Basic College Mathematics
with Early Integers

Elayn Martin-Gay

University of New Orleans

PEARSON

Prentice
Hall

Upper Saddle River, New Jersey 07458

Library of Congress Cataloging-in-Publication Data

Martin-Gay, K. Elayn
  Basic college mathematics with early integers / Elayn Martin-Gay.—1st ed.
    p. cm.
  Includes index.
  ISBN 0-13-222749-5 (pbk.: alk. paper) — ISBN 0-13-223048-8 (alk. paper)
  1. Mathematics—Textbooks. I. Title.

QA39.3.M37 2007
510—dc22

Executive Editor: *Paul Murphy*
Editor in Chief: *Christine Hoag*
Project Manager: *Mary Beckwith*
Production Management: *Elm Street Publishing Services, Inc.*
Senior Managing Editor: *Linda Mihatov Behrens*
Executive Managing Editor: *Kathleen Schiaparelli*
Media Project Manager, Developmental Math: *Audra J. Walsh*
Media Production Editor: *Raegan Keida*
Managing Editor, Digital Supplements: *Nicole M. Jackson*
Manufacturing Buyer: *Alan Fischer*
Manufacturing Manager: *Alexis Heydt-Long*
Director of Marketing: *Patrice Jones*
Senior Marketing Manager: *Kate Valentine*
Marketing Assistant: *Jennifer de Leeuwerk*
Development Editor: *Laura Wheel*
Editor in Chief, Development: *Carol Trueheart*
Editorial Assistant: *Abigail Rethore*
Art Director: *Maureen Eide*
Interior/Cover Designer: *Suzanne Behnke*
Art Editor: *Thomas Benfatti*
Creative Director: *Juan R. López*
Director of Creative Services: *Paul Belfanti*
Cover Photo: *Holt Studios Ltd/Animals Animals/Earth Scenes*
Manager, Cover Visual Research & Permissions: *Karen Sanatar*
Director, Image Resource Center: *Melinda Reo*
Manager, Rights and Permissions: *Zina Arabia*
Manager, Visual Research: *Beth Brenzel*
Image Permission Coordinator: *Craig Jones*
Photo Researcher: *Teri Stratford*
Composition: *Interactive Composition Corporation*
Art Studios: *Scientific Illustrators and Laserwords*

 © 2007 by Prentice-Hall, Inc.
Pearson Prentice Hall
Pearson Education, Inc.
Upper Saddle River, New Jersey 07458

Pearson Prentice Hall™ is a trademark of Pearson Education, Inc.

Photo Credits appear on page I7, which constitutes a continuation of the copyright page.

Printed in the United States of America
10 9 8 7 6 5 4 3 2 1

ISBN: (paperback) 0-13-222749-5; (case bound) 0-13-223048-8

Pearson Education LTD., *London*
Pearson Education Australia PTY., Limited, *Sydney*
Pearson Education Singapore, Pte. Ltd.
Pearson Education North Asia Ltd., *Hong Kong*
Pearson Education Canada, Ltd., *Canada*
Pearson Educacíon de Mexico, S.A. de C.V.
Pearson Education—Japan, *Tokyo*
Pearson Education Malaysia, Pte. Ltd.

*To my mother, Barbara M. Miller,
and her husband, Leo Miller, and to the memory of
my father, Robert J. Martin*

Contents

1 The Whole Numbers   1

2 Integers and Introduction to Variables   111

9 Geometry 616

Tools to Help Students Succeed

Your textbook includes a number of features designed to help you succeed in this math course—as well as the next math course you take. These features include:

Feature	Benefit	Page
Well-crafted Exercise Sets: We learn math by doing math	The exercise sets in your text offer an ample number of exercises carefully ordered so you can master basic mathematical skills and concepts while developing all-important problem solving skills. Exercise sets include Mixed Practice exercises to help you master multiple key concepts, as well as Mental Math, Writing, Applications, Concept Check, Concept Extension, and Review exercises.	260–266
Solutions-to-Selected Exercises: Built-in solutions at the back of the text	If you need to review problems you find difficult, this built-in solutions manual at the back of the text provides the step-by-step solutions to every other odd-numbered exercise in the exercise sets.	A21
Study Skills Builders: Maximize your chances for success	Study Skills Builders reinforce the material in *Section 1.1—Tips for Success in Mathematics*. Study Skills Builders are a great resource for study ideas and self-assessment to maximize your opportunity for success in this course. Take your new study skills with you to help you succeed in your next math course.	129
The Bigger Picture: Succeed in this math course and the next one you take	The Bigger Picture focuses on the key concept of this course—operations (addition, subtraction, multiplication, division)—and asks you to keep an ongoing outline so you can recognize and perform operations on different types of numbers. A strong foundation in operations on different sets of numbers will help you succeed in this basic math course, as well as the next math course you take.	266
Examples: Step-by-step instruction for you	Examples in the text provide you with clear, concise step-by-step instructions to help you learn. Annotations in the examples provide additional instruction.	230
Helpful Hints: Help where you'll need it most	Helpful Hints provide tips and advice at exact locations where students need it most. Strategically placed where you might have the most difficulty, Helpful Hints will help you work through common trouble spots.	231
Practice Problems: Immediate reinforcement	Practice Problems offer immediate reinforcement after every example. Try each Practice Problem after studying the corresponding example to make sure you have a good working knowledge of the concept.	230
Integrated Review: Mid-chapter progress check	To ensure that you understand the key concepts covered in the first sections of the chapter, work the exercises in the Integrated Review before you continue with the rest of the chapter.	227
Vocabulary Check: Key terms and vocabulary	Make sure you understand key terms and vocabulary in each chapter with the Vocabulary Check.	268
Chapter Highlights: Study smart	Chapter Highlights outline the key concepts of the chapter along with examples to help you focus your studying efforts as you prepare for your test.	268–272
Chapter Test: Take a practice test	In preparation for your classroom test, take this practice test to make sure you understand the key topics in the chapter. Be sure to use the **Chapter Test Prep Video CD** included with this text to see the author present a fully worked-out solution to each exercise in the Chapter Test.	286

Martin-Gay's CD VIDEO RESOURCES Help Students Succeed

Martin-Gay's **Chapter Test Prep Video CD (available with this text)**

- Provides students with help during their most "teachable moment"—while they are studying for a test.

- Text author Elayn Martin-Gay presents step-by-step solutions to the exact exercises found in each Chapter Test in the book.

- Easy video navigation allows students to instantly access the worked-out solutions to the exercises they want to review.

- A close-captioned option for the hearing impaired is provided.

Martin-Gay's **CD Lecture Series (with Tips for Success in Mathematics)**

- Text author Elayn Martin-Gay presents the key concepts from every section of the text in 10–15 minute mini-lectures.

- Students can easily review a section or a specific topic before a homework assignment, quiz, or test.

- Includes fully worked-out solutions to exercises marked with a CD Video icon (⊙) in each section.

- Includes *Section 1.1, Tips for Success in Mathematics.*

- A close-captioned option for the hearing impaired is provided.

- Ask your bookstore for information about Martin-Gay's *Basic College Mathematics with Early Integers* CD Lecture Series, or visit www.prenhall.com.

Additional Resources to Help You Succeed

Student Study Pack

A single, easy-to-use package—available bundled with your textbook or by itself—for purchase through your bookstore. This package contains the following resources to help you succeed:

Student Solutions Manual
- Contains worked-out solutions to odd-numbered exercises from each section exercise set, Practice Problems, Mental Math exercises, and all exercises found in the Chapter Review and Chapter Tests.

Prentice Hall Math Tutor Center
- Staffed by qualified math instructors who provide students with tutoring on examples and odd-numbered exercises from the textbook. Tutoring is available via telephone, fax, email, or the Internet.

Martin-Gay's CD Lecture Series
- Text author Elayn Martin-Gay presents the key concepts from every section of the text with 10–15 minute mini-lectures. Students can easily review a section or a specific topic before a homework assignment, quiz, or test.
- Includes fully worked-out solutions to exercises marked with a CD Video icon () in each section. Also includes *Section 1.1, Tips for Success in Mathematics.*

Online Homework and Tutorial Resources

MyMathLab

MyMathLab is a series of text specific, easily customizable, online courses for Prentice Hall textbooks in mathematics and statistics. MyMathLab is powered by Course Compass™—Pearson Education's online teaching and learning environment—and by MathXL®—our online homework, tutorial, and assessment system. MyMathLab gives instructors the tools they need to deliver all or a portion of their course online, whether students are in a lab setting or working from home. MyMathLab provides a rich and flexible set of course materials, featuring free-response exercises that are algorithmically generated for unlimited practice and mastery. Students can also use online tools, such as video lectures, animations, and a multimedia textbook, to independently improve their understanding and performance. MyMathLab is available to qualified adopters. For more information, visit our Web site at www.mymathlab.com or contact your Prentice Hall sales representative. (MyMathLab must be set up and assigned by your instructor.)

MathXL® www.mathxl.com

MathXL is a powerful online homework, tutorial, and assessment system that accompanies the text. With MathXL, instructors can create, edit, and assign online homework and tests using algorithmically generated exercises correlated to your textbook. All student work is tracked in MathXL's online gradebook. Students can take chapter tests in MathXL and receive personalized study plans based on their test results. The study plan diagnoses weaknesses and links students directly to tutorial exercises for the objectives they need to study and retest. Students can also access supplemental animations and video clips directly from selected exercises. MathXL is available to qualified adopters. For more information, visit our Web site at www.mathxl.com, or contact your Prentice Hall sales representative for a product demonstration. (MathXL must be set up and assigned by your instructor.)

Preface

Basic College Mathematics with Early Integers was written to provide a solid foundation in the basics of college mathematics, including the topics of whole numbers, integers, fractions, decimals, ratio, and proportion, percent, and measurement as well as introductions to geometry, statistics and probability, and algebra topics. Integers are introduced in Chapter 2, and integrated throughout the text. This allows students to gain confidence and mastery by working with integers throughout the course. Specific care was taken to make sure students have the most up-to-date relevant text preparation for their next mathematics course or for nonmathematical courses that require an understanding of basic mathematical concepts. I have tried to achieve this by writing a user-friendly text that is keyed to objectives and contains many worked-out examples. As suggested by AMATYC and the NCTM Standards (plus Addenda), real-life and real-data applications, data interpretation, conceptual understanding, problem solving, writing, cooperative learning, appropriate use of technology, mental mathematics, number sense, estimation, critical thinking, and geometric concepts are emphasized and integrated throughout the book.

Highlights of *Basic College Mathematics with Early Integers*

Exercise Sets

- Three forms of mixed sections of exercises are included.
  - **Mixed Practice** exercises combining objectives within a section
  - **Mixed Practice** exercises combining previous sections
  - **Mixed Review** exercises included at the end of the Chapter Review

  These exercises require students to determine the problem type and strategy needed in order to solve it. In doing so, students need to think about key concepts to proceed with a correct method of solving—just as they would need to do on a test.

- **Concept Check exercises** are included in the section exercise sets. These exercises are related to the Concept Check(s) found within the section. They help students measure their understanding of key concepts by focusing on common trouble areas. These exercises may ask students to identify a common error, and/or provide an explanation.

- **Concept Extensions** exercises extend the concepts and require students to combine several skills or concepts to solve the exercises in this section.

Emphasis on Study Skills and Student Success

- **Study Skills Builders** Found at the end of many exercise sets, Study Skills Builders allow instructors to assign exercises that will help students improve their study skills and take responsibility for their part of the learning process. Study Skills Builders reinforce the material found in Section 1.1, "Tips for Success in Mathematics" and serve as an excellent tool for self-assessment.

- **The Bigger Picture** is a recurring feature that focuses on the key concepts of the course—operations, sets of numbers, and solving equations—and helps students develop an outline to recognize and perform operations on different sets of numbers or to solve different types of equations. By working the exercises and developing this outline throughout the text, students can begin to transition from thinking "section by section" to thinking about how the mathematics in this course is part of the "bigger picture" of mathematics in general. A completed outline is provided in Appendix B so students have a model for their work.

- **Chapter Test Prep Video CD** provides students with help during their most "teachable moment"—while they are studying for a test. Included with every copy of the student edition of the text, this video CD provides fully worked-out solutions by the author to every exercise from each Chapter Test in the text. The easy video navigation allows students to instantly access the solutions to the exercises they want to review. The problems are solved by the author in the same manner as in the text.

- **Chapter Test files in TestGen** provide algorithms specific to each exercise from each Chapter Test in the text. Allows for easy replication of Chapter Tests with consistent, algorithmically generated problem types for additional assignments or assessment purposes.

Key Pedagogical Features

The following key features are included in the text:

Problem Solving Process   This is formally introduced in Chapter 1 with a four-step process that is integrated throughout the text. The four steps are **Understand, Translate, Solve,** and **Interpret.** The repeated use of these steps in a variety of examples shows their wide applicability. Reinforcing the steps can increase students' comfort level and confidence in tackling problems.

Exercise Sets   The exercise sets have been carefully examined. Special focus was placed on making sure that even- and odd-numbered exercises are paired.

Examples   Detailed step-by-step examples are included throughout. Many of these reflect real life. Additional instructional support is provided in the annotated examples.

Practice Problems   Throughout the text, each worked-out example has a parallel Practice Problem. These invite students to be actively involved in the learning process. Students should try each Practice Problem after finishing the corresponding example. Learning by doing will help students grasp ideas before moving on to other concepts. Answers to the Practice Problems are provided at the bottom of each page.

Helpful Hints   Helpful Hints contain practical advice on applying mathematical concepts. Strategically placed where students are most likely to need immediate reinforcement, Helpful Hints help students avoid common trouble areas and mistakes.

Concept Checks   This feature allows students to gauge their grasp of an idea as it is being presented in the text. Concept Checks stress conceptual understanding at the point-of-use and help suppress misconceived notions before they start. Answers appear at the bottom of the page. Exercises related to Concept Checks are included in the exercise sets.

Selected Solutions   Solutions to every-other odd exercise are included in the back of the text. This built-in solutions manual allows students to check their work.

Integrated Reviews   A unique, mid-chapter exercise set that helps students assimilate new skills and concepts that they have learned separately over several sections. These reviews provide yet another opportunity for students to work with "mixed" exercises as they master the topics.

Vocabulary Check   Provides an opportunity for students to become more familiar with the use of mathematical terms as they strengthen their verbal skills. These appear at the end of each chapter before the Chapter Highlights.

Chapter Highlights   Found at the end of every chapter, these contain key definitions and concepts with examples to help students understand and retain what they have learned and help them organize their notes and study for tests.

Chapter Review The end of every chapter contains a comprehensive review of topics introduced in the chapter. The Chapter Review offers exercises keyed to every section in the chapter, as well as Mixed Review exercises that are not keyed to sections.

Chapter Test and Chapter Test Prep Video CD The Chapter Test is structured to include those problems that involve common student errors. The **Chapter Test Prep Video CD** gives students instant author access to a step-by-step video solution of each exercise in the Chapter Test.

Cumulative Review Follows every chapter in the text (except Chapter 1). Each odd-numbered exercise contained in the Cumulative Review is an earlier worked example in the text that is referenced in the back of the book along with the answer.

Mental Math Found at the beginning of an exercise set, these mental warm-ups reinforce concepts found in the accompanying section and increase student's confidence before they tackle an exercise set.

Writing Exercises ✎ These exercises occur in almost every exercise set and require students to provide a written response to explain concepts or justify their thinking.

Applications Real-world and real-data applications have been included throughout the text. These exercises occur in almost every exercise set and show the relevance of mathematics and help students gradually, and continuously develop their problem solving skills.

Review Exercises These exercises occur in each exercise set (except in Chapter 1) and are keyed to earlier sections. They review concepts learned earlier in the text that will be needed in the next section or chapter.

Exercise Set Resource Icons at the opening of each exercise set remind students of the resources available for extra practice and support:

CD/Video for Review   MyMathLab   MathXL®

PH Math/Tutor Center   Student Solutions Manual

See Student Resource descriptions pages xviii–xvix for details on the individual resources available.

Exercise Icons These icons facilitate the assignment of specialized exercises and let students know what resources can support them.

    CD Video icon: exercise worked on Martin-Gay's CD Lecture Series.

    △ Triangle icon: identifies exercises involving geometric concepts.

    ✎ Pencil icon: indicates a written response is needed.

    Calculator icon: optional exercises intended to be solved using a scientific or graphing calculator.

Group Activities Found at the end of each chapter, these activities are for individual or group completion, and are usually hands-on or data-based activities that extend the concepts found in the chapter allowing students to make decisions and interpretations and to think and write about algebra.

Optional: Calculator Exploration Boxes and Calculator Exercises The optional Calculator Explorations provide key strokes and exercises at appropriate points to provide an opportunity for students to become familiar with these tools. Section exercises that are best completed by using a calculator are identified by ▦ for ease of assignment.

A Word about Textbook Design and Student Success

The design of developmental mathematics textbooks has become increasingly important. As students and instructors have told Prentice Hall in focus groups and market research surveys, these textbooks cannot look "cluttered" or "busy." A "busy" design can distract a student from what is most important in the text. It can also heighten math anxiety.

As a result of the conversations and meetings we have had with students and instructors, we concluded the design of this text should be understated and focused on the most important pedagogical elements. Students and instructors helped us to identify the primary elements that are central to student success. These primary elements include:

- Exercise Sets

- Examples and Practice Problems

- Helpful Hints

- Rules, Property, and Definition boxes

As you will notice in this text, these primary features are the most prominent elements in the design. We have made every attempt to make sure these elements are the features the eye is drawn to. The remaining features, the secondary elements in the design, blend into the "fabric" or "grain" of the overall design. These secondary elements complement the primary elements without becoming distractions.

Prentice Hall's thanks goes to all of the students and instructors (as noted by the author in Acknowledgments) who helped us develop the design of this text. At every step in the design process, their feedback proved valuable in helping us to make the right decisions. Thanks to your input, we're confident the design of this text will be both practical and engaging as it serves its educational and learning purposes.

Sincerely,

Paul Murphy

Executive Editor
Developmental Mathematics
Prentice Hall

Instructor and Student Resources

The following resources are available to help instructors and students use this text more effectively.

Instructor Resources

Annotated Instructor's Edition (0-13-222750-9)

- Answers to all exercises printed on the same text page
- Teaching Tips throughout the text placed at key points
- Includes Vocabulary Check at the beginning of relevant sections
- General tips and suggestions for classroom or group activities

Instructor Solutions Manual (0-13-222797-5)

- Solutions to the even-numbered exercises
- Solutions to every Mental Math exercise
- Solutions to every Practice Problem
- Solutions to every exercise in the Integrated Reviews, Chapter Reviews, Chapter Tests, and Cumulative Reviews

Instructor's Resource Manual with Tests (0-13-222798-3)

- Includes Mini-Lectures for every section from the text
- Group Activities
- Free Response Test Forms, Multiple Choice Test Forms, Cumulative Tests, and Additional Exercises
- Answers to all items

TestGen (0-13-238737-9)

- Enables instructors to build, edit, print, and administer tests
- Features a computerized bank of questions developed to cover all text objectives
- Available on dual-platform Windows/Macintosh CD-ROM

Instructor Adjunct Resource Kit

The Martin-Gay Instructor/Adjunct Resource Kit (IARK) contains tools and resources to help adjuncts and instructors succeed in the classroom. The IARK includes:

- Instructor-to-Instructor CD Videos that offer tips, suggestions, and strategies for engaging students and presenting key topics
- PDF files of the Instructor Solutions Manual and the Instructor's Resource Manual
- TestGen

MyMathLab Instructor Version (0-13-147898-2)
MyMathLab www.mymathlab.com

MyMathLab is a series of text specific, easily customizable, online courses for Prentice Hall textbooks in mathematics and statistics. MyMathLab is powered by Course Compass™—Pearson Education's online teaching and learning environment—and by MathXL®—our online homework, tutorial, and assessment system. MyMathLab gives instructors the tools they need to deliver all or a portion of their course online, whether students are in a lab setting or working from home. MyMathLab provides a rich and flexible set of course materials, featuring free-response exercises that are algorithmically generated for unlimited practice and mastery. Students can also use online tools, such as video lectures, animations, and a multimedia textbook, to independently improve their understanding and performance. Instructors can use

MyMathLab's homework and test managers to select and assign online exercises correlated directly to the text, and they can import TestGen tests into MyMathLab for added flexibility. MyMathLab's online gradebook—designed specifically for mathematics and statistics—automatically tracks students' homework and test results and gives the instructor control over how to calculate final grades. Instructors can also add offline (paper-and-pencil) grades to the gradebook. MyMathLab is available to qualified adopters. For more information, visit our website at www.mymathlab.com or contact your Prentice Hall sales representative.

MathXL Instructor Version (0-13-147895-8)
MathXL® www.mathxl.com

MathXL is a powerful online homework, tutorial, and assessment system that accompanies the text. With MathXL, instructors can create, edit, and assign online homework and tests using algorithmically generated exercises correlated to your textbook. All student work is tracked in MathXL's online gradebook. Students can take chapter tests in MathXL and receive personalized study plans based on their test results. The study plan diagnoses weaknesses and links students directly to tutorial exercises for the objectives they need to study and retest. Students can also access supplemental animations and video clips directly from selected exercises. MathXL is available to qualified adopters. For more information, visit our Web site at www.mathxl.com, or contact your Prentice Hall sales representative for a product demonstration.

Interact Math® Tutorial Web site www.interactmath.com

Get practice and tutorial help online! This interactive tutorial Web site provides algorithmically generated practice exercises that correlate directly to the exercises in your textbook. You can retry an exercise as many times as you like with new values each time for unlimited practice and mastery. Every exercise is accompanied by an interactive guided solution that gives you helpful feedback if you enter an incorrect answer, and you can also view a worked-out sample problem that steps you through an exercise similar to the one you're working on.

Student Resources

Student Solutions Manual (0-13-222795-9)

- Solutions to the odd-numbered section exercises
- Solutions to the Practice Problems
- Solutions to every Mental Math exercise
- Solutions to every exercise found in the Chapter Reviews and Chapter Tests

Martin-Gay's CD Lecture Series (0-13-222790-8)

- Perfect for review of a section or a specific topic, these mini-lectures by Elayn Martin-Gay cover the key concepts from each section of the text in approximately 10–15 minutes
- Includes fully worked-out solutions to exercises in each section marked with a 💿
- Includes coverage of Section 1.1, "Tips for Success Mathematics"
- Closed-captioned for the hearing impaired

Prentice Hall Math Tutor Center (0-13-064604-0)

- Staffed by qualified math instructors who provide students with tutoring on examples and odd-numbered exercises from the textbook
- Tutoring is available via toll-free telephone, toll-free fax, e-mail, or the Internet
- Whiteboard technology allows tutors and students to see problems worked while they "talk" in real time over the Internet during tutoring sessions

Basic College Mathematics with Early Integers Student Study Pack

The Student Study Pack includes:

- Martin-Gay's CD Lecture Series
- Student Solutions Manual
- Prentice Hall Math Tutor Center access code

Chapter Test Prep Video CD—Standalone (0-13-222788-6)

- Includes fully worked-out solutions to every problem from each Chapter Test in the text.

MathXL Tutorials on CD—Standalone (0-13-199846-3)

- Provides algorithmically generated practice exercises that correlate to exercises at the end of sections.
- Every exercise is accompanied by an example and a guided solution, selected exercises include a video clip.
- The software recognizes student errors and provides feedback. It can also generate printed summaries of students progress.

Interact Math® Tutorial Web Site www.interactmath.com

Get practice and tutorial help online! This interactive tutorial Web site provides algorithmically generated practice exercises that correlate directly to the exercises in your textbook. You can retry an exercise as many times as you like with new values each time for unlimited practice and mastery. Every exercise is accompanied by an interactive guided solution that gives you helpful feedback if you enter an incorrect answer, and you can also view a worked-out sample problem that steps you through an exercise similar to the one you're working on.

Acknowledgments

There are many people who helped me develop this text, and I will attempt to thank some of them here. Carrie Green was *invaluable* for contributing to the overall accuracy of the text. Chris Callac, Laura Wheel, and Lori Mancuso were *invaluable* for their many suggestions and contributions during the development and writing of this text. Ingrid Benson provided guidance throughout the production process.

A special thanks to my editor, Paul Murphy, for all of his assistance, support, and contributions to this project. A very special thank you goes to my project manager, Mary Beckwith, for being there 24/7/365, as my students say. Last, my thanks to the staff at Prentice Hall for all their support: Linda Behrens, Alan Fischer, Patty Burns, Tom Benfatti, Paul Belfanti, Maureen Eide, Suzanne Behnke, Kate Valentine, Patrice Jones, Chris Hoag, Paul Corey, and Tim Bozik.

I would like to thank the following reviewers of portions of this manuscript:

Anita Aikman, *Collin County Community College*

Sheila Anderson, *Housatonic Community College*

Adrianne Arata, *College of the Siskyous*

Cedric Atkins, *Mott Community College*

Laurel Berry, *Bryant & Stratton College*

Connie Buller, *Metropolitan Community College*

Lisa Feintech, *Cabrillo College*

Chris Ford, *Shasta College*

Cindy Fowler, *Central Piedmont Communty College*

Pam Gerszewski, *College of the Albemarle*

Doug Harley, *Del Mar College*

Sonya Johnson, *Central Piedmont Community College*

Deborah Jones, *High Tech College*

Nancy Lange, *Inver Hills Community College*

Paul Laverty, *Wachusett Commmunity College*

Donna Martin, *Florida Community College–Jacksonville*

Robbin Miller, *Erie Community College*

Kris Mundunuri, *Long Beach City College*

Gary Piercy, *Moraine Valley Community College*

Marilyn Platt, *Gaston Community College*

Carolyn Poos, *Southwestern Illinois Community College*

Johnny Reaves, *Central Piedmont Community College*

Mary Lee Seitz, *Erie Community College*

Rhonda Watts, *College of the Albemarle*

I would also like to thank the following dedicated group of instructors who participated in our focus groups, Martin-Gay Summits, and our design review for the series. Their feedback and insights have helped to strengthen the texts. These instructors include:

Cedric Atkins, *Mott Community College*

Laurel Berry, *Bryant & Stratton*

Bob Brown, *Community College of Baltimore County–Essex*

Lisa Brown, *Community College of Baltimore County–Essex*

Gail Burkett, *Palm Beach Community College*

Cheryl Cantwell, *Seminole Community College*

Jackie Cohen, *Augusta State College*

Janice Ervin, *Central Piedmont Community College*

Pauline Hall, *Iowa State College*

Sonya Johnson, *Central Piedmont Community College*

Irene Jones, *Fullerton College*

Nancy Lange, *Inver Hills Community College*

Jean McArthur, *Joliet Junior College*

Marica Molle, *Metropolitan Community College*

Linda Padilla, *Joliet Junior College*

Carole Shapero, *Oakton Community College*

Jennifer Strehler, *Oakton Community College*

Tanomo Taguchi, *Fullerton College*

Leigh Ann Wheeler, *Greenville Technical Community College*

Valerie Wright, *Central Piedmont Community College*

A special thank you to those students who participated in our design review: Katherine Browne, Mike Bulfin, Nancy Canipe, Ashley Carpenter, Jeff Chojnachi, Roxanne Davis, Mike Dieter, Amy Dombrowski, Kay Herring, Todd Jaycox, Kaleena Levan, Matt Montgomery, Tony Plese, Abigail Polkinghorn, Harley Price, Eli Robinson, Avery Rosen, Robyn Schott, Cynthia Thomas, and Sherry Ward.

Additional Acknowledgments

As usual, I would like to thank my husband, Clayton, for his constant encouragement. I would also like to thank my children, Eric and Bryan, for providing most of the cooking and humor in our household. I would also like to thank my extended family for their help and wonderful sense of humor. Their contributions are too numerous to list. They are Rod and Karen Pasch; Peter, Michael, Christopher, Matthew, and Jessica Callac; Stuart and Earline Martin; Josh, Mandy, Bailey, Ethan, and Avery Barnes; Mark, Sabrina, and Madison Martin; Leo and Barbara Miller; and Jewett Gay.

Elayn Martin-Gay

About the Author

Elayn Martin-Gay has taught mathematics at the University of New Orleans for more than 25 years. Her numerous teaching awards include the local University Alumni Association's Award for Excellence in Teaching, and Outstanding Developmental Educator at University of New Orleans, presented by the Louisiana Association of Developmental Educators.

Prior to writing textbooks, Elayn Martin-Gay developed an acclaimed series of lecture videos to support developmental mathematics students in their quest for success. These highly successful videos originally served as the foundation material for her texts. Today, the videos are specific to each book in the Martin-Gay series. The author has also created Chapter Test Prep Videos to help students during their most "teachable moment"—as they prepare for a test, along with Instructor-to-Instructor videos that provide teaching tips, hints, and suggestions for each developmental mathematics course, including basic mathematics, prealgebra, beginning algebra, and intermediate algebra.

Elayn is the author of 10 published textbooks as well as multimedia interactive mathematics, all specializing in developmental mathematics courses. She has participated as an author across the broadest range of educational materials: textbooks, videos, tutorial software, and Interactive Math courseware. All of these components are designed to work together. This offers an opportunity of various combinations for an integrated teaching and learning package offering great consistency for the student.

Applications Index

Basic College Mathematics
with Early Integers

1

The Whole Numbers

Whole numbers are the basic building blocks of mathematics. The whole numbers answer the question "How many?"

This chapter covers basic operations on whole numbers. Knowledge of these operations provides a good foundation on which to build further mathematical skills.

Yosemite National Park was established on October 1, 1890, and it is a favorite tourist destination in the Sierra Nevada Mountains in central California. Its nearly 750,000 acres are home to many of nature's most beautiful sites, including rock formations, giant sequoias, and waterfalls. In Exercise 65, Section 1.3, we will see how whole numbers can be used to measure the height of Yosemite Falls, the highest waterfall in the United States.

Highest U.S. Waterfalls

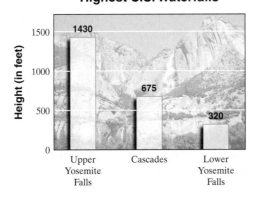

A Get Ready for This Course.

B Understand Some General Tips for Success.

C Understand How to Use This Text.

D Get Help As Soon As You Need It.

E Learn How to Prepare for and Take an Exam.

F Develop Good Time Management.

1.1 TIPS FOR SUCCESS IN MATHEMATICS

Before reading this section, remember that your instructor is your best source of information. Please see your instructor for any additional help or information.

Objective **A** Getting Ready for This Course

Now that you have decided to take this course, remember that a *positive attitude* will make all the difference in the world. Your belief that you can succeed is just as important as your commitment to this course. Make sure you are ready for this course by having the time and positive attitude that it takes to succeed.

Next, make sure that you have scheduled your math course at a time that will give you the best chance for success. For example, if you are also working, you may want to check with your employer to make sure that your work hours will not conflict with your course schedule.

On the day of your first class period, double-check your schedule and allow yourself extra time to arrive on time in case of traffic problems or difficulty locating your classroom. Make sure that you bring at least your textbook, paper, and a writing instrument. Are you required to have a lab manual, graph paper, calculator, or some other supply besides this text? If so, bring this material with you also.

Objective **B** General Tips for Success

Below are some general tips that will increase your chance for success in a mathematics class. Many of these tips will also help you in other courses you may be taking.

Exchange names and phone numbers or e-mail addresses with at least one other person in class. This contact person can be a great help if you miss an assignment or want to discuss math concepts or exercises that you find difficult.

Choose to attend all class periods. If possible, sit near the front of the classroom. This way, you will see and hear the presentation better. It may also be easier for you to participate in classroom activities.

Do your homework. You've probably heard the phrase "practice makes perfect" in relation to music and sports. It also applies to mathematics. You will find that the more time you spend solving mathematics exercises, the easier the process becomes. Be sure to schedule enough time to complete your assignments before the next class period.

Check your work. Review the steps you made while working a problem. Learn to check your answers in the original problems. You may also compare your answers with the answers to selected exercises section in the back of the book. If you have made a mistake, try to figure out what went wrong. Then correct your mistake. If you can't find what went wrong, don't erase your work or throw it away. Bring your work to your instructor, a tutor in a math lab, or a classmate. It is easier for someone to find where you had trouble if they look at your original work.

Learn from your mistakes. Everyone, even your instructor, makes mistakes. Use your errors to learn and to become a better math student. The key is finding and understanding your errors. Was your mistake a careless one, or did you make it because you can't read your own math writing? If so, try to work more slowly or write more neatly and make a conscious effort to carefully check your work. Did you make a mistake because you don't understand a concept? If so, take the time to review the concept or ask questions to better understand it.

Know how to get help if you need it. It's all right to ask for help. In fact, it's a good idea to ask for help whenever there is something that you don't understand. Make sure you know when your instructor has office hours and how to find his or her office. Find out whether math tutoring services are available on your campus. Check on the hours, location, and requirements of the tutoring service. Know whether software is available and how to access this resource.

Organize your class materials, including homework assignments, graded quizzes and tests, and notes from your class or lab. All of these items will make valuable references throughout your course and when studying for upcoming tests and the final exam. Make sure that you can locate these materials when you need them.

Read your textbook before class. Reading a mathematics textbook is unlike reading a novel or a newspaper. Your pace will be much slower. It is helpful to have paper and a pencil with you when you read. Try to work out examples on your own as you encounter them in your text. You should also write down any questions that you want to ask in class. When you read a mathematics textbook, sometimes some of the information in a section will be unclear. But after you hear a lecture or watch a video on that section, you will understand it much more easily than if you had not read your text beforehand.

Don't be afraid to ask questions. You are not the only person in class with questions. Other students are normally grateful that someone has spoken up.

Hand in assignments on time. This way you can be sure that you will not lose points for being late. Show every step of a problem and be neat and organized. Also be sure that you understand which problems are assigned for homework. If allowed, you can always double-check the assignment with another student in your class.

Objective C Using This Text

There are many helpful resources that are available to you in this text. It is important that you become familiar with and use these resources. They should increase your chances for success in this course.

- *Practice Problems.* Each example in every section has a parallel Practice Problem. As you read a section, try each Practice Problem after you've finished the corresponding example. This "learn-by-doing" approach will help you grasp ideas before you move on to other concepts.

- *Chapter Test Prep Video CD.* This book contains a CD. This CD contains all of the Chapter Test exercises worked out by the author. This supplement is very helpful before a classroom chapter test.

- *Lecture Video CDs.* Exercises marked with a ⊙ are fully worked out by the author on video CDs. Check with your instructor for the availability of these video CDs.

- *Symbols at the beginning of an exercise set.* If you need help with a particular section, the symbols listed at the beginning of each exercise set will remind you of the numerous supplements available.

- *Objectives.* The main section of exercises in each exercise set is referenced by an objective, such as A or B, and also an example(s). There is also often a section of exercises entitled "Mixed Practice," which is referenced by two or more objectives or sections. These are mixed exercises written to prepare you for your next exam. Use all of this referencing if you have trouble completing an assignment from the exercise set.

- *Icons (Symbols).* Make sure that you understand the meaning of the icons that are beside many exercises. ⊙ tells you that the corresponding exercise may be viewed on the video segment that corresponds to that section. ✎ tells you that this exercise is a writing exercise in which you should answer in complete sentences. △ icon tells you that the exercise involves geometry.

- *Integrated Reviews.* Found in the middle of each chapter, these reviews offer you a chance to practice—in one place—the many concepts that you have learned separately over several sections.

- *End of Chapter Opportunities.* There are many opportunities at the end of each chapter to help you understand the concepts of the chapter.

  Chapter Highlights contain chapter summaries and examples.

  Chapter Reviews contain review problems. The first part is organized section by section and the second part contains a set of mixed exercises.

  Chapter Tests are sample tests to help you prepare for an exam. The Chapter Test Prep Video CD, found in this text, contains all the Chapter Test exercises worked by the author.

  Cumulative Reviews are reviews consisting of material from the beginning of the book to the end of that particular chapter.

- *Study Skills Builder.* This feature is found at the end of many exercise sets. In order to increase your chance of success in this course, please read and answer the questions in the Study Skills Builder.

- *The Bigger Picture.* This feature contains the directions for building an outline to be used throughout the course. The purpose of this outline is to help you make the transition from thinking "section by section" to thinking about how the mathematics in this course is part of a bigger picture.

See the Preface at the beginning of this text for a more thorough explanation of the features of this text.

Objective **D** Getting Help

If you have trouble completing assignments or understanding the mathematics, get help as soon as you need it! This tip is presented as an objective on its own because it is so important. In mathematics, usually the material presented in one section builds on your understanding of the previous section. This means that if you don't understand the concepts covered during a class period, there is a good chance that you will not understand the concepts covered during the next class period. If this happens to you, get help as soon as you can.

Where can you get help? Many suggestions have been made in this section on where to get help, and now it is up to you to do it. Try your instructor, a tutoring center, or a math lab, or you may want to form a study group with fellow classmates. If you do decide to see your instructor or go to a tutoring center, make sure that you have a neat notebook and are ready with your questions.

Objective **E** Preparing for and Taking an Exam

Make sure that you allow yourself plenty of time to prepare for a test. If you think that you are a little "math anxious," it may be that you are not preparing for a test in a way that will ensure success. The way that you prepare for a test in mathematics is important. To prepare for a test:

1. Review your previous homework assignments.

2. Review any notes from class and section-level quizzes you have taken. (If this is a final exam, also review chapter tests you have taken.)

3. Review concepts and definitions by reading the Highlights at the end of each chapter.

4. Practice working out exercises by completing the Chapter Review found at the end of each chapter. (If this is a final exam, go through a Cumulative Review. There is one found at the end of each chapter except Chapter 1. Choose the review found at the end of the latest chapter that you have covered in your course.) *Don't stop here!*

5. It is important that you place yourself in conditions similar to test conditions to find out how you will perform. In other words, as soon as you feel that you know the material, get a few blank sheets of paper and take a sample test. There is a Chapter Test available at the end of each chapter, or you can work selected

problems from the Chapter Review. Your instructor may also provide you with a review sheet. During this sample test, do not use your notes or your textbook. Then check your sample test. If you are not satisfied with the results, study the areas that you are weak in and try again.

6. On the day of the test, allow yourself plenty of time to arrive at where you will be taking your exam.

When taking your test:

1. Read the directions on the test carefully.
2. Read each problem carefully as you take the test. Make sure that you answer the question asked.
3. Watch your time and pace yourself so that you can attempt each problem on your test.
4. If you have time, check your work and answers.
5. Do not turn your test in early. If you have extra time, spend it double-checking your work.

Objective F Managing Your Time

As a college student, you know the demands that classes, homework, work, and family place on your time. Some days you probably wonder how you'll ever get everything done. One key to managing your time is developing a schedule. Here are some hints for making a schedule:

1. Make a list of all of your weekly commitments for the term. Include classes, work, regular meetings, extracurricular activities, etc. You may also find it helpful to list such things as laundry, regular workouts, grocery shopping, etc.
2. Next, estimate the time needed for each item on the list. Also make a note of how often you will need to do each item. Don't forget to include time estimates for the reading, studying, and homework you do outside of your classes. You may want to ask your instructor for help estimating the time needed.
3. In the exercise set that follows, you are asked to block out a typical week on the schedule grid given. Start with items with fixed time slots like classes and work.
4. Next, include the items on your list with flexible time slots. Think carefully about how best to schedule items such as study time.
5. Don't fill up every time slot on the schedule. Remember that you need to allow time for eating, sleeping, and relaxing! You should also allow a little extra time in case some items take longer than planned.
6. If you find that your weekly schedule is too full for you to handle, you may need to make some changes in your workload, classload, or in other areas of your life. You may want to talk to your advisor, manager or supervisor at work, or someone in your college's academic counseling center for help with such decisions.

1. What is your instructor's name?

2. What are your instructor's office location and office hours?

3. What is the best way to contact your instructor?

4. Do you have the name and contact information of at least one other student in class?

5. Will your instructor allow you to use a calculator in this class?

6. Is tutorial software available to you? If so, what type and where?

7. Is there a tutoring service available on campus? If so, what are its hours? What services are available?

8. Have you attempted this course before? If so, write down ways that you might improve your chances of success during this second attempt.

9. List some steps that you can take if you begin having trouble understanding the material or completing an assignment.

10. How many hours of studying does your instructor advise for each hour of instruction?

11. What does the ✏ icon in this text mean?

12. What does the 💿 icon in this text mean?

13. What does the △ icon in this text mean?

14. Search the minor columns in your text. What are Practice Problems?

15. When might be the best time to work a Practice Problem?

16. Where are the answers to Practice Problems?

17. What answers are contained in this text and where are they?

18. What solutions are contained in this text and where are they?

19. What and where are Integrated Reviews?

20. What video CD is contained in this book, where is it, and what material is on it?

21. Chapter Highlights are found at the end of each chapter. Find the Chapter 1 Highlights and explain how you might use it and how it might be helpful.

22. Chapter Reviews are found at the end of each chapter. Find the Chapter 1 Review and explain how you might use it and how it might be useful.

23. Chapter Tests are found at the end of each chapter. Find the Chapter 1 Test and explain how you might use it and how it might be helpful when preparing for an exam on Chapter 1. Include how the Chapter Test Prep Video in this book may help.

24. Read or reread objective **F** and fill out the schedule grid below.

	Monday	Tuesday	Wednesday	Thursday	Friday	Saturday	Sunday
7:00 a.m.							
8:00 a.m.							
9:00 a.m.							
10:00 a.m.							
11:00 a.m.							
12:00 a.m.							
1:00 p.m.							
2:00 p.m.							
3:00 p.m.							
4:00 p.m.							
5:00 p.m.							
6:00 p.m.							
7:00 p.m.							
8:00 p.m.							
9:00 p.m.							

1.2 PLACE VALUE AND NAMES FOR NUMBERS

Objectives

 Find the Place Value of a Digit in a Whole Number.

 Write a Whole Number in Words and in Standard Form.

 Write a Whole Number in Expanded Form.

 Read Tables.

The **digits** 0, 1, 2, 3, 4, 5, 6, 7, 8, and 9 can be used to write numbers. For example, the **whole numbers** are

0, 1, 2, 3, 4, 5, 6, 7, 8, 9, 10, 11, . . .

The three dots (. . .) after the 11 mean that this list continues indefinitely. That is, there is no largest whole number. The smallest whole number is 0.

Objective Finding the Place Value of a Digit in a Whole Number

The position of each digit in a number determines its **place value.** For example, the distance (in miles) between the planet Mercury and the planet Earth can be represented by the whole number 48,337,000.

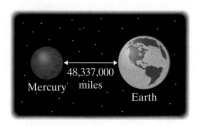

Below is a place-value chart for this whole number.

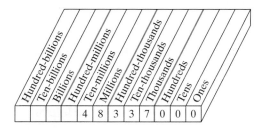

The two 3s in 48,337,000 represent different amounts because of their different placements. The place value of the 3 on the left is hundred-thousands. The place value of the 3 on the right is ten-thousands.

EXAMPLES Find the place value of the digit 4 in each whole number.

1. 48,761
↑
ten-thousands

2. 249
↑
tens

3. 524,007,656
↑
millions

 Work Practice Problems 1–3

Objective Writing a Whole Number in Words and in Standard Form

A whole number such as 1,083,664,500 is written in **standard form.** Notice that commas separate the digits into groups of three, starting from the right. Each group of three digits is called a **period.** The names of the first four periods are shown in blue.

PRACTICE PROBLEMS 1–3

Find the place value of the digit 7 in each whole number.
1. 72,589,620
2. 67,890
3. 50,722

Answers
1. ten-millions, **2.** thousands,
3. hundreds

7

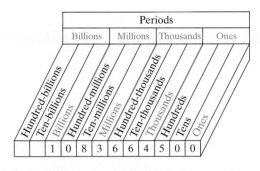

Writing a Whole Number in Words

To write a whole number in words, write the number in each period followed by the name of the period. (The ones period is usually not written.) This same procedure can be used to read a whole number.

For example, we write 1,083,664,500 as

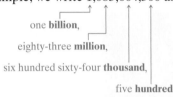

one **billion,**

eighty-three **million,**

six hundred sixty-four **thousand,**

five **hundred**

> **Helpful Hint** Notice the commas after the name of each period.

> **Helpful Hint** The name of the ones period is not used when reading and writing whole numbers. For example,
>
> 9,265
>
> is read as
>
> "nine **thousand,** two **hundred** sixty-five."

PRACTICE PROBLEMS 4–6

Write each number in words.

4. 67

5. 395

6. 12,804

EXAMPLES Write each number in words.

4. 85   eighty-five

5. 126   one hundred twenty-six

6. 27,034   twenty-seven thousand, thirty-four

⬛ **Work Practice Problems 4–6**

> **Helpful Hint** The word "and" is *not* used when reading and writing whole numbers. It is used when reading and writing mixed numbers and some decimal values, as shown later in this text.

PRACTICE PROBLEM 7

Write 321,670,200 in words.

EXAMPLE 7 Write 106,052,447 in words.

Solution: 106,052,447 is written as

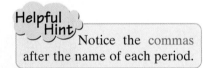

one hundred six **million,** fifty-two **thousand,** four **hundred** forty-seven

⬛ **Work Practice Problem 7**

Answers

4. sixty-seven, **5.** three hundred ninety-five, **6.** twelve thousand, eight hundred four, **7.** three hundred twenty-one million, six hundred seventy thousand, two hundred

✔ **Concept Check Answer**

false

✔ **Concept Check** True or false? When writing a check for $2600, the word name we write for the dollar amount of the check is "two thousand sixty." Explain your answer.

Writing a Whole Number in Standard Form

To write a whole number in standard form, write the number in each period, followed by a comma.

EXAMPLES Write each number in standard form.

8. sixty-one 61

9. eight hundred five 805

10. two million, five hundred sixty-four thousand, three hundred fifty

2,564,350

11. nine thousand, three hundred eighty-six

9,386 or 9386

Work Practice Problems 8–11

PRACTICE PROBLEMS 8–11

Write each number in standard form.

8. twenty-nine

9. seven hundred ten

10. twenty-six thousand, seventy-one

11. six thousand, five hundred seven

Helpful Hint A comma may or may not be inserted in a four-digit number. For example, both

9,386 and 9386

are acceptable ways of writing nine thousand, three hundred eighty-six.

Objective C Writing a Whole Number in Expanded Form

The place value of a digit can be used to write a number in expanded form. The **expanded form** of a number shows each digit of the number with its place value. For example, 5672 is written in expanded form as

5 ↑ digit	thousands ↑ place value	+	6 ↑ digit	hundreds ↑ place value	+	7 ↑ digit	tens ↑ place value	+	2 ↑ digit	ones ↑ place value
	↓			↓			↓			↓
5672 =	5000	+		600	+		70	+		2

EXAMPLE 12 Write 706,449 in expanded form.

Solution: $700{,}000 + 6000 + 400 + 40 + 9$

Work Practice Problem 12

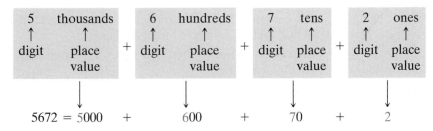

Write thousands or 1000 in numbers?

PRACTICE PROBLEM 12

Write 1,047,608 in expanded form.

Objective D Reading Tables

Now that we know about place value and names for whole numbers, we introduce one way that whole number data may be presented. **Tables** are often used to organize and display facts that involve numbers. The following table shows the countries that won the most medals during the 2004 Olympic summer games. (Although the medals are truly won by athletes from the various countries, for simplicity we will state that countries have won the medals.)

Answers

8. 29, **9.** 710, **10.** 26,071, **11.** 6507, **12.** $1{,}000{,}000 + 40{,}000 + 7000 + 600 + 8$

Most Medals—2004 Olympic Summer Games

Country	Gold	Silver	Bronze	Total	Country	Gold	Silver	Bronze	Total
United States	35	39	27	101	Italy	10	11	11	32
Russia	27	27	38	92	Great Britain	9	9	12	30
China	32	17	14	63	South Korea	9	12	9	30
Australia	17	16	16	49	Cuba	9	7	11	27
Germany	14	16	18	48	Ukraine	9	5	9	23
Japan	16	9	12	37	Netherlands	4	9	9	22
France	11	9	13	33	(*Source:* ESPN.com)				

For example, by reading from left to right along the row marked "U.S." we find that the United States won 35 gold, 39 silver, and 27 bronze medals during the 2004 Summer Games.

PRACTICE PROBLEM 13

Use the Summer Games table to answer the following questions:

a. How many bronze medals did Australia win during the Summer Games of the 2004 Olympics?

b. Which countries shown won more than 30 gold medals?

EXAMPLE 13 Use the Summer Games table to answer each question.

a. How many total medals did China win during the 2004 Summer Games of the Olympics?

b. Which country shown won fewer gold medals than Great Britain?

Solution:

a. Find "China" in the left column. Then read from left to right until the "Total" column is reached. We find that China won 63 total medals.

b. Great Britain won 9 gold medals while Netherlands won 4, so Netherlands won fewer gold medals than Great Britain.

▢ **Work Practice Problem 13**

Answers

13. a. 16,   **b.** United States and China

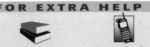

Objective A *Determine the place value of the digit 5 in each whole number. See Examples 1 through 3.*

1. 352

2. 905

3. 5890

4. 6527

5. 62,500,000

6. 79,050,000

7. 5,070,099

8. 51,682,700

Objective B *Write each whole number in words. See Examples 4 through 7.*

9. 542

10. 316

11. 7896

12. 5445

13. 26,990

14. 42,009

15. 1,620,000

16. 3,204,000

17. 53,520,170

18. 47,033,107

Write each number in the sentence in words. See Examples 4 through 7.

19. At this writing, the population of Bermuda is 64,482. (*Source:* 2004 *World Almanac*)

20. Each Home Depot store in the United States and Canada stocks at least 40,000 different kinds of building materials, home improvement supplies, and lawn and garden products. (*Source:* The Home Depot, Inc.)

21. The world's tallest building, the Taipei 101 building in Taiwan is 1679 feet tall. (*Source:* Council on Tall Buildings and Urban Habitat)

22. In a recent year, there were 3895 patients in the United States waiting for a heart transplant. (*Source:* United Network for Organ Sharing)

23. Each day, UPS delivers 13,600,000 packages and documents worldwide. (*Source:* United Parcel Service of America, Inc.)

24. Liz Harold has the number 16,820,409 showing on her calculator display.

25. The highest point in Idaho is at Granite Peak, at an elevation of 12,662 feet. (*Source:* U.S. Geological Survey)

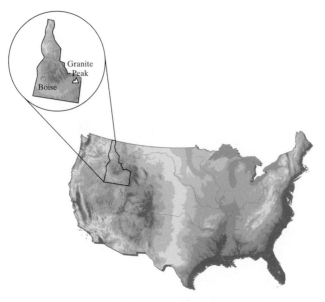

26. The highest point in New Mexico is Wheeler Peak, at an elevation of 13,161 feet. (*Source:* U.S. Geological Survey)

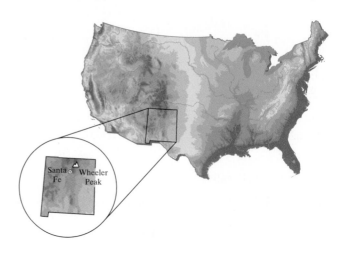

27. The Goodyear blimp *Eagle* holds 202,700 cubic feet of helium. (*Source:* The Goodyear Tire & Rubber Company)

28. In a recent year, zinc mines in the United States mined 799,000 metric tons of zinc. (*Source:* U.S. Dept. of Interior)

Write each whole number in standard form. See Examples 8 through 11.

29. Six thousand, five hundred eighty-seven

30. Three thousand, three hundred seventy-nine

31. Twenty-nine thousand, nine hundred

32. Forty-two thousand, six

33. Sixteen million, five hundred four thousand, nineteen

34. Ten million, thirty-seven thousand, sixteen

35. Three million, fourteen

36. Seven million, twelve

Write the whole number in each sentence in standard form. See Examples 8 through 11.

37. The International Space station orbits above Earth at an altitude of two hundred twenty miles. (*Source:* NASA)

38. The average distance between the surfaces of the Earth and the Moon is about two hundred thirty-four thousand miles.

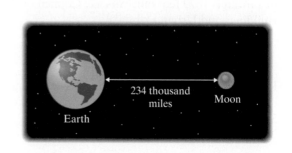

39. The price for a 2005 Porsche Carrera GT is four hundred forty thousand, two hundred seventy-six dollars. (*Source:* Porsche Cars North America)

40. You might know that the zip code for Beverly Hills, California, is 90210, but did you know that one of its area codes is three hundred ten?

41. The Disney/Pixar film *Finding Nemo* set the world record for opening weekend income when it took in seventy million, two hundred fifty-one thousand, seven hundred ten dollars during the weekend of May 30, 2003. (*Source: Guinness Book,* 2005)

42. In 2004, there were one hundred eight million, four hundred thousand U.S. households that owned at least one television set. (*Source:* Nielsen Media Research)

43. The world's tallest self-supporting structure is the CN Tower in Toronto, Canada. It is one thousand, eight hundred fifteen feet tall. (*Source: The World Almanac,* 2005)

44. As of 2004, there were one thousand, eight hundred twenty-four species classified as either threatened or endangered in the United States. (*Source:* U.S. Fish & Wildlife Service)

45. Hank Aaron holds the career record for home runs in Major League baseball since 1974, with a total of seven hundred fifty-five home runs. (*Source:* Major League Baseball)

46. Barry Bonds is approaching Hank Aaron's career record for home runs in Major League baseball (see Exercise 45). Barry has seven hundred three home runs through 2004.

Objective **C** *Write each whole number in expanded form. See Example 12.*

47. 406

48. 789

49. 5290

50. 6040

51. 62,407

52. 20,215

53. 30,680

54. 99,032

55. 39,680,000

56. 47,703,029

Objectives **B** **C** **D** **Mixed Practice** *The table shows the six tallest mountains in New England and their elevations. Use this table to answer Exercises 57 through 62. See Example 13.*

Mountain (State)	Elevation (in feet)
Boott Spur (NH)	5492
Mt. Adams (NH)	5774
Mt. Clay (NH)	5532
Mt. Jefferson (NH)	5712
Mt. Sam Adams (NH)	5584
Mt. Washington (NH)	6288
Source: U.S. Geological Survey	

Elevation in feet

57. Write the elevation of Mt. Clay in standard form and then in words.

58. Write the elevation of Mt. Washington in standard form and then in words.

59. Write the height of Boott Spur in expanded form.

60. Write the height of Mt. Jefferson in expanded form.

61. Which mountain is the tallest in New England?

62. Which mountain is the second tallest in New England?

The table shows the top ten popular breeds of dogs in 2003 according to the American Kennel Club. Use this table to answer Exercises 63 through 68. See Example 13.

Top Ten American Kennel Club Registrations in 2003			
Breed	**Number of Registered Dogs**	**Average Dog Maximum Height (in inches)**	**Average Dog Maximum Weight (in pounds)**
Beagle	45,033	15	30
Boxer	34,136	25	70
Chihuahua	24,930	9	6
Dachshund	39,473	9	25
German shepherd dog	43,950	26	95
Golden retriever	52,530	24	80
Labrador retriever	144,934	25	75
Poodle (standard, miniature, and toy)	32,176	standard: 26	standard: 70
Shih Tzu	26,935	11	16
Yorkshire terrier	38,256	9	7

(*Source:* American Kennel Club)

63. Which breed has more dogs registered, Chihuahua or Golden retriever?

64. Which breed has fewer dogs registered, Beagle or Yorkshire terrier?

65. Which breed has the most American Kennel Club registrations? Write the number of registrations for this breed in words.

66. Which of the listed breeds has the fewest registrations? Write the number of registered dogs for this breed in words.

67. What is the maximum weight of an average-size Dachshund?

68. What is the maximum height of an average-size Yorkshire terrier?

Concept Extensions

69. Write the largest four-digit number that can be made from the digits 3, 6, 7, and 2 if each digit must be used once.

_____ _____ _____ _____

70. Write the largest five-digit number that can be made using the digits 4, 5, and 3 if each digit must be used at least once.

_____ _____, _____ _____ _____

Check to see whether each number written in standard form matches the number written in words. If not, correct the number in words. See the Concept Check in this section.

71.

60–8124/7233
1000613331   1401

DATE

PAY TO
THE ORDER OF $ *105.00*

One Hundred Fifty and ⁰⁰/₁₀₀ ——— DOLLARS

FIRST STATE BANK
OF FARTHINGTON
FARTHINGTON, IL 64422

MEMO

⑆621497260⑆ 1000613331⑈ 1401

72.

60–8124/7233
1000613331   1402

DATE

PAY TO
THE ORDER OF $ *7030.00*

Seven Thousand Thirty and ⁰⁰/₁₀₀ ——— DOLLARS

FIRST STATE BANK
OF FARTHINGTON
FARTHINGTON, IL 64422

MEMO

⑆621497260⑆ 1000613331⑈ 1402

73. If a number is given in words, describe the process used to write this number in standard form.

74. If a number is written in standard form, describe the process used to write this number in expanded form.

75. The Pro-Football Hall of Fame was established on September 7, 1963, in this town. Use the information and the diagram to the right to find the name of the town.

- Alliance is east of Massillon.
- Dover is between Canton and New Philadelphia.
- Massillon is not next to Alliance.
- Canton is north of Dover.

Pro-Football
Hall of Fame

OHIO

76. The world's fastest super computer is Japan's Earth Simulator, which is programmed to simulate weather patterns and other massive systems. It can perform thirty-five trillion calculations in a second. Look up "trillion" in a dictionary and use the definition to write this number in standard form. (*Source:* 2005 *World Almanac*)

1.3 ADDING WHOLE NUMBERS AND PERIMETER

Objective A Adding Whole Numbers

The iPod is a hard drive–based portable audio player. As of 2004, it is the most popular digital music player in the United States.

Suppose that a small computer store received a shipment of two iPods one day and an additional four iPods the next day. The **total** shipment in the two days can be found by adding 2 and 4.

$$2 \text{ iPods} + 4 \text{ iPods} = 6 \text{ iPods}$$

The **sum** (or total) is 6 iPods. Each of the numbers 2 and 4 is called an **addend,** and the process of finding the sum is called **addition.**

$$\underset{\text{addend}}{2} \quad + \quad \underset{\text{addend}}{4} \quad = \quad \underset{\text{sum}}{6}$$

To add whole numbers, we add the digits in the ones place, then the tens place, then the hundreds place, and so on. For example, let's add $2236 + 160$.

$$
\begin{array}{r}
2236 \\
+160 \\
\hline
2396
\end{array}
$$

Line up numbers vertically so that the place values correspond. Then add digits in corresponding place values, starting with the ones place.

sum of ones
sum of tens
sum of hundreds
sum of thousands

EXAMPLE 1 Add: $23 + 136$

Solution:
$$
\begin{array}{r}
23 \\
+136 \\
\hline
159
\end{array}
$$

■ **Work Practice Problem 1**

When the sum of digits in corresponding place values is more than 9, **carrying** is necessary. For example, to add $365 + 89$, add the ones-place digits first.

Carrying
$$
\begin{array}{r}
\overset{1}{3}65 \\
+\ 89 \\
\hline
4
\end{array}
$$
5 ones + 9 ones = **14 ones** or **1 ten** + **4 ones**
Write the 4 ones in the ones place and carry the 1 ten to the tens place.

Next, add the tens-place digits.

$$
\begin{array}{r}
\overset{1\ 1}{3}65 \\
+\ 89 \\
\hline
54
\end{array}
$$
1 ten + 6 tens + 8 tens = **15 tens** or **1 hundred** + **5 tens**
Write the 5 tens in the tens place and carry the 1 hundred to the hundreds place.

Next, add the hundreds-place digits.

$$
\begin{array}{r}
\overset{1\ 1}{3}65 \\
+\ 89 \\
\hline
454
\end{array}
$$
1 hundred + 3 hundreds = 4 hundreds
Write the 4 hundreds in the hundreds place.

PRACTICE PROBLEM 1

Add: $7235 + 542$

Answer

1. 7777

16

EXAMPLE 2 Add: 34,285 + 149,761

Solution:
$$\begin{array}{r} \overset{1\ 1\ \ 1}{34{,}285} \\ +\ 149{,}761 \\ \hline 184{,}046 \end{array}$$

■ **Work Practice Problem 2**

✔**Concept Check** What is wrong with the following computation?

$$\begin{array}{r} 394 \\ +\ 283 \\ \hline 577 \end{array}$$

Before we continue adding whole numbers, let's review some properties of addition that you may have already discovered. The first property that we will review is the **addition property of 0.** This property reminds us that the sum of 0 and any number is that same number.

Addition Property of 0

The sum of 0 and any number is that number. For example,

$$7 + 0 = 7$$
$$0 + 7 = 7$$

Next, notice that we can add any two whole numbers in any order and the sum is the same. For example,

$$4 + 5 = 9 \quad \text{and} \quad 5 + 4 = 9$$

We call this special property of addition the **commutative property of addition.**

Commutative Property of Addition

Changing the **order** of two addends does not change their sum. For example,

$$2 + 3 = 5 \quad \text{and} \quad 3 + 2 = 5$$

Another property that can help us when adding numbers is the **associative property of addition.** This property states that when adding numbers, the grouping of the numbers can be changed without changing the sum. We use parentheses to group numbers. They indicate which numbers to add first. For example, let's use two different groupings to find the sum of 2 + 1 + 5.

$$\underbrace{(2 + 1)} + 5 = 3 + 5 = 8$$

Also,

$$2 + \underbrace{(1 + 5)} = 2 + 6 = 8$$

Both groupings give a sum of 8.

PRACTICE PROBLEM 2
Add: 27,364 + 92,977

Answer
2. 120,341

✔ **Concept Check Answer**
forgot to carry 1 hundred to the hundreds place

Associative Property of Addition

Changing the **grouping** of addends does not change their sum. For example,

$$3 + (5 + 7) = 3 + 12 = 15 \quad \text{and} \quad (3 + 5) + 7 = 8 + 7 = 15$$

The commutative and associative properties tell us that we can add whole numbers using any order and grouping that we want.

    When adding several numbers, it is often helpful to look for two or three numbers whose sum is 10, 20, and so on. Why? Adding multiples of 10 such as 10 and 20 is easier.

PRACTICE PROBLEM 3

Add: $11 + 7 + 8 + 9 + 13$

EXAMPLE 3 Add: $13 + 2 + 7 + 8 + 9$

Solution: $13 + 2 + 7 + 8 + 9 = 39$

$$20 + 10 + 9$$

$$39$$

◻ **Work Practice Problem 3**

Feel free to use the process of Example 3 anytime when adding.

PRACTICE PROBLEM 4

Add: $19 + 5042 + 638 + 526$

EXAMPLE 4 Add: $1647 + 246 + 32 + 85$

Solution:

$$
\begin{array}{r}
^{1\,2\,2}\\
1647\\
246\\
32\\
+\quad 85\\
\hline
2010
\end{array}
$$

◻ **Work Practice Problem 4**

Objective B Finding the Perimeter of a Polygon

In geometry addition is used to find the perimeter of a polygon. A **polygon** can be described as a flat figure formed by line segments connected at their ends. (For more review, see Appendix A.3.) Geometric figures such as triangles, squares, and rectangles are called polygons.

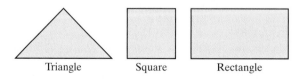

Triangle   Square   Rectangle

    The **perimeter** of a polygon is the *distance around* the polygon. This means that the perimeter of a polygon is the sum of the lengths of its sides.

Answers

3. 48, **4.** 6225

EXAMPLE 5 Find the perimeter of the polygon shown.

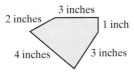

Solution: To find the perimeter (distance around), we add the lengths of the sides.

2 in. + 3 in. + 1 in. + 3 in. + 4 in. = 13 in.

The perimeter is 13 inches.

■ **Work Practice Problem 5**

To make the addition appear simpler, we will often not include units with the addends. If you do this, make sure units are included in the final answer.

 EXAMPLE 6 **Calculating the Perimeter of a Building**

The largest commercial building in the world under one roof is the flower auction building of the cooperative VBA in Aalsmeer, Netherlands. The floor plan is a rectangle that measures 776 meters by 639 meters. Find the perimeter of this building. (A meter is a unit of length in the metric system.) (*Source: The Handy Science Answer Book*, Visible Ink Press)

Solution: Recall that opposite sides of a rectangle have the same length. To find the perimeter of this building, we add the lengths of the sides. The sum of the lengths of its sides is

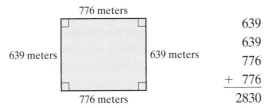

$$\begin{array}{r} 639 \\ 639 \\ 776 \\ + 776 \\ \hline 2830 \end{array}$$

The perimeter of the building is 2830 meters.

■ **Work Practice Problem 6**

Objective C Solving Problems by Adding

Often, real-life problems occur that can be solved by writing an addition statement. The first step in solving any word problem is to *understand* the problem by reading it carefully. Descriptions of problems solved through addition *may* include any of these key words or phrases:

Key Words or Phrases	Example	Symbols
added to	5 added to 7	7 + 5
plus	0 plus 78	0 + 78
increased by	12 increased by 6	12 + 6
more than	11 more than 25	25 + 11
total	the total of 8 and 1	8 + 1
sum	the sum of 4 and 133	4 + 133

To solve a word problem that involves addition, we first use the facts given to write an addition statement. Then we write the corresponding solution of the real-life

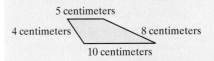

problem. It is sometimes helpful to write the statement in words (brief phrases) and then translate to numbers.

PRACTICE PROBLEM 7

Texas produces 90 million pounds of pecans per year. Georgia is the world's top pecan producer and produces 15 million pounds more pecans than Texas. How much does Georgia produce? (*Source: Absolute Trivia.com*)

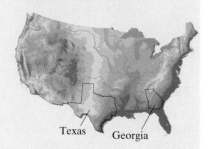

EXAMPLE 7 Finding a Salary

The governor's salary in the state of Alabama was recently increased by $1706. If the old salary was $94,655, find the new salary. (*Source: The World Almanac and Book of Facts*, 2003 and 2005)

Montgomery

Solution: The key phrase here is "increased by," which suggests that we add. To find the new salary, we add the increase, $1706, to the old salary.

In Words		Translate to Numbers
old salary	→	94,655
+ increase	→	+ 1 706
new salary	→	96,361

The Alabama governor's salary is now $96,361.

Work Practice Problem 7

Graphs can be used to visualize data. The graph shown next is called a **bar graph.** For this bar graph, the height of each bar is labeled above the bar. To check this height, follow the top of each bar to the vertical line to the left. For example, the second bar is labeled 15. Follow the top of that bar to the left until the vertical line is reached, halfway between 10 and 20, or 15.

PRACTICE PROBLEM 8

Use the graph in Example 8 to answer the following:

a. Which rating had the least number of Best Picture nominees?

b. Find the total number of Best Picture nominees that were rated PG, PG-13, or R.

EXAMPLE 8 Reading a Bar Graph

The graph below shows the ratings of Best Picture nominees since PG-13 was introduced in 1984. In this graph, each bar represents a different rating, and the height of each bar represents the number of Best Picture nominees for that rating.

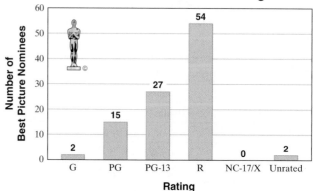

Source: Academy of Motion Picture Arts and Sciences; Internet Movie Database

a. Which rating did most Best Picture nominees have?

b. Find the total number of Best Picture nominees that were rated G, PG, or PG-13.

Solution:

a. The rating for most Best Picture nominees is the one corresponding to the highest bar, which is an R rating.

b. The key word here is "total." To find the total number of Best Picture nominees that were rated G, PG, or PG-13, we add.

In Words		Translate to Numbers
G-rated nominees	$\rightarrow$	2
PG-rated nominees	$\rightarrow$	15
PG-13–rated nominees	$\rightarrow$	$+\ 27$
Total		44

The number of Best Picture nominees rated G, PG, or PG-13 is 44.

■ **Work Practice Problem 8**

▦ **CALCULATOR EXPLORATIONS**   Adding Numbers

To add numbers on a calculator, find the keys marked $\boxed{+}$ and $\boxed{=}$ or $\boxed{\text{ENTER}}$.

For example, to add 5 and 7 on a calculator, press the keys $\boxed{5}\ \boxed{+}\ \boxed{7}\ \boxed{=}$ or $\boxed{\text{ENTER}}$.

The display will read $\boxed{\qquad 12}$.
Thus, 5 + 7 = 12.

To add 687, 981, and 49 on a calculator, press the keys $\boxed{687}\ \boxed{+}\ \boxed{981}\ \boxed{+}\ \boxed{49}\ \boxed{=}$ or $\boxed{\text{ENTER}}$.
The display will read $\boxed{\qquad 1717}$.

Thus, 687 + 981 + 49 = 1717. (Although entering 687, for example, requires pressing more than one key, here numbers are grouped together for easier reading.)

Use a calculator to add.

1. 89 + 45

2. 76 + 97

3. 285 + 55

4. 8773 + 652

5.
985
1210
562
+ 77

6.
465
9888
620
+1550

Mental Math

Find each sum.

1. $9 + 7$ **2.** $20 + 30$ **3.** $5000 + 4000$ **4.** $4300 + 26$ **5.** $1620 + 0$ **6.** $6 + 126 + 4$

1.3 EXERCISE SET

FOR EXTRA HELP

Student Solutions Manual   PH Math/Tutor Center   CD/Video for Review   Math XL MathXL®   MyMathLab MyMathLab

Objective **A** *Add. See Examples 1 through 4.*

1. $\begin{array}{r} 14 \\ +22 \end{array}$
2. $\begin{array}{r} 27 \\ +31 \end{array}$
3. $\begin{array}{r} 62 \\ +230 \end{array}$
4. $\begin{array}{r} 37 \\ +542 \end{array}$
5. $\begin{array}{r} 12 \\ 13 \\ +24 \end{array}$

6. $\begin{array}{r} 23 \\ 45 \\ +30 \end{array}$
7. $\begin{array}{r} 5267 \\ +\ 132 \end{array}$
8. $\begin{array}{r} 236 \\ +6243 \end{array}$
9. $53 + 64$
10. $41 + 74$

11. $22 + 490$ **12.** $35 + 470$ **13.** $22{,}781 + 186{,}297$ **14.** $17{,}427 + 821{,}059$

15. $\begin{array}{r} 8 \\ 9 \\ 2 \\ 5 \\ +1 \end{array}$
16. $\begin{array}{r} 3 \\ 5 \\ 8 \\ 5 \\ +7 \end{array}$
17. $\begin{array}{r} 6 \\ 21 \\ 14 \\ 9 \\ +12 \end{array}$
18. $\begin{array}{r} 12 \\ 4 \\ 8 \\ 26 \\ +10 \end{array}$

19. $\begin{array}{r} 81 \\ 17 \\ 23 \\ 79 \\ +12 \end{array}$
20. $\begin{array}{r} 64 \\ 28 \\ 56 \\ 25 \\ +32 \end{array}$
21. $62 + 18 + 14$
22. $23 + 49 + 18$

23. $40 + 800 + 70$ **24.** $30 + 900 + 20$ **25.** $7542 + 49 + 682$

26. $1624 + 32 + 976$ **27.** $24 + 9006 + 489 + 2407$ **28.** $16 + 1056 + 748 + 7770$

29. 627
         628
      + 629

30. 427
         383
      + 229

31. 6820
         4271
      + 5626

32. 6789
         4321
      + 5555

33. 507
         593
      + 10

34. 864
          33
      + 356

35. 4200
         2107
      + 2692

36. 5000
         1400
      + 3021

37.   49
            628
          5 762
      + 29,462

38.   26
             582
           4 763
      + 62,511

39. 121,742
          57,279
          26,586
      + 426,782

40. 504,218
         321,920
          38,507
      + 594,687

Objective **B** *Find the perimeter of each figure. See Examples 5 and 6.*

△ **41.**

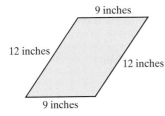

9 inches
12 inches
12 inches
9 inches

△ **42.**

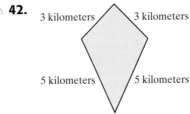

3 kilometers   3 kilometers
5 kilometers   5 kilometers

43.

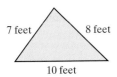

7 feet   8 feet
10 feet

△ **44.**

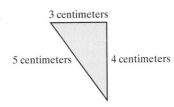

3 centimeters
5 centimeters   4 centimeters

△ **45.**

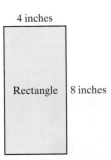

4 inches
Rectangle   8 inches

△ **46.**

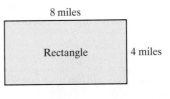

8 miles
Rectangle   4 miles

△ **47.**

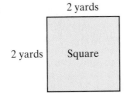

2 yards
2 yards   Square

△ **48.**

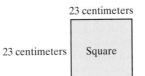

23 centimeters
23 centimeters   Square

△ **49.**

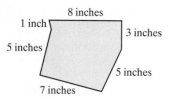

△ **50.**

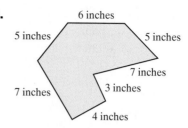

Objectives Ⓐ Ⓑ Ⓒ **Mixed Practice** *Solve. See Examples 1 through 8.*

51. Find the sum of 297 and 1796.

52. Find the sum of 802 and 6487.

53. Find the total of 76, 39, 8, 17, and 126.

54. Find the total of 89, 45, 2, 19, and 341.

55. What is 452 increased by 92?

56. What is 712 increased by 38?

57. What is 2686 plus 686 plus 80?

58. What is 3565 plus 565 plus 70?

59. The highest point in South Carolina is Sassafras Mountain at 3560 feet above sea level. The highest point in North Carolina is Mt. Mitchell, whose peak is 3124 feet increased by the height of Sassafras Mountain. Find the height of Mt. Mitchell. (*Source: U.S. Geological Survey*)

60. The distance from Kansas City, Kansas, to Hays, Kansas, is 285 miles. Colby, Kansas, is 98 miles farther from Kansas City than Hays. Find the total distance from Kansas City to Colby.

△ **61.** Leo Callier is installing an invisible fence in his backyard. How many feet of wiring are needed to enclose the yard below?

△ **62.** A homeowner is considering installing gutters around her home. Find the perimeter of her rectangular home.

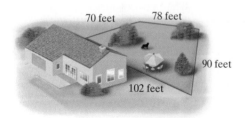

63. In 2003, Harley-Davidson sold 228,400 of its motorcycles domestically. In addition, 62,747 Harley-Davidson motorcycles were sold internationally. What was the total number of Harley-Davidson motorcycles sold in 2003? (*Source:* Harley-Davidson, Inc.)

64. Dan Marino holds the NFL career record for most passes completed. He completed 2305 passes from the beginning of his NFL career in 1983 through 1989. He completed another 2662 passes from 1990 through 1999, his last season before retiring from professional football. How many total passes did he complete during his NFL career? (*Source:* National Football League)

65. The highest waterfall in the United States is Yosemite Falls in Yosemite National Park in California. Yosemite Falls is made up of three sections, as shown in the graph. What is the total height of Yosemite Falls? (*Source:* U.S. Department of the Interior)

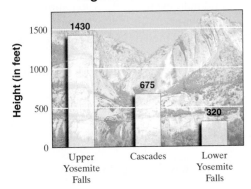

Highest U.S. Waterfalls

66. Jordan White, a nurse at Mercy Hospital, is recording fluid intake on a patient's medical chart. During his shift, the patient had the following types and amounts of intake measured in cubic centimeters (cc). What amount should Jordan record as the total fluid intake for this patient?

Oral	Intravenous	Blood
240	500	500
100	200	
355		

67. The State of Alaska has 1795 miles of urban highways and 11,460 miles of rural highways. Find the total highway mileage in Alaska. (*Source:* U.S. Federal Highway Administration)

68. The state of Hawaii has 1851 miles of urban highways and 2291 miles of rural highways. Find the total highway mileage in Hawaii. (*Source:* U.S. Federal Highway Administration)

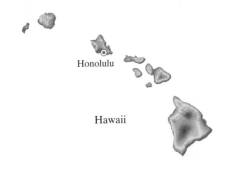

69. The largest permanent Monopoly board is made of granite and located in San Jose, California. Find the perimeter of the square playing board.

31 ft

31 ft

70. The smallest commercially available jigsaw puzzle is a 1000-piece puzzle manufactured in Spain. Find the perimeter of this rectangular-shaped puzzle.

12 in.

18 in.

71. The two top-selling automobiles in the United States are the Honda Accord, with sales of 397,750 and the Toyota Camry with sales of 369,562 in 2003. What is the total amount of Accords and Camrys sold in 2003? (*Source:* J. D. Power and Associates)

72. In the country of New Zealand, there are 40,748,693 more sheep than there are people. If the human population of New Zealand is 3,951,307, what is the sheep population? (*Source:* Food and Agricultural Organization of the United States)

73. In 2004, there were 5670 Blockbuster video rental stores located in the United States and 3197 located outside the United States. How many Blockbuster rental stores were located worldwide? (*Source:* Blockbuster Inc.)

74. Wilma Rudolph, who won three gold medals in track and field events in the 1960 Summer Olympics, was born in 1940. Marion Jones, who also won three gold medals in track and field events but in the 2000 Summer Olympics, was born 35 years later. In what year was Marion Jones born?

The table shows the number of Target stores in ten states. Use this table to answer Exercises 75 through 80.

The Top States for Target Stores in 2003	
State	**Number of Stores**
Arizona	36
California	184
Florida	78
Georgia	38
Illinois	62
New York	37
Michigan	51
Minnesota	65
Ohio	44
Texas	104
(*Source:* Target Corporation)	

75. Which state has the most Target stores?

76. Which of the states listed in the table has the fewest number of Target stores?

77. What is the total number of Target stores located in the three states with the most Target stores?

78. How many Target stores are located in the ten states listed in the table?

79. Which pair of neighboring states have more Target stores combined, Florida and Georgia or Michigan and Ohio?

80. Target operates stores in 47 states. There are 526 Target stores located in the states not listed in the table. How many Target stores are in the United States?

Concept Extensions

81. In your own words, explain the commutative property of addition.

82. In your own words, explain the associative property of addition.

83. Give any three whole numbers whose sum is 100.

84. Give any four whole numbers whose sum is 25.

85. Find the perimeter of the figure.

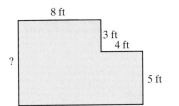

8 ft
3 ft
4 ft
?
5 ft
?

86. Add: 78,962 + 129,968,350 + 36,462,880

87. Add: 56,468,980 + 1,236,785 + 986,768,000

Check each addition below. If it is incorrect, find the correct answer. See the Concept Check in this section.

88.
```
   566
   932
+  871
  2369
```

89.
```
   773
   659
+  481
  1913
```

90.
```
    14
   173
    86
+  257
   520
```

91.
```
    19
   214
    49
+  651
   923
```

📖 STUDY SKILLS BUILDER

Learning New Terms?

Many of the terms used in this text may be new to you. It will be helpful to make a list of new mathematical terms and symbols as you encounter them and to review them frequently. Placing these new terms (including page references) on 3 × 5 index cards might help you later when you're preparing for a quiz.

Answer the following.

1. Name one way you might place a word and its definition on a 3 × 5 card.

2. How do new terms stand out in this text so that they can be found?

1.4 SUBTRACTING WHOLE NUMBERS

Objective **A** Subtracting Whole Numbers

If you have $5 and someone gives you $3, you have a total of $8, since $5 + 3 = 8$. Similarly, if you have $8 and then someone borrows $3, you have $5 left. **Subtraction** is finding the **difference** of two numbers.

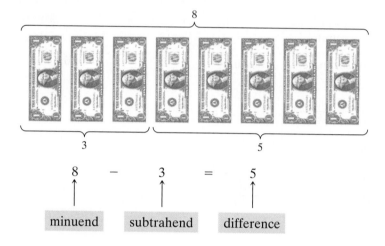

$$8 \quad - \quad 3 \quad = \quad 5$$

minuend   subtrahend   difference

Notice that addition and subtraction are very closely related. In fact, subtraction is defined in terms of addition.

$8 - 3 = 5$ because $5 + 3 = 8$

This means that subtraction can be *checked* by addition, and we say that addition and subtraction are reverse operations.

PRACTICE PROBLEM 1

Subtract. Check each answer by adding.
a. $14 - 9$
b. $20 - 8$
c. $9 - 9$
d. $4 - 0$

EXAMPLE 1 Subtract. Check each answer by adding.

a. $12 - 9$ b. $11 - 6$ c. $5 - 5$ d. $7 - 0$

Solution:

a. $12 - 9 = 3$ because $3 + 9 = 12$
b. $11 - 6 = 5$ because $5 + 6 = 11$
c. $5 - 5 = 0$ because $0 + 5 = 5$
d. $7 - 0 = 7$ because $7 + 0 = 7$

Work Practice Problem 1

Look again at Examples 1(c) and 1(d).

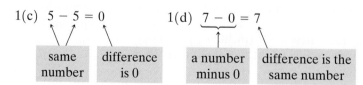

1(c) $5 - 5 = 0$ — same number, difference is 0

1(d) $7 - 0 = 7$ — a number minus 0, difference is the same number

These two examples illustrate the subtraction properties of 0.

Answers

1. **a.** 5, **b.** 12, **c.** 0, **d.** 4

Subtraction Properties of 0

The difference of any number and that same number is 0. For example,

$$11 - 11 = 0$$

The difference of any number and 0 is that same number. For example,

$$45 - 0 = 45$$

To subtract whole numbers we subtract the digits in the ones place, then the tens place, then the hundreds place, and so on. When subtraction involves numbers of two or more digits, it is more convenient to subtract vertically. For example, to subtract 893 − 52,

```
  893  ←——— minuend          Line up the numbers vertically so that the minuend is on top
 − 52  ←——— subtrahend        and the place values correspond. Subtract in corresponding
  ───                          places, starting with the ones place.
  841  ←——— difference
   ↑↑↑
    │ │ 3 − 2
    │ 9 − 5
    8 − 0
```

To check, add.

```
  difference   or       841
 + subtrahend         +  52
  ──────────           ─────
   minuend               893  ←——— Since this is the original minuend,
                                    the problem checks.
```

EXAMPLE 2   Subtract: 7826 − 505. Check by adding.

Solution: 7826 ←   **Check:**   7321
                  −505   +505
                  ─────   ─────
                  7321   7826

■ **Work Practice Problem 2**

Objective B Subtracting with Borrowing

When subtracting vertically, if a digit in the second number (subtrahend) is larger than the corresponding digit in the first number (minuend), **borrowing** is necessary. For example, consider

```
   8 1
 − 6 3
```

Since the 3 in the ones place of 63 is larger than the 1 in the ones place of 81, borrowing is necessary. We borrow 1 ten from the tens place and add it to the ones place.

Borrowing

```
   8  − 1 = 7  →    7 11  ←—1 ten + 1 one = 11 ones
  tens  ten  tens   8̸ 1̸
                   − 6 3
```

Now we subtract the ones-place digits and then the tens-place digits.

$$\begin{array}{r} {}^{7\ 11}\!\!\!\not{8}\not{1} \\ -63 \\ \hline 18 \end{array}$$ ←—11 − 3 = 8
          ⌐—— 7 − 6 = 1

Check:

$$\begin{array}{r} 18 \\ +63 \\ \hline 81 \end{array}$$ The original minuend

PRACTICE PROBLEM 3

Subtract. Check by adding.

a. $\begin{array}{r} 227 \\ -175 \\ \hline \end{array}$

b. $\begin{array}{r} 1136 \\ -\ 914 \\ \hline \end{array}$

c. $\begin{array}{r} 8627 \\ -4119 \\ \hline \end{array}$

EXAMPLE 3 Subtract: 543 − 29. Check by adding.

Solution: $\begin{array}{r} {}^{3\ 13}\!\!\!5\not{4}\not{3} \\ -29 \\ \hline 514 \end{array}$ **Check:** $\begin{array}{r} 514 \\ +29 \\ \hline 543 \end{array}$

Work Practice Problem 3

Sometimes we may have to borrow from more than one place. For example, to subtract 7631 − 152, we first borrow from the tens place.

$$\begin{array}{r} {}^{2\ 11}\!\!\!76\not{3}\not{1} \\ -\ 152 \\ \hline 9 \end{array}$$ ←—11 − 2 = 9

In the tens place, 5 is greater than 2, so we borrow again. This time we borrow from the hundreds place.

⌐—— 6 hundreds − **1 hundred** = 5 hundreds

$$\begin{array}{r} {}^{5\ \not{2}\ 11}_{\ \ 12}\!\!\!7\not{6}\not{3}\not{1} \\ -\ 152 \\ \hline 7479 \end{array}$$ **1 hundred** + 2 tens
                    or
   10 tens + 2 tens = **12 tens**

Check:

$$\begin{array}{r} 7479 \\ +\ 152 \\ \hline 7631 \end{array}$$ The original minuend

PRACTICE PROBLEM 4

Subtract. Check by adding.

a. $\begin{array}{r} 400 \\ -164 \\ \hline \end{array}$

b. $\begin{array}{r} 200 \\ -\ 45 \\ \hline \end{array}$

c. $\begin{array}{r} 1000 \\ -\ 762 \\ \hline \end{array}$

EXAMPLE 4 Subtract: 900 − 174. Check by adding.

Solution: In the ones place, 4 is larger than 0, so we borrow from the tens place. But the tens place of 900 is 0, so to borrow from the tens place we must first borrow from the hundreds place.

$$\begin{array}{r} {}^{8\ \ 10}\!\!\!\not{9}\not{0}0 \\ -174 \\ \hline \end{array}$$

Answers

3. **a.** 52,   **b.** 222,   **c.** 4508,
4. **a.** 236,   **b.** 155,   **c.** 238

Now borrow from the tens place.

$$
\begin{array}{r}
\overset{9}{\cancel{8}}\ \overset{\cancel{10}}{\cancel{0}}\ \overset{10}{\cancel{0}} \\
-\ 1\ 7\ 4 \\
\hline
7\ 2\ 6
\end{array}
$$

Check:

$$
\begin{array}{r}
726 \\
+\ 174 \\
\hline
900
\end{array}
$$

🔲 **Work Practice Problem 4**

Objective C Solving Problems by Subtracting

Descriptions of real-life problems that suggest solving by subtraction include these key words or phrases:

Key Words or Phrases	Examples	Symbols
subtract	subtract 5 from 8	$8 - 5$
difference	the difference of 10 and 2	$10 - 2$
less	17 less 3	$17 - 3$
less than	2 less than 20	$20 - 2$
take away	14 take away 9	$14 - 9$
decreased by	7 decreased by 5	$7 - 5$
subtracted from	9 subtracted from 12	$12 - 9$

✔ **Concept Check** In each of the following problems, identify which number is the minuend and which number is the subtrahend.

  a. What is the result when 9 is subtracted from 20?
  b. What is the difference of 15 and 8?
  c. Find a number that is 15 fewer than 23.

EXAMPLE 5 **Finding the Radius of a Planet**

The radius of Venus is 6052 kilometers. The radius of Mercury is 3612 kilometers less than the radius of Venus. Find the radius of Mercury. (*Source:* National Space Science Data Center)

Venus
6052 kilometers

Mercury
?

Continued on next page

Solution:

In Words		Translate to Numbers
radius of Venus	$\longrightarrow$	6052
− 3612	$\longrightarrow$	− 3612
radius of Mercury	$\longrightarrow$	2440

The radius of Mercury is 2440 kilometers.

▣ **Work Practice Problem 5**

PRACTICE PROBLEM 6

During a sale, the price of a new suit is decreased by $47. If the original price was $92, find the sale price of the suit.

EXAMPLE 6 **Calculating Miles per Gallon**

A subcompact car gets 42 miles per gallon of gas. A full-size car gets 17 miles per gallon of gas. Find the difference between the subcompact car miles per gallon and the full-size car miles per gallon.

Solution:

In Words		Translate to Numbers
subcompact miles per gallon	$\longrightarrow$	$\overset{3\ \ 12}{\cancel{4}\ \cancel{2}}$
− full-size miles per gallon	$\longrightarrow$	− 1 7
difference in miles per gallon		2 5

The difference in the subcompact car miles per gallon and the full-size car miles per gallon is 25 miles per gallon.

▣ **Work Practice Problem 6**

> **Helpful Hint**
> Since subtraction and addition are reverse operations, don't forget that a subtraction problem can be checked by adding.

▦ **CALCULATOR EXPLORATIONS**   Subtracting Numbers

To subtract numbers on a calculator, find the keys marked ⎡−⎤ and ⎡=⎤ or ⎡ENTER⎤.

For example, to find 83 − 49 on a calculator, press the keys

⎡83⎤ ⎡−⎤ ⎡49⎤ ⎡=⎤ or ⎡ENTER⎤.

The display will read ⎡   34 ⎤. Thus, 83 − 49 = 34.

Use a calculator to subtract.

1. 865 − 95   **2.** 76 − 27

3. 147 − 38   **4.** 366 − 87

5. 9625 − 647   **6.** 10,711 − 8925

Answer

6. $45

Mental Math

Find each difference. See Example 1.

1. $9 - 2$ **2.** $6 - 6$ **3.** $5 - 0$ **4.** $44 - 22$ **5.** $93 - 93$

6. $700 - 400$ **7.** $700 - 300$ **8.** $700 - 700$ **9.** $600 - 100$ **10.** $600 - 0$

1.4 EXERCISE SET

Objective A *Subtract. Check by adding. See Examples 1 and 2.*

1.
$$\begin{array}{r} 67 \\ -23 \\ \hline \end{array}$$

2.
$$\begin{array}{r} 72 \\ -41 \\ \hline \end{array}$$

3.
$$\begin{array}{r} 389 \\ -124 \\ \hline \end{array}$$

4.
$$\begin{array}{r} 572 \\ -321 \\ \hline \end{array}$$

5.
$$\begin{array}{r} 167 \\ -32 \\ \hline \end{array}$$

6.
$$\begin{array}{r} 286 \\ -45 \\ \hline \end{array}$$

7. $2677 - 423$

8. $5766 - 324$

9. $6998 - 1453$

10. $4912 - 2610$

 11.
$$\begin{array}{r} 749 \\ -149 \\ \hline \end{array}$$

12.
$$\begin{array}{r} 257 \\ -257 \\ \hline \end{array}$$

Objectives A B Mixed Practice *Subtract. Check by adding. See Examples 1 through 4.*

 13.
$$\begin{array}{r} 62 \\ -37 \\ \hline \end{array}$$

14.
$$\begin{array}{r} 55 \\ -29 \\ \hline \end{array}$$

15.
$$\begin{array}{r} 70 \\ -25 \\ \hline \end{array}$$

16.
$$\begin{array}{r} 80 \\ -37 \\ \hline \end{array}$$

17.
$$\begin{array}{r} 938 \\ -792 \\ \hline \end{array}$$

18.
$$\begin{array}{r} 436 \\ -275 \\ \hline \end{array}$$

19.
$$\begin{array}{r} 922 \\ -634 \\ \hline \end{array}$$

20.
$$\begin{array}{r} 674 \\ -299 \\ \hline \end{array}$$

21.
$$\begin{array}{r} 600 \\ -432 \\ \hline \end{array}$$

22.
$$\begin{array}{r} 300 \\ -149 \\ \hline \end{array}$$

23.
$$\begin{array}{r} 142 \\ -36 \\ \hline \end{array}$$

24.
$$\begin{array}{r} 773 \\ -29 \\ \hline \end{array}$$

25.
$$\begin{array}{r} 923 \\ -476 \\ \hline \end{array}$$

26.
$$\begin{array}{r} 813 \\ -227 \\ \hline \end{array}$$

27.
$$\begin{array}{r} 6283 \\ -560 \\ \hline \end{array}$$

28.
$$\begin{array}{r} 5349 \\ -720 \\ \hline \end{array}$$

29.
$$\begin{array}{r} 533 \\ -29 \\ \hline \end{array}$$

30.
$$\begin{array}{r} 724 \\ -16 \\ \hline \end{array}$$

31.
$$\begin{array}{r} 200 \\ -111 \\ \hline \end{array}$$

32.
$$\begin{array}{r} 300 \\ -211 \\ \hline \end{array}$$

33.
$$\begin{array}{r} 1983 \\ -1904 \\ \hline \end{array}$$

34.
$$\begin{array}{r} 1983 \\ -1914 \\ \hline \end{array}$$

35.
$$\begin{array}{r} 56,422 \\ -16,508 \\ \hline \end{array}$$

36.
$$\begin{array}{r} 76,652 \\ -29,498 \\ \hline \end{array}$$

37. 50,000 − 17,289   **38.** 40,000 − 23,582   **39.** 7020 − 1979

40. 6050 − 1878   **41.** 51,111 − 19,898   **42.** 62,222 − 39,898

Objective **C** *Solve. See Examples 5 and 6.*

43. Subtract 5 from 9.

44. Subtract 9 from 21.

45. Find the difference of 41 and 21.

46. Find the difference of 16 and 5.

47. Subtract 56 from 63.

48. Subtract 41 from 59.

49. Find 108 less 36.

50. Find 25 less 12.

51. Find 12 subtracted from 100.

52. Find 86 subtracted from 90.

53. Dyllis King is reading a 503-page book. If she has just finished reading page 239, how many more pages must she read to finish the book?

54. When Lou and Judy Zawislak began a trip, the odometer read 55,492. When the trip was over, the odometer read 59,320. How many miles did they drive on their trip?

55. In 1997, the hole in the Earth's ozone layer over Antartica was about 21 million square kilometers in size. In 2001, the hole had grown to 25 million square kilometers. By how much has the hole grown from 1997 to 2001? (*Source:* U.S. Environmental Protection Agency EPA)

56. Bamboo can grow to 98 feet while Pacific giant kelp (a type of seaweed) can grow to 197 feet. How much taller is the kelp than the bamboo?

Bamboo

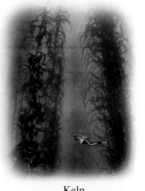
Kelp

57. The peak of Mt. McKinley in Alaska is 20,320 feet above sea level. The peak of Long's Peak in Colorado is 14,255 feet above sea level. How much higher is the peak of Mt. McKinley than Long's Peak? (*Source:* U.S. Geological Survey)

Mt. McKinley, Alaska   Long's Peak, Colorado

58. On one day in May the temperature in Paddin, Indiana, dropped 27 degrees from 2 p.m. to 4 p.m. If the temperature at 2 p.m. was 73° Fahrenheit, what was the temperature at 4 p.m.?

59. During the 2003–2004 regular season, Kevin Garnett of the Minnesota Timberwolves led the NBA in total points scored with 1987. The Sacramento Kings' Predrag Stojakovic placed second for total points scored with 1964. How many more points did Garnett score than Stojakovic during the 2003–2004 regular season? (*Source:* National Basketball Association)

60. In 2002, Americans bought 243,199 Ford Focus cars. In 2003, 13,846 fewer Focuses were sold in the United States. How many Focuses were sold in the United States in 2003? (*Source:* Ford Motor Company)

61. Buhler Gomez has a total of $538 in his checking account. If he writes a check for his electric bill of $129, how much money will be left in his account?

62. Pat Salanki's blood cholesterol level is 243. The doctor tells him it should be decreased to 185. How much of a decrease is this?

63. The distance from Kansas City to Denver is 645 miles. Hays, Kansas, lies on the road between the two and is 287 miles from Kansas City. What is the distance between Hays and Denver?

64. Alan Little is trading his car in on a new car. The new car costs $15,425. His car is worth $7998. How much more money does he need to buy the new car?

65. A new VCR with remote control costs $525. Prunella Pasch has $914 in her savings account. How much will she have left in her savings account after she buys the VCR?

66. A stereo that regularly sells for $547 is discounted by $99 in a sale. What is the sale price?

67. The population of Florida grew from 12,937,926 in 1990 to 15,982,378 in 2000. What was Florida's population increase over this time period? (*Source:* U.S. Census Bureau)

68. The population of El Paso, Texas, was 515,342 in 1990 and 563,662 in 2000. By how much did the population of El Paso grow from 1990 to 2000? (*Source:* U.S. Census Bureau)

El Paso

69. In 2000, there were 29,393 cocker spaniels registered with the American Kennel Club. In 2003, there were 10,357 fewer cocker spaniels registered. How many cocker spaniels were registered with the AKC in 2003? (*Source:* American Kennel Club)

70. In the United States, there were 41,589 tornadoes from 1950 through 2000. In all, 13,205 of these tornadoes occurred from 1990 through 2000. How many tornadoes occurred during the period prior to 1990? (*Source:* Storm Prediction Center, National Weather Service)

71. Until recently, the world's largest permanent maze was located in Ruurlo, Netherlands. This maze of beech hedges covers 94,080 square feet. A new hedge maze using hibiscus bushes at the Dole Plantation in Wahiawa, Hawaii, covers 100,000 square feet. How much larger is the Dole Plantation maze than the Ruurlo maze? (*Source: The Guinness Book of Records*)

72. There were only 27 California condors in the entire world in 1987. By 2004, the number of California condors had increased to 221. How much of an increase was this? (*Source:* California Department of Fish and Game)

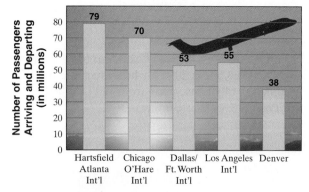

The bar graph shows the top five U.S. airports according to number of passengers arriving and departing in 2003. Use this graph to answer Exercises 73 through 76.

Top Five Airports in U.S.

Source: Airports Council International

73. Which airport is the busiest?

74. Which airports have fewer than 60 million passengers per year?

75. How many more passengers per year does the Chicago O'Hare International Airport have than the Denver Airport?

76. How many more passengers per year does the Hartsfield Atlanta International Airport have than the Dallas/Ft. Worth International Airport?

The table shows the top ten leading advertisers in the United States in 2003 and the amount of money each spent in that year on advertising. Use this table to answer Exercises 77 through 80.

Advertiser	Amount Spent on Advertising in 2003 (in millions of dollars)
DaimlerChrysler AG	2318
General Motors Corp.	3430
Pfizer	2839
Ford Motor Co.	2234
Johnson & Johnson	1996
Sony Corp.	1815
Walt Disney Co.	2129
Toyota Motor Corp.	1683
Time Warner	3097
Procter & Gamble Co.	3323
Source: Television Bureau of Advertising, Inc.	

77. Which companies spent more than $3000 million on advertising?

78. Which companies shown spent fewer than $2000 million on advertising?

79. How much more money did General Motors Corp. spend on advertising than DaimlerChrysler AG?

80. How much more money did Pfizer spend on advertising than Toyota Motor Corp.?

Mixed Practice (*Sections 1.3 and 1.4*) *Add or subtract as indicated.*

81.
$$\begin{array}{r} 986 \\ +\ 48 \end{array}$$

82.
$$\begin{array}{r} 986 \\ -\ 48 \end{array}$$

83. $76 - 67$

84. $80 + 93 + 17 + 9 + 2$

85.
$$\begin{array}{r} 9000 \\ -\ 482 \end{array}$$

86.
$$\begin{array}{r} 10,000 \\ -\ 1786 \end{array}$$

87.
$$\begin{array}{r} 10,962 \\ 4851 \\ +\ 7063 \end{array}$$

88.
$$\begin{array}{r} 12,468 \\ 3211 \\ +\ 1988 \end{array}$$

Concept Extensions

For each exercise, identify which number is the minuend and which number is the subtrahend. See the Concept Check in this section.

89.
$$\begin{array}{r} 48 \\ -\ 1 \end{array}$$

90.
$$\begin{array}{r} 2863 \\ -\ 1904 \end{array}$$

91. Subtract 7 from 70.

92. Find 86 decreased by 25.

Solve.

93. Jo Keen and Trudy Waterbury were candidates for student government president. Who won the election if the votes were cast as follows? By how many votes did the winner win?

Class	Candidate	
	Jo	Trudy
Freshman	276	295
Sophomore	362	122
Junior	201	312
Senior	179	18

94. Two students submitted advertising budgets for a student government fund-raiser.

	Student A	Student B
Radio ads	$600	$300
Newspaper ads	$200	$400
Posters	$150	$240
Handbills	$120	$170

If $1200 is available for advertising, how much excess would each budget have?

Identify each answer as correct or incorrect. Use addition to check. If the answer is incorrect, then write the correct answer.

95. $\begin{array}{r} 741 \\ -\ 56 \\ \hline 675 \end{array}$

96. $\begin{array}{r} 478 \\ -\ 89 \\ \hline 389 \end{array}$

97. $\begin{array}{r} 1029 \\ -\ 888 \\ \hline 141 \end{array}$

98. $\begin{array}{r} 7615 \\ -\ 547 \\ \hline 7168 \end{array}$

Fill in the missing digits in each problem.

99. $\begin{array}{r} 526\_ \\ -2\_85 \\ \hline \_28\_4 \end{array}$

100. $\begin{array}{r} 10,\_4\_ \\ -8\_5\_4 \\ \hline \_710 \end{array}$

101. Is there a commutative property of subtraction? In other words, does order matter when subtracting? Why or why not?

102. Explain why the phrase "Subtract 7 from 10" translates to "10 − 7."

103. The local college library is having a Million Pages of Reading promotion. The freshmen have read a total of 289,462 pages; the sophomores have read a total of 369,477 pages; the juniors have read a total of 218,287 pages; and the seniors have read a total of 121,685 pages. Have they reached a goal of one million pages? If not, how many more pages need to be read?

1.5 ROUNDING AND ESTIMATING

Objectives

A Round Whole Numbers.

B Use Rounding to Estimate Sums and Differences.

C Solve Problems by Estimating.

Objective **A** Rounding Whole Numbers

Rounding a whole number means approximating it. A rounded whole number is often easier to use, understand, and remember than the precise whole number. For example, instead of trying to remember the Iowa state population as 2,851,792, it is much easier to remember it rounded to the nearest million: 3 million people.

To understand rounding, let's first understand how we can visualize whole numbers by points on a line. The line below is called a **number line.** This number line has equally spaced marks for each whole number. The arrow to the right simply means that there is no largest whole number.

To **graph** a whole number, we darken the point representing the location of the whole number. For example, the number 4 is graphed below.

On the number line, the whole number 36 is closer to 40 than 30, so 36 rounded to the nearest ten is 40.

The whole number 52 rounded to the nearest ten is 50 because 52 is closer to 50 than to 60.

In trying to round 25 to the nearest ten, we see that 25 is halfway between 20 and 30. It is not closer to either number. In such a case, we round to the larger ten, that is, to 30.

To round a whole number without using a number line, follow these steps:

Rounding Whole Numbers to a Given Place Value

Step 1: Locate the digit to the right of the given place value.

Step 2: If this digit is 5 or greater, add 1 to the digit in the given place value and replace each digit to its right by 0.

Step 3: If this digit is less than 5, replace it and each digit to its right by 0.

PRACTICE PROBLEM 1

Round to the nearest ten.

a. 46

b. 731

c. 125

 EXAMPLE 1 Round 568 to the nearest ten.

Solution: 5 6(8)   The digit to the right of the tens place is the ones place, which is circled.

↑ tens place

5 6(8)   Since the circled digit is 5 or greater, add 1 to the 6 in the tens place and replace the digit to the right by 0.

Add 1.   Replace with 0.

We find that 568 rounded to the nearest ten is 570.

⬛ **Work Practice Problem 1**

PRACTICE PROBLEM 2

Round to the nearest thousand.

a. 56,702

b. 7444

c. 291,500

EXAMPLE 2 Round 278,362 to the nearest thousand.

Solution:

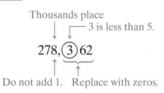

Thousands place

3 is less than 5.

278,(3)62

Do not add 1.   Replace with zeros.

The number 278,362 rounded to the nearest thousand is 278,000.

⬛ **Work Practice Problem 2**

PRACTICE PROBLEM 3

Round to the nearest hundred.

a. 2777

b. 38,152

c. 762,955

EXAMPLE 3 Round 248,982 to the nearest hundred.

Solution:

Hundreds place

8 is greater than or equal to 5.

248,9(8)2

Add 1.   9 + 1 = 10, so replace the digit 9 by 0 and carry 1 to the place value to the left.

Add 1.   Replace with zeros.

The number 248,982 rounded to the nearest hundred is 249,000.

⬛ **Work Practice Problem 3**

✔ **Concept Check** Round each of the following numbers to the nearest *hundred*. Explain your reasoning.

a. 79   b. 33

Answers

1. a. 50,   b. 730,   c. 130,
2. a. 57,000,   b. 7000,   c. 292,000,
3. a. 2800,   b. 38,200,   c. 763,000

✔ **Concept Check Answers**

a. 100,   b. 0

Objective B Estimating Sums and Differences

By rounding addends, we can estimate sums. An estimated sum is appropriate when an exact sum is not necessary. To estimate the sum shown, round each number to the nearest hundred and then add.

768	rounds to	800
1952	rounds to	2000
225	rounds to	200
+ 149	rounds to	+ 100
		3100

The estimated sum is 3100, which is close to the exact sum of 3094.

EXAMPLE 4

Round each number to the nearest hundred to find an estimated sum.

```
  294
  625
 1071
+ 349
```

Solution:

294	rounds to	300
625	rounds to	600
1071	rounds to	1100
+ 349	rounds to	+ 300
		2300

The estimated sum is 2300. (The exact sum is 2339.)

🔲 **Work Practice Problem 4**

PRACTICE PROBLEM 4

Round each number to the nearest ten to find an estimated sum.

```
  79
  35
  42
  21
+ 98
```

EXAMPLE 5

Round each number to the nearest hundred to find an estimated difference.

```
  4725
- 2879
```

Solution:

4725	rounds to	4700
- 2879	rounds to	- 2900
		1800

The estimated difference is 1800. (The exact difference is 1846.)

🔲 **Work Practice Problem 5**

PRACTICE PROBLEM 5

Round each number to the nearest thousand to find an estimated difference.

```
  4725
- 2879
```

Objective C Solving Problems by Estimating

Making estimates is often the quickest way to solve real-life problems when solutions do not need to be exact.

PRACTICE PROBLEM 6

Tasha Kilbey is trying to estimate how far it is from Grove, Kansas, to Hays, Kansas. Round each given distance on the map to the nearest ten to estimate the total distance.

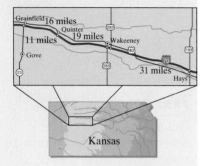

EXAMPLE 6 Estimating Distances

Jose Guillermo is trying to estimate quickly the distance from Temple, Texas, to Brenham, Texas. Round each distance given on the map to the nearest ten to estimate the total distance.

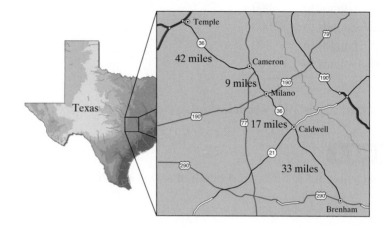

Solution:

Distance		Estimation
42	rounds to	40
9	rounds to	10
17	rounds to	20
+33	rounds to	+ 30
		100

It is approximately 100 miles from Temple to Brenham. (The exact distance is 101 miles.)

Work Practice Problem 6

PRACTICE PROBLEM 7

In a recent year, there were 120,624 reported cases of chicken pox, 22,866 reported cases of tuberculosis, and 45,970 reported cases of salmonellosis in the United States. Round each number to the nearest ten-thousand to estimate the total number of cases reported for these diseases. (*Source:* Centers for Disease Control and Prevention)

EXAMPLE 7 Estimating Data

In three recent years the numbers of reported cases of mumps in the United States were 906, 1537, and 1692. Round each number to the nearest hundred to estimate the total number of cases reported over this period. (*Source:* Centers for Disease Control and Prevention)

Solution:

Number of Cases		Estimation
906	rounds to	900
1537	rounds to	1500
+ 1692	rounds to	+ 1700
		4100

The approximate number of cases reported over this period was 4100.

Work Practice Problem 7

Answers

6. 80 mi, **7.** 190,000

Objective *Round each whole number to the given place. See Examples 1 through 3.*

1. 632 to the nearest ten

2. 273 to the nearest ten

 3. 635 to the nearest ten

4. 275 to the nearest ten

5. 1792 to the nearest hundred

6. 9394 to the nearest hundred

7. 395 to the nearest ten

8. 898 to the nearest ten

9. 51,096 to the nearest thousand

10. 82,198 to the nearest thousand

11. 42,682 to the nearest thousand

12. 42,682 to the nearest ten-thousand

13. 248,695 to the nearest hundred

14. 179,406 to the nearest hundred

15. 36,499 to the nearest thousand

16. 96,501 to the nearest thousand

17. 99,995 to the nearest ten

18. 39,994 to the nearest ten

19. 59,725,642 to the nearest ten-million

20. 39,523,698 to the nearest million

Complete the table by estimating the given number to the given place value.

		Tens	Hundreds	Thousands
21.	5281			
22.	7619			
23.	9444			
24.	7777			
25.	14,876			
26.	85,049			

Round each number to the indicated place.

27. The number of active duty U.S. Air Force personnel in 2004 was 379,884. Round this number to the nearest thousand. (*Source:* U.S. Department of Defense)

28. The number of passengers handled in 2004 by the Hartsfield Atlanta International Airport was 79,086,792. Round this number to the nearest hundred-thousand. (*Source:* Airports Council International)

29. It takes 10,759 days for Saturn to make a complete orbit around the Sun. Round this number to the nearest hundred. (*Source:* National Space Science Data Center)

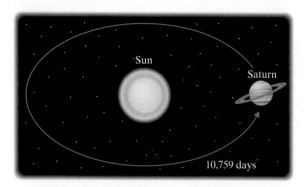

Sun

Saturn

10,759 days

30. Kareem Abdul-Jabbar holds the NBA record for points scored, a total of 38,387 over his NBA career. Round this number to the nearest thousand. (*Source:* National Basketball Association)

31. The most valuable brand in the world in 2003 was Coca-Cola, with an estimated brand value of $70,450,000,000. Round this to the nearest billion. (*Source: Interbrand/Business Week*)

32. According to the 2000 U.S. Census, the population of the United States was 281,421,906. Round this population figure to the nearest million. (*Source:* U.S. Census Bureau)

33. The average salary for a Major League baseball player during the 2004 season was $2,486,609. Round this average salary to the nearest hundred-thousand. (*Source:* Major League Baseball Players Association)

34. In 2004, the Procter & Gamble Company had $51,407,000,000 in sales. Round this sales figure to the nearest billion. (*Source:* The Procter & Gamble Company)

35. The United States currently has 158,722,000 cellular mobile phone users (about 54% of population) while Austria has 7,094,500 users (about 88% of population). Round each of the user numbers to the nearest million. (*Note:* We will study percents in a later chapter.) (*Source:* Siemens AG, International Telecom Statistics, 2003)

36. In 2003, U.S. farms produced 144,649,000 bushels of oats. Round the oat production figure to the nearest ten-million. (*Source:* U.S. Department of Agriculture)

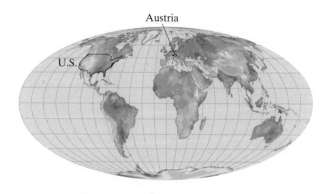

Austria

U.S.

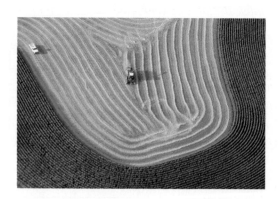

Objective B *Estimate the sum or difference by rounding each number to the nearest ten. See Examples 4 and 5.*

37.	**38.**	**39.**	**40.**
29	62	649	555
35	72	− 272	− 235
42	15		
+ 16	+ 19		

Estimate the sum or difference by rounding each number to the nearest hundred. See Examples 4 and 5.

41. 1812
1776
+ 1945

42. 2010
2001
+ 1984

43. 1774
− 1492

44. 1989
− 1870

45. 2995
1649
+ 3940

46. 799
1655
+ 271

Two of the given calculator answers below are incorrect. Find them by estimating each sum.

47. 362 + 419   781

48. 522 + 785   1307

49. 432 + 679 + 198   1139

50. 229 + 443 + 606   1278

51. 7806 + 5150   12,956

52. 5233 + 4988   9011

> **Helpful Hint**
> Estimation is useful to check for incorrect answers when using a calculator. For example, pressing a key too hard may result in a double digit, while pressing a key too softly may result in the digit not appearing in the display.

Objective C *Solve each problem by estimating. See Examples 6 and 7.*

53. Campo Appliance Store advertises three refrigerators on sale at $799, $1299, and $999. Round each cost to the nearest hundred to estimate the total cost.

54. Jared Nuss scored 89, 92, 100, 67, 75, and 89 on his biology tests. Round each score to the nearest ten to estimate his total score.

55. Round each distance given on the map to the nearest ten miles to estimate the total distance from Stockton to LaCrosse.

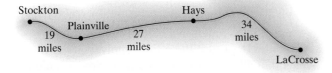

Stockton — Plainville — 19 miles — 27 miles — Hays — 34 miles — LaCrosse

56. The Gonzales family took a trip and traveled 458, 489, 377, 243, 69, and 702 miles on six consecutive days. Round each distance to the nearest hundred to estimate the distance they traveled.

57. The peak of Mt. McKinley, in Alaska, is 20,320 feet above sea level. The top of Mt. Rainier, in Washington, is 14,410 feet above sea level. Round each height to the nearest thousand to estimate the difference in elevation of these two peaks. (*Source:* U.S. Geological Survey)

58. A student is pricing new car stereo systems. One system sells for $1895 and another system sells for $1524. Round each price to the nearest hundred dollars to estimate the difference in price of these systems.

59. In 2003 the population of Chicago was 2,896,121, and the population of Philadelphia was 1,479,339. Round each population to the nearest hundred-thousand to estimate how much larger Chicago was than Philadelphia. (*Source:* U.S. Census Bureau, 2003 census)

60. The distance from Kansas City to Boston is 1429 miles and from Kansas City to Chicago, 530 miles. Round each distance to the nearest hundred to estimate how much farther Boston is from Kansas City than Chicago is.

61. In the 1964 presidential election, Lyndon Johnson received 41,126,233 votes and Barry Goldwater received 27,174,898 votes. Round each number of votes to the nearest million to estimate the number of votes by which Johnson won the election.

62. Enrollment figures at Normal State University showed an increase from 49,713 credit hours in 2003 to 51,746 credit hours in 2004. Round each number to the nearest thousand to estimate the increase.

63. Head Start is a national program that provides developmental and social services for America's low-income preschool children ages three to five. Enrollment figures in Head Start programs showed an increase from 857,664 children in 2000 to 909,608 children in 2003. Round each number of children to the nearest thousand to estimate this increase. (*Source:* Head Start Bureau)

64. In 2002, General Motors produced 244,356 Saturn cars. Similarly, in 2003 only 183,448 Saturns were produced. Round each number of cars to the nearest thousand to estimate the decrease in Saturn production from 2002 to 2003. (*Source:* General Motors Corporation)

Mixed Practice (Sections 1.2 and 1.5) *The following table (from Section 1.4) shows a few of the top leading advertisers in the United States for 2003 and the amount of money spent in that year on advertising. Complete this table. The first line is completed for you.*

	Advertiser	Amount Spent on Advertising in 2003 (in millions of dollars)	Amount Written in Standard Form	Standard Form Rounded to Nearest Hundred-Million	Standard Form Rounded to Nearest Billion
	DaimlerChrysler AG	2318	$2,318,000,000	$2,300,000,000	$2,000,000,000
65.	General Motors Corp.	3430			
66.	Pfizer	2839			
67.	Ford Motor Co.	2234			
68.	Johnson & Johnson	1996			
	(*Source:* Television Bureau of Advertising, Inc.)				

Concept Extensions

69. Find one number that when rounded to the nearest hundred is 4600.

70. Find one number that when rounded to the nearest ten is 4600.

71. A number rounded to the nearest hundred is 8600.
  a. Determine the smallest possible number.
  b. Determine the largest possible number.

72. On August 23, 1989, it was estimated that 1,500,000 people joined hands in a human chain stretching 370 miles to protest the fiftieth anniversary of the pact that allowed what was then the Soviet Union to annex the Baltic nations in 1939. If the estimate of the number of people is to the nearest hundred-thousand, determine the largest possible number of people in the chain.

73. In your own words, explain how to round a number to the nearest thousand.

△ **74.** Estimate the perimeter of the triangle by first rounding the length of each side to the nearest hundred.

5950 miles   7693 miles
8203 miles

75. Estimate the perimeter of the rectangle by first rounding the length of each side to the nearest ten.

54 meters
Rectangle   17 meters

1.6 MULTIPLYING WHOLE NUMBERS AND AREA

Objectives

Ⓐ Use the Properties of Multiplication.

Ⓑ Multiply Whole Numbers.

Ⓒ Multiply by Whole Numbers Ending in Zero(s).

Ⓓ Find the Area of a Rectangle.

Ⓔ Solve Problems by Multiplying Whole Numbers.

Multiplication Shown as Repeated Addition Suppose that we wish to count the number of laptops provided in a computer class. The laptops are arranged in 5 rows, and each row has 6 laptops.

6 laptops in each row

1

2

3
⋮

Adding 5 sixes gives the total number of laptops:
$6 + 6 + 6 + 6 + 6 = 30$ laptops. When each addend is the same, we refer to this as **repeated addition.**

Multiplication is repeated addition but with different notation.

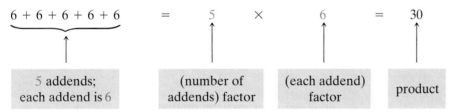

| $6 + 6 + 6 + 6 + 6$ | $=$ | 5 | $\times$ | 6 | $=$ | 30 |

| 5 addends; each addend is 6 | (number of addends) factor | (each addend) factor | product |

The $\times$ is called a **multiplication sign.** The numbers 5 and 6 are called **factors.** The number 30 is called the **product.** The notation 5×6 is read as "five times six." The symbols $\cdot$ and $(\ )$ can also be used to indicate multiplication.

$$5 \times 6 = 30, \quad 5 \cdot 6 = 30, \quad (5)(6) = 30, \quad \text{and} \quad 5(6) = 30$$

✔ Concept Check

a. Rewrite $4 + 4 + 4 + 4 + 4 + 4 + 4$ using multiplication.

b. Rewrite 3×16 as repeated addition. Is there more than one way to do this? If so, show all ways.

Objective Ⓐ Using the Properties of Multiplication

As with addition, we memorize products of one-digit whole numbers and then use certain properties of multiplication to multiply larger numbers. (If necessary, review the multiplication of one-digit numbers in Appendix A.2.) Notice in the appendix that when any number is multiplied by 0, the result is always 0. This is called the **multiplication property of 0.**

✔ Concept Check Answers
a. $7 \times 4 = 28$,
b. $16 + 16 + 16 = 48$; yes,
$3 + 3 + 3 + 3 + 3 + 3 + 3 + 3 +$
$3 + 3 + 3 + 3 + 3 + 3 + 3 + 3 = 48$

Multiplication Property of 0

The product of 0 and any number is 0. For example,

$$5 \cdot 0 = 0 \quad \text{and} \quad 0 \cdot 8 = 0$$

Also notice in the appendix that when any number is multiplied by 1, the result is always the original number. We call this result the **multiplication property of 1.**

Multiplication Property of 1

The product of 1 and any number is that same number. For example,

$$1 \cdot 9 = 9 \quad \text{and} \quad 6 \cdot 1 = 6$$

PRACTICE PROBLEM 1

Multiply.
a. 3×0
b. $4(1)$
c. $(0)(34)$
d. $1 \cdot 76$

EXAMPLE 1 Multiply.

a. 6×1　　**b.** $0(8)$　　**c.** $1 \cdot 45$　　**d.** $(75)(0)$

Solution:

a. $6 \times 1 = 6$　　**b.** $0(8) = 0$
c. $1 \cdot 45 = 45$　　**d.** $(75)(0) = 0$

▢ **Work Practice Problem 1**

Like addition, multiplication is commutative and associative. Notice that when multiplying two numbers, the order of these numbers can be changed without changing the product. For example,

$$3 \cdot 5 = 15 \quad \text{and} \quad 5 \cdot 3 = 15$$

This property is the **commutative property of multiplication.**

Commutative Property of Multiplication

Changing the **order** of two factors does not change their product. For example,

$$9 \cdot 2 = 18 \quad \text{and} \quad 2 \cdot 9 = 18$$

Another property that can help us when multiplying is the **associative property of multiplication.** This property states that when multiplying numbers, the grouping of the numbers can be changed without changing the product. For example,

$$(2 \cdot 3) \cdot 4 = 6 \cdot 4 = 24$$

Also,

$$2 \cdot (3 \cdot 4) = 2 \cdot 12 = 24$$

Both groupings give a product of 24.

Answers
1. a. 0, **b.** 4, **c.** 0, **d.** 76

Associative Property of Multiplication

Changing the **grouping** of factors does not change their product. From above, we know that for example,

$$(2 \cdot 3) \cdot 4 = 2 \cdot (3 \cdot 4)$$

With these properties, along with the **distributive property,** we can find the product of any whole numbers. The distributive property says that multiplication **distributes** over addition. For example, notice that $3(2 + 5)$ simplifies to the same number as $3 \cdot 2 + 3 \cdot 5$.

$$3(2 + 5) = 3(7) = 21$$

$$3 \cdot 2 + 3 \cdot 5 = 6 + 15 = 21$$

Since $3(2 + 5)$ and $3 \cdot 2 + 3 \cdot 5$ both simplify to 21, then

$$3(2 + 5) = 3 \cdot 2 + 3 \cdot 5$$

Notice in $3(2 + 5) = 3 \cdot 2 + 3 \cdot 5$ that each number inside the parentheses is multiplied by 3.

Distributive Property

Multiplication distributes over addition. For example,

$$2(3 + 4) = 2 \cdot 3 + 2 \cdot 4$$

EXAMPLE 2 Rewrite each using the distributive property.

a. $3(4 + 5)$ 　　　**b.** $10(6 + 8)$ 　　　**c.** $2(7 + 3)$

Solution: Using the distributive property, we have

a. $3(4 + 5) = 3 \cdot 4 + 3 \cdot 5$
b. $10(6 + 8) = 10 \cdot 6 + 10 \cdot 8$
c. $2(7 + 3) = 2 \cdot 7 + 2 \cdot 3$

■ **Work Practice Problem 2**

Objective B Multiplying Whole Numbers

Let's use the distributive property to multiply $7(48)$. To do so, we begin by writing the expanded form of 48 (see Section 1.2) and then applying the distributive property.

$$7(48) = 7(40 + 8) \quad \text{Write 48 in expanded form.}$$
$$ = 7 \cdot 40 + 7 \cdot 8 \quad \text{Apply the distributive property.}$$
$$ = 280 + 56 \quad \text{Multiply.}$$
$$ = 336 \quad \text{Add.}$$

PRACTICE PROBLEM 2

Rewrite each using the distributive property.
a. $5(2 + 3)$
b. $9(8 + 7)$
c. $3(6 + 1)$

This is how we multiply whole numbers. When multiplying whole numbers, we will use the following notation.

$$
\begin{array}{r}
\overset{5}{4}8 \\
\times\,7 \\
\hline
336
\end{array}
$$

$7 \cdot 4 = 28$ and $28 + 5 = 33$ $336 \longleftarrow 7 \cdot 8 = 56$

Write 6 in the ones place and carry 5 to the tens place.

PRACTICE PROBLEM 3
Multiply.

a. $\begin{array}{r} 36 \\ \times\,4 \\ \hline \end{array}$ b. $\begin{array}{r} 132 \\ \times\,9 \\ \hline \end{array}$

EXAMPLE 3 Multiply:

a. $\begin{array}{r} 25 \\ \times\,8 \\ \hline \end{array}$ b. $\begin{array}{r} 246 \\ \times\,5 \\ \hline \end{array}$

Solution:

a. $\begin{array}{r} \overset{4}{2}5 \\ \times\,8 \\ \hline 200 \end{array}$ b. $\begin{array}{r} \overset{2\,3}{2}46 \\ \times\,5 \\ \hline 1230 \end{array}$

▣ **Work Practice Problem 3**

To multiply larger whole numbers, use the following similar notation. Multiply 89×52.

Step 1

$$
\begin{array}{r}
\overset{1}{8}9 \\
\times\,52 \\
\hline
178
\end{array}
$$

$\longleftarrow$ Multiply 89×2.

Step 2

$$
\begin{array}{r}
\overset{4}{8}9 \\
\times\,52 \\
\hline
178 \\
4450
\end{array}
$$

$\longleftarrow$ Multiply 89×50.

Step 3

$$
\begin{array}{r}
89 \\
\times\,52 \\
\hline
178 \\
4450 \\
\hline
4628
\end{array}
$$

Add.

The numbers 178 and 4450 are called **partial products.** The sum of the partial products, 4628, is the product of 89 and 52.

PRACTICE PROBLEM 4
Multiply.

a. $\begin{array}{r} 594 \\ \times\,72 \\ \hline \end{array}$ b. $\begin{array}{r} 306 \\ \times\,81 \\ \hline \end{array}$

EXAMPLE 4 Multiply: 236×86

Solution:

$$
\begin{array}{r}
236 \\
\times\,86 \\
\hline
1\,416 \\
18\,880 \\
\hline
20{,}296
\end{array}
$$

$\leftarrow 6(236)$
$\leftarrow 80(236)$
Add.

▣ **Work Practice Problem 4**

PRACTICE PROBLEM 5
Multiply.

a. $\begin{array}{r} 726 \\ \times\,142 \\ \hline \end{array}$ b. $\begin{array}{r} 288 \\ \times\,4 \\ \hline \end{array}$

EXAMPLE 5 Multiply: 631×125

Solution:

$$
\begin{array}{r}
631 \\
\times\,125 \\
\hline
3\,155 \\
12\,620 \\
63\,100 \\
\hline
78{,}875
\end{array}
$$

$\leftarrow 5(631)$
$\leftarrow 20(631)$
$\leftarrow 100(631)$
Add.

▣ **Work Practice Problem 5**

Answers
3. a. 144, **b.** 1188,
4. a. 42,768, **b.** 24,786,
5. a. 103,092, **b.** 1152

✔**Concept Check** Find and explain the error in the following multiplication problem.

$$
\begin{array}{r}
102 \\
\times\ 33 \\
\hline
306 \\
306 \\
\hline
612
\end{array}
$$

Objective C Multiplying by Whole Numbers Ending in Zero(s)

Interesting patterns occur when we multiply by a number that ends in zeros. To see these patterns, let's multiply a number, say 34, by 10, then 100, then 1000.

1 zero
$34 \cdot 10 = 340$ 1 zero attached to 34.

2 zeros
$34 \cdot 100 = 3400$ 2 zeros attached to 34.

3 zeros
$34 \cdot 1000 = 34,000$ 3 zeros attached to 34.

These patterns help us develop a shortcut for multiplying by whole numbers ending in zeros.

To multiply by 10, 100, 1000 and so on,
    Form the product by attaching the number of zeros in that number to the other factor.
    For example, $41 \cdot 100 = 4100$.
                                2 zeros

EXAMPLES Multiply.

6. $176 \cdot 1000 = 176,000$ Attach 3 zeros.

7. $2041 \cdot 100 = 204,100$ Attach 2 zeros.

▣ **Work Practice Problems 6–7**

We can use a similar format to multiply by any whole number ending in zeros. For example, since

$$15 \cdot 500 = 15 \cdot 5 \cdot 100,$$

we find the product by multiplying 15 and 5, then attaching two zeros to the product.

$$
\begin{array}{r}
\overset{2}{15} \\
\times\ 5 \\
\hline
75
\end{array}
\qquad 15 \cdot 500 = 7500
$$

PRACTICE PROBLEMS 6–7

Multiply.
6. $75 \cdot 100$
7. $808 \cdot 1000$

Answers
6. 7500, **7.** 808,000

✔ **Concept Check Answer**

$$
\begin{array}{r}
102 \\
\times\ 33 \\
\hline
306 \\
3060 \\
\hline
3366
\end{array}
$$

PRACTICE PROBLEMS 8–9

Multiply.

8. $35 \cdot 3000$

9. $600 \cdot 600$

EXAMPLES Multiply.

8. $25 \cdot 9000 = 225,000$ Attach 3 zeros.

$$\begin{array}{r} \overset{4}{25} \\ \times 9 \\ \hline 225 \end{array}$$

9. $20 \cdot 7000 = 140,000$ Attach 4 zeros.

$$2 \cdot 7$$

▪ **Work Practice Problems 8–9**

Objective D Finding the Area of a Rectangle

A special application of multiplication is finding the area of a region. Area measures the amount of surface of a region. For example, we measure a plot of land or the living space of a home by area. The figures show two examples of units of area measure. (A centimeter is a unit of length in the metric system.)

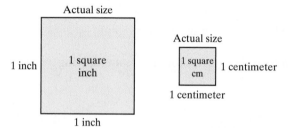

To measure the area of a geometric figure such as the rectangle shown, count the number of square units that cover the region.

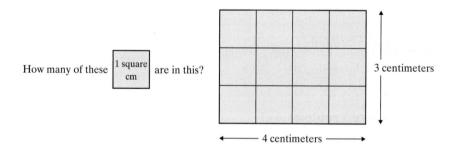

This rectangular region contains 12 square units, each 1 square centimeter. Thus, the area is 12 square centimeters. This total number of squares can be found by counting or by multiplying **4 · 3**(length · width).

Area of a rectangle = length · width

= (4 centimeters)(3 centimeters)

= 12 square centimeters

In this section, we find the areas of rectangles only. In later sections, we find the areas of other geometric regions.

Answers

8. 105,000, **9.** 360,000

EXAMPLE 10 Finding the Area of a State

The state of Colorado is in the shape of a rectangle whose length is 380 miles and whose width is 280 miles. Find its area.

Solution:

The area of a rectangle is the product of its length and its width.

$$
\begin{aligned}
\text{Area} &= \text{length} \cdot \text{width} \\
&= (380 \text{ miles})(280 \text{ miles}) \\
&= 106{,}400 \text{ square miles}
\end{aligned}
$$

The area of Colorado is 106,400 square miles.

■ Work Practice Problem 10

Objective E Solving Problems by Multiplying

There are several words or phrases that indicate the operation of multiplication. Some of these are as follows:

Key Words or Phrases	Example	Symbols
multiply	multiply 5 by 7	$5 \cdot 7$
product	the product of 3 and 2	$3 \cdot 2$
times	10 times 13	$10 \cdot 13$

Many key words or phrases describing real-life problems that suggest addition might be better solved by multiplication instead. For example, to find the **total** cost of 8 shirts, each selling for $27, we can either add $27 + 27 + 27 + 27 + 27 + 27 + 27 + 27$, or we can multiply $8(27)$.

EXAMPLE 11 Finding DVD Space

A digital video disc (DVD) can hold about 4800 megabytes (MB) of information. How many megabytes can 12 DVDs hold?

Solution:

Twelve DVDs will hold 12×4800 megabytes.

In Words		Translate to Numbers
megabytes per disk	$\rightarrow$	4800
+ DVDs	$\rightarrow$	$\times$ 12
		9600
		48000
total megabytes		57,600

Twelve DVDs will hold 57,600 megabytes.

■ Work Practice Problem 11

PRACTICE PROBLEM 10

The state of Wyoming is in the shape of a rectangle whose length is 360 miles and whose width is 280 miles. Find its area.

PRACTICE PROBLEM 11

A particular computer printer can print 15 pages per minute in color. How many pages can it print in 45 minutes?

Answers
10. 100,800 sq mi, **11.** 675 pages

PRACTICE PROBLEM 12

Softball T-shirts come in two styles: plain at $6 each and striped at $7 each. The team orders 4 plain shirts and 5 striped shirts. Find the total cost of the order.

EXAMPLE 12 **Budgeting Money**

Earline Martin agrees to take her children and their cousins to the San Antonio Zoo. The ticket price for each child is $4 and for each adult, $6. If 8 children and 1 adult plan to go, how much money is needed for admission?

Solution: If the price of one child's ticket is $4, the price for 8 children is $8 \cdot 4 = \$32$. The price of one adult ticket is $6, so the total cost is

In Words		Translate to Numbers
price of 8 children	→	32
+ price of 1 adult	→	+ 6
total cost		38

The total cost is $38.

■ **Work Practice Problem 12**

PRACTICE PROBLEM 13

If an average page in a book contains 171 words, estimate, rounding each number to the nearest hundred, the total number of words contained on 395 pages.

EXAMPLE 13 **Estimating Word Count**

The average page of a book contains 259 words. Estimate, rounding each number to the nearest hundred, the total number of words contained on 212 pages.

Solution: The exact number of words is 259×212. Estimate this product by rounding each factor to the nearest hundred.

259   rounds to   300
$\times 212$ rounds to $\times 200$,

$$300 \times 200 = 60,000$$
$$3 \cdot 2 = 6$$

There are approximately 60,000 words contained on 212 pages.

■ **Work Practice Problem 13**

CALCULATOR EXPLORATIONS Multiplying Numbers

To multiply numbers on a calculator, find the keys marked $\boxed{\times}$ and $\boxed{=}$ or $\boxed{\text{ENTER}}$. For example, to find $31 \cdot 66$ on a calculator, press the keys $\boxed{31}$ $\boxed{\times}$ $\boxed{66}$ $\boxed{=}$ or $\boxed{\text{ENTER}}$. The display will read $\boxed{2046}$. Thus, $31 \cdot 66 = 2046$.

Use a calculator to multiply.

1. 72×48 **2.** 81×92
3. $163 \cdot 94$ **4.** $285 \cdot 144$
5. $983(277)$ **6.** $1562(843)$

Answers

12. $59,   **13.** 80,000 words

Mental Math

Objective *Multiply. See Example 1.*

1. $1 \cdot 24$

2. $55 \cdot 1$

3. $0 \cdot 19$

4. $27 \cdot 0$

5. $8 \cdot 0 \cdot 9$

6. $7 \cdot 6 \cdot 0$

7. $87 \cdot 1$

8. $1 \cdot 41$

1.6 EXERCISE SET

FOR EXTRA HELP

Student Solutions Manual | PH Math/Tutor Center | CD/Video for Review | MathXL MathXL® | MyMathLab MyMathLab

Objective *Use the distributive property to rewrite each expression. See Example 2.*

1. $4(3 + 9)$

2. $5(8 + 2)$

3. $2(4 + 6)$

4. $6(1 + 4)$

5. $10(11 + 7)$

6. $12(12 + 3)$

Objective *Multiply. See Example 3.*

7.
$$\begin{array}{r} 42 \\ \times\ 6 \\ \hline \end{array}$$

8.
$$\begin{array}{r} 79 \\ \times\ 3 \\ \hline \end{array}$$

9.
$$\begin{array}{r} 624 \\ \times\ 3 \\ \hline \end{array}$$

10.
$$\begin{array}{r} 638 \\ \times\ 5 \\ \hline \end{array}$$

 11. 277×6

12. 882×2

13. 1062×5

14. 9021×3

Multiply. See Examples 4 and 5.

15.
$$\begin{array}{r} 98 \\ \times 14 \\ \hline \end{array}$$

16.
$$\begin{array}{r} 91 \\ \times 72 \\ \hline \end{array}$$

17.
$$\begin{array}{r} 231 \\ \times\ 47 \\ \hline \end{array}$$

18.
$$\begin{array}{r} 526 \\ \times\ 23 \\ \hline \end{array}$$

19.
$$\begin{array}{r} 809 \\ \times\ 14 \\ \hline \end{array}$$

20.
$$\begin{array}{r} 307 \\ \times\ 16 \\ \hline \end{array}$$

21. $(620)(40)$

22. $(720)(80)$

23. $(998)(12)(0)$

24. $(593)(47)(0)$

25. $(590)(1)(10)$

26. $(240)(1)(20)$

27. 1234×48

28. 1357×79

 29. 609×234

30. 505×127

31.
$$\begin{array}{r} 5621 \\ \times\ 324 \\ \hline \end{array}$$

32.
$$\begin{array}{r} 1234 \\ \times\ 567 \\ \hline \end{array}$$

33.
$$\begin{array}{r} 1941 \\ \times 2035 \\ \hline \end{array}$$

34.
$$\begin{array}{r} 1876 \\ \times 1407 \\ \hline \end{array}$$

35.
$$\begin{array}{r} 589 \\ \times 110 \\ \hline \end{array}$$

36.
$$\begin{array}{r} 426 \\ \times 110 \\ \hline \end{array}$$

Objective **C** *Multiply. See Examples 6 through 9.*

37. 8×100 **38.** 6×100 **39.** 11×1000 **40.** 26×1000 **41.** $7406 \cdot 10$ **42.** $9054 \cdot 10$

43. $6 \cdot 4000$ **44.** $3 \cdot 9000$ **45.** $50 \cdot 900$ **46.** $70 \cdot 300$ **47.** $41 \cdot 80,000$ **48.** $27 \cdot 50,000$

Objectives **D** **E** **Mixed Practice** *Estimate the products by rounding each factor to the nearest hundred. See Example 13.*

49. 576×354 **50.** 982×650 **51.** 604×451 **52.** 111×999

Without actually calculating, mentally round, multiply, and choose the best estimate.

53. $38 \times 42 =$
    a. 16
    b. 160
    c. 1600
    d. 16,000

54. 2872×12
    a. 2872
    b. 28,720
    c. 287,200
    d. 2,872,000

55. $612 \times 29 =$
    a. 180
    b. 1800
    c. 18,000
    d. 180,000

56. 706×409
    a. 280
    b. 2800
    c. 28,000
    d. 280,000

Find the area of each rectangle. See Example 10.

57.

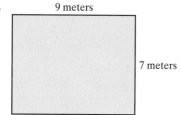

9 meters

7 meters

58.

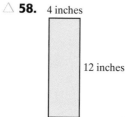

4 inches

12 inches

59.

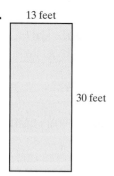

13 feet

30 feet

60.

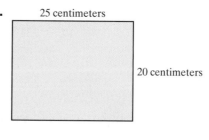

25 centimeters

20 centimeters

Solve. See Examples 10 through 13.

61. Multiply 70 by 11.

62. Multiply 80 by 12.

63. Find the product of 9 and 600.

64. Find the product of 4 and 400.

65. Find 2 times 2240.

66. Find 3 times 3310.

67. One tablespoon of olive oil contains 125 calories. How many calories are in 3 tablespoons of olive oil? (*Source: Home and Garden Bulletin No. 72,* U.S. Department of Agriculture).

68. One ounce of hulled sunflower seeds contains 14 grams of fat. How many grams of fat are in 6 ounces of hulled sunflower seeds? (*Source: Home and Garden Bulletin No. 72,* U.S. Department of Agriculture).

69. The textbook for a course in Civil War history costs $54. There are 35 students in the class. Find the total cost of the history books for the class.

70. The seats in the mathematics lecture hall are arranged in 12 rows with 34 seats in each row. Find how many seats are in this room.

71. A case of canned peas has *two layers* of cans. In each layer are 8 rows with 12 cans in each row.
   a. How many cans are in 1 layer?
   b. How many cans are in a case?

72. An apartment building has *three floors*. Each floor has five rows of apartments with four apartments in each row.
   a. How many apartments are on 1 floor?
   b. How many apartments are in the building?

△ **73.** A plot of land measures 90 feet by 110 feet. Find its area.

△ **74.** A house measures 45 feet by 60 feet. Find the floor area of the house.

△ **75.** The largest hotel lobby can be found at the Hyatt Regency in San Francisco, CA. It is in the shape of a rectangle that measures 350 feet by 160 feet. Find its area.

△ **76.** Recall from an earlier section that the largest commercial building in the world under one roof is the flower auction building of the cooperative VBA in Aalsmeer, Netherlands. The floor plan is a rectangle that measures 776 meters by 639 meters. Find the area of this building. (A meter is a unit of length in the metric system.) (*Source: The Handy Science Answer Book,* Visible Ink Press)

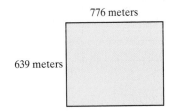

776 meters

639 meters

77. A pixel is a rectangular dot on a graphing calculator screen. If a graphing calculator screen contains 62 pixels in a row and 94 pixels in a column, find the total number of pixels on a screen.

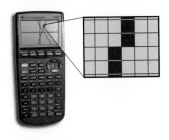

78. A compact disc (CD) can hold 700 megabytes (MB) of information. How many MBs can 17 discs hold?

79. A line of print on a computer contains 60 characters (letters, spaces, punctuation marks). Find how many characters there are in 25 lines.

80. An average cow eats 3 pounds of grain per day. Find how much grain a cow eats in a year. (Assume 365 days in 1 year.)

81. One ounce of Planters® Dry Roasted Peanuts has 160 calories. How many calories are in 8 ounces? (*Source:* RJR Nabisco, Inc.)

82. One ounce of Planters® Dry Roasted Peanuts has 13 grams of fat. How many grams of fat are in 8 ounces? (*Source:* RJR Nabisco, Inc.)

83. The diameter of the planet Saturn is 9 times as great as the diameter of Earth. The diameter of Earth is 7927 miles. Find the diameter of Saturn.

84. The planet Uranus orbits the Sun every 84 Earth years. Find how many Earth days two orbits take. (Assume 365 days in 1 year.)

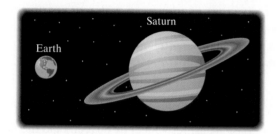

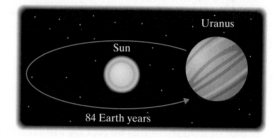

85. The Thespian club at a local community college is ordering T-shirts. T-shirts size S, M, or L cost $10 each and T-shirts size XL or XXL cost $12 each. Use the table below to find the total cost. (The first row is filled in for you.)

T-Shirt Size	Number of Shirts Ordered	Cost per Shirt	Cost per Size Ordered
S	3	$10	$30
M	5		
L	10		
XL	2		
XXL	2		

Total Cost ____

86. A field trip to the planetarium is planned by the student teacher of a third-grade class. For parent supervisors, the cost is $10 per person. For the third grade students, the cost is $8 per person. For the teacher and student teacher, the cost is $5 per person. Use the table below to find the total cost. (The first row is filled in for you.)

Person	Number of Persons	Cost per Person	Cost per Category
Teacher/ student teacher	2	$5	$10
Third graders	25		
Parents	5		

Total Cost ____

87. Hershey's main chocolate factory in Hershey, Pennsylvania, uses 700,000 quarts of milk each day. How many quarts of milk would be used during the month of March, assuming that chocolate is made at the factory every day of the month? (*Source:* Hershey Foods Corp.)

88. Among older Americans (age 65 years and older), there are about 4 times as many widows as widowers. There were 1,974,000 widowers in 2002. How many widows were there in 2002? (*Sources:* Administration on Aging, U.S. Census Bureau)

Mixed Practice (*Sections 1.3, 1.4, 1.6*) *Perform each indicated operation.*

89.   126
      + 8

90.   126
      − 8

91.   126
      × 8

92. 47 + 26 + 10 + 231 + 50

93. Find the sum of 18 and 6.

94. Find the product of 18 and 6.

95. Find the difference of 18 and 6.   **96.** Find the total of 18 and 6.

Concept Extensions

Solve. See the first Concept Check in this section.

97. Rewrite $3 + 3 + 3 + 3 + 3$ using multiplication.

98. Rewrite $11 + 11 + 11 + 11 + 11 + 11$ using multiplication.

99. a. Rewrite $4 \cdot 7$ as repeated addition.
　　b. Explain why there is more than one way to do this.

100. a. Rewrite $2 \cdot 5$ as repeated addition.
　　　b. Explain why there is more than one way to do this.

Find and explain the error in each multiplication problem. See the second Concept Check in this section.

101.
$$\begin{array}{r} 203 \\ \times\ 14 \\ \hline 812 \\ 203 \\ \hline 1015 \end{array}$$

102.
$$\begin{array}{r} 31 \\ \times\ 50 \\ \hline 155 \end{array}$$

Fill in the missing digits in each problem.

103.
$$\begin{array}{r} 4\_ \\ \times\ \ \_3 \\ \hline 126 \\ 3780 \\ \hline 3906 \end{array}$$

104.
$$\begin{array}{r} \_7 \\ \times\ 6\_ \\ \hline 171 \\ 3420 \\ \hline 3591 \end{array}$$

105. Explain how to multiply two 2-digit numbers using partial products.

106. During the NBA's 2003–2004 season, Kevin Garnett of the Minnesota Timberwolves scored 11 three-point field goals, 793 two-point field goals, and 368 free throws (worth one point each). How many points did Garnett score during the 2003–2004 season? (*Source:* National Basketball Association)

107. A window washer in New York City is bidding for a contract to wash the windows of a 23-story building. To write a bid, the number of windows in the building is needed. If there are 7 windows in each row of windows on 2 sides of the building and 4 windows per row on the other 2 sides of the building, find the total number of windows.

1.7 DIVIDING WHOLE NUMBERS

Suppose three people pooled their money and bought a raffle ticket at a local fund-raiser. Their ticket was the winner and they won a $60 cash prize. They then divided the prize into three equal parts so that each person received $20.

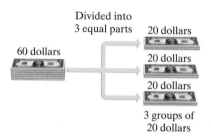

Objective **A** Dividing Whole Numbers

The process of separating a quantity into equal parts is called **division.** The division above can be symbolized by several notations.

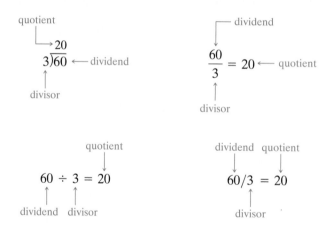

(In the notation $\frac{60}{3}$, the bar separating 60 and 3 is called a **fraction bar.**) Just as subtraction is the reverse of addition, division is the reverse of multiplication. This means that division can be checked by multiplication.

$$3\overline{)60}^{\,20} \quad \text{because} \quad 20 \cdot 3 = 60$$

$$\boxed{\text{Quotient}} \cdot \boxed{\text{Divisor}} = \boxed{\text{Dividend}}$$

Since multiplication and division are related in this way, you can use the multiplication table in Appendix A.2 to review quotients of one-digit divisors if necessary.

EXAMPLE 1 Find each quotient. Check by multiplying.

a. $42 \div 7$ **b.** $\dfrac{81}{9}$ **c.** $4\overline{)24}$

Solution:

a. $42 \div 7 = 6$ because $6 \cdot 7 = 42$

b. $\dfrac{81}{9} = 9$ because $9 \cdot 9 = 81$

c. $4\overline{)24}^{\,6}$ because $6 \cdot 4 = 24$

▣ **Work Practice Problem 1**

EXAMPLE 2 Find each quotient. Check by multiplying.

a. $1\overline{)8}$ **b.** $11 \div 1$ **c.** $\dfrac{9}{9}$ **d.** $7 \div 7$ **e.** $\dfrac{10}{1}$ **f.** $6\overline{)6}$

Solution:

a. $1\overline{)8}^{\,8}$ because $8 \cdot 1 = 8$

b. $11 \div 1 = 11$ because $11 \cdot 1 = 11$

c. $\dfrac{9}{9} = 1$ because $1 \cdot 9 = 9$

d. $7 \div 7 = 1$ because $1 \cdot 7 = 7$

e. $\dfrac{10}{1} = 10$ because $10 \cdot 1 = 10$

f. $6\overline{)6}^{\,1}$ because $1 \cdot 6 = 6$

▣ **Work Practice Problem 2**

Example 2 illustrates the important properties of division described next:

Division Properties of 1

The quotient of any number and that same number is 1. For example,

$$8 \div 8 = 1 \qquad \frac{7}{7} = 1 \qquad 4\overline{)4}^{\,1}$$

The quotient of any number and 1 is that same number. For example,

$$9 \div 1 = 9 \qquad \frac{6}{1} = 6 \qquad 1\overline{)3}^{\,3} \qquad \frac{0}{1} = 0$$

EXAMPLE 3 Find each quotient. Check by multiplying.

a. $9\overline{)0}$ **b.** $0 \div 12$ **c.** $\dfrac{0}{5}$ **d.** $\dfrac{3}{0}$

Solution:

a. $9\overline{)0}^{\,0}$ because $0 \cdot 9 = 0$ **b.** $0 \div 12 = 0$ because $0 \cdot 12 = 0$

c. $\dfrac{0}{5} = 0$ because $0 \cdot 5 = 0$

Continued on next page

Find each quotient. Check by multiplying.

a. $8\overline{)48}$

b. $35 \div 5$

c. $\dfrac{49}{7}$

Find each quotient. Check by multiplying.

a. $\dfrac{8}{8}$ **b.** $3 \div 1$

c. $1\overline{)12}$ **d.** $2 \div 1$

e. $\dfrac{5}{1}$ **f.** $11 \div 11$

Find each quotient. Check by multiplying.

a. $\dfrac{0}{7}$ **b.** $5\overline{)0}$

c. $9 \div 0$ **d.** $0 \div 6$

Answers
1. a. 6, **b.** 7, **c.** 7, **2. a.** 1, **b.** 3,
c. 12, **d.** 2, **e.** 5, **f.** 1,
3. a. 0, **b.** 0, **c.** undefined, **d.** 0

d. If $\dfrac{3}{0}$ = a **number,** then the **number** times 0 = 3. Recall from Section 1.6 that any number multiplied by 0 is 0 and not 3. We say, then, that $\dfrac{3}{0}$ is **undefined.**

🔲 **Work Practice Problem 3**

Example 3 illustrates important division properties of 0.

Division Properties of 0

The quotient of 0 and any number (except 0) is 0. For example,

$$0 \div 9 = 0 \qquad \frac{0}{5} = 0 \qquad 14\overline{)0}^{\,0}$$

The quotient of any number and 0 is not a number. We say that

$$\frac{3}{0}, \quad 0\overline{)3}, \quad \text{and} \quad 3 \div 0$$

are **undefined.**

Objective B Performing Long Division

When dividends are larger, the quotient can be found by a process called **long division.** For example, let's divide 2541 by 3.

$$3\overline{)2541}$$

We can't divide 3 into 2, so we try dividing 3 into the first two digits.

$$3\overline{)2541}^{\,8} \qquad 25 \div 3 = 8 \text{ with 1 left, so our best estimate is 8. We place 8 over the 5 in 25.}$$

Next, multiply 8 and 3 and subtract this product from 25. Make sure that this difference is less than the divisor.

$$
\begin{array}{r}
8 \\
3\overline{)2541} \\
-24 \\
\hline
1
\end{array}
\qquad
\begin{array}{l}
8(3) = 24 \\
25 - 24 = 1, \text{ and 1 is less than the divisor 3.}
\end{array}
$$

Bring down the next digit and go through the process again.

$$
\begin{array}{r}
84 \\
3\overline{)2541} \\
-24\downarrow \\
\hline
14 \\
-12 \\
\hline
2
\end{array}
\qquad
\begin{array}{l}
14 \div 3 = 4 \text{ with 2 left} \\
\\
\\
4(3) = 12 \\
14 - 12 = 2
\end{array}
$$

Once more, bring down the next digit and go through the process.

$$
\begin{array}{r}
847 \\
3\overline{)2541} \\
-24 \\
\hline
14 \\
-12\downarrow \\
\hline
21 \\
-21 \\
\hline
0
\end{array}
\qquad
\begin{array}{l}
21 \div 3 = 7 \\
\\
\\
\\
\\
7(3) = 21 \\
21 - 21 = 0
\end{array}
$$

The quotient is 847. To check, see that $847 \times 3 = 2541$.

EXAMPLE 4 Divide: 3705 ÷ 5. Check by multiplying.

Solution:

$$\begin{array}{r} 7 \\ 5\overline{)3705} \\ -35\downarrow \\ \hline 20 \end{array}$$

37 ÷ 5 = 7 with 2 left. Place this estimate, 7, over the 7 in 37.

7(5) = 35

37 − 35 = 2, and 2 is less than the divisor 5.

└── Bring down the 0.

$$\begin{array}{r} 74 \\ 5\overline{)3705} \\ -35 \\ \hline 20 \\ -20\downarrow \\ \hline 05 \end{array}$$

20 ÷ 5 = 4

4(5) = 20

20 − 20 = 0, and 0 is less than the divisor 5.

└── Bring down the 5.

$$\begin{array}{r} 741 \\ 5\overline{)3705} \\ -35 \\ \hline 20 \\ -20\downarrow \\ \hline 5 \\ -5 \\ \hline 0 \end{array}$$

5 ÷ 5 = 1

1(5) = 5

5 − 5 = 0

Check:

$$\begin{array}{r} 741 \\ \times \quad 5 \\ \hline 3705 \end{array}$$

▣ **Work Practice Problem 4**

Helpful Hint Since division and multiplication are reverse operations, don't forget that a division problem can be checked by multiplying.

EXAMPLE 5 Divide and check: 1872 ÷ 9

Solution:

$$\begin{array}{r} 208 \\ 9\overline{)1872} \\ -18\downarrow\downarrow \\ \hline 07 \\ -0\downarrow \\ \hline 72 \\ -72 \\ \hline 0 \end{array}$$

2(9) − 18

18 − 18 = 0; bring down the 7.

0(9) = 0

7 − 0 = 7; bring down the 2.

8(9) = 72

72 − 72 = 0

Check: 208 · 9 = 1872

▣ **Work Practice Problem 5**

PRACTICE PROBLEM 4

Divide. Check by multiplying.

a. 5382 ÷ 6

b. 2212 ÷ 4

c. 753 ÷ 3

PRACTICE PROBLEM 5

Divide and check.

a. 3$\overline{)2115}$

b. 7$\overline{)28,700}$

Answers
4. a. 897, **b.** 553, **c.** 251,
5. a. 705, **b.** 4100

Naturally, quotients don't always "come out even." Making 4 rows out of 26 chairs, for example, isn't possible if each row is supposed to have exactly the same number of chairs. Each of 4 rows can have 6 chairs, but 2 chairs are still left over.

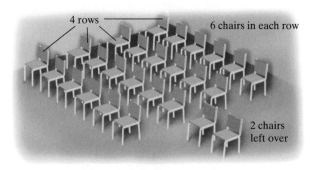

We signify "leftovers" or **remainders** in this way:

$$\begin{array}{r} 6 R\,2 \\ 4\overline{)26} \end{array}$$

The **whole number part of the quotient** is 6; the **remainder part of the quotient** is 2. Checking by multiplying,

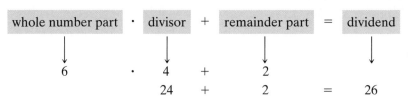

whole number part	·	divisor	+	remainder part	=	dividend
6	·	4	+	2		
		24	+	2	=	26

PRACTICE PROBLEM 6

Divide and check.

a. $5\overline{)949}$

b. $6\overline{)4399}$

EXAMPLE 6 Divide and check: $2557 \div 7$

Solution:

$$\begin{array}{r} 365 R\,2 \\ 7\overline{)2557} \\ \underline{-21}\!\downarrow\!\downarrow \\ 45 \\ \underline{-42}\!\downarrow \\ 37 \\ \underline{-35} \\ 2 \end{array}$$

$3(7) = 21$
$25 - 21 = 4$; bring down the 5.
$6(7) = 42$
$45 - 42 = 3$; bring down the 7.
$5(7) = 35$
$37 - 35 = 2$; the remainder is 2.

Check: $\quad 365 \quad \cdot \quad 7 \quad + \quad 2 \quad = \quad 2557$

whole number part	·	divisor	+	remainder part	=	dividend

☐ **Work Practice Problem 6**

Answers

6. a. 189 R 4, **b.** 733 R 1

EXAMPLE 7 Divide and check: 56,717 ÷ 8

Solution:

```
      7089  R 5
  8)56717
   −56↓│││
      07││        7(8) = 56
     −0↓│         Subtract and bring down the 7.
      71│         0(8) = 0
    −64↓          Subtract and bring down the 1.
      77          8(8) = 64
    −72           Subtract and bring down the 7.
       5          9(8) = 72
                  Subtract. The remainder is 5.
```

Check:

$$7089 \quad \cdot \quad 8 \quad + \quad 5 \quad = \quad 56{,}717$$

| whole number part | · | divisor | + | remainder part | = | dividend |

■ Work Practice Problem 7

When the divisor has more than one digit, the same pattern applies. For example, let's find 1358 ÷ 23.

```
       5      135 ÷ 23 = 5 with 20 left over. Our estimate is 5.
  23)1358
   −115↓      5(23) = 115
     208      135 − 115 = 20. Bring down the 8.
```

Now we continue estimating.

```
      59   R 1   208 ÷ 23 = 9 with 1 left over.
  23)1358
   −115
     208
    −207        9(23) = 207
       1        208 − 207 = 1. The remainder is 1.
```

To check, see that 59 · 23 + 1 = 1358.

EXAMPLE 8 Divide: 6819 ÷ 17

Solution:

```
      401  R 2
  17)6819
   −68↓          4(17) = 68
     01│         Subtract and bring down the 1.
    −0↓          0(17) = 0
     19          Subtract and bring down the 9.
   −17           1(17) = 17
     2           Subtract. The reminder is 2.
```

To check, see that 401 · 17 + 2 = 6819.

■ Work Practice Problem 8

PRACTICE PROBLEM 7

Divide and check.

a. 5)40,841

b. 7)22,430

PRACTICE PROBLEM 8

Divide: 5740 ÷ 19

PRACTICE PROBLEM 9

Divide: $16{,}589 \div 247$

EXAMPLE 9 Divide: $51{,}600 \div 403$

Solution:
$$
\begin{array}{r}
128 \ \ \text{R } 16 \\
403\overline{)51600} \\
-403 \\
\hline
1130 \\
-806 \\
\hline
3240 \\
-3224 \\
\hline
16
\end{array}
$$

$1(403) = 403$
Subtract and bring down the 0.
$2(403) = 806$
Subtract and bring down the 0.
$8(403) = 3224$
Subtract. The remainder is 16.

To check, see that $128 \cdot 403 + 16 = 51{,}600$.

■ **Work Practice Problem 9**

Division Shown as Repeated Subtraction To further understand division, recall from Section 1.6 that addition and multiplication are related in the following manner:

$$\underbrace{3 + 3 + 3 + 3}_{\text{4 addends; each addend is 3}} = 4 \times 3 = 12$$

In other words, multiplication is repeated addition. Likewise, division is repeated subtraction.

For example, let's find

$$35 \div 8$$

by repeated subtraction. Keep track of the number of times 8 is subtracted from 35. We are through when we can subtract no more because the difference is less than 8.

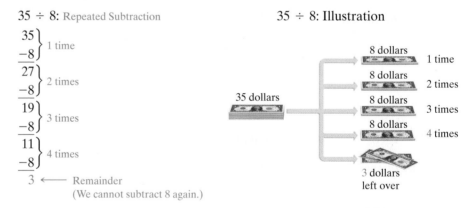

$35 \div 8$: Repeated Subtraction

$$
\begin{array}{l}
\left.\begin{array}{r}35\\-8\end{array}\right\} \text{1 time} \\
\left.\begin{array}{r}27\\-8\end{array}\right\} \text{2 times} \\
\left.\begin{array}{r}19\\-8\end{array}\right\} \text{3 times} \\
\left.\begin{array}{r}11\\-8\end{array}\right\} \text{4 times} \\
\ \ 3 \longleftarrow \text{Remainder}
\end{array}
$$
(We cannot subtract 8 again.)

$35 \div 8$: Illustration

35 dollars

8 dollars — 1 time
8 dollars — 2 times
8 dollars — 3 times
8 dollars — 4 times

3 dollars left over

Thus, $35 \div 8 = 4 \text{ R } 3$.

To check, perform the same multiplication as usual, but finish by adding in the remainder.

whole number part of quotient	·	divisor	+	remainder	=	dividend
↓		↓		↓		↓
4	·	8	+	3	=	35

Answer

9. $67 \text{ R } 40$

Objective **C** Solving Problems by Dividing

Below are some key words and phrases that may indicate the operation of division:

Key Words or Phrases	Examples	Symbols
divide	divide 10 by 5	$10 \div 5$ or $\dfrac{10}{5}$
quotient	the quotient of 64 and 4	$64 \div 4$ or $\dfrac{64}{4}$
divided by	9 divided by 3	$9 \div 3$ or $\dfrac{9}{3}$
divided or **shared equally among**	$100 divided equally among five people	$100 \div 5$ or $\dfrac{100}{5}$

✔**Concept Check** Which of the following is the correct way to represent "the quotient of 20 and 5"? Or are both correct? Explain your answer.

a. $5 \div 20$

b. $20 \div 5$

EXAMPLE 10 **Finding Shared Earnings**

Zachary, Tyler, and Stephanie McMillan share a paper route to earn money for college expenses. The total in their fund after expenses was $2895. How much is each person's equal share?

Solution:

In words: | Each person's share | = | total money | ÷ | number of persons

Translate: Each person's share = 2895 ÷ 3

Then

$$\begin{array}{r} 965 \\ 3\overline{)2895} \\ -27 \\ \hline 19 \\ -18 \\ \hline 15 \\ -15 \\ \hline 0 \end{array}$$

Each person's share is $965.

■ **Work Practice Problem 10**

PRACTICE PROBLEM 10

Marina, Manual, and Min bought 120 high-density computer diskettes to share equally. How many diskettes did each person get?

Answer

10. 40 diskettes

✔ **Concept Check Answers**

a. incorrect, **b.** correct

PRACTICE PROBLEM 11

Peanut butter and cheese cracker sandwiches come in 6 sandwiches to a package. How many full packages are formed with 195 sandwiches?

EXAMPLE 11 **Calculating Shipping Needs**

How many boxes are needed to ship 56 pairs of Nikes to a shoe store in Texarkana if 9 pairs of shoes will fit in each shipping box?

Solution:

In words:	number of boxes	=	total pairs of shoes	÷	how many pairs in a box

Translate:	number or boxes	=	56	÷	9

$$\begin{array}{r} 6 \text{ R2} \\ 9\overline{)56} \\ -54 \\ \hline 2 \end{array}$$

There are 6 full boxes with 2 pairs of shoes left over, so 7 boxes will be needed.

■ **Work Practice Problem 11**

PRACTICE PROBLEM 12

Calculators can be packed 24 to a box. If 497 calculators are to be packed but only full boxes are shipped, how many full boxes will be shipped? How many calculators are left over and not shipped?

EXAMPLE 12 **Dividing Holiday Favors Among Students**

Mary Schultz has 48 kindergarten students. She buys 260 stickers as Thanksgiving Day favors for her students. How many stickers will each person receive? How many stickers will be left over?

Solution:

In words:	Number of stickers for each person	=	number of stickers	÷	number of students

Translate:	Number of stickers for each person	=	260	÷	48

$$\begin{array}{r} 5 \text{ R20} \\ 48\overline{)260} \\ -240 \\ \hline 20 \end{array}$$

Each student will receive 5 stickers. The stickers cannot be divided equally among her students since there is a nonzero remainder. There will be 20 stickers left over.

■ **Work Practice Problem 12**

Objective D Finding Averages

A special application of division (and addition) is finding the average of a list of numbers. The **average** of a list of numbers is the sum of the numbers divided by the *number* of numbers.

$$\text{average} = \frac{\text{sum of numbers}}{\textit{number of numbers}}$$

Answers

11. 32 full packages,
12. 20 full boxes; 17 calculators left over

EXAMPLE 13 **Averaging Scores**

Liam Reilly's scores in his mathematics class so far are 93, 86, 71, and 82. Find his average score.

Solution: To find his average score, we find the sum of his scores and divide by 4, the number of scores.

$$\begin{array}{r} 93 \\ 86 \\ 71 \\ +82 \\ \hline 332 \text{ sum} \end{array}$$

$$\text{average} = \frac{332}{4} = 83$$

$$\begin{array}{r} 83 \\ 4\overline{)332} \\ -32 \\ \hline 12 \\ -12 \\ \hline 0 \end{array}$$

His average score is 83.

Work Practice Problem 13

PRACTICE PROBLEM 13

To compute a safe time to wait for reactions to occur after allergy shots are administered, a lab technician is given a list of elapsed times between administered shots and reactions. Find the average of the times 5 minutes, 7 minutes, 20 minutes, 6 minutes, 9 minutes, 3 minutes, and 48 minutes.

Answer

13. 14 min

CALCULATOR EXPLORATIONS Dividing Numbers

To divide numbers on a calculator, find the keys marked $\div$ and $=$ or ENTER . For example, to find $435 \div 5$ on a calculator, press the keys 435 $\div$ 5 $=$ or ENTER . The display will read 87 . Thus, $435 \div 5 = 87$.

Use a calculator to divide.

1. $848 \div 16$　　**2.** $564 \div 12$　　**3.** $95\overline{)5890}$　　**4.** $27\overline{)1053}$

5. $\dfrac{32,886}{126}$　　**6.** $\dfrac{143,088}{264}$　　**7.** $0 \div 315$　　**8.** $315 \div 0$

Mental Math

Objective A *Find each quotient. See Examples 1 through 3.*

1. $40 \div 8$　　**2.** $72 \div 9$　　**3.** $45 \div 5$　　**4.** $24 \div 3$　　**5.** $0 \div 5$

6. $0 \div 8$　　**7.** $9 \div 1$　　**8.** $12 \div 1$　　**9.** $\dfrac{16}{16}$　　**10.** $\dfrac{49}{49}$

11. $\dfrac{25}{5}$　　**12.** $\dfrac{45}{9}$　　**13.** $6 \div 0$　　**14.** $\dfrac{12}{0}$　　**15.** $7 \div 1$

16. $6 \div 6$　　**17.** $0 \div 4$　　**18.** $7 \div 0$　　**19.** $16 \div 2$　　**20.** $18 \div 3$

1.7 EXERCISE SET

FOR EXTRA HELP

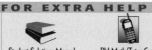
Student Solutions Manual

PH Math/Tutor Center

CD/Video for Review

Math XL
MathXL®

MyMathLab
MyMathLab

Objective Ⓐ Ⓑ **Mixed Practice** *Divide and then check by multiplying. See Examples 1 through 5.*

1. $3\overline{)78}$ **2.** $5\overline{)85}$ **3.** $6\overline{)222}$ **4.** $8\overline{)640}$ **5.** $3\overline{)1014}$ **6.** $4\overline{)2104}$

7. $\dfrac{20}{0}$ **8.** $\dfrac{0}{20}$ **9.** $48 \div 6$ **10.** $56 \div 8$ **11.** $125 \div 5$ **12.** $121 \div 11$

Divide and then check by multiplying. See Examples 6 and 7.

13. $9\overline{)589}$ **14.** $7\overline{)426}$ **15.** $5\overline{)1129}$ **16.** $3\overline{)1240}$

17. $186 \div 5$ **18.** $167 \div 3$ **19.** $2125 \div 8$ **20.** $3333 \div 4$

Divide and then check by multiplying. See Examples 8 and 9.

21. $23\overline{)1127}$ **22.** $42\overline{)2016}$ **23.** $55\overline{)715}$ **24.** $23\overline{)736}$ **25.** $97\overline{)9449}$

26. $1938 \div 44$ **27.** $3718 \div 18$ **28.** $7224 \div 12$ **29.** $6578 \div 13$ **30.** $5670 \div 14$

31. $9299 \div 46$ **32.** $2539 \div 64$ **33.** $\dfrac{10,620}{236}$ **34.** $\dfrac{5781}{123}$ **35.** $\dfrac{10,194}{103}$

36. $\dfrac{23,048}{240}$ **37.** $20,619 \div 102$ **38.** $40,853 \div 203$ **39.** $244,989 \div 423$ **40.** $164,592 \div 543$

Divide. See Examples 1 through 9.

41. $7\overline{)133}$ **42.** $9\overline{)153}$ **43.** $3\overline{)1540}$ **44.** $5\overline{)3017}$

45. $30\overline{)62,486}$ **46.** $50\overline{)85,747}$ **47.** $139\overline{)699,170}$ **48.** $213\overline{)866,910}$

Objective Ⓒ *Solve. See Examples 10 through 12.*

49. Find the quotient of 85 and 4.

50. Find the quotient of 90 and 7.

51. Find 100 divided by 35.

52. Find 121 divided by 29.

70

53. Find the quotient of 62 and 3.

54. Find the quotient of 78 and 5.

55. Kathy Gomez teaches Spanish lessons for $85 per student for a 5-week session. From one group of students, she collects $4930. Find how many students are in the group.

56. Martin Thieme teaches American Sign Language classes for $55 per student for a 7-week session. He collects $1430 from the group of students. Find how many students are in the group.

57. Twenty-one people pooled their money and bought lottery tickets. One ticket won a prize of $5,292,000. Find how many dollars each person received.

58. The gravity of Jupiter is 318 times as strong as the gravity of Earth, so objects on Jupiter weigh 318 times as much as they weigh on Earth. If a person would weigh 52,470 pounds on Jupiter, find how much the person weighs on Earth.

59. A truck hauls wheat to a storage granary. It carries a total of 5810 bushels of wheat in 14 trips. How much does the truck haul each trip if each trip it hauls the same amount?

60. An 18-hole golf course is 5580 yards long. If the distance to each hole is the same, find the distance between holes.

61. The white stripes dividing the lanes on a highway are 25 feet long, and the spaces between them are 25 feet long. Let's call a "lane divider" a stripe followed by a space. Find how many whole "lane dividers" there are in 1 mile of highway. (A mile is 5280 feet.)

62. There is a bridge over highway I-35 every three miles. The first bridge is at the beginning of a 265-mile stretch of highway. Find how many bridges there are over 265 miles of I-35.

63. Wendy Holladay has a piece of rope 185 feet long that she wants to cut into pieces for an experiment in her second-grade class. Each piece of rope is to be 8 feet long. Determine whether she has enough rope for her 22-student class. Determine the amount extra or the amount short.

64. Jesse White is in the requisitions department of Central Electric Lighting Company. Light poles along a highway are placed 492 feet apart. The first light pole is at the beginning of a 1-mile strip. Find how many poles he should order for the 1-mile strip of highway. (A mile is 5280 feet.)

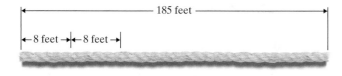

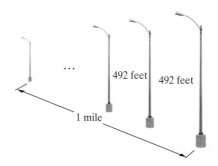

65. Priest Holmes of the Kansas City Chiefs led the NFL in touchdowns during the 2003 football season, scoring a total of 162 points from touchdowns. If a touchdown is worth 6 points, how many touchdowns did Priest make during 2003? (*Source:* National Football League)

66. Broad Peak in Pakistan is the twelfth-tallest mountain in the world. Its elevation is 26,400 feet. A mile is 5280 feet. How many miles tall is Broad Peak? (*Source:* National Geographic Society)

67. Find how many yards are in 1 mile. (A mile is 5280 feet; a yard is 3 feet.)

68. Find how many whole feet are in 1 rod. (A mile is 5280 feet; 1 mile is 320 rods.)

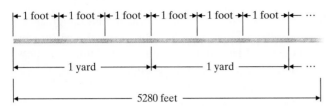

Objective D *Find the average of each list of numbers. See Example 13.*

69. 14, 22, 45, 18, 30, 27

70. 37, 26, 15, 29, 51, 22

71. 204, 968, 552, 268

72. 121, 200, 185, 176, 163

73. 86, 79, 81, 69, 80

74. 92, 96, 90, 85, 92, 79

The normal monthly temperature in degrees Fahrenheit for Minneapolis, Minnesota, is given in the graph. Use this graph to answer Exercises 75 and 76. (Source: National Climatic Data Center)

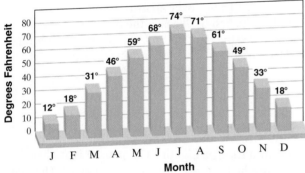

Normal Monthly Temperature (in Fahrenheit) for Minneapolis, Minnesota

75. Find the average temperature for December, January, and February.

76. Find the average temperature for the entire year.

Mixed Practice (*Sections 1.3, 1.4, 1.6, 1.7*) *Perform each indicated operation. Watch the operation symbol.*

77. 78 + 236 + 42 + 8506

78. 23 + 407 + 92 + 7011

79.
$$\begin{array}{r} 635 \\ \times\ 46 \\ \hline \end{array}$$

80.
$$\begin{array}{r} 712 \\ \times\ 54 \\ \hline \end{array}$$

81.
$$\begin{array}{r} 635 \\ -\ 46 \\ \hline \end{array}$$

82.
$$\begin{array}{r} 712 \\ -\ 54 \\ \hline \end{array}$$

83. $\dfrac{86}{0}$

84. $\dfrac{0}{80}$

85. 211 ÷ 28

86. 304 ÷ 31

Concept Extensions

Match each word phrase to the correct translation. (Not all letter choices will be used.) See the Concept Check in this section.

87. The quotient of 35 and 7

a. 100 ÷ 10

88. The quotient of 100 and 10

b. 10 ÷ 100

89. 100 divided by 10

c. 7 ÷ 35

90. 35 divided by 7

d. 35 ÷ 7

The following table shows the top five leading U.S. advertisers in 2003 and the amount of money spent in that year on advertising. Use this table to answer Exercises 91 and 92.

Company	2003 Advertising Expenditures
General Motors Corp.	$3,430,000,000
DaimlerChrysler AG	$2,318,000,000
Procter & Gamble Co.	$3,323,000,000
Pfizer	$2,839,000,000
Time Warner Inc.	$3,097,000,000
(*Source:* Crain Communications)	

91. Find the average amount of money spent on ads for the year by the top two companies.

92. Find the average amount of money spent on ads by DaimlerChrysler AG, Procter & Gamble Co., Pfizer, and Time Warner Inc.

In Example 13 in this section, we found that the average of 93, 86, 71, and 82 is 83. Use this information to answer Exercises 93 and 94.

93. If the number 71 is removed from the list of numbers, does the average increase or decrease? Explain why.

94. If the number 93 is removed from the list of numbers, does the average increase or decrease? Explain why.

95. Without computing it, tell whether the average of 126, 135, 198, 113 is 86. Explain why it is or why it is not.

96. If the area of a rectangle is 30 square feet and its width is 3 feet, what is its length?

97. Write down any two numbers whose quotient is 15.

98. Find $26 \div 5$ using the process of repeated subtraction.

 THE BIGGER PICTURE Operations on Sets of Numbers

This is a special feature that we begin in this section. Among other concepts introduced later in the text, it is very important for you to be able to perform operations on different sets of numbers. To help you remember these operations, we begin an outline below and continually expand this outline throughout this text. Although suggestions are given, this outline should be in your own words. Once you complete the new portion of your outline, try the exercises below. Remember: Study your outline often as you proceed through this text.

I. Some Operations on Sets of Numbers

   A. Whole Numbers

      1. Add or Subtract:

$$\begin{array}{r} 14 \\ +\ 39 \\ \hline 53 \end{array} \qquad \begin{array}{r} 300 \\ -\ 27 \\ \hline 273 \end{array}$$

2. Multiply or Divide:

$$\begin{array}{r} 238 \\ \times\ 47 \\ \hline 1666 \\ 9520 \\ \hline 11186 \end{array} \qquad \begin{array}{r} 127\ \text{R}\ 2 \\ 7\overline{)891} \\ -7 \\ \hline 19 \\ -14 \\ \hline 51 \\ -49 \\ \hline 2 \end{array}$$

Perform indicated operations.

1. $73 + 45$

2. $73 - 45$

3. 73×45

4. $2592 \div 29$

5. $0 \cdot 28$

6. $0 \div 11$

7. $19 \cdot 1$

8. $36 \div 0$

9. $64 \div 1$

10. $2000 - 156$

Operations on Whole Numbers

1. _____

2. _____

3. _____

4. _____

5. _____

6. _____

7. _____

8. _____

9. _____

10. _____

11. _____

12. _____

13. _____

14. _____

15. _____

16. _____

17. _____

18. _____

19. _____

20. _____

21. _____

22. _____

23. _____

24. _____

25. _____

26. _____

27. _____

28. _____

29. _____

30. _____

Perform each indicated operation.

1. $\begin{array}{r} 23 \\ 46 \\ +79 \\ \hline \end{array}$

2. $\begin{array}{r} 7006 \\ -\ 451 \\ \hline \end{array}$

3. $\begin{array}{r} 36 \\ \times 45 \\ \hline \end{array}$

4. $8\overline{)4496}$

5. $1 \cdot 79$

6. $\dfrac{36}{0}$

7. $9 \div 1$

8. $9 \div 9$

9. $0 \cdot 13$

10. $7 \cdot 0 \cdot 8$

11. $0 \div 2$

12. $12 \div 4$

13. $4219 - 1786$

14. $1861 + 7965$

15. $5\overline{)1068}$

16. $\begin{array}{r} 1259 \\ \times\ \ 63 \\ \hline \end{array}$

17. $3 \cdot 9$

18. $45 \div 5$

19. $\begin{array}{r} 207 \\ -\ 69 \\ \hline \end{array}$

20. $\begin{array}{r} 207 \\ +\ 69 \\ \hline \end{array}$

21. $7\overline{)7695}$

22. $9\overline{)1000}$

23. $32\overline{)21,222}$

24. $65\overline{)70,000}$

25. $4000 - 2976$

26. $10,000 - 101$

27. $\begin{array}{r} 303 \\ \times 101 \\ \hline \end{array}$

28. $(475)(100)$

29. Find the total of 57 and 8.

30. Find the product of 57 and 8.

31. Find the quotient of 57 and 8.

32. Find the difference of 57 and 8.

33. Subtract 14 from 100.

34. Find the difference of 43 and 21.

Complete the table by rounding the given number to the given place value.

		Tens	Hundreds	Thousands
35.	8625			
36.	1553			
37.	10,901			
38.	432,198			

Find the perimeter and area of each figure.

△ **39.**

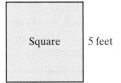

Square   5 feet

△ **40.**

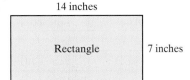

14 inches

Rectangle   7 inches

Find the perimeter of each figure.

△ **41.**

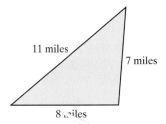

11 miles

7 miles

8 miles

△ **42.**

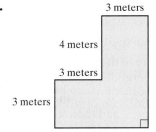

3 meters

4 meters

3 meters

3 meters

3 meters

Find the average of each list of numbers.

43. 19, 15, 25, 37, 24

44. 108, 131, 98, 159

45. The Mackinac Bridge is a suspension bridge that connects the lower and upper peninsulas of Michigan across the Straits of Mackinac. Its total length is 26,372 feet. The Lake Pontchartrain Bridge is a twin concrete trestle bridge in Slidell, Louisiana. Its total length is 28,547 feet. Which bridge is longer and by how much? (*Sources:* Mackinac Bridge Authority and Federal Highway Administration, Bridge Division)

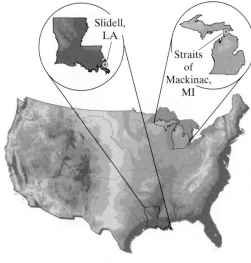

Slidell, LA

Straits of Mackinac, MI

46. In North America, the average toy expenditure per child is $328 per year. On average, how much is spent on toys for a child by the time he or she reaches age 18? (*Source:* The NPD Group Worldwide)

31. _____

32. _____

33. _____

34. _____

35. see table _____

36. see table _____

37. see table _____

38. see table _____

39. _____

40. _____

41. _____

42. _____

43. _____

44. _____

45. _____

46. _____

A Solve Problems by Adding, Subtracting, Multiplying, or Dividing Whole Numbers.

B Solve Problems That Require More Than One Operation.

1.8 AN INTRODUCTION TO PROBLEM SOLVING

Objective **A** Solving Problems Involving Addition, Subtraction, Multiplication, or Division

In this section, we decide which operation to perform in order to solve a problem. Don't forget the key words and phrases that help indicate which operation to use. Some of these are listed below and were introduced earlier in the chapter. Also included are several words and phrases that translate to the symbol "=".

Addition (+)	Subtraction (−)	Multiplication (·)	Division (÷)	Equality (=)
sum	difference	product	quotient	equals
plus	minus	times	divide	is equal to
added to	subtract	multiply	shared equally	is/was
more than	less than	multiply by	among	yields
increased by	decreased by	of	divided by	
total	less	double/triple	divided into	

The following problem-solving steps may be helpful to you:

Problem-Solving Steps

1. UNDERSTAND the problem. Some ways of doing this are to read and reread the problem, construct a drawing and look for key words to identify an operation.

2. TRANSLATE the problem. That is, write the problem in short form using words, and then translate to numbers and symbols.

3. SOLVE the problem. It is helpful to estimate the solution by rounding. Then carry out the indicated operation from Step 2.

4. INTERPRET the results. *Check* the proposed solution in the stated problem and *state* your conclusions. Write your results with the correct units attached.

EXAMPLE 1 Calculating the Length of a River

The Hudson River in New York State is 306 miles long. The Snake River in the northwestern United States is 732 miles longer than the Hudson River. How long is the Snake River? (*Source:* U.S. Department of the Interior)

Solution:

1. UNDERSTAND. Read and reread the problem, and then draw a picture. Notice that we are told that the Snake River is 732 miles longer than the Hudson River. The phrase "longer than" means that we add.

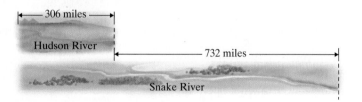

PRACTICE PROBLEM 1

PRACTICE PROBLEM 1

The Bank of America Building is the second-tallest building in San Francisco, California, at 779 feet. The tallest building in San Francisco is the Transamerica Pyramid, which is 74 feet taller than the Bank of America Building. How tall is the Transamerica Pyramid? (*Source: The World Almanac, 2005*)

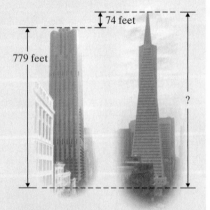

Bank of America   Transamerica Pyramid

Answer

1. 853 ft

2. TRANSLATE.

In words:

| Snake River | is | 732 miles | longer than | the Hudson River |

Translate: Snake River   =   732   +   306

3. SOLVE: Let's see if our answer is reasonable by also estimating. We will estimate each addend to the nearest hundred.

$$
\begin{array}{r}
732 \quad \text{rounds to} \quad 700 \\
+306 \quad \text{rounds to} \quad \underline{300} \\
\hline
1038 \quad \text{exact} \qquad 1000 \quad \text{estimate}
\end{array}
$$

4. INTERPRET. *Check* your work. The answer is reasonable since 1038 is close to our estimated answer of 1000. *State* your conclusion: The Snake River is 1038 miles long.

■ **Work Practice Problem 1**

EXAMPLE 2 **Filling a Shipping Order**

How many cases can be filled with 9900 cans of jalapeños if each case holds 48 cans? How many cans will be left over? Will there be enough cases to fill an order for 200 cases?

Solution:

1. UNDERSTAND. Read and reread the problem. Draw a picture to help visualize the situation.

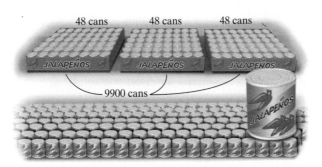

48 cans   48 cans   48 cans

9900 cans

Since each case holds 48 cans, we want to know how many 48s there are in 9900. We find this by dividing.

2. TRANSLATE.

In words:

| Number of cases | is | 9900 | divided by | 48 |

Translate: Number of cases   =   9900   ÷   48

3. SOLVE: Let's estimate a reasonable solution before we actually divide. Since 9900 rounded to the nearest thousand is 10,000 and 48 rounded to the nearest ten is 50, $10,000 \div 50 = 200$. Now find the exact quotient.

$$
\begin{array}{r}
206 \text{ R } 12 \\
48 \overline{)9900} \\
-96 \\
\hline
300 \\
-288 \\
\hline
12
\end{array}
$$

Continued on next page

PRACTICE PROBLEM 2

Four friends bought a lottery ticket and won $65,000. If each person is to receive the same amount of money, how much does each person receive?

Answer
2. $16,250

4. INTERPRET. *Check* your work. The answer is reasonable since 206 R 12 is close to our estimate of 200. *State* your conclusion: 206 cases will be filled, with 12 cans left over. There will be enough cases to fill an order for 200 cases.

▣ **Work Practice Problem 2**

PRACTICE PROBLEM 3

The director of the learning lab also needs to include in the budget a line for 425 blank CDs at a cost of $4 each. What is this total cost for the blank CDs?

EXAMPLE 3 Calculating Budget Costs

The director of a learning lab at a local community college is working on next year's budget. Thirty-three new DVD players are needed at a cost of $187 each. What is the total cost of these DVD players?

Solution:

1. UNDERSTAND. Read and reread the problem, and then draw a diagram.

33 DVD Players

$ 187 $ 187 $ 187

From the phrase "total cost," we might decide to solve this problem by adding. This would work, but repeated addition, or multiplication, would save time.

2. TRANSLATE.

In words:	Total cost	is	number of DVD players	times	cost of a DVD player
	↓	↓	↓	↓	↓
Translate:	Total cost	=	33	×	$187

3. SOLVE: Once again, let's estimate a reasonable solution.

$$
\begin{array}{r}
187 \\
\times\ 33 \\
\hline
561 \\
5610 \\
\hline
6171
\end{array}
\quad
\begin{array}{l}
\text{rounds to} \\
\text{rounds to} \\
\end{array}
\quad
\begin{array}{r}
200 \\
\times\ 30 \\
\hline
6000 \\
\end{array}
$$

187 rounds to 200
× 33 rounds to × 30
561   6000 estimate
5610
6171 exact

4. INTERPRET. *Check* your work. *State* your conclusion: The total cost of the video players is $6171.

▣ **Work Practice Problem 3**

PRACTICE PROBLEM 4

In 2002, the average salary of a public school teacher in North Dakota was $32,300. For the same year, the average salary for a public school teacher in South Dakota was $1000 less than this. What was the average public school teacher's salary in South Dakota? (*Source:* National Education Association)

EXAMPLE 4 Calculating a Public School Teacher's Salary

In 2002, the average salary of a public school teacher in California was $54,300. For the same year, the average salary for a public school teacher in Louisiana was $18,000 less than this. What was the average public school teacher's salary in Louisiana? (*Source:* National Education Association)

Solution:

1. UNDERSTAND. Read and reread the problem. Notice that we are told that the Louisiana salary is $18,000 less than the California salary. The phrase "less than" indicates subtraction.

Answers

3. $1700,   4. $31,300

2. TRANSLATE. Remember that order matters when subtracting, so be careful when translating.

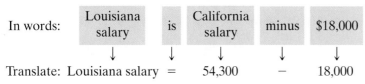

In words:
| Louisiana salary | is | California salary | minus | $18,000 |

Translate: Louisiana salary = 54,300 − 18,000

3. SOLVE: This time, instead of estimating, let's check by adding

$$
\begin{array}{r}
54{,}300 \\
-18{,}000 \\
\hline
36{,}300
\end{array}
\qquad
\textbf{Check:}
\qquad
\begin{array}{r}
\overset{1}{3}6{,}300 \\
+18{,}000 \\
\hline
54{,}300
\end{array}
$$

4. INTERPRET. *Check* your work. The check is above. *State* your conclusion: The average Louisiana teacher's salary in 2002 was $36,300.

◼ **Work Practice Problem 4**

Objective Ⓑ Solving Problems That Require More Than One Operation

We must sometimes use more than one operation to solve a problem.

△ **EXAMPLE 5** **Planting a New Garden**

A gardener bought enough plants to fill a rectangular garden with length 30 feet and width 20 feet. Because of shading problems from a nearby tree, the gardener changed the width of the garden to 15 feet. If the area is to remain the same, what is the new length of the garden?

Solution:

1. UNDERSTAND. Read and reread the problem. Then draw a picture to help visualize the problem.

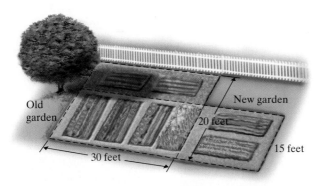

2. TRANSLATE. Since the area of the new garden is to be the same as the area of the old garden, let's find the area of the old garden. Recall that

Area = length × width = 30 feet × 20 feet = 600 square feet

Continued on next page

PRACTICE PROBLEM 5

A gardener is trying to decide how much fertilizer to buy for his yard. He knows that his lot is in the shape of a rectangle that measures 90 feet by 120 feet. He also knows that the floor of his house is in the shape of a rectangle that measures 45 feet by 65 feet. How much area of the lot is not covered by the house?

Answer

5. 7875 sq ft

Thus, the area of the new garden is to be 600 square feet. Also, we need to see how many 15s there are in 600. This means division. In other words,

In words: [New length] = [Area of garden] ÷ [New width]

↓   ↓   ↓

Translate: New length =   600   ÷   15

Since the area of the new garden is to be 600 square feet also, we need to see how many 15s there are in 600. This means division.

3. SOLVE.

$$\begin{array}{r} 40 \\ 15\overline{)600} \\ -60 \\ \hline 00 \end{array}$$

4. INTERPRET. *Check* your work. *State* your conclusion: The length of the new garden is 40 feet.

Work Practice Problem 5

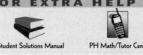

Objective **A** *Solve. See Examples 1 through 4.*

1. 41 increased by 8 is what number?

2. What is the product of 12 and 9?

3. What is the quotient of 1185 and 5?

4. 78 decreased by 12 is what number?

5. What is the total of 35 and 7?

6. What is the difference of 48 and 8?

7. 60 times 10 is what number?

8. 60 divided by 10 is what number?

9. A vacant lot in the shape of a rectangle measures 120 feet by 80 feet.
  a. What is the perimeter of the lot?
  b. What is the area of the lot?

10. A parking lot in the shape of a rectangle measures 100 feet by 150 feet.
  a. What is the perimeter of the lot?
  b. What is the area of the parking lot?

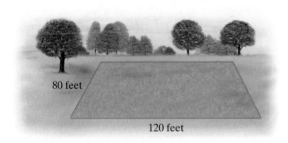

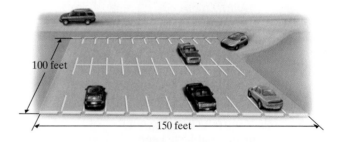

11. The Henrick family bought a house for $85,700 and later sold the house for $101,200. How much money did they make by selling the house?

12. Three people dream of equally sharing a $147 million lottery. How much would each person receive if they have the winning ticket?

13. There are 24 hours in a day. How many hours are in a week?

14. There are 60 minutes in an hour. How many minutes are in a day?

15. The country with the most higher education establishments is India, with 8407 of these establishments. In second place is the United States, with 2649 fewer higher education establishments. Find how many of these establishments there are in the United States.

17. Yellowstone National Park in Wyoming was the first national park in the United States. It was created in 1872. One of the more recent additions to the National Park System is Governors Island National Monument in New York. It was established in 2001. How much older is Yellowstone than Governors Island? (*Source:* National Park Service)

19. Since their introduction, the number of LEGO building bricks that have been sold is equivalent to the world's current population of approximately 6 billion people owning 52 LEGO bricks each. About how many LEGO bricks have been sold since their introduction? (*Source:* LEGO Company)

21. The three most common city names in the United States are Fairview, Midway, and Riverside. There are 287 towns named Fairview, 252 named Midway, and 180 named Riverside. Find the total number of towns named Fairview, Midway, and Riverside.

16. The Goodyear Tire & Rubber Company maintains a fleet of five blimps. The *Spirit of Goodyear* can hold 202,700 cubic feet of helium. Its smaller sister, the *Spirit of Europe,* can hold 132,700 fewer cubic feet of helium than *Spirit of Goodyear*. How much helium can *Spirit of Europe* hold? (*Source:* Goodyear Tire & Rubber Company)

18. Razor scooters were introduced in 2000. Radio Flyer Wagons were first introduced 83 years earlier. In what year were Radio Flyer Wagons introduced? (*Source:* Toy Industry Association, Inc.)

20. In 2003, the average weekly pay for a production worker in the United States was $517 per week. At that rate, how much would a production worker have earned working a 52-week year? (*Source:* U.S. Bureau of Labor Statistics)

22. In the game of Monopoly, a player must own all properties in a color group before building houses. The yellow color-group properties are Atlantic Avenue, Ventnor Avenue, and Marvin Gardens. These cost $260, $260, and $280, respectively, when purchased from the bank. What total amount must a player pay to the bank before houses can be built on the yellow properties? (*Source:* Hasbro, Inc.)

23. In 2003, the average weekly pay for a Financial Records Processing Supervisor in the United States was $840. If such a supervisor works 40 hours in one week, what is his or her hourly pay? (*Source:* U.S. Bureau of Labor Statistics)

24. In 2003, the average weekly pay for a computer programmer in the United States was $1160. If a computer programmer works 40 hours in one week, what is his or her hourly pay? (*Source:* U.S. Bureau of Labor Statistics)

25. Three ounces of canned tuna in oil has 165 calories. How many calories does 1 ounce have? (*Source: Home and Garden Bulletin No. 72,* U.S. Department of Agriculture)

26. A whole cheesecake has 3360 calories. If the cheesecake is cut into 12 equal pieces, how many calories will each piece have? (*Source: Home and Garden Bulletin No. 72,* U.S. Department of Agriculture)

27. The estimated 2003 U.S. population is 290,800,000 people. Between Memorial Day and Labor Day, 7 billion hot dogs are consumed. Approximately how many hot dogs are consumed per person between Memorial and Labor Days? Divide, but do not give remainder portion of quotient. (*Source:* U.S. Census Bureau, National Hot Dog and Sausage Council)

28. Diana Taurasi of the WNBA's Phoenix Mercury scored an average of 17 points per basketball game during the 2004 regular season. She played a total of 34 games during the season. What was the total number of points she scored during 2004? (*Source:* Women's National Basketball Association)

29. The May Department Stores Company operates Lord & Taylor, Foley's, Filene's, Kaufmann's, and other department stores around the country. It also operates 73 Robinsons-May and Meier & Frank stores in California, Oregon, Nevada, and Arizona. In 2003, Robinsons-May and Meier & Frank had sales of $2,446,000,050. What is the average amount of sales made by each of the 73 stores? (*Source:* The May Department Stores Company)

30. In 2003, the United States Postal Service delivered approximately 859,000,000 pieces of Priority Mail. The total weight of all items sent Priority Mail that year was approximately 1,718,000,000 pounds. What was the average weight of an item sent Priority Mail during 2003? (*Source:* United States Postal Service)

31. The enrollment of all students in elementary and secondary schools in the United States in 2008 is projected to be 54,268,000. Of these students, 16,234,000 are expected to be enrolled in secondary schools. How many students are expected to be enrolled in elementary schools in 2008? (*Source:* National Center for Education Statistics)

32. Kroger now operates convenience stores, food/grocery type stores, and department stores. In 2003, Kroger operated a total of 3774 stores. Of this total, 802 were convenience stores and 2532 were food/grocery type stores. How many department stores did Kroger operate in 2003? (*Source:* The Kroger Company)

33. The length of the southern boundary of the conterminous United States is 1933 miles. The length of the northern boundary of the conterminous United States is 2054 miles longer than this. What is the length of the northern boundary? (*Source:* U.S. Geological Survey)

34. In humans, 14 muscles are required to smile. It takes 29 more muscles to frown. How many muscles does it take to frown?

2054 miles longer

1933 miles

35. Marcel Rockett receives a paycheck every four weeks. Find how many paychecks he receives in a year. (A year has 52 weeks.)

36. A loan of $6240 is to be paid in 48 equal payments. How much is each payment?

Objective **B** *Solve. See Example 5.*

37. Find the total cost of 3 sweaters at $38 each and 5 shirts at $25 each.

38. Find the total cost of 10 computers at $2100 each and 7 boxes of diskettes at $12 each.

39. A college student has $950 in an account. She spends $205 from the account on books and then deposits $300 in the account. How much money is now in the account?

40. The temperature outside was 57°F (degrees Fahrenheit). During the next few hours, it decreased by 18 degrees and then increased by 23 degrees. Find the new temperature.

The table shows the menu from Corky's, a concession stand at the county fair. Use this menu to answer Exercises 41 and 42.

41. A hungry college student is debating between the following two orders:
   a. a hamburger, an order of onion rings, a candy bar, and a soda.
   b. a hot dog, an apple, an order of french fries, and a soda.
   Which order will be cheaper? By how much?

Corky's Concession Stand Menu	
Item	**Price**
Hot dog	$3
Hamburger	$4
Soda	$1
Onion rings	$3
French fries	$2
Apple	$1
Candy bar	$2

42. A family of four is debating between the following two orders:
   a. 6 hot dogs, 4 orders of onion rings, and 4 sodas.
   b. 4 hamburgers, 4 orders of french fries, 2 apples, and 4 sodas.
   Will the family save any money by ordering (b) instead of (a)? If so, how much?

Objectives **A** **B** **Mixed Practice** *Use the bar graph to answer Exercises 43 through 50.*

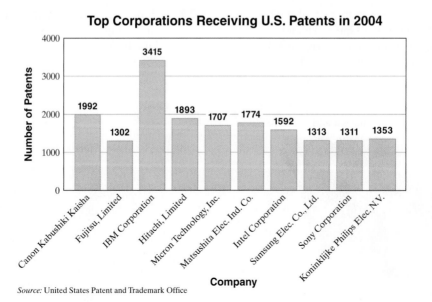

Top Corporations Receiving U.S. Patents in 2004

Source: United States Patent and Trademark Office

43. Which company listed received the most patents in 2004?

44. Which company listed received the fewest patents in 2004?

45. How many more patents did the company with the most patents receive than the company with the fewest patents?

46. How many more patents did Samsung receive than Sony?

47. How many more patents did Canon receive than Hitachi?

48. Which company received more patents, Matsushita or Fujitsu? How many more patents did it receive?

Find the average number of patents for the companies listed. Do not show remainders. Give whole number answers only.

49. The three companies with the greatest number of patents.

50. The four companies with the least number of patents shown.

Solve.

51. The learning lab at a local university is receiving new equipment. Twenty-two computers are purchased for $615 each and three printers for $408 each. Find the total cost for this equipment.

52. The washateria near the local community college is receiving new equipment. Thirty-six washers are purchased for $585 each and ten dryers are purchased for $388 each. Find the total cost for this equipment.

53. The American Heart Association recommends consuming no more than 2400 milligrams of salt per day. (This is about the amount in 1 teaspoon of salt.) How many milligrams of sodium is this in a week?

54. This semester a particular student pays $1750 for room and board, $709 for a meal ticket plan, and $2168 for tuition. What is her total bill?

△ **55.** The Meish's yard is in the shape of a rectangle and measures 50 feet by 75 feet. In their yard, they have a rectangular swimming pool that measures 15 feet by 25 feet.
   a. Find the area of the entire yard.
   b. Find the area of the swimming pool.
   c. Find the area of the yard that is not part of the swimming pool.

56. The community is planning to construct a rectangular-shaped playground within the local park. The park is in the shape of a square and measures 100 yards on each side. The playground is to measure 15 yards by 25 yards.
   a. Find the area of the entire park.
   b. Find the area of the playground.
   c. Find the area of the park that is not part of the playground.

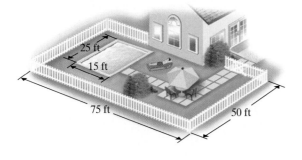

Concept Extensions

57. In 2003, the United States Postal Service issued approximately 202,500,000 money orders worth approximately $48,551,700,000. Round the value of the money orders issued to the nearest hundred-million to estimate the average value of each money order. (*Source:* United States Postal Service)

58. In 2003, there were about 2000 Hilton Hotels worldwide with a total of 348,483 guestrooms. Round the number of guestrooms to the nearest thousand to estimate the average number of guestrooms per hotel. (*Source:* Hilton Hotels Corporation)

59. Write an application of your own that uses the term "bank account" and the numbers 1036 and 524.

 STUDY SKILLS BUILDER

Are You Familiar with Your Textbook Supplements?

There are many student supplements available for additional study. Below, I have listed some of these. See the preface of this text or your instructor for further information.

Chapter Test Prep Video CD. This material is found in your textbook and is fully explained there. The CD contains video clips solutions to the Chapter Test exercises in this text and are excellent help when studying for chapter tests.

Lecture Video CDs. These video segments are keyed to each section of the text. The material is presented by me, Elayn Martin-Gay, and I have placed a video icon by the exercises in the text that I have worked on the video.

The Student Solutions Manual. This contains worked out solutions to odd-numbered exercises as well as every exercise in the Integrated Reviews, Chapter Reviews, Chapter Tests, and Cumulative Reviews.

Prentice Hall Tutor Center. Mathematics questions may be phoned, faxed, or emailed to this center.

MyMathLab, MathXL, and Interact Math. These are computer and Internet tutorials. This supplement may already be available to you somewhere on campus, for example at your local learning resource lab. Take a moment and find the name and location of any such lab on campus.

As usual, your instructor is your best source of information.

Let's see how you are doing with textbook supplements:

1. Name one way the Chapter Test Prep Video can help you prepare for a chapter test.

2. List any textbook supplements that you have found useful.

3. Have you located and visited a learning resource lab located on your campus?

4. List the textbook supplements that are currently housed in your campus' learning resource lab.

1.9 EXPONENTS, SQUARE ROOTS, AND ORDER OF OPERATIONS

Objectives

A Write Repeated Factors Using Exponential Notation.

B Evaluate Expressions Containing Exponents.

C Evaluate the Square Root of a Perfect Square.

D Use the Order of Operations.

E Find the Area of a Square.

Objective **A** Using Exponential Notation

In the product $2 \cdot 2 \cdot 2 \cdot 2 \cdot 2$, notice that 2 is a factor several times. When this happens, we can use a shorthand notation, called an **exponent,** to write the repeated multiplication.

$\underbrace{2 \cdot 2 \cdot 2 \cdot 2 \cdot 2}_{\text{2 is a factor 5 times}}$ can be written as

2^5 Read as "two to the fifth power."

with exponent and base labeled.

This is called **exponential notation.** The **exponent,** 5, indicates how many times the **base,** 2, is a factor.

The table below shows examples of reading exponential notation in words.

Expression	In Words
5^2	"five to the second power" or "five squared."
5^3	"five to the third power" or "five cubed."
5^4	"five to the fourth power."

Usually, an exponent of 1 is not written, so when no exponent appears, we assume that the exponent is 1. For example, $2 = 2^1$ and $7 = 7^1$.

EXAMPLES Write using exponential notation.

1. $4 \cdot 4 \cdot 4 = 4^3$
2. $7 \cdot 7 = 7^2$
3. $5 \cdot 5 \cdot 5 \cdot 5 = 5^4$
4. $6 \cdot 6 \cdot 6 \cdot 8 \cdot 8 \cdot 8 \cdot 8 \cdot 8 = 6^3 \cdot 8^5$

▣ **Work Practice Problems 1–4**

Objective **B** Evaluating Exponential Expressions

To **evaluate** an exponential expression, we write the expression as a product and then find the value of the product.

EXAMPLES Evaluate.

5. $8^2 = 8 \cdot 8 = 64$
6. $9^1 = 9$
7. $2^5 = 2 \cdot 2 \cdot 2 \cdot 2 \cdot 2 = 32$
8. $5 \cdot 6^2 = 5 \cdot 6 \cdot 6 = 180$

▣ **Work Practice Problems 5–8**

PRACTICE PROBLEMS 1–4

Write using exponential notation.
1. $2 \cdot 2 \cdot 2$
2. $3 \cdot 3$
3. $10 \cdot 10 \cdot 10 \cdot 10 \cdot 10 \cdot 10$
4. $5 \cdot 5 \cdot 4 \cdot 4 \cdot 4$

PRACTICE PROBLEMS 5–8

Evaluate.
5. 2^3 6. 5^2
7. 10^1 8. $4 \cdot 5^2$

Answers
1. 2^3,   2. 3^2,   3. 10^6,   4. $5^2 \cdot 4^3$,
5. 8,   6. 25,   7. 10,   8. 100

Example 8 illustrates an important property: An exponent applies only to its base. The exponent 2, in $5 \cdot 6^2$, applies only to its base, 6.

> **Helpful Hint**
> An exponent applies only to its base. For example, $4 \cdot 2^3$ means $4 \cdot 2 \cdot 2 \cdot 2$.

> **Helpful Hint**
> Don't forget that 2^4, for example, is *not* $2 \cdot 4$. The expression 2^4 means repeated multiplication of the same factor.
> $$2^4 = 2 \cdot 2 \cdot 2 \cdot 2 = 16, \quad \text{whereas } 2 \cdot 4 = 8$$

✔ **Concept Check** Which of the following statements is correct?

a. 3^6 is the same as $6 \cdot 6 \cdot 6$.
b. "Eight to the fourth power" is the same as 8^4.
c. "Ten squared" is the same as 10^3.
d. 11^2 is the same as $11 \cdot 2$.

Objective C Evaluating Square Roots

A **square root** of a number is one of two identical factors of the number. For example,

$$7 \cdot 7 = 49, \text{ so a square root of 49 is 7.}$$

We use this symbol $\sqrt{}$ (called a radical sign) for finding square roots. Since
$$7 \cdot 7 = 49, \text{ then } \sqrt{49} = 7.$$

PRACTICE PROBLEMS 9–11

Find each square root.

9. $\sqrt{100}$
10. $\sqrt{4}$
11. $\sqrt{1}$

EXAMPLES Find each square root.

9. $\sqrt{25} = 5$ because $5 \cdot 5 = 25$
10. $\sqrt{81} = 9$ because $9 \cdot 9 = 81$
11. $\sqrt{0} = 0$ because $0 \cdot 0 = 0$

■ **Work Practice Problems 9–11**

> **Helpful Hint**
> Make sure you understand the difference between squaring a number and finding the square root of a number.
> $$9^2 = 9 \cdot 9 = 81 \quad \sqrt{9} = 3 \text{ because } 3 \cdot 3 = 9$$

Answers
9. 10, **10.** 2, **11.** 1

✔ **Concept Check Answer**
b

Not every square root simplifies to a whole number. We will study this more in a later chapter. In this section, we will find square roots of perfect squares only.

A **perfect square** is the product of a whole number multiplied by itself. It may be helpful to study the perfect squares below.

Perfect Squares

$0 = 0 \cdot 0$	$9 = 3 \cdot 3$	$36 = 6 \cdot 6$	$81 = 9 \cdot 9$	$144 = 12 \cdot 12$	$225 = 15 \cdot 15$
$1 = 1 \cdot 1$	$16 = 4 \cdot 4$	$49 = 7 \cdot 7$	$100 = 10 \cdot 10$	$169 = 13 \cdot 13$	$256 = 16 \cdot 16$
$4 = 2 \cdot 2$	$25 = 5 \cdot 5$	$64 = 8 \cdot 8$	$121 = 11 \cdot 11$	$196 = 14 \cdot 14$	$289 = 17 \cdot 17$

Objective D Using the Order of Operations

Suppose that you are in charge of taking inventory at a local bookstore. An employee has given you the number of a certain book in stock as the expression

$$3 + 2 \cdot 10$$

To calculate the value of this expression, do you add first or multiply first? If you add first, the answer is 50. If you multiply first, the answer is 23.

Mathematical symbols wouldn't be very useful if two values were possible for one expression. Thus, mathematicians have agreed that, given a choice, we multiply first.

$$3 + 2 \cdot 10 = 3 + 20 \quad \text{Multiply.}$$
$$= 23 \quad \text{Add.}$$

This agreement is one of several **order of operations** agreements.

Order of Operations

1. Perform all operations within parentheses ( ), brackets [ ], or other grouping symbols such as fraction bars or square roots.
2. Evaluate any expressions with exponents.
3. Multiply or divide in order from left to right.
4. Add or subtract in order from left to right.

Below we practice using order of operations to simplify expressions.

EXAMPLE 12 Simplify: $2 \cdot 4 - 3 \div 3$

Solution: There are no parentheses and no exponents, so we start by multiplying and dividing, from left to right.

$$2 \cdot 4 - 3 \div 3 = 8 - 3 \div 3 \quad \text{Multiply.}$$
$$= 8 - 1 \quad \text{Divide.}$$
$$= 7 \quad \text{Subtract.}$$

▣ **Work Practice Problem 12**

PRACTICE PROBLEM 12

Simplify: $8 \cdot 2 - 16 \div 4$

Answer
12. 12

PRACTICE PROBLEM 13
Simplify: $36 \div 3 \cdot 2^2$

EXAMPLE 13 Simplify: $4^2 \div 2 \cdot 4$

Solution: We start by evaluating 4^2.

$4^2 \div 2 \cdot 4 = 16 \div 2 \cdot 4$ Write 4^2 as 16.

Next we multiply or divide *in order* from left to right. Since division appears before multiplication from left to right, we divide first, then multiply.

$16 \div 2 \cdot 4 = 8 \cdot 4$ Divide.
$\qquad\qquad = 32$ Multiply.

■ **Work Practice Problem 13**

PRACTICE PROBLEM 14
Simplify: $(9 - 8)^3 + 3 \cdot 2^4$

EXAMPLE 14 Simplify: $(8 - 6)^2 + 2^3 \cdot 3$

Solution: $(8 - 6)^2 + 2^3 \cdot 3 = 2^2 + 2^3 \cdot 3$ Simplify inside parentheses.

$\qquad\qquad = 4 + 8 \cdot 3$ Write 2^2 as 4 and 2^3 as 8.
$\qquad\qquad = 4 + 24$ Multiply.
$\qquad\qquad = 28$ Add.

■ **Work Practice Problem 14**

PRACTICE PROBLEM 15
Simplify:
$24 \div [20 - (3 \cdot 4)] + 2^3 - 5$

EXAMPLE 15 Simplify: $4^3 + [3^2 - (10 \div 2)] - 7 \cdot 3$

Solution: Here we begin with the innermost set of parentheses.

$4^3 + [3^2 - (10 \div 2)] - 7 \cdot 3 = 4^3 + [3^2 - 5] - 7 \cdot 3$ Simplify inside parentheses.

$\qquad\qquad = 4^3 + [9 - 5] - 7 \cdot 3$ Write 3^3 as 9.

$\qquad\qquad = 4^3 + 4 - 7 \cdot 3$ Simplify inside brackets.

$\qquad\qquad = 64 + 4 - 7 \cdot 3$ Write 4^3 as 64.

$\qquad\qquad = 64 + 4 - 21$ Multiply.

$\qquad\qquad = 47$ Add and subtract from left to right.

■ **Work Practice Problem 15**

PRACTICE PROBLEM 16
Simplify: $\dfrac{49 + 4 \cdot 3 - 5^2}{3(1 + 1)}$

EXAMPLE 16 Simplify: $\dfrac{7 - 2 \cdot 3 + 3^2}{5(2 - 1)}$

Solution: Here, the fraction bar is like a grouping symbol. We simplify above and below the fraction bar separately.

$\dfrac{7 - 2 \cdot 3 + 3^2}{5(2 - 1)} = \dfrac{7 - 2 \cdot 3 + 9}{5(1)}$ Evaluate 3^2 and $(2 - 1)$.

$\qquad\qquad = \dfrac{7 - 6 + 9}{5}$ Multiply $2 \cdot 3$ in the numerator and multiply $5(1)$ in the denominator.

$\qquad\qquad = \dfrac{10}{5}$ Add and subtract from left to right.

$\qquad\qquad = 2$ Divide.

■ **Work Practice Problem 16**

Answers
13. 48, **14.** 49, **15.** 6, **16.** 6

EXAMPLE 17 Simplify: $64 \div \sqrt{64} \cdot 2 + 4$

Solution: $64 \div \sqrt{64} \cdot 2 + 4 = \underline{64 \div 8} \cdot 2 + 4$ Find the square root.

$= \underline{8 \cdot 2} + 4$ Divide.

$= 16 + 4$ Multiply.

$= 20$ Add.

🔲 **Work Practice Problem 17**

PRACTICE PROBLEM 17
Simplify: $81 \div \sqrt{81} \cdot 5 + 7$

Objective E Finding the Area of a Square

Since a square is a special rectangle, we can find its area by finding the product of its length and its width.

Area of a rectangle = length · width

By recalling that each side of a square has the same measurement, we can use the following procedure to find its area:

Area of a square = length · width

$= $ side · side

$= (\text{side})^2$

Square   Side

Side

EXAMPLE 18 Find the area of a square whose side measures 5 inches.

Solution: Area of a square $= (\text{side})^2$

$= (5 \text{ inches})^2$

$= 25$ square inches

5 inches

The area of the square is 25 square inches.

🔲 **Work Practice Problem 18**

PRACTICE PROBLEM 18

Find the area of a square whose side measures 11 centimeters.

Answers
17. 52,   **18.** 121 sq cm

🖩 CALCULATOR EXPLORATIONS

Exponents

To evaluate an exponent such as 4^7 on a calculator, find the keys marked $\boxed{y^x}$ or $\boxed{\wedge}$ and $\boxed{=}$ or $\boxed{\text{ENTER}}$. To evaluate 4^7, press the keys $\boxed{4}$ $\boxed{y^x}$ (or $\boxed{\wedge}$) $\boxed{7}$ $\boxed{=}$ or $\boxed{\text{ENTER}}$. The display will read $\boxed{\qquad 16384}$. Thus, $4^7 = 16{,}384$.

Use a calculator to evaluate.

1. 3^6 **2.** 5^6 **3.** 4^5

4. 7^6 **5.** 2^{11} **6.** 6^8

Order of Operations

To see whether your calculator has the order of operations built in, evaluate $5 + 2 \cdot 3$ by pressing the keys $\boxed{5}$ $\boxed{+}$ $\boxed{2}$ $\boxed{\times}$ $\boxed{3}$ $\boxed{=}$ or $\boxed{\text{ENTER}}$. If the display reads $\boxed{11}$, your calculator does have the order of operations

built in. This means that most of the time you can key in a problem exactly as it is written and the calculator will perform operations in the proper order. When evaluating an expression containing parentheses, key in the parentheses. (If an expression contains brackets, key in parentheses.) For example, to evaluate $2[25 - (8 + 4)] - 11$, press the keys $\boxed{2}$ $\boxed{\times}$ $\boxed{(}$ $\boxed{25}$ $\boxed{-}$ $\boxed{(}$ $\boxed{8}$ $\boxed{+}$ $\boxed{4}$ $\boxed{)}$ $\boxed{)}$ $\boxed{-}$ $\boxed{11}$ $\boxed{=}$ or $\boxed{\text{ENTER}}$.

The display will read $\boxed{\qquad 15}$.

Use a calculator to evaluate.

7. $7^4 + 5^3$

8. $12^4 - 8^4$

9. $63 \cdot 75 - 43 \cdot 10$

10. $8 \cdot 22 + 7 \cdot 16$

11. $4(15 \div 3 + 2) - 10 \cdot 2$

12. $155 - 2(17 + 3) + 185$

1.9 EXERCISE SET

Objective A *Write using exponential notation. See Examples 1 through 4.*

1. $3 \cdot 3 \cdot 3 \cdot 3$

2. $5 \cdot 5 \cdot 5$

3. $7 \cdot 7 \cdot 7 \cdot 7 \cdot 7 \cdot 7 \cdot 7 \cdot 7$

4. $6 \cdot 6 \cdot 6 \cdot 6 \cdot 6$

5. $12 \cdot 12 \cdot 12$

6. $10 \cdot 10$

7. $6 \cdot 6 \cdot 5 \cdot 5 \cdot 5$

8. $4 \cdot 4 \cdot 4 \cdot 3 \cdot 3$

9. $9 \cdot 9 \cdot 9 \cdot 8$

10. $7 \cdot 7 \cdot 7 \cdot 4$

11. $3 \cdot 2 \cdot 2 \cdot 2 \cdot 2 \cdot 2$

12. $4 \cdot 6 \cdot 6 \cdot 6 \cdot 6$

13. $3 \cdot 2 \cdot 2 \cdot 5 \cdot 5 \cdot 5$

14. $6 \cdot 6 \cdot 2 \cdot 9 \cdot 9 \cdot 9 \cdot 9$

Objective B *Evaluate. See Examples 5 through 8.*

15. 7^2

16. 6^2

17. 5^3

18. 6^3

19. 2^6

20. 2^7

21. 1^{10}

22. 1^{12}

23. 7^1

24. 8^1

25. 3^5

26. 5^4

27. 2^8

28. 3^3

29. 4^3

30. 4^4

31. 9^2

32. 12^2

33. 9^3

34. 8^3

35. 10^2

36. 10^3

37. 20^1

38. 14^1

39. 3^6

40. 4^5

41. $3 \cdot 2^4$

42. $5 \cdot 3^2$

43. $2 \cdot 3^3$

44. $2 \cdot 7^2$

Objective **C** *Find each square root. See Examples 9 through 11.*

45. $\sqrt{9}$ **46.** $\sqrt{36}$ **47.** $\sqrt{64}$ **48.** $\sqrt{121}$

49. $\sqrt{144}$ **50.** $\sqrt{0}$ **51.** $\sqrt{16}$ **52.** $\sqrt{169}$

Objective **D** *Simplify. See Examples 12 through 16. (This section does not contain square roots.)*

53. $15 + 3 \cdot 2$ **54.** $24 + 6 \cdot 3$ **55.** $28 \div 7 \cdot 2 + 3$ **56.** $100 \div 10 \cdot 5 + 4$

57. $28 \div 4 - 3$ **58.** $42 \div 7 - 6$ **59.** $14 + \dfrac{24}{8}$ **60.** $32 + \dfrac{8}{2}$

61. $6 \cdot 5 + 8 \cdot 2$ **62.** $3 \cdot 4 + 9 \cdot 1$ **63.** $\dfrac{6 + 8 \div 2}{1^7}$ **64.** $\dfrac{6 + 9 \div 3}{3^2}$

65. $(3 + 5^2) \div 2 \cdot 3^2$ **66.** $(13 + 6^2) \div 7 \cdot 4^2$ **67.** $6^2 \cdot (10 - 8) + 2^3 + 5^2$

68. $5^3 \div (10 + 15) + 9^2 + 3^3$ **69.** $\dfrac{18 + 6}{2^4 - 2^2}$ **70.** $\dfrac{15 + 17}{5^2 - 3^2}$

71. $(2 + 5) \cdot (8 - 3)$ **72.** $(9 - 7) \cdot (12 + 18)$ **73.** $\dfrac{7(9 - 6) + 3}{3^2 - 3}$

74. $\dfrac{5(12 - 7) - 4}{5^2 - 18}$ **75.** $5 \div 0 + 24$ **76.** $18 - 7 \div 0$

77. $2^3 \cdot 4 - (10 \div 5)$

78. $2^4 \cdot 3 - (100 \div 10)$

79. $3^4 - [35 - (12 - 6)]$

80. $[40 - (8 - 2)] - 2^5$

81. $(7 \cdot 5) + [9 \div (3 \div 3)]$

82. $(18 \div 6) + [(3 + 5) \cdot 2]$

83. $8 \cdot [2^2 + (6 - 1) \cdot 2] - 50 \cdot 2$

84. $35 \div [3^2 + (9 - 7) - 2^2] + 10 \cdot 3$

85. $\dfrac{9^2 + 2^2 - 1^2}{8 \div 2 \cdot 3 \cdot 1 \div 3}$

86. $\dfrac{5^2 - 2^3 + 1^4}{10 \div 5 \cdot 4 \cdot 1 \div 4}$

Simplify. See Examples 12 through 17. (This section does contain square roots.)

87. $6 \cdot \sqrt{9} + 3 \cdot \sqrt{4}$

88. $3 \cdot \sqrt{25} + 2 \cdot \sqrt{81}$

89. $4 \cdot \sqrt{49} - 0 \div \sqrt{100}$

90. $7 \cdot \sqrt{36} - 0 \div \sqrt{64}$

91. $\dfrac{\sqrt{4} + 4^2}{5(20 - 16) - 3^2 - 5}$

92. $\dfrac{\sqrt{9} + 9^2}{3(10 - 6) - 2^2 - 1}$

93. $\sqrt{81} \div \sqrt{9} + 4^2 \cdot 2 - 10$

94. $\sqrt{100} \div \sqrt{4} + 3^3 \cdot 2 - 20$

95. $[\sqrt{225} \div (11 - 6) + 2^2] + (\sqrt{25} - \sqrt{1})^2$

96. $[\sqrt{169} \div (20 - 7) + 2^5] - (\sqrt{4} + \sqrt{9})^2$

97. $7^2 - \{18 - [40 \div (4 \cdot 2) + \sqrt{4}] + 5^2\}$

98. $29 - \{5 + 3[8 \cdot (10 - \sqrt{64})] - 50\}$

Objective 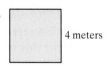 *Find the area of each square. See Example 18.*

△ **99.**

20 miles

△ **100.**

4 meters

△ **101.**

8 centimeters

△ **102.**

31 feet

Concept Extensions

Answer the following true or false. See the Concept Check in this section.

103. "Five to the sixth power" is the same as 6^5.

104. "Seven cubed" is the same as 7^3.

105. 2^5 is the same as $5 \cdot 5$.

106. 4^9 is the same as $4 \cdot 9$.

Insert grouping symbols (parentheses) so that each given expression evaluates to the given number.

107. $2 + 3 \cdot 6 - 2$; evaluate to 28

108. $2 + 3 \cdot 6 - 2$; evaluate to 20

109. $24 \div 3 \cdot 2 + 2 \cdot 5$; evaluate to 14

110. $24 \div 3 \cdot 2 + 2 \cdot 5$; evaluate to 15

△ **111.** A building contractor is bidding on a contract to install gutters on seven homes in a retirement community, all in the shape shown. To estimate the cost of materials, she needs to know the total perimeter of all seven homes. Find the total perimeter.

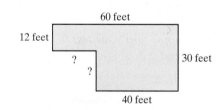

60 feet

12 feet

? ?

40 feet

30 feet

Simplify.

▦ **112.** $25^3 \cdot (45 - 7 \cdot 5) \cdot 5$

▦ **113.** $(7 + 2^4)^5 - (3^5 - 2^4)^2$

✎ **114.** Explain why $2 \cdot 3^2$ is not the same as $(2 \cdot 3)^2$.

115. Write an expression that simplifies to 5. Use multiplication, division, addition, subtraction, and at least one set of parentheses.

THE BIGGER PICTURE   Operations on Sets of Numbers

Continue your outline started in Section 1.7. Suggestions are once again written to help you complete this part of your outline.

I. **Some Operations on Sets of Numbers**

   A. **Whole Numbers**

      1. **Add or Subtract** (Sections 1.3, 1.4)

      2. **Multiply or Divide** (Sections 1.6, 1.7)

      3. **Exponent:** $3^4 = \overbrace{3 \cdot 3 \cdot 3 \cdot 3}^{\text{4 factors of 3}} = 81$

      4. **Square Root:** $\sqrt{25} = 5$ *because* $5 \cdot 5 = 25$

      5. **Order of Operations:**

$$24 \div 3 \cdot 2 - (2 + 8)$$
$$= 24 \div 3 \cdot 2 - (10) \quad \text{Parentheses.}$$
$$= 8 \cdot 2 - 10 \quad \text{Multiply or divide from left to right.}$$
$$= 16 - 10 \quad \text{Multiply or divide from left to right.}$$
$$= 6 \quad \text{Add or subtract from left to right.}$$

Perform the indicated operations.

1. 4^3

2. $2^3 \cdot 6^1$

3. $\sqrt{81}$

4. $\sqrt{9} \cdot \sqrt{25}$

5. $2 + 5(10 - 6)$

6. $20 \div 2 \cdot 5$

7. $867 - 179$

8. $\begin{array}{r} 72 \\ \times\,30 \\ \hline \end{array}$

9. $626 \div 58$

10. $3[(7 - 3)^2 - (25 - 22)^2] + \sqrt{36}$

 STUDY SKILLS BUILDER

What to Do the Day of an Exam?

Your first exam may be soon. On the day of an exam, don't forget to try the following:

• Allow yourself plenty of time to arrive.

• Read the directions on the test carefully.

• Read each problem carefully as you take your test. Make sure that you answer the question asked.

• Watch your time and pace yourself so that you may attempt each problem on your test.

• Check your work and answers.

• ***Do not turn your test in early.*** If you have extra time, spend it double-checking your work.

Good luck!

Answer the following questions based on your most recent mathematics exam, whenever that was.

1. How soon before class did you arrive?

2. Did you read the directions on the test carefully?

3. Did you make sure you answered the question asked for each problem on the exam?

4. Were you able to attempt each problem on your exam?

5. If your answer to question 4 is no, list reasons why.

6. Did you have extra time on your exam?

7. If your answer to question 6 is yes, describe how you spent that extra time.

CHAPTER 1   Group Activity

Modeling Subtraction of Whole Numbers

A mathematical concept can be represented or modeled in many different ways. For instance, subtraction can be represented by the following symbolic model:

$$11 - 4$$

The following verbal models can also represent subtraction of these same quantities:

"Four subtracted from eleven" or
"Eleven take away four"

Physical models can also represent mathematical concepts. In these models, a number is represented by that many objects. For example, the number 5 can be represented by five pennies, squares, paper clips, tiles, or bottle caps.

A physical representation of the number 5

Take-Away Model for Subtraction: 11 − 4

- Start with 11 objects.
- Take 4 objects away.
- How many objects remain?

Comparison Model for Subtraction: 11 − 4

- Start with a set of 11 of one type of object and a set of 4 of another type of object.

- Make as many pairs that include one object of each type as possible.

- How many more objects left are in the larger set?

Missing Addend Model for Subtraction: 11 − 4

- Start with 4 objects.
- Continue adding objects until a total of 11 is reached.
- How many more objects were needed to give a total of 11?

Group Activity

Use an appropriate physical model for subtraction to solve each of the following problems. Explain your reasoning for choosing each model.

1. Javier has assembled 12 computer components so far this shift. If his quota is 20 components, how many more components must he assemble to reach his quota?

2. Yuko has 14 daffodil bulbs to plant in her yard. She planted 5 bulbs in the front yard. How many bulbs does she have left for planting in the backyard?

3. Todd is 19 years old and his sister Tanya is 13 years old. How much older is Todd than Tanya?

Chapter 1 Vocabulary Check

Fill in each blank with one of the words or phrases listed below.

difference	area	square root	addend	divisor	minuend
place value	factor	quotient	subtrahend	exponent	digits
sum	whole numbers	perimeter	dividend	product	

1. The _____ are 0, 1, 2, 3, . . .
2. The _____ of a polygon is its distance around or the sum of the lengths of its sides.
3. The position of each digit in a number determines its _____.
4. An _____ is a shorthand notation for repeated multiplication of the same factor.
5. To find the _____ of a rectangle, multiply length times width.
6. A _____ of a number is one of two identical factors of the number.
7. The _____ used to write numbers are 0, 1, 2, 3, 4, 5, 6, 7, 8, and 9.

Use the facts below for Exercises 8 through 17.

$$2 \cdot 3 = 6 \qquad 4 + 17 = 21 \qquad 20 - 9 = 11 \qquad 5\overline{)35}\,^{7}$$

8. The 21 above is called the _____.
9. The 5 above is called the _____.
10. The 35 above is called the _____.
11. The 7 above is called the _____.
12. The 3 above is called a _____.
13. The 6 above is called the _____.
14. The 20 above is called the _____.
15. The 9 above is called the _____.
16. The 11 above is called the _____.
17. The 4 above is called an _____.

Helpful Hint

Are you preparing for your test? Don't forget to take the Chapter 1 Test on page 109. Then check your answers at the back of the text and use the Chapter Test Prep Video CD to see the fully worked-out solutions to any of the exercises you want to review.

1 Chapter Highlights

DEFINITIONS AND CONCEPTS	EXAMPLES
Section 1.2 Place Value and Names for Numbers	
The **whole numbers** are 0, 1, 2, 3, 4, 5, . . . The position of each digit in a number determines its **place value.** A place-value chart is shown next with the names of the periods given.	0, 14, 968, 5,268,619

Periods			
Billions	Millions	Thousands	Ones

Hundred-billions, Ten-billions, Billions, Hundred-millions, Ten-millions, Millions, Hundred-thousands, Ten-thousands, Thousands, Hundreds, Tens, Ones

DEFINITIONS AND CONCEPTS	**EXAMPLES**

Section 1.2   Place Value and Names for Numbers (*continued*)

To write a whole number in words, write the number in each period followed by the name of the period. (The name of the ones period is not included.)	9,078,651,002 is written as nine billion, seventy-eight million, six hundred fifty-one thousand, two.
To write a whole number in standard form, write the number in each period, followed by a comma.	Four million, seven hundred six thousand, twenty-eight is written as 4,706,028.

Section 1.3   Adding Whole Numbers and Perimeter

To add whole numbers, add the digits in the ones place, then the tens place, then the hundreds place, and so on, carrying when necessary.

Find the sum:

$$\begin{array}{r} \overset{2\,1\,1}{2689} \leftarrow \text{ addend}\\ 1735 \leftarrow \text{ addend}\\ +\;\;662 \leftarrow \text{ addend}\\ \hline 5086 \leftarrow \text{ sum} \end{array}$$

The **perimeter** of a polygon is its distance around or the sum of the lengths of its sides.

Find the perimeter of the polygon shown.

The perimeter is 5 feet + 3 feet + 9 feet + 2 feet = 19 feet.

Section 1.4   Subtracting Whole Numbers

To subtract whole numbers, subtract the digits in the ones place, then the tens place, then the hundreds place, and so on, borrowing when necessary.

Subtract:

$$\begin{array}{r} \overset{8\,15}{7\cancel{9}\cancel{5}4} \leftarrow \text{ minuend}\\ -5673 \leftarrow \text{ subtrahend}\\ \hline 2281 \leftarrow \text{ difference} \end{array}$$

Section 1.5   Rounding and Estimating

ROUNDING WHOLE NUMBERS TO A GIVEN PLACE VALUE

Step 1. Locate the digit to the right of the given place value.

Step 2. If this digit is 5 or greater, add 1 to the digit in the given place value and replace each digit to its right with 0.

Step 3. If this digit is less than 5, replace it and each digit to its right with 0.

Round 15,721 to the nearest thousand.

15,⑦21   Since the circled digit is 5 or greater, add 1 to the given place value and replace digits to its right with zeros.

Add 1 ⤴ Replace with zeros.

15,721 rounded to the nearest thousand is 16,000.

Section 1.6   Multiplying Whole Numbers and Area

To multiply 73 and 58, for example, multiply 73 and 8, then 73 and 50. The sum of these partial products is the product of 73 and 58. Use the notation to the right.

$$\begin{array}{r} 73 \leftarrow \text{ factor}\\ \times\;58 \leftarrow \text{ factor}\\ \hline 584 \leftarrow \;73 \times 8\\ 3650 \leftarrow \;73 \times 50\\ \hline 4234 \leftarrow \text{ product} \end{array}$$

continued

DEFINITIONS AND CONCEPTS	EXAMPLES
Section 1.6 Multiplying Whole Numbers and Area (*continued*)	

To find the **area** of a rectangle, multiply length times width.	Find the area of the rectangle shown. 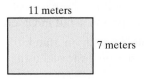 area of rectangle = length · width = (11 meters)(7 meters) = 77 square meters
To multiply by 10, 100, 1000, and so on, form the product by attaching the number of 0s in that number to the other factor.	$39 \cdot 1000 = 39{,}000$ Attach 3 zeros. $200 \cdot 4000 = 800{,}000$ Attach 5 zeros. $2 \cdot 4$

Section 1.7 Dividing Whole Numbers	

DIVISION PROPERTIES OF 0 The quotient of 0 and any number (except 0) is 0. The quotient of any number and 0 is not a number. We say that this quotient is undefined.	$\dfrac{0}{5} = 0$ $\dfrac{7}{0}$ is undefined
To divide larger whole numbers, use the process called **long division** as shown to the right.	$$\begin{array}{r} 507 \ \text{R } 2 \quad \leftarrow \text{quotient} \\ \text{divisor} \rightarrow 14\overline{)7100} \leftarrow \text{dividend} \\ -70\downarrow \quad \quad 5(14)=70 \\ \overline{10} \quad \quad \text{Subtract and bring down the 0.} \\ -0\downarrow \quad \quad 0(14)=0 \\ \overline{100} \quad \quad \text{Subtract and bring down the 0.} \\ -98 \quad \quad 7(14)=98 \\ \overline{2} \quad \quad \text{Subtract. The remainder is 2.} \end{array}$$ To check, see that $507 \cdot 14 + 2 = 7100$.
The **average** of a list of numbers is $$\text{average} = \frac{\text{sum of numbers}}{\text{number of numbers}}$$	Find the average of 23, 35, and 38. $$\text{average} = \frac{23 + 35 + 38}{3} = \frac{96}{3} = 32$$

Section 1.8 An Introduction to Problem Solving	

PROBLEM-SOLVING STEPS **1.** UNDERSTAND the problem.	Suppose that 225 tickets are sold for each performance of a play. How many tickets are sold for 5 performances? **1.** UNDERSTAND. Read and reread the problem. Since we want the number of tickets for 5 performances, we multiply.

Definitions and Concepts	**Examples**

Section 1.8   An Introduction to Problem Solving (*continued*)

2. TRANSLATE the problem.

2. TRANSLATE.

number of tickets	is	number of performances	times	tickets per performance
↓	↓	↓	↓	↓

Number of tickets	=	5	·	225

3. SOLVE the problem.

3. SOLVE: See if the answer is reasonable by also estimating.

$$
\begin{array}{c}
\overset{1\;2}{225} \\
\underline{\times\quad 5} \\
1125 \quad \text{exact}
\end{array}
\qquad
\begin{array}{c}
\text{rounds to} \\
\\
\\
\end{array}
\qquad
\begin{array}{c}
200 \\
\underline{\times\quad 5} \\
1000 \quad \text{estimate}
\end{array}
$$

4. INTERPRET the results.

4. INTERPRET. **Check** your work. The product is reasonable since 1125 is close to our estimated answer of 1000, and **state** your conclusion: There are 1125 tickets sold for 5 performances.

Section 1.9   Exponents, Square Roots, and Order of Operations

An **exponent** is a shorthand notation for repeated multiplication of the same factor.

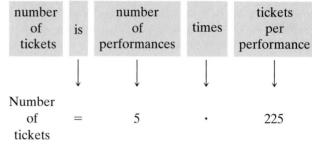

$$3^4 = \underbrace{3 \cdot 3 \cdot 3 \cdot 3}_{\text{4 factors of 3}} = 81$$

base

A **square root** of a number is one of two identical factors of the number.

$$\sqrt{36} = 6 \quad \text{because} \quad 6 \cdot 6 = 36$$
$$\sqrt{121} = 11 \quad \text{because} \quad 11 \cdot 11 = 121$$
$$\sqrt{0} = 0 \quad \text{because} \quad 0 \cdot 0 = 0$$

Order of Operations

1. Perform all operations within parentheses ( ), brackets [ ], or other grouping symbols such as square roots or fraction bars.
2. Evaluate any expressions with exponents.
3. Multiply or divide in order from left to right.
4. Add or subtract in order from left to right.

Simplify: $\dfrac{5 + 3^2}{2(7 - 6)}$

Simplify above and below the fraction bar separately.

$$\frac{5 + 3^2}{2(7 - 6)} = \frac{5 + 9}{2(1)} \quad \begin{array}{l}\text{Evaluate } 3^2 \text{ above the fraction bar.} \\ \text{Subtract: } 7 - 6 \text{ below the fraction bar.}\end{array}$$

$$= \frac{14}{2} \quad \begin{array}{l}\text{Add.} \\ \text{Multiply.}\end{array}$$

$$= 7 \quad \text{Divide.}$$

The **area of a square** is (side)².

Find the area of a square with side length 9 inches.

$$
\begin{aligned}
\text{Area of the square} &= (\text{side})^2 \\
&= (9 \text{ inches})^2 \\
&= 81 \text{ square inches}
\end{aligned}
$$

1 CHAPTER REVIEW

(1.2) *Determine the place value of the digit 4 in each whole number.*

1. 5480

2. 46,200,120

Write each whole number in words.

3. 5480

4. 46,200,120

Write each whole number in expanded form.

5. 6279

6. 403,225,000

Write each whole number in standard form.

7. Fifty-nine thousand, eight hundred

8. Six billion, three hundred four million

The following table shows the populations of the ten largest cities in the United States. Use this table to answer Exercises 9 through 12 and other exercises throughout this review.

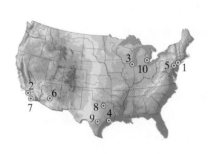

Rank	City	2000	1990	1980
1	New York, NY	8,008,278	7,322,564	7,071,639
2	Los Angeles, CA	3,694,820	3,485,398	2,968,528
3	Chicago, IL	2,896,016	2,783,726	3,005,072
4	Houston, TX	1,953,631	1,630,553	1,595,138
5	Philadelphia, PA	1,517,550	1,585,577	1,688,210
6	Phoenix, AZ	1,321,045	983,403	789,704
7	San Diego, CA	1,223,400	1,110,549	875,538
8	Dallas, TX	1,188,580	1,006,877	904,599
9	San Antonio, TX	1,144,646	935,933	785,940
10	Detroit, MI	951,270	1,027,974	1,203,368

(*Source:* U.S. Census Bureau)

9. Find the population of Houston, Texas, in 1990.

10. Find the population of Los Angeles, California, in 1980.

11. Which city had the smallest population in 1990?

12. Which city had the largest population in 1990?

(1.3) *Add.*

13. $17 + 46$

14. $28 + 39$

15. $25 + 8 + 15$

16. $27 + 9 + 41$

17. $932 + 24$

18. $819 + 21$

19. $567 + 7383$

20. $463 + 6787$

21. $91 + 3623 + 497$

22. $82 + 1647 + 238$

Solve.

23. Find the sum of 86, 331, and 909.

24. Find the sum of 49, 529, and 308.

25. What is 26,481 increased by 865?

26. What is 38,556 increased by 744?

27. The distance from Chicago to New York City is 714 miles. The distance from New York City to New Delhi, India, is 7318 miles. Find the total distance from Chicago to New Delhi if traveling by air through New York City.

28. Susan Summerline earned salaries of $62,589, $65,340, and $69,770 during the years 2002, 2003, and 2004, respectively. Find her total earnings during those three years.

Find the perimeter of each figure.

△ **29.**

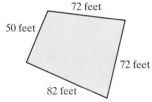

72 feet
50 feet
72 feet
82 feet

△ **30.** 11 kilometers   20 kilometers
35 kilometers

(1.4) *Subtract and then check.*

31. $93 - 79$

32. $61 - 27$

33. $462 - 397$

34. $583 - 279$

35. $4000 - 86$

36. $8000 - 92$

Solve.

37. Subtract 7965 from 25,862.

38. Subtract 4349 from 39,007.

Use the city population table for Exercises 39 and 40.

39. Find the increase in population for Phoenix, Arizona, from 1980 to 2000.

40. Find the decrease in population for Detroit, Michigan, from 1990 to 2000.

41. Bob Roma is proofreading the Yellow Pages for his county. If he has finished 315 pages of the total 712 pages, how many pages does he have left to proofread?

42. Shelly Winters bought a new car listed at $28,425. She received a discount of $1599 and a factory rebate of $1200. Find how much she paid for the car.

The following bar graph shows the monthly savings account balance for a freshman attending a local community college. Use this graph to answer Exercises 43 through 46.

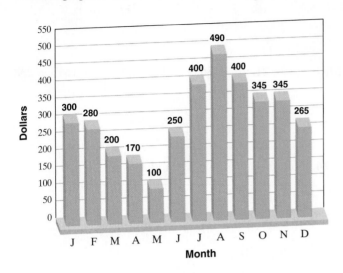

43. During what month was the balance the least?

44. During what month was the balance the greatest?

45. By how much did his balance decrease from February to April?

46. By how much did his balance increase from June to August?

(1.5) *Round to the given place.*

47. 93 to the nearest ten

48. 45 to the nearest ten

49. 467 to the nearest ten

50. 493 to the nearest hundred

51. 4832 to the nearest hundred

52. 57,534 to the nearest thousand

53. 49,683,712 to the nearest million

54. 768,542 to the nearest hundred-thousand

55. In 2003, there were 73,365,880 households in the United States subscribing to cable television services. Round this number to the nearest million. (*Source:* Nielsen Media Research-NTI)

56. In 2003, the total number of employees working for U.S. airlines was 570,868. Round this number to the nearest thousand. (*Source:* The Air Transport Association of America, Inc.)

Estimate the sum or difference by rounding each number to the nearest hundred.

57. $4892 + 647 + 1876$

58. $5925 - 1787$

59. A group of students took a week-long driving trip and traveled 628, 290, 172, 58, 508, 445, and 383 miles on seven consecutive days. Round each distance to the nearest hundred to estimate the distance they traveled.

60. According to the city population table, the 2000 population of Los Angeles was 3,694,820, and for Dallas it was 1,188,580. Round each number to the nearest hundred-thousand and estimate how much larger Los Angeles is than Dallas.

(1.6) *Multiply.*

61. $\begin{array}{r} 273 \\ \times\ 7 \\ \hline \end{array}$

62. $\begin{array}{r} 349 \\ \times\ 4 \\ \hline \end{array}$

63. $\begin{array}{r} 47 \\ \times 30 \\ \hline \end{array}$

64. $\begin{array}{r} 69 \\ \times 42 \\ \hline \end{array}$

65. 20(8)(5) **66.** 25(9)(4) **67.** 48 **68.** 77
× 77 × 22

69. 49 · 49 · 0 **70.** 62 · 88 · 0 **71.** 586 **72.** 242
× 29 × 37

73. 642 **74.** 347 **75.** 1026 **76.** 2107
× 177 × 129 × 401 × 302

77. 375 · 1000 **78.** 108 · 1000 **79.** 30 · 400 **80.** 50 · 700

81. 1700 · 3000 **82.** 1900 · 4000

Solve.

83. Find the product of 5 and 230. **84.** Find the product of 6 and 820.

85. Multiply 9 and 12. **86.** Multiply 8 and 14.

87. One ounce of Swiss cheese contains 8 grams of fat. How many grams of fat are in 3 ounces of Swiss cheese? (*Source: Home and Garden Bulletin No. 72*, U.S. Department of Agriculture)

88. There were 5283 students enrolled at Weskan State University in the fall semester. Each paid $927 in tuition. Find the total tuition collected.

Find the area of each rectangle.

△ **89.**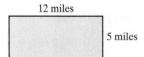
12 miles
5 miles

△ **90.**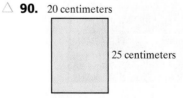
20 centimeters
25 centimeters

(1.7) *Divide and then check.*

91. $\frac{18}{6}$ **92.** $\frac{36}{9}$ **93.** 42 ÷ 7 **94.** 35 ÷ 5 **95.** 27 ÷ 5

96. 18 ÷ 4 **97.** 16 ÷ 0 **98.** 0 ÷ 8 **99.** 9 ÷ 9 **100.** 10 ÷ 1

101. $918 \div 0$ **102.** $0 \div 668$ **103.** $5\overline{)167}$ **104.** $8\overline{)159}$ **105.** $26\overline{)626}$

106. $19\overline{)680}$ **107.** $47\overline{)23,792}$ **108.** $53\overline{)48,111}$ **109.** $207\overline{)578,291}$ **110.** $306\overline{)615,732}$

Solve.

111. Find the quotient of 92 and 5.

112. Find the quotient of 86 and 4.

113. One foot is 12 inches. Find how many feet there are in 5496 inches.

114. One mile is 1760 yards. Find how many miles there are in 22,880 yards.

115. Find the average of the numbers 76, 49, 32, and 47.

116. Find the average of the numbers 23, 85, 62, and 66.

(1.8) *Solve.*

117. A box can hold 24 cans of corn. How many boxes can be filled with 648 cans of corn?

118. If a ticket to a movie costs $6, how much do 32 tickets cost?

119. Aspirin was 100 years old in 1997 and was the first U.S. drug made in tablet form. Today, people take 11 billion tablets a year for heart disease prevention and 4 billion tablets a year for headaches. How many more tablets are taken a year for heart disease prevention? (*Source:* Bayer Market Research)

120. The cost to banks when a person uses an ATM (Automatic Teller Machine) is 27¢. The cost to banks when a person deposits a check with a teller is 48¢ more. How much is this cost?

121. A golf pro orders shirts for the company sponsoring a local charity golfing event. Shirts size large cost $32 while shirts size extra-large cost $38. If 15 large shirts and 11 extra-large shirts are ordered, find the cost.

122. Two rectangular pieces of land are purchased: one that measures 65 feet by 110 feet and one that measures 80 feet by 200 feet. Find the total area of land purchased. (*Hint:* Find the area of each rectangle, then add.)

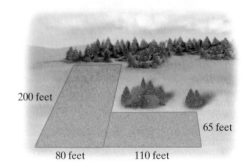

200 feet   65 feet

80 feet   110 feet

(1.9) *Simplify.*

123. 7^2 **124.** 5^3 **125.** $5 \cdot 3^2$ **126.** $4 \cdot 10^2$

127. $18 \div 3 + 7$ **128.** $12 - 8 \div 4$ **129.** $\dfrac{5(6^2 - 3)}{3^2 + 2}$ **130.** $\dfrac{7(16 - 8)}{2^3}$

131. $48 \div 8 \cdot 2$

132. $27 \div 9 \cdot 3$

133. $2 + 3[1^5 + (20 - 17) \cdot 3] + 5 \cdot 2$

134. $21 - [2^4 - (7 - 5) - 10] + 8 \cdot 2$

Simplify. These exercises contain roots.

135. $\sqrt{81}$

136. $\sqrt{4}$

137. $\sqrt{1}$

138. $\sqrt{0}$

139. $4 \cdot \sqrt{25} - 2 \cdot 7$

140. $8 \cdot \sqrt{49} - 3 \cdot 9$

141. $\left(\sqrt{36} - \sqrt{16}\right)^3 \cdot [10^2 \div (3 + 17)]$

142. $\left(\sqrt{49} - \sqrt{25}\right)^3 \cdot [9^2 \div (2 + 7)]$

143. $\dfrac{5 \cdot 7 - 3 \cdot \sqrt{25}}{2\left(\sqrt{121} - 3^2\right)}$

144. $\dfrac{4 \cdot 8 - 1 \cdot \sqrt{121}}{3\left(\sqrt{81} - 2^3\right)}$

Find the area of each square.

△ **145.** A square with side length of 7 meters.

△ **146.**

3 inches

Mixed Review

Perform the indicated operations.

147. $375 - 68$

148. $729 - 47$

149. 723×3

150. 629×4

151. $264 + 39 + 598$

152. $593 + 52 + 766$

153. $13\overline{)5962}$

154. $18\overline{)4267}$

155. 1968×36

156. 5324×18

157. $2000 - 356$

158. $9000 - 519$

Round to the given place.

159. 736 to the nearest ten

160. 258,371 to the nearest thousand

161. 1999 to the nearest hundred

162. 44,499 to the nearest ten thousand

Write each whole number in words.

163. 36,911

164. 154,863

Write each whole number in standard form.

165. Seventy thousand, nine hundred forty-three

166. Forty-three thousand, four hundred one

Simplify.

167. 4^3

168. 5^3

169. $\sqrt{144}$

170. $\sqrt{100}$

171. $24 \div 4 \cdot 2$

172. $\sqrt{256} - 3 \cdot 5$

173. $\dfrac{8(7-4)-10}{4^2-3^2}$

174. $\dfrac{\left(15+\sqrt{9}\right)\cdot(8-5)}{2^3+1}$

Solve.

175. 36 divided by 9 is what number?

176. What is the product of 2 and 12?

177. 16 increased by 8 is what number?

178. 7 subtracted from 21 is what number?

The following table shows the top-grossing movies for 2003 and 2004. Use this table to answer Exercises 179 and 180.

Movie (2003)	Gross	Movie (2004)	Gross
The Lord of the Rings: The Return of the King	$377,019,000	Shrek 2	$436,471,000
Finding Nemo	$339,714,000	Spider-Man 2	$373,378,000
Pirates of the Caribbean: The Curse of the Black Pearl	$305,389,000	The Passion of the Christ	$370,275,000
The Matrix Reloaded	$281,492,000	Harry Potter and the Prisoner of Azkaban	$249,359,000
Bruce Almighty	$242,590,000	The Incredibles	$242,426,000
(*Source:* Internet Movie Database)			

179. How much more did the top grossing film in 2004 make than the top-grossing film in 2003?

180. Find the total gross of the animated films *Finding Nemo* and *The Incredibles*.

181. A manufacturer of drinking glasses ships his delicate stock in special boxes that can hold 32 glasses. If 1714 glasses are manufactured, how many full boxes are filled? Are there any glasses left over?

182. A teacher orders 2 small white boards for $27 each and 8 boxes of dry erase pens for $4 each. What is her total bill before taxes?

1 CHAPTER TEST

 Use the Chapter Test Prep Video CD to see the fully worked-out solutions to any of the exercises you want to review.

Simplify.

1. Write 82,426 in words.

2. Write "four hundred two thousand, five hundred fifty" in standard form.

3. $59 + 82$

4. $600 - 487$

5. $\begin{array}{r} 496 \\ \times\ \ 30 \\ \hline \end{array}$

6. $52,896 \div 69$

7. $2^3 \cdot 5^2$

8. $\sqrt{4} \cdot \sqrt{25}$

9. $0 \div 49$

10. $62 \div 0$

11. $(2^4 - 5) \cdot 3$

12. $16 + 9 \div 3 \cdot 4 - 7$

13. $\dfrac{64 \div 8 \cdot 2}{\left(\sqrt{9} - \sqrt{4}\right)^2 + 1}$

14. $2[(6 - 4)^2 + (22 - 19)^2] + 10$

15. $5698 \cdot 1000$

16. $8000 \cdot 1400$

17. Round 52,369 to the nearest thousand.

Estimate each sum or difference by rounding each number to the nearest hundred.

18. $6289 + 5403 + 1957$

19. $4267 - 2738$

1. _____

2. _____

3. _____

4. _____

5. _____

6. _____

7. _____

8. _____

9. _____

10. _____

11. _____

12. _____

13. _____

14. _____

15. _____

16. _____

17. _____

18. _____

19. _____

20. _____

21. _____

22. _____

23. _____

24. _____

25. _____

26. _____

27. _____

28. _____

29. _____

Solve.

20. Subtract 15 from 107.

21. Find the sum of 15 and 107.

22. Find the product of 15 and 107.

23. Find the quotient of 107 and 15.

24. Twenty-nine cans of Sherwin-Williams paint cost $493. How much was each can?

25. Jo McElory is looking at two new refrigerators for her apartment. One costs $599 and the other costs $725. How much more expensive is the higher-priced one?

26. One tablespoon of white granulated sugar contains 45 calories. How many calories are in 8 tablespoons of white granulated sugar? (_Source: Home and Garden Bulletin No. 72, U.S. Department of Agriculture_)

27. A small business owner recently ordered 11 digital cameras that cost $430 each and 5 printers that cost $205 each. Find the total cost for these items.

Find the perimeter and the area of each figure.

△ **28.**

| Square | 5 centimeters |

△ **29.**

20 yards

| Rectangle | 10 yards |

2

Integers and Introduction to Variables

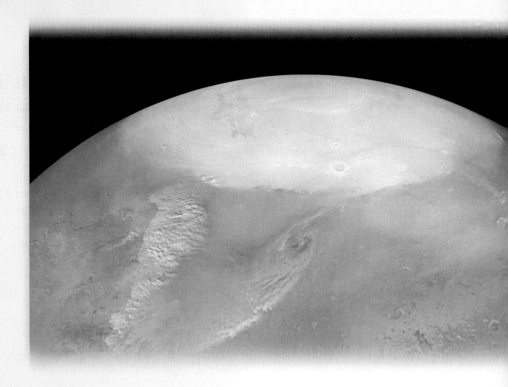

Thus far, we have studied whole numbers, but these numbers are not sufficient for representing many situations in real life. For example, to express 5 degrees below zero or $100 in debt, numbers less than 0 are needed. This chapter is devoted to integers, which include numbers less than 0, and to operations on these numbers.

Have you ever wondered about the weather on other planets? Scientists do! Information from satellites, probes, and telescopes tells of extreme atmospheric conditions of our Solar System neighbors. Pluto's distance from the Sun contributes to its frigid temperatures, some recorded as low as 338°F *below zero*. Compare that to the extreme heat of Venus, where temperatures on the surface are in excess of 800°F. In Exercises 63–66 on page 143, we will see how integers can be used to compare average daily temperatures of several planets in our Solar System.

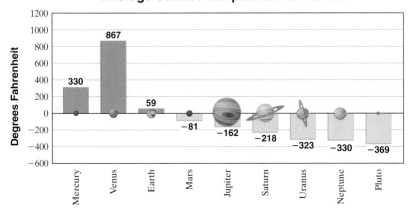

Average Surface Temperature of Planets*

*(For some planets, the temperature given is the temperature where the atmosphere pressure equals 1 Earth atmosphere; *Source: The World Almanac*, 2005)

2.1 INTRODUCTION TO VARIABLES AND ALGEBRAIC EXPRESSIONS

Objective **A** Evaluating Algebraic Expressions

Perhaps the most important quality of mathematics is that it is a science of patterns. Communicating about patterns is often made easier by using a letter to represent all the numbers fitting a pattern. We call such a letter a **variable.** For example, in Section 1.3 we presented the addition property of 0, which states that the sum of 0 and any number is that number. We might write

$$0 + 1 = 1$$
$$0 + 2 = 2$$
$$0 + 3 = 3$$
$$0 + 4 = 4$$
$$0 + 5 = 5$$
$$0 + 6 = 6$$
$$\vdots$$

continuing indefinitely. This is a pattern, and all whole numbers fit the pattern. We can communicate this pattern for all whole numbers by letting a letter, such as a, represent all whole numbers. We can then write

$$0 + a = a$$

Using variable notation is a primary goal of learning **algebra.** We now take some important first steps in beginning to use variable notation.

A combination of operations on letters (variables) and numbers is called an **algebraic expression** or simply an **expression.**

Algebraic Expressions

$$3 + x \qquad 5 \cdot y \qquad 2 \cdot z - 1 + x$$

If two variables or a number and a variable are next to each other, with no operation sign between them, the operation is multiplication. For example,

$$2x \quad \text{means} \quad 2 \cdot x$$

and

$$xy \text{ or } x(y) \quad \text{means} \quad x \cdot y$$

Also, the meaning of an exponent remains the same when the base is a variable. For example,

$$x^2 = \underbrace{x \cdot x}_{2 \text{ factors of } x} \text{ and } y^5 = \underbrace{y \cdot y \cdot y \cdot y \cdot y}_{5 \text{ factors of } y}$$

Algebraic expressions such as $3x$ have different values depending on replacement values for x. For example, if x is 2, then $3x$ becomes

$$3x = 3 \cdot 2$$
$$= 6$$

If x is 7, then $3x$ becomes

$$3x = 3 \cdot 7$$
$$= 21$$

Replacing a variable in an expression by a number and then finding the value of the expression is called **evaluating the expression** for the variable. When finding the value of an expression, remember to follow the order of operations given in Section 1.9.

EXAMPLE 1 Evaluate $x + 7$ if x is 8.

Solution: Replace x with 8 in the expression $x + 7$.

$$x + 7 = 8 + 7 \qquad \text{Replace } x \text{ with 8.}$$
$$= 15 \qquad \text{Add.}$$

Work Practice Problem 1

When we write a statement such as "x is 5," we can use an equals symbol to represent "is" so that

x is 5   can be written as $x = 5$.

EXAMPLE 2 Evaluate $2(x - y)$ for $x = 8$ and $y = 4$.

Solution: $2(x - y) = 2(8 - 4)$ Replace x with 8 and y with 4.
$$= 2(4) \qquad \text{Subtract.}$$
$$= 8 \qquad \text{Multiply.}$$

Work Practice Problem 2

EXAMPLE 3 Evaluate $\dfrac{x - 5y}{y}$ for $x = 21$ and $y = 3$.

Solution: $\dfrac{x - 5y}{y} = \dfrac{21 - 5(3)}{3}$ Replace x with 21 and y with 3.

$$= \frac{21 - 15}{3} \qquad \text{Multiply.}$$

$$= \frac{6}{3} \qquad \text{Subtract.}$$

$$= 2 \qquad \text{Divide.}$$

Work Practice Problem 3

EXAMPLE 4 Evaluate $x^2 + z - 3$ for $x = 5$ and $z = 4$.

Solution: $x^2 + z - 3 = 5^2 + 4 - 3$ Replace x with 5 and z with 4.
$$= 25 + 4 - 3 \qquad \text{Evaluate } 5^2.$$
$$= 26 \qquad \text{Add and subtract from left to right.}$$

Work Practice Problem 4

PRACTICE PROBLEM 1
Evaluate $x - 2$ if x is 5.

PRACTICE PROBLEM 2
Evaluate $y(x - 3)$ for $x = 3$ and $y = 7$.

PRACTICE PROBLEM 3
Evaluate $\dfrac{y + 6}{x}$ for $x = 2$ and $y = 8$.

PRACTICE PROBLEM 4
Evaluate $25 - z^3 + x$ for $z = 2$ and $x = 1$.

Answers

1. 3, **2.** 0, **3.** 7, **4.** 18

Helpful Hint

If you are having difficulty replacing variables with numbers, first replace each variable with a set of parentheses, then insert the replacement number within the parentheses.

Example:

$$x^2 + z - 3 = (\ )^2 + (\ ) - 3$$
$$= (5)^2 + (4) - 3$$
$$= 25 + 4 - 3$$
$$= 26$$

✔**Concept Check** What's wrong with the solution to the following problem?

Evaluate $3x + 2y$ for $x = 2$ and $y = 3$.

Solution: $3x + 2y = 3(3) + 2(2)$
$$= 9 + 4$$
$$= 13$$

PRACTICE PROBLEM 5

Evaluate $\dfrac{5(F - 32)}{9}$ for $F = 41$.

EXAMPLE 5 The expression $\dfrac{5(F - 32)}{9}$ can be used to write degrees Fahrenheit F as degrees Celsius C. Find the value of this expression for $F = 86$.

Solution:
$$\frac{5(F - 32)}{9} = \frac{5(86 - 32)}{9}$$
$$= \frac{5(54)}{9}$$
$$= \frac{270}{9}$$
$$= 30$$

Thus 86°F is the same temperature as 30°C.

■ **Work Practice Problem 5**

Objective **B** Translating Phrases into Variable Expressions

To aid us in solving problems later, we practice translating verbal phrases into algebraic expressions. Recall from Section 1.8 that certain key words and phrases suggest addition, subtraction, multiplication, or division. These are reviewed next.

Addition (+)	Subtraction (−)	Multiplication (·)	Division (÷)
sum	difference	product	quotient
plus	minus	times	divide
added to	subtract	multiply	shared equally
more than	less than	multiply by	among
increased by	decreased by	of	divided by
total	less	double/triple	divided into

Answer

5. 5

✔ **Concept Check Answer**

$3x + 2y = 3(2) + 2(3)$
$$= 6 + 6$$
$$= 12$$

EXAMPLE 6 Write as an algebraic expression. Use x to represent "a number."

a. 7 increased by a number
b. 15 decreased by a number
c. The product of 2 and a number
d. The quotient of a number and 5
e. 2 subtracted from a number

Solution:

a. In words:　7　increased by　a number
　　　Translate:　7　　　+　　　　x

b. In words:　15　decreased by　a number
　　　Translate:　15　　　−　　　　x

c. In words:
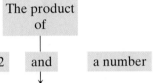
　　Translate:　2　　·　　　x　　or $2x$

d. In words:
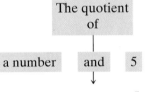
　　Translate:　　x　　÷　　5　　or $\dfrac{x}{5}$

e. In words:
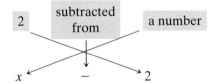
　　Translate:　x　　　−　　　2

Work Practice Problem 6

Helpful Hint

　　　　Remember that order is important when subtracting. Study the order of numbers and variables below.

Phrase	Translation
a number *decreased by* 5	$x - 5$
a number *subtracted from* 5	$5 - x$

PRACTICE PROBLEM 6

Write as an algebraic expression. Use x to represent "a number."

a. Twice a number.
b. 8 increased by a number.
c. 10 minus a number.
d. 10 subtracted from a number.
e. The quotient of 6 and a number.

Answers
6. a. $2x$, **b.** $8 + x$, **c.** $10 - x$,
d. $x - 10$, **e.** $6 \div x$ or $\dfrac{6}{x}$

FOR EXTRA HELP

Student Solutions Manual

PH Math/Tutor Center

CD/Video for Review

Math XL
MathXL®

MyMathLab
MyMathLab

Objective Ⓐ *Evaluate each expression for $x = 2$, $y = 5$, and $z = 3$. See Examples 1 through 5.*

1. $3 + 2z$

2. $7 + 3z$

3. $6xz - 5x$

4. $4yz + 2x$

5. $z - x + y$

6. $x + 5y - z$

7. $3x - z$

8. $2y + 5z$

9. $y^3 - 4x$

10. $y^3 - z$

11. $2xy^2 - 6$

12. $3yz^2 + 1$

13. $8 - (y - x)$

14. $5 + (2x - 1)$

15. $y^4 + (z - x)$

16. $x^4 - (y - z)$

17. $\dfrac{6xy}{z}$

18. $\dfrac{8yz}{15}$

19. $\dfrac{2y - 2}{x}$

20. $\dfrac{6 + 3x}{z}$

21. $\dfrac{x + 2y}{z}$

22. $\dfrac{2z + 6}{3}$

23. $\dfrac{5x}{y} - \dfrac{10}{y}$

24. $\dfrac{70}{2y} - \dfrac{15}{z}$

25. $2y^2 - 4y + 3$

26. $3z^2 - z + 10$

27. $(3y - 2x)^2$

28. $(4y + 3z)^2$

29. $(xy + 1)^2$

30. $(xz - 5)^4$

31. $2y(4z - x)$

32. $3x(y + z)$

33. $xy(5 + z - x)$

34. $xz(2y + x - z)$

35. $\dfrac{7x + 2y}{3x}$

36. $\dfrac{6z + 2y}{4}$

37. The expression $16t^2$ gives the distance in feet that an object falls after t seconds. Complete the table by evaluating $16t^2$ for each given value of t.

t	1	2	3	4
$16t^2$				

38. The expression $\dfrac{5(F - 32)}{9}$ gives the equivalent degrees Celsius for F degrees Fahrenheit. Complete the table by evaluating this expression for each given value of F.

F	50	59	68	77
$\dfrac{5(F - 32)}{9}$				

Objective **B** *Write each phrase as a variable expression. Use x to represent "a number." See Example 6.*

39. The sum of a number and five

40. Ten plus a number

41. The total of a number and eight

42. The difference of a number and five hundred

43. Twenty decreased by a number

44. A number less thirty

45. The product of 512 and a number

46. A number times twenty

47. A number divided by 2

48. The quotient of six and a number

49. The sum of seventeen and a number added to the product of five and the number

50. The difference of twice a number, and four

51. The product of five and a number

52. The quotient of twenty and a number, decreased by three

53. A number subtracted from 11

54. Twelve subtracted from a number

55. A number less 5

56. The product of a number and 7

57. 6 divided by a number

58. The sum of a number and 7

59. Fifty decreased by eight times a number

60. Twenty decreased by twice a number

Concept Extensions

Solve. See the Concept Check in this section. Determine whether each expression is correctly evaluated for $x = 2$, $y = 0$, and $z = 7$.

61. $2y + 3z \stackrel{?}{=} 2(2) + 3(7)$

$ \stackrel{?}{=} 4 + 21$

$ \stackrel{?}{=} 25$

62. $2z - 4x \stackrel{?}{=} 2(7) - 4(2)$

$ \stackrel{?}{=} 14 - 8$

$ \stackrel{?}{=} 6$

63. $\dfrac{4z}{2x} \stackrel{?}{=} \dfrac{4(7)}{2(2)}$

$\phantom{\dfrac{4z}{2x}} \stackrel{?}{=} \dfrac{28}{4}$

$\phantom{\dfrac{4z}{2x}} \stackrel{?}{=} 7$

64. $\dfrac{2xy}{z} \stackrel{?}{=} \dfrac{2(2)(0)}{7}$

$\phantom{\dfrac{2xy}{z}} \stackrel{?}{=} \dfrac{0}{7}$

$\phantom{\dfrac{2xy}{z}}$ is undefined

Use a calculator to evaluate each expression for $x = 23$ and $y = 72$.

65. $x^4 - y^2$

66. $2(x + y)^2$

67. $x^2 + 5y - 112$

68. $16y - 20x + x^3$

69. If x is a whole number, which expression is the largest: $2x$, $5x$, or $\dfrac{x}{3}$? Explain your answer.

70. If x is a whole number, which expression is the smallest: $2x$, $5x$, or $\dfrac{x}{3}$? Explain your answer.

71. In Exercise 37, what do you notice about the value of $16t^2$ as t gets larger?

72. In Exercise 38, what do you notice about the value of $\dfrac{5(F - 32)}{9}$ as F gets larger?

STUDY SKILLS BUILDER

Have You Decided to Complete This Course Successfully?

Ask yourself if one of your current goals is to complete this course successfully.

If it is not a goal of yours, ask yourself why? One common reason is fear of failure. Amazingly enough, fear of failure alone can be strong enough to keep many of us from doing our best in any endeavor.

Another common reason is that you simply haven't taken the time to make successfully completing this course one of your goals. How do you do this? Start by writing this goal in your mathematics notebook. Then list steps you will take to ensure success. A great first step is to read or reread Section 1.1 and make a commitment to try the suggestions in that section.

Good luck, and don't forget that a positive attitude will make a big difference.

Let's see how you are doing.

1. Have you decided to make "successfully completing this course" a goal of yours? If no, please list reasons why this has not happened. Study your list and talk to your instructor about this.

2. If your answer to question 1 is yes, take a moment and list in your notebook further specific goals that will help you achieve this major goal of successfully completing this course. (For example, "My goal this semester is not to miss any of my mathematics classes.")

3. Rate your commitment to this course with a number between 1 and 5. Use the diagram below to help.

High Commitment	Average Commitment	Not committed at all
5	4	3	2	1

4. If you have rated your personal commitment level (from the exercise above) as a 1, 2, or 3, list the reasons why this is so. Then determine whether it is possible to increase your commitment level to a 4 or 5.

A Represent Real-Life Situations with Integers.

B Graph Integers on a Number Line.

C Compare Integers.

D Find the Absolute Value of a Number.

E Find the Opposite of a Number.

F Read Bar Graphs Containing Integers.

2.2 INTRODUCTION TO INTEGERS

Objective A Representing Real-Life Situations

Thus far in this text, all numbers have been 0 or greater than 0. Numbers greater than 0 are called **positive numbers.** However, sometimes situations exist that cannot be represented by a number greater than 0. For example,

0° — 5 degrees below 0°

Sea level
20 feet below sea level

To represent these situations, we need numbers less than 0.

Extending the number line to the left of 0 allows us to picture **negative numbers,** which are numbers that are less than 0.

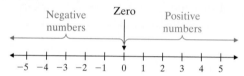

Negative numbers   Zero   Positive numbers

−5 −4 −3 −2 −1   0   1   2   3   4   5

When a single + sign or no sign is in front of a number, the number is a positive number. When a single − sign is in front of a number, the number is a negative number. Together, we call positive numbers, negative numbers, and zero the **signed numbers.**

−5 indicates "negative five."

5 and +5 both indicate "positive five."

The number 0 is neither positive nor negative.

Some signed numbers are integers. The **integers** consist of the numbers labeled on the number line above. The integers are

..., −3, −2, −1, 0, 1, 2, 3, ...

Now we have numbers to represent the situations previously mentioned.

5 degrees below 0   −5°

20 feet below sea level   −20 feet

> **Helpful Hint**
> Notice that 0 is neither positive or negative.

> **Helpful Hint**
> A − sign, such as the one in −1, tells us that the number is to the left of 0 on the number line. −1 is read "negative one."
> A + sign or no sign tells us that a number lies to the right of 0 on the number line. For example, 3 and +3 both mean "positive three."

EXAMPLE 1 Representing Depth with an Integer

Jack Mayfield, a miner for the Molly Kathleen Gold Mine, is presently 150 feet below the surface of the Earth. Represent this position using an integer.

Solution: If 0 represents the surface of the Earth, then 150 feet below the surface can be represented by -150.

🔲 **Work Practice Problem 1**

Objective **B** Graphing Integers

EXAMPLE 2 Graph $0, -3, 2,$ and -2 on the number line.

Solution:

🔲 **Work Practice Problem 2**

Objective **C** Comparing Integers

We compare integers just as we compare whole numbers. For any two numbers graphed on a number line, the number to the **right** is the **greater number** and the number to the **left** is the **smaller number**. Recall that the inequality symbol $>$ means "is greater than" and the inequality symbol $<$ means "is less than."

Both -5 and -7 are graphed on the number line below.

On the graph, -7 is **to the left of** -5, so -7 **is less than** -5, written as

$$-7 < -5$$

We can also write

$$-5 > -7$$

since -5 is **to the right** of -7, so -5 **is greater than** -7.

✔ **Concept Check** Is there a largest positive number? Is there a smallest negative number? Explain.

EXAMPLE 3 Insert $<$ or $>$ between each pair of numbers to make a true statement.

a. -7 7 **b.** 0 -4 **c.** -9 -11

Solution:

a. -7 is to the left of 7 on a number line, so $-7 < 7$.
b. 0 is to the right of -4 on a number line, so $0 > -4$.
c. -9 is to the right of -11 on a number line, so $-9 > -11$.

🔲 **Work Practice Problem 3**

Helpful Hint
    If you think of $<$ and $>$ as arrowheads, notice that in a true statement the arrow always points to the smaller number.

$$5 > -4 \qquad -3 < -1$$
smaller   smaller
number   number

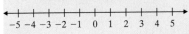 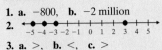

Objective D Finding the Absolute Value of a Number

The **absolute value** of a number is the number's distance from 0 on the number line. The symbol for absolute value is | |. For example, |3| is read as "the absolute value of 3."

$|3| = 3$ because 3 is 3 units from 0.

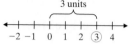
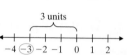

$|-3| = 3$ because -3 is 3 units from 0.

EXAMPLE 4 Simplify.

a. $|-2|$ **b.** $|5|$ **c.** $|0|$

Solution:

a. $|-2| = 2$ because -2 is 2 units from 0.

b. $|5| = 5$ because 5 is 5 units from 0.

c. $|0| = 0$ because 0 is 0 units from 0.

▢ **Work Practice Problem 4**

Helpful Hint

Since the absolute value of a number is that number's *distance* from 0, the absolute value of a number is always 0 or positive. It is never negative.

$$|0| = 0 \qquad |-6| = 6$$

zero   a positive number

Objective E Finding Opposites

Two numbers that are the same distance from 0 on the number line but are on opposite sides of 0 are called **opposites**.

4 and -4 are opposites.

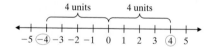

When two numbers are opposites, we say that each is the opposite of the other. Thus **4 is the opposite of** -4 and -4 **is the opposite of 4**.

The phrase "the opposite of" is written in symbols as "−." For example,

The opposite of	5	is	−5
↓	↓	↓	↓
−	(5)	=	−5

The opposite of	−3	is	3
↓	↓	↓	↓
−	(−3)	=	3

or

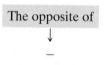

In general, we have the following:

Opposites

If a is a number, then $-(-a) = a$.

Notice that because "the opposite of" is written as "$-$", to find the opposite of a number we place a "$-$" sign in front of the number.

EXAMPLE 5 Find the opposite of each number.

a. 11　　b. -2　　c. 0

Solution:

a. The opposite of 11 is -11.
b. The opposite of -2 is $-(-2)$ or 2.
c. The opposite of 0 is 0.

Helpful Hint
Remember that 0 is neither positive nor negative.

Work Practice Problem 5

✔ **Concept Check** True or false? The number 0 is the only number that is its own opposite.

EXAMPLE 6 Simplify.

a. $-(-4)$　　b. $-|-5|$　　c. $-|6|$

Solution:

a. $-(-4) = 4$　　The opposite of negative 4 is 4.

b. $-|-5| = -5$　　The opposite of the absolute value of -5 is the opposite of 5, or -5.

c. $-|6| = -6$　　The opposite of the absolute value of 6 is the opposite of 6, or -6.

Work Practice Problem 6

EXAMPLE 7 Evaluate $-|-x|$ if $x = -2$.

Solution: Carefully replace x with -2; then simplify.

$$-|-x| = -|-(-2)|$$　　Replace x with -2.

Then $-|-(-2)| = -|2| = -2$.

Work Practice Problem 7

PRACTICE PROBLEM 5

Find the opposite of each number.

a. 7　　　　b. -17

PRACTICE PROBLEM 6

Simplify.

a. $-|-2|$　　　　b. $-|5|$
c. $-(-11)$

PRACTICE PROBLEM 7

Evaluate $-|x|$ if $x = -9$.

Answers
5. a. -7,　b. 17,
6. a. -2,　b. -5,　c. 11,
7. -9

✔ **Concept Check Answer**
True

Objective F Reading Bar Graphs Containing Integers

The bar graph below shows the average temperature (in Fahrenheit) of the known planets. Notice that a negative temperature is illustrated by a bar below the horizontal line representing 0°F, and a positive temperature is illustrated by a bar above the horizontal line representing 0°F.

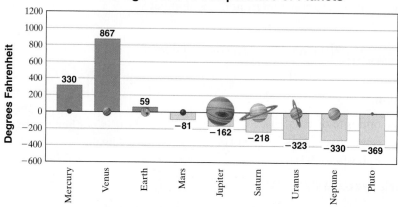

Average Surface Temperature of Planets*

*(For some planets, the temperature given is the temperature where the atmosphere pressure equals 1 Earth atmosphere; *Source: The World Almanac*, 2005)

PRACTICE PROBLEM 8

Which planet has the highest average temperature?

EXAMPLE 8   Which planet has the lowest average temperature?

Solution   The planet with the lowest average temperature is the one that corresponds to the bar that extends the furthest in the negative direction (downward.) Pluto has the lowest average temperature of −369°F.

▦ **Work Practice Problem 8**

Answer

8. Venus; 867°F

2.2 EXERCISE SET

FOR EXTRA HELP

Student Solutions Manual

PH Math/Tutor Center

CD/Video for Review

Math XL
MathXL®

MyMathLab
MyMathLab

Objective Ⓐ *Represent each quantity by an integer. See Example 1.*

1. A worker in a silver mine in Nevada works 1445 feet underground.

2. A scuba diver is swimming 35 feet below the surface of the water in the Gulf of Mexico.

3. The peak of Mount Elbert in Colorado is 14,433 feet above sea level. (*Source:* U.S. Geological Survey)

4. The lowest elevation in the United States is found at Death Valley, California, at an elevation of 282 feet below sea level. (*Source:* U.S. Geological Survey)

5. The record high temperature in Nevada is 118 degrees above zero Fahrenheit. (*Source:* National Climatic Data Center)

6. The Minnesota Viking football team lost 15 yards on a play.

7. The average depth of the Atlantic Ocean is 11,730 feet below the surface of the ocean. (*Source:* 2005 *World Almanac*)

8. The Dow Jones stock market average fell 317 points in one day.

9. Gateway, Inc., manufactures personal computers. In the second quarter of fiscal year 2004, Gateway posted a net loss of $339 million. (*Source:* Gateway, Inc.)

10. For the second quarter of fiscal year 2004, Gateway reported a loss of 91¢ per share.

11. Two divers are exploring the bottom of a trench in the Pacific Ocean. Joe is at 135 feet below the surface of the ocean and Sara is at 157 feet below the surface. Represent each quantity by an integer and determine who is deeper in the water.

12. The temperature on one January day in Chicago was 10° below 0° Celsius. Represent this quantity by an integer and tell whether this temperature is cooler or warmer than 5° below 0° Celsius.

13. In a recent year, the number of music cassette singles shipped to retailers reflected a 45 percent loss from the previous year. Write an integer to represent the percent loss in cassette singles shipped. (*Source:* Recording Industry Association of America)

14. In a recent year, the number of music CDs shipped to retailers reflected a 7 percent loss from the previous year. Write an integer to represent the percent loss in CDs shipped. (*Source:* Recording Industry Association of America)

Objective Ⓑ *Graph each integer in the list on the same number line. See Example 2.*

15. 1, 2, 4, 6

16. 3, 5, 2, 0

17. 1, −1, −2, −4, −7

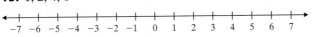

18. 2, −2, −4, 6

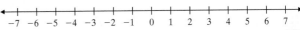

19. 0, 2, 5, 7

20. 0, 3, 6, 10

21. 0, −2, −7, −5

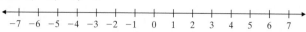

22. 0, −7, 3, −6

Objective **C** *Insert* $<$ *or* $>$ *between each pair of integers to make a true statement. See Example 3.*

23. −4   0

24. −8   0

25. −7   −5

26. −12   −10

27. −30   −35

28. −27   −29

29. −26   26

30. 13   −13

Objective **D** *Simplify. See Example 4.*

31. $|5|$

32. $|7|$

33. $|-8|$

34. $|-19|$

35. $|0|$

36. $|100|$

37. $|-5|$

38. $|-10|$

Objective **E** *Find the opposite of each integer. See Example 5.*

39. 5

40. 8

41. −4

42. −6

43. 23

44. 123

45. −10

46. −23

Objectives **C** **D** **E** **Mixed Practice** *Simplify. See Example 6.*

47. $|-7|$

48. $|-11|$

49. $-|20|$

50. $-|43|$

51. $-|-3|$

52. $-|-18|$

53. $-(-8)$

54. $-(-7)$

55. $|-14|$

56. $-(-14)$

57. $-(-29)$

58. $-|-29|$

Evaluate. See Example 7.

59. $|-x|$ if $x = -8$

60. $-|x|$ if $x = -8$

61. $-|-x|$ if $x = 3$

62. $-|-x|$ if $x = 7$

63. $|x|$ if $x = -23$

64. $|x|$ if $x = 23$

65. $-|x|$ if $x = 4$

66. $|-x|$ if $x = 1$

Insert $<, >,$ *or* $=$ *between each pair of numbers to make a true statement. See Examples 3 through 6.*

67. −3   −5

68. −17   −6

69. $|-9|$ $|-14|$

70. $|-8|$ $|-4|$

71. $|-33|$ $-(-33)$

72. $-|17|$ $-(-17)$

73. $-|-10|$ $-(-10)$

74. $|-24|$ $-(-24)$

75. 0   −9   **76.** −45   0   **77.** |0| |−9| **78.** |−45| |0|

79. −|−2| −|−10| **80.** −|−8| −|−4| **81.** −(−12)   −(−18)   **82.** −22   −(−38)

Objectives **D** **E** **Mixed Practice** *Fill in the chart. See Examples 4 through 7.*

	Number	Absolute Value of Number	Opposite of Number
83.	25		
84.	−13		
85.			−84
86.			2

Objective **F** *The bar graph shows elevation of selected lakes. Use this graph For Exercises 87 through 90* (*Source:* U.S. Geological Survey). *See Example 8.*

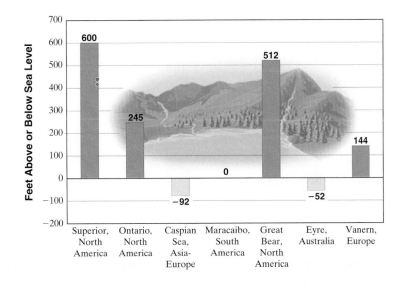

87. Which lake has an elevation at sea level?

88. Which lake shown has the lowest elevation?

89. Which lake shown has the second lowest elevation?

90. Which lake shown has the highest elevation?

Use the bar graph from Example 8 to answer Exercises 91 through 94.

91. Which planet has an average temperature closest to 0°F?

92. Which planet has a negative average temperature closest to 0°F?

93. Which planet has an average temperature closest to −200°F?

94. Which planet has an average temperature closest to −300°F?

Review

Add. See Section 1.3.

95. $0 + 13$

96. $9 + 0$

97. $15 + 20$

98. $20 + 15$

99. $47 + 236 + 77$

100. $362 + 37 + 90$

Concept Extensions

Write the given numbers in order from least to greatest.

101. $2^2, -|3|, -(-5), -|-8|$

102. $|10|, 2^3, -|-5|, -(-4)$

103. $|-1|, -|-6|, -(-6), -|1|$

104. $1^4, -(-3), -|7|, |-20|$

105. $-(-2), 5^2, -10, -|-9|, |-12|$

106. $3^3, -|-11|, -(-10), -4, -|2|$

Choose all numbers for x from each given list that make each statement true.

107. $|x| > 8$
  a. 0   **b.** -5 **c.** 8   **d.** -12

108. $|x| > 4$
  a. 0   **b.** 4   **c.** -1 **d.** -100

109. Evaluate: $-(-|-5|)$

110. Evaluate: $-(-|-(-7)|)$

Answer true or false for Exercises 111 through 115.

111. If $a > b$, then a must be a positive number.

112. The absolute value of a number is *always* a positive number.

113. A positive number is always greater than a negative number.

114. Zero is always less than a positive number.

115. The number $-a$ is always a negative number. (*Hint:* Read "$-$" as "the opposite of.")

116. Given the number line $\xleftarrow{\;\bullet\;\;\;\bullet\;\;|\;\;|\;\;|\;}\rightarrow$, is it true that $b < a$?
$\quad\quad a\;\;b\;-1\;\;0\;\;1$

117. Write in your own words how to find the absolute value of a signed number.

118. Explain how to determine which of two signed numbers is larger.

For Exercises 119 and 120, see the first Concept Check in this section.

119. Is there a largest negative number? If so, what is it?

120. Is there a smallest positive number? If so, what is it?

STUDY SKILLS BUILDER

Organizing a Notebook

It's never too late to get organized. If you need ideas about organizing a notebook for your mathematics course, try some of these:

- Use a spiral or ring binder notebook with pockets and use it for mathematics only.
- Start each page by writing the book's section number you are working on at the top.
- When your instructor is lecturing, take notes. **Always** include any examples your instructor works for you.
- Place your worked-out homework exercises in your notebook immediately after the lecture notes from that section. This way, a section's worth of material is together.
- Homework exercises: Attempt all assigned homework. For odd-numbered exercises, you are not through until you check your answers against the back of the book. Correct any exercises with incorrect answers. You may want to place a "?" by any homework exercises or notes that you need to ask questions about. Also, consider placing a "!" by any notes or exercises you feel are important.

- Place graded quizzes in the pockets of your notebook. If you are using a binder, you can place your quizzes in a special section of your binder.

Let's check your notebook organization by answering the following questions.

1. Do you have a spiral or ring binder notebook for your mathematics course only?
2. Have you ever had to flip through several sheets of notes and work in your mathematics notebook to determine what section's work you are in?
3. Are you now writing the textbook's section number at the top of each notebook page?
4. Have you ever lost or had trouble finding a graded quiz or test?
5. Are you now placing all your graded work in a dedicated place in your notebook?
6. Are you attempting all of your homework and placing all of your work in your notebook?
7. Are you checking and correcting your homework in your notebook? If not, why not?
8. Are you writing in your notebook the examples your instructor works for you in class?

2.3 ADDING INTEGERS

Objective **A** Adding Integers

Adding integers can be visualized using a number line. A positive number can be represented on the number line by an arrow of appropriate length pointing to the right, and a negative number by an arrow of appropriate length pointing to the left.

Both arrows represent 2 or +2. They both point to the right and they are both 2 units long.

Both arrows represent -3. They both point to the left and they are both 3 units long.

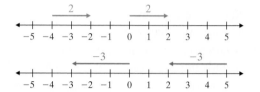

EXAMPLE 1 Add using a number line: $5 + (-2)$

PRACTICE PROBLEM 1

Add using a number line:
$5 + (-1)$

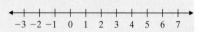

Solution: To add integers on a number line, such as $5 + (-2)$, we start at 0 on the number line and draw an arrow representing 5. From the tip of this arrow, we draw another arrow representing -2. The tip of the second arrow ends at their sum, 3.

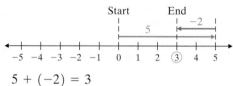

$$5 + (-2) = 3$$

▨ **Work Practice Problem 1**

EXAMPLE 2 Add using a number line: $-1 + (-4)$

Start at 0 and draw an arrow representing -1. From the tip of this arrow, we draw another arrow representing -4. The tip of the second arrow ends at their sum, -5.

PRACTICE PROBLEM 2

Add using a number line:
$-6 + (-2)$

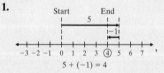

Solution:

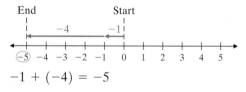

$$-1 + (-4) = -5$$

▨ **Work Practice Problem 2**

PRACTICE PROBLEM 3

Add using a number line:
$-8 + 3$

EXAMPLE 3 Add using a number line: $-7 + 3$

Solution:

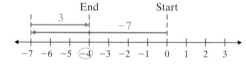

▨ **Work Practice Problem 3**

Answers

1.
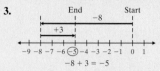
$5 + (-1) = 4$

2.
$-6 + (-2) = -8$

3.
$-8 + 3 = -5$

Using a number line each time we add two numbers can be time consuming. Instead, we can notice patterns in the previous examples and write rules for adding signed numbers.

Rules for adding signed numbers depend on whether we are adding numbers with the same sign or different signs. When adding two numbers with the same sign, as in Example 2, notice that the sign of the sum is the same as the sign of the addends.

Adding Two Numbers with the Same Sign

Step 1 Add their absolute values.

Step 2 Use their common sign as the sign of the sum.

EXAMPLE 4 Add: $-2 + (-21)$

Solution:

Step 1: $|-2| = 2, |-21| = 21$, and $2 + 21 = 23$.

Step 2: Their common sign is negative, so the sum is negative:

$$-2 + (-21) = -23$$

Work Practice Problem 4

EXAMPLES Add.

5. $-5 + (-1) = -6$
6. $2 + 6 = 8$

Work Practice Problems 5–6

When adding two numbers with different signs, as in Examples 1 and 3, the sign of the result may be positive, negative, or the result may be 0.

Adding Two Numbers with Different Signs

Step 1 Find the larger absolute value minus the smaller absolute value.

Step 2 Use the sign of the number with the larger absolute value as the sign of the sum.

EXAMPLE 7 Add: $-2 + 5$

Solution:

Step 1: $|-2| = 2, |5| = 5$, and $5 - 2 = 3$.

Step 2: 5 has the larger absolute value and its sign is an understood +:

$$-2 + 5 = +3 \text{ or } 3$$

Work Practice Problem 7

EXAMPLE 8 Add: $3 + (-7)$

Solution:

Step 1: $|3| = 3, |-7| = 7$, and $7 - 3 = 4$.

Step 2: -7 has the larger absolute value and its sign is $-$:

$$3 + (-7) = -4$$

Work Practice Problem 8

EXAMPLES Add.

9. $-18 + 10 = -8$
10. $12 + (-8) = 4$
11. $0 + (-5) = -5$ The sum of 0 and any number is the number.

Work Practice Problems 9–11

PRACTICE PROBLEM 4
Add: $(-3) + (-9)$

PRACTICE PROBLEMS 5–6
Add.

5. $-12 + (-3)$
6. $9 + 5$

PRACTICE PROBLEM 7
Add: $-3 + 9$

PRACTICE PROBLEM 8
Add: $2 + (-8)$

PRACTICE PROBLEMS 9–11
Add.

9. $-46 + 20$
10. $8 + (-6)$
11. $-2 + 0$

Answers
4. -12,   **5.** -15,   **6.** 14,   **7.** 6,
8. -6,   **9.** -26,   **10.** 2,   **11.** -2

Recall that numbers such as 7 and -7 are called opposites. In general, the sum of a number and its opposite is always 0.

$$7 + (-7) = 0 \qquad -26 + 26 = 0 \qquad 1008 + (-1008) = 0$$

opposites   opposites   opposites

If a is a number, then

$-a$ is its opposite. Also,

$$\left. \begin{array}{l} a + (-a) = 0 \\ -a + a = 0 \end{array} \right\}$$ The sum of a number and its opposite is 0.

PRACTICE PROBLEMS 12–13

Add.
12. $15 + (-15)$
13. $-80 + 80$

EXAMPLES Add.

12. $-21 + 21 = 0$
13. $36 + (-36) = 0$

▣ **Work Practice Problems 12–13**

✔ **Concept Check** What is wrong with the following calculation?

$$6 + (-22) = 16$$

In the following examples, we add three or more integers. Remember that by the associative and commutative properties for addition, we may add numbers in any order that we wish. In Examples 14 and 15, let's add the numbers from left to right.

PRACTICE PROBLEM 14

Add: $8 + (-3) + (-13)$

EXAMPLE 14 Add: $(-3) + 4 + (-11)$

Solution: $(-3) + 4 + (-11) = 1 + (-11)$
$$= -10$$

▣ **Work Practice Problem 14**

PRACTICE PROBLEM 15

Add: $5 + (-3) + 12 + (-14)$

EXAMPLE 15 Add: $1 + (-10) + (-8) + 9$

Solution: $1 + (-10) + (-8) + 9 = -9 + (-8) + 9$
$$= -17 + 9$$
$$= -8$$

The sum will be the same if we add the numbers in any order. To see this, let's add the positive numbers together and then the negative numbers together first.

$$1 + 9 = 10 \qquad \text{Add the positive numbers.}$$
$$(-10) + (-8) = -18 \qquad \text{Add the negative numbers.}$$
$$10 + (-18) = -8 \qquad \text{Add these results.}$$

The sum is -8.

▣ **Work Practice Problem 15**

Helpful Hint

Don't forget that addition is commutative and associative. In other words, numbers may be added in any order.

Answers
12. 0,   **13.** 0,   **14.** -8,   **15.** 0

✔ **Concept Check Answer**
$6 + (-22) = -16$

Objective **B** Evaluating Algebraic Expressions

We can continue our work with algebraic expressions by evaluating expressions given integer replacement values.

EXAMPLE 16 Evaluate $2x + y$ for $x = 3$ and $y = -5$.

Solution: Replace x with 3 and y with -5 in $2x + y$.

$$2x + y = 2 \cdot 3 + (-5)$$
$$= 6 + (-5)$$
$$= 1$$

▢ **Work Practice Problem 16**

EXAMPLE 17 Evaluate $x + y$ for $x = -2$ and $y = -10$.

Solution: $x + y = (-2) + (-10)$ Replace x with -2 and y with -10.
$$= -12$$

▢ **Work Practice Problem 17**

Objective 🄲 Solving Problems by Adding Integers

Next, we practice solving problems that require adding integers.

EXAMPLE 18 **Calculating Temperature**

On January 6, the temperature in Caribou, Maine, at 8 a.m. was $-12°$ Fahrenheit. By 9 a.m., the temperature had risen 4 degrees, and by 10 a.m. it had risen 6 degrees from the 9 a.m. temperature. What was the temperature at 10 a.m.?

Solution:

In words:

temperature at 10 a.m.	=	8 a.m. temperature	+	rise of 4°	+	rise of 6°

↓   ↓   ↓   ↓

Translate:

$$\text{temperature at 10 a.m.} = -12 + (+4) + (+6)$$
$$= -8 + (+6)$$
$$= -2$$

The temperature was $-2°$F at 10 a.m.

▢ **Work Practice Problem 18**

PRACTICE PROBLEM 16

Evaluate $x + 3y$ for $x = -4$ and $y = 1$.

PRACTICE PROBLEM 17

Evaluate $x + y$ for $x = -11$ and $y = -6$.

PRACTICE PROBLEM 18

If the temperature was $-8°$ Fahrenheit at 6 a.m., and it rose 4 degrees by 7 a.m. and then rose another 7 degrees in the hour from 7 a.m. to 8 a.m., what was the temperature at 8 a.m.?

Answers
16. -1,   **17.** -17,   **18.** $3°$F

📟 **CALCULATOR EXPLORATIONS** Entering Negative Numbers

To enter a negative number on a calculator, find the key marked 〔 +/− 〕. (Some calculators have a key marked 〔 CHS 〕 and some calculators have a special key 〔 (−) 〕 for entering a negative sign.) To enter the number -2, for example, press the keys 〔 2 〕 〔 +/− 〕. The display will read 〔 −2 〕.

To find $-32 + (-131)$, press the keys

〔 32 〕 〔 +/− 〕 〔 + 〕 〔 131 〕 〔 +/− 〕 〔 = 〕 or

〔 (−) 〕 〔 32 〕 〔 + 〕 〔 (−) 〕 〔 131 〕 〔 ENTER 〕

The display will read 〔 −163 〕. Thus $-32 + (-131) = -163$.

Use a calculator to perform each indicated operation.

1. $-256 + 97$
2. $811 + (-1058)$
3. $6(15) + (-46)$
4. $-129 + 10(48)$
5. $-108,650 + (-786,205)$
6. $-196,662 + (-129,856)$

Mental Math

Add.

1. $5 + 0$ **2.** $(-2) + 0$ **3.** $0 + (-35)$ **4.** $0 + 3$

5. $-12 + 12$ **6.** $48 + (-48)$ **7.** $28 + (-28)$ **8.** $-9 + 9$

2.3 EXERCISE SET

Objective **A** *Add using a number line. See Examples 1 through 3.*

1. $-1 + (-6)$

2. $9 + (-4)$

3. $-4 + 7$

4. $10 + (-3)$

5. $-13 + 7$

6. $-6 + (-5)$

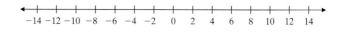

Add. See Examples 4 through 13.

7. $23 + 12$ **8.** $15 + 42$ **9.** $-6 + (-2)$ **10.** $-5 + (-4)$ **11.** $-43 + 43$

12. $-62 + 62$ **13.** $6 + (-2)$ **14.** $8 + (-3)$ **15.** $-6 + 8$ **16.** $-8 + 12$

17. $3 + (-5)$ **18.** $5 + (-9)$ **19.** $-2 + (-7)$ **20.** $-6 + (-1)$ **21.** $-12 + (-12)$

22. $-23 + (-23)$ **23.** $-25 + (-32)$ **24.** $-45 + (-90)$ **25.** $-123 + (-100)$ **26.** $-500 + (-230)$

27. $-7 + 7$ **28.** $-10 + 10$ **29.** $12 + (-5)$ **30.** $24 + (-10)$ **31.** $-6 + 3$

32. $-8 + 2$ **33.** $-12 + 3$ **34.** $-15 + 5$ **35.** $56 + (-26)$ **36.** $89 + (-37)$

37. $-37 + 57$ **38.** $-25 + 65$ **39.** $-42 + 93$ **40.** $-64 + 164$ **41.** $34 + (-67)$

42. $42 + (-83)$ **43.** $124 + (-144)$ **44.** $325 + (-375)$ **45.** $-82 + (-43)$ **46.** $-56 + (-33)$

Add. See Examples 14 and 15.

47. $-4 + 2 + (-5)$ **48.** $-1 + 5 + (-8)$ **49.** $-52 + (-77) + (-117)$

50. $-103 + (-32) + (-27)$ **51.** $12 + (-4) + (-4) + 12$ **52.** $18 + (-9) + 5 + (-2)$

53. $(-10) + 14 + 25 + (-16)$ **54.** $34 + (-12) + (-11) + 213$

Objective **A** **Mixed Practice** *Add. See Examples 1 through 15.*

55. $-8 + (-14) + (-11)$ **56.** $-10 + (-6) + (-1)$ **57.** $-26 + 5$

58. $-35 + (-12)$ **59.** $5 + (-1) + 17$ **60.** $3 + (-23) + 6$

61. $-14 + (-31)$ **62.** $-100 + 70$ **63.** $13 + 14 + (-18)$

64. $(-45) + 22 + 20$ **65.** $-87 + 87$ **66.** $-87 + 0$

67. $-3 + (-8) + 12 + (-1)$ **68.** $-16 + 6 + (-14) + (-20)$

69. $0 + (-103)$ **70.** $94 + (-94)$

Objective **B** *Evaluate $x + y$ for the given replacement values. See Examples 16 and 17.*

71. $x = -2$ and $y = 3$ **72.** $x = -7$ and $y = 11$ **73.** $x = -20$ and $y = -50$

74. $x = -1$ and $y = -29$ **75.** $x = 3$ and $y = -30$ **76.** $x = 13$ and $y = -17$

Objective **C** *Solve. See Example 18.*

77. Find the sum of -8 and 25.

78. Find the sum of -30 and 10.

79. Find the sum of -31, -9, and 30.

80. Find the sum of -49, -2, and 40.

81. Suppose a deep-sea diver dives from the surface to 165 feet below the surface. He then dives down 16 more feet. Use positive and negative numbers to represent this situation. Then find the diver's present depth.

82. Suppose a diver dives from the surface to 248 meters below the surface and then swims up 6 meters, down 17 meters, down another 24 meters, and then up 23 meters. Use positive and negative numbers to represent this situation. Then find the diver's depth after these movements.

In some card games, it is possible to have positive and negative scores. The table shows the scores for two teams playing a series of four card games. Use this table to answer Exercises 83 and 84.

	Game 1	Game 2	Game 3	Game 4
Team 1	−2	−13	20	2
Team 2	5	11	−7	−3

83. Find each team's total score after four games. If the winner is the team with the greater score, find the winning team.

84. Find each team's total score after three games. If the winner is the team with the greater score, which team was winning after three games?

The bar graph below shows the yearly net income for Apple, Inc. Net income is one indication of a company's health. It measures revenue (money taken in) minus cost (money spent). Use this graph for Exercises 85 through 88. (Source: Apple, Inc.)

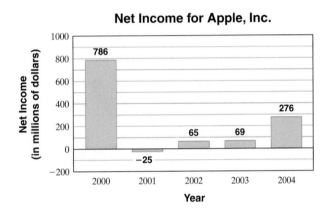

Net Income for Apple, Inc.

85. What was the net income (in dollars) for Apple, Inc. in 2000?

86. What was the net income (in dollars) for Apple, Inc. in 2001?

87. Find the total net income for years 2000 and 2001.

88. Find the total net income for all the years shown.

89. The temperature at 4 p.m. on February 2 was −10° Celsius. By 11 p.m. the temperature had risen 12 degrees. Find the temperature at 11 p.m.

90. Scores in golf can be positive or negative integers. For example, a score of 3 *over* par can be represented by +3 and a score of 5 *under* par can be represented by −5. If Fred Couples had scores of 3 over par, 6 under par, and 7 under par for three games of golf, what was his total score?

A small business company reports the following net incomes. Use this table for Exercises 91 and 92.

Year	Net Income (in Dollars)
2001	$75,083
2002	−$10,412
2003	−$1,786
2004	$96,398

91. Find the sum of the net incomes for 2002 and 2003.

92. Find the net income sum for all four years shown.

93. The all-time record low temperature for Wyoming is −66°F, which was recorded on February 9, 1933. Kansas's all-time record low temperature is 26°F higher than Wyoming's record low. What is Kansas's record low temperature? (*Source:* National Climatic Data Center)

94. The all-time record low temperature for New York is −52°F, which occurred on February 13, 1905. In Mississippi, the lowest temperature ever recorded is 33°F higher than New York's all-time low temperature. What is the all-time record low temperature for Mississippi? (*Source:* National Climatic Data Center)

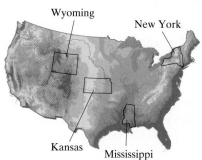

95. The deepest spot in the Pacific Ocean is the Mariana Trench, which has an elevation of 10,924 meters below sea level. The bottom of the Pacific's Aleutian Trench has an elevation 3245 meters higher than that of the Mariana Trench. Use a negative number to represent the depth of the Aleutian Trench. (*Source:* Defense Mapping Agency)

96. The deepest spot in the Atlantic Ocean is the Puerto Rico Trench, which has an elevation of 8605 meters below sea level. The bottom of the Atlantic's Cayman Trench has an elevation 1070 meters above the level of the Puerto Rico Trench. Use a negative number to represent the depth of the Cayman Trench. (*Source:* Defense Mapping Agency)

Review

Subtract. See Section 1.4.

97. $44 - 0$

98. $91 - 0$

99. $200 - 59$

100. $400 - 18$

Concept Extensions

101. Name 2 numbers whose sum is −17.

102. Name 2 numbers whose sum is −30.

Each calculation below is incorrect. Find the error and correct. See the Concept Check in this section.

103. $7 + (-10) \stackrel{?}{=} 17$

104. $-10 + (-12) \stackrel{?}{=} -120$

105. $-4 + 14 \stackrel{?}{=} -18$

106. $-15 + (-17) \stackrel{?}{=} 32$

For Exercises 107 through 110, determine whether each statement is true or false.

107. The sum of two negative numbers is always a negative number.

108. The sum of two positive numbers is always a positive number.

109. The sum of a positive number and a negative number is always a negative number.

110. The sum of zero and a negative number is always a negative number.

111. In your own words, explain how to add two negative numbers.

112. In your own words, explain how to add a positive number and a negative number.

2.4 SUBTRACTING INTEGERS

In Section 2.2, we discussed the opposite of an integer.

The opposite of 3 is -3.
The opposite of -6 is 6.

In this section, we use opposites to subtract integers.

Objective **A** Subtracting Integers

To subtract integers, we will write the subtraction problem as an addition problem. To see how to do this, study the examples below.

$$10 - 4 = 6$$
$$10 + (-4) = 6$$

Since both expressions simplify to 6, this means that

$$10 - 4 = 10 + (-4) = 6$$

Also,

$$3 - 2 = 3 + (-2) = 1$$
$$15 - 1 = 15 + (-1) = 14$$

Thus, to subtract two numbers, we add the first number to the opposite of the second number. (The opposite of a number is also known as its **additive inverse.**)

Subtracting Two Numbers

If a and b are numbers, then $a - b = a + (-b)$.

PRACTICE PROBLEMS 1–4

Subtract.

1. $12 - 7$ **2.** $-6 - 4$
3. $11 - (-14)$ **4.** $-9 - (-1)$

EXAMPLES Subtract.

subtraction	=	first number	+	opposite of the second number		
1. $8 - 5$	=	8	+	(-5)	=	3
2. $-4 - 10$	=	-4	+	(-10)	=	-14
3. $6 - (-5)$	=	6	+	5	=	11
4. $-11 - (-7)$	=	-11	+	7	=	-4

Work Practice Problems 1–4

PRACTICE PROBLEMS 5–7

Subtract.

5. $5 - 9$ **6.** $-12 - 4$
7. $-2 - (-7)$

EXAMPLES Subtract.

5. $-10 - 5 = -10 + (-5) = -15$

6. $8 - 15 = 8 + (-15) = -7$

7. $-4 - (-5) = -4 + 5 = 1$

Work Practice Problems 5–7

Answers
1. 5, **2.** -10, **3.** 25, **4.** -8,
5. -4, **6.** -16, **7.** 5

Helpful Hint

To visualize subtraction, try the following:
The difference between $5°F$ and $-2°F$ can be found by subtracting. That is,

$$5 - (-2) = 5 + 2 = 7$$

Can you visually see from the thermometer on the right that there is actually 7 degrees between $5°F$ and $-2°F$?

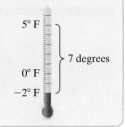

5° F

0° F

−2° F

7 degrees

✔ **Concept Check**   What is wrong with the following calculation?

$$-9 - (-6) = -15$$

EXAMPLE 8   Subtract 7 from −3.

Solution: To subtract 7 *from* −3, we find

$$-3 - 7 = -3 + (-7) = -10$$

⌨ **Work Practice Problem 8**

Objective B Adding and Subtracting Integers

If a problem involves adding or subtracting more than two integers, we rewrite differences as sums and add. Recall that by associative and commutative properties, we may add numbers in any order. In Examples 9 and 10, we will add from left to right.

EXAMPLE 9   Simplify: $7 - 8 - (-5) - 1$

Solution:

$$
\begin{aligned}
7 - 8 - (-5) - 1 &= \underline{7 + (-8)} + 5 + (-1) \\
&= \underline{-1 + 5} + (-1) \\
&= \underline{4 + (-1)} \\
&= 3
\end{aligned}
$$

⌨ **Work Practice Problem 9**

EXAMPLE 10   Simplify: $7 + (-12) - 3 - (-8)$

Solution:

$$
\begin{aligned}
7 + (-12) - 3 - (-8) &= \underline{7 + (-12)} + (-3) + 8 \\
&= \underline{-5 + (-3)} + 8 \\
&= \underline{-8 + 8} \\
&= 0
\end{aligned}
$$

⌨ **Work Practice Problem 10**

Objective C Evaluating Expressions

Now let's practice evaluating expressions when the replacement values are integers.

EXAMPLE 11   Evaluate $x - y$ for $x = -3$ and $y = 9$.

Solution: Replace x with −3 and y with 9 in $x - y$.

$$
\begin{aligned}
x &- y \\
\downarrow \quad &\downarrow \quad \downarrow \\
= (-3) &- \quad 9 \\
= (-3) &+ (-9) \\
&= -12
\end{aligned}
$$

⌨ **Work Practice Problem 11**

PRACTICE PROBLEM 8
Subtract 5 from −10.

PRACTICE PROBLEM 9
Simplify: $-4 - 3 - 7 - (-5)$

PRACTICE PROBLEM 10
Simplify:
$3 + (-5) - 6 - (-4)$

PRACTICE PROBLEM 11
Evaluate $x - y$ for $x = -2$ and $y = 14$.

Answers
8. −15, **9.** −9, **10.** −4, **11.** −16

✔ **Concept Check Answer**
$-9 - (-6) = -3$

PRACTICE PROBLEM 12

Evaluate $y - z$ for $y = -3$ and $z = -4$.

EXAMPLE 12 Evaluate $a - b$ for $a = 8$ and $b = -6$.

Solution: Watch your signs carefully!

$$\begin{array}{ccc} a & - & b \\ \downarrow & \downarrow & \downarrow \\ = 8 & - & (-6) \\ = 8 & + & 6 \\ = 14 & & \end{array}$$

Replace a with 8 and b with -6.

> **Helpful Hint**
> Watch carefully when replacing variables in the expression $a - b$. Make sure that all symbols are inserted and accounted for.

▢ **Work Practice Problem 12**

Objective D Solving Problems by Subtracting Integers

Solving problems often requires subtraction of integers.

PRACTICE PROBLEM 13

The highest point in Asia is the top of Mount Everest, at a height of 29,028 feet above sea level. The lowest point is the Dead Sea, which is 1312 feet below sea level. How much higher is Mount Everest than the Dead Sea? (*Source:* National Geographic Society)

EXAMPLE 13 Finding a Change in Elevation

The highest point in the United States is the top of Mount McKinley, at a height of 20,320 feet above sea level. The lowest point is Death Valley, California, which is 282 feet below sea level. How much higher is Mount McKinley than Death Valley? (*Source:* U.S. Geological Survey)

Solution:

1. UNDERSTAND. Read and reread the problem. To find "how much higher," we subtract. Don't forget that since Death Valley is 282 feet *below* sea level, we represent its height by -282. Draw a diagram to help visualize the problem.

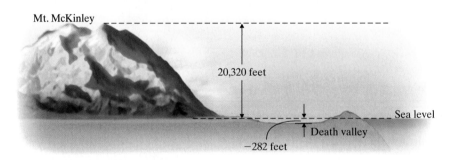

2. TRANSLATE.

In words:	how much higher is Mt. McKinley	=	height of Mt. McKinley	minus	height of Death Valley
	↓	↓	↓	↓	↓
Translate:	how much higher is Mt. McKinley	=	20,320	−	(-282)

3. SOLVE:

$$20{,}320 - (-282) = 20{,}320 + 282 = 20{,}602$$

4. INTERPRET. Check and state your conclusion: Mount McKinley is 20,602 feet higher than Death Valley.

▢ **Work Practice Problem 13**

Answers

12. 1, **13.** 30,340 ft

Mental Math

Subtract.

1. $5 - 5$ **2.** $7 - 7$ **3.** $8642 - 8642$ **4.** $9012 - 9012$

2.4 EXERCISE SET

Objective A *Subtract. See Examples 1 through 8.*

1. $-5 - (-5)$ **2.** $-6 - (-6)$ **3.** $8 - 3$ **4.** $5 - 2$ **5.** $3 - 8$

6. $2 - 5$ **7.** $7 - (-7)$ **8.** $12 - (-12)$ **9.** $-5 - (-8)$ **10.** $-25 - (-25)$

11. $-14 - 4$ **12.** $-2 - 42$ **13.** $2 - 16$ **14.** $8 - 9$ **15.** $22 - 55$

16. $17 - 63$ **17.** $362 - (-40)$ **18.** $844 - (-20)$ **19.** $-4 - 10$ **20.** $-5 - 8$

21. $-7 - (-3)$ **22.** $-12 - (-5)$ **23.** $16 - 23$ **24.** $16 - 45$

Solve. See Example 8.

25. Subtract 18 from -20. **26.** Subtract 10 from -22. **27.** Find the difference of -20 and -3.

28. Find the difference of -8 and -13. **29.** Subtract -11 from 2. **30.** Subtract -50 from -50.

Mixed Practice *(Sections 2.3, 2.4)* *Add or subtract as indicated.*

31. $-21 + (-17)$ **32.** $-35 + (-11)$ **33.** $9 - 20$ **34.** $7 - 30$

35. $-49 - 78$ **36.** $-105 - 68$ **37.** $48 - 59$ **38.** $86 - 98$

Objective **B** *Simplify. See Examples 9 and 10.*

39. $7 - 3 - 2$

40. $8 - 4 - 1$

41. $12 - 5 - 7$

42. $30 - 7 - 12$

43. $-5 - 8 - (-12)$

44. $-10 - 6 - (-9)$

45. $-10 + (-5) - 12$

46. $-15 + (-8) - 4$

47. $12 - (-34) + (-6)$

48. $23 - (-17) + (-9)$

49. $-(-6) - 12 + (-16)$

50. $-(-9) - 7 + (-23)$

51. $-9 - (-12) + (-7) - 4$

52. $-6 - (-8) + (-12) - 7$

53. $-3 + 4 - (-23) - 10$

54. $5 + (-18) - (-21) - 2$

Objective **C** *Evaluate $x - y$ for the given replacement values. See Examples 11 and 12.*

55. $x = -3$ and $y = 5$

56. $x = -7$ and $y = 1$

57. $x = 6$ and $y = -30$

58. $x = 9$ and $y = -2$

59. $x = -4$ and $y = -4$

60. $x = -8$ and $y = -10$

61. $x = 1$ and $y = -18$

62. $x = 14$ and $y = -12$

Objective **D** *Solve. See Example 13.*

The bar graph from Section 2.2 showing the average temperature in Fahrenheit of known planets is reprinted below. Notice that a negative temperature is illustrated by a bar below the horizontal line representing 0°F, and a positive temperature is illustrated by a bar above the horizontal line representing 0°F.

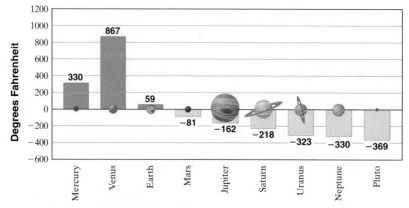

Average Surface Temperature of Planets*

*(For some planets, the temperature given is the temperature where the atmosphere pressure equals 1 Earth atmosphere; Source: The World Almanac, 2005)

63. Find the difference in temperature between Earth and Pluto.

64. Find the difference in temperature between Venus and Mars.

65. Find the difference in temperature between the two plants with the lowest temperature.

66. Find the difference in temperature between Jupiter and Saturn.

67. The coldest temperature ever recorded on Earth was −129°F in Antarctica. The warmest temperature ever recorded was 136°F in the Sahara Desert. How many degrees warmer is 136°F than −129°F? (*Source: Questions Kids Ask,* Grolier Limited, 1991, and *The World Almanac,* 2005)

68. The coldest temperature ever recorded in the United States was −80°F in Alaska. The warmest temperature ever recorded was 134°F in California. How many degrees warmer is 134°F than −80°F? (*Source: The World Almanac,* 2005)

Solve.

69. Aaron Aiken has $125 in his checking account. He writes a check for $117, makes a deposit of $45, and then writes another check for $69. Find the balance in his account. (Write the amount as an integer.)

70. In the card game canasta, it is possible to have a negative score. If Juan Santanilla's score is 15, what is his new score if he loses 20 points?

71. The temperature on a February morning is −6° Celsius at 6 a.m. If the temperature drops 3 degrees by 7 a.m., rises 4 degrees between 7 a.m. and 8 a.m., and then drops 7 degrees between 8 a.m. and 9 a.m., find the temperature at 9 a.m.

72. Mauna Kea in Hawaii has an elevation of 13,796 feet above sea level. The Mid-America Trench in the Pacific Ocean has an elevation of 21,857 feet below sea level. Find the difference in elevation between those two points. (*Source:* National Geographic Society and Defense Mapping Agency)

Some places on Earth lie below sea level, which is the average level of the surface of the oceans. Use this diagram to answer Exercises 73 through 76. (Source: Fantastic Book of Comparisons, Russell Ash, 1999)

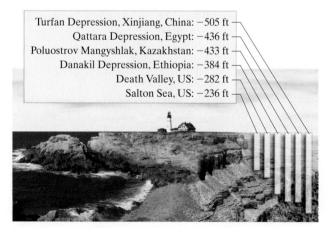

Turfan Depression, Xinjiang, China: −505 ft
Qattara Depression, Egypt: −436 ft
Poluostrov Mangyshlak, Kazakhstan: −433 ft
Danakil Depression, Ethiopia: −384 ft
Death Valley, US: −282 ft
Salton Sea, US: −236 ft

73. Find the difference in elevation between Death Valley and Quattâra Depression.

74. Find the difference in elevation between Danakil and Turfan Depressions.

75. Find the difference in elevation between the two lowest elevations shown.

76. Find the difference in elevation between the highest elevation shown and the lowest elevation shown.

The bar graph shows heights of selected lakes. For Exercises 77 through 80, find the difference in elevation for the lakes listed. (*Source:* U.S. Geological Survey)

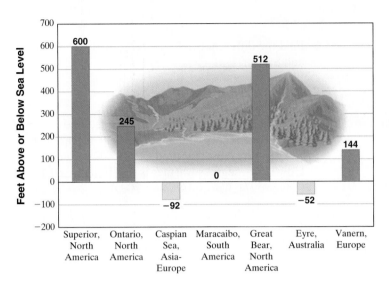

77. Lake Superior and Lake Eyre

78. Great Bear Lake and Caspian Sea

79. Lake Maracaibo and Lake Vanern

80. Lake Eyre and Caspian Sea

Solve.

81. The difference between a country's exports and imports is called the country's *trade balance.* In 2003, the United States had $725 billion in exports and $1257 billion in imports. What was the U.S. trade balance in 2003? (*Source:* U.S. Department of Commerce)

82. In 2003, the United States exported 375 million barrels of petroleum products and imported 4476 million barrels of petroleum products. What was the U.S. trade balance for petroleum products in 2003? (*Source:* U.S. Energy Information Administration)

Review

Multiply. See Section 1.6.

83. $8 \cdot 0$

84. $0 \cdot 8$

85. $1 \cdot 8$

86. $8 \cdot 1$

87. $\begin{array}{r} 23 \\ \times\, 46 \\ \hline \end{array}$

88. $\begin{array}{r} 51 \\ \times\, 89 \\ \hline \end{array}$

Concept Extensions

89. Name two numbers whose difference is -3.

90. Name two numbers whose difference is -10.

Each calculation below is incorrect. Find the error and correct. See the Concept Check in this section.

91. $9 - (-7) \stackrel{?}{=} 2$

92. $-4 - 8 \stackrel{?}{=} 4$

93. $10 - 30 \stackrel{?}{=} 20$

94. $-3 - (-10) \stackrel{?}{=} -13$

Simplify. (Hint: Find the absolute values first.)

95. $|-3| - |-7|$

96. $|-12| - |-5|$

97. $|-6| - |6|$

98. $|-9| - |9|$

99. $|-17| - |-29|$

100. $|-23| - |-42|$

For Exercises 101 and 102, determine whether each statement is true or false.

101. $|-8 - 3| = 8 - 3$

102. $|-2 - (-6)| = |-2| - |-6|$

103. In your own words, explain how to subtract one signed number from another.

104. A student explains to you that the first step to simplify $8 + 12 \cdot 5 - 100$ is to add 8 and 12. Is the student correct? Explain why or why not.

INTEGRATED REVIEW
Sections 2.1–2.4

Integers

1. _____

2. _____

3. _____

4. see number line

5. _____

6. _____

7. _____

8. _____

9. _____

10. _____

11. _____

12. _____

13. _____

14. _____

15. _____

16. _____

17. _____

18. _____

19. _____

Represent each quantity by an integer.

1. The peak of Mount Everest in Asia is 29,028 feet above sea level. (*Source:* U.S. Geological Survey)

2. The Marianas Trench in the Pacific Ocean is 35,840 feet below sea level. (*Source:* The World Almanac)

3. The deepest hole ever drilled in the Earth's crust is in Russia and its depth is over 7 miles below sea level. (*Source: Fantastic Book of Comparisons*)

4. Graph the signed numbers on the given number line. $-4, 0, -1, 3$

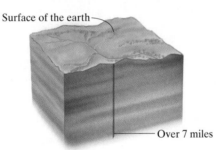

Surface of the earth

Over 7 miles

Insert < or > between each pair of numbers to make a true statement.

5. $0 \quad -3$ **6.** $-15 \quad -5$ **7.** $-1 \quad 1$ **8.** $-2 \quad -7$

Simplify.

9. $|-1|$ **10.** $-|-4|$ **11.** $|-8|$ **12.** $-(-5)$

Find the opposite of each number.

13. 6 **14.** -3 **15.** 89 **16.** 0

Add or subtract as indicated.

17. $-7 + 12$ **18.** $-9 + (-11)$ **19.** $25 + (-35)$

20. $1 - 3$

21. $26 - (-26)$

22. $-2 - 1$

23. $-18 - (-102)$

24. $-8 + (-6) + 20$

25. $-11 - 7 - (-19)$

26. $-4 + (-8) - 16 - (-9)$

27. Subtract 14 from 26.

28. Subtract -8 from -12.

29. Find the sum of -17 and -27.

Choose all numbers for x from each given list that make each statement true.

30. $|x| > 0$
   a. 0   **b.** 18   **c.** -3 **d.** -21

31. $|x| > -5$
   a. 0   **b.** 3   **c.** -1 **d.** -1000

Evaluate the expressions below for x = -1 and y = 11.

32. $x + y$

33. $x - y$

34. $y - x$

35. $y + x$

36. $5y - x$

37. $x - 3y$

20. _____

21. _____

22. _____

23. _____

24. _____

25. _____

26. _____

27. _____

28. _____

29. _____

30. _____

31. _____

32. _____

33. _____

34. _____

35. _____

36. _____

37. _____

2.5 MULTIPLYING AND DIVIDING INTEGERS

Multiplying and dividing integers is similar to multiplying and dividing whole numbers. One difference is that we need to determine whether the result is a positive number or a negative number.

Objective **A** Multiplying Integers

Consider the following pattern of products.

First factor decreases by 1 each time.

$$3 \cdot 2 = 6$$
$$2 \cdot 2 = 4$$
$$1 \cdot 2 = 2$$
$$0 \cdot 2 = 0$$

Product decreases by 2 each time.

This pattern can be continued, as follows.

$$-1 \cdot 2 = -2$$
$$-2 \cdot 2 = -4$$
$$-3 \cdot 2 = -6$$

This suggests that the product of a negative number and a positive number is a negative number.

What is the sign of the product of two negative numbers? To find out, we form another pattern of products. Again, we decrease the first factor by 1 each time, but this time the second factor is negative.

$$2 \cdot (-3) = -6$$
$$1 \cdot (-3) = -3$$
$$0 \cdot (-3) = 0$$

Product increases by 3 each time.

This pattern continues as:

$$-1 \cdot (-3) = 3$$
$$-2 \cdot (-3) = 6$$
$$-3 \cdot (-3) = 9$$

This suggests that the product of two negative numbers is a positive number. Thus we can determine the sign of a product when we know the signs of the factors.

Multiplying Numbers

The product of two numbers having the same sign is a positive number.

Product of Like Signs

$$(+)(+) = +$$
$$(-)(-) = +$$

The product of two numbers having different signs is a negative number.

Product of Different Signs

$$(-)(+) = -$$
$$(+)(-) = -$$

EXAMPLES Multiply.

1. $-7 \cdot 3 = -21$
2. $-2(-5) = 10$
3. $0 \cdot (-4) = 0$
4. $10(-8) = -80$

▣ **Work Practice Problems 1-4**

PRACTICE PROBLEMS 1-4

Multiply.

1. $-2 \cdot 6$ 2. $-4(-3)$
3. $0 \cdot (-10)$ 4. $5(-15)$

Recall that by the associative and commutative properties for multiplication, we may multiply numbers in any order that we wish. In Example 5, we multiply from left to right.

EXAMPLES Multiply.

5. $\overbrace{7(-6)}(-2) = -42(-2)$
$\qquad\qquad = 84$

6. $\overbrace{(-2)(-3)}(-4) = 6(-4)$
$\qquad\qquad\quad = -24$

7. $(-1)(-2)(-3)(-4) = -1(-24)$ We have -24 from Example 6.
$\qquad\qquad\qquad\qquad = 24$

▣ **Work Practice Problems 5-7**

PRACTICE PROBLEMS 5-7

Multiply.

5. $7(-2)(-4)$
6. $(-5)(-6)(-1)$
7. $(-2)(-5)(-6)(-1)$

✔ **Concept Check** What is the sign of the product of five negative numbers? Explain.

Recall from our study of exponents that $2^3 = 2 \cdot 2 \cdot 2 = 8$. We can now work with bases that are negative numbers. For example,

$(-2)^3 = (-2)(-2)(-2) = -8$

EXAMPLE 8 Evaluate: $(-5)^2$

Solution: Remember that $(-5)^2$ means 2 factors of -5.

$(-5)^2 = (-5)(-5) = 25$

▣ **Work Practice Problem 8**

PRACTICE PROBLEM 8

Evaluate $(-3)^4$.

Helpful Hint

Have you noticed a pattern when multiplying signed numbers?
If we let $(-)$ represent a negative number and $(+)$ represent a positive number, then

The product of an even number of negative numbers is a positive result.

$(-)(-) = (+)$
$(-)(-)(-) = (-)$ ← The product of an odd number of negative numbers is a negative result.
$(-)(-)(-)(-) = (+)$
$(-)(-)(-)(-)(-) = (-)$

Notice in Example 8 the parentheses around -5 in $(-5)^2$. With these parentheses, -5 is the base that is squared. Without parentheses, such as -5^2, only the 5 is squared. In other words, $-5^2 = -(5 \cdot 5) = -25$.

Answers

1. -12, 2. 12, 3. 0, 4. -75,
5. 56, 6. -30, 7. 60, 8. 81

✔ **Concept Check Answer**
Negative

PRACTICE PROBLEM 9

Evaluate: -9^2

EXAMPLE 9 Evaluate: -7^2

Solution: Remember that without parentheses, only the 7 is squared.

$$-7^2 = -(7 \cdot 7) = -49$$

💻 **Work Practice Problem 9**

Helpful Hint

Make sure you understand the difference between Examples 8 and 9.

⟶ parentheses, so -5 is squared

$$(-5)^2 = (-5)(-5) = 25$$

⟶ no parentheses, so only the 7 is squared

$$-7^2 = -(7 \cdot 7) = -49$$

Objective B Dividing Integers

Division of integers is related to multiplication of integers. The sign rules for division can be discovered by writing a related multiplication problem. For example,

$$\frac{6}{2} = 3 \qquad \text{because } 3 \cdot 2 = 6$$

$$\frac{-6}{2} = -3 \qquad \text{because } -3 \cdot 2 = -6$$

$$\frac{6}{-2} = -3 \qquad \text{because } -3 \cdot (-2) = 6$$

$$\frac{-6}{-2} = 3 \qquad \text{because } 3 \cdot (-2) = -6$$

Helpful Hint

Just as for whole numbers, division can be checked by multiplication.

Dividing Numbers

The quotient of two numbers having the same sign is a positive number.

The quotient of two numbers having different signs is a negative number.

Quotient of Like Signs

$$\frac{(+)}{(+)} = + \qquad \frac{(-)}{(-)} = +$$

Quotient of Different Signs

$$\frac{(+)}{(-)} = - \qquad \frac{(-)}{(+)} = -$$

PRACTICE PROBLEMS 10–12

Divide.

10. $\dfrac{28}{-7}$ **11.** $-18 \div (-2)$

12. $\dfrac{-60}{10}$

EXAMPLES Divide.

10. $\dfrac{-12}{6} = -2$

11. $-20 \div (-4) = 5$

12. $\dfrac{48}{-3} = -16$

💻 **Work Practice Problems 10–12**

Answers

9. -81,   **10.** -4,   **11.** 9,   **12.** -6

✔ Concept Check Answer

$$\frac{-27}{-9} = 3$$

✔ **Concept Check** What is wrong with the following calculation.

$$\frac{-27}{-9} \times = -3$$

EXAMPLES Divide, if possible.

13. $\dfrac{0}{-5} = 0$ because $0 \cdot -5 = 0$

14. $\dfrac{-7}{0}$ is undefined because there is no number that gives a product of -7 when multiplied by 0.

◻ **Work Practice Problems 13–14**

PRACTICE PROBLEMS 13–14

Divide, if possible.

13. $\dfrac{-1}{0}$ **14.** $\dfrac{0}{-2}$

Objective **C** Evaluating Expressions

Next, we practice evaluating expressions given integer replacement values.

EXAMPLE 15 Evaluate xy for $x = -2$ and $y = 7$.

Solution: Recall that xy means $x \cdot y$.
Replace x with -2 and y with 7 in xy.

$-2 \cdot 7$

$$xy = -2 \cdot 7$$
$$= -14$$

◻ **Work Practice Problem 15**

PRACTICE PROBLEM 15

Evaluate xy for $x = 5$ and $y = -9$.

EXAMPLE 16 Evaluate $\dfrac{x}{y}$ for $x = -24$ and $y = 6$.

Solution: $\dfrac{x}{y} = \dfrac{-24}{6}$ Replace x with -24 and y with 6.
$$= -4$$

◻ **Work Practice Problem 16**

PRACTICE PROBLEM 16

Evaluate $\dfrac{x}{y}$ for $x = -9$ and $y = -3$.

Objective **D** Solving Problems by Multiplying and Dividing Integers

Many real-life problems involve multiplication and division of signed numbers.

EXAMPLE 17 Calculating Total Golf Score

A professional golfer finished seven strokes under par (-7) for each of three days of a tournament. What was his total score for the tournament?

Solution:

1. UNDERSTAND. Read and reread the problem. Although the key word is "total," since this is repeated addition of the same number we multiply.

2. TRANSLATE.

In words:	golfer's total score	=	number of days	·	score each day
	↓	↓	↓	↓	↓
Translate:	golfer's total	=	3	·	(-7)

3. SOLVE: $3 \cdot (-7) = -21$

4. INTERPRET. Check and state your conclusion: The golfer's total score is -21, or 21 strokes under par.

◻ **Work Practice Problem 17**

PRACTICE PROBLEM 17

A card player had a score of -12 for each of four games. Find her total score.

Answers

13. undefined, **14.** 0, **15.** -45,
16. 3, **17.** -48

2.5 EXERCISE SET

Objective A *Multiply. See Examples 1 through 4.*

1. $-2(-3)$ **2.** $5(-3)$ **3.** $-4(9)$ **4.** $-7(-2)$

5. $8(-8)$ **6.** $-9(9)$ **7.** $0(-14)$ **8.** $-6(0)$

Multiply. See Examples 5 through 7.

9. $6(-4)(2)$ **10.** $-2(3)(-7)$ **11.** $-1(-2)(-4)$ **12.** $8(-3)(3)$

13. $-4(4)(-5)$ **14.** $-2(-5)(-4)$ **15.** $10(-5)(0)$ **16.** $2(-1)(3)(-2)$

17. $-5(3)(-1)(-1)$ **18.** $3(0)(-4)(-8)$

Evaluate. See Examples 8 and 9.

19. -2^2 **20.** -2^4 **21.** $(-3)^3$ **22.** $(-1)^4$

23. -5^2 **24.** -4^3 **25.** $(-2)^3$ **26.** $(-3)^2$

Objective B *Find each quotient. See Examples 10 through 14.*

27. $-24 \div 6$ **28.** $90 \div (-9)$ **29.** $\dfrac{-30}{6}$ **30.** $\dfrac{56}{-8}$

31. $\dfrac{-88}{-11}$ **32.** $\dfrac{-32}{4}$ **33.** $\dfrac{0}{14}$ **34.** $\dfrac{-13}{0}$

35. $\dfrac{2}{0}$ **36.** $\dfrac{0}{-5}$ **37.** $\dfrac{39}{-3}$ **38.** $\dfrac{-24}{-12}$

Objectives A B Mixed Practice *Multiply or divide as indicated.*

39. $-12(0)$ **40.** $0(-100)$ **41.** $-4(3)$ **42.** $-6 \cdot 2$ **43.** $-9 \cdot 6$

44. $-12(13)$ **45.** $-7(-6)$ **46.** $-9(-5)$ **47.** $-3(-4)(-2)$ **48.** $-7(-5)(-3)$

49. $(-4)^2$ **50.** $(-5)^2$ **51.** $-\dfrac{10}{5}$ **52.** $-\dfrac{25}{5}$ **53.** $-\dfrac{56}{8}$

54. $-\dfrac{49}{7}$ **55.** $-12 \div 3$ **56.** $-15 \div 3$ **57.** $4(-4)(-3)$ **58.** $6(-5)(-2)$

152

59. $-30(6)(-2)(-3)$ **60.** $-20 \cdot 5 \cdot (-5) \cdot (-3)$ **61.** $3 \cdot (-2) \cdot 0$ **62.** $-5(4)(0)$

63. $\dfrac{100}{-20}$ **64.** $\dfrac{45}{-9}$ **65.** $240 \div (-40)$ **66.** $480 \div (-8)$

67. $\dfrac{-12}{-4}$ **68.** $\dfrac{-36}{-3}$ **69.** -1^4 **70.** -2^3

71. $(-3)^5$ **72.** $(-9)^2$ **73.** $-2(3)(5)(-6)$ **74.** $-1(2)(7)(-3)$

75. $(-1)^{32}$ **76.** $(-1)^{33}$ **77.** $-2(-2)(-5)$ **78.** $-2(-2)(-3)(-2)$

79. $-42 \cdot 23$ **80.** $-56 \cdot 43$ **81.** $25 \cdot (-82)$ **82.** $70 \cdot (-23)$

Objective **C** *Evaluate ab for the given replacement values. See Example 15.*

83. $a = -4$ and $b = 7$ **84.** $a = 5$ and $b = -1$ **85.** $a = 3$ and $b = -2$

86. $a = -9$ and $b = -6$ **87.** $a = -5$ and $b = -5$ **88.** $a = -8$ and $b = 8$

Evaluate $\dfrac{x}{y}$ for the given replacement values. See Example 16.

89. $x = 5$ and $y = -5$ **90.** $x = 9$ and $y = -3$ **91.** $x = -12$ and $y = 0$

92. $x = -10$ and $y = -10$ **93.** $x = -36$ and $y = -6$ **94.** $x = 0$ and $y = -5$

Evaluate xy and also $\dfrac{x}{y}$ for the given replacement values.

95. $x = -4$ and $y = -2$ **96.** $x = 20$ and $y = -5$ **97.** $x = 0$ and $y = -6$ **98.** $x = -3$ and $y = 0$

Objective **D** *Solve. See Example 17.*

99. Find the quotient of -27 and 9.   **100.** Find the quotient of -63 and -3.

101. Find the product of -51 and -6.   **102.** Find the product of -49 and 5.

103. A football team lost four yards on each of three consecutive plays. Represent the total loss as a product of signed numbers and find the total loss.

104. Joe Norstrom lost $400 on each of seven consecutive days in the stock market. Represent his total loss as a product of signed numbers and find his total loss.

105. A deep-sea diver must move up or down in the water in short steps in order to keep from getting a physical condition called the "bends." Suppose a diver moves down from the surface in five steps of 20 feet each. Represent his total movement as a product of signed numbers and find the product.

106. A weather forecaster predicts that the temperature will drop five degrees each hour for the next six hours. Represent this drop as a product of signed numbers and find the total drop in temperature.

107. During the third quarter of 2004, Delta Airlines posted a net income of −$646 million. If this continued, what would Delta's net income have been after four quarters? (*Source:* Delta Airlines)

108. During the third quarter of 2004, AMR Corporation, the parent company of American Airlines, Inc., posted a net income of −$214 million. If this continued, what would AMR's net income have been after four quarters? (*Source:* AMR Corporation)

109. In 1987, there were only 27 California Condors in the entire world. Thanks to conservation efforts, in 2004 there were 221 California Condors. (*Source:* California Department of Fish and Game)

   a. Find the change in the number of California Condors from 1987 to 2004.
   b. Find the average change per year in the California Condor population over the period in part a. Round to the nearest whole.

110. In 2000, a total of 76 million music cassettes were shipped to retailers in the United States. In 2004, this number had dropped to approximately 16 music cassettes. (*Source:* Recording Industry Association of America)

   a. Find the change in the number of music cassettes shipped to retailers from 2000 to 2004.
   b. Find the average change per year in the number of music cassettes shipped to retailers over this period.

The graph shows melting points in degrees Celsius of selected elements. Use this graph to answer Exercises 111 through 114.

111. The melting point of nitrogen is 3 times the melting point of radon. Find the melting point of nitrogen.

112. The melting point of rubidium is −1 times the melting point of mercury. Find the melting point of rubidium.

113. The melting point of argon is −3 times the melting point of potassium. Find the melting point of argon.

114. The melting point of strontium is −11 times the melting point of radon. Find the melting point of strontium.

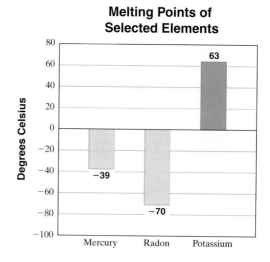

Melting Points of Selected Elements

Review

Perform each indicated operation. See Section 1.9.

115. $(3 \cdot 5)^2$

116. $(12 - 3) \cdot (18 - 10)$

117. $90 + 12^2 - 5^3$

118. $3 \cdot (7 - 4) + 2 \cdot 5^2$

119. $12 \div 4 - 2 + 7$

120. $12 \div (4 - 2) + 7$

Concept Extensions

Mixed Practice (*Sections 2.3, 2.4, 2.5*) *Perform indicated operations.*

121. $-87 \div 3$

122. $-9(-10)$

123. $-9 - 10$

124. $-4 + (-3) + 21$

125. $-4 - 15 - (-11)$

126. $-16 - (-2)$

In Exercises 127 through 130, determine whether each statement is true or false.

127. The product of two negative numbers is always a negative number.

128. The product of a positive number and a negative number is always a negative number.

129. The quotient of two negative numbers is always a positive number.

130. The quotient of zero and a negative number is always zero.

Solve. For Exercises 131 and 132, see the first Concept Check in this section.

131. What is the sign of the product of seven negative numbers?

132. What is the sign of the product of ten negative numbers?

Without actually finding the product, write the list of numbers in Exercises 133 and 134 in order from least to greatest. For help, see a helpful hint box in this section.

133. $(-2)^{12}, (-2)^{17}, (-5)^{12}, (-5)^{17}$

134. $(-1)^{50}, (-1)^{55}, 0^{15}, (-7)^{20}, (-7)^{23}$

135. In your own words, explain how to divide two integers.

136. In your own words, explain how to multiply two integers.

THE BIGGER PICTURE   Operations on Sets of Numbers

Continue your outline from Sections 1.7 and 1.9. Suggestions are once again written to help you complete this part of your outline. Notice that this part of the outline has to do with operations on integers.

I. **Operations on Sets of Numbers**

    A. **Whole Numbers**

        1. **Add or Subtract** (Sections 1.3, 1.4)

        2. **Multiply or Divide** (Sections 1.6, 1.7)

        3. **Exponent** (Section 1.9)

        4. **Square Root** (Section 1.9)

        5. **Order of Operations** (Section 1.9)

    B. **Integers**

        1. **Add:**

$$-5 + (-2) = -7$$ Adding like signs. Add absolute value. Attach the common sign.

$$-5 + 2 = -3$$ Adding unlike signs. Subtract absolute values. Attach the sign of the number with the larger absolute value.

        2. **Subtract:** Add the first number to the opposite of the second number.

$$7 - 10 = 7 + (-10) = -3$$

        3. **Multiply or Divide:** Multiply or divide as usual. If the signs of the two numbers are the same, the answer is positive. If the signs of the two numbers are different, the answer is negative.

$$-5 \cdot 5 = -25, \quad \frac{-32}{-8} = 4$$

Perform the indicated operations.

1. $-9 + 14$

2. $-5(-11)$

3. $5 - 11$

4. $58 - |-70|$

5. $18 + (-30)$

6. $(-9)^2$

7. -9^2

8. $-10 + (-24)$

9. $1 - (-9)$

10. $-15 - 15$

11. $-3(2)(-5)$

12. $\dfrac{|-88|}{-|-8|}$

13. $2 + 4(7 - 9)^3$

14. $-100 - (-20)$

15. $1 + 2(7)$

16. $30 \div 2 \cdot 3$

2.6 ORDER OF OPERATIONS

Objective **A** Simplifying Expressions

Objectives

A Simplify Expressions by Using the Order of Operations.

B Evaluate an Algebraic Expression.

We first discussed the order of operations in Chapter 1. In this section, you are given an opportunity to practice using the order of operations when expressions contain signed numbers. The rules for the order of operations from Section 1.9 are repeated here.

Order of Operations

1. Perform all operations within parentheses ( ), brackets [ ], or other grouping symbols such as square roots or fraction bars.

2. Evaluate any expressions with exponents.

3. Multiply or divide in order from left to right.

4. Add or subtract in order from left to right.

EXAMPLE 1 Simplify: $\dfrac{-6(2)}{-3}$

Solution: First we multiply -6 and 2. Then we divide.

$$\frac{-6(2)}{-3} = \frac{-12}{-3}$$
$$= 4$$

■ Work Practice Problem 1

EXAMPLE 2 Simplify: $\dfrac{12 - 16}{-1 + 3}$

Solution: We simplify above and below the fraction bar separately. Then we divide.

$$\frac{12 - 16}{-1 + 3} = \frac{-4}{2}$$
$$= -2$$

■ Work Practice Problem 2

EXAMPLE 3 Simplify: $60 + 30 + (-2)^3$

Solution: $60 + 30 + (-2)^3 = 60 + 30 + (-8)$ Write $(-2)^3$ as -8.
$$= 90 + (-8) \qquad \text{Add from left to right.}$$
$$= 82$$

■ Work Practice Problem 3

EXAMPLE 4 Simplify: $-4^2 + (-3)^2 - 1^3$

Solution:

$$-4^2 + (-3)^2 - 1^3 = -16 + 9 - 1 \qquad \text{Simplify expressions with exponents.}$$
$$= -7 - 1 \qquad \text{Add or subtract from left to right.}$$
$$= -8$$

■ Work Practice Problem 4

PRACTICE PROBLEM 1

Simplify: $\dfrac{25}{5(-1)}$

PRACTICE PROBLEM 2

Simplify: $\dfrac{-18 + 6}{-3 - 1}$

PRACTICE PROBLEM 3

Simplify: $20 + 50 + (-4)^3$

PRACTICE PROBLEM 4

Simplify: $-2^3 + (-4)^2 + 1^5$

Answers
1. -5,   **2.** 3,   **3.** 6,   **4.** 9

PRACTICE PROBLEM 5

Simplify:

$2(2 - 8) + (-12) - \sqrt{9}$

EXAMPLE 5 Simplify: $3(4 - 7) + (-2) - \sqrt{25}$

Solution:

$$
\begin{aligned}
3(4 - 7) + (-2) - \sqrt{25} &= 3(-3) + (-2) - 5 & \text{Simplify inside parentheses and} \\
& & \text{replace } \sqrt{25} \text{ with 5.} \\
&= -9 + (-2) - 5 & \text{Multiply.} \\
&= -11 - 5 & \text{Add or subtract from left to right.} \\
&= -16
\end{aligned}
$$

🖥 **Work Practice Problem 5**

PRACTICE PROBLEM 6

Simplify:

$(-5) \cdot |-4| + (-3) + 2^3$

EXAMPLE 6 Simplify: $(-3) \cdot |-5| - (-2) + 4^2$

Solution:

$$
\begin{aligned}
(-3) \cdot |-5| - (-2) + 4^2 &= (-3) \cdot 5 - (-2) + 4^2 & \text{Write } |-5| \text{ as 5.} \\
&= (-3) \cdot 5 - (-2) + 16 & \text{Write } 4^2 \text{ as 16.} \\
&= -15 - (-2) + 16 & \text{Multiply.} \\
&= -13 + 16 & \text{Add or subtract from left to right.} \\
&= 3
\end{aligned}
$$

🖥 **Work Practice Problem 6**

PRACTICE PROBLEM 7

Simplify:

$-4[-2 + 5(-3 + 5)] - 7$

EXAMPLE 7 Simplify: $-2[-3 + 2(-1 + 6)] - 5$

Solution: Here we begin with the innermost set of parentheses.

$$
\begin{aligned}
-2[-3 + 2(-1 + 6)] - 5 &= -2[-3 + 2(5)] - 5 & \text{Write } -1 + 6 \text{ as 5.} \\
&= -2[-3 + 10] - 5 & \text{Multiply.} \\
&= -2(7) - 5 & \text{Add.} \\
&= -14 - 5 & \text{Multiply.} \\
&= -19 & \text{Subtract.}
\end{aligned}
$$

🖥 **Work Practice Problem 7**

✔ **Concept Check** True or false? Explain your answer. The result of

$-4(3 - 7) - 8(9 - 6)$

is positive because there are four negative signs.

Objective **B** Evaluating Expressions

Now we practice evaluating expressions.

PRACTICE PROBLEM 8

Evaluate x^2 and $-x^2$ for $x = -12$.

EXAMPLE 8 Evaluate x^2 and $-x^2$ for $x = -11$.

Solution: $x^2 = (-11)^2 = (-11)(-11) = 121$

$-x^2 = -(-11)^2 = -(-11)(-11) = -121$

🖥 **Work Practice Problem 8**

Answers

5. -27, **6.** -15, **7.** -39,
8. 144; -144

✔ **Concept Check Answer**

false; $-4(3 - 7) - 8(9 - 6) = -8$

EXAMPLE 9 Evaluate $6z^2$ for $z = 2$ and $z = -2$.

Solution: $6z^2 = 6(2)^2 = 6(4) = 24$

$6z^2 = 6(-2)^2 = 6(4) = 24$

▥ **Work Practice Problem 9**

PRACTICE PROBLEM 9

Evaluate $5y^2$ for $y = 3$ and $y = -3$.

EXAMPLE 10 Evaluate $x + 2y - z$ for $x = 3$ and $y = -5$ and $z = -4$.

Solution: Replace x with 3, y with -5, z with -4 and simplify.

$x + 2y - z = 3 + 2(-5) - (-4)$ Let $x = 3$, $y = -5$, and $z = -4$.

$= 3 + (-10) + 4$ Replace $2(-5)$ with its product, -10.

$= -3$ Add.

▥ **Work Practice Problem 10**

PRACTICE PROBLEM 10

Evaluate $x^2 + y$ for $x = -5$ and $y = -2$.

Helpful Hint

Remember to rewrite the subtraction sign as shown in Example 10.

EXAMPLE 11 Evaluate $7 - x^2$ for $x = -4$.

Solution: Replace x with -4 and simplify carefully!

$7 - x^2 = 7 - (-4)^2$

$= 7 - 16$ $(-4)^2 = (-4)(-4) = 16$

$= -9$ Subtract.

▥ **Work Practice Problem 11**

PRACTICE PROBLEM 11

Evaluate $4 - x^2$ for $x = -9$.

Answers

9. 45; 45, **10.** 23, **11.** −77

CALCULATOR EXPLORATIONS Simplifying an Expression Containing a Fraction Bar

Recall that even though most calculators follow the order of operations, parentheses must sometimes be inserted. For example, to simplify $\dfrac{-8 + 6}{-2}$ on a calculator, enter parentheses about the expression above the fraction bar so that it is simplified separately.

To simplify $\dfrac{-8 + 6}{-2}$, press the keys

$\boxed{(}\ \boxed{8}\ \boxed{+/-}\ \boxed{+}\ \boxed{6}\ \boxed{)}\ \boxed{\div}\ \boxed{2}\ \boxed{+/-}\ \boxed{=}$ or

$\boxed{(}\ \boxed{(-)}\ \boxed{8}\ \boxed{+}\ \boxed{6}\ \boxed{)}\ \boxed{\div}\ \boxed{(-)}\ \boxed{2}\ \boxed{ENTER}$

The display will read $\boxed{1}$.

Thus, $\dfrac{-8 + 6}{-2} = 1$.

Use a calculator to simplify.

1. $\dfrac{-120 - 360}{-10}$

2. $\dfrac{4750}{-2 + (-17)}$

3. $\dfrac{-316 + (-458)}{28 + (-25)}$

4. $\dfrac{-234 + 86}{-18 + 16}$

Mental Math

Identify the base and exponent of each expression. Do not simplify.

1. -3^2

2. $(-3)^2$

3. $4 \cdot 2^3$

4. $9 \cdot 5^6$

5. $(-7)^5$

6. -9^4

7. $5^7 \cdot 10$

8. $2^8 \cdot 11$

2.6 EXERCISE SET

FOR EXTRA HELP

Student Solutions Manual • PH Math/Tutor Center • CD/Video for Review • MathXL® • MyMathLab

Objective A *Simplify. See Examples 1 through 7.*

1. $(-4)^3$

2. -2^4

3. -4^3

4. $(-2)^4$

5. $6 \cdot 2^2$

6. $5 \cdot 2^3$

7. $-1(-2) + 1$

8. $3 + (-8) \div 2$

9. $9 - 12 - 4$

10. $10 - 23 - 12$

11. $4 + 3(-6)$

12. $-8 + 4(3)$

13. $5(-9) + 2$

14. $7(-6) + 3$

15. $(-10) + 4 \div 2$

16. $(-12) + 6 \div 3$

17. $6 + 7 \cdot 3 - 40$

18. $5 + 9 \cdot 4 - 52$

19. $\dfrac{16 - 13}{-3}$

20. $\dfrac{20 - 15}{-1}$

21. $\dfrac{24}{10 + (-4)}$

22. $\dfrac{88}{-8 - 3}$

23. $5(-3) - (-12)$

24. $7(-4) - (-6)$

25. $(-19) - 12(3)$

26. $(-24) - 14(2)$

27. $-8 + 4^2$

28. $-12 + 3^3$

29. $[8 + (-4)]^2$

30. $[9 + (-2)]^3$

31. $8 \cdot 6 - 3 \cdot 5 + (-20)$

32. $7 \cdot 6 - 6 \cdot 5 + (-10)$

33. $16 - (-3)^4$

34. $20 - (-5)^2$

35. $|5 + 3| \cdot 2^3$

36. $|-3 + 7| \cdot 7^2$

37. $7 \cdot 8^2 + 4$

38. $10 \cdot 5^3 + 7$

39. $5^3 - (4 - 2^3)$

40. $8^2 - (5 - 2)^4$

41. $|3 - 12| \div 3$

42. $|12 - 19| \div 7$

43. $-(-2)^2$

44. $-(-2)^3$

160

45. $(5 - 9)^2 \div (4 - 2)^2$

46. $(2 - 7)^2 \div (4 - 3)^4$

47. $|8 - 24| \cdot (-2) \div (-2)$

48. $|3 - 15| \cdot (-4) \div (-16)$

49. $(-12 - 20) \div 16 - 25$

50. $(-20 - 5) \div 5 - 15$

51. $5(5 - 2) + (-5)^2 - 6$

52. $3 \cdot (8 - 5) + (-4) - 10$

53. $(2 - 7) \cdot (6 - 19)$

54. $(4 - 12) \cdot (8 - 17)$

55. $2 - 7 \cdot 6 - 19$

56. $4 - 12 \cdot 8 - 17$

57. $(-36 \div 6) - (4 \div 4)$

58. $(-4 \div 4) - (8 \div 8)$

59. $-5^2 - 6^2$

60. $-4^4 - 5^4$

61. $(-5)^2 - 6^2$

62. $(-4)^4 - (5)^4$

63. $(10 - 4^2)^2$

64. $(11 - 3^2)^3$

65. $2(8 - 10)^2 - 5(1 - 6)^2$

66. $-3(4 - 8)^2 + 5(14 - 16)^3$

67. $3(-10) \div [5(-3) - 7(-2)]$

68. $12 - [7 - (3 - 6)] + (2 - 3)^3$

69. $\dfrac{(-7)(-3) - (4)(3)}{3[7 \div (3 - 10)]}$

70. $\dfrac{10(-1) - (-2)(-3)}{2[-8 \div (-2 - 2)]}$

71. $-5[4 + 5(-3 + 5)] + 11$

72. $-2[1 + 3(7 - 12)] - 35$

Objective **B** *Evaluate each expression for $x = -2$, $y = 4$, and $z = -1$. See Examples 8 through 11.*

73. $x + y + z$

74. $x - y - z$

75. $2x - 3y - 4z$

76. $5x - y + 4z$

77. $x^2 - y$

78. $x^2 + z$

79. $\dfrac{5y}{z}$

80. $\dfrac{4x}{y}$

Evaluate each expression for $x = -3$ and $z = -4$. See Examples 8 through 11.

81. x^2

82. z^2

83. $-z^2$

84. $-x^2$

85. $10 - x^2$

86. $3 - z^2$

87. $2x^3 - z$

88. $3z^2 - x$

Review

Perform each indicated operation. See Sections 1.3, 1.4, 1.6, and 1.7.

89. $45 \cdot 90$

90. $90 \div 45$

91. $90 - 45$

92. $45 + 90$

Find the perimeter of each figure. See Section 1.3.

△ **93.** Square

8 in.

△ **94.** Parallelogram

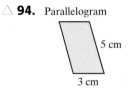

5 cm

3 cm

△ **95.** Rectangle

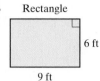

6 ft

9 ft

△ **96.** Triangle

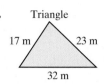

17 m   23 m

32 m

Concept Extensions

Recall that the average of a list of numbers is

$$average = \frac{sum\ of\ numbers}{number\ of\ numbers}$$

Use this for Exercises 97 through 100.

Find the average of each list of numbers.

97. $-10, 8, -4, 2, 7, -5, -12$

98. $-18, -8, -1, -1, 0, 4$

The graph shows some monthly normal temperatures for Barrow, Alaska.

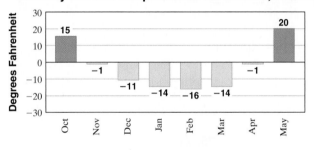

Monthly Normal Temperatures for Barrow, Alaska

99. Use this graph to find the average of the temperatures for months January through May.

100. Find the average of the temperatures for the months October through April.

Insert parentheses where needed so that each expression evaluates to the given number.

101. $2 \cdot 7 - 5 \cdot 3$; evaluates to 12

102. $7 \cdot 3 - 4 \cdot 2$; evaluates to 34

103. $-6 \cdot 10 - 4$; evaluates to -36

104. $2 \cdot 8 \div 4 - 20$; evaluates to -36

105. Are parentheses necessary in the expression $3 + (4 \cdot 5)$? Explain your answer.

106. Are parentheses necessary in the expression $(3 + 4) \cdot 5$? Explain your answer.

107. Discuss the effect parentheses have in an exponential expression. For example, what is the difference between $(-6)^2$ and -6^2?

108. Discuss the effect parentheses have in an exponential expression. For example, what is the difference between $(2 \cdot 4)^2$ and $2 \cdot 4^2$?

Evaluate.

 109. $(-12)^4$

110. $(-17)^6$

111. $(xy + z)^x$ for $x = 2$, $y = -5$, and $z = 7$

112. $5(ab + 3)^b$ for $a = -2$, $b = 3$

STUDY SKILLS BUILDER

How Are Your Homework Assignments Going?

It is very important in mathematics to keep up with homework. Why? Many concepts build on each other. Often your understanding of a day's concepts depends on an understanding of the previous day's material.

Remember that completing your homework assignment involves a lot more than attempting a few of the problems assigned.

To complete a homework assignment, remember these four things:

- Attempt all of it.
- Check it.
- Correct it.
- If needed, ask questions about it.

Take a moment and review your completed homework assignments. Answer the questions below based on this review.

1. Approximate how much of your homework you have attempted.

2. Approximate how much of your homework you have checked (if possible).

3. If you are able to check your homework, have you corrected it when errors have been found?

4. When working homework, if you do not understand a concept, what do you do?

CHAPTER 2   Group Activity

Magic Squares
Sections 2.2–2.4

A magic square is a set of numbers arranged in a square table so that the sum of the numbers in each column, row, and diagonal is the same. For instance, in the magic square below, the sum of each column, row, and diagonal is 15. Notice that no number is used more than once in the magic square.

2	9	4
7	5	3
6	1	8

The properties of magic squares have been known for a very long time and once were thought to be good luck charms. The ancient Egyptians and Greeks understood their patterns. A magic square even made it into a famous work of art. The engraving titled *Melencolia I,* created by German artist Albrecht Dürer in 1514, features the following four-by-four magic square on the building behind the central figure.

16	3	2	13
5	10	11	8
9	6	7	12
4	15	14	1

Exercises

1. Verify that what is shown in the Dürer engraving is, in fact, a magic square. What is the common sum of the columns, rows, and diagonals?

2. Negative numbers can also be used in magic squares. Complete the following magic square:

		−2
	−1	
0		−4

3. Use the numbers −16, −12, −8, −4, 0, 4, 8, 12, and 16 to form a magic square:

Chapter 2 Vocabulary Check

Fill in each blank with one of the words or phrases listed below.

signed   positive   opposites   negative   absolute value   variable   integers

1. Two numbers that are the same distance from 0 on the number line but are on opposite sides of 0 are called

_____ .

2. Together, positive numbers, negative numbers, and 0 are called _____ numbers.
3. The _____ of a number is that number's distance from 0 on a number line.
4. The _____ are . . . , $-3, -2, -1, 0, 1, 2, 3, \ldots$.
5. A letter used to represent a number is called

a _____ .

6. The _____ numbers are numbers less than zero.
7. The _____ numbers are numbers greater than zero.

> **Helpful Hint**
>
> Are you preparing for your test? Don't forget to take the Chapter 2 Test on page 173. Then check your answers at the back of the text and use the Chapter Test Prep Video CD to see the fully worked-out solutions to any of the exercises you want to review.

2 Chapter Highlights

DEFINITIONS AND CONCEPTS	EXAMPLES
Section 2.1 Introduction to Variables and Algebraic Expressions	

A letter used to represent a number is called a **variable.**	Variables: $x, \quad y, \quad z, \quad a, \quad b$
A combination of operations on variables and numbers is called an **algebraic expression.**	Algebraic expressions: $3 + x, \quad 7y, \quad x^3 + y - 10$
Replacing a variable in an expression by a number, and then finding the value of the expression is called **evaluating the expression** for the variable.	Evaluate $2x + y$ for $x = 22$ and $y = 4$. $\begin{aligned} 2x + y &= 2 \cdot 22 + 4 &&\text{Replace } x \text{ with 22 and } y \text{ with 4.} \\ &= 44 + 4 &&\text{Multiply.} \\ &= 48 &&\text{Add.} \end{aligned}$

Section 2.2 Introduction to Integers	
Together, positive numbers, negative numbers, and 0 are called **signed numbers.**	$-432, -10, 0, 15$
The **integers** are . . . , $-3, -2, -1, 0, 1, 2, 3, \ldots$.	
The **absolute value** of a number is that number's distance from 0 on a number line. The symbol for absolute value is $\vert \quad \vert$.	$\vert -2 \vert = 2$ 2 units $-3\ -2\ -1\quad 0\quad 1\quad 2\quad 3$ $\vert 2 \vert = 2$ 2 units $-3\ -2\ -1\quad 0\quad 1\quad 2\quad 3$
Two numbers that are the same distance from 0 on the number line but are on opposite sides of 0 are called **opposites.**	5 and -5 are opposites. 5 units 5 units $-5\ -4\ -3\ -2\ -1\quad 0\quad 1\quad 2\quad 3\quad 4\quad 5$
If a is a number, then $-(-a) = a$.	$-(-11) = 11$. Do not confuse with 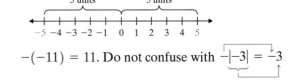 $-\vert -3 \vert = -3$

DEFINITIONS AND CONCEPTS	**EXAMPLES**
Section 2.3 Adding Integers	

ADDING TWO NUMBERS WITH THE SAME SIGN	Add:
Step 1. Add their absolute values.	$$-3 + (-2) = -5$$
Step 2. Use their common sign as the sign of the sum.	$$-7 + (-15) = -22$$
ADDING TWO NUMBERS WITH DIFFERENT SIGNS	$$-6 + 4 = -2$$
Step 1. Find the larger absolute value minus the smaller absolute value.	$$17 + (-12) = 5$$
Step 2. Use the sign of the number with the larger absolute value as the sign of the sum.	$$-32 + (-2) + 14 = -34 + 14$$ $$= -20$$

Section 2.4 Subtracting Integers	

SUBTRACTING TWO NUMBERS	Subtract:
If a and b are numbers, then $a - b = a + (-b)$.	$$-35 - 4 = -35 + (-4) = -39$$ $$3 - 8 = 3 + (-8) = -5$$ $$-10 - (-12) = -10 + 12 = 2$$ $$7 - 20 - 18 - (-3) = 7 + (-20) + (-18) + (+3)$$ $$= -13 + (-18) + 3$$ $$= -31 + 3$$ $$= -28$$

Section 2.5 Multiplying and Dividing Integers	

MULTIPLYING NUMBERS	Multiply:
The product of two numbers having the same sign is a positive number. The product of two numbers having unlike signs is a negative number.	$$(-7)(-6) = 42$$ $$9(-4) = -36$$
	Evaluate:
	$$(-3)^2 = (-3)(-3) = 9$$
DIVIDING NUMBERS	Divide:
The quotient of two numbers having the same sign is a positive number. The quotient of two numbers having unlike signs is a negative number.	$$-100 \div (-10) = 10$$ $$\frac{14}{-2} = -7, \quad \frac{0}{-3} = 0, \quad \frac{22}{0} \text{ is undefined.}$$

DEFINITIONS AND CONCEPTS	**EXAMPLES**
Section 2.6 Order of Operations	

ORDER OF OPERATIONS

1. Perform all operations within parentheses ( ), brackets [ ], or other grouping symbols such as square roots or fraction bars.
2. Evaluate any expressions with exponents.
3. Multiply or divide in order from left to right.
4. Add or subtract in order from left to right.

Simplify:

$$3 + 2 \cdot (-5) = 3 + (-10)$$
$$= -7$$

$$\frac{-2(5 - 7)}{-7 + |-3|} = \frac{-2(-2)}{-7 + 3}$$
$$= \frac{4}{-4}$$
$$= -1$$

STUDY SKILLS BUILDER

Are You Prepared for a Test on Chapter 2?

Below I have listed some *common trouble areas* for students in Chapter 2. After studying for your test—but before taking your test—read these.

- Don't forget the difference between $-(-5)$ and $-|-5|$.

  $-(-5) = 5$ The opposite of -5 is 5.

  $-|-5| = -5$ The opposite of the absolute value of -5 is the opposite of 5, which is -5.

- Remember how to simplify $(-7)^2$ and -7^2.

  $(-7)^2 = (-7)(-7) = 49$

  $-7^2 = -(7)(7) = -49$

- Don't forget order of operations.

  $1 + 3(4 - 6) = 1 + 3(-2)$ Simplify inside parentheses.
  $= 1 + (-6)$ Multiply.
  $= -5$ Add.

Remember: This is simply a checklist of common trouble spots. For a review of Chapter 2, see the Highlights and Chapter Review at the end of this chapter.

2 CHAPTER REVIEW

(2.1) *Evaluate each expression for x = 5, y = 0, and z = 2.*

1. $\dfrac{2x}{z}$

2. $4x - 3$

3. $\dfrac{x + 7}{y}$

4. $\dfrac{y}{5x}$

5. $x^3 - 2z$

6. $\dfrac{7 + x}{3z}$

7. $(y + z)^2$

8. $\dfrac{100}{x} + \dfrac{y}{3}$

Translate each phrase into a variable expression.

9. Five subtracted from a number

10. Seven more than a number

11. Ten divided by a number

12. The product of 5 and a number

The map below shows selected cities and their normal high and low temperatures. Use this map as indicated throughout the rest of this Chapter Review to fill in each missing temperature in the picture. The table on the next page may help to insert missing temperatures. Exercise 49 is the first exercise to use this map.

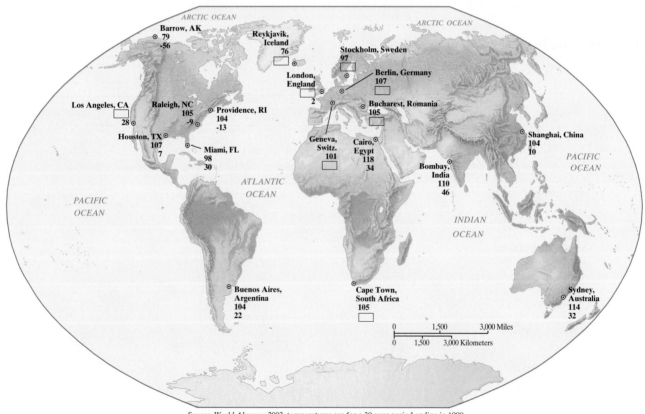

Source: World Almanac 2003; temperatures are for a 30-year period ending in 1990.

Extreme High and Low Temperatures for Selected Locations (in degrees Fahrenheit)					
	Max	**Min**		**Max**	**Min**
Berlin, Germany	107		Barrow, Alaska	79	−56
Raleigh, NC	105	−9	London, England		2
Houston, TX	107	7	Cairo, Egypt	118	34
Miami, FL	98	30	Sydney, Australia	114	32
Los Angeles, CA		28	Shanghai, China	104	10
Bucharest, Romania	105		Reykjavik, Iceland	76	
Geneva, Switzerland	101		Capetown, South Africa	105	
Providence, RI	104	−13	Buenos Aires, Argentina	104	22
Stockholm, Sweden	97		Bombay, India	110	46

(2.2) *Represent each quantity by an integer.*

13. A gold miner is working 1435 feet down in a mine.

14. A mountain peak is 7562 meters above sea level.

Graph each integer in the list on the same number line.

15. $-2, -5, 0, 5$

16. $-7, -1, 0, 7$

Simplify.

17. $|-12|$

18. $|0|$

19. $-|6|$

20. $-(-9)$

21. $-|-9|$

22. $-(-2)$

Insert $<$ or $>$ between each pair of integers to make a true statement.

23. $-18 \quad -20$

24. $-5 \quad 5$

25. $|-123| \quad -|-198|$

26. $8 - |-12| \quad -|-16|$

Find the opposite of each integer.

27. -12

28. $-(-3)$

Answer true or false for each statement.

29. If $a < b$, then a must be a negative number.

30. The absolute value of an integer is always 0 or a positive number.

31. A negative number is always less than a positive number.

32. If a is a negative number, then $-a$ is a positive number.

(2.3) *Add.*

33. $5 + (-3)$ **34.** $18 + (-4)$ **35.** $-12 + 16$ **36.** $-23 + 40$

37. $-8 + (-15)$ **38.** $-5 + (-17)$ **39.** $-24 + 3$ **40.** $-89 + 19$

41. $15 + (-15)$ **42.** $-24 + 24$ **43.** $-43 + (-108)$ **44.** $-100 + (-506)$

45. The temperature at 5 a.m. on a day in January was $-15°$ Celsius. By 6 a.m. the temperature had fallen 5 degrees. Use a signed number to represent the temperature at 6 a.m.

46. A diver starts out at 127 feet below the surface and then swims downward another 23 feet. Use a signed number to represent the diver's current depth.

47. During the 2004 PGA Masters Tournament, the winner, Phil Mickelson, had scores of $0, -3, -3,$ and -3 over four rounds of golf. What was his total score for the tournament? (*Source:* Professional Golfer's Association)

48. During the 2004 U.S. Open golf tournament, the winner, Retief Goosen, had a score of -4. The third-place finisher, Jeff Maggert, had a score that was 5 points more than the winning score. What was Jeff Maggert's score in the U.S. Open? (*Source:* Professional Golfer's Association)

For Exercises 49 and 50, use the map at the beginning of this Chapter Review.

49. The high temperature for London, England, is 155 degrees greater than the low temperature for Barrow, Alaska. Find the high temperature for London.

50. The high temperature for Los Angeles, California, is 125 degrees greater than the low temperature for Providence, Rhode Island. Find the high temperature for Los Angeles.

(2.4) *Subtract.*

51. $12 - 4$ **52.** $-12 - 4$ **53.** $8 - 19$ **54.** $-8 - 19$

55. $7 - (-13)$ **56.** $-6 - (-14)$ **57.** $16 - 16$ **58.** $-16 - 16$

59. $-12 - (-12)$ **60.** $|-5| - |-12|$ **61.** $-(-5) - 12 + (-3)$ **62.** $-8 + |-12| - 10 - |-3|$

Solve.

63. Josh Weidner has \$142 in his checking account. He writes a check for \$125, makes a deposit for \$43, and then writes another check for \$85. Represent the balance in his account by an integer.

64. If the elevation of Lake Superior is 600 feet above sea level and the elevation of the Caspian Sea is 92 feet below sea level, find the difference of the elevations.

For Exercises 65 and 66, use the map at the beginning of this Chapter Review.

65. The low temperature for Reykjavik is 35 degrees less than the low temperature for Sydney, Australia. Find the low temperature for Reykjavik.

66. The low temperature for Berlin, Germany, is 14 degrees less than the low temperature for Shanghai, China. Find the low temperature for Berlin.

Answer true or false for each statement.

67. $|-5| - |-6| = 5 - 6$

68. $|-5 - (-6)| = 5 + 6$

69. If $b > a$, then $b - a$ is a positive number.

70. If $b < a$, then $b - a$ is a negative number.

(2.5) *Multiply.*

71. $-3(-7)$

72. $-6(3)$

73. $-4(16)$

74. $-5(-12)$

75. $(-5)^2$

76. $(-1)^5$

77. $12(-3)(0)$

78. $-1(6)(2)(-2)$

Divide.

79. $-15 \div 3$

80. $\dfrac{-24}{-8}$

81. $\dfrac{0}{-3}$

82. $\dfrac{-46}{0}$

83. $\dfrac{100}{-5}$

84. $\dfrac{-72}{8}$

85. $\dfrac{-38}{-1}$

86. $\dfrac{45}{-9}$

87. A football team lost 5 yards on each of two consecutive plays. Represent the total loss by a product of integers, and find the product.

88. A race horse bettor lost $50 on each of four consecutive races. Represent the total loss by a product of integers, and find the product.

For Exercises 89 through 92, use the map at the beginning of this Chapter Review.

89. The low temperature for Bucharest, Romania is 2 times the low temperature for Raleigh, North Carolina. Find the low temperature for Bucharest.

90. The low temperature for Geneva, Switzerland is the same as the low temperature for Miami, Florida divided by −10. Find the low temperature for Geneva.

91. The low temperature for Capetown, South Africa is the same as the low temperature for Barrow, Alaska divided by −2. Find the low temperature for Capetown.

92. The low temperature for Stockholm, Sweden, is 2 times the low temperature for Providence, Rhode Island. Find the low temperature for Stockholm.

(2.6) *Simplify.*

93. $(-7)^2$

94. -7^2

95. -2^5

96. $(-2)^5$

97. $5 - 8 + 3$

98. $-3 + 12 + (-7) - 10$

99. $-10 + 3 \cdot (-2)$

100. $5 - 10 \cdot (-3)$

101. $16 \cdot (-2) + 4$ **102.** $3 \cdot (-12) - 8$ **103.** $5 + 6 \div (-3)$ **104.** $-6 + (-10) \div (-2)$

105. $16 + (-3) \cdot 12 \div 4$ **106.** $(-12) + 25 \cdot 1 \div (-5)$ **107.** $4^3 - (8 - 3)^2$ **108.** $4^3 - 90$

109. $-(-4) \cdot |-3| - 5$ **110.** $|5 - 1|^2 \cdot (-5)$ **111.** $\dfrac{(-4)(-3) - (-2)(-1)}{-10 + 5}$ **112.** $\dfrac{4(12 - 18)}{-10 \div (-2 - 3)}$

Find the average of each list of numbers.

113. $-18, 25, -30, 7, 0, -2$ **114.** $-45, -40, -30, -25$

Evaluate each expression for $x = -2$ and $y = 1$.

115. $2x - y$ **116.** $y^2 + x^2$ **117.** $\dfrac{3x}{6}$ **118.** $\dfrac{5y - x}{-y}$

119. x^2 **120.** $-x^2$ **121.** $7 - x^2$ **122.** $100 - x^3$

Mixed Review

Perform the indicated operations.

123. $(-4)^2$ **124.** -4^2 **125.** $-6 + (-9)$ **126.** $-16 - 3$

127. $-4(-12)$ **128.** $\dfrac{84}{-4}$ **129.** $-76 - (-97)$ **130.** $-9 + 4$

131. Joe owed his mother $32. He gave her $23. Write his financial situation as a signed number.

132. The temperature at noon on a Monday in December was $-11°$C. By noon on Tuesday, it had warmed by $17°$C. What was the temperature at noon on Tuesday?

133. The top of the mountain has an altitude of 12,923 feet. The bottom of the valley is 195 feet below sea level. Find the difference between these two elevations.

134. Wednesday's lowest temperature was $-18°$C. The cold weather continued and by Friday it had dropped another $9°$C. What was the temperature on Friday?

Simplify.

135. $(3 - 7)^2 \div (6 - 4)^3$ **136.** $(4 + 6)^2 \div (2 - 7)^2$ **137.** $3(4 + 2) + (-6) - 3^2$

138. $4(5 - 3) - (-2) + 3^3$ **139.** $2 - 4 \cdot 3 + \sqrt{25}$ **140.** $4 - 6 \cdot 5 + \sqrt{1}$

141. $\dfrac{-|-14| - 6}{7 + 2(-3)}$ **142.** $5(7 - 6)^3 - 4(2 - 3)^2 + 2^4$

2 CHAPTER TEST

Remember to use the Chapter Test Prep Video CD to see the fully worked-out solutions to any of the exercises you want to review.

Answers

Simplify each expression.

1. $-5 + 8$

2. $18 - 24$

3. $5 \cdot (-20)$

4. $(-16) \div (-4)$

5. $(-18) + (-12)$

6. $-7 - (-19)$

7. $(-5) \cdot (-13)$

8. $\dfrac{-25}{-5}$

9. $|-25| + (-13)$

10. $14 - |-20|$

11. $|5| \cdot |-10|$

12. $\dfrac{|-10|}{-|-5|}$

13. $(-8) + 9 \div (-3)$

14. $-7 + (-32) - 12 + 5$

15. $(-5)^3 - 24 \div (-3)$

16. $(5 - 9)^2 \cdot (8 - 2)^3$

17. $-(-7)^2 \div 7 \cdot (-4)$

18. $3 - (8 - 2)^3$

1. _____

2. _____

3. _____

4. _____

5. _____

6. _____

7. _____

8. _____

9. _____

10. _____

11. _____

12. _____

13. _____

14. _____

15. _____

16. _____

17. _____

18. _____

19. _____

20. _____

21. _____

22. _____

23. _____

24. _____

25. _____

26. _____

27. _____

28. _____

29. _____

30. _____

31. _____

32. _____

33. _____

34. _____

35. _____

36. a. _____

b. _____

19. $-6 + (-15) \div (-3)$

20. $\dfrac{4}{2} - \dfrac{8^2}{16}$

21. $\dfrac{-3(-2) + 12}{-1(-4 - 5)}$

22. $\dfrac{|25 - 30|^2}{2(-6) + 7}$

23. $5(-8) - [6 - (2 - 4)] + (12 - 16)^2$

24. $-2^3 - 2^2$

Evaluate each expression for $x = 0$, $y = -3$, and $z = 2$.

25. $3x + y$

26. $|y| + |x| + |z|$

27. $\dfrac{3z}{2y}$

28. $2y^3$

29. $10 - y^2$

30. $7x + 3y - 4z$

31. Mary Dunstan, a diver, starts at sea level and then makes 4 successive descents of 22 feet. After the descents, what is her elevation?

32. Aaron Hawn has $129 in his checking account. He writes a check for $79, withdraws $40 from an ATM, and then deposits $35. Represent the new balance in his account by an integer.

33. Mt. Washington in New Hampshire has an elevation of 6288 feet above sea level. The Romanche Gap in the Atlantic Ocean has an elevation of 25,354 feet below sea level. Represent the difference in elevation between these two points by an integer. (*Source:* National Geographic Society and Defense Mapping Agency)

34. Lake Baykal in Siberian Russia is the deepest lake in the world with a maximum depth of 5315 feet. The elevation of the lake's surface is 1495 feet above sea level. What is the elevation (with respect to sea level) of the deepest point in the lake? (*Source:* U.S. Geological Survey)

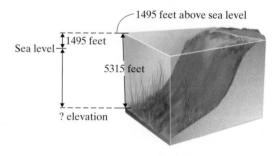

35. Find the average of $-12, -13, 0, 9$.

36. Translate the following phrases into mathematical expressions. Use x to represent "a number."

a. The product of a number and 17

b. Twice a number subtracted from 20

Find the place value of the digit 4 in each whole number.

1. 48,761

2. 3408

3. 249

4. 694,298

5. 524,007,656

6. 267,401,818

7. Insert $<$ or $>$ to make a true statement.
   a. $-7 \quad 7$
   b. $0 \quad -4$
   c. $-9 \quad -11$

8. Insert $<$ or $>$ to make a true statement
   a. $12 \quad 4$
   b. $13 \quad 31$
   c. $82 \quad 79$

9. Add:
   $13 + 2 + 7 + 8 + 9$

10. Add: $11 + 3 + 9 + 16$

11. Subtract: $7826 - 505$
   Check by adding.

12. Subtract: $3285 - 272$
   Check by adding.

13. The radius of Venus is 6052 kilometers. The radius of Mercury is 3612 kilometers less than the radius of Venus. Find the radius of Mercury. (*Source:* National Space Science Data Center)

14. C.J. Dufour wants to buy a digital camera. She has $762 in her savings account. If the camera costs $237, how much money will she have in her account after buying the camera?

15. Round 568 to the nearest ten.

16. Round 568 to the nearest hundred.

17. Round each number to the nearest hundred to find an estimated difference.
   $$\begin{array}{r} 4725 \\ -2879 \\ \hline \end{array}$$

18. Round each number to the nearest thousand to find an estimated difference.
   $$\begin{array}{r} 8394 \\ -2913 \\ \hline \end{array}$$

19. Rewrite each using the distributive property.
   a. $3(4 + 5)$
   b. $10(6 + 8)$
   c. $2(7 + 3)$

20. Rewrite each using the distributive property.
   a. $5(2 + 12)$
   b. $9(3 + 6)$
   c. $4(8 + 1)$

21. Multiply: 631×125

22. Multiply: 299×104

23. Find each quotient. Check by multiplying.
   a. $42 \div 7$
   b. $\dfrac{81}{9}$
   c. $4\overline{)24}$

24. Find each quotient. Check by multiplying.
   a. $\dfrac{35}{5}$
   b. $64 \div 8$
   c. $4\overline{)48}$

Answers

1. _____
2. _____
3. _____
4. _____
5. _____
6. _____
7. a. _____
   b. _____
   c. _____
8. a. _____
   b. _____
   c. _____
9. _____
10. _____
11. _____
12. _____
13. _____
14. _____
15. _____
16. _____
17. _____
18. _____
19. a. _____
    b. _____
    c. _____
20. a. _____
    b. _____
    c. _____
21. _____
22. _____
23. a. _____
    b. _____
    c. _____
24. a. _____
    b. _____
    c. _____

25. _____

26. _____

27. _____

28. _____

29. _____

30. _____

31. _____

32. _____

33. _____

34. _____

35. _____

36. _____

37. _____

38. _____

39. a. _____

 b. _____

 c. _____

40. a. _____

 b. _____

41. _____

42. _____

43. _____

44. _____

45. _____

46. _____

47. _____

48. _____

49. _____

50. _____

25. Divide: $3705 \div 5$
Check by multiplying.

26. Divide: $3648 \div 8$
Check by multiplying.

27. How many boxes are needed to ship 56 pairs of Nikes to a shoe store in Texarkana if 9 pairs of shoes will fit in each shipping box?

28. Mrs. Mallory's first grade class is going to the zoo. She pays a total of $324 for 36 admission tickets. How much did each ticket cost?

Evaluate.

29. 8^2

30. 5^3

31. 7^1

32. 4^1

33. $5 \cdot 6^2$

34. $2^3 \cdot 7$

35. Simplify: $\dfrac{7 - 2 \cdot 3 + 3^2}{5(2 - 1)}$

36. Simplify: $\dfrac{6^2 + 4 \cdot 4 + 2^3}{37 - 5^2}$

37. Evaluate $x + 7$ if x is 8.

38. Evaluate $5 + x$ if x is 9.

39. Simplify:
 a. $|-2|$
 b. $|5|$
 c. $|0|$

40. Simplify:
 a. $|4|$
 b. $|-7|$

41. Add: $-2 + 5$

42. Add: $8 + (-3)$

43. Evaluate $a - b$ for $a = 8$ and $b = -6$.

44. Evaluate $x - y$ for $x = -2$ and $y = -7$.

45. Multiply: $-7 \cdot 3$

46. Multiply: $5(-2)$

47. Multiply: $0 \cdot (-4)$

48. Multiply: $-6 \cdot 9$

49. Simplify: $3(4 - 7) + (-2) - \sqrt{25}$

50. Simplify: $4 - 8(7 - 3) - (-1)$

3

Fractions

Fractions are numbers and, like whole numbers and integers, they can be added, subtracted, multiplied, and divided. Fractions are very useful and appear frequently in everyday language, in common phrases such as "half an hour," "quarter of a pound," and "third of a cup." This chapter reviews the concept of fractions and demonstrates how to add, subtract, multiply, and divide fractions.

You may have heard before that the surface of the earth is about $\frac{1}{4}$ land and $\frac{3}{4}$ water, but what about the individual continents and oceans?

In Section 3.4, Exercises 45 through 48, and Section 3.5, Exercises 81 and 82, we use fractions to help us see the relative sizes of the continents and oceans.

Arctic Ocean

$\frac{7}{100}$ Europe $\frac{30}{100}$

North America

Asia

$\frac{16}{100}$ Atlantic Ocean   Africa   Pacific Ocean

Pacific Ocean

South America $\frac{20}{100}$ Indian Ocean

Australia

$\frac{12}{100}$ $\frac{6}{100}$

$\frac{9}{100}$

Antarctica

3.1 INTRODUCTION TO FRACTIONS AND MIXED NUMBERS

A Identify the Numerator and the Denominator of a Fraction.

B Write a Fraction to Represent Parts of Figures or Real-Life Data.

C Identify Proper Fractions, Improper Fractions, and Mixed Numbers.

D Review Division Properties for 0 and 1.

Objective **A** Identifying Numerators and Denominators

Whole numbers are used to count whole things or units, such as cars, horses, dollars, and people. To refer to a part of a whole, fractions can be used. Here are some examples of **fractions.** Study these examples for a moment.

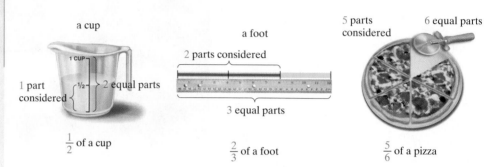

$\frac{1}{2}$ of a cup $\frac{2}{3}$ of a foot $\frac{5}{6}$ of a pizza

In a fraction, the top number is called the **numerator** and the bottom number is called the **denominator.** The bar between the numbers is called the **fraction bar.**

Names	Fraction	Meaning
numerator ⟶	5	⟵ number of parts being considered
denominator ⟶	6	⟵ number of equal parts in the whole

EXAMPLES Identify the numerator and the denominator of each fraction.

1. $\frac{3}{7}$ ← numerator
       ← denominator

2. $\frac{13}{5}$ ← numerator
       ← denominator

☐ **Work Practice Problems 1–2**

Helpful Hint

$\frac{3}{7}$ ← Remember that the bar in a fraction means division. Since division by 0 is undefined, a fraction with a denominator of 0 is undefined.

Objective **B** Writing Fractions to Represent Parts of Figures or Real-Life Data

One way to become familiar with the concept of fractions is to visualize fractions with shaded figures. We can then write a fraction to represent the shaded area of the figure (or diagram).

PRACTICE PROBLEMS 1–2

Identify the numerator and the denominator of each fraction.

1. $\frac{9}{2}$ **2.** $\frac{10}{17}$

Answers

1. numerator = 9, denominator = 2,
2. numerator = 10, denominator = 17

EXAMPLES Write a fraction to represent the shaded part of each figure.

3. In this figure, 2 of the 5 equal parts are shaded. Thus, the fraction is $\frac{2}{5}$.

$\frac{2}{5}$ ← number of parts shaded
  ← number of equal parts

4. In this figure, 3 of the 10 rectangles are shaded. Thus, the fraction is $\frac{3}{10}$.

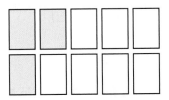

$\frac{3}{10}$ ← number of parts shaded
   ← number of equal parts

🔲 **Work Practice Problems 3–4**

EXAMPLES Write a fraction to represent the shaded part of the diagram.

5.

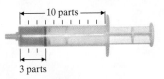

The fraction is $\frac{3}{10}$.   3 parts

6.

3 parts

1 part
shaded

The fraction is $\frac{1}{3}$.

🔲 **Work Practice Problems 5–6**

EXAMPLES Draw a figure and then shade a part of it to represent each fraction.

7. $\frac{5}{6}$ of a figure

We will use a geometric figure such as a rectangle. Since the denominator is 6, we divide it into 6 equal parts. Then we shade 5 of the equal parts.

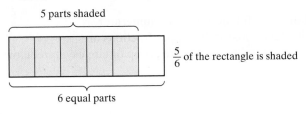

5 parts shaded

$\frac{5}{6}$ of the rectangle is shaded

6 equal parts

Continued on next page

PRACTICE PROBLEMS 3–4

Write a fraction to represent the shaded part of each figure.

3.

4.

PRACTICE PROBLEMS 5–6

Write a fraction to represent the part of the whole shown.

5. Just consider this part of the syringe

6.

PRACTICE PROBLEMS 7–8

Draw and shade a part of a figure to represent each fraction.

7. $\frac{2}{3}$ of a figure

8. $\frac{7}{11}$ of a figure

Answers

3. $\frac{3}{8}$, **4.** $\frac{1}{6}$, **5.** $\frac{7}{10}$, **6.** $\frac{9}{16}$

7. answers may vary; for example,

8. answer on page 180.

8. $\frac{3}{8}$ of a figure

If you'd like, our figure can consist of 8 triangles of the same size. We will shade 3 of the triangles.

3 triangles shaded

8 triangles

$\frac{3}{8}$ of the diagram is shaded

▣ **Work Practice Problems 7–8**

✔ Concept Check If ☐☐☐☐☐☐ represents $\frac{6}{7}$ of a whole diagram, sketch the whole diagram.

PRACTICE PROBLEM 9

Of the nine planets in our solar system, seven are farther from the Sun than Venus is. What fraction of the planets are farther from the Sun than Venus is?

EXAMPLE 9 **Writing Fractions from Real-Life Data**

Of the nine planets in our solar system, two are closer to the Sun than the Earth. What fraction of the planets are closer to the Sun than the Earth?

Solution: The fraction of planets closer to the Sun than Earth is:

$\frac{2}{9}$ ← number of planets closer
← number of planets in our solar system

Thus, $\frac{2}{9}$ of the planets in our solar system are closer to the Sun than the Earth.

▣ **Work Practice Problem 9**

Objective C Identifying Proper Fractions, Improper Fractions, and Mixed Numbers

A **proper fraction** is a fraction whose numerator is less than its denominator. Proper fractions are less than 1. For example, the shaded portion of the triangle's area is represented by $\frac{2}{3}$.

$\frac{2}{3}$

An **improper fraction** is a fraction whose numerator is greater than or equal to its denominator. Improper fractions are greater than or equal to 1. The shaded part of the group of circles' area below is $\frac{9}{4}$.

Answers

8. answers may vary; for example,

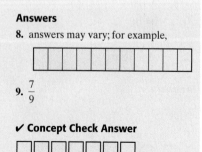

9. $\frac{7}{9}$

✔ **Concept Check Answer**

☐☐☐☐☐☐☐

The shaded part of the rectangle's area is $\frac{6}{6}$. (Recall from earlier that $\frac{6}{6}$ simplifies to 1 and notice that 1 whole figure or rectangle is shaded below.)

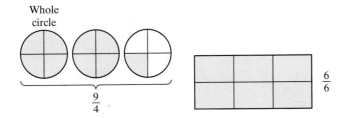

A **mixed number** contains a whole number and a fraction. Mixed numbers are greater than 1. Earlier, we wrote the shaded part of the group of circles below as the improper fraction $\frac{9}{4}$. Now let's write the shaded part as a mixed number. The shaded part of the group of circles' area is $2\frac{1}{4}$. (Read "two and one-fourth.")

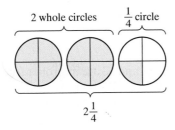

EXAMPLE 10 Identify each number as a proper fraction, improper fraction, or mixed number.

a. $\frac{6}{7}$ is a proper fraction

b. $\frac{13}{12}$ is an improper fraction

c. $\frac{2}{2}$ is an improper fraction

d. $\frac{99}{101}$ is a proper fraction

e. $1\frac{7}{8}$ is a mixed number

f. $\frac{93}{74}$ is an improper fraction

☐ **Work Practice Problem 10**

PRACTICE PROBLEM 10

Identify each number as a proper fraction, improper fraction, or mixed number.

a. $\frac{5}{8}$

b. $\frac{7}{7}$

c. $\frac{14}{13}$

d. $\frac{13}{14}$

e. $5\frac{1}{4}$

f. $\frac{100}{49}$

Helpful Hint

The mixed number $2\frac{1}{4}$ represents $2 + \frac{1}{4}$.

The mixed number $-3\frac{1}{5}$ represents $-\left(3 + \frac{1}{5}\right)$ or $-3 - \frac{1}{5}$. We review this later in this chapter.

Answers

10. a. proper fraction, **b.** improper fraction, **c.** improper fraction, **d.** proper fraction, **e.** mixed number, **f.** improper fraction

Copyright 2007 Pearson Education, Inc.

PRACTICE PROBLEMS 11–12

Represent the shaded part of each figure group as both an improper fraction and a mixed number.

11.

12.

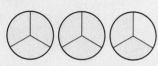

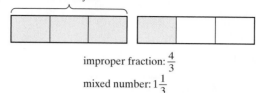 **EXAMPLES** Represent the shaded part of each figure group's area as both an improper fraction and a mixed number.

11.   Whole object

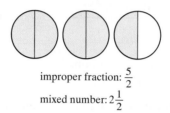

improper fraction: $\frac{4}{3}$

mixed number: $1\frac{1}{3}$

12.

improper fraction: $\frac{5}{2}$

mixed number: $2\frac{1}{2}$

▣ **Work Practice Problems 11–12**

✔ **Concept Check**   If you were to estimate $2\frac{1}{8}$ by a whole number, would you choose 2 or 3? Why?

The fractions in Examples 11 and 12 are improper fractions. Notice that the value of each is greater than or equal to 1. This is always true since the numerator of an improper fraction is greater than or equal to the denominator.

Objective ⒟ Reviewing Division Properties for 0 and 1

Before we continue further, don't forget from Section 1.7 that the fraction bar indicates division. Let's review some division properties for 1 and 0.

Helpful Hint   Notice the fraction $\frac{11}{1} = 11$, or also $11 = \frac{11}{1}$.

$$\frac{9}{9} = 1 \text{ because } 1 \cdot 9 = 9 \qquad -\frac{11}{1} = -11 \text{ because } -11 \cdot 1 = -11$$

$$\frac{0}{6} = 0 \text{ because } 0 \cdot 6 = 0 \qquad \frac{6}{0} \text{ is } \textit{undefined} \text{ because there is no number that}$$

when multiplied by 0 gives 6.

In general, we can say the following.

Let n be any integer except 0.

$$\frac{n}{n} = 1 \qquad \frac{0}{n} = 0$$

$$\frac{n}{1} = n \qquad \frac{n}{0} \text{ is undefined.}$$

Answers

11. $\frac{8}{3}, 2\frac{2}{3}$,   **12.** $\frac{5}{4}, 1\frac{1}{4}$

✔ **Concept Check Answer**

2, answers may vary

EXAMPLES Simplify.

13. $\frac{5}{5} = 1$ **14.** $\frac{-2}{-2} = 1$ **15.** $\frac{0}{-5} = 0$

16. $\frac{-5}{1} = -5$ **17.** $\frac{41}{1} = 41$ **18.** $\frac{19}{0}$ is undefined

☐ **Work Practice Problems 13–18**

Notice from Example 16 that we can have negative fractions. In fact,

$$\frac{-5}{1} = -5, \qquad \frac{5}{-1} = -5, \qquad \text{and} \quad -\frac{5}{1} = -5$$

Because all of the fractions equal -5, we have

$$\frac{-5}{1} = \frac{5}{-1} = -\frac{5}{1}$$

This means that the negative sign in a fraction can be written in the numerator, the denominator, or in front of the fraction. Remember this as we work with negative fractions.

> **Helpful Hint**
>
> Remember, for example, that
>
> $$-\frac{2}{3} = \frac{-2}{3} = \frac{2}{-3}$$

PRACTICE PROBLEMS 13–18

Simplify.

13. $\frac{9}{9}$ **14.** $\frac{-6}{-6}$ **15.** $\frac{0}{-1}$

16. $\frac{4}{1}$ **17.** $\frac{-13}{0}$ **18.** $\frac{-13}{1}$

Answers

13. 1, **14.** 1, **15.** 0, **16.** 4,
17. undefined, **18.** −13

Mental Math

Objectives A C **Mixed Practice** *Identify the numerator and the denominator of each fraction and identify each fraction as proper or improper. See Examples 1, 2, and 10.*

1. $\frac{1}{2}$

2. $\frac{1}{4}$

3. $\frac{10}{3}$

4. $\frac{53}{21}$

5. $\frac{15}{15}$

6. $\frac{26}{26}$

3.1 EXERCISE SET

FOR EXTRA HELP

Student Solutions Manual   PH Math/Tutor Center   CD/Video for Review   Math XL MathXL®   MyMathLab MyMathLab

Objectives B C **Mixed Practice** *Write a proper or improper fraction to represent the shaded part of each. If an improper fraction is appropriate, write the shaded figure as (a) an improper fraction and (b) a mixed number. See Examples 3 through 6 and 11 and 12.*

1.

2.

3.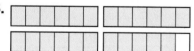

4.

5.

6.

7.

8.

9.

10.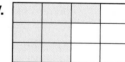

11.

12.

13.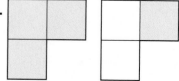

14.

15.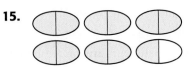

16.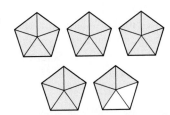

17.

18.

19.

1 mile

20.

Objective B *Draw and shade a part of a diagram to represent each fraction. See Examples 7 and 8.*

21. $\frac{1}{5}$ of a diagram

22. $\frac{1}{16}$ of a diagram

23. $\frac{7}{8}$ of a diagram

24. $\frac{3}{5}$ of a diagram

25. $\frac{6}{7}$ of a diagram

26. $\frac{7}{9}$ of a diagram

27. $\frac{4}{4}$ of a diagram

28. $\frac{6}{6}$ of a diagram

Write each fraction. See Example 9.

29. Of the 131 students at a small private school, 42 are freshmen. What fraction of the students are freshmen?

30. Of the 78 executives at a private accounting firm, 61 are women. What fraction of the executives are women?

31. Use Exercise 29 to answer a and b.

    a. How many students are *not* freshmen?

    b. What fraction of the students are *not* freshmen?

32. Use Exercise 30 to answer a and b.

    a. How many of the executives are men?

    b. What fraction of the executives are men?

33. As of 2005, the United States has had 43 different presidents. A total of eight U.S. presidents were born in the state of Virginia, more than any other state. What fraction of U.S. presidents were born in Virginia? (*Source: 2005 World Almanac and Book of Facts*)

Eight U.S. Presidents

34. Of the nine planets in our solar system, four have days that are longer than the 24-hour Earth day. What fraction of the planets have longer days than Earth has? (*Source:* National Space Science Data Center)

35. The hard drive in Aaron Hawn's computer can hold 70 gigabytes of information. He has currently used 27 gigabytes. What fraction of his hard drive has he used?

36. There are 12 inches in a foot. What fractional part of a foot does 5 inches represent?

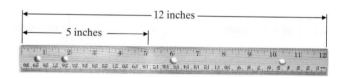

37. There are 31 days in the month of March. What fraction of the month does 11 days represent?

Mon.	Tue.	Wed.	Thu.	Fri.	Sat.	Sun.
					1	2
3	4	5	6	7	8	9
10	11	12	13	14	15	16
17	18	19	20	21	22	23
24	25	26	27	28	29	30
31						

38. There are 60 minutes in an hour. What fraction of an hour does 37 minutes represent?

39. In a basic college mathematics class containing 31 students, there are 18 freshmen, 10 sophomores, and 3 juniors. What fraction of the class is sophomores?

40. In a family with 11 children, there are 4 boys and 7 girls. What fraction of the children is girls?

41. Thirty-three states in the United States contain federal Indian reservations.

  a. What fraction of the states contain Indian reservations?

  b. How many states do not contain Indian reservations?

  c. What fraction of the states do not contain Indian reservations? (*Source:* Tiller Research, Inc., Albuquerque, NM)

42. Consumer fireworks are legal in 40 states in the United States.

  a. In what fraction of the states are consumer fireworks legal?

  b. In how many states are consumer fireworks illegal?

  c. In what fraction of the states are consumer fireworks illegal? (*Source:* United States Fireworks Safety Council)

43. A bag contains 50 red or blue marbles. If 21 marbles are blue,

  a. What *fraction* of the marbles are blue?

  b. How many marbles are red?

  c. What *fraction* of the marbles are red?

44. An art dealer is taking inventory. His shop contains a total of 37 pieces, which are all sculptures, watercolor paintings, or oil paintings. If there are 15 watercolor paintings and 17 oil paintings, answer each question.

  a. What fraction of the inventory is watercolor paintings?

  b. What fraction of the inventory is oil paintings?

  c. How many sculptures are there?

  d. What fraction of the inventory is sculptures?

Objective D *Simplify by dividing. See Examples 13 through 18.*

45. $\dfrac{12}{12}$

46. $\dfrac{-3}{-3}$

47. $\dfrac{-5}{1}$

48. $\dfrac{-10}{1}$

49. $\dfrac{0}{-2}$

50. $\dfrac{0}{-8}$

51. $\dfrac{-8}{-8}$

52. $\dfrac{-14}{-14}$

53. $\dfrac{-9}{0}$

54. $\dfrac{-7}{0}$

55. $\dfrac{3}{1}$

56. $\dfrac{5}{5}$

Review

Simplify. See Section 1.9.

57. 3^2

58. 4^3

59. 5^3

60. 3^4

Write each using exponents.

61. $7 \cdot 7 \cdot 7 \cdot 7 \cdot 7$

62. $5 \cdot 5 \cdot 5 \cdot 5$

63. $2 \cdot 2 \cdot 2 \cdot 3$

64. $4 \cdot 4 \cdot 10 \cdot 10 \cdot 10$

Concept Extensions

Write each fraction in two other equivalent ways by inserting the negative sign in different places.

65. $-\dfrac{11}{2} = = $

66. $\dfrac{-13}{15} = = $

67. $\dfrac{45}{-57} = = $

68. In your own words, explain why $\dfrac{0}{10} = 0$ and $\dfrac{10}{0}$ are undefined.

Identify the larger fraction for each pair.

69. $\dfrac{1}{2}$ or $\dfrac{2}{3}$ (*Hint:* Represent each fraction by the shaded part of equivalent figures. Then compare the shaded areas.)

70. $\dfrac{7}{4}$ or $\dfrac{3}{5}$ (*Hint:* Identify each as a proper fraction or an improper fraction.)

Solve. See the Concept Check in this section.

71. If ◯◯◯◯ represents $\dfrac{4}{9}$ of a whole diagram, sketch the whole diagram.

72. If △△ represents $\dfrac{1}{3}$ of a whole diagram, sketch the whole diagram.

73. The Wendy's Corporation owns restaurants with five different names, as shown on the bar graph. What fraction of restaurants owned by Wendy's corporation are named "Wendy's" restaurants? (*Source:* The Wendy's Corporation)

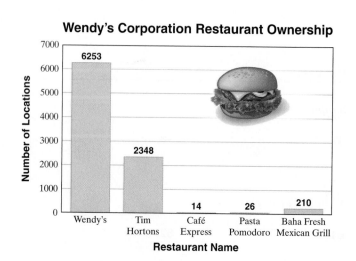

Wendy's Corporation Restaurant Ownership

74. The Public Broadcasting Service (PBS) provides programming to the noncommercial public TV stations of the United States. The table shows a breakdown of the public television licensees by type. Each licensee operates one or more PBS member TV stations. What fraction of the public television licensees are universities or colleges? (*Source:* The Public Broadcast Service)

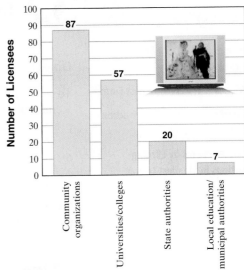

Public Television Licensees

75. Habitat for Humanity is a nonprofit organization that helps provide affordable housing to families in need. Habitat for Humanity does its work of building and renovating houses through 1651 local affiliates in the United States and 634 international affiliates. What fraction of the total Habitat for Humanity affiliates are located in the United States? (*Hint:* First find the total number of affiliates.) (*Source:* Habitat for Humanity International)

76. The United States Marine Corps (USMC) has five principal training centers in California, three in North Carolina, two in South Carolina, one in Arizona, one in Hawaii, and one in Virginia. What fraction of the total USMC principal training centers are located in California? (*Source:* U.S. Department of Defense)

 STUDY SKILLS BUILDER

How Well Do You Know Your Textbook?

The questions below will determine whether you are familiar with your textbook. For help, see Section 1.1 in this text.

1. What does the 🌐 icon mean?

2. What does the ✎ icon mean?

3. What does the △ icon mean?

4. Where can you find a review for each chapter? What answers to this review can be found in the back of your text?

5. Each chapter contains an overview of the chapter along with examples. What is this feature called?

6. Each chapter contains a review of vocabulary. What is this feature called?

7. There is a CD in your text. What content is contained on this CD?

8. What is the location of the section that is entirely devoted to study skills?

9. There are Practice Problems that are contained in the margin of the text. What are they and how can they be used?

3.2 FACTORS AND SIMPLEST FORM

Objective Ⓐ Writing a Number as a Product of Prime Numbers

To perform operations on fractions, it is necessary to be able to factor a number. Remember that factoring a number means writing a number as a product. We first practice writing a number as a product of prime numbers.

Recall from Section 1.6 that since $12 = 2 \cdot 6$, the numbers 2 and 6 are called *factors* of 12. A **factor** is any number that divides a number evenly (with a remainder of 0).

Of all the ways to factor a number, one special way is called the **prime factorization.** To help us write prime factorizations, we first review prime and composite numbers.

> ### Prime Numbers
>
> A **prime number** is a natural number that has exactly two different factors, 1 and itself.

The first several prime numbers are

2, 3, 5, 7, 11, 13, 17

It would be helpful to memorize these.

If a natural number other than 1 is not a prime number, it is called a **composite number.**

> ### Composite Numbers
>
> A **composite number** is any natural number, other than 1, that is not prime.

 Helpful Hint

The natural number 1 is neither prime nor composite.

Now we are ready to define, then find, **prime factorizations** of numbers.

> ### Prime Factorization
>
> The **prime factorization** of a number is the factorization in which all the factors are prime numbers.

Earlier, we wrote $12 = 2 \cdot 6$. Although 2 and 6 are factors of 12, the product $2 \cdot 6$ is *not* the prime factorization of 12 because 6 is *not* a prime number.

The prime factorization of 12 is $2 \cdot 2 \cdot 3$ because

$12 = 2 \cdot 2 \cdot 3$ and each number is a prime number.

There is only one prime factorization for any given number. In other words, the prime factorization of a number is unique.

Helpful Hint

Don't forget that multiplication is commutative, so $2 \cdot 2 \cdot 3$ can also be written as $2 \cdot 3 \cdot 2$ or $3 \cdot 2 \cdot 2$ or $2^2 \cdot 3$. Any one of these can be called *the prime factorization of* 12.

One method for finding the prime factorization of a number is by using a factor tree, as shown in the next example.

EXAMPLE 1 Write the prime factorization of 45.

Solution: We can begin by writing 45 as the product of two numbers, say 5 and 9.

$$
\begin{array}{c}
45 \\
\diagup \quad \diagdown \\
5 \quad \cdot \quad 9
\end{array}
$$

The number 5 is prime but 9 is not, so we write 9 as $3 \cdot 3$.

$$
\begin{array}{c}
45 \\
\diagup \quad \diagdown \\
5 \quad \cdot \quad 9 \\
\diagup \quad \diagup \diagdown \\
5 \quad \cdot \quad 3 \quad \cdot \quad 3
\end{array}
\Big\} \; \text{A factor tree}
$$

Each factor is now a prime number, so the prime factorization of 45 is $3 \cdot 3 \cdot 5$ or $3^2 \cdot 5$.

 Work Practice Problem 1

✔ **Concept Check** True or false? Two different numbers can have exactly the same prime factorization. Explain your answer.

EXAMPLE 2 Write the prime factorization of 80.

Solution: Write 80 as a product of two numbers. Continue this process until all factors are prime.

$$
\begin{array}{c}
80 \\
\diagup \quad \diagdown \\
8 \quad \cdot \quad 10 \\
\diagup\diagdown \quad \quad \diagup \diagdown \\
4 \; \cdot 2 \cdot 2 \; \cdot \; 5 \\
\diagup\diagdown \quad | \quad | \quad | \\
2 \cdot 2 \cdot 2 \cdot 2 \cdot 5
\end{array}
$$

All factors are now prime, so the prime factorization of 80 is

$$2 \cdot 2 \cdot 2 \cdot 2 \cdot 5 \quad \text{or} \quad 2^4 \cdot 5.$$

Work Practice Problem 2

Helpful Hint

It makes no difference which factors you start with. The prime factorization of a number will be the same.

$$
\begin{array}{c}
80 \\
\diagup \quad \diagdown \\
20 \quad \cdot \quad 4 \\
\diagup\diagdown \quad | \quad \diagup\diagdown \\
4 \; \cdot \; 5 \cdot 2 \cdot 2 \\
\diagup\diagdown \quad | \quad | \quad | \\
2 \cdot 2 \cdot 5 \cdot 2 \cdot 2
\end{array}
\; \begin{array}{l}\text{Same factors as} \\ \text{in Example 2}\end{array}
$$

PRACTICE PROBLEM 1

Use a factor tree to find the prime factorization of each number.

a. 30   **b.** 56   **c.** 72

PRACTICE PROBLEM 2

Write the prime factorization of 117.

There are a few quick **divisibility tests** to determine whether a number is divisible by the primes 2, 3, or 5. (A number is divisible by 2, for example, if 2 divides it evenly.)

Divisibility Tests

A whole number is divisible by:

- **2** if the last digit is 0, 2, 4, 6, or 8.

  13↓2 is divisible by 2 since the last digit is a 2.

- **3** if the sum of the digits is divisible by 3.

  144 is divisible by 3 since 1 + 4 + 4 = 9 is divisible by 3.

- **5** if the last digit is 0 or 5.

  111↓5 is divisible by 5 since the last digit is a 5.

Helpful Hint

Here are a few other divisibility tests you may find interesting. A whole number is divisible by:

- **4** if its last two digits are divisible by 4.

  1712 is divisible by 4.

- **6** if it's divisible by 2 and 3.

  9858 is divisible by 6.

- **9** if the sum of its digits is divisible by 9.

  5238 is divisible by 9 since 5 + 2 + 3 + 8 = 18 is divisible by 9.

When finding the prime factorization of larger numbers, you may want to use the procedure shown in Example 3.

PRACTICE PROBLEM 3

Write the prime factorization of 297.

EXAMPLE 3 Write the prime factorization of 252.

Solution: For this method, we divide prime numbers into the given number. Since the ones digit of 252 is 2, we know that 252 is divisible by 2.

$$\begin{array}{r} 126 \\ 2\overline{)252} \end{array}$$

126 is divisible by 2 also.

$$\begin{array}{r} 63 \\ 2\overline{)126} \\ 2\overline{)252} \end{array}$$

63 is not divisible by 2 but is divisible by 3. Divide 63 by 3 and continue in this same manner until the quotient is a prime number.

$$\begin{array}{r} 7 \\ 3\overline{)21} \\ 3\overline{)63} \\ 2\overline{)126} \\ 2\overline{)252} \end{array}$$

Helpful Hint

The order of choosing prime numbers does not matter. For consistency, we use the order 2, 3, 5, 7, ...

The prime factorization of 252 is $2 \cdot 2 \cdot 3 \cdot 3 \cdot 7$ or $2^2 \cdot 3^2 \cdot 7$.

Work Practice Problem 3

Answer

3. $3^3 \cdot 11$

In this text, we will write the factorization of a number from the smallest factor to the largest factor.

✔ **Concept Check** True or false? The prime factorization of 60 is $2 \cdot 5 \cdot 6$. Explain your reasoning.

Objective B Writing Fractions in Simplest Form

Fractions that represent the same portion of a whole are called **equivalent fractions.**

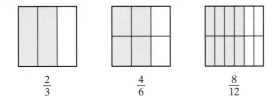

$$\frac{2}{3} \qquad \frac{4}{6} \qquad \frac{8}{12}$$

For example, $\frac{2}{3}, \frac{4}{6},$ and $\frac{8}{12}$ all represent the same shaded portion of the rectangle's area, so they are equivalent fractions.

$$\frac{2}{3} = \frac{4}{6} = \frac{8}{12}$$

A special form of a fraction is called **simplest form.**

Simplest Form of a Fraction

A fraction is written in **simplest form** or **lowest terms** when the numerator and the denominator have no common factors other than 1.

For example, the fraction $\frac{2}{3}$ *is* in simplest form because 2 and 3 have no common factor other than 1. The fraction $\frac{4}{6}$ *is not* in simplest form because 4 and 6 both have a factor of 2. That is, 2 is a common factor of 4 and 6. The process of writing a fraction in simplest form is called **simplifying** the fraction.

To simplify $\frac{4}{6}$ and write it as $\frac{2}{3}$, let's first study a few properties. Recall from Section 3.1 that any nonzero whole number n divided by itself is 1.

Any nonzero number n divided by itself is 1.

$$\frac{5}{5} = 1, \quad \frac{17}{17} = 1, \quad \frac{24}{24} = 1, \text{ or, in general, } \frac{n}{n} = 1$$

Also, in general, if $\frac{a}{b}$ and $\frac{c}{d}$ are fractions (with b and d not 0), the following is true.

$$\frac{a \cdot c}{b \cdot d} = \frac{a}{b} \cdot \frac{c}{d}*$$

These properties allow us to do the following:

$$\frac{4}{6} = \frac{2 \cdot 2}{2 \cdot 3} = \frac{2}{2} \cdot \frac{2}{3} = 1 \cdot \frac{2}{3} = \frac{2}{3} \qquad \text{When 1 is multiplied by a number, the result is the same number.}$$

$\llcorner$ This is 1

Note: We will study this concept further in the next section.

PRACTICE PROBLEM 4

Write in simplest form: $\dfrac{30}{45}$

EXAMPLE 4 Write in simplest form: $\dfrac{12}{20}$

Solution: Notice that 12 and 20 have a common factor of 4.

$$\frac{12}{20} = \frac{4 \cdot 3}{4 \cdot 5} = \frac{4}{4} \cdot \frac{3}{5} = 1 \cdot \frac{3}{5} = \frac{3}{5}$$

Since 3 and 5 have no common factors (other than 1), $\dfrac{3}{5}$ is in simplest form.

◼ **Work Practice Problem 4**

If you have trouble finding common factors, write the prime factorization of the numerator and the denominator.

PRACTICE PROBLEM 5

Write in simplest form: $\dfrac{39}{51}$

EXAMPLE 5 Write in simplest form: $\dfrac{42}{66}$

Solution: Let's write the prime factorizations of 42 and 66.

$$\frac{42}{66} = \frac{2 \cdot 3 \cdot 7}{2 \cdot 3 \cdot 11} = \frac{2}{2} \cdot \frac{3}{3} \cdot \frac{7}{11} = 1 \cdot 1 \cdot \frac{7}{11} = \frac{7}{11}$$

◼ **Work Practice Problem 5**

In the example above, you may have saved time by noticing that 42 and 66 have a common factor of 6.

$$\frac{42}{66} = \frac{6 \cdot 7}{6 \cdot 11} = \frac{6}{6} \cdot \frac{7}{11} = 1 \cdot \frac{7}{11} = \frac{7}{11}$$

Helpful Hint

Writing the prime factorizations of the numerator and the denominator is helpful in finding any common factors.

The method for simplifying negative fractions is the same as for positive fractions.

PRACTICE PROBLEM 6

Write in simplest form: $-\dfrac{9}{50}$

EXAMPLE 6 Write in simplest form: $-\dfrac{10}{27}$

Solution:

$$-\frac{10}{27} = -\frac{2 \cdot 5}{3 \cdot 3 \cdot 3} \qquad \text{Prime factorizations of 10 and 27.}$$

Since 10 and 27 have no common factors, $-\dfrac{10}{27}$ is already in simplest form.

◼ **Work Practice Problem 6**

PRACTICE PROBLEM 7

Write in simplest form: $\dfrac{49}{112}$

EXAMPLE 7 Write in simplest form: $\dfrac{30}{108}$

Solution:

$$\frac{30}{108} = \frac{2 \cdot 3 \cdot 5}{2 \cdot 2 \cdot 3 \cdot 3 \cdot 3} = \frac{2}{2} \cdot \frac{3}{3} \cdot \frac{5}{2 \cdot 3 \cdot 3} = 1 \cdot 1 \cdot \frac{5}{18} = \frac{5}{18}$$

◼ **Work Practice Problem 7**

We can use a shortcut procedure with common factors when simplifying.

$$\frac{4}{6} = \frac{\overset{1}{\cancel{2}} \cdot 2}{\underset{1}{\cancel{2}} \cdot 3} = \frac{1 \cdot 2}{1 \cdot 3} = \frac{2}{3} \qquad \text{Divide out the common factor of 2 in the numerator and denominator.}$$

Answers

4. $\dfrac{2}{3}$, **5.** $\dfrac{13}{17}$, **6.** $-\dfrac{9}{50}$, **7.** $\dfrac{7}{16}$

This procedure is possible because dividing out a common factor in the numerator and denominator is the same as removing a factor of 1 in the product.

Writing a Fraction in Simplest Form

To write a fraction in simplest form, write the prime factorization of the numerator and the denominator and then divide both by all common factors.

EXAMPLE 8 Write in simplest form: $-\dfrac{72}{26}$

Solution:

$$-\frac{72}{26} = -\frac{\overset{1}{\cancel{2}} \cdot 2 \cdot 2 \cdot 3 \cdot 3}{\underset{1}{\cancel{2}} \cdot 13} = -\frac{1 \cdot 2 \cdot 2 \cdot 3 \cdot 3}{1 \cdot 13} = -\frac{36}{13}$$

Work Practice Problem 8

✔ **Concept Check** Which is the correct way to simplify the fraction $\dfrac{15}{25}$? Or are both correct? Explain.

a. $\dfrac{15}{25} = \dfrac{3 \cdot \overset{1}{\cancel{5}}}{5 \cdot \underset{1}{\cancel{5}}} = \dfrac{3}{5}$ **b.** $\dfrac{1\overset{1}{\cancel{5}}}{2\underset{1}{\cancel{5}}} = \dfrac{11}{21}$

EXAMPLE 9 Write in simplest form: $\dfrac{6}{60}$

Solution:

$$\frac{6}{60} = \frac{\overset{1}{\cancel{2}} \cdot \overset{1}{\cancel{3}}}{\underset{1}{\cancel{2}} \cdot 2 \cdot \underset{1}{\cancel{3}} \cdot 5} = \frac{1 \cdot 1}{1 \cdot 2 \cdot 1 \cdot 5} = \frac{1}{10}$$

Work Practice Problem 9

Helpful Hint

Be careful when all factors of the numerator or denominator are divided out. In Example 9, the numerator was $1 \cdot 1 = 1$, so the final result was $\dfrac{1}{10}$.

In the fraction of Example 9, $\dfrac{6}{60}$, you may have immediately noticed that the largest common factor of 6 and 60 is 6. If so, you may simply divide out that common factor.

$$\frac{6}{60} = \frac{\overset{1}{\cancel{6}}}{\underset{1}{\cancel{6}} \cdot 10} = \frac{1}{1 \cdot 10} = \frac{1}{10} \qquad \text{Divide out the common factor of 6.}$$

Notice that the result, $\dfrac{1}{10}$, is in simplest form. If it were not, we would repeat the same procedure until the result was in simplest form.

PRACTICE PROBLEM 8

Write in simplest form: $-\dfrac{64}{20}$

PRACTICE PROBLEM 9

Write in simplest form: $\dfrac{8}{56}$

Answers

8. $-\dfrac{16}{5}$, **9.** $\dfrac{1}{7}$

✔ **Concept Check Answers**

a. correct, **b.** incorrect

Objective C Determining Whether Two Fractions Are Equivalent

Recall that two fractions are equivalent if they represent the same part of a whole. One way to determine whether two fractions are equivalent is to see whether they simplify to the same fraction.

PRACTICE PROBLEM 10

Determine whether $\frac{7}{9}$ and $\frac{21}{27}$ are equivalent.

EXAMPLE 10 Determine whether $\frac{16}{40}$ and $\frac{10}{25}$ are equivalent.

Solution: Simplify each fraction.

$$\frac{16}{40} = \frac{\overset{1}{\cancel{8}} \cdot 2}{\underset{1}{\cancel{8}} \cdot 5} = \frac{1 \cdot 2}{1 \cdot 5} = \frac{2}{5}$$

Since these fractions are the same, $\frac{16}{40} = \frac{10}{25}$.

$$\frac{10}{25} = \frac{2 \cdot \overset{1}{\cancel{5}}}{5 \cdot \underset{1}{\cancel{5}}} = \frac{2 \cdot 1}{5 \cdot 1} = \frac{2}{5}$$

🔲 **Work Practice Problem 10**

There is a shortcut method you may use to check or test whether two fractions are equivalent. In the example above, we learned that the fractions are equivalent, or

$$\frac{16}{40} = \frac{10}{25}$$

In this example above, we call $25 \cdot 16$ and $40 \cdot 10$ **cross products** because they are the products one obtains by multiplying across.

Cross Products

$$25 \cdot 16 \qquad \frac{16}{40} = \frac{10}{25} \qquad 40 \cdot 10$$

Notice that these cross products are equal

$$25 \cdot 16 = 400, \quad 40 \cdot 10 = 400$$

In general, this is true for equivalent fractions.

Equality of Fractions

$$8 \cdot 6 \qquad \frac{6}{24} \overset{?}{=} \frac{2}{8} \qquad 24 \cdot 2$$

Since the cross products ($8 \cdot 6 = 48$ and $24 \cdot 2 = 48$) are equal, the fractions are equal.

Note: If the cross products are not equal, the fractions are not equal.

Answer

10. equivalent

EXAMPLE 11 Determine whether $\frac{8}{11}$ and $\frac{19}{26}$ are equivalent.

Solution: Let's check cross products.

$$26 \cdot 8 = 208 \qquad \frac{8}{11} \stackrel{?}{=} \frac{19}{26} \qquad 11 \cdot 19 = 209$$

Since $208 \neq 209$, then $\frac{8}{11} \neq \frac{19}{26}$.

■ **Work Practice Problem 11**

PRACTICE PROBLEM 11

Determine whether $\frac{4}{13}$ and $\frac{5}{18}$ are equivalent.

Helpful Hint

"Not equal to" symbol

Objective D **Solving Problems by Writing Fractions in Simplest Form**

Many real-life problems can be solved by writing fractions. To make the answers clearer, these fractions should be written in simplest form.

EXAMPLE 12 **Calculating the Fraction of Memorials in Washington, D.C.**

There are 28 national memorials in the United States. Seven of these are located in Washington, D.C. What fraction of the national memorials in the United States can be found in Washington, D.C.? Write the fraction in simplest form. (*Source:* National Park Service)

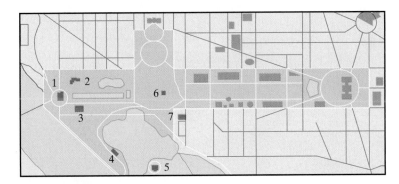

PRACTICE PROBLEM 12

Eighty pigs were used in a recent study of olestra, a calorie-free fat substitute. A group of 12 of these pigs were fed a diet high in fat. What fraction of the pigs were fed the high-fat diet in this study? Write your answer in simplest form. (*Source:* from a study conducted by the Procter & Gamble Company)

Solution: First we determine the fraction of national memorials located in Washington, D.C.

$$\frac{7}{28} \quad \begin{array}{l} \leftarrow \text{ number of national memorials in Washington, D.C.} \\ \leftarrow \text{ total number of national memorials in U.S.} \end{array}$$

Next we simplify the fraction.

$$\frac{7}{28} = \frac{\overset{1}{\cancel{7}}}{\underset{1}{\cancel{7}} \cdot 4} = \frac{1}{1 \cdot 4} = \frac{1}{4}$$

Thus, $\frac{1}{4}$ of the United States' national memorials are in Washington, D.C.

■ **Work Practice Problem 12**

Answers

11. not equivalent, **12.** $\frac{3}{20}$

▦ CALCULATOR EXPLORATIONS   Simplifying Fractions

Scientific Calculator

Many calculators have a fraction key, such as $\boxed{a_{\,b/c}}$, that allows you to simplify a fraction on the calculator. For example, to simplify $\dfrac{324}{612}$, enter

$$\boxed{3}\ \boxed{2}\ \boxed{4}\ \boxed{a_{\,b/c}}\ \boxed{6}\ \boxed{1}\ \boxed{2}\ \boxed{=}$$

The display will read

$$\boxed{\qquad 9\,|\,17 \qquad}$$

which represents $\dfrac{9}{17}$, the original fraction simplified.

> ### Helpful Hint
> The Calculator Explorations boxes in this chapter provide only an introduction to fraction keys on calculators. Any time you use a calculator, there are both advantages and limitations to its use. Never rely solely on your calculator. It is very important that you understand how to perform all operations on fractions by hand in order to progress through later topics. For further information, talk to your instructor.

Use your calculator to simplify each fraction.

1. $\dfrac{128}{224}$

2. $\dfrac{231}{396}$

3. $\dfrac{340}{459}$

4. $\dfrac{999}{1350}$

5. $\dfrac{810}{432}$

6. $\dfrac{315}{225}$

7. $\dfrac{243}{54}$

8. $\dfrac{689}{455}$

Mental Math

1. Is 2430 divisible by 2? By 3? By 5?

Write the prime factorization of each number.

2. 15   **3.** 10   **4.** 6   **5.** 21

6. 4   **7.** 9   **8.** 14

3.2 EXERCISE SET

FOR EXTRA HELP

Student Solutions Manual   PH Math/Tutor Center   CD/Video for Review   MathXL®   MyMathLab

Objective A *Write the prime factorization of each number. See Examples 1 through 3.*

1. 20   **2.** 12   **3.** 48   **4.** 75

5. 45   **6.** 64   **7.** 162   **8.** 128

9. 110   **10.** 130   **11.** 85   **12.** 93

13. 240   **14.** 836   **15.** 828   **16.** 504

Objective B *Write each fraction in simplest form. See Examples 4 through 9.*

17. $\dfrac{3}{12}$ **18.** $\dfrac{5}{30}$ **19.** $\dfrac{4}{42}$ **20.** $\dfrac{9}{48}$ **21.** $\dfrac{14}{16}$

22. $\dfrac{22}{34}$ **23.** $\dfrac{20}{30}$ **24.** $\dfrac{70}{80}$ **25.** $\dfrac{35}{50}$ **26.** $\dfrac{25}{55}$

27. $-\dfrac{63}{81}$ **28.** $-\dfrac{21}{49}$ **29.** $\dfrac{24}{40}$ **30.** $\dfrac{36}{54}$ **31.** $\dfrac{27}{64}$

32. $\dfrac{32}{63}$ **33.** $\dfrac{25}{40}$ **34.** $\dfrac{36}{42}$ **35.** $-\dfrac{40}{64}$ **36.** $-\dfrac{28}{60}$

37. $\dfrac{36}{24}$ **38.** $\dfrac{60}{36}$ **39.** $\dfrac{90}{120}$ **40.** $\dfrac{60}{150}$ **41.** $\dfrac{70}{196}$

42. $\dfrac{98}{126}$ **43.** $\dfrac{66}{308}$ **44.** $\dfrac{65}{234}$ **45.** $-\dfrac{55}{85}$ **46.** $-\dfrac{78}{90}$

47. $\dfrac{189}{216}$ **48.** $\dfrac{144}{162}$ **49.** $\dfrac{224}{16}$ **50.** $\dfrac{270}{15}$

Objective **C** *Determine whether each pair of fractions is equivalent. See Examples 10 and 11.*

51. $\dfrac{3}{6}$ and $\dfrac{4}{8}$ **52.** $\dfrac{3}{9}$ and $\dfrac{2}{6}$ **53.** $\dfrac{7}{11}$ and $\dfrac{5}{8}$ **54.** $\dfrac{2}{5}$ and $\dfrac{4}{11}$

55. $\dfrac{10}{15}$ and $\dfrac{6}{9}$ **56.** $\dfrac{4}{10}$ and $\dfrac{6}{15}$ **57.** $\dfrac{3}{9}$ and $\dfrac{6}{18}$ **58.** $\dfrac{2}{8}$ and $\dfrac{7}{28}$

59. $\dfrac{10}{13}$ and $\dfrac{12}{15}$ **60.** $\dfrac{16}{20}$ and $\dfrac{9}{12}$ **61.** $\dfrac{8}{18}$ and $\dfrac{12}{24}$ **62.** $\dfrac{6}{21}$ and $\dfrac{14}{35}$

Objective **D** *Solve. Write each fraction in simplest form. See Example 12.*

63. A work shift for an employee at McDonald's consists of 8 hours. What fraction of the employee's work shift is represented by 2 hours?

64. Two thousand baseball caps were sold one year at the U.S. Open Golf Tournament. What fractional part of this total does 200 caps represent?

65. There are 5280 feet in a mile. What fraction of a mile is represented by 2640 feet?

66. There are 100 centimeters in 1 meter. What fraction of a meter is 20 centimeters?

67. Fifteen states in the United States have Ritz-Carlton hotels. (*Source:* Ritz-Carlton Hotel Company, LLC)

   a. What fraction of states can claim at least one Ritz-Carlton hotel?

   b. How many states do not have a Ritz-Carlton hotel?

   c. Write the fraction of states without a Ritz-Carlton hotel.

68. There were 74 national monuments in the United States. Ten of these monuments are located in New Mexico. (*Source:* National Park Service)

   a. What fraction of the national monuments in the United States can be found in New Mexico?

   b. How many of the national monuments in the United States are found outside New Mexico?

   c. Write the fraction of national monuments found in states other than New Mexico.

69. The outer wall of the Pentagon is 24 inches wide. Ten inches is concrete, 8 inches is brick, and 6 inches is limestone. What fraction of the wall is concrete? (*Source: USA Today, 1/28/2000*)

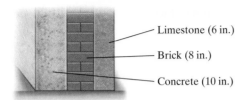

— Limestone (6 in.)

— Brick (8 in.)

— Concrete (10 in.)

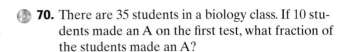

70. There are 35 students in a biology class. If 10 students made an A on the first test, what fraction of the students made an A?

71. As Internet usage grows in the United States, more and more state governments are placing services online. Twenty-eight states have Web sites that allow residents to pay their state income tax online.

   a. How many states do not have this type of Web site?

   b. What fraction of states do not have this type of Web site? (*Source:* Center for Digital Government)

72. Chris Callac just bought a brand new 2005 Toyota Camry for $22,000. His old car was traded in for $10,000.

   a. How much of his purchase price was not covered by his trade-in?

   b. What fraction of the purchase price was not covered by the trade-in?

Review

Multiply. See Section 1.6.

73. $\begin{array}{r} 91 \\ \times\ 4 \\ \hline \end{array}$
   74. $\begin{array}{r} 73 \\ \times\ 8 \\ \hline \end{array}$
   75. $\begin{array}{r} 387 \\ \times\ \ 6 \\ \hline \end{array}$
   76. $\begin{array}{r} 562 \\ \times\ \ 9 \\ \hline \end{array}$
   77. $\begin{array}{r} 72 \\ \times\ 35 \\ \hline \end{array}$
   78. $\begin{array}{r} 238 \\ \times\ 26 \\ \hline \end{array}$

Concept Extensions

79. In your own words, define equivalent fractions.

80. Given a fraction, say $\frac{3}{8}$, how many fractions are there that are equivalent to it? Explain your answer.

Write each fraction in simplest form.

81. $\dfrac{3975}{6625}$

82. $\dfrac{9506}{12,222}$

There are generally considered to be eight basic blood types. The table shows the number of people with the various blood types in a typical group of 100 blood donors. Use the table to answer Exercises 83 through 86. Write each answer in simplest form.

Distribution of Blood Types in Blood Donors	
Blood Type	**Number of People**
O Rh-positive	37
O Rh-negative	7
A Rh-positive	36
A Rh-negative	6
B Rh-positive	9
B Rh-negative	1
AB Rh-positive	3
AB Rh-negative	1
(*Source:* American Red Cross Biomedical Services)	

83. What fraction of blood donors have blood type A Rh-positive?

84. What fraction of blood donors have an O blood type?

85. What fraction of blood donors have an AB blood type?

86. What fraction of blood donors have a B blood type?

Find the prime factorization of each number.

87. 34,020

88. 131,625

89. In your own words, define a prime number.

90. The number 2 is a prime number. All other even natural numbers are composite numbers. Explain why.

91. Two students have different prime factorizations for the same number. Is this possible? Explain.

The following graph is called a circle graph or pie chart. Each sector (shaped like a piece of pie) shows the fraction of entering college freshmen who expect to major in each discipline shown. The whole circle represents the entire class of college freshmen. Use this graph to answer Exercises 92 through 95.

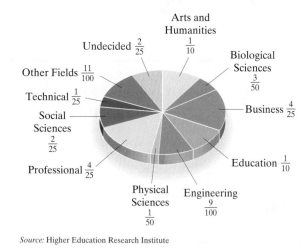

Undecided $\frac{2}{25}$

Arts and Humanities $\frac{1}{10}$

Other Fields $\frac{11}{100}$

Biological Sciences $\frac{3}{50}$

Technical $\frac{1}{25}$

Social Sciences $\frac{2}{25}$

Business $\frac{4}{25}$

Professional $\frac{4}{25}$

Education $\frac{1}{10}$

Physical Sciences $\frac{1}{50}$

Engineering $\frac{9}{100}$

Source: Higher Education Research Institute

92. What fraction of entering college freshmen plan to major in education?

93. What fraction of entering college freshmen plan to major in social sciences?

94. Why is the Professional sector the same size as the Business sector?

95. Why is the Physical Sciences sector smaller than the Biological Sciences sector?

Use the following numbers for Exercises 96 through 99.

8691　　786　　1235　　2235　　85　　105　　22　　222　　900　　1470

96. List the numbers divisible by both 2 and 3.

97. List the numbers that are divisible by both 3 and 5.

98. The answers to Exercise 96, are also divisible by what number? Tell why.

99. The answers to Exercise 97 are also divisible by what number? Tell why.

3.3 MULTIPLYING AND DIVIDING FRACTIONS

Objectives

A Multiply Fractions.

B Evaluate Exponential Expressions with Fractional Bases.

C Divide Fractions.

D Multiply and Divide Given Fractional Replacement Values.

E Solve Applications That Require Multiplication of Fractions.

Objective **A** Multiplying Fractions

Let's use a diagram to discover how fractions are multiplied. For example, to multiply $\frac{1}{2}$ and $\frac{3}{4}$, we find $\frac{1}{2}$ of $\frac{3}{4}$. To do this, we begin with a diagram showing $\frac{3}{4}$ of a rectangle's area shaded.

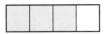 $\frac{3}{4}$ of the rectangle's area is shaded.

To find $\frac{1}{2}$ of $\frac{3}{4}$, we heavily shade $\frac{1}{2}$ of the part that is already shaded.

By counting smaller rectangles, we see that $\frac{3}{8}$ of the larger rectangle is now heavily shaded, so that

$$\frac{1}{2} \text{ of } \frac{3}{4} \text{ is } \frac{3}{8}, \text{ or } \frac{1}{2} \cdot \frac{3}{4} = \frac{3}{8}$$ Notice that $\frac{1}{2} \cdot \frac{3}{4} = \frac{1 \cdot 3}{2 \cdot 4} = \frac{3}{8}$.

Multiplying Fractions

To multiply two fractions, multiply the numerators and multiply the denominators.

If a, b, c, and d represent numbers, and b and d are not 0, we have

$$\frac{a}{b} \cdot \frac{c}{d} = \frac{a \cdot c}{b \cdot d}$$

EXAMPLES Multiply.

1. $\frac{2}{3} \cdot \frac{5}{11} = \frac{2 \cdot 5}{3 \cdot 11} = \frac{10}{33}$

This fraction is in simplest form since 10 and 33 have no common factors other than 1.

2. $\frac{1}{4} \cdot \frac{1}{2} = \frac{1 \cdot 1}{4 \cdot 2} = \frac{1}{8}$

■ **Work Practice Problems 1–2**

PRACTICE PROBLEMS 1–2

Multiply.

1. $\frac{3}{8} \cdot \frac{5}{7}$ **2.** $\frac{1}{3} \cdot \frac{1}{6}$

Answers

1. $\frac{15}{56}$, **2.** $\frac{1}{18}$

PRACTICE PROBLEM 3

Multiply and simplify: $\dfrac{6}{55} \cdot \dfrac{5}{8}$

EXAMPLE 3 Multiply and simplify: $\dfrac{6}{7} \cdot \dfrac{14}{27}$

Solution:

$$\frac{6}{7} \cdot \frac{14}{27} = \frac{6 \cdot 14}{7 \cdot 27}$$

We can simplify by finding the prime factorizations and using our shortcut procedure of dividing out common factors in the numerator and denominator.

$$\frac{6 \cdot 14}{7 \cdot 27} = \frac{2 \cdot \cancel{3} \cdot 2 \cdot \cancel{7}}{\cancel{7} \cdot \cancel{3} \cdot 3 \cdot 3} = \frac{2 \cdot 2}{3 \cdot 3} = \frac{4}{9}$$

⬛ **Work Practice Problem 3**

Helpful Hint

Remember that the shortcut procedure above is the same as removing factors of 1 in the product.

$$\frac{6 \cdot 14}{7 \cdot 27} = \frac{2 \cdot 3 \cdot 2 \cdot 7}{7 \cdot 3 \cdot 3 \cdot 3} = \frac{7}{7} \cdot \frac{3}{3} \cdot \frac{2 \cdot 2}{3 \cdot 3} = 1 \cdot 1 \cdot \frac{4}{9} = \frac{4}{9}$$

Helpful Hint

In simplifying a product, don't forget that it may be possible to identify common factors without actually writing the prime factorization. For example,

$$\frac{10}{11} \cdot \frac{1}{20} = \frac{10 \cdot 1}{11 \cdot 20} = \frac{\cancel{10} \cdot 1}{11 \cdot \cancel{10} \cdot 2} = \frac{1}{11 \cdot 2} = \frac{1}{22}$$

PRACTICE PROBLEM 4

Multiply and simplify: $\dfrac{4}{15} \cdot \dfrac{3}{8}$

EXAMPLE 4 Multiply and simplify: $\dfrac{23}{32} \cdot \dfrac{4}{7}$

Solution: Notice that 4 and 32 have a common factor of 4.

$$\frac{23}{32} \cdot \frac{4}{7} = \frac{23 \cdot 4}{32 \cdot 7} = \frac{23 \cdot \cancel{4}}{\cancel{4} \cdot 8 \cdot 7} = \frac{23}{8 \cdot 7} = \frac{23}{56}$$

⬛ **Work Practice Problem 4**

After multiplying two fractions, always check to see whether the product can be simplified.

PRACTICE PROBLEM 5

Multiply.

5. $\dfrac{1}{2} \cdot \left(-\dfrac{11}{28}\right)$

EXAMPLE 5 Multiply: $-\dfrac{1}{4} \cdot \dfrac{1}{2}$

Solution: Recall that the product of a negative number and a positive number is a negative number.

$$-\frac{1}{4} \cdot \frac{1}{2} = -\frac{1 \cdot 1}{4 \cdot 2} = -\frac{1}{8}$$

⬛ **Work Practice Problem 5**

Answers

3. $\dfrac{3}{44}$, 4. $\dfrac{1}{10}$, 5. $-\dfrac{11}{56}$

EXAMPLES Multiply.

6. $\dfrac{6}{13} \cdot \dfrac{26}{30} = \dfrac{6 \cdot 26}{13 \cdot 30} = \dfrac{\overset{1}{\cancel{6}} \cdot \overset{1}{\cancel{13}} \cdot 2}{\cancel{13} \cdot \cancel{6} \cdot 5} = \dfrac{2}{5}$

7. $\dfrac{1}{3} \cdot \dfrac{2}{5} \cdot \dfrac{9}{16} = \dfrac{1 \cdot 2 \cdot 9}{3 \cdot 5 \cdot 16} = \dfrac{1 \cdot \overset{1}{\cancel{2}} \cdot \overset{1}{\cancel{3}} \cdot 3}{\cancel{3} \cdot 5 \cdot \underset{1}{\cancel{2}} \cdot 8} = \dfrac{3}{40}$

🔲 **Work Practice Problems 6–7**

Objective B Evaluating Expressions with Fractional Bases

The base of an exponential expression can also be a fraction.

$$\left(\dfrac{1}{3}\right)^4 = \underbrace{\dfrac{1}{3} \cdot \dfrac{1}{3} \cdot \dfrac{1}{3} \cdot \dfrac{1}{3}}_{\frac{1}{3} \text{ is a factor 4 times.}} = \dfrac{1 \cdot 1 \cdot 1 \cdot 1}{3 \cdot 3 \cdot 3 \cdot 3} = \dfrac{1}{81}$$

EXAMPLE 8 Evaluate.

a. $\left(\dfrac{2}{5}\right)^4 = \dfrac{2}{5} \cdot \dfrac{2}{5} \cdot \dfrac{2}{5} \cdot \dfrac{2}{5} = \dfrac{2 \cdot 2 \cdot 2 \cdot 2}{5 \cdot 5 \cdot 5 \cdot 5} = \dfrac{16}{625}$

b. $\left(-\dfrac{1}{4}\right)^2 = \left(-\dfrac{1}{4}\right) \cdot \left(-\dfrac{1}{4}\right) = \dfrac{1 \cdot 1}{4 \cdot 4} = \dfrac{1}{16}$

🔲 **Work Practice Problem 8**

Objective C Dividing Fractions

Before we can divide fractions, we need to know how to find the **reciprocal** of a fraction.

Reciprocal of a Fraction

Two numbers are **reciprocals** of each other if their product is 1. The reciprocal of the fraction $\dfrac{a}{b}$ is $\dfrac{b}{a}$ because $\dfrac{a}{b} \cdot \dfrac{b}{a} = \dfrac{a \cdot b}{b \cdot a} = 1$.

For example,

The reciprocal of $\dfrac{2}{5}$ is $\dfrac{5}{2}$ because $\dfrac{2}{5} \cdot \dfrac{5}{2} = \dfrac{10}{10} = 1$.

The reciprocal of 5 is $\dfrac{1}{5}$ because $5 \cdot \dfrac{1}{5} = \dfrac{5}{1} \cdot \dfrac{1}{5} = \dfrac{5}{5} = 1$.

The reciprocal of $-\dfrac{7}{11}$ is $-\dfrac{11}{7}$ because $-\dfrac{7}{11} \cdot -\dfrac{11}{7} = \dfrac{77}{77} = 1$.

Helpful Hint

Every number has a reciprocal except 0. The number 0 has no reciprocal because there is no number such that $0 \cdot a = 1$.

PRACTICE PROBLEMS 6–7

Multiply.

6. $\dfrac{4}{11} \cdot \dfrac{33}{16}$

7. $\dfrac{1}{6} \cdot \dfrac{3}{10} \cdot \dfrac{25}{16}$

PRACTICE PROBLEM 8

Evaluate.

a. $\left(\dfrac{3}{4}\right)^3$ b. $\left(-\dfrac{4}{5}\right)^2$

Answers

6. $\dfrac{3}{4}$,   7. $\dfrac{5}{64}$,   8. a. $\dfrac{27}{64}$,   b. $\dfrac{16}{25}$

Division of fractions has the same meaning as division of whole numbers. For example,

$10 \div 5$ means: How many 5s are there in 10?

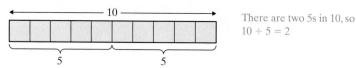

There are two 5s in 10, so $10 \div 5 = 2$

$\dfrac{3}{4} \div \dfrac{1}{8}$ means: How many $\dfrac{1}{8}$s are there in $\dfrac{3}{4}$?

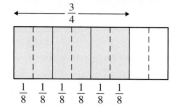

There are six $\dfrac{1}{8}$s in $\dfrac{3}{4}$, so $\dfrac{3}{4} \div \dfrac{1}{8} = 6$

We use reciprocals to divide fractions.

Dividing Fractions

To divide two fractions, multiply the first fraction by the reciprocal of the second fraction.

If a, b, c, and d represent numbers, and b, c, and d are not 0, then

$$\frac{a}{b} \div \frac{c}{d} = \frac{a}{b} \cdot \underset{\uparrow \text{reciprocal}}{\frac{d}{c}} = \frac{a \cdot d}{b \cdot c}$$

For example,

$$\overset{\text{multiply by reciprocal}}{\frac{3}{4} \div \frac{1}{8}} = \frac{3}{4} \cdot \frac{8}{1} = \frac{3 \cdot 8}{4 \cdot 1} = \frac{3 \cdot 2 \cdot \overset{1}{\cancel{4}}}{\underset{1}{\cancel{4}} \cdot 1} = \frac{6}{1} \text{ or } 6$$

Just as when you are multiplying fractions, always check to see whether your answer can be simplified when you divide fractions.

PRACTICE PROBLEMS 9–11

Divide and simplify.

9. $\dfrac{3}{2} \div \dfrac{14}{5}$ **10.** $\dfrac{8}{7} \div \dfrac{2}{9}$

11. $\dfrac{4}{9} \div \dfrac{1}{2}$

EXAMPLES Divide and simplify.

9. $\dfrac{7}{8} \div \dfrac{2}{9} = \dfrac{7}{8} \cdot \dfrac{9}{2} = \dfrac{7 \cdot 9}{8 \cdot 2} = \dfrac{63}{16}$

10. $\dfrac{5}{16} \div \dfrac{3}{4} = \dfrac{5}{16} \cdot \dfrac{4}{3} = \dfrac{5 \cdot 4}{16 \cdot 3} = \dfrac{5 \cdot \overset{1}{\cancel{4}}}{\underset{1}{\cancel{4}} \cdot 4 \cdot 3} = \dfrac{5}{12}$

11. $\dfrac{2}{5} \div \dfrac{1}{2} = \dfrac{2}{5} \cdot \dfrac{2}{1} = \dfrac{2 \cdot 2}{5 \cdot 1} = \dfrac{4}{5}$

◻ **Work Practice Problems 9–11**

Answers

9. $\dfrac{15}{28}$,   **10.** $\dfrac{36}{7}$,   **11.** $\dfrac{8}{9}$

> **Helpful Hint**
>
> When dividing by a fraction, do not look for common factors to divide out until you rewrite the division as multiplication.
>
> Do **not** try to divide out these two 2s.
>
> $$\frac{1}{2} \div \frac{2}{3} = \frac{1}{2} \cdot \frac{3}{2} = \frac{3}{4}$$

EXAMPLE 12 Divide: $-\dfrac{5}{16} \div -\dfrac{3}{4}$

Solution: Recall that the quotient (or product) of two negative numbers is a positive number.

$$-\frac{5}{16} \div -\frac{3}{4} = -\frac{5}{16} \cdot -\frac{4}{3} = \frac{5 \cdot \overset{1}{\cancel{4}}}{\underset{1}{\cancel{4}} \cdot 4 \cdot 3} = \frac{5}{12}$$

🔲 **Work Practice Problem 12**

✔ **Concept Check** Which of the following is the correct way to divide $\dfrac{2}{5}$ by $\dfrac{3}{4}$? Or are both correct? Explain.

a. $\dfrac{5}{2} \cdot \dfrac{3}{4}$ **b.** $\dfrac{2}{5} \cdot \dfrac{4}{3}$

✔ **Concept Check** Which is the correct way to divide $\dfrac{3}{5}$ by $\dfrac{5}{12}$? Explain.

a. $\dfrac{3}{5} \div \dfrac{5}{12} = \dfrac{3}{5} \cdot \dfrac{12}{5}$ **b.** $\dfrac{3}{5} \div \dfrac{5}{12} = \dfrac{5}{3} \cdot \dfrac{5}{12}$

Objective D Multiplying and Dividing with Fractional Replacement Values

EXAMPLE 13 If $x = \dfrac{7}{8}$ and $y = -\dfrac{1}{3}$, evaluate **(a)** xy and **(b)** $x \div y$.

Solution: Replace x with $\dfrac{7}{8}$ and y with $-\dfrac{1}{3}$.

a. $xy = \dfrac{7}{8} \cdot -\dfrac{1}{3}$

$= -\dfrac{7 \cdot 1}{8 \cdot 3}$

$= -\dfrac{7}{24}$

b. $x \div y = \dfrac{7}{8} \div -\dfrac{1}{3}$

$= \dfrac{7}{8} \cdot -\dfrac{3}{1}$

$= -\dfrac{7 \cdot 3}{8 \cdot 1}$

$= -\dfrac{21}{8}$

🔲 **Work Practice Problem 13**

Objective E Solving Problems by Multiplying Fractions

To solve real-life problems that involve multiplying fractions, we use our four problem-solving steps from Chapter 1. In Example 14, a new key word that implies multiplication is used. That key word is "**of.**"

PRACTICE PROBLEM 12

Divide: $\dfrac{10}{4} \div \dfrac{2}{9}$

PRACTICE PROBLEM 13

If $x = -\dfrac{3}{4}$ and $y = \dfrac{9}{2}$, evaluate (a) xy, and (b) $x \div y$.

> **Helpful Hint**
>
> "of" usually translates to multiplication.

Answers

12. $\dfrac{45}{4}$, 13. **a.** $-\dfrac{27}{8}$, **b.** $-\dfrac{1}{6}$

✔ **Concept Check Answers**

a. incorrect, **b.** correct; **a.** correct, **b.** incorrect

PRACTICE PROBLEM 14

About $\frac{1}{3}$ of all plant and animal species in the United States are at risk of becoming extinct. There are 20,439 known species of plants and animals in the United States. How many species are at risk of extinction? (*Source:* The Nature Conservancy)

EXAMPLE 14 Finding the Number of Roller Coasters in an Amusement Park

Cedar Point is an amusement park located in Sandusky, Ohio. Its collection of 68 rides is the largest in the world. Of the rides, $\frac{7}{34}$ are roller coasters. How many roller coasters are in Cedar Point's collection of rides? (*Source:* Cedar Fair, L.P.)

Solution:

1. UNDERSTAND the problem. To do so, read and reread the problem. We are told that $\frac{7}{34}$ of Cedar Point's rides are roller coasters. The word "of" here means multiplication.

2. TRANSLATE.

In words:	Number of roller coasters	is	$\frac{7}{34}$	of	total rides at Cedar Point
	↓	↓	↓	↓	↓
Translate:	Number of roller coasters	=	$\frac{7}{34}$	·	68

3. SOLVE: Before we solve, let's estimate a reasonable answer. The fraction $\frac{7}{34}$ is less than $\frac{1}{2}$ (draw a diagram, if needed), and $\frac{1}{2}$ of 68 rides is 34 rides, so the number of roller coasters should be less than 34.

$$\frac{7}{34} \cdot 68 = \frac{7}{34} \cdot \frac{68}{1} = \frac{7 \cdot 68}{34 \cdot 1} = \frac{7 \cdot \overset{1}{\cancel{34}} \cdot 2}{\underset{1}{\cancel{34}} \cdot 1} = \frac{14}{1} \quad \text{or} \quad 14$$

4. INTERPRET. *Check* your work. From our estimate, our answer is reasonable. *State* your conclusion: The number of roller coasters at Cedar Point is 14.

🔲 **Work Practice Problem 14**

Helpful Hint

To help visualize a fractional part of a whole number, look at the diagram below.

$\frac{1}{5}$ of 60 = ?

$\frac{1}{5}$ of 60 is 12.

Answer

14. 6813 species

Mental Math

Find each product.

1. $\dfrac{1}{3} \cdot \dfrac{2}{5}$

2. $\dfrac{2}{3} \cdot \dfrac{4}{7}$

3. $\dfrac{6}{5} \cdot \dfrac{1}{7}$

4. $\dfrac{7}{3} \cdot \dfrac{2}{3}$

5. $\dfrac{3}{1} \cdot \dfrac{3}{8}$

6. $\dfrac{2}{1} \cdot \dfrac{7}{11}$

3.3 EXERCISE SET

FOR EXTRA HELP

Student Solutions Manual | PH Math/Tutor Center | CD/Video for Review | MathXL® | MyMathLab

Objective **A** *Multiply. Write the product in simplest form. See Examples 1 through 7.*

1. $\dfrac{7}{8} \cdot \dfrac{2}{3}$

2. $\dfrac{5}{9} \cdot \dfrac{7}{4}$

3. $-\dfrac{2}{7} \cdot \dfrac{5}{8}$

4. $\dfrac{5}{8} \cdot -\dfrac{1}{3}$

5. $-\dfrac{1}{2} \cdot -\dfrac{2}{15}$

6. $-\dfrac{3}{8} \cdot -\dfrac{5}{12}$

7. $\dfrac{6}{5} \cdot \dfrac{1}{7}$

8. $\dfrac{7}{3} \cdot \dfrac{1}{4}$

9. $\dfrac{2}{7} \cdot \dfrac{5}{8}$

10. $\dfrac{7}{8} \cdot \dfrac{2}{3}$

11. $\dfrac{5}{28} \cdot \dfrac{2}{25}$

12. $\dfrac{4}{35} \cdot \dfrac{5}{24}$

13. $0 \cdot \dfrac{8}{9}$

14. $\dfrac{11}{12} \cdot 0$

15. $\dfrac{18}{20} \cdot \dfrac{36}{99}$

16. $\dfrac{5}{32} \cdot \dfrac{64}{100}$

17. $\dfrac{11}{20} \cdot \dfrac{1}{7} \cdot \dfrac{5}{22}$

18. $\dfrac{27}{32} \cdot \dfrac{10}{13} \cdot \dfrac{16}{30}$

Objective **B** *Evaluate. See Example 8.*

19. $\left(\dfrac{1}{5}\right)^3$

20. $\left(-\dfrac{1}{2}\right)^4$

21. $\left(-\dfrac{2}{3}\right)^2$

22. $\left(\dfrac{8}{9}\right)^2$

23. $\left(-\dfrac{2}{3}\right)^3 \cdot \dfrac{1}{2}$

24. $\left(-\dfrac{3}{4}\right)^3 \cdot \dfrac{1}{3}$

Objective **C** *Divide. Write all quotients in simplest form. See Examples 9 through 12.*

25. $\dfrac{2}{3} \div \dfrac{5}{6}$

26. $\dfrac{5}{8} \div \dfrac{2}{3}$

27. $-\dfrac{6}{15} \div \dfrac{12}{5}$

28. $-\dfrac{4}{15} \div -\dfrac{8}{3}$

29. $\dfrac{8}{9} \div -\dfrac{1}{2}$

30. $\dfrac{10}{11} \div -\dfrac{4}{5}$ **31.** $-\dfrac{2}{3} \div 4$ **32.** $-\dfrac{5}{6} \div 10$ **33.** $\dfrac{1}{10} \div \dfrac{10}{1}$ **34.** $\dfrac{3}{13} \div \dfrac{13}{3}$

35. $\dfrac{7}{45} \div \dfrac{4}{25}$ **36.** $\dfrac{14}{52} \div \dfrac{1}{13}$ **37.** $\dfrac{3}{25} \div \dfrac{27}{40}$ **38.** $\dfrac{6}{15} \div \dfrac{7}{10}$ **39.** $\dfrac{8}{13} \div 0$

40. $0 \div \dfrac{4}{11}$ **41.** $0 \div \dfrac{7}{8}$ **42.** $\dfrac{2}{3} \div 0$

Objectives **A** **B** **C** **Mixed Practice** *Perform each indicated operation. See Examples 1 through 12.*

43. $\dfrac{2}{3} \cdot \dfrac{5}{9}$ **44.** $\dfrac{8}{15} \cdot \dfrac{5}{32}$ **45.** $-\dfrac{5}{28} \cdot \dfrac{35}{25}$ **46.** $\dfrac{24}{45} \cdot -\dfrac{5}{8}$ **47.** $-\dfrac{3}{5} \div -\dfrac{4}{5}$

48. $-\dfrac{11}{16} \div -\dfrac{13}{16}$ **49.** $\left(-\dfrac{3}{4}\right)^2$ **50.** $\left(-\dfrac{1}{2}\right)^5$ **51.** $7 \div \dfrac{2}{11}$ **52.** $-100 \div \dfrac{1}{2}$

53. $\dfrac{4}{8} \div \dfrac{3}{16}$ **54.** $\dfrac{9}{2} \div \dfrac{16}{15}$ **55.** $\left(\dfrac{1}{2} \cdot \dfrac{2}{3}\right) \div \dfrac{5}{6}$ **56.** $\left(\dfrac{3}{4} \cdot \dfrac{8}{9}\right) \div \dfrac{2}{5}$

Objective **D** *Given the following replacement values, evaluate (**a**) xy and (**b**) x ÷ y. See Example 13.*

57. $x = \dfrac{2}{5}$ and $y = \dfrac{5}{6}$

   a.

   b.

58. $x = \dfrac{8}{9}$ and $y = \dfrac{1}{4}$

   a.

   b.

59. $x = -\dfrac{4}{5}$ and $y = \dfrac{9}{11}$

   a.

   b.

60. $x = \dfrac{7}{6}$ and $y = -\dfrac{1}{2}$

   a.

   b.

Objective **E** *Solve. Write each answer in simplest form. For Exercises 61 through 64, recall that "of" translates to multiplication. See Example 14.*

61. Find $\dfrac{1}{4}$ of 200.   **62.** Find $\dfrac{1}{5}$ of 200.   **63.** Find $\dfrac{5}{6}$ of 24.   **64.** Find $\dfrac{5}{8}$ of 24.

Solve. See Example 14.

65. Each turn of a screw sinks it $\frac{3}{16}$ of an inch deeper into a piece of wood. Find how deep the screw is after 8 turns.

$\frac{3}{16}$ inch

66. A veterinarian's dipping vat holds 36 gallons of liquid. She normally fills it $\frac{5}{6}$ full of a medicated flea dip solution. Find how many gallons of solution are normally in the vat.

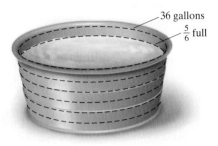

36 gallons

$\frac{5}{6}$ full

67. The Oregon National Historic Trail is 2,170 miles long. It begins in Independence, Missouri, and ends in Oregon City, Oregon. Manfred Coulon has hiked $\frac{2}{5}$ of the trail before. How many miles has he hiked? (*Source:* National Park Service)

Oregon City

Independence

68. Movie theater owners received a total of $7660 million in movie admission tickets. About $\frac{7}{10}$ of this amount was for R-rated movies. Find the amount of money received from R-rated movies. (*Source:* Motion Picture Association of America)

△ **69.** The radius of a circle is one-half of its diameter as shown. If the diameter of a circle is $\frac{3}{8}$ of an inch, what is its radius?

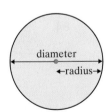

diameter

←radius→

70. An estimate for an adult's waist measurement is found by multiplying the neck size (in inches) by 2. Jock's neck measures $\frac{36}{2}$ inches. Estimate his waist measurement.

71. A patient was told that no more than $\frac{1}{5}$ of his calories should come from fat. If his diet consists of 3000 calories a day, how many of these calories can come from fat?

72. A recipe calls for $\frac{1}{3}$ of a cup of flour. How much flour should be used if only $\frac{1}{2}$ of the recipe is being made?

73. A special on a cruise to the Bahamas is advertised to be $\frac{2}{3}$ of the regular price. If the regular price is $2757, what is the sale price?

74. The Gonzales recently sold their house for $102,000, but $\frac{3}{50}$ of this amount goes to the real estate companies that helped them sell their house. How much money do the Gonzales pay to the real estate companies?

Find the area of each rectangle. Recall that area = length · width.

△ **75.**

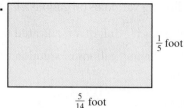

$\frac{1}{5}$ foot

$\frac{5}{14}$ foot

△ **76.**

$\frac{1}{2}$ mile

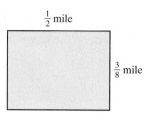

$\frac{3}{8}$ mile

*The following graph is called a **circle graph** or **pie chart.** Each sector (shaped like a piece of pie) shows the fractional part of a car's total mileage that falls into a particular category. The whole circle represents a car's total mileage.*

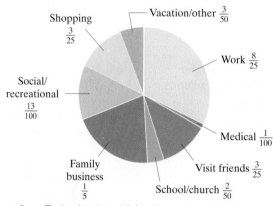

Shopping $\frac{3}{25}$

Vacation/other $\frac{3}{50}$

Work $\frac{8}{25}$

Social/ recreational $\frac{13}{100}$

Medical $\frac{1}{100}$

Family business $\frac{1}{5}$

Visit friends $\frac{3}{25}$

School/church $\frac{2}{50}$

Source: The American Automobile Manufacturers Association and The National Automobile Dealers Association

In one year, a family drove 12,000 miles in the family car. Use the circle graph to determine how many of these miles might be expected to fall in the categories shown in Exercises 77 through 80.

77. Work

78. Shopping

79. Family business

80. Medical

Review

Perform each indicated operation. See Sections 1.3 and 1.4.

81.
$$\begin{array}{r} 27 \\ 76 \\ + \ 98 \\ \hline \end{array}$$

82.
$$\begin{array}{r} 811 \\ 42 \\ + \ 69 \\ \hline \end{array}$$

83.
$$\begin{array}{r} 968 \\ - \ 772 \\ \hline \end{array}$$

84.
$$\begin{array}{r} 882 \\ - \ 773 \\ \hline \end{array}$$

Concept Extensions

85. In your own words, describe how to divide fractions.

86. In your own words, explain how to multiply fractions.

Simplify.

87. $\frac{42}{25} \cdot \frac{125}{36} \div \frac{7}{6}$

88. $\left(\frac{8}{13} \cdot \frac{39}{16} \cdot \frac{8}{9} \right)^2 \div \frac{1}{2}$

89. The FedEx Express air fleet includes 258 Cessnas. These Cessnas make up $\dfrac{129}{320}$ of the FedEx fleet. How many aircraft make up the entire FedEx Express air fleet? (*Source:* FedEx Corporation)

90. One-third of all native flowering plant species in the United States are at risk of becoming extinct. That translates into 5144 at-risk flowering plant species. Based on this data, how many flowering plant species are native to the United States overall? (*Source:* The Nature Conservancy)

(*Hint:* How many $\dfrac{1}{3}$s are in 5144?)

91. If $\dfrac{3}{4}$ of 36 students on a first bus are girls and $\dfrac{2}{3}$ of the 30 students on a second bus are *boys,* how many students on the two buses are girls?

92. According to the 2000 census, in that year there were 34,800,000 Americans age 65 or older. About $\dfrac{11}{20}$ of these older Americans had annual incomes *under* \$15,000. How many older Americans had incomes greater than or equal to \$15,000? (*Source:* U.S. Census Bureau)

93. In 2004, there were approximately 10,600 commercial radio stations broadcasting in the United States. Of these stations, $\dfrac{32}{265}$ were news/talk stations. How many radio stations were news/talk stations in 2004? (*Source:* Corporation for Public Broadcasting)

 THE BIGGER PICTURE   **Operations on Sets of Numbers**

Continue your outline from Sections 1.7, 1.9, and 2.5. Suggestions are once again written to help you complete this part of your outline, Section I.C. Fractions.

I. Operations on Sets of Numbers

  A. Whole Numbers

    1. Add or Subtract (Sections 1.3, 1.4)

    2. Multiply or Divide (Sections 1.6, 1.7)

    3. Exponent (Section 1.9)

    4. Square Root (Section 1.9)

    5. Order of Operations (Section 1.9)

  B. Integers

    1. Add (Section 2.3)

    2. Subtract (Section 2.4)

    3. Multiply or Divide (Section 2.5)

  C. Fractions

    1. Simplify: Factor the numerator and denominator. Then divide out factors of 1 by dividing out common factors in the numerator and denominator.

$$\text{Simplify: } \frac{20}{28} = \frac{\overset{1}{\cancel{4}} \cdot 5}{\underset{1}{\cancel{4}} \cdot 7} = \frac{5}{7}$$

    2. Multiply: Numerator times numerator over denominator times denominator. $\dfrac{5}{9} \cdot \dfrac{2}{7} = \dfrac{10}{63}$

    3. Divide: First fraction times the reciprocal of the second fraction.

$$\frac{2}{11} \div \frac{3}{4} = \frac{2}{11} \cdot \frac{4}{3} = \frac{8}{33}$$

Perform the indicated operations.

1. $\dfrac{2}{3} \cdot \dfrac{8}{9}$ **2.** $\dfrac{2}{3} \div \dfrac{8}{9}$

3. $12 \cdot \dfrac{1}{9}$ **4.** $4\dfrac{1}{2} \div 1\dfrac{7}{8}$

5. $\sqrt{64}$ **6.** $3^2 \cdot 2^3$

7. $\dfrac{11}{20} \cdot \dfrac{5}{8} \cdot \dfrac{4}{33}$ **8.** $20 \div \dfrac{1}{2}$

9. $3 + 4(18 - 16)^3$ **10.** $100 - 76$

A Add or Subtract Like Fractions.

B Solve Problems by Adding or Subtracting Like Fractions.

C Find the Least Common Denominator of a List of Fractions.

D Write Equivalent Fractions.

3.4 ADDING AND SUBTRACTING LIKE FRACTIONS AND LEAST COMMON DENOMINATOR

Fractions with the same denominator are called **like fractions.** Fractions that have different denominators are called **unlike fractions.**

Like Fractions

$\frac{2}{5}$ and $\frac{3}{5}$
↑___↑ same denominator

$\frac{5}{21}, \frac{16}{21}$, and $\frac{7}{21}$
↑___↑___↑ same denominator

Unlike Fractions

$\frac{2}{5}$ and $\frac{3}{4}$
↑___↑ different denominators

$\frac{5}{7}$ and $\frac{5}{9}$
↑___↑ different denominators

Objective **A** Adding or Subtracting Like Fractions

To see how we add like fractions (fractions with the same denominator), study the figures below:

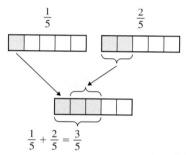

$$\frac{1}{5} + \frac{2}{5} = \frac{3}{5}$$

A similar figure can be used to illustrate subtracting fractions.

Adding or Subtracting Like Fractions (Fractions with the Same Denominator)

If a, b, and c, are numbers and b is not 0, then

$$\frac{a}{b} + \frac{c}{b} = \frac{a+c}{b} \qquad \text{and also} \qquad \frac{a}{b} - \frac{c}{b} = \frac{a-c}{b}$$

In other words, to add or subtract fractions with the same denominator, add or subtract their numerators and write the sum or difference over the **common** denominator.

For example,

$$\frac{1}{4} + \frac{2}{4} = \frac{1+2}{4} = \frac{3}{4}$$
Add the numerators.
Keep the denominator.

$$\frac{4}{5} - \frac{2}{5} = \frac{4-2}{5} = \frac{2}{5}$$
Subtract the numerators.
Keep the denominator.

Helpful Hint

As usual, don't forget to write all answers in simplest form.

EXAMPLES Add and simplify.

1. $\dfrac{2}{7} + \dfrac{3}{7} = \dfrac{2+3}{7} = \dfrac{5}{7}$ ← Add the numerators.
   ← Keep the common denominator.

2. $\dfrac{3}{16} + \dfrac{7}{16} = \dfrac{3+7}{16} = \dfrac{10}{16} = \dfrac{\overset{1}{\cancel{2}} \cdot 5}{\underset{1}{\cancel{2}} \cdot 8} = \dfrac{5}{8}$

3. $\dfrac{7}{8} + \dfrac{6}{8} + \dfrac{3}{8} = \dfrac{7+6+3}{8} = \dfrac{16}{8}$ or 2

🔲 **Work Practice Problems 1–3**

✔ **Concept Check** Find and correct the error in the following:

$$\dfrac{1}{5} + \dfrac{1}{5} = \dfrac{2}{10}$$

EXAMPLES Subtract and simplify.

4. $\dfrac{8}{9} - \dfrac{1}{9} = \dfrac{8-1}{9} = \dfrac{7}{9}$ ← Subtract the numerators.
   ← Keep the common denominator.

5. $\dfrac{7}{8} - \dfrac{5}{8} = \dfrac{7-5}{8} = \dfrac{2}{8} = \dfrac{\overset{1}{\cancel{2}}}{\underset{1}{\cancel{2}} \cdot 4} = \dfrac{1}{4}$

🔲 **Work Practice Problems 4–5**

From our earlier work, we know that

$$\dfrac{-12}{6} = \dfrac{12}{-6} = -\dfrac{12}{6}$$

In general, the following is true:

$$\dfrac{-a}{b} = \dfrac{a}{-b} = -\dfrac{a}{b} \quad \text{as long as } b \text{ is not } 0.$$

EXAMPLE 6 Add: $-\dfrac{11}{8} + \dfrac{6}{8}$

Solution: $-\dfrac{11}{8} + \dfrac{6}{8} = \dfrac{-11+6}{8}$

$$= \dfrac{-5}{8} \quad \text{or} \quad -\dfrac{5}{8}$$

🔲 **Work Practice Problem 6**

EXAMPLE 7 Subtract: $\dfrac{3}{4} - \dfrac{7}{4}$

Solution: $\dfrac{3}{4} - \dfrac{7}{4} = \dfrac{3-7}{4} = \dfrac{3+(-7)}{4} = \dfrac{-4}{4} = -1$

🔲 **Work Practice Problem 7**

PRACTICE PROBLEMS 1–3

Add and simplify.

1. $\dfrac{5}{9} + \dfrac{2}{9}$

2. $\dfrac{5}{8} + \dfrac{1}{8}$

3. $\dfrac{10}{11} + \dfrac{1}{11} + \dfrac{7}{11}$

PRACTICE PROBLEMS 4–5

Subtract and simplify.

4. $\dfrac{7}{12} - \dfrac{2}{12}$ 5. $\dfrac{9}{10} - \dfrac{1}{10}$

PRACTICE PROBLEM 6

Add: $-\dfrac{8}{5} + \dfrac{4}{5}$

PRACTICE PROBLEM 7

Subtract: $\dfrac{2}{5} - \dfrac{7}{5}$

Answers

1. $\dfrac{7}{9}$, 2. $\dfrac{3}{4}$, 3. $\dfrac{18}{11}$, 4. $\dfrac{5}{12}$, 5. $\dfrac{4}{5}$

6. $-\dfrac{4}{5}$, 7. -1

✔ **Concept Check Answer**

We don't add denominators together; correct solution: $\dfrac{1}{5} + \dfrac{1}{5} = \dfrac{2}{5}$.

PRACTICE PROBLEM 8

Subtract: $\dfrac{4}{11} - \dfrac{6}{11} - \dfrac{3}{11}$

EXAMPLE 8 Subtract: $\dfrac{3}{7} - \dfrac{6}{7} - \dfrac{3}{7}$

Solution: $\dfrac{3}{7} - \dfrac{6}{7} - \dfrac{3}{7} = \dfrac{3 - 6 - 3}{7} = \dfrac{-6}{7}$ or $-\dfrac{6}{7}$

☐ **Work Practice Problem 8**

Helpful Hint

Recall that

$$\dfrac{-6}{7} = -\dfrac{6}{7} \quad \left(\text{Also, } \dfrac{6}{-7} = -\dfrac{6}{7}, \text{ if needed.}\right)$$

Objective **B** **Solving Problems by Adding or Subtracting Like Fractions**

Many real-life problems involve finding the perimeters of square or rectangular areas such as pastures, swimming pools, and so on. We can use our knowledge of adding fractions to find perimeters.

PRACTICE PROBLEM 9

Find the perimeter of the square.

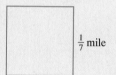

$\dfrac{1}{7}$ mile

EXAMPLE 9 Find the perimeter of the rectangle.

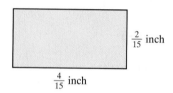

$\dfrac{2}{15}$ inch

$\dfrac{4}{15}$ inch

Solution: Recall that perimeter means distance around and that opposite sides of a rectangle are the same length.

$\dfrac{4}{15}$ inch

$\dfrac{2}{15}$ inch $\dfrac{2}{15}$ inch

$\dfrac{4}{15}$ inch

$$\text{Perimeter} = \dfrac{2}{15} + \dfrac{4}{15} + \dfrac{2}{15} + \dfrac{4}{15} = \dfrac{2 + 4 + 2 + 4}{15}$$

$$= \dfrac{12}{15} = \dfrac{\overset{1}{\cancel{3}} \cdot 4}{\underset{1}{\cancel{3}} \cdot 5} = \dfrac{4}{5}$$

The perimeter of the rectangle is $\dfrac{4}{5}$ inch.

☐ **Work Practice Problem 9**

We can combine our skills in adding and subtracting fractions with our four problem-solving steps from Chapter 1 to solve many kinds of real-life problems.

Answers

8. $-\dfrac{5}{11}$, **9.** $\dfrac{4}{7}$ mi

EXAMPLE 10 **Calculating Distance**

The distance from home to the World Gym is $\frac{7}{8}$ of a mile and from home to the post office is $\frac{3}{8}$ of a mile. How much farther is it from home to the World Gym than from home to the post office?

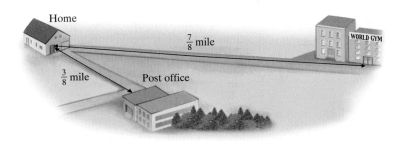

Home

$\frac{7}{8}$ mile

WORLD GYM

$\frac{3}{8}$ mile   Post office

Solution:

1. UNDERSTAND. Read and reread the problem. The phrase "How much farther" tells us to subtract distances.

2. TRANSLATE.

In words:	distance farther	is	home to World Gym distance	minus	home to post office distance
	↓	↓	↓	↓	↓
Translate:	distance farther	=	$\frac{7}{8}$	−	$\frac{3}{8}$

3. SOLVE: $\frac{7}{8} - \frac{3}{8} = \frac{7-3}{8} = \frac{4}{8} = \frac{\overset{1}{\cancel{4}}}{2 \cdot \cancel{4}} = \frac{1}{2}$

4. INTERPRET. *Check* your work. *State* your conclusion: The distance from home to the World Gym is $\frac{1}{2}$ mile farther than from home to the post office.

▢ **Work Practice Problem 10**

Objective **C** Finding the Least Common Denominator

In the next section, we will add and subtract fractions that have different denominators. To add or subtract fractions that have unlike, or different, denominators, we first write them as equivalent fractions with a common denominator.

Although any common denominator can be used to add or subtract unlike fractions, we will use the **least common denominator (LCD).** The LCD of a list of fractions is the same as the **least common multiple (LCM)** of the denominators. Why do we use this number as the common denominator? Since the LCD is the *smallest* of all common denominators, operations are usually less tedious with this number.

The **least common denominator (LCD)** of a list of fractions is the smallest positive number divisible by all the denominators in the list. (The least common denominator is also the **least common multiple (LCM)** of the denominators.)

For example, the LCD of $\frac{1}{4}$ and $\frac{3}{10}$ is 20 because 20 is the smallest positive number divisible by both 4 and 10.

PRACTICE PROBLEM 10

A jogger ran $\frac{13}{4}$ miles on Monday and $\frac{7}{4}$ miles on Wednesday. How much farther did he run on Monday than on Wednesday?

Answer

10. $\frac{3}{2}$ mi

Finding the LCD (or LCM): Method 1

One way to find the LCD is to see whether the larger denominator is divisible by the smaller denominator. If so, the larger number is the LCD. If not, then check consecutive multiples of the larger denominator until the LCD is found.

> ### Method 1: Finding the LCM of a List of Numbers (or Denominators) Using Multiples of the Largest Number
>
> **Step 1:** Write the multiples of the largest denominator (starting with the number itself) until a multiple common to all denominators in the list is found.
>
> **Step 2:** The multiple found in Step 1 is the LCM.

PRACTICE PROBLEM 11

Find the LCM of 8 and 16.

EXAMPLE 11 Find the LCM of 7 and 14.

Solution: We write the multiples of 14 until we find one that is also a multiple of 7.

$14 \cdot 1 = 14$ A multiple of 7

The LCM of 7 and 14 is 14.

▣ **Work Practice Problem 11**

PRACTICE PROBLEM 12

Find the LCM of 25 and 30.

EXAMPLE 12 Find the LCM of 12 and 20.

Solution: We write the multiples of 20 until we find one that is also a multiple of 12.

$20 \cdot 1 = 20$ Not a multiple of 12
$20 \cdot 2 = 40$ Not a multiple of 12
$20 \cdot 3 = 60$ A multiple of 12

The LCM of 12 and 20 is 60.

▣ **Work Practice Problem 12**

Method 1 for finding multiples works fine for smaller numbers, but may get tedious for larger numbers. A second method that uses prime factorization may be easier to use for larger numbers.

Finding the LCD (or LCM): Method 2

For example, to find the LCM of 270 and 84, let's look at the prime factorization of each.

$$270 = 2 \cdot 3 \cdot 3 \cdot 3 \cdot 5$$
$$84 = 2 \cdot 2 \cdot 3 \cdot 7$$

Recall that the LCM must be a multiple of both 270 and 84. Thus, to build the LCM, we will circle the greatest number of factors for each different prime number. The LCM is the product of the circled factors.

Prime Number Factors

270 =	2 ·	(3 · 3 · 3) ·	(5)
84 =	(2 · 2) ·	3 ·	(7)

$$\text{LCM} = 2 \cdot 2 \cdot 3 \cdot 3 \cdot 3 \cdot 5 \cdot 7 = 3780$$

The number 3780 is the smallest number that both 270 and 84 divide into evenly.

This method 2 is summarized below:

Method 2: Finding the LCM of a List of Numbers Using Prime Factorization

Step 1: Write the prime factorization of each number.

Step 2: For each different prime factor in Step 1, circle the greatest number of times that factor occurs in any one factorization.

Step 3: The LCM is the product of the circled factors.

EXAMPLE 13 Find the LCM of 72 and 60.

Solution: First we write the prime factorization of each number.

$$72 = 2 \cdot 2 \cdot 2 \cdot 3 \cdot 3$$
$$60 = 2 \cdot 2 \cdot 3 \cdot 5$$

For the prime factors shown, we circle the greatest number of factors found in either factorization.

$$72 = \boxed{2 \cdot 2 \cdot 2} \cdot \boxed{3 \cdot 3}$$
$$60 = 2 \cdot 2 \cdot 3 \cdot \boxed{5}$$

The LCM is the product of the circled factors.

$$\text{LCM} = 2 \cdot 2 \cdot 2 \cdot 3 \cdot 3 \cdot 5 = 360$$

The LCM is 360.

▣ **Work Practice Problem 13**

PRACTICE PROBLEM 13

Find the LCM of 40 and 108.

Helpful Hint If you prefer working with exponents, circle the factor with the greatest exponent.

Example 13:

$$72 = \boxed{2^3} \cdot \boxed{3^2}$$
$$60 = 2^2 \cdot 3 \cdot \boxed{5}$$
$$\text{LCD} = 2^3 \cdot 3^2 \cdot 5 = 360$$

Helpful Hint If the number of factors of a prime number are equal, circle either one, but not both. For example,

$$12 = \boxed{2 \cdot 2} \cdot \boxed{3}$$
$$15 = 3 \cdot \boxed{5}$$

Circle either 3 but not both.

The LCM is $2 \cdot 2 \cdot 3 \cdot 5 = 60$.

EXAMPLE 14 Find the LCM of 15, 18, and 54.

Solution:
$$15 = 3 \cdot \boxed{5}$$
$$18 = \boxed{2} \cdot 3 \cdot 3$$
$$54 = 2 \cdot \boxed{3 \cdot 3 \cdot 3}$$

The LCM is $2 \cdot 3 \cdot 3 \cdot 3 \cdot 5$ or 270.

▣ **Work Practice Problem 14**

PRACTICE PROBLEM 14

Find the LCM of 20, 24, and 45.

Answers
13. 1080, **14.** 360

Objective D Writing Equivalent Fractions

To add or subtract unlike fractions in the next section, we first write equivalent fractions with the LCM as the denominator. Recall from Section 3.2 that fractions that represent the same portion of a whole are called "equivalent fractions."

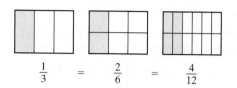

$$\frac{1}{3} \quad = \quad \frac{2}{6} \quad = \quad \frac{4}{12}$$

To write $\frac{1}{3}$ as an equivalent fraction with a denominator of 12, we multiply by 1 in the form of $\frac{4}{4}$.

$$\frac{1}{3} = \frac{1}{3} \cdot 1 = \frac{1}{3} \cdot \frac{4}{4} = \frac{1 \cdot 4}{3 \cdot 4} = \frac{4}{12}$$

$$\frac{4}{4} = 1$$

So $\frac{1}{3} = \frac{4}{12}$.

To write an equivalent fraction,

$$\frac{a}{b} = \frac{a}{b} \cdot \frac{c}{c} = \frac{a \cdot c}{b \cdot c}$$

where a, b, and c are nonzero numbers.

✔ **Concept Check** Which of the following is not equivalent to $\frac{3}{4}$?

a. $\frac{6}{8}$ **b.** $\frac{18}{24}$ **c.** $\frac{9}{14}$ **d.** $\frac{30}{40}$

PRACTICE PROBLEM 15

Write an equivalent fraction with the indicated denominator: $\frac{7}{8} = \frac{}{56}$

Answer

15. $\frac{49}{56}$

✔ **Concept Check Answer**

c

EXAMPLE 15 Write an equivalent fraction with the indicated denominator.

$$\frac{3}{4} = \frac{}{20}$$

Solution: In the denominators, since $4 \cdot 5 = 20$, we will multiply by 1 in the form of $\frac{5}{5}$.

$$\frac{3}{4} = \frac{3}{4} \cdot \frac{5}{5} = \frac{3 \cdot 5}{4 \cdot 5} = \frac{15}{20}$$

Thus, $\frac{3}{4} = \frac{15}{20}$.

■ **Work Practice Problem 15**

Helpful Hint

To check Example 15, write $\dfrac{15}{20}$ in simplest form.

$$\frac{15}{20} = \frac{3 \cdot \overset{1}{\cancel{5}}}{4 \cdot \underset{1}{\cancel{5}}} = \frac{3}{4}, \text{ the original fraction.}$$

If the original fraction is in lowest terms, we can check our work by writing the new equivalent fraction in simplest form. This form should be the original fraction.

EXAMPLE 16 Write an equivalent fraction with the indicated denominator.

$$\frac{1}{2} = \frac{}{14}$$

Solution: Since $2 \cdot 7 = 14$, we multiply by 1 in the form of $\dfrac{7}{7}$.

$$\frac{1}{2} = \frac{1}{2} \cdot \frac{7}{7} = \frac{1 \cdot 7}{2 \cdot 7} = \frac{7}{14}$$

Thus, $\dfrac{1}{2} = \dfrac{7}{14}$.

Work Practice Problem 16

✔**Concept Check** True or false? When the fraction $\dfrac{2}{9}$ is rewritten as an equivalent fraction with 27 as the denominator, the result is $\dfrac{2}{27}$.

PRACTICE PROBLEM 16

Write an equivalent fraction with the indicated denominator.

$$\frac{3}{5} = \frac{}{15}$$

Answer

16. $\dfrac{9}{15}$

✔ Concept Check Answer

false; the correct result would be $\dfrac{6}{27}$

Mental Math

State whether the fractions in each list are like or unlike fractions.

1. $\dfrac{7}{8}, \dfrac{7}{10}$

2. $\dfrac{2}{3}, \dfrac{4}{9}$

3. $\dfrac{9}{10}, \dfrac{1}{10}$

4. $\dfrac{8}{11}, \dfrac{2}{11}$

5. $\dfrac{2}{31}, \dfrac{30}{31}, \dfrac{19}{31}$

6. $\dfrac{3}{10}, \dfrac{3}{11}, \dfrac{3}{13}$

7. $\dfrac{5}{12}, \dfrac{7}{12}, \dfrac{12}{11}$

8. $\dfrac{1}{5}, \dfrac{2}{5}, \dfrac{4}{5}$

3.4 EXERCISE SET

FOR EXTRA HELP

Student Solutions Manual  PH Math/Tutor Center CD/Video for Review MathXL® MyMathLab

Objective A *Add and simplify. See Examples 1 through 3, and 6.*

1. $\dfrac{1}{7} + \dfrac{2}{7}$

2. $\dfrac{9}{17} + \dfrac{2}{17}$

3. $\dfrac{1}{10} + \dfrac{1}{10}$

4. $\dfrac{1}{4} + \dfrac{1}{4}$

5. $\dfrac{2}{9} + \dfrac{4}{9}$

6. $\dfrac{3}{10} + \dfrac{2}{10}$

7. $-\dfrac{6}{20} + \dfrac{1}{20}$

8. $-\dfrac{1}{8} + \dfrac{3}{8}$

9. $-\dfrac{3}{14} + \left(-\dfrac{4}{14}\right)$

10. $-\dfrac{5}{24} + \left(-\dfrac{7}{24}\right)$

11. $\dfrac{10}{11} + \dfrac{3}{11}$

12. $\dfrac{13}{17} + \dfrac{9}{17}$

13. $\dfrac{4}{13} + \dfrac{2}{13} + \dfrac{1}{13}$

14. $\dfrac{5}{11} + \dfrac{1}{11} + \dfrac{2}{11}$

15. $-\dfrac{7}{18} + \dfrac{3}{18} + \dfrac{2}{18}$

16. $-\dfrac{7}{15} + \dfrac{3}{15} + \dfrac{1}{15}$

Subtract and simplify. See Examples 4, 5, and 7.

17. $\dfrac{10}{11} - \dfrac{4}{11}$

18. $\dfrac{9}{13} - \dfrac{5}{13}$

19. $\dfrac{4}{5} - \dfrac{1}{5}$

20. $\dfrac{7}{8} - \dfrac{4}{8}$

21. $\dfrac{7}{4} - \dfrac{3}{4}$

22. $\dfrac{18}{5} - \dfrac{3}{5}$

23. $\dfrac{7}{8} - \dfrac{1}{8}$

24. $\dfrac{5}{6} - \dfrac{1}{6}$

25. $-\dfrac{25}{12} - \dfrac{15}{12}$

26. $-\dfrac{30}{20} - \dfrac{15}{20}$

27. $\dfrac{11}{10} - \dfrac{3}{10}$

28. $\dfrac{14}{15} - \dfrac{4}{15}$

29. $-\dfrac{27}{33} - \left(-\dfrac{8}{33}\right)$

30. $-\dfrac{37}{45} - \left(-\dfrac{18}{45}\right)$

Mixed Practice *Perform the indicated operation. See Examples 1 through 7.*

31. $\dfrac{8}{21} + \dfrac{5}{21}$

32. $\dfrac{7}{37} + \dfrac{9}{37}$

33. $\dfrac{99}{100} - \dfrac{9}{100}$

34. $\dfrac{85}{200} - \dfrac{15}{200}$

35. $-\dfrac{13}{28} - \dfrac{13}{28}$

36. $-\dfrac{15}{26} - \dfrac{15}{26}$

37. $-\dfrac{3}{16} + \left(-\dfrac{7}{16}\right) + \left(-\dfrac{2}{16}\right)$

38. $-\dfrac{5}{18} + \left(-\dfrac{1}{18}\right) + \left(-\dfrac{6}{18}\right)$

Objective B *Find the perimeter of each figure. (Hint: Recall that perimeter means distance around.) See Example 9.*

39.

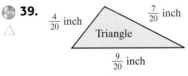

40.

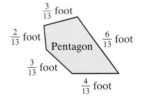

41.

$\frac{5}{12}$ meter | Rectangle |

$\frac{7}{12}$ meter

42.

Square | $\frac{1}{6}$ centimeter

Solve. Write each answer in simplest form. See Example 10.

43. Emil Vasquez, a bodybuilder, worked out $\dfrac{7}{8}$ of an hour one morning before school and $\dfrac{5}{8}$ of an hour that evening. How long did he work out that day?

44. A recipe for Heavenly Hash cake calls for $\dfrac{3}{4}$ cup of sugar and later $\dfrac{1}{4}$ cup of sugar. How much sugar is needed to make the recipe?

The map of the world below shows the fraction of the world's surface land area taken up by each continent. In other words, the continent of Africa makes up $\frac{20}{100}$ of the land in the world. Use this map for Exercises 45 through 48.

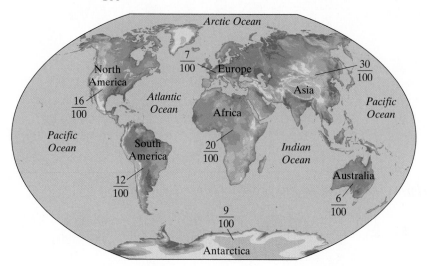

45. Find the fractional part of the world's land area within the continents of North America and South America.

46. Find the fractional part of the world's land area within the continents of Asia and Africa.

47. How much greater is the fractional part of the continent of Antarctica than the fractional part of the continent of Europe?

48. How much greater is the fractional part of the continent of Asia than the continent of Australia?

Solve.

49. A railroad inspector must inspect $\frac{19}{20}$ of a mile of railroad track. If she has already inspected $\frac{5}{20}$ of a mile, how much more does she need to inspect?

50. Scott Davis has run $\frac{11}{8}$ miles already and plans to complete $\frac{16}{8}$ miles. To do this, how much farther must he run?

51. In the United States, about $\frac{7}{20}$ of all households own two television sets. Approximately $\frac{8}{20}$ of all households own 3 or more television sets. What fraction of U.S. households own 2 or more television sets? (*Source:* Neilsen Media Research)

52. In a recent survey, $\frac{55}{100}$ of people said that visiting family and friends would be their pleasure trip of choice while $\frac{29}{100}$ of people surveyed said that going to a beach resort would be their pleasure trip of choice. What fraction of people surveyed said visiting family and friends or going to a beach resort? (*Source:* American Express)

53. In 2004, the fraction of states in the United States with maximum interstate highway speed limits up to and including 70 mph was $\frac{37}{50}$. The fraction of states with 70 mph speed limits was $\frac{16}{50}$. What fraction of states had speed limits that were less than 70 mph? (*Source:* Insurance Institute for Highway Safety)

54. When people take aspirin, $\frac{31}{50}$ of the time it is used to treat some type of pain. Approximately $\frac{7}{50}$ of all aspirin use is for treating headaches. What fraction of aspirin use is for treating pain other than headaches? (*Source:* Bayer Market Research)

Objective C *Find the LCM of each list of numbers. See Examples 11 through 14.*

55. 9, 15   **56.** 15, 20   **57.** 24, 36   **58.** 42, 70   **59.** 8, 24

60. 15, 90   **61.** 6, 7   **62.** 13, 8   **63.** 25, 15, 6   **64.** 4, 14, 20

65. 30, 36, 50   **66.** 21, 28, 42   **67.** 50, 72, 120   **68.** 70, 98, 100

Objective D *Write each fraction as an equivalent fraction with the given denominator. See Examples 15 and 16.*

69. $\dfrac{4}{7} = \dfrac{}{35}$ **70.** $\dfrac{3}{5} = \dfrac{}{20}$ **71.** $\dfrac{1}{2} = \dfrac{}{30}$ **72.** $\dfrac{1}{3} = \dfrac{}{30}$ **73.** $\dfrac{4}{9} = \dfrac{}{81}$

74 $\dfrac{5}{11} = \dfrac{}{88}$ **75.** $\dfrac{15}{13} = \dfrac{}{78}$ **76.** $\dfrac{9}{7} = \dfrac{}{84}$ **77.** $\dfrac{14}{17} = \dfrac{}{68}$ **78.** $\dfrac{19}{21} = \dfrac{}{126}$

Review

Write the prime factorization of each number. See Section 3.2.

79. 10   **80.** 12   **81.** 8   **82.** 20

Concept Extensions

Perform each indicated operation.

83. $\dfrac{3}{8} + \dfrac{7}{8} - \dfrac{5}{8}$ **84.** $\dfrac{12}{20} - \dfrac{1}{20} - \dfrac{3}{20}$ **85.** $\dfrac{4}{11} + \dfrac{5}{11} - \dfrac{3}{11} + \dfrac{2}{11}$ **86.** $\dfrac{9}{12} + \dfrac{1}{12} - \dfrac{3}{12} - \dfrac{5}{12}$

Find and correct the error. See the Concept Check in this section.

87.
$$\dfrac{2}{7} + \dfrac{9}{7} = \dfrac{11}{14}$$

88.
$$\dfrac{3}{4} - \dfrac{1}{4} = \dfrac{2}{8} = \dfrac{1}{4}$$

Solve.

89. In your own words, explain how to add like fractions.

90. In your own words, explain how to subtract like fractions.

91. Use the map of the world for Exercises 45 through 48 and find the sum of all the continents' fractions. Explain your answer.

92. Mike Cannon jogged $\dfrac{3}{8}$ of a mile from home and then rested. Then he continued jogging further from home for another $\dfrac{3}{8}$ of a mile until he discovered his watch had fallen off. He walked back along the same path for $\dfrac{4}{8}$ of a mile until he found his watch. Find how far he was from his home.

Write each fraction as an equivalent fraction with the indicated denominator.

93. $\dfrac{37}{165} = \dfrac{}{3630}$

94. $\dfrac{108}{215} = \dfrac{}{4085}$

95. In your own words, explain how to find the LCM of two numbers.

96. In your own words, explain how to write a fraction as an equivalent fraction with a given denominator.

Solve. See the Concept Checks in this section.

97. Which of the following are equivalent to $\dfrac{2}{3}$?

    a. $\dfrac{10}{15}$ **b.** $\dfrac{40}{60}$

    c. $\dfrac{16}{20}$ **d.** $\dfrac{200}{300}$

98. True or False? When the fraction $\dfrac{7}{12}$ is rewritten with a denominator of 48, the result is $\dfrac{11}{48}$. If false, give the correct fraction.

Summary on Fractions and Operations on Fractions

Use a fraction to represent the shaded area of each figure. If the fraction is improper, also write the fraction as a mixed number.

1.

2.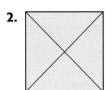

Solve.

3. In a survey, 73 people out of 85 get fewer than 8 hours of sleep each night. What fraction of people in the survey get fewer than 8 hours of sleep?

4. Sketch a diagram to represent $\frac{9}{13}$.

Simplify.

5. $\dfrac{11}{-11}$ **6.** $\dfrac{17}{1}$ **7.** $\dfrac{0}{-3}$ **8.** $\dfrac{7}{0}$

Write the prime factorization of each composite number. Write any repeated factors using exponents.

9. 65 **10.** 70 **11.** 315 **12.** 441

Write each fraction in simplest form.

13. $\dfrac{2}{14}$ **14.** $\dfrac{24}{20}$ **15.** $-\dfrac{56}{60}$ **16.** $-\dfrac{72}{80}$

17. $\dfrac{54}{135}$ **18.** $\dfrac{90}{240}$ **19.** $\dfrac{165}{210}$ **20.** $\dfrac{245}{385}$

Determine whether each pair of fractions is equivalent.

21. $\dfrac{7}{8}$ and $\dfrac{9}{10}$ **22.** $\dfrac{10}{12}$ and $\dfrac{15}{18}$

Answers

1. _____
2. _____
3. _____
4. _____
5. _____
6. _____
7. _____
8. _____
9. _____
10. _____
11. _____
12. _____
13. _____
14. _____
15. _____ 16. _____
17. _____ 18. _____
19. _____ 20. _____
21. _____
22. _____

23. a. _____

b. _____

c. _____

24. a. _____

b. _____

c. _____

25. _____

26. _____

27. _____

28. _____

29. _____

30. _____

31. _____

32. _____

33. _____

34. _____

35. _____

36. _____

37. _____

38. _____

39. _____

40. _____

41. _____

42. _____

43. _____

44. _____

23. Of the 50 states, 2 states are not adjacent to any other states.
  a. What fraction of the states are not adjacent to other states?
  b. How many states are adjacent to other states?
  c. What fraction of the states are adjacent to other states?

24. In a recent year, 460 films were released and rated. Of these, 275 were rated PG-13. (_Source:_ Motion Picture Association)
  a. What fraction were rated PG-13?
  b. How many films were rated other than PG-13?
  c. What fraction of films were rated other than PG-13?

Find the LCM of each list of numbers.

25. $5, 6$ **26.** $2, 14$ **27.** $6, 18, 30$

Write each fraction as an equivalent fraction with the indicated denominator.

28. $\dfrac{7}{9} = \dfrac{}{36}$ **29.** $\dfrac{11}{15} = \dfrac{}{75}$ **30.** $\dfrac{5}{6} = \dfrac{}{48}$

Perform the indicated operation.

31. $\dfrac{9}{10} + \dfrac{3}{10}$ **32.** $\dfrac{9}{10} - \dfrac{3}{10}$ **33.** $\dfrac{9}{10} \cdot \dfrac{2}{3}$ **34.** $\dfrac{9}{10} \div \dfrac{2}{3}$

35. $\dfrac{21}{70} - \dfrac{3}{70}$ **36.** $\dfrac{21}{70} + \dfrac{3}{70}$ **37.** $\dfrac{21}{25} \div \dfrac{3}{70}$ **38.** $\dfrac{21}{25} \cdot \dfrac{3}{70}$

39. $-\dfrac{7}{9} \cdot \dfrac{4}{5}$ **40.** $-\dfrac{3}{11} \div \left(-\dfrac{3}{10}\right)$ **41.** $-\dfrac{14}{27} - \dfrac{4}{27}$ **42.** $-\dfrac{8}{45} + \dfrac{6}{45}$

43. A contractor is using 18 acres of his land to sell $\dfrac{3}{4}$-acre lots. How many lots can he sell?

44. Suppose that the cross-section of a piece of pipe looks like the diagram shown. What is the inner diameter?

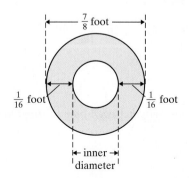

3.5 ADDING AND SUBTRACTING UNLIKE FRACTIONS

Objectives

A Add or Subtract Unlike Fractions.

B Write Fractions in Order.

C Evaluate Expressions Given Fractional Replacement Values.

D Solve Problems by Adding or Subtracting Unlike Fractions.

Objective A Adding and Subtracting Unlike Fractions

In this section we add and subtract fractions with unlike denominators. To add or subtract these unlike fractions, we first write the fractions as equivalent fractions with a common denominator and then add or subtract the like fractions. The common denominator that we use is the least common multiple (LCM) of the denominators. This denominator is called the **least common denominator (LCD).**

To begin, let's add the unlike fractions $\frac{3}{4} + \frac{1}{6}$.

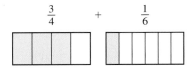

The LCM of denominators 4 and 6 is 12. This means that the number 12 is also the LCD. So we write each fraction as an equivalent fraction with a denominator of 12.

$$\frac{3}{4} = \frac{3}{4} \cdot \frac{3}{3} = \frac{9}{12} \text{ and } \frac{1}{6} = \frac{1}{6} \cdot \frac{2}{2} = \frac{2}{12} \qquad \text{Remember } \frac{3}{3} = 1 \text{ and } \frac{2}{2} = 1.$$

Now we can add, just as in Section 3.4.

$$\frac{3}{4} + \frac{1}{6} = \frac{9}{12} + \frac{2}{12} = \frac{11}{12}$$

$$\frac{9}{12} + \frac{2}{12} = \frac{11}{12}$$

Adding or Subtracting Unlike Fractions

Step 1: Find the LCM of the denominators of the fractions. This number is the least common denominator (LCD).

Step 2: Write each fraction as an equivalent fraction whose denominator is the LCD.

Step 3: Add or subtract the like fractions.

Step 4: Write the sum or difference in simplest form.

PRACTICE PROBLEM 1

Add: $\dfrac{1}{6} + \dfrac{3}{18}$

EXAMPLE 1 Add: $\dfrac{2}{5} + \dfrac{4}{15}$

Solution:

Step 1: The LCM of the denominators 5 and 15 is 15. Thus, the LCD is 15. In later examples, we shall simply say, for example, that the LCD of 5 and 15 is 15.

Step 2: $\dfrac{2}{5} = \dfrac{2}{5} \cdot \dfrac{3}{3} = \dfrac{6}{15}, \quad \dfrac{4}{15} = \dfrac{4}{15}$ ← This fraction already has a denominator of 15.

└ Multiply by 1 in the form $\dfrac{3}{3}$

Step 3: $\dfrac{2}{5} + \dfrac{4}{15} = \dfrac{6}{15} + \dfrac{4}{15} = \dfrac{10}{15}$

Step 4: Write in simplest form.

$$\dfrac{10}{15} = \dfrac{2 \cdot \overset{1}{\cancel{5}}}{3 \cdot \underset{1}{\cancel{5}}} = \dfrac{2}{3}$$

▢ **Work Practice Problem 1**

PRACTICE PROBLEM 2

Add: $\dfrac{5}{6} + \dfrac{2}{9}$

EXAMPLE 2 Add: $\dfrac{2}{15} + \dfrac{3}{10}$

Solution:

Step 1: The LCD of 15 and 10 is 30.

Step 2: $\dfrac{2}{15} = \dfrac{2}{15} \cdot \dfrac{2}{2} = \dfrac{4}{30} \qquad \dfrac{3}{10} = \dfrac{3}{10} \cdot \dfrac{3}{3} = \dfrac{9}{30}$

Step 3: $\dfrac{2}{15} + \dfrac{3}{10} = \dfrac{4}{30} + \dfrac{9}{30} = \dfrac{13}{30}$

Step 4: $\dfrac{13}{30}$ is in simplest form.

▢ **Work Practice Problem 2**

PRACTICE PROBLEM 3

Add: $-\dfrac{1}{5} + \dfrac{3}{20}$

EXAMPLE 3 Add: $-\dfrac{1}{6} + \dfrac{1}{2}$

Solution: The LCD of the denominators 6 and 2 is 6.

$$-\dfrac{1}{6} + \dfrac{1}{2} = \dfrac{-1}{6} + \dfrac{1 \cdot 3}{2 \cdot 3}$$

$$= \dfrac{-1}{6} + \dfrac{3}{6}$$

$$= \dfrac{2}{6}$$

Next, simplify $\dfrac{2}{6}$.

$$\dfrac{2}{6} = \dfrac{\overset{1}{\cancel{2}}}{\underset{1}{\cancel{2}} \cdot 3} = \dfrac{1}{3}$$

▢ **Work Practice Problem 3**

Answers

1. $\dfrac{1}{3}$, 2. $\dfrac{19}{18}$, 3. $-\dfrac{1}{20}$

✔ **Concept Check** Find and correct the error in the following:

$$\frac{2}{9} + \frac{4}{11} = \frac{6}{20} = \frac{3}{10}$$

EXAMPLE 4 Subtract: $\frac{2}{5} - \frac{3}{20}$

Solution:

Step 1: The LCD of 5 and 20 is 20.

Step 2: $\frac{2}{5} = \frac{2}{5} \cdot \frac{4}{4} = \frac{8}{20}$ $\quad \frac{3}{20} = \frac{3}{20}$ ← The fraction already has a denominator of 20.

Step 3: $\frac{2}{5} - \frac{3}{20} = \frac{8}{20} - \frac{3}{20} = \frac{5}{20}$

Step 4: Write in simplest form.

$$\frac{5}{20} = \frac{\overset{1}{\cancel{5}}}{\underset{1}{\cancel{5}} \cdot 4} = \frac{1}{4}$$

 Work Practice Problem 4

EXAMPLE 5 Subtract: $\frac{2}{3} - \frac{10}{11}$

Solution:

Step 1: The LCD of 3 and 11 is 33.

Step 2: $\frac{2}{3} = \frac{2}{3} \cdot \frac{11}{11} = \frac{22}{33}$ $\quad \frac{10}{11} = \frac{10}{11} \cdot \frac{3}{3} = \frac{30}{33}$

Step 3: $\frac{2}{3} - \frac{10}{11} = \frac{22}{33} - \frac{30}{33} = \frac{-8}{33}$ or $-\frac{8}{33}$

Step 4: $-\frac{8}{33}$ is in simplest form.

Work Practice Problem 5

> **Helpful Hint**
>
> Remember that $-\frac{a}{b} = \frac{a}{-b} = \frac{-a}{b}$. For example, $-\frac{8}{33} = \frac{8}{-33} = \frac{-8}{33}$.

EXAMPLE 6 Find: $-\frac{3}{4} - \frac{1}{14} + \frac{6}{7}$

Solution: The LCD of 4, 14, and 7 is 28.

$$-\frac{3}{4} - \frac{1}{14} + \frac{6}{7} = -\frac{3 \cdot 7}{4 \cdot 7} - \frac{1 \cdot 2}{14 \cdot 2} + \frac{6 \cdot 4}{7 \cdot 4}$$

$$= -\frac{21}{28} - \frac{2}{28} + \frac{24}{28}$$

$$= \frac{1}{28}$$

Work Practice Problem 6

PRACTICE PROBLEM 4

Subtract: $\frac{7}{12} - \frac{5}{24}$

PRACTICE PROBLEM 5

Subtract: $\frac{3}{7} - \frac{9}{10}$

PRACTICE PROBLEM 6

Find: $\frac{5}{8} - \frac{1}{3} - \frac{1}{12}$

Answers

4. $\frac{3}{8}$, **5.** $-\frac{33}{70}$, **6.** $\frac{5}{24}$

✔ **Concept Check Answer**

When adding unlike fractions, we don't add the denominators. Correct solution:

$$\frac{2}{9} + \frac{4}{11} = \frac{22}{99} + \frac{36}{99} = \frac{58}{99}$$

✔*Concept Check*   Find and correct the error in the following:

$$\frac{7}{12} - \frac{3}{4} = \frac{4}{8} = \frac{1}{2}.$$

Objective B Writing Fractions in Order

One important application of the least common denominator is to use the LCD to help order or compare fractions.

EXAMPLE 7   Insert < or > to form a true sentence.

$$\frac{3}{4} \qquad \frac{9}{11}$$

Solution: The LCD for these fractions is 44. Let's write each fraction as an equivalent fraction with a denominator of 44.

$$\frac{3}{4} = \frac{3 \cdot 11}{4 \cdot 11} = \frac{33}{44} \qquad \frac{9}{11} = \frac{9 \cdot 4}{11 \cdot 4} = \frac{36}{44}$$

Since $33 < 36$, then $\dfrac{33}{44} < \dfrac{36}{44}$ or

$$\frac{3}{4} < \frac{9}{11}$$

▨ **Work Practice Problem 7**

EXAMPLE 8   Insert < or > to form a true sentence.

$$-\frac{2}{7} \qquad -\frac{1}{3}$$

Solution: The LCD is 21.

$$-\frac{2}{7} = -\frac{2 \cdot 3}{7 \cdot 3} = -\frac{6}{21} \qquad -\frac{1}{3} = -\frac{1 \cdot 7}{3 \cdot 7} = -\frac{7}{21}$$

Since $-6 > -7$, then $-\dfrac{6}{21} > -\dfrac{7}{21}$ or

$$-\frac{2}{7} > -\frac{1}{3}$$

▨ **Work Practice Problem 8**

Objective C Evaluating Expressions Given Fractional Replacement Values

EXAMPLE 9   Evaluate $x - y$ if $x = \dfrac{7}{18}$ and $y = \dfrac{2}{9}$.

Solution: Replace x with $\dfrac{7}{18}$ and y with $\dfrac{2}{9}$ in the expression $x - y$.

$$x - y = \frac{7}{18} - \frac{2}{9}$$

PRACTICE PROBLEM 7

Insert < or > to form a true sentence.

$$\frac{3}{8} \qquad \frac{7}{20}$$

PRACTICE PROBLEM 8

Insert < or > to form a true sentence.

$$-\frac{17}{20} \qquad -\frac{4}{5}$$

PRACTICE PROBLEM 9

Evaluate $x + y$ if $x = \dfrac{5}{11}$ and $y = \dfrac{4}{9}$.

Answers

7. >, **8.** <, **9.** $\dfrac{89}{99}$

✔ **Concept Check Answer**

$$\frac{7}{12} - \frac{3}{4} = \frac{7}{12} - \frac{9}{12} = -\frac{2}{12} = -\frac{1}{6}$$

The LCD of the denominators 18 and 9 is 18. Then

$$\frac{7}{18} - \frac{2}{9} = \frac{7}{18} - \frac{2 \cdot 2}{9 \cdot 2}$$

$$= \frac{7}{18} - \frac{4}{18}$$

$$= \frac{3}{18} = \frac{1}{6} \qquad \text{Simplified.}$$

Work Practice Problem 9

Objective D Solving Problems by Adding or Subtracting Unlike Fractions

Very often, real-world problems involve adding or subtracting unlike fractions.

EXAMPLE 10 Finding Total Weight

A freight truck has $\frac{1}{4}$ ton of computers, $\frac{1}{3}$ ton of televisions, and $\frac{3}{8}$ ton of small appliances. Find the total weight of its load.

$\frac{1}{4}$ ton of computers | $\frac{1}{3}$ ton of televisions | $\frac{3}{8}$ ton of appliances

Solution:

1. UNDERSTAND. Read and reread the problem. The phrase "total weight" tells us to add.

2. TRANSLATE.

In words:	total weight	is	weight of computers	plus	weight of televisions	plus	weight of appliances
	↓	↓	↓	↓	↓	↓	↓
Translate:	total weight	=	$\frac{1}{4}$	+	$\frac{1}{3}$	+	$\frac{3}{8}$

3. SOLVE: The LCD is 24.

$$\frac{1}{4} + \frac{1}{3} + \frac{3}{8} = \frac{1}{4} \cdot \frac{6}{6} + \frac{1}{3} \cdot \frac{8}{8} + \frac{3}{8} \cdot \frac{3}{3}$$

$$= \frac{6}{24} + \frac{8}{24} + \frac{9}{24}$$

$$= \frac{23}{24}$$

4. INTERPRET. *Check* the solution. *State* your conclusion: The total weight of the truck's load is $\frac{23}{24}$ ton.

Work Practice Problem 10

PRACTICE PROBLEM 10

To repair her sidewalk, a homeowner must pour small amounts of cement in three different locations. She needs $\frac{3}{5}$ of a cubic yard, $\frac{2}{10}$ of a cubic yard, and $\frac{2}{15}$ of a cubic yard for these locations. Find the total amount of cement the homeowner needs.

Answer

10. $\frac{14}{15}$ cu yd

PRACTICE PROBLEM 11

Find the difference in length of two boards if one board is $\frac{4}{5}$ of a foot long and the other is $\frac{2}{3}$ of a foot long.

EXAMPLE 11 **Calculating Flight Time**

A flight from Tucson to Phoenix, Arizona, requires $\frac{5}{12}$ of an hour. If the plane has been flying $\frac{1}{4}$ of an hour, find how much time remains before landing.

Solution:

1. UNDERSTAND. Read and reread the problem. The phrase "how much time remains" tells us to subtract.

2. TRANSLATE.

In words:	time remaining	is	flight time from Tucson to Phoenix	minus	flight time already passed
	↓	↓	↓	↓	↓
Translate:	time remaining	=	$\frac{5}{12}$	−	$\frac{1}{4}$

3. SOLVE: The LCD is 12.

$$\frac{5}{12} - \frac{1}{4} = \frac{5}{12} - \frac{1}{4} \cdot \frac{3}{3}$$

$$= \frac{5}{12} - \frac{3}{12}$$

$$= \frac{2}{12} = \frac{\overset{1}{\cancel{2}}}{\underset{1}{\cancel{2}} \cdot 6} = \frac{1}{6}$$

4. INTERPRET. *Check* the solution. *State* your conclusion: The flight time remaining is $\frac{1}{6}$ of an hour.

▢ **Work Practice Problem 11**

Answer

11. $\frac{2}{15}$ ft

CALCULATOR EXPLORATIONS Performing Operations on Fractions

Scientific Calculator

Many calculators have a fraction key, such as $\boxed{a\ b/c}$, that allows you to enter fractions, perform operations on fractions, and will give the result as a fraction. If your calculator has a fraction key, use it to calculate

$$\frac{3}{5} + \frac{4}{7}$$

Enter the keystrokes

$\boxed{3}\ \boxed{a\ b/c}\ \boxed{5}\ \boxed{+}\ \boxed{4}\ \boxed{a\ b/c}\ \boxed{7}\ \boxed{=}$

The display should read $\boxed{1\_6\ |\ 35}$

which represents the mixed number $1\frac{6}{35}$. Let's write the result as a fraction. To convert from mixed number notation to fractional notation, press

$\boxed{2^{nd}}\ \boxed{d/c}$

The display now reads $\boxed{41\ |\ 35}$

which represents $\frac{41}{35}$, the sum in fractional notation.

Graphing Calculator

Graphing calculators also allow you to perform operations on fractions and will give exact fractional results. The fraction option on a graphing calculator may be found under the $\boxed{MATH}$ menu. To perform the addition above, try the keystrokes.

$\boxed{3}\ \boxed{\div}\ \boxed{5}\ \boxed{+}\ \boxed{4}\ \boxed{\div}\ \boxed{7}\ \boxed{MATH}\ \boxed{ENTER}$
$\boxed{ENTER}$

The display should read

$\boxed{3/5 + 4/7 \blacktriangleright \text{Frac } 41/35}$

Use a calculator to add the following fractions. Give each sum as a fraction.

1. $\dfrac{1}{16} + \dfrac{2}{5}$ **2.** $\dfrac{3}{20} + \dfrac{2}{25}$ **3.** $\dfrac{4}{9} + \dfrac{7}{8}$

4. $\dfrac{9}{11} + \dfrac{5}{12}$ **5.** $\dfrac{10}{17} + \dfrac{12}{19}$ **6.** $\dfrac{14}{31} + \dfrac{15}{21}$

Mental Math

Find the LCD of each pair of fractions.

1. $\dfrac{1}{2}, \dfrac{2}{3}$ **2.** $\dfrac{1}{2}, \dfrac{3}{4}$ **3.** $\dfrac{1}{6}, \dfrac{5}{12}$ **4.** $\dfrac{2}{5}, \dfrac{7}{10}$

5. $\dfrac{4}{7}, \dfrac{1}{8}$ **6.** $\dfrac{23}{24}, \dfrac{1}{3}$ **7.** $\dfrac{11}{12}, \dfrac{3}{4}$ **8.** $\dfrac{2}{3}, \dfrac{3}{11}$

3.5 EXERCISE SET

Objective A *Add or subtract as indicated. See Examples 1 through 6.*

1. $\dfrac{2}{3} + \dfrac{1}{6}$ **2.** $\dfrac{5}{6} + \dfrac{1}{12}$ **3.** $\dfrac{1}{2} - \dfrac{1}{3}$ **4.** $\dfrac{2}{3} - \dfrac{1}{4}$ **5.** $-\dfrac{2}{11} + \dfrac{2}{33}$

6. $-\dfrac{5}{9} + \dfrac{1}{3}$ **7.** $\dfrac{3}{14} - \dfrac{3}{7}$ **8.** $\dfrac{2}{15} - \dfrac{2}{5}$ **9.** $\dfrac{11}{35} + \dfrac{2}{7}$ **10.** $\dfrac{2}{5} + \dfrac{3}{25}$

11. $2 - \dfrac{5}{12}$ **12.** $5 - \dfrac{3}{20}$ **13.** $\dfrac{5}{12} - \dfrac{1}{9}$ **14.** $\dfrac{7}{12} - \dfrac{5}{18}$ **15.** $\dfrac{5}{7} + 1$

16. $-10 + \dfrac{7}{10}$ **17.** $\dfrac{5}{11} + \dfrac{4}{9}$ **18.** $\dfrac{7}{18} + \dfrac{2}{9}$ **19.** $\dfrac{2}{3} - \dfrac{1}{6}$ **20.** $\dfrac{5}{6} - \dfrac{1}{12}$

21. $\dfrac{1}{3} + \dfrac{1}{9} + \dfrac{1}{27}$ **22.** $\dfrac{1}{4} + \dfrac{1}{16} + \dfrac{1}{64}$ **23.** $-\dfrac{2}{11} - \dfrac{2}{33}$ **24.** $-\dfrac{5}{9} - \dfrac{1}{3}$ **25.** $\dfrac{9}{14} - \dfrac{3}{7}$

26. $\dfrac{4}{5} - \dfrac{2}{15}$ **27.** $\dfrac{11}{35} - \dfrac{2}{7}$ **28.** $\dfrac{2}{5} - \dfrac{3}{25}$ **29.** $\dfrac{1}{9} - \dfrac{5}{12}$ **30.** $\dfrac{5}{18} - \dfrac{7}{12}$

31. $\dfrac{7}{15} - \dfrac{5}{12}$ **32.** $\dfrac{5}{8} - \dfrac{3}{20}$ **33.** $\dfrac{5}{7} - \dfrac{1}{8}$ **34.** $\dfrac{10}{13} - \dfrac{7}{10}$ **35.** $\dfrac{7}{8} + \dfrac{3}{16}$

36. $-\dfrac{7}{18} - \dfrac{2}{9}$ **37.** $\dfrac{5}{9} + \dfrac{3}{9}$ **38.** $\dfrac{4}{13} - \dfrac{1}{13}$ **39.** $-\dfrac{2}{5} + \dfrac{1}{3} - \dfrac{3}{10}$

40. $-\dfrac{1}{3} - \dfrac{1}{4} + \dfrac{2}{5}$ **41.** $-\dfrac{5}{6} - \dfrac{3}{7}$ **42.** $\dfrac{1}{2} - \dfrac{3}{29}$ **43.** $\dfrac{7}{9} - \dfrac{1}{6}$

44. $\dfrac{9}{16} - \dfrac{3}{8}$ **45.** $\dfrac{5}{11} + \dfrac{3}{13}$ **46.** $\dfrac{3}{7} + \dfrac{9}{17}$ **47.** $\dfrac{7}{30} - \dfrac{5}{12}$

48. $\dfrac{7}{30} - \dfrac{3}{20}$ **49.** $\dfrac{6}{5} - \dfrac{3}{4} + \dfrac{1}{2}$ **50.** $\dfrac{6}{5} + \dfrac{3}{4} - \dfrac{1}{2}$ **51.** $\dfrac{4}{5} + \dfrac{4}{9}$

52. $\dfrac{11}{12} - \dfrac{7}{24}$ **53.** $-\dfrac{9}{12} + \dfrac{17}{24} - \dfrac{1}{6}$ **54.** $-\dfrac{5}{14} + \dfrac{3}{7} - \dfrac{1}{2}$ **55.** $\dfrac{1}{1000} - \dfrac{1}{100}$ **56.** $\dfrac{1}{500} - \dfrac{1}{50}$

Objective **B** *Insert $<$ or $>$ to form a true sentence. See Examples 7 and 8.*

57. $\dfrac{2}{7}$ $\dfrac{3}{10}$ **58.** $\dfrac{5}{9}$ $\dfrac{6}{11}$ **59.** $\dfrac{5}{6}$ $-\dfrac{13}{15}$

60. $-\dfrac{7}{8}$ $-\dfrac{5}{6}$ **61.** $-\dfrac{3}{4}$ $-\dfrac{11}{14}$ **62.** $-\dfrac{2}{9}$ $-\dfrac{3}{13}$

Objective **C** *Evaluate each expression if $x = \dfrac{1}{3}$ and $y = \dfrac{3}{4}$. See Example 9.*

63. $x + y$ **64.** $x - y$ **65.** xy

66. $x \div y$ **67.** $2y + x$ **68.** $2x + y$

Objective **E** *Find the perimeter of each geometric figure. (Hint: Recall that perimeter means distance around.)*

△ **69.**
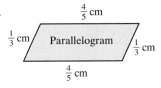

△ **70.**
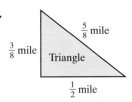

△ **71.**
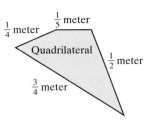

△ **72.**
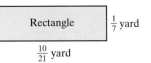

Solve. See Examples 10 and 11.

73. Killer bees have been known to chase people for up to $\dfrac{1}{4}$ of a mile, while domestic European honeybees will normally chase a person for no more than 100 feet, or $\dfrac{5}{264}$ of a mile. How much farther will a killer bee chase a person than a domestic honeybee? (*Source:* Coachella Valley Mosquito & Vector Control District)

74. The slowest mammal is the three-toed sloth from South America. The sloth has an average ground speed of $\dfrac{1}{10}$ mph. In the trees, it can accelerate to $\dfrac{17}{100}$ mph. How much faster can a sloth travel in the trees? (*Source: The Guiness Book of World Records*)

75. Given the following diagram, find its total length.

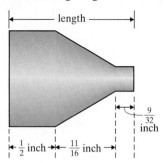

76. Given the following diagram, find its total width.

77. About $\frac{13}{20}$ of American students ages 10 to 17 name math, science, or art as their favorite subject in school. Art is the favorite subject for about $\frac{4}{25}$ of the American students ages 10 to 17. For what fraction of students this age is math or science their favorite subject? (*Source:* Peter D. Hart Research Associates for the National Science Foundation)

78. Together, the United States' and Japan's postal services handle $\frac{49}{100}$ of the world's mail volume. Japan's postal service alone handles $\frac{3}{50}$ of the world's mail. What fraction of the world's mail is handled by the postal service of the United States? (*Source:* United States Postal Service)

The table gives the fraction of Americans who eat pasta at various intervals. Use this table to answer Exercises 79 and 80.

How Often Americans Eat Pasta	
Frequency	**Fraction**
3 times per week	$\frac{31}{100}$
1 or 2 times per week	$\frac{23}{50}$
1 or 2 times per month	$\frac{17}{100}$
Less often	$\frac{3}{50}$
(*Source:* Princeton Survey Research)	

79. What fraction of Americans eat pasta 1, 2, or 3 times a week?

80. What fraction of Americans eat pasta 1 or 2 times a month or less often?

The map of the world now shows the fraction of the water's surface area taken up by each ocean. Use this map for Exercises 81 and 82.

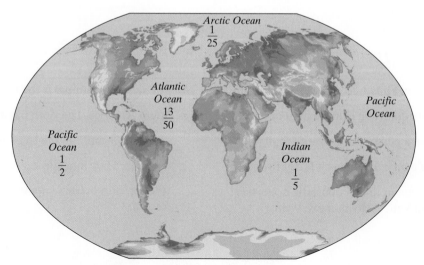

81. What fraction of the world's water surface area is accounted for by the Pacific and Atlantic Oceans?

82. What fraction of the world's water surface area is accounted for by the Arctic and Indian Oceans?

Review

Use order of operations to simplify.

83. $50 \div 5 \cdot 2$

84. $8 - 6 \cdot 4 - 7$

85. $(8 - 6) \cdot (4 - 7)$

86. $50 \div (5 \cdot 2)$

Concept Extensions

For each sum below, do the following:

a. *Draw three rectangles of the same size and represent each fraction in the sum, one fraction per rectangle, by shading.*
b. *Using these rectangles as estimates, determine whether there is an error in the sum.*
c. *If there is an error, correctly calculate the sum.*

See the Concept Check in this section.

87. $\dfrac{3}{5} + \dfrac{4}{5} = \dfrac{7}{10}$

88. $\dfrac{5}{8} + \dfrac{3}{4} = \dfrac{8}{12}$

Subtract from left to right.

89. $\dfrac{2}{3} - \dfrac{1}{4} - \dfrac{2}{540}$

90. $\dfrac{9}{10} - \dfrac{7}{200} - \dfrac{1}{3}$

Perform each indicated operation.

91. $\dfrac{30}{55} + \dfrac{1000}{1760}$

92. $\dfrac{19}{26} - \dfrac{968}{1352}$

93. In your own words, describe how to add or subtract two fractions with different denominators.

STUDY SKILLS BUILDER

Are You Organized?

Have you ever had trouble finding a completed assignment? When it's time to study for a test, are your notes neat and organized? Have you ever had trouble reading your own mathematics handwriting? (Be honest—I have.)

When any of these things happen, it's time to get organized. Here are a few suggestions:

Write your notes and complete your homework assignment in a notebook with pockets (spiral or ring binder.) Take class notes in this notebook, and then follow the notes with your completed homework assignment. When you receive graded papers or handouts, place them in the notebook pocket so that you will not lose them.

Remember to mark (possibly with an exclamation point) any note(s) that seem extra important to you. Also remember to mark (possibly with a question mark) any notes or homework that you are having trouble with. Don't forget to see your instructor or a math tutor to help you with the concepts or exercises that you are having trouble understanding.

Also, if you are having trouble reading your own handwriting, *slow down* and write your mathematics work clearly!

Exercises

1. Have you been completing your assignments on time?

2. Have you been correcting any exercises you may be having difficulty with?

3. If you are having trouble with a mathematical concept or correcting any homework exercises, have you visited your instructor, a tutor, or your campus math lab?

4. Are you taking lecture notes in your mathematics course? (By the way, these notes should include worked-out examples solved by your instructor.)

5. Is your mathematics course material (handouts, graded papers, lecture notes) organized?

6. If your answer to Exercise 5 is no, take a moment and review your course material. List at least two ways that you might better organize it. Then read the Study Skills Builder on organizing a notebook in Chapter 2.

3.6 COMPLEX FRACTIONS, ORDER OF OPERATIONS, AND MIXED NUMBERS

Objectives

A Simplify Complex Fractions.

B Review the Order of Operations.

C Evaluate Expressions Given Replacement Values.

D Write Mixed Numbers as Improper Fractions.

E Write Improper Fractions as Mixed Numbers or Whole Numbers.

Objective A Simplifying Complex Fractions

Thus far, we have studied operations on fractions. We now practice simplifying fractions whose numerators or denominators themselves contain fractions. These fractions are called **complex fractions.**

Complex Fraction

A fraction whose numerator or denominator or both numerator and denominator contain fractions is called a **complex fraction.**

Examples of complex fractions are

$$\frac{\frac{1}{4}}{\frac{3}{2}} \qquad \frac{\frac{1}{2}+\frac{3}{8}}{\frac{3}{4}-\frac{1}{6}} \qquad \frac{\frac{4}{5}-2}{\frac{3}{10}}$$

Method 1 for Simplifying Complex Fractions

Two methods are presented to simplify complex fractions. The first method makes use of the fact that a fraction bar means division.

EXAMPLE 1 Simplify: $\dfrac{\frac{1}{4}}{\frac{3}{2}}$

Solution: Since a fraction bar means division, the complex fraction

$\dfrac{\frac{1}{4}}{\frac{3}{2}}$ can be written as $\dfrac{1}{4} \div \dfrac{3}{2}$. Then divide as usual to simplify.

$$\frac{1}{4} \div \frac{3}{2} = \frac{1}{4} \cdot \frac{2}{3} \qquad \text{Multiply by the reciprocal.}$$

$$= \frac{1 \cdot \cancel{2}^{1}}{\cancel{2} \cdot 2 \cdot 3}$$

$$= \frac{1}{6}$$

■ **Work Practice Problem 1**

EXAMPLE 2 Simplify: $\dfrac{\frac{1}{2}+\frac{3}{8}}{\frac{3}{4}-\frac{1}{6}}$

Solution: Recall the order of operations. Since the fraction bar is considered a grouping symbol, we simplify the numerator and the denominator of the complex fraction separately. Then we divide.

$$\frac{\frac{1}{2}+\frac{3}{8}}{\frac{3}{4}-\frac{1}{6}} = \frac{\frac{1 \cdot 4}{2 \cdot 4}+\frac{3}{8}}{\frac{3 \cdot 3}{4 \cdot 3}-\frac{1 \cdot 2}{6 \cdot 2}} = \frac{\frac{4}{8}+\frac{3}{8}}{\frac{9}{12}-\frac{2}{12}} = \frac{\frac{7}{8}}{\frac{7}{12}}$$

PRACTICE PROBLEM 1

Simplify: $\dfrac{\frac{7}{10}}{\frac{1}{5}}$

PRACTICE PROBLEM 2

Simplify: $\dfrac{\frac{1}{2}+\frac{1}{6}}{\frac{3}{4}-\frac{2}{3}}$

Answers

1. $\dfrac{7}{2}$, 2. $\dfrac{8}{1}$ or 8

Continued on next page

Thus,

$$\frac{\dfrac{1}{2} + \dfrac{3}{8}}{\dfrac{3}{4} - \dfrac{1}{6}} = \frac{\dfrac{7}{8}}{\dfrac{7}{12}}$$

$$= \frac{7}{8} \div \frac{7}{12} \qquad \text{Rewrite the quotient using the } \div \text{ sign.}$$

$$= \frac{7}{8} \cdot \frac{12}{7} \qquad \text{Multiply by the reciprocal.}$$

$$= \frac{7 \cdot 3 \cdot 4}{2 \cdot 4 \cdot 7} \qquad \text{Multiply.}$$

$$= \frac{3}{2} \qquad \text{Simplify.}$$

■ **Work Practice Problem 2**

Method 2 for Simplifying Complex Fractions

The second method for simplifying complex fractions is to multiply the numerator and the denominator of the complex fraction by the LCD of all the fractions in its numerator and its denominator. Since this LCD is divisible by all denominators, this has the effect of leaving sums and differences of integers in the numerator and the denominator. Let's use this second method to simplify the complex fraction in Example 2 again.

PRACTICE PROBLEM 3

Use Method 2 to simplify:

$$\frac{\dfrac{1}{2} + \dfrac{1}{6}}{\dfrac{3}{4} - \dfrac{2}{3}}$$

EXAMPLE 3 Simplify: $\dfrac{\dfrac{1}{2} + \dfrac{3}{8}}{\dfrac{3}{4} - \dfrac{1}{6}}$

Solution: The complex fraction contains fractions with denominators 2, 8, 4, and 6. The LCD is 24. By the fundamental property of fractions, we can multiply the numerator and the denominator of the complex fraction by 24. Notice below that by the distributive property, this means that we multiply each term in the numerator and denominator by 24.

$$\frac{\dfrac{1}{2} + \dfrac{3}{8}}{\dfrac{3}{4} - \dfrac{1}{6}} = \frac{24\left(\dfrac{1}{2} + \dfrac{3}{8}\right)}{24\left(\dfrac{3}{4} - \dfrac{1}{6}\right)}$$

$$= \frac{\left(24 \cdot \dfrac{1}{2}\right) + \left(24 \cdot \dfrac{3}{8}\right)}{\left(24 \cdot \dfrac{3}{4}\right) - \left(24 \cdot \dfrac{1}{6}\right)} \qquad \text{Apply the distributive property.}$$

$$= \frac{12 + 9}{18 - 4} \qquad \text{Multiply.}$$

$$= \frac{21}{14}$$

$$= \frac{7 \cdot 3}{7 \cdot 2} = \frac{3}{2} \qquad \text{Simplify.}$$

■ **Work Practice Problem 3**

The simplified result is the same, of course, no matter which method is used.

EXAMPLE 4 Simplify: $\dfrac{\dfrac{4}{5} - 2}{\dfrac{3}{10}}$

Solution: Use the second method and multiply the numerator and the denominator of the complex fraction by the LCD of all fractions. Recall that $2 = \dfrac{2}{1}$. The LCD of the denominators 5, 1, and 10 is 10.

$$\frac{\frac{4}{5} - \frac{2}{1}}{\frac{3}{10}} = \frac{10\left(\frac{4}{5} - \frac{2}{1}\right)}{10\left(\frac{3}{10}\right)}$$ Multiply the numerator and denominator by 10.

$$= \frac{\left(10 \cdot \frac{4}{5}\right) - \left(10 \cdot \frac{2}{1}\right)}{10 \cdot \frac{3}{10}}$$ Apply the distributive property.

$$= \frac{8 - 20}{3}$$ Multiply.

$$= \frac{-12}{3} = -4$$ Simplify.

Work Practice Problem 4

PRACTICE PROBLEM 4

Simplify: $\dfrac{\dfrac{3}{4}}{\dfrac{3}{5} - 1}$

Helpful Hint

Don't forget to multiply the numerator and the denominator of the complex fraction by the same number—the LCD.

Objective B Reviewing the Order of Operations

At this time, it is probably a good idea to review the order of operations on expressions containing fractions. Before we do so, let's review how we perform operations on fractions.

	Review of Operations on Fractions	
Operation	**Procedure**	**Example**
Multiply	Multiply the numerators and multiply the denominators.	$\dfrac{5}{9} \cdot \dfrac{1}{2} = \dfrac{5 \cdot 1}{9 \cdot 2} = \dfrac{5}{18}$
Divide	Multiply the first fraction by the reciprocal of the second fraction.	$\dfrac{2}{3} \div \dfrac{11}{13} = \dfrac{2}{3} \cdot \dfrac{13}{11} = \dfrac{2 \cdot 13}{3 \cdot 11} = \dfrac{26}{33}$
Add or Subtract	1. Write each fraction as an equivalent fraction whose denominator is the LCD 2. Add or subtract numerators and write the result over the common denominator.	$\dfrac{3}{4} + \dfrac{1}{8} = \dfrac{3}{4} \cdot \dfrac{2}{2} + \dfrac{1}{8} = \dfrac{6}{8} + \dfrac{1}{8} = \dfrac{7}{8}$

Now let's review order of operations.

Order of Operations

1. Perform all operations within parentheses ( ), brackets [ ], or other grouping symbols such as square roots or fraction bars.
2. Evaluate any expressions with exponents.
3. Multiply or divide in order from left to right.
4. Add or subtract in order from left to right.

Answer

4. $-\dfrac{15}{8}$

PRACTICE PROBLEM 5

Simplify: $\left(2 - \dfrac{2}{3}\right)^3$

EXAMPLE 5 Simplify: $\left(\dfrac{4}{5}\right)^2 - 1$

Solution: According to the order of operations, first evaluate $\left(\dfrac{4}{5}\right)^2$.

$\left(\dfrac{4}{5}\right)^2 - 1 = \dfrac{16}{25} - 1$ Write $\left(\dfrac{4}{5}\right)^2$ as $\dfrac{16}{25}$.

Next, combine the fractions. The LCD of 25 and 1 is 25.

$\dfrac{16}{25} - 1 = \dfrac{16}{25} - \dfrac{25}{25}$ Write 1 as $\dfrac{25}{25}$.

$\qquad = \dfrac{-9}{25}$ or $-\dfrac{9}{25}$ Subtract.

▣ **Work Practice Problem 5**

PRACTICE PROBLEM 6

Simplify: $\left(-\dfrac{1}{2} + \dfrac{1}{5}\right)\left(\dfrac{7}{8} + \dfrac{1}{8}\right)$

EXAMPLE 6 Simplify: $\left(\dfrac{1}{4} + \dfrac{2}{3}\right)\left(\dfrac{11}{12} + \dfrac{1}{4}\right)$

Solution: First perform operations inside parentheses. Then multiply.

$\left(\dfrac{1}{4} + \dfrac{2}{3}\right)\left(\dfrac{11}{12} + \dfrac{1}{4}\right) = \left(\dfrac{1 \cdot 3}{4 \cdot 3} + \dfrac{2 \cdot 4}{3 \cdot 4}\right)\left(\dfrac{11}{12} + \dfrac{1 \cdot 3}{4 \cdot 3}\right)$ Each LCD is 12.

$\qquad = \left(\dfrac{3}{12} + \dfrac{8}{12}\right)\left(\dfrac{11}{12} + \dfrac{3}{12}\right)$

$\qquad = \left(\dfrac{11}{12}\right)\left(\dfrac{14}{12}\right)$ Add.

$\qquad = \dfrac{11 \cdot 2 \cdot 7}{2 \cdot 6 \cdot 12}$ Multiply.

$\qquad = \dfrac{77}{72}$ Simplify.

▣ **Work Practice Problem 6**

✔ **Concept Check** What should be done first to simplify the expression $\dfrac{1}{5} \cdot \dfrac{5}{2} - \left(\dfrac{2}{3} + \dfrac{4}{5}\right)^2$?

Objective **C** Evaluating Algebraic Expressions

EXAMPLE 7 Evaluate $2x + y^2$ if $x = -\dfrac{1}{2}$ and $y = \dfrac{1}{3}$.

Solution: Replace x and y with the given values and simplify.

$2x + y^2 = 2\left(-\dfrac{1}{2}\right) + \left(\dfrac{1}{3}\right)^2$ Replace x with $-\dfrac{1}{2}$ and y with $\dfrac{1}{3}$.

$\qquad = 2\left(-\dfrac{1}{2}\right) + \dfrac{1}{9}$ Write $\left(\dfrac{1}{3}\right)^2$ as $\dfrac{1}{9}$.

$\qquad = -1 + \dfrac{1}{9}$ Multiply.

$\qquad = -\dfrac{9}{9} + \dfrac{1}{9}$ The LCD is 9.

$\qquad = -\dfrac{8}{9}$ Add.

▣ **Work Practice Problem 7**

PRACTICE PROBLEM 7

Evaluate $-\dfrac{3}{5} - xy$ if $x = \dfrac{3}{10}$ and $y = \dfrac{2}{3}$.

Answers

5. $\dfrac{64}{27}$,   **6.** $-\dfrac{3}{10}$,   **7.** $-\dfrac{4}{5}$

✔ **Concept Check Answer**

Add inside parentheses.

Helpful Hint

If you find it difficult replacing a variable with a number, try the following. First, replace the variable with a set of parentheses, then place the replacement number between the parentheses.

If $x = \dfrac{4}{5}$, find $2x + x^2$.

$$2x + x^2 = 2(\ ) + (\ )^2$$

$$= 2\left(\frac{4}{5}\right) + \left(\frac{4}{5}\right)^2 \cdots$$

then continue simplifying.

Objective D Writing Mixed Numbers as Improper Fractions

Notice from Section 3.1 that mixed numbers and improper fractions were both used to represent the shaded area of the figure groups. For example,

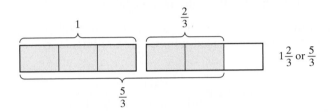

The following steps may be used to write a mixed number as an improper fraction:

Writing a Mixed Number as an Improper Fraction

To write a mixed number as an improper fraction:

Step 1: Multiply the denominator of the fraction by the whole number.

Step 2: Add the numerator of the fraction to the product from Step 1.

Step 3: Write the sum from Step 2 as the numerator of the improper fraction over the original denominator.

For example,

$$1\frac{2}{3} = \frac{\overset{\text{Step 1}}{3 \cdot 1} + \overset{\text{Step 2}}{2}}{3} = \frac{3 + 2}{3} = \frac{5}{3}$$

Step 3

EXAMPLE 8 Write each as an improper fraction.

a. $4\dfrac{2}{9} = \dfrac{9 \cdot 4 + 2}{9} = \dfrac{36 + 2}{9} = \dfrac{38}{9}$

b. $1\dfrac{8}{11} = \dfrac{11 \cdot 1 + 8}{11} = \dfrac{11 + 8}{11} = \dfrac{19}{11}$

◼ **Work Practice Problem 8**

PRACTICE PROBLEM 8

Write each as an improper fraction.

a. $2\dfrac{5}{7}$ **b.** $5\dfrac{1}{3}$

c. $9\dfrac{3}{10}$ **d.** $1\dfrac{1}{5}$

Answers

8. **a.** $\dfrac{19}{7}$, **b.** $\dfrac{16}{3}$, **c.** $\dfrac{93}{10}$, **d.** $\dfrac{6}{5}$

Objective E Writing Improper Fractions as Mixed Numbers or Whole Numbers

Just as there are times when an improper fraction is preferred, sometimes a mixed or a whole number better suits a situation. To write improper fractions as mixed or whole numbers, we use division. Recall once again from Section 1.7 that the fraction bar means division. This means that the fraction

$$\frac{5}{3} \begin{array}{l}\text{numerator}\\ \text{denominator}\end{array} \quad \text{means } 3\overline{)5}$$

Writing an Improper Fraction as a Mixed Number or a Whole Number

To write an improper fraction as a mixed number or a whole number:

Step 1: Divide the denominator into the numerator.

Step 2: The whole number part of the mixed number is the quotient. The fraction part of the mixed number is the remainder over the original denominator.

$$\text{quotient}\frac{\text{remainder}}{\text{original denominator}}$$

For example,

$$\frac{5}{3} : 3\overline{)5}\ \ \frac{3}{2} \qquad \frac{5}{3} = 1\frac{2}{3}$$

PRACTICE PROBLEM 9

Write each as a mixed number or a whole number.

a. $\frac{8}{5}$ **b.** $\frac{17}{6}$ **c.** $\frac{48}{4}$

d. $\frac{75}{13}$ **e.** $\frac{51}{7}$ **f.** $\frac{21}{20}$

EXAMPLE 9 Write each as a mixed number or a whole number.

a. $\frac{30}{7}$ **b.** $\frac{16}{15}$ **c.** $\frac{84}{6}$

Solution:

a. $\frac{30}{7} : 7\overline{)30}\ \frac{28}{2}$ $\frac{30}{7} = 4\frac{2}{7}$

b. $\frac{16}{15} : 15\overline{)16}\ \frac{15}{1}$ $\frac{16}{15} = 1\frac{1}{15}$

c. $\frac{84}{6} : 6\overline{)84}\ \frac{6}{24}\ \frac{24}{0}$ $\frac{84}{6} = 14$ Since the remainder is 0, the result is the whole number 14.

Helpful Hint
When the remainder is 0, the improper fraction is a whole number. For example, $\frac{92}{4} = 23$.

$$4\overline{)92}\ \frac{8}{12}\ \frac{12}{0}$$

Answers

9. a. $1\frac{3}{5}$, **b.** $2\frac{5}{6}$, **c.** 12,

d. $5\frac{10}{13}$, **e.** $7\frac{2}{7}$, **f.** $1\frac{1}{20}$

Work Practice Problem 9

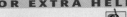
Objective A *Simplify each complex fraction. See Examples 1 through 4.*

1. $\dfrac{\frac{1}{8}}{\frac{3}{4}}$

2. $\dfrac{\frac{2}{3}}{\frac{2}{7}}$

3. $\dfrac{\frac{9}{10}}{\frac{21}{10}}$

4. $\dfrac{\frac{14}{5}}{\frac{7}{5}}$

5. $\dfrac{\frac{2}{27}}{\frac{4}{9}}$

6. $\dfrac{\frac{3}{11}}{\frac{1}{2}}$

7. $\dfrac{\frac{3}{4}+\frac{2}{5}}{\frac{1}{2}+\frac{3}{5}}$

8. $\dfrac{\frac{7}{6}+\frac{2}{3}}{\frac{3}{2}-\frac{8}{9}}$

9. $\dfrac{\frac{3}{4}}{5-\frac{1}{8}}$

10. $\dfrac{\frac{3}{10}+2}{\frac{2}{5}}$

Objective B *Use the order of operations to simplify each expression. See Examples 5 and 6.*

11. $\dfrac{1}{5}+\dfrac{1}{3}\cdot\dfrac{1}{4}$

12. $\dfrac{1}{2}+\dfrac{1}{6}\cdot\dfrac{1}{3}$

13. $\dfrac{5}{6}\div\dfrac{1}{3}\cdot\dfrac{1}{4}$

14. $\dfrac{7}{8}\div\dfrac{1}{4}\cdot\dfrac{1}{7}$

15. $2^2-\left(\dfrac{1}{3}\right)^2$

16. $3^2-\left(\dfrac{1}{2}\right)^2$

17. $\left(\dfrac{2}{9}+\dfrac{4}{9}\right)\left(\dfrac{1}{3}-\dfrac{9}{10}\right)$

18. $\left(\dfrac{1}{5}-\dfrac{1}{10}\right)\left(\dfrac{1}{5}+\dfrac{1}{10}\right)$

19. $\left(\dfrac{7}{8}-\dfrac{1}{2}\right)\div\dfrac{3}{11}$

20. $\left(-\dfrac{2}{3}-\dfrac{7}{3}\right)\div\dfrac{4}{9}$

21. $2\cdot\left(\dfrac{1}{4}+\dfrac{1}{5}\right)+2$

22. $\dfrac{2}{5}\cdot\left(5-\dfrac{1}{2}\right)-1$

23. $\left(\dfrac{3}{4}\right)^2\div\left(\dfrac{3}{4}-\dfrac{1}{12}\right)$

24. $\left(\dfrac{8}{9}\right)^2\div\left(2-\dfrac{2}{3}\right)$

25. $\left(\dfrac{2}{3}-\dfrac{5}{9}\right)^2$

26. $\left(1-\dfrac{2}{5}\right)^3$

27. $\left(\dfrac{3}{4}+\dfrac{1}{8}\right)^2-\left(\dfrac{1}{2}+\dfrac{1}{8}\right)$

28. $\left(\dfrac{1}{6}+\dfrac{1}{3}\right)^3+\left(\dfrac{2}{5}\cdot\dfrac{3}{4}\right)^2$

Objective C *Evaluate each expression if $x=-\dfrac{1}{3}$, $y=\dfrac{2}{5}$, and $z=\dfrac{5}{6}$. See Example 7.*

29. $5y-z$

30. $2z-x$

31. $\dfrac{x}{z}$

32. $\dfrac{y+x}{z}$

33. x^2-yz

34. $(1+x)(1+z)$

Objectives A B Mixed Practice *Simplify the following. See Examples 1 through 6.*

35. $\dfrac{\frac{5}{24}}{\frac{1}{12}}$

36. $\dfrac{\frac{7}{10}}{\frac{14}{25}}$

37. $\left(\dfrac{3}{2}\right)^3+\left(\dfrac{1}{2}\right)^3$

38. $\left(\dfrac{5}{21} \div \dfrac{1}{2}\right) + \left(\dfrac{1}{7} \cdot \dfrac{1}{3}\right)$

39. $\left(-\dfrac{1}{3}\right)^2 + \dfrac{1}{3}$

40. $\left(-\dfrac{3}{4}\right)^2 + \dfrac{3}{8}$

41. $\dfrac{2 + \dfrac{1}{6}}{1 - \dfrac{4}{3}}$

42. $\dfrac{3 - \dfrac{1}{2}}{4 + \dfrac{1}{5}}$

43. $\left(1 - \dfrac{2}{5}\right)^2$

44. $\left(-\dfrac{1}{2}\right)^2 - \left(\dfrac{3}{4}\right)^2$

45. $\left(\dfrac{3}{4} - 1\right)\left(\dfrac{1}{8} + \dfrac{1}{2}\right)$

46. $\left(\dfrac{1}{10} + \dfrac{3}{20}\right)\left(\dfrac{1}{5} - 1\right)$

47. $\left(-\dfrac{2}{9} - \dfrac{7}{9}\right)^4$

48. $\left(\dfrac{5}{9} - \dfrac{2}{3}\right)^2$

49. $\dfrac{\dfrac{1}{2} - \dfrac{3}{8}}{\dfrac{3}{4} + \dfrac{1}{2}}$

50. $\dfrac{\dfrac{7}{10} + \dfrac{1}{2}}{\dfrac{4}{5} + \dfrac{3}{4}}$

Objective **D** *Write each mixed number as an improper fraction. See Example 8.*

51. $2\dfrac{1}{3}$ **52.** $6\dfrac{3}{4}$ **53.** $3\dfrac{3}{5}$ **54.** $2\dfrac{5}{9}$ **55.** $6\dfrac{5}{8}$ **56.** $7\dfrac{3}{8}$

57. $2\dfrac{11}{15}$ **58.** $1\dfrac{13}{17}$ **59.** $11\dfrac{6}{7}$ **60.** $12\dfrac{2}{5}$ **61.** $6\dfrac{6}{13}$ **62.** $8\dfrac{9}{10}$

63. $9\dfrac{7}{20}$ **64.** $10\dfrac{14}{27}$ **65.** $166\dfrac{2}{3}$ **66.** $114\dfrac{2}{7}$

Objective **E** *Write each improper fraction as a mixed number or a whole number. See Example 9.*

67. $\dfrac{17}{5}$ **68.** $\dfrac{13}{7}$ **69.** $\dfrac{37}{8}$ **70.** $\dfrac{64}{9}$ **71.** $\dfrac{47}{15}$ **72.** $\dfrac{65}{12}$

73. $\dfrac{225}{15}$ **74.** $\dfrac{196}{14}$ **75.** $\dfrac{182}{175}$ **76.** $\dfrac{149}{143}$ **77.** $\dfrac{737}{112}$ **78.** $\dfrac{901}{123}$

Review

Perform each indicated operation. See Section 3.5.

79. $3 + \dfrac{1}{2}$ **80.** $2 + \dfrac{2}{3}$ **81.** $9 - \dfrac{5}{6}$ **82.** $4 - \dfrac{1}{5}$

Concept Extensions

83. In your own words, explain how to write an improper fraction as a mixed number.

84. In your own words, explain how to write a mixed number as an improper fraction.

Recall that to find the average of two numbers, find their sum and divide by 2. For example, the average of $\frac{1}{2}$ and $\frac{3}{4}$ is

$\dfrac{\frac{1}{2}+\frac{3}{4}}{2}$. *Find the average of each pair of numbers.*

85. $\dfrac{1}{2}, \dfrac{3}{4}$

86. $\dfrac{3}{5}, \dfrac{9}{10}$

87. $\dfrac{1}{4}, \dfrac{2}{14}$

88. $\dfrac{5}{6}, \dfrac{7}{9}$

89. Two positive numbers, a and b, are graphed below. Where should the graph of their average lie?

Answer true or false for each statement.

90. It is possible for the average of two numbers to be greater than both numbers.

91. It is possible for the average of two numbers to be less than both numbers.

92. The sum of two negative fractions is always a negative number.

93. The sum of a negative fraction and a positive fraction is always a positive number.

94. It is possible for the sum of two fractions to be a whole number.

95. It is possible for the difference of two fractions to be a whole number.

96. What operation should be performed first to simplify

$$\frac{1}{5} \cdot \frac{5}{2} - \left(\frac{2}{3} + \frac{4}{5}\right)^2$$

Explain your answer.

97. A student is to evaluate $x - y$ when $x = \dfrac{1}{5}$ and $y = -\dfrac{1}{7}$. This student is asking you if he should evaluate $\dfrac{1}{5} - \dfrac{1}{7}$. What do you tell this student and why?

Each expression contains one addition, one subtraction, one multiplication, and one division. Write the operations in the order that they should be performed. Do not actually simplify. See the Concept Check in this section.

98. $[9 + 3(4 - 2)] \div \dfrac{10}{21}$

99. $[30 - 4(3 + 2)] \div \dfrac{5}{2}$

100. $\dfrac{1}{3} \div \left(\dfrac{2}{3}\right)\left(\dfrac{4}{5}\right) - \dfrac{1}{4} + \dfrac{1}{2}$

101. $\left(\dfrac{5}{6} - \dfrac{1}{3}\right) \cdot \dfrac{1}{3} + \dfrac{1}{2} \div \dfrac{9}{8}$

PRACTICE PROBLEM 1

Graph the numbers on a number line.

$$-4, -4\frac{1}{2}, 1\frac{3}{4}, \frac{1}{8}, -\frac{1}{2}$$

3.7 OPERATIONS ON MIXED NUMBERS

Objective **A** Graphing Fractions and Mixed Numbers

Just as we graphed whole numbers and integers on a number line, we can graph fractions. This will help us visualize rounding and estimating operations with mixed numbers.

Recall that $5\frac{2}{3}$ means $5 + \frac{2}{3}$ and

$-4\frac{1}{6}$ means $-4 - \frac{1}{6}$

EXAMPLE 1 Graph the numbers on a number line:

$$\frac{1}{2}, -\frac{3}{4}, 2\frac{2}{3}, -3, -3\frac{1}{8}$$

Solution: Remember that $2\frac{2}{3}$ means $2 + \frac{2}{3}$.

Also, $-3\frac{1}{8}$ means $-3 - \frac{1}{8}$, so $-3\frac{1}{8}$ lies to the left of -3.

☐ **Work Practice Problem 1**

✔ **Concept Check** Which of the following are equivalent to 9?

a. $7\frac{6}{3}$ **b.** $8\frac{4}{4}$ **c.** $8\frac{9}{9}$ **d.** $\frac{18}{2}$ **e.** all of these

Objective **B** Multiplying or Dividing with Mixed Numbers or Whole Numbers

When multiplying or dividing a fraction and a mixed or a whole number, remember that mixed and whole numbers can be written as fractions.

> **Multiplying or Dividing Fractions and Mixed Numbers or Whole Numbers**
>
> To multiply or divide with mixed numbers or whole numbers, first write any mixed or whole numbers as fractions and then multiply or divide as usual.

(Note: If an exercise contains a mixed number, we will write the answer as a mixed number, if possible.)

Answer

1.

✔ Concept Check Answer

e

EXAMPLE 2 Multiply: $3\frac{1}{3} \cdot \frac{7}{8}$

Solution: The mixed number $3\frac{1}{3}$ can be written as the fraction $\frac{10}{3}$. Then,

$$3\frac{1}{3} \cdot \frac{7}{8} = \frac{10}{3} \cdot \frac{7}{8} = \frac{\overset{1}{\cancel{2}} \cdot 5 \cdot 7}{3 \cdot \underset{1}{\cancel{2}} \cdot 4} = \frac{35}{12} \quad \text{or} \quad 2\frac{11}{12}$$

🔲 **Work Practice Problem 2**

Don't forget that a whole number can be written as a fraction by writing the whole number over 1. For example,

$$20 = \frac{20}{1} \quad \text{and} \quad 7 = \frac{7}{1}$$

EXAMPLE 3 Multiply.

$$\frac{3}{4} \cdot 20 = \frac{3}{4} \cdot \frac{20}{1} = \frac{3 \cdot 20}{4 \cdot 1} = \frac{3 \cdot \overset{1}{\cancel{4}} \cdot 5}{\underset{1}{\cancel{4}} \cdot 1} = \frac{15}{1} \quad \text{or} \quad 15$$

🔲 **Work Practice Problem 3**

When both numbers to be multiplied are mixed or whole numbers, it is a good idea to estimate the product to see if your answer is reasonable. To do this, we first practice rounding mixed numbers to the nearest whole. If the fraction part of the mixed number is $\frac{1}{2}$ or greater, we round the whole number part up. If the fraction part of the mixed number is less than $\frac{1}{2}$, then we do not round the whole number part up. Study the table below for examples.

Mixed Number	Rounding
$5\frac{1}{4}$ $\frac{1}{4}$ is less than $\frac{1}{2}$ $\frac{1}{4}$ $\frac{1}{2}$	Thus, $5\frac{1}{4}$ rounds to 5.
$3\frac{9}{16}$ ← 9 is greater than 8 → Half of 16 is 8.	Thus, $3\frac{9}{16}$ rounds to 4.
$1\frac{3}{7}$ ← 3 is less than $3\frac{1}{2}$. → Half of 7 is $3\frac{1}{2}$.	Thus, $1\frac{3}{7}$ rounds to 1.

EXAMPLES Multiply. Check by estimating.

4. $1\frac{2}{3} \cdot 2\frac{1}{4} = \frac{5}{3} \cdot \frac{9}{4} = \frac{5 \cdot 9}{3 \cdot 4} = \frac{5 \cdot \overset{1}{\cancel{3}} \cdot 3}{\underset{1}{\cancel{3}} \cdot 4} = \frac{15}{4} \text{ or } 3\frac{3}{4}$ Exact

Let's check by estimating.

$1\frac{2}{3}$ rounds to 2, $2\frac{1}{4}$ rounds to 2, and $2 \cdot 2 = 4$ Estimate

The estimate is close to the exact value, so our answer is reasonable.

Continued on next page

5. $7 \cdot 2\frac{11}{14} = \frac{7}{1} \cdot \frac{39}{14} = \frac{7 \cdot 39}{1 \cdot 14} = \frac{\overset{1}{\cancel{7}} \cdot 39}{1 \cdot 2 \cdot \cancel{7}} = \frac{39}{2}$ or $19\frac{1}{2}$ Exact

To estimate,

$2\frac{11}{14}$ rounds to 3 and $7 \cdot 3 = 21$. Estimate

The estimate is close to the exact value, so our answer is reasonable.

🔲 **Work Practice Problems 4–5**

✔ **Concept Check**

Find the error.

$2\frac{1}{4} \cdot \frac{1}{2} = 2\frac{1 \cdot 1}{4 \cdot 2} = 2\frac{1}{8}$

PRACTICE PROBLEMS 6–8

Divide.

6. $\frac{4}{9} \div 7$ **7.** $\frac{8}{15} \div 3\frac{4}{5}$

8. $3\frac{2}{7} \div 2\frac{3}{14}$

EXAMPLES Divide.

6. $\frac{3}{4} \div 5 = \frac{3}{4} \div \frac{5}{1} = \frac{3}{4} \cdot \frac{1}{5} = \frac{3 \cdot 1}{4 \cdot 5} = \frac{3}{20}$

7. $\frac{11}{18} \div 2\frac{5}{6} = \frac{11}{18} \div \frac{17}{6} = \frac{11}{18} \cdot \frac{6}{17} = \frac{11 \cdot 6}{18 \cdot 17} = \frac{11 \cdot \overset{1}{\cancel{6}}}{\cancel{6} \cdot 3 \cdot 17} = \frac{11}{51}$

8. $5\frac{2}{3} \div 2\frac{5}{9} = \frac{17}{3} \div \frac{23}{9} = \frac{17}{3} \cdot \frac{9}{23} = \frac{17 \cdot 9}{3 \cdot 23} = \frac{17 \cdot \overset{1}{\cancel{3}} \cdot 3}{\cancel{3} \cdot 23} = \frac{51}{23}$ or $2\frac{5}{23}$

🔲 **Work Practice Problems 6–8**

Objective ◉ Adding or Subtracting Mixed Numbers

✔ **Concept Check** Which of the following are equivalent to 7?

a. $6\frac{5}{5}$ **b.** $6\frac{7}{7}$ **c.** $5\frac{8}{4}$

d. $6\frac{17}{17}$ **e.** all of these

We can add or subtract mixed numbers, too, by first writing each mixed number as an improper fraction. But it is often easier to add or subtract the whole-number parts and add or subtract the proper-fraction parts vertically.

Adding or Subtracting Mixed Numbers

To add or subtract mixed numbers, add or subtract the fraction parts and then add or subtract the whole number parts.

For example,

$$2\frac{2}{7}$$
$$+\,6\frac{3}{7}$$

$8\frac{5}{7}$ ← Add the fractions;
then add the whole numbers

EXAMPLE 9 Add: $2\frac{1}{3} + 5\frac{3}{8}$. Check by estimating.

Solution: The LCD of 3 and 8 is 24.

$$2\frac{1 \cdot 8}{3 \cdot 8} = 2\frac{8}{24}$$
$$+\,5\frac{3 \cdot 3}{8 \cdot 3} = 5\frac{9}{24}$$
$$7\frac{17}{24}$$ ← Add the fractions
Add the whole numbers

To check by estimating, we round as usual. The fraction $2\frac{1}{3}$ rounds to 2, $5\frac{3}{8}$ rounds to 5, and $2 + 5 = 7$, our estimate.

Our exact answer is close to 7, so our answer is reasonable.

■ **Work Practice Problem 9**

Helpful Hint

When adding or subtracting mixed numbers and whole numbers, it is a good idea to estimate to see if your answer is reasonable.

EXAMPLE 10 Add: $3\frac{4}{5} + 1\frac{4}{15}$

Solution: The LCD of 5 and 15 is 15.

$$3\frac{4}{5} = 3\frac{12}{15}$$
$$+\,1\frac{4}{15} = 1\frac{4}{15}$$ Add the fractions; then add the whole numbers.
$$4\frac{16}{15}$$ Notice that the fraction part is improper.

Since $\frac{16}{15}$ is $1\frac{1}{15}$ we can write the sum as

$$4\frac{16}{15} = 4 + 1\frac{1}{15} = 5\frac{1}{15}$$

■ **Work Practice Problem 10**

PRACTICE PROBLEM 9

Add: $4\frac{2}{5} + 5\frac{1}{6}$

PRACTICE PROBLEM 10

Add: $2\frac{5}{14} + 5\frac{6}{7}$

Answers

9. $9\frac{17}{30}$, **10.** $8\frac{3}{14}$

Copyright 2007 Pearson Education, Inc.

PRACTICE PROBLEM 11

Add: $10 + 2\dfrac{6}{7} + 3\dfrac{1}{5}$

EXAMPLE 11 Add: $1\dfrac{4}{5} + 4 + 2\dfrac{1}{2}$

Solution: The LCD of 5 and 2 is 10.

$$1\dfrac{4}{5} = 1\dfrac{8}{10}$$

$$4 \phantom{\dfrac{4}{5}} = 4$$

$$\underline{+\,2\dfrac{1}{2} = 2\dfrac{5}{10}}$$

$$7\dfrac{13}{10} = 7 + 1\dfrac{3}{10} = 8\dfrac{3}{10}$$

■ **Work Practice Problem 11**

PRACTICE PROBLEM 12

Subtract: $29\dfrac{7}{9} - 13\dfrac{5}{18}$

EXAMPLE 12 Subtract: $9\dfrac{3}{7} - 5\dfrac{2}{21}$. Check by estimating.

Solution: The LCD of 7 and 21 is 21.

$$9\dfrac{3}{7} \;=\; 9\dfrac{9}{21} \;\leftarrow\; \text{The LCD of 7 and 21 is 21.}$$

$$\underline{-5\dfrac{2}{21} = -5\dfrac{2}{21}}$$

$$4\dfrac{7}{21} \;\leftarrow\; \text{Subtract the fractions.}$$
$$\uparrow$$
$$\text{Subtract the whole numbers.}$$

Then $4\dfrac{7}{21}$ simplifies to $4\dfrac{1}{3}$. The difference is $4\dfrac{1}{3}$.

To check, $9\dfrac{3}{7}$ rounds to 9, $5\dfrac{2}{21}$ rounds to 5, and $9 - 5 = 4$, our estimate.

Our exact answer is close to 4, so our answer is reasonable.

■ **Work Practice Problem 12**

When subtracting mixed numbers, borrowing may be needed, as shown in the next example.

PRACTICE PROBLEM 13

Subtract: $9\dfrac{7}{15} - 5\dfrac{3}{5}$

EXAMPLE 13 Subtract: $7\dfrac{3}{14} - 3\dfrac{6}{7}$

Solution: The LCD of 7 and 14 is 14.

$$7\dfrac{3}{14} \;=\; 7\dfrac{3}{14}$$

$$\underline{-3\dfrac{6}{7} \;=\; -3\dfrac{12}{14}}$$

Notice that we cannot subtract $\dfrac{12}{14}$ from $\dfrac{3}{14}$, so we borrow from the whole number 7.

borrow 1 from 7

$$7\dfrac{3}{14} = 6 + 1\dfrac{3}{14} = 6 + \dfrac{17}{14} \text{ or } 6\dfrac{17}{14}$$

Answers

11. $16\dfrac{2}{35}$, **12.** $16\dfrac{1}{2}$, **13.** $3\dfrac{13}{15}$

Now subtract.

$$7\frac{3}{14} = \ 7\frac{3}{14} = \ 6\frac{17}{14}$$
$$-3\frac{6}{7} = -3\frac{12}{14} = -3\frac{12}{14}$$
$$3\frac{5}{14} \leftarrow \text{Subtract the fractions.}$$
$$\uparrow$$
$$\text{Subtract the whole numbers.}$$

▣ **Work Practice Problem 13**

✔ **Concept Check** In the subtraction problem $5\frac{1}{4} - 3\frac{3}{4}$, $5\frac{1}{4}$ must be rewritten because $\frac{3}{4}$ cannot be subtracted from $\frac{1}{4}$. Why is it incorrect to rewrite $5\frac{1}{4}$ as $5\frac{5}{4}$?

EXAMPLE 14 Subtract: $12 - 8\frac{3}{7}$

Solution:

$$12 \ = \ 11\frac{7}{7} \ \text{Borrow 1 from 12 and write it as } \frac{7}{7}.$$
$$-8\frac{3}{7} = -8\frac{3}{7}$$
$$3\frac{4}{7} \leftarrow \text{Subtract the fractions.}$$
$$\uparrow$$
$$\text{Subtract the whole numbers.}$$

▣ **Work Practice Problem 14**

Objective D Solving Problems Containing Mixed Numbers

Now that we know how to perform operations on mixed numbers, we can solve real-life problems.

EXAMPLE 15 Finding Legal Lobster Size

Lobster fishermen must measure the upper body shells of the lobsters they catch. Lobsters that are too small are thrown back into the ocean. Each state has its own size standard for lobsters to help control the breeding stock. In 1988, Massachusetts increased its legal lobster size from $3\frac{3}{16}$ inches to $3\frac{7}{32}$ inches. How much of an increase was this? (*Source:* Peabody Essex Museum, Salem, Massachusetts)

Solution:

1. UNDERSTAND. Read and reread the problem carefully. The word "increase" found in the problem might make you think that we add to solve the problem. But the phrase "how much of an increase" tells us to subtract to find the increase.

Continued on next page

PRACTICE PROBLEM 14

Subtract: $25 - 10\frac{2}{9}$

PRACTICE PROBLEM 15

The measurement around the trunk of a tree just below shoulder height is called its girth. The largest known American beech tree in the United States has a girth of $23\frac{1}{4}$ feet. The largest known sugar maple tree in the United States has a girth of $19\frac{5}{12}$ feet. How much larger is the girth of the largest known American beech tree than the girth of the largest known sugar maple tree? (*Source: American Forests*)

Girth

Answers

14. $14\frac{7}{9}$, **15.** $3\frac{5}{6}$ ft

✔ **Concept Check Answer**

Rewrite $5\frac{1}{4}$ as $4\frac{5}{4}$ by borrowing from the 5.

2. TRANSLATE.

In words:

| increase | is | new lobster size | minus | old lobster size |

$$\downarrow \qquad \downarrow \qquad \downarrow \qquad \downarrow \qquad \downarrow$$

Translate: $\quad$ increase $\quad = \quad 3\dfrac{7}{32} \quad - \quad 3\dfrac{3}{16}$

3. SOLVE: Before we solve, let's estimate. The fraction $3\dfrac{7}{32}$ rounds to 3, $3\dfrac{3}{16}$ rounds to 3, and $3 - 3 = 0$. The increase is not 0, but will be very small.

$$
\begin{aligned}
3\dfrac{7}{32} &= 3\dfrac{7}{32} \\
-3\dfrac{3}{16} &= 3\dfrac{6}{32} \\
\hline
&\qquad \dfrac{1}{32}
\end{aligned}
$$

4. INTERPRET. *Check* your work. Our estimate tells us that the exact increase of $\dfrac{1}{32}$ inch is reasonable. *State* your conclusion: The increase in lobster size is $\dfrac{1}{32}$ of an inch.

▣ **Work Practice Problem 15**

A designer of women's clothing designs a woman's dress that requires $2\dfrac{1}{7}$ yards of material.

How many dresses can be made from a 30-yard bolt of material?

EXAMPLE 16 **Calculating Manufacturing Materials Needed**

In a manufacturing process, a metal-cutting machine cuts strips $1\dfrac{3}{5}$ inches long from a piece of metal stock. How many such strips can be cut from a 48-inch piece of stock?

Solution:

1. UNDERSTAND the problem. To do so, read and reread the problem. Then draw a diagram:

We want to know how many $1\dfrac{3}{5}$s there are in 48.

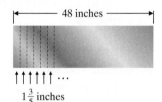

2. TRANSLATE.

In words:

| Number of strips | is | 48 | divided by | $1\dfrac{3}{5}$ |

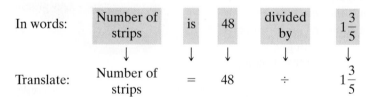

Translate:

Number of strips $\quad = \quad 48 \quad \div \quad 1\dfrac{3}{5}$

3. SOLVE: Let's estimate a reasonable answer. The mixed number $1\dfrac{3}{5}$ rounds to 2 and $48 \div 2 = 24$.

$$48 \div 1\dfrac{3}{5} = 48 \div \dfrac{8}{5} = \dfrac{48}{1} \cdot \dfrac{5}{8} = \dfrac{48 \cdot 5}{1 \cdot 8} = \dfrac{\overset{1}{\cancel{8}} \cdot 6 \cdot 5}{1 \cdot \underset{1}{\cancel{8}}} = \dfrac{30}{1} \text{ or } 30$$

4. INTERPRET. *Check* your work. Since the exact answer of 30 is close to our estimate of 24, our answer is reasonable. *State* your conclusion: Thirty strips can be cut from the 48-inch piece of stock.

▣ **Work Practice Problem 16**

Answer

16. 14 dresses

Objective ⓔ **Operating on Negative Mixed Numbers**

To perform operations on negative mixed numbers, let's first practice writing these numbers as negative fractions and negative fractions as negative mixed numbers.

To understand negative mixed numbers, we simply need to know that, for example,

$$-3\frac{2}{5} \text{ means } -\left(3\frac{2}{5}\right)$$

Thus, to write a negative mixed number as a fraction, we do the following.

$$-3\frac{2}{5} = -\left(3\frac{2}{5}\right) = -\left(\frac{17}{5}\right) \quad \text{or} \quad -\frac{17}{5}$$

$$3\frac{2}{5} = \frac{5\cdot3+2}{5} = \frac{17}{5}$$

EXAMPLES Write each as a fraction.

17. $-1\frac{7}{8} = -\frac{8\cdot1+7}{8} = -\frac{15}{8}$ Write $1\frac{7}{8}$ as an improper fraction and keep the negative sign.

18. $-23\frac{1}{2} = -\frac{2\cdot23+1}{2} = -\frac{47}{2}$ Write $23\frac{1}{2}$ as an improper fraction and keep the negative sign.

■ **Work Practice Problems 17–18**

To write a negative fraction as a negative mixed number, we use a similar procedure. We simply disregard the negative sign, convert the improper fraction to a mixed number, then reinsert the negative sign.

EXAMPLES Write each as a mixed number.

19. $-\frac{22}{5} = -4\frac{2}{5}$

$$\begin{array}{r} 4 \\ 5\overline{)22} \\ -20 \\ \hline 2 \end{array} \qquad \frac{22}{5} = 4\frac{2}{5}$$

20. $-\frac{9}{4} = -2\frac{1}{4}$

$$\begin{array}{r} 2 \\ 4\overline{)9} \\ -8 \\ \hline 1 \end{array} \qquad \frac{9}{4} = 2\frac{1}{4}$$

■ **Work Practice Problems 19–20**

We multiply or divide with negative mixed numbers the same way that we multiply or divide with positive mixed numbers. First, write each mixed number as a fraction.

PRACTICE PROBLEMS 17–18

Write each as a fraction

17. $-7\frac{3}{7}$

18. $-4\frac{10}{11}$

PRACTICE PROBLEMS 19–20

Write each as a mixed number.

19. $-\frac{29}{8}$

20. $-\frac{31}{5}$

Answers

17. $-\frac{52}{7}$, 18. $-\frac{54}{11}$, 19. $-3\frac{5}{8}$,

20. $-6\frac{1}{5}$

PRACTICE PROBLEMS 21–22

21. $3\frac{3}{4} \cdot \left(-2\frac{3}{5}\right)$

22. $-1\frac{2}{7} \div 4\frac{1}{4}$

EXAMPLES Perform the indicated operations.

21. $-4\frac{2}{5} \cdot 1\frac{3}{11} = -\frac{22}{5} \cdot \frac{14}{11} = -\frac{22 \cdot 14}{5 \cdot 11} = -\frac{2 \cdot 11 \cdot 14}{5 \cdot 11} = -\frac{28}{5}$ or $-5\frac{3}{5}$

22. $-2\frac{1}{3} \div \left(-2\frac{1}{2}\right) = -\frac{7}{3} \div \left(-\frac{5}{2}\right) = -\frac{7}{3} \cdot \left(-\frac{2}{5}\right) = \frac{7 \cdot 2}{3 \cdot 5} = \frac{14}{15}$

Work Practice Problems 21–22

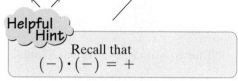

Helpful Hint

Recall that $(-) \cdot (-) = +$

To add or subtract with negative mixed numbers, we must be very careful! Problems arise because recall that

$$-3\frac{2}{5} \text{ means } -\left(3\frac{2}{5}\right)$$

This means that

$$-3\frac{2}{5} = -\left(3\frac{2}{5}\right) = -\left(3 + \frac{2}{5}\right) = -3 - \frac{2}{5} \quad \text{This can sometimes be easily overlooked.}$$

To avoid problems, we will add or subtract negative mixed numbers by rewriting as addition and recalling how to add signed numbers.

PRACTICE PROBLEM 23

Add: $7\frac{2}{3} + \left(-11\frac{3}{4}\right)$

EXAMPLE 23 Add: $6\frac{3}{5} + \left(-9\frac{7}{10}\right)$

Solution: Here we are adding two numbers with different signs. Recall that we then subtract the absolute values and keep the sign of the larger absolute value.

Since $-9\frac{7}{10}$ has the larger absolute value, the answer is negative.

First, subtract absolute values:

$$9\frac{7}{10} = 9\frac{7}{10}$$
$$-6\frac{3 \cdot 2}{5 \cdot 2} = -6\frac{6}{10}$$
$$\overline{\phantom{-6\frac{3 \cdot 2}{5 \cdot 2}}} \quad \overline{3\frac{1}{10}}$$

Thus,

$$6\frac{3}{5} + \left(-9\frac{7}{10}\right) = -3\frac{1}{10} \quad \text{The result is negative since } -9\frac{7}{10} \text{ has the larger absolute value.}$$

Work Practice Problem 23

Answers

21. $-9\frac{3}{4}$, **22.** $-\frac{36}{119}$, **23.** $-4\frac{1}{12}$

EXAMPLE 24 Subtract: $-11\frac{5}{6} - 20\frac{4}{9}$

Solution: Let's write as an equivalent addition: $-11\frac{5}{6} + \left(-20\frac{4}{9}\right)$. Here, we are adding two numbers with like signs. Recall that we add their absolute values and keep the common negative sign.

First, add absolute values:

$$11\frac{5 \cdot 3}{6 \cdot 3} = \quad 11\frac{15}{18}$$

$$+20\frac{4 \cdot 2}{9 \cdot 2} = +20\frac{8}{18}$$

$$\overline{\qquad\qquad\qquad 31\frac{23}{18} \text{ or } 32\frac{5}{18}}$$

Since $\frac{23}{18} = 1\frac{5}{18}$

Thus,

$$-11\frac{5}{6} - 20\frac{4}{9} = -32\frac{5}{18}$$

Keep the common sign.

■ **Work Practice Problem 24**

PRACTICE PROBLEM 24

Subtract: $-9\frac{2}{7} - 15\frac{11}{14}$

Answer

24. $-25\frac{1}{14}$

CALCULATOR EXPLORATIONS

Converting Between Mixed-Number and Fraction Notation

If your calculator has a fraction key, such as $\boxed{a\ b/c}$, you can use it to convert between mixed-number notation and fraction notation.

To write $13\frac{7}{16}$ as an improper fraction, press

$$\boxed{1}\ \boxed{3}\ \boxed{a\ b/c}\ \boxed{7}\ \boxed{a\ b/c}\ \boxed{1}\ \boxed{6}\ \boxed{\text{2nd}}\ \boxed{d/c}$$

The display will read

$$\boxed{215\,|\,16}$$

which represents $\frac{215}{16}$. Thus $13\frac{7}{16} = \frac{215}{16}$

To convert $\frac{190}{13}$ to a mixed number, press

$$\boxed{1}\ \boxed{9}\ \boxed{0}\ \boxed{a\ b/c}\ \boxed{1}\ \boxed{3}\ \boxed{=}$$

The display will read

$$\boxed{14\_8/13}$$

which represents $14\frac{8}{13}$. Thus $\frac{190}{13} = 14\frac{8}{13}$.

Write each mixed number as a fraction and each fraction as a mixed number.

1. $25\frac{5}{11}$ **2.** $67\frac{14}{15}$ **3.** $107\frac{31}{35}$

4. $186\frac{17}{21}$ **5.** $\frac{365}{14}$ **6.** $\frac{290}{13}$

7. $\frac{2769}{30}$ **8.** $\frac{3941}{17}$

Mental Math

Choose the best estimate for each sum or difference.

1. $3\frac{7}{8} + 2\frac{1}{5}$

    a. 6 **b.** 5 **c.** 1 **d.** 2

3. $8\frac{1}{3} + 1\frac{1}{2}$

    a. 4 **b.** 10 **c.** 6 **d.** 16

2. $3\frac{7}{8} - 2\frac{1}{5}$

    a. 6 **b.** 5 **c.** 1 **d.** 2

4. $8\frac{1}{3} - 1\frac{1}{2}$

    a. 4 **b.** 10 **c.** 6 **d.** 16

3.7 EXERCISE SET

FOR EXTRA HELP

 Student Solutions Manual   PH Math/Tutor Center   CD/Video for Review Math XL MathXL® MyMathLab MyMathLab

Objective A *Graph each list of numbers on the given number line. See Example 1.*

1. $-2, -2\frac{2}{3}, 0, \frac{7}{8}, -\frac{1}{3}$

$$\xleftrightarrow{\hspace{0.2cm}|\hspace{0.2cm}|\hspace{0.2cm}|\hspace{0.2cm}|\hspace{0.2cm}|\hspace{0.2cm}|\hspace{0.2cm}|\hspace{0.2cm}|\hspace{0.2cm}|\hspace{0.2cm}|\hspace{0.2cm}|}$$
$$-5\ -4\ -3\ -2\ -1\ \ 0\ \ 1\ \ 2\ \ 3\ \ 4\ \ 5$$

2. $-1, -1\frac{1}{4}, -\frac{1}{4}, 3\frac{1}{4}, 3$

$$\xleftrightarrow{\hspace{0.2cm}|\hspace{0.2cm}|\hspace{0.2cm}|\hspace{0.2cm}|\hspace{0.2cm}|\hspace{0.2cm}|\hspace{0.2cm}|\hspace{0.2cm}|\hspace{0.2cm}|\hspace{0.2cm}|\hspace{0.2cm}|}$$
$$-5\ -4\ -3\ -2\ -1\ \ 0\ \ 1\ \ 2\ \ 3\ \ 4\ \ 5$$

3. $4, \frac{1}{3}, -3, -3\frac{4}{5}, 1\frac{1}{3}$

$$\xleftrightarrow{\hspace{0.2cm}|\hspace{0.2cm}|\hspace{0.2cm}|\hspace{0.2cm}|\hspace{0.2cm}|\hspace{0.2cm}|\hspace{0.2cm}|\hspace{0.2cm}|\hspace{0.2cm}|\hspace{0.2cm}|\hspace{0.2cm}|}$$
$$-5\ -4\ -3\ -2\ -1\ \ 0\ \ 1\ \ 2\ \ 3\ \ 4\ \ 5$$

4. $3, \frac{3}{8}, -4, -4\frac{1}{3}, -\frac{9}{10}$

$$\xleftrightarrow{\hspace{0.2cm}|\hspace{0.2cm}|\hspace{0.2cm}|\hspace{0.2cm}|\hspace{0.2cm}|\hspace{0.2cm}|\hspace{0.2cm}|\hspace{0.2cm}|\hspace{0.2cm}|\hspace{0.2cm}|\hspace{0.2cm}|}$$
$$-5\ -4\ -3\ -2\ -1\ \ 0\ \ 1\ \ 2\ \ 3\ \ 4\ \ 5$$

Objective B *Multiply or divide. For those exercises marked, find an exact answer and an estimated answer. See Examples 2 through 8.*

5. $2\frac{2}{3} \cdot \frac{1}{7}$

6. $\frac{5}{9} \cdot 4\frac{1}{5}$

7. $8 \div 1\frac{5}{7}$

8. $5 \div 3\frac{3}{4}$

9. $2\frac{1}{5} \cdot 3\frac{1}{2}$

Exact:

Estimate:

10. $2\frac{1}{4} \cdot 7\frac{1}{8}$

Exact:

Estimate:

11. $3\frac{4}{5} \cdot 6\frac{2}{7}$

Exact:

Estimate:

12. $5\frac{5}{6} \cdot 7\frac{3}{5}$

Exact:

Estimate:

13. $5 \cdot 2\frac{1}{2}$

14. $6 \cdot 3\frac{1}{3}$

 **15.** $3\frac{2}{3} \cdot 1\frac{1}{2}$

16. $2\frac{4}{5} \cdot 2\frac{5}{8}$

 **17.** $2\frac{2}{3} \div \frac{1}{7}$

18. $\frac{5}{9} \div 4\frac{1}{5}$

Objective C *Add. For those exercises marked, find an exact sum and an estimated sum. See Examples 9 through 11.*

19. $4\frac{7}{10}$
$+2\frac{1}{10}$

Exact:

Estimate:

20. $7\frac{4}{9}$
$+3\frac{2}{9}$

Exact:

Estimate:

21. $10\frac{3}{14}$
$+ 3\frac{4}{7}$

Exact:

Estimate:

22. $12\frac{5}{12}$
$+ 4\frac{1}{6}$

Exact:

Estimate:

23. $9\dfrac{1}{5}$
$+8\dfrac{2}{25}$

Exact:

Estimate:

24. $6\dfrac{2}{13}$
$+8\dfrac{7}{26}$

25. $12\dfrac{3}{14}$
10
$+25\dfrac{5}{12}$

26. $8\dfrac{2}{9}$
32
$+\ 9\dfrac{10}{21}$

27. $15\dfrac{4}{7}$
$+9\dfrac{11}{14}$

28. $23\dfrac{3}{5}$
$+8\dfrac{8}{15}$

29. $3\dfrac{5}{8}$
$2\dfrac{1}{6}$
$+7\dfrac{3}{4}$

30. $4\dfrac{1}{3}$
$9\dfrac{2}{5}$
$+3\dfrac{1}{6}$

Subtract. For those exercises marked, find an exact difference and an estimated difference. See Examples 12 through 14.

31. $4\dfrac{7}{10}$
$-2\dfrac{1}{10}$

Exact:

Estimate:

32. $7\dfrac{4}{9}$
$-3\dfrac{2}{9}$

Exact:

Estimate:

33. $10\dfrac{13}{14}$
$-\ 3\dfrac{4}{7}$

Exact:

Estimate:

34. $12\dfrac{5}{12}$
$-\ 4\dfrac{1}{6}$

Exact:

Estimate:

35. $9\dfrac{1}{5}$
$-8\dfrac{6}{25}$

Exact:

Estimate:

36. $5\dfrac{2}{13}$
$-4\dfrac{7}{26}$

37. 6
$-2\dfrac{4}{9}$

38. 8
$-1\dfrac{7}{10}$

39. $63\dfrac{1}{6}$
$-47\dfrac{5}{12}$

40. $86\dfrac{2}{15}$
$-27\dfrac{3}{10}$

Objectives **B** **C** **Mixed Practice** *Perform each indicated operation. See Examples 2 through 14.*

41. $2\dfrac{3}{4}$
$+1\dfrac{1}{4}$

42. $5\dfrac{5}{8}$
$+2\dfrac{3}{8}$

43. $15\dfrac{4}{7}$
$-9\dfrac{11}{14}$

44. $23\dfrac{3}{5}$
$-8\dfrac{8}{15}$

45. $3\dfrac{1}{9}\cdot 2$

46. $4\dfrac{1}{2}\cdot 3$

47. $1\dfrac{2}{3}\div 2\dfrac{1}{5}$

48. $5\dfrac{1}{5}\div 3\dfrac{1}{4}$

49. $22\dfrac{4}{9} + 13\dfrac{5}{18}$

50. $15\dfrac{3}{25} - 5\dfrac{2}{5}$

51. $5\dfrac{2}{3} - 3\dfrac{1}{6}$

52. $5\dfrac{3}{8} - 2\dfrac{13}{16}$

53.
$$15\dfrac{1}{5}$$
$$20\dfrac{3}{10}$$
$$+37\dfrac{2}{15}$$
$$\overline{\phantom{+37\dfrac{2}{15}}}$$

54.
$$7\dfrac{3}{7}$$
$$15$$
$$+20\dfrac{1}{2}$$
$$\overline{\phantom{+20\dfrac{1}{2}}}$$

55. $6\dfrac{4}{7} - 5\dfrac{11}{14}$

56. $47\dfrac{5}{12} - 23\dfrac{19}{24}$

Objective **D** *Solve. Write each answer in simplest form. See Examples 15 and 16.*

57. A patient is to take $3\dfrac{1}{3}$ tablespoons of medicine per day in 4 equally divided doses. How much medicine is to be taken in each dose?

58. If there are $13\dfrac{1}{3}$ grams of fat in 4 ounces of lean hamburger meat, how many grams of fat are in an ounce?

59. A sidewalk is built 6 bricks wide by laying each brick side by side. How many inches wide is the sidewalk if each brick measures $3\dfrac{1}{4}$ inches wide?

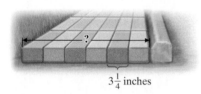

$3\dfrac{1}{4}$ inches

60. The nutrition label on a can of crushed pineapple shows 9 grams of carbohydrates for each cup of pineapple. How many grams of carbohydrates are in a $2\dfrac{1}{2}$-cup can?

61. At this writing, the smallest digital camera is the SPYZ camera from a Japanese company called Che-ez! The face of the camera measures $2\dfrac{9}{25}$ inches by $1\dfrac{13}{25}$ inches and is slightly bigger than a Zippo lighter. Find the area of the face of this camera.

(Area = length · width)

$1\dfrac{13}{25}$ in.

$2\dfrac{9}{25}$ in.

62. As part of his research, famous tornado expert Dr. T. Fujita studied approximately 31,050 tornadoes that occurred in the United States between 1916 and 1985. He found that roughly $\dfrac{7}{10}$ of these tornadoes occurred during April, May, June, and July. How many of these tornadoes occurred during these four months? (*Source: U.S. Tornadoes Part 1*, T. Fujita, University of Chicago)

△ **63.** To prevent intruding birds, birdhouses built for Eastern Bluebirds should have an entrance hole measuring $1\frac{1}{2}$ inches in diameter. Entrance holes in bird houses for Mountain Bluebirds should measure $1\frac{9}{16}$ inches in diameter. How much wider should entrance holes for Mountain Bluebirds be than for Eastern Bluebirds? (*Source:* North American Bluebird Society)

64. If the total weight allowable without overweight charges is 50 pounds and the traveler's luggage weighs $60\frac{5}{8}$ pounds, on how many pounds will the traveler's overweight charges be based?

65. Charlotte Dowlin has $15\frac{2}{3}$ feet of plastic pipe. She cuts off a $2\frac{1}{2}$-foot length and then a $3\frac{1}{4}$-foot length. If she now needs a 10-foot piece of pipe, will the remaining piece do? If not, by how much will the piece be short?

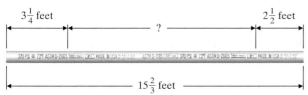

$3\frac{1}{4}$ feet   ? $2\frac{1}{2}$ feet

$15\frac{2}{3}$ feet

66. A trim carpenter cuts a board $3\frac{3}{8}$ feet long from one 6 feet long. How long is the remaining piece?

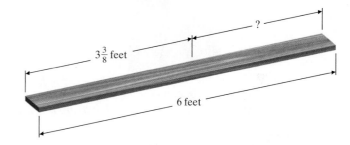

$3\frac{3}{8}$ feet   ?

6 feet

💿 **67.** If Tucson's average annual rainfall is $11\frac{1}{4}$ inches and Yuma's is $3\frac{3}{5}$ inches, how much more rain, on average, does Tucson get than Yuma?

68. A pair of crutches needs adjustment. One crutch is 43 inches and the other is $41\frac{5}{8}$ inches. Find how much the short crutch should be lengthened to make both crutches the same length.

69. A heart attack patient in rehabilitation walked on a treadmill $12\frac{3}{4}$ miles over 4 days. How many miles is this per day?

70. A local restaurant is selling hamburgers from a booth on Memorial Day. A total of $27\frac{3}{4}$ pounds of hamburger have been ordered. How many quarter-pound hamburgers can this make?

△ **71.** The area of the rectangle below is 12 square meters. If its width is $2\frac{4}{7}$ meters, find its length.

Rectangle $2\frac{4}{7}$ meters

△ **72.** The perimeter of the square below is $23\frac{1}{2}$ feet. Find the length of each side.

Square

73. Located on an island in New York City's harbor, the Statue of Liberty is one of the largest statues in the world. The copper figure is $46\frac{1}{20}$ meters tall from feet to tip of torch. The figure stands on a pedestal that is $46\frac{47}{50}$ meters feet tall. What is the overall height of the Statue of Liberty from the base of the pedestal to the tip of the torch? (*Source:* National Park Service)

74. The record for largest rainbow trout ever caught is $42\frac{1}{8}$ pounds and was set in Alaska in 1970. The record for largest tiger trout ever caught is $20\frac{13}{16}$ pounds and was set in Michigan in 1978. How much more did the record-setting rainbow trout weigh than the record-setting tiger trout? (*Source:* International Game Fish Association)

The following table lists some upcoming total eclipses of the Sun that will be visible in North America. The duration of each eclipse is listed in the table. Use the table to answer Exercises 75 through 78.

Total Solar Eclipses Visible from North America	
Date of Eclipse	**Duration (in Minutes)**
August 1, 2008	$2\frac{9}{20}$
August 21, 2017	$2\frac{2}{3}$
April 8, 2024	$4\frac{7}{15}$
(*Source:* NASA/Goddard Space Flight Center)	

75. What is the total duration for the three eclipses?

76. What is the total duration for the two eclipses occuring in even-numbered years?

77. How much longer will the April 8, 2024, eclipse be than the August 21, 2017, eclipse?

78. How much longer will the August 21, 2017, eclipse be than the August 1, 2008, eclipse?

Find the perimeter.

△ **79.**

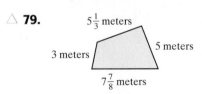

5 meters
$5\frac{1}{3}$ meters
3 meters
$7\frac{7}{8}$ meters

△ **80.**

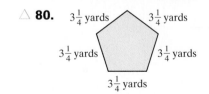

$3\frac{1}{4}$ yards
$3\frac{1}{4}$ yards
$3\frac{1}{4}$ yards
$3\frac{1}{4}$ yards
$3\frac{1}{4}$ yards

Objective 🄴 *Perform the indicated operations. See Examples 17 through 24.*

81. $-4\frac{2}{5} \cdot 2\frac{3}{10}$

82. $-3\frac{5}{6} \div \left(-3\frac{2}{3}\right)$

83. $-5\frac{1}{8} - 19\frac{3}{4}$

84. $17\frac{5}{9} + \left(-14\frac{2}{3}\right)$

85. $-31\frac{2}{15} + 17\frac{3}{20}$

86. $-1\frac{5}{7} \cdot \left(-2\frac{1}{2}\right)$

87. $1\frac{3}{4} \div \left(-3\frac{1}{2}\right)$

88. $-31\frac{7}{8} - \left(-26\frac{5}{12}\right)$

89. $11\frac{7}{8} - 13\frac{5}{6}$

90. $-20\frac{2}{5} + \left(-30\frac{3}{10}\right)$

91. $-7\frac{3}{10} \div (-100)$

92. $-4\frac{1}{4} \div 2\frac{3}{8}$

Review

Evaluate each expression. See Section 1.9.

93. $20 \div 10 \cdot 2$

94. $36 - 5 \cdot 6 + 10$

95. $2 + 3(8 \cdot 7 - 1)$

96. $2(10 - 2 \cdot 5) + 13$

Concept Extensions

Solve. See the Concept Checks in this section.

97. Which of the following are equivalent to 10?

   a. $9\frac{5}{5}$ **b.** $9\frac{100}{100}$ **c.** $6\frac{44}{11}$ **d.** $8\frac{13}{13}$

98. Which of the following are equivalent to $7\frac{3}{4}$?

   a. $6\frac{7}{4}$ **b.** $5\frac{11}{4}$ **c.** $7\frac{12}{16}$ **d.** all of them

Solve. See the Concept Check in this section.

99. A student asked you to check her work below. Is it correct? If not, where is the error?

   $$20\frac{2}{3} \div 10\frac{1}{2} = 2\frac{1}{3}.$$

Choose the best estimate for each quotient.

100. $10\frac{1}{4} \div 2\frac{1}{16}$

   a. 8   **b.** 5   **c.** 20   **d.** 12

101. $20\frac{1}{4} \div \frac{5}{6}$

   a. 5   **b.** $5\frac{1}{8}$ **c.** 20   **d.** 10

102. $\frac{11}{12} \div 16\frac{1}{5}$

   a. $\frac{1}{16}$ **b.** 4   **c.** 8   **d.** 16

103. $12\frac{2}{13} \div 3\frac{7}{8}$

   a. 4   **b.** 9   **c.** 36   **d.** 3

104. In your own words, describe how to divide mixed numbers.

105. In your own words, explain how to multiply
   a. fractions
   b. mixed numbers

106. In your own words, explain how to round a mixed number to the nearest whole number.

Solve. See the Concept Check in this section.

107. A student asked you to check his work below. Is it correct? If not, where is the error?

$$3\frac{2}{3} \cdot 1\frac{1}{7} = 3\frac{2}{21}$$

Solve.

108. Explain in your own words why $9\frac{13}{9}$ is equal to $10\frac{4}{9}$.

109. In your own words, explain
   a. when to borrow when subtracting mixed numbers, and
   b. how to borrow when subtracting mixed numbers.

 THE BIGGER PICTURE   **Operations on Sets of Numbers**

Continue your outline from Sections 1.7, 1.9, 2.5, and 3.3. Suggestions are once again written to help you complete this part of your outline.

I. Operations on Sets of Numbers

   A. Whole Numbers
   1. **Add or Subtract** (Sections 1.3, 1.4)
   2. **Multiply or Divide** (Sections 1.6, 1.7)
   3. **Exponent** (Section 1.9)
   4. **Square Root** (Section 1.9)
   5. **Order of Operations** (Section 1.9)

   B. Integers
   1. **Add** (Section 2.3)
   2. **Subtract** (Section 2.4)
   3. **Multiply or Divide** (Section 2.5)

   C. Fractions
   1. **Simplify** (Section 3.2)
   2. **Multiply** (Section 3.3)
   3. **Divide** (Section 3.3)
   4. **Add or Subtract:** Must have same denominators. If not, find the LCD, and write each fraction as an equivalent fraction with the LCD as denominator.

$$\frac{2}{5} + \frac{1}{15} = \frac{2}{5} \cdot \frac{3}{3} + \frac{1}{15} = \frac{6}{15} + \frac{1}{15} = \frac{7}{15}$$

Perform indicated operations.

1. $\dfrac{3}{17} + \dfrac{2}{17}$

2. $\dfrac{9}{10} - \dfrac{1}{10}$

3. $\dfrac{2}{3} + \dfrac{3}{10}$

4. $\dfrac{23}{24} - \dfrac{11}{12}$

5. $\dfrac{7}{8} + \dfrac{19}{20}$

6. $\dfrac{3^3}{4^3}$

7.
$$\begin{array}{r} 16 \\ -\ 3\frac{4}{7} \\ \hline \end{array}$$

8.
$$\begin{array}{r} 2\frac{5}{8} \\ 1\frac{1}{6} \\ +5\frac{3}{4} \\ \hline \end{array}$$

9. $\dfrac{6}{11} \cdot \dfrac{8}{9}$

10. $2\dfrac{4}{15} \div 1\dfrac{4}{5}$

CHAPTER 3 Group Activity

Sections 3.1, 3.6, 3.7

This activity may be completed by working in groups or individually.

Lobsters are normally classified by weight. Use the weight classification table to answer the questions in this activity.

Classification of Lobsters	
Class	**Weight (in Pounds)**
Chicken	1 to $1\frac{1}{8}$
Quarter	$1\frac{1}{4}$
Half	$1\frac{1}{2}$ to $1\frac{3}{4}$
Select	$1\frac{3}{4}$ to $2\frac{1}{2}$
Large select	$2\frac{1}{2}$ to $3\frac{1}{2}$
Jumbo	Over $3\frac{1}{2}$

(*Source:* The Maine Lobster Promotion Council)

1. A lobster fisher has kept four lobsters from a lobster trap. Classify each lobster if they have the following weights:

   a. $1\frac{7}{8}$ pounds

   b. $1\frac{9}{16}$ pounds

   c. $2\frac{3}{4}$ pounds

   d. $2\frac{3}{8}$ pounds

2. A recipe requires 5 pounds of lobster. Using the minimum weight for each class, decide whether a chicken, half, and select lobster will be enough for the recipe, and explain your reasoning. If not, suggest a better choice of lobsters to meet the recipe requirements.

3. A lobster market customer has selected two chickens, a select, and a large select. What is the most that these four lobsters could weigh? What is the least that these four lobsters could weigh?

4. A lobster market customer wishes to buy three quarters. If lobsters sell for $7 per pound, how much will the customer owe for her purchase?

5. Why do you think there is no classification for lobsters weighing under 1 pound?

Chapter 3 Vocabulary Check

Fill in each blank with one of the words or phrases listed below.

mixed number	equivalent	0	undefined
composite number	improper fraction	simplest form	prime factorization
prime number	proper fraction	numerator	denominator
reciprocals	like	least common denominator	

1. Two numbers are _____ of each other if their product is 1.
2. A _____ is a natural number greater than 1 that is not prime.
3. Fractions that represent the same portion of a whole are called _____ fractions.
4. An _____ is a fraction whose numerator is greater than or equal to its denominator.
5. A _____ is a natural number greater than 1 whose only factors are 1 and itself.
6. A fraction is in _____ when the numerator and the denominator have no factors in common other than 1.
7. A _____ is one whose numerator is less than its denominator.
8. A _____ contains a whole number part and a fraction part.
9. In the fraction $\frac{7}{9}$, the 7 is called the _____ and the 9 is called the _____.
10. The _____ of a number is the factorization in which all the factors are prime numbers.
11. The fraction $\frac{3}{0}$ is _____.
12. The fraction $\frac{0}{5}$ = _____.
13. Fractions that have the same denominator are called _____ fractions.
14. The LCM of the denominators in a list of fractions is called the _____.

> **Helpful Hint**
> Are you preparing for your test? Don't forget to take the Chapter 3 Test on page 280. Then check your answers at the back of the text and use the Chapter Test Prep Video CD to see the fully worked-out solutions to any of the exercises you want to review.

3 Chapter Highlights

DEFINITIONS AND CONCEPTS	**EXAMPLES**
Section 3.1 Introduction to Fractions and Mixed Numbers	

A **fraction** is of the form
 	
$\frac{\text{numerator}}{\text{denominator}}$ ← number of parts being considered
            ← number of equal parts in the whole
	Write a fraction to represent the shaded part of the figure.
	
	$\frac{3}{8}$ ← number of parts shaded
	      ← number of equal parts

DEFINITIONS AND CONCEPTS	**EXAMPLES**

Section 3.1   Introduction to Fractions and Mixed Numbers (*continued*)

A fraction is called a **proper fraction** if its numerator is less than its denominator.	Proper Fractions: $\dfrac{1}{3}, \dfrac{2}{5}, \dfrac{7}{8}, \dfrac{100}{101}$
A fraction is called an **improper fraction** if its numerator is greater than or equal to its denominator.	Improper Fractions: $\dfrac{5}{4}, \dfrac{2}{2}, \dfrac{9}{7}, \dfrac{101}{100}$
A **mixed number** contains a whole number and a fraction.	Mixed Numbers: $1\dfrac{1}{2}, 5\dfrac{7}{8}, 25\dfrac{9}{10}$

Section 3.2   Factors and Simplest Form

A **prime number** is a natural number that has exactly two different factors, 1 and itself.

$$2, 3, 5, 7, 11, 13, 17, \ldots$$

A **composite number** is any natural number other than 1 that is not prime.

$$4, 6, 8, 9, 10, 12, 14, 15, 16, \ldots$$

The prime factorization of a number is the factorization in which all the factors are prime numbers.

Write the prime factorization of 60.

$$60 = 6 \cdot 10$$
$$= 2 \cdot 3 \cdot 2 \cdot 5 \quad \text{or} \quad 2^2 \cdot 3 \cdot 5$$

Fractions that represent the same portion of a whole are called **equivalent fractions.**

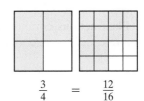

$$\frac{3}{4} \quad = \quad \frac{12}{16}$$

A fraction is in **simplest form** or **lowest terms** when the numerator and the denominator have no common factors other than 1.

The fraction $\dfrac{2}{3}$ is in simplest form.

To write a fraction in simplest form, write the prime factorizations of the numerator and the denominator and then divide both by all common factors.

Write in simplest form: $\dfrac{30}{36}$

$$\frac{30}{36} = \frac{2 \cdot 3 \cdot 5}{2 \cdot 2 \cdot 3 \cdot 3} = \frac{2}{2} \cdot \frac{3}{3} \cdot \frac{5}{2 \cdot 3} = 1 \cdot 1 \cdot \frac{5}{6} = \frac{5}{6}$$

$$\text{or} \quad \frac{30}{36} = \frac{\overset{1}{\cancel{2}} \cdot \overset{1}{\cancel{3}} \cdot 5}{\underset{1}{\cancel{2}} \cdot 2 \cdot \underset{1}{\cancel{3}} \cdot 3} = \frac{5}{6}$$

Two fractions are equivalent if

Method 1.   They simplify to the same fraction.

Determine whether $\dfrac{7}{8}$ and $\dfrac{21}{24}$ are equivalent.

$\dfrac{7}{8}$ is in simplest form

Method 2.   Their cross products are equal.

$$\frac{21}{24} = \frac{\overset{1}{\cancel{3}} \cdot 7}{\underset{1}{\cancel{3}} \cdot 8} = \frac{1 \cdot 7}{1 \cdot 8} = \frac{7}{8}$$

$$\begin{array}{cc} 24 \cdot 7 & 8 \cdot 21 \\ = 168 & \dfrac{7}{8} = \dfrac{21}{24} \quad = 168 \end{array}$$

Since $168 = 168, \dfrac{7}{8} = \dfrac{21}{24}$

Since both simplify to $\dfrac{7}{8}$, then $\dfrac{7}{8} = \dfrac{21}{24}$.

DEFINITIONS AND CONCEPTS	EXAMPLES

Section 3.3   Multiplying and Dividing Fractions

To multiply two fractions, multiply the numerators and multiply the denominators.	Multiply. $$\frac{7}{8} \cdot \frac{3}{5} = \frac{7 \cdot 3}{8 \cdot 5} = \frac{21}{40}$$ $$\frac{3}{4} \cdot \frac{1}{6} = \frac{3 \cdot 1}{4 \cdot 6} = \frac{\overset{1}{\cancel{3}} \cdot 1}{4 \cdot \underset{1}{\cancel{3}} \cdot 2} = \frac{1}{8}$$
To find the **reciprocal** of a fraction, interchange its numerator and denominator.	The reciprocal of $\frac{3}{5}$ is $\frac{5}{3}$.
To divide two fractions, multiply the first fraction by the reciprocal of the second fraction.	Divide. $$\frac{3}{10} \div \frac{7}{9} = \frac{3}{10} \cdot \frac{9}{7} = \frac{3 \cdot 9}{10 \cdot 7} = \frac{27}{70}$$

Section 3.4   Adding and Subtracting Like Fractions and Least Common Denominator

Fractions that have the same denominator are called **like fractions.**	$\frac{1}{3}$ and $\frac{2}{3}$; $\frac{5}{7}$ and $\frac{6}{7}$

To add or subtract like fractions, combine the numerators and place the sum or difference over the common denominator.	$\dfrac{2}{7} + \dfrac{3}{7} = \dfrac{5}{7}$ ← Add the numerators.
	         ← Keep the common denominator.
	
	$\dfrac{7}{8} - \dfrac{4}{8} = \dfrac{3}{8}$ ← Subtract the numerators.
	         ← Keep the common denominator.

The **least common multiple (LCM)** is the smallest number that is a multiple of all numbers in a list of numbers.	The LCM of 2 and 6 is 6 because 6 is the smallest number that is a multiple of both 2 and 6.
METHOD 1 FOR FINDING THE LCM OF A LIST OF NUMBERS USING MULTIPLES **Step 1.** Write the multiples of the largest number (starting with the number itself) until a multiple common to all numbers in the list is found. **Step 2.** The multiple found in Step 1 is the LCM.	Find the LCM of 4 and 6 using Method 1. $\quad 6 \cdot 1 = 6$ Not a multiple of 4 $\quad 6 \cdot 2 = 12$ A multiple of 4 The LCM is 12.
METHOD 2 FOR FINDING THE LCM OF A LIST OF NUMBERS USING PRIME FACTORIZATION **Step 1.** Write the prime factorization of each number. **Step 2.** For each different prime factor in Step 1, circle the greatest number of times that factor occurs in any one factorization. **Step 3.** The LCM is the product of the circled factors.	Find the LCM of 6 and 20 using Method 2. $\quad 6 = 2 \cdot \boxed{3}$ $\quad 20 = \boxed{2 \cdot 2} \cdot \boxed{5}$ The LCM is $\quad 2 \cdot 2 \cdot 3 \cdot 5 = 60$
Equivalent fractions represent the same portion of a whole.	Write an equivalent fraction with the indicated denominator. $$\frac{2}{8} = \frac{}{16}$$ $$\frac{2 \cdot 2}{8 \cdot 2} = \frac{4}{16}$$

DEFINITIONS AND CONCEPTS	**EXAMPLES**

Section 3.5 Adding and Subtracting Unlike Fractions

TO ADD OR SUBTRACT FRACTIONS WITH UNLIKE DENOMINATORS	Add: $\dfrac{3}{20} + \dfrac{2}{5}$
Step 1. Find the LCD.	**Step 1.** The LCD of 20 and 5 is 20.
Step 2. Write each fraction as an equivalent fraction whose denominator is the LCD.	**Step 2.** $\dfrac{3}{20} = \dfrac{3}{20}; \dfrac{2}{5} = \dfrac{2}{5} \cdot \dfrac{4}{4} = \dfrac{8}{20}$
Step 3. Add or subtract the like fractions.	**Step 3.** $\dfrac{3}{20} + \dfrac{2}{5} = \dfrac{3}{20} + \dfrac{8}{20} = \dfrac{11}{20}$
Step 4. Write the sum or difference in simplest form.	**Step 4.** $\dfrac{11}{20}$ is in simplest form.

Section 3.6 Complex Fractions, Order of Operations, and Mixed Numbers

A fraction whose numerator or denominator or both contain fractions is called a **complex fraction**.	Complex Fractions:
	$\dfrac{\frac{11}{4}}{\frac{7}{10}}, \quad \dfrac{\frac{1}{6} - 11}{\frac{4}{3}}$
One method for simplifying complex fractions is to multiply the numerator and the denominator of the complex fraction by the LCD of all fractions in its numerator and its denominator.	$\dfrac{\frac{1}{6} - 11}{\frac{4}{3}} = \dfrac{6\left(\frac{1}{6} - 11\right)}{6\left(\frac{4}{3}\right)} = \dfrac{6\left(\frac{1}{6}\right) - 6(11)}{6\left(\frac{4}{3}\right)}$
	$= \dfrac{1 - 66}{8} = \dfrac{-65}{8} = -\dfrac{65}{8}$
TO WRITE A MIXED NUMBER AS AN IMPROPER FRACTION	
1. Multiply the denominator of the fraction by the whole number.	$5\frac{2}{7} = \dfrac{5 \cdot 7 + 2}{7} = \dfrac{35 + 2}{7} = \dfrac{37}{7}$
2. Add the numerator of the fraction to the product from Step 1.	
3. Write this sum from Step 2 as the numerator of the improper fraction over the original denominator.	

continued

DEFINITIONS AND CONCEPTS	EXAMPLES

Section 3.6   Complex Fractions, Order of Operations, and Mixed Numbers (*continued*)

TO WRITE AN IMPROPER FRACTION AS A MIXED NUMBER OR A WHOLE NUMBER

1. Divide the denominator into the numerator.
2. The whole number part of the mixed number is the quotient. The fraction is the remainder over the original denominator.

$$\text{quotient} \frac{\text{remainder}}{\text{original denominator}}$$

$$\frac{17}{3} = 5\frac{2}{3}$$

$$\begin{array}{r} 5 \\ 3\overline{)17} \\ \underline{15} \\ 2 \end{array}$$

Section 3.7   Operations on Mixed Numbers

To multiply with mixed numbers or whole numbers, first write any mixed or whole numbers as fractions and then multiply as usual.

To divide with mixed numbers or whole numbers, first write any mixed or whole numbers as fractions and then divide as usual.

$$2\frac{1}{3} \cdot \frac{1}{9} = \frac{7}{3} \cdot \frac{1}{9} = \frac{7 \cdot 1}{3 \cdot 9} = \frac{7}{27}$$

$$2\frac{5}{8} \div 3\frac{7}{16} = \frac{21}{8} \div \frac{55}{16} = \frac{21}{8} \cdot \frac{16}{55} = \frac{21 \cdot 16}{8 \cdot 55}$$

$$= \frac{21 \cdot 2 \cdot \overset{1}{\cancel{8}}}{\underset{1}{\cancel{8}} \cdot 55} = \frac{42}{55}$$

To add or subtract with mixed numbers, add or subtract the fractions and then add or subtract the whole numbers.

Add: $2\frac{1}{2} + 5\frac{7}{8}$

$$2\frac{1}{2} = 2\frac{4}{8}$$

$$\underline{+5\frac{7}{8} = 5\frac{7}{8}}$$

$$7\frac{11}{8} = 7 + 1\frac{3}{8} = 8\frac{3}{8}$$

STUDY SKILLS BUILDER

Tips for Studying for an Exam

To prepare for an exam, try the following study techniques:

- Start the study process days before your exam.
- Make sure that you are up-to-date on your assignments.
- If there is a topic that you are unsure of, use one of the many resources that are available to you. For example,

    See your instructor.

    Visit a learning resource center on campus.

    Read the textbook material and examples on the topic.

    View a video on the topic.

- Reread your notes and carefully review the Chapter Highlights at the end of any chapter.
- Work the review exercises at the end of the chapter. Check your answers and correct any mistakes. If you have trouble, use a resource listed above.
- Find a quiet place to take the Chapter Test found at the end of the chapter. Do not use any resources when taking this sample test. This way, you will have a clear indication of how prepared you are for your exam. Check your answers and make sure that you correct any missed exercises.
- Get lots of rest the night before the exam. It's hard to show how well you know the material if your brain is foggy from lack of sleep.

Good luck and keep a positive attitude.

Let's see how you did on your last exam.

1. How many days before your last exam did you start studying for that exam?
2. Were you up-to-date on your assignments at that time or did you need to catch up on assignments?

3. List the most helpful text supplement (if you used one).
4. List the most helpful campus supplement (if you used one).
5. List your process for preparing for a mathematics test.
6. Was this process helpful? In other words, were you satisfied with your performance on your exam?
7. If not, what changes can you make in your process that will make it more helpful to you?

Are You Prepared for a Test on Chapter 3?

Below I have listed some *common trouble areas* for students in Chapter 3. After studying for your test—but before taking your test—read these.

Make sure you remember how to perform different operations on fractions!!! Try to add, subtract, multiply, then divide $\frac{3}{5}$ and $\frac{7}{15}$. Check your results below.

$$\frac{3}{5} + \frac{7}{15} = \frac{3}{5} \cdot \frac{3}{3} + \frac{7}{15} = \frac{9}{15} + \frac{7}{15} = \frac{16}{15} \text{ or } 1\frac{1}{15}$$

To add or subtract, the fractions must have a common denominator.

$$\frac{3}{5} - \frac{7}{15} = \frac{3}{5} \cdot \frac{3}{3} - \frac{7}{15} = \frac{9}{15} - \frac{7}{15} = \frac{2}{15}$$

$$\frac{3}{5} \cdot \frac{7}{15} = \frac{3 \cdot 7}{5 \cdot 15} = \frac{\overset{1}{\cancel{3}} \cdot 7}{5 \cdot \underset{1}{\cancel{3}} \cdot 5} = \frac{7}{25}$$

To multiply, multiply numerators and multiply denominators.

$$\frac{3}{5} \div \frac{7}{15} = \frac{3}{5} \cdot \frac{15}{7} = \frac{3 \cdot 15}{5 \cdot 7} = \frac{3 \cdot 3 \cdot \overset{1}{\cancel{5}}}{\underset{1}{\cancel{5}} \cdot 7} = \frac{9}{7} \text{ or } 1\frac{2}{7}$$

To divide, multiply by the reciprocal.

3 CHAPTER REVIEW

(3.1) *Determine whether each number is an improper fraction, a proper fraction, or a mixed number.*

1. $\dfrac{11}{23}$ **2.** $\dfrac{9}{8}$ **3.** $\dfrac{1}{2}$ **4.** $2\dfrac{1}{4}$

Write a fraction to represent the shaded area. If the fraction is proper, write the shaded area as a mixed number, also.

5.   **6.**  **7.**   **8.**

9. A basketball player made 11 free throws out of 12 during a game. What fraction of free throws did the player make?

10. A new car lot contained 23 blue cars out of a total of 131 cars.
  a. How many cars on the lot are not blue?
  b. What fraction of cars on the lot are not blue?

Simplify by dividing.

11. $\dfrac{23}{23}$ **12.** $\dfrac{-12}{12}$ **13.** $\dfrac{3}{-3}$ **14.** $\dfrac{-20}{-20}$

15. $\dfrac{0}{-1}$ **16.** $\dfrac{-1}{0}$ **17.** $\dfrac{4}{0}$ **18.** $\dfrac{-15}{1}$

(3.2) *Find the prime factorization of each number.*

19. 68 **20.** 90 **21.** 785 **22.** 255

Write each fraction in simplest form.

23. $\dfrac{12}{28}$ **24.** $\dfrac{15}{27}$ **25.** $-\dfrac{25}{75}$ **26.** $-\dfrac{36}{72}$

27. $\dfrac{29}{32}$

28. $\dfrac{18}{23}$

29. $\dfrac{48}{6}$

30. $\dfrac{54}{9}$

31. There are 12 inches in a foot. What fractional part of a foot does 8 inches represent?

```
        12 inches
 ├──── = 1 foot ────┤
 ┌─┬─┬─┬─┬─┬─┬─┬─┬─┬─┬─┬─┐
 └─┴─┴─┴─┴─┴─┴─┴─┴─┴─┴─┴─┘
 ├────── 8 ──────┤
```

32. Six out of 15 cars are white. What fraction of cars are *not* white?

Determine whether each two fractions are equivalent.

33. $\dfrac{10}{34}$ and $\dfrac{4}{14}$

34. $\dfrac{30}{50}$ and $\dfrac{9}{15}$

(3.3) *Multiply. Write each answer in simplest form.*

35. $-\dfrac{3}{5} \cdot \dfrac{1}{2}$

36. $\dfrac{6}{7} \cdot \dfrac{5}{12}$

37. $-\dfrac{24}{5} \cdot \left(-\dfrac{15}{8}\right)$

38. $\dfrac{39}{3} \cdot \dfrac{7}{13} \cdot \dfrac{5}{21}$

39. $\left(-\dfrac{1}{3}\right)^3$

40. $\left(-\dfrac{5}{12}\right)^2$

41. Evaluate xy if $x = \dfrac{2}{3}$ and $y = \dfrac{1}{5}$.

42. Evaluate ab if $a = -7$ and $b = \dfrac{9}{10}$.

Find the reciprocal of each number.

43. 7

44. $\dfrac{14}{23}$

Divide. Write each answer in simplest form.

45. $-\dfrac{3}{4} \div \dfrac{3}{8}$

46. $\dfrac{21}{4} \div \dfrac{7}{5}$

47. $\dfrac{5}{3} \div (-2)$

48. $-\dfrac{9}{2} \div -\dfrac{1}{3}$

49. Evaluate $x \div y$ if $x = \dfrac{9}{7}$ and $y = \dfrac{3}{4}$.

50. Evaluate $a \div b$ if $a = -5$ and $b = \dfrac{2}{3}$.

Find the area of each figure.

△ **51.**

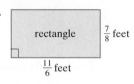

rectangle — $\frac{7}{8}$ feet

$\frac{11}{6}$ feet

△ **52.**

square — $\frac{2}{3}$ meter

(3.4) *Add or subtract as indicated. Simplify your answers.*

53. $\dfrac{4}{50} + \dfrac{2}{50}$

54. $\dfrac{1}{15} - \dfrac{11}{15}$

55. $\dfrac{4}{21} - \dfrac{1}{21}$

56. $\dfrac{3}{20} - \dfrac{7}{20} - \dfrac{2}{20}$

Solve.

57. One evening Mark Alorenzo did $\dfrac{3}{8}$ of his homework before supper, another $\dfrac{2}{8}$ of it while his children did their homework, and $\dfrac{1}{8}$ after his children went to bed. What part of his homework did he do that evening?

△ **58.** The Simpsons will be fencing in their land, which is in the shape of a rectangle. In order to do this, they need to find its perimeter. Find the perimeter of their land.

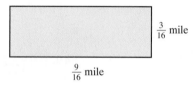

$\frac{3}{16}$ mile

$\frac{9}{16}$ mile

Find the LCM of each list of numbers.

59. 5, 11

60. 20, 24

61. 12, 21, 63

62. 6, 8, 18

Write each fraction as an equivalent fraction with the given denominator.

63. $\dfrac{7}{8} = \dfrac{}{64}$

64. $\dfrac{10}{13} = \dfrac{}{26}$

65. $\dfrac{4}{15} = \dfrac{}{60}$

66. $\dfrac{5}{12} = \dfrac{}{60}$

(3.5) *Add or subtract as indicated. Simplify your answers.*

67. $\dfrac{7}{18} + \dfrac{2}{9}$

68. $\dfrac{4}{15} + \dfrac{1}{5}$

69. $\dfrac{4}{13} - \dfrac{1}{26}$

70. $-\dfrac{7}{12} + \dfrac{1}{9}$

71. $\dfrac{1}{3} + \dfrac{9}{14}$

72. $-\dfrac{7}{18} - \dfrac{5}{24}$

73. $\dfrac{11}{15} - \dfrac{4}{9}$

74. $\dfrac{2}{3} - \dfrac{2}{9} - \dfrac{1}{6}$

Find the perimeter of each figure.

75.

$\frac{2}{9}$ meter | Rectangle | $\frac{5}{6}$ meter

△ **76.** $\frac{1}{5}$ foot $\frac{3}{5}$ foot $\frac{7}{10}$ foot

77. Find the difference in length of two scarves if one scarf is $\frac{5}{12}$ of a yard long and the other is $\frac{2}{3}$ of a yard long.

78. Truman Kalzote cleaned $\frac{3}{5}$ of his house yesterday and $\frac{1}{10}$ of it today. How much of the house has been cleaned?

Insert < or > to form a true statement.

79. $\frac{5}{11}$ _ $\frac{6}{11}$

80. $\frac{4}{35}$ _ $\frac{3}{35}$

81. $-\frac{5}{14}$ _ $-\frac{16}{42}$

82. $-\frac{6}{35}$ _ $-\frac{17}{105}$

(3.6) *Simplify each complex fraction.*

83. $\dfrac{\frac{2}{5}}{\frac{7}{10}}$

84. $\dfrac{2 + \frac{3}{4}}{1 - \frac{1}{8}}$

Evaluate each expression if $x = \frac{1}{2}$, $y = -\frac{2}{3}$, and $z = \frac{4}{5}$.

85. y^2

86. $x - z$

Write each improper fraction as a mixed number or a whole number.

87. $\frac{15}{4}$

88. $\frac{39}{13}$

89. $\frac{7}{7}$

90. $\frac{125}{4}$

Write each mixed number as an improper fraction.

91. $2\frac{1}{5}$

92. $3\frac{8}{9}$

Evaluate each expression. Use the order of operations to simplify.

93. $\frac{5}{13} \div \frac{1}{2} \cdot \frac{4}{5}$

94. $\frac{2}{27} - \left(\frac{1}{3}\right)^2$

95. $\frac{9}{10} \cdot \frac{1}{3} - \frac{2}{5} \cdot \frac{1}{11}$

96. $-\frac{2}{7} \cdot \left(\frac{1}{5} + \frac{3}{10}\right)$

(3.7) *Perform operations as indicated. Simplify your answers. Estimate where noted.*

97. $31\dfrac{2}{7} + 14\dfrac{10}{21}$

98. $\begin{array}{r} 7\dfrac{3}{8} \\[4pt] 9\dfrac{5}{6} \\[4pt] +\,3\dfrac{1}{12} \\ \hline \end{array}$

99. $\begin{array}{r} 9\dfrac{3}{5} \\[4pt] -\,4\dfrac{1}{7} \\ \hline \end{array}$

100. $\begin{array}{r} 8\dfrac{3}{11} \\[4pt] -\,5\dfrac{1}{5} \\ \hline \end{array}$

101. $1\dfrac{5}{8} \cdot 3\dfrac{1}{5}$

Exact:

Estimate:

102. $3\dfrac{6}{11} \cdot 1\dfrac{7}{13}$

Exact:

Estimate:

103. $6\dfrac{3}{4} \div 1\dfrac{2}{7}$

104. $5\dfrac{1}{2} \div 2\dfrac{1}{11}$

105. A truck traveled 341 miles on $15\dfrac{1}{2}$ gallons of gas. How many miles might we expect the truck to travel on 1 gallon of gas?

106. Herman Heltznutt walks 5 days a week for a total distance of $5\dfrac{1}{4}$ miles per week. If he walks the same distance each day, find the distance he walks each day.

107. There are $7\dfrac{1}{3}$ grams of fat in each ounce of hamburger. How many grams of fat are in a 5-ounce hamburger patty?

108. An art teacher needs 45 pieces of PVC piping for an art project. If each piece needs to be $\dfrac{3}{4}$ inch long, find the total length of piping she needs.

Find the unknown measurements.

△ **109.**

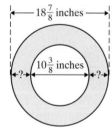

△ **110.**

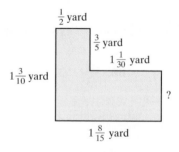

Perform the indicated operations.

111. $-12\dfrac{1}{7} + \left(-15\dfrac{3}{14}\right)$

112. $-3\dfrac{1}{5} \div \left(-2\dfrac{7}{10}\right)$

113. $-2\dfrac{1}{4} \cdot 1\dfrac{3}{4}$

114. $23\dfrac{7}{8} - 24\dfrac{7}{10}$

Mixed Review

Perform indicated operations. Write each answer in simplest form. Estimate where noted.

115. $\dfrac{7}{8} \cdot \dfrac{2}{3}$

116. $\dfrac{6}{15} \cdot \dfrac{5}{8}$

117. $\dfrac{18}{5} \div \dfrac{2}{5}$

118. $\dfrac{9}{2} \div \dfrac{1}{3}$

119. $\dfrac{5}{12} - \dfrac{3}{12}$

120. $\dfrac{3}{10} - \dfrac{1}{10}$

121. $\dfrac{2}{3} + \dfrac{1}{4}$

122. $\dfrac{5}{11} + \dfrac{2}{55}$

123. $4\dfrac{1}{6} \cdot 2\dfrac{2}{5}$

Exact:

Estimate:

124. $5\dfrac{2}{3} \cdot 2\dfrac{1}{4}$

Exact:

Estimate:

125. $\dfrac{7}{2} \div 1\dfrac{1}{2}$

126. $1\dfrac{3}{5} \div \dfrac{1}{4}$

127. $\begin{array}{r} 7\dfrac{3}{4} \\ +5\dfrac{2}{3} \\ \hline \end{array}$

128. $\begin{array}{r} 2\dfrac{7}{8} \\ +9\dfrac{1}{2} \\ \hline \end{array}$

129. $\begin{array}{r} 12\dfrac{3}{5} \\ -9\dfrac{1}{7} \\ \hline \end{array}$

130. $\begin{array}{r} 32\dfrac{10}{21} \\ -24\dfrac{3}{7} \\ \hline \end{array}$

Evaluate each expression. Use the order of operations to simplify.

131. $\dfrac{2}{5} + \left(\dfrac{2}{5}\right)^2 - \dfrac{3}{25}$

132. $\left(\dfrac{5}{6} - \dfrac{3}{4}\right)^2$

133. $-\dfrac{3}{8} \cdot \left(\dfrac{2}{3} - \dfrac{4}{9}\right)$

Solve.

134. Two packages to be mailed weigh $3\dfrac{3}{4}$ pounds and $2\dfrac{3}{5}$ pounds. Find their combined weight.

135. A ribbon $5\dfrac{1}{2}$ yards long is cut from a reel of ribbon with 50 yards on it. Find the length of the piece remaining on the reel.

△ **136.** A slab of natural granite is purchased and a rectangle with length $5\dfrac{1}{2}$ feet and width $7\dfrac{4}{11}$ feet is cut from it. Find the area of the rectangle.

137. An area of Mississippi received $23\dfrac{1}{2}$ inches of rain in $30\dfrac{1}{2}$ hours. How many inches per 1 hour is this?

$7\frac{4}{11}$ feet

$5\frac{1}{2}$ feet

Answers

Write a fraction to represent the shaded area.

1.

Write the mixed number as an improper fraction.

2. $7\dfrac{2}{3}$

Write the improper fraction as a mixed number.

3. $\dfrac{75}{4}$

Write each fraction in simplest form.

4. $\dfrac{24}{210}$

5. $-\dfrac{42}{70}$

Determine whether these fractions are equivalent.

6. $\dfrac{5}{7}$ and $\dfrac{8}{11}$

7. $\dfrac{6}{27}$ and $\dfrac{14}{63}$

Find the prime factorization of each number.

8. 84

9. 495

10. Find the LCM of 8, 9, and 12.

Perform each indicated operation. Simplify your answers.

11. $\dfrac{7}{9} + \dfrac{1}{9}$

12. $-\dfrac{8}{15} - \dfrac{2}{15}$

13. $\dfrac{4}{4} \div \dfrac{3}{4}$

14. $-\dfrac{4}{3} \cdot \dfrac{4}{4}$

15. $\dfrac{1}{6} + \dfrac{3}{14}$

16. $\dfrac{7}{8} - \dfrac{1}{3}$

17. $-\dfrac{2}{3} \cdot -\dfrac{8}{15}$

18. $8 \div \dfrac{1}{2}$

19. $\dfrac{6}{21} - \dfrac{1}{7}$

20. $\dfrac{16}{25} - \dfrac{1}{2}$

21. $\dfrac{3}{8} \cdot \dfrac{16}{6} \cdot \dfrac{4}{11}$

22. $5\dfrac{1}{4} \div \dfrac{7}{12}$

Answers column:

1. _____
2. _____
3. _____
4. _____
5. _____
6. _____
7. _____
8. _____
9. _____
10. _____
11. _____
12. _____
13. _____
14. _____
15. _____
16. _____
17. _____ 18. _____
19. _____ 20. _____
21. _____ 22. _____

280

23. $\dfrac{11}{12} - \dfrac{3}{8} + \dfrac{5}{24}$ **24.** $\begin{array}{r} 3\dfrac{7}{8} \\ 7\dfrac{2}{5} \\ +2\dfrac{3}{4} \\ \hline \end{array}$ **25.** $\begin{array}{r} 19 \\ -2\dfrac{3}{11} \\ \hline \end{array}$ **26.** $-\dfrac{16}{3} \div -\dfrac{3}{12}$

27. $3\dfrac{1}{3} \cdot 6\dfrac{3}{4}$ **28.** $-\dfrac{2}{7} \cdot \left(6 - \dfrac{1}{6}\right)$ **29.** $\dfrac{1}{2} \div \dfrac{2}{3} \cdot \dfrac{3}{4}$

30. $\left(-\dfrac{3}{4}\right)^2 \div \left(\dfrac{2}{3} + \dfrac{5}{6}\right)$ **31.** Find the average of $\dfrac{5}{6}, \dfrac{4}{3},$ and $\dfrac{7}{12}.$

Simplify the complex fraction.

32. $\dfrac{5 + \dfrac{3}{7}}{2 - \dfrac{1}{2}}$

Evaluate the expression for the given replacement value.

33. $-5x; x = -\dfrac{1}{2}$

Solve.

34. A carpenter cuts a piece $2\dfrac{3}{4}$ feet long from a cedar plank that is $6\dfrac{1}{2}$ feet long. How long is the remaining piece?

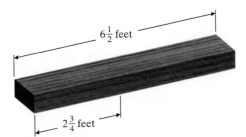

$6\dfrac{1}{2}$ feet

$2\dfrac{3}{4}$ feet

The circle graph below shows us how the average consumer spends money. For example, $\dfrac{7}{50}$ of your spending goes for food. Use this information for Exercises 35 through 37.

Consumer Spending

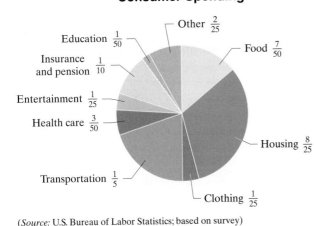

Other $\frac{2}{25}$
Education $\frac{1}{50}$
Insurance and pension $\frac{1}{10}$
Entertainment $\frac{1}{25}$
Health care $\frac{3}{50}$
Transportation $\frac{1}{5}$
Food $\frac{7}{50}$
Housing $\frac{8}{25}$
Clothing $\frac{1}{25}$

(*Source:* U.S. Bureau of Labor Statistics; based on survey)

35. What fraction of spending goes for housing and food combined?

36. What fraction of spending goes for education, transportation, and clothing?

37. Suppose your family spent $47,000 on the items in the graph. How much might we expect was spent on health care?

Find the perimeter and area of the figure.

△ **38.**

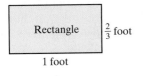

Rectangle $\frac{2}{3}$ foot

1 foot

39. During a 258-mile trip, a car used $10\dfrac{3}{4}$ gallons of gas. How many miles would we expect the car to travel on 1 gallon of gas?

23. _____

24. _____

25. _____

26. _____

27. _____

28. _____

29. _____

30. _____

31. _____

32. _____

33. _____

34. _____

35. _____

36. _____

37. _____

38. _____

39. _____

Write each number in words.

Answers

1. 126

2. 115

1. _____

3. 27,034

4. 6573

2. _____

3. _____

5. Add: 23 + 136

6. Add: 587 + 44

4. _____

7. Subtract: 543 − 29. Check by adding.

8. Subtract: 995 − 62. Check by adding.

5. _____

6. _____

7. _____

9. Round 278,362 to the nearest thousand.

10. Round 1436 to the nearest ten.

8. _____

9. _____

11. A digital video disc (DVD) can hold about 4800 megabytes (MB) of information. How many megabytes can 12 DVDs hold?

12. On a trip across country, Daniel Daunis travels 435 miles per day. How many total miles does he travel in 3 days?

10. _____

11. _____

12. _____

13. Divide and check: 56,717 ÷ 8

14. Divide and check: 4558 ÷ 12

13. _____

14. _____

15. _____

Write using exponential notation.

15. $4 \cdot 4 \cdot 4$

16. $7 \cdot 7$

16. _____

17. _____

17. $6 \cdot 6 \cdot 6 \cdot 8 \cdot 8 \cdot 8 \cdot 8 \cdot 8$

18. $9 \cdot 9 \cdot 9 \cdot 9 \cdot 5 \cdot 5$

18. _____

19. _____

20. _____

19. Evaluate $2(x - y)$ if $x = 8$ and $y = 4$.

20. Evaluate $8a + 3(b - 5)$ if $a = 5$ and $b = 9$.

21. Jack Mayfield, a miner for the Molly Kathleen Gold Mine, is presently 150 feet below the surface of the Earth. Represent this position using an integer.

22. The temperature on a cold day in Minneapolis, MN is 21° F below zero. Represent this temperature using an integer.

23. Add using a number line: $-7 + 3$

24. Add using a number line: $-3 + 8$

25. Simplify: $7 - 8 - (-5) - 1$

26. Simplify: $6 + (-8) - (-9) + 3$

27. Evaluate: $(-5)^2$

28. Evaluate: -2^4

29. Simplify: $3(4 - 7) + (-2) - \sqrt{25}$

30. Simplify: $(20 - 5^2)^2$

31. Write the prime factorization of 45.

32. Write the prime factorization of 92.

Multiply.

33. $\dfrac{2}{3} \cdot \dfrac{5}{11}$

34. $\dfrac{1}{7} \cdot \dfrac{2}{5}$

35. $\dfrac{1}{4} \cdot \dfrac{1}{2}$

36. $\dfrac{3}{5} \cdot \dfrac{1}{5}$

37. Write a fraction to represent the shaded part of the figure.

38. Write the prime factorization of 156.

39. Write each as an improper fraction.

   a. $4\dfrac{2}{9}$ **b.** $1\dfrac{8}{11}$

40. Write $7\dfrac{4}{5}$ as an improper fraction.

41. Write in simplest form: $\dfrac{42}{66}$

42. Write in simplest form: $\dfrac{70}{105}$

43. Multiply: $3\dfrac{1}{3} \cdot \dfrac{7}{8}$

44. Multiply: $\dfrac{2}{3} \cdot 4$

45. Divide and simplify: $\dfrac{5}{16} \div \dfrac{3}{4}$

46. Divide: $1\dfrac{1}{10} \div 5\dfrac{3}{5}$

21. _____

22. _____

23. _____

24. _____

25. _____

26. _____

27. _____

28. _____

29. _____

30. _____

31. _____

32. _____

33. _____

34. _____

35. _____

36. _____

37. _____

38. _____

39. a. _____

   b. _____

40. _____

41. _____

42. _____

43. _____

44. _____

45. _____

46. _____

4

Decimals

Decimal numbers represent parts of a whole, just like fractions. In this chapter, we learn to perform arithmetic operations using decimals and to analyze the relationship between fractions and decimals. We also learn how decimals are used in the real world.

Video rental chains are suffering losses in revenue and this trend is predicted to continue. With many discount chains offering cheap DVDs, consumers are choosing to purchase rather than rent. There are also more rent-by-mail and video-on-demand companies competing for your business.

In Section 4.2, Exercise 79, we calculate the predicted loss of revenue for video rental stores.

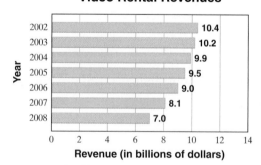

Video Rental Revenues

Source: Forrester Research; Note: Many of these years are projections.

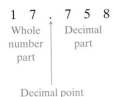

INTRODUCTION TO DECIMALS

Objective Ⓐ Decimal Notation and Writing Decimals in Words

Like fractional notation, decimal notation is used to denote a part of a whole. Numbers written in decimal notation are called **decimal numbers,** or simply **decimals.** The decimal 17.758 has three parts.

$$
\underset{\substack{\text{Whole}\\\text{number}\\\text{part}}}{1\ 7}\ .\ \underset{\substack{\text{Decimal}\\\text{part}}}{7\ 5\ 8}
$$

Decimal point

In Section 1.2, we introduced place value for whole numbers. Place names and place values for the whole number part of a decimal number are exactly the same, as shown next. Place names and place values for the decimal part are also shown.

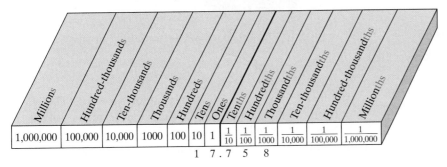

Notice that the value of each place is $\frac{1}{10}$ of the value of the place to its left. For example,

$$
\underset{\text{ones}}{1} \cdot \underset{\text{tenths}}{\frac{1}{10}} = \frac{1}{10} \qquad \text{and} \qquad \underset{\text{tenths}}{\frac{1}{10}} \cdot \frac{1}{10} = \underset{\text{hundredths}}{\frac{1}{100}}
$$

The decimal number 17.758 means

1 ten	+	7 ones	+	7 tenths	+	5 hundredths	+	8 thousandths

or $1 \cdot 10$	+	$7 \cdot 1$	+	$7 \cdot \dfrac{1}{10}$	+	$5 \cdot \dfrac{1}{100}$	+	$8 \cdot \dfrac{1}{1000}$
or 10	+	7	+	$\dfrac{7}{10}$	+	$\dfrac{5}{100}$	+	$\dfrac{8}{1000}$

Writing (or Reading) a Decimal in Words

Step 1: Write the whole number part in words.

Step 2: Write "and" for the decimal point.

Step 3: Write the decimal part in words as though it were a whole number, followed by the place value of the last digit.

Objectives

Ⓐ Know the Meaning of Place Value for a Decimal Number and Write Decimals in Words.

Ⓑ Write Decimals in Standard Form.

Ⓒ Write Decimals as Fractions.

Ⓓ Compare Decimals.

Ⓔ Round Decimals to a Given Place Value.

Helpful Hint
Notice that place values to the left of the decimal point end in "s." Place values to the right of the decimal point end in "ths."

285

PRACTICE PROBLEM 1

Write each decimal in words.

a. 0.08   **b.** −500.025

c. 0.0329

EXAMPLE 1 Write each decimal in words.

a. 0.3   **b.** −5.82   **c.** 21.093

Solution:

a. Three tenths

b. Negative five and eighty-two hundredths

c. Twenty-one and ninety-three thousandths

▣ Work Practice Problem 1

PRACTICE PROBLEM 2

Write the decimal 97.28 in words.

EXAMPLE 2 Write the decimal in the following sentence in words: The Golden Jubilee Diamond is a 545.67 carat cut diamond. (*Source: The Guinness Book of Records*)

Solution: five hundred forty-five and sixty-seven hundredths

▣ Work Practice Problem 2

PRACTICE PROBLEM 3

Write the decimal 72.1085 in words.

EXAMPLE 3 Write the decimal in the following sentence in words: The oldest known fragments of the Earth's crust are Zircon crystals; they were discovered in Australia and are thought to be 4.276 billion years old. (*Source: The Guinness Book of Records*)

Solution: four and two hundred seventy-six thousandths

▣ Work Practice Problem 3

Suppose that you are paying for a purchase of $368.42 at Circuit City by writing a check. Checks are usually written using the following format.

Answers

1. a. eight hundredths,   **b.** negative five hundred and twenty-five thousandths,   **c.** three hundred twenty-nine ten-thousandths

2. ninety-seven and twenty-eight hundredths,   **3.** seventy-two and one thousand eighty-five ten-thousandths

EXAMPLE 4 Fill in the check to Camelot Music to pay for your purchase of $92.98.

Solution:

■ **Work Practice Problem 4**

Objective B Writing Decimals in Standard Form

A decimal written in words can be written in standard form by reversing the preceding procedure.

EXAMPLES Write each decimal in standard form.

5. Forty-eight and twenty-six hundredths is

48.26

       hundredths place

6. Six and ninety-five thousandths is

6.095

       thousandths place

■ **Work Practice Problems 5–6**

> **Helpful Hint**
>
> When converting a decimal from words to decimal notation, make sure the last digit is in the correct place by inserting 0s if necessary. For example,
>
> Two and thirty-eight thousandths is 2.038
>
>   thousandths place

Objective C Writing Decimals as Fractions

Once you master reading and writing decimals, writing a decimal as a fraction follows naturally.

Decimal	In Words	Fraction
0.7	seven tenths	$\frac{7}{10}$
0.51	fifty-one hundredths	$\frac{51}{100}$
0.009	nine thousandths	$\frac{9}{1000}$
0.05	five hundredths	$\frac{5}{100} = \frac{1}{20}$

PRACTICE PROBLEM 4

Fill in the check to CLECO (Central Louisiana Electric Company) to pay for your monthly electric bill of $207.40.

PRACTICE PROBLEMS 5–6

Write each decimal in standard form.

5. Three hundred and ninety-six hundredths

6. Thirty-nine and forty-two thousandths

Answers

4. CLECO; 207.40; Two hundred seven and $\frac{40}{100}$, **5.** 300.96, **6.** 39.042

Notice that the number of decimal places in a decimal number is the same as the number of zeros in the denominator of the equivalent fraction. We can use this fact to write decimals as fractions.

$$0.51 = \frac{51}{100} \qquad 0.009 = \frac{9}{1000}$$

2 decimal places   2 zeros   3 decimal places   3 zeros

EXAMPLE 7 Write 0.43 as a fraction.

Solution: $0.43 = \dfrac{43}{100}$

2 decimal places   2 zeros

▪ **Work Practice Problem 7**

EXAMPLE 8 Write 5.7 as a mixed number.

Solution: $5.7 = 5\dfrac{7}{10}$

1 decimal place   1 zero

▪ **Work Practice Problem 8**

EXAMPLES Write each decimal as a fraction or a mixed number. Write your answer in simplest form.

9. $0.125 = \dfrac{125}{1000} = \dfrac{1}{8}$

10. $23.5 = 23\dfrac{5}{10} = 23\dfrac{\overset{1}{\cancel{5}}}{2\cdot\underset{1}{\cancel{5}}} = 23\dfrac{1}{2\cdot 1} = 23\dfrac{1}{2}$

11. $-105.083 = -105\dfrac{83}{1000}$

▪ **Work Practice Problems 9–11**

Later in the chapter, we write fractions as decimals. If you study Examples 7–11, you already know how to write fractions with denominators of 10, 100, 1000, and so on, as decimals.

Objective D Comparing Decimals

One way to compare positive decimals is by comparing digits in corresponding places. To see why this works, let's compare 0.5 or $\dfrac{5}{10}$ and 0.8 or $\dfrac{8}{10}$. We know

$$\frac{5}{10} < \frac{8}{10} \text{ since } 5 < 8, \text{ so}$$

$$0.5 < 0.8 \text{ since } 5 < 8$$

This leads to the following.

Comparing Two Positive Decimals

Compare digits in the same places from left to right. When two digits are not equal, the number with the larger digit is the larger decimal. If necessary, insert 0s after the last digit to the right of the decimal point to continue comparing.

Compare hundredths place digits

28.253   28.263
  ↑   ↑
  5   <   6
so 28.253   <   28.263

Helpful Hint

For any decimal, writing 0s after the last digit to the right of the decimal point does not change the value of the number.

7.6 = 7.60 = 7.600, and so on

When a whole number is written as a decimal, the decimal point is placed to the right of the ones digit.

25 = 25.0 = 25.00, and so on

EXAMPLE 12 Insert $<$, $>$, or $=$ to form a true statement.

0.378   0.368

Solution: 0. 3 78   0. 3 68   The tenths places are the same.

0.3 7 8   0.3 6 8   The hundredths places are different.

Since $7 > 6$, then $0.378 > 0.368$.

Work Practice Problem 12

EXAMPLE 13 Insert $<$, $>$, or $=$ to form a true statement.

0.052   0.236

Solution: 0. 0 52 $<$ 0. 2 36   0 is smaller than 2 in the tenths place.
                ↑   ↑

Work Practice Problem 13

We can also use a number line to compare decimals. This is especially helpful when comparing negative decimals. Remember, the number whose graph is to the left is smaller and the number whose graph is to the right is larger.

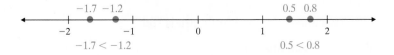

$-1.7 < -1.2$ $0.5 < 0.8$

PRACTICE PROBLEM 12

Insert $<$, $>$, or $=$ to form a true statement.
13.208   13.28

PRACTICE PROBLEM 13

Insert $<$, $>$, or $=$ to form a true statement.
0.12   0.086

Answers
12. $<$,   **13.** $>$

Helpful Hint

If you have trouble comparing two negative decimals, try the following: Compare their absolute values. Then to correctly compare the negative decimals, reverse the direction of the inequality symbol.

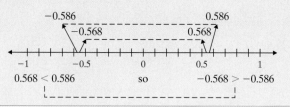

$0.568 < 0.586$ so $-0.568 > -0.586$

PRACTICE PROBLEM 14

Insert $<$, $>$, or $=$ to form a true statement.
$$-0.029 \quad -0.0209$$

EXAMPLE 14 Insert $<$, $>$, or $=$ to form a true statement.

$$-0.0101 \quad -0.00109$$

Solution: Since $0.0101 > 0.00109$, then $-0.0101 \; < \; -0.00109$

■ **Work Practice Problem 14**

Objective ■ Rounding Decimals

We **round the decimal part** of a decimal number in nearly the same way as we round whole numbers. The only difference is that we drop digits to the right of the rounding place, instead of replacing these digits with 0s. For example,

24.954   rounded to the nearest hundredth is   24.95.

Rounding Decimals to a Place Value to the Right of the Decimal Point

Step 1: Locate the digit to the right of the given place value.

Step 2: If this digit is 5 or greater, add 1 to the digit in the given place value and drop all digits to its right. If this digit is less than 5, drop all digits to the right of the given place.

PRACTICE PROBLEM 15

Round 123.7817 to the nearest thousandth.

EXAMPLE 15 Round 736.2359 to the nearest tenth.

Solution:

Step 1: We locate the digit to the right of the tenths place.

tenths place

736.2 **3** 59

digit to the right

Step 2: Since this digit to the right is less than 5, we drop it and all digits to its right.

Thus, 736.2359 rounded to the nearest tenth is 736.2.

■ **Work Practice Problem 15**

Answers
14. $-0.029 < -0.0209$, **15.** 123.782

The same steps for rounding can be used when the decimal is negative.

EXAMPLE 16 Round −0.027 to the nearest hundredth.

Solution:

Step 1: Locate the digit to the right of the hundredths place.

hundredths place

−0.02 7

digit to the right

Step 2: Since this digit to the right is 5 or greater, we add 1 to the hundredths digit and drop all digits to its right.

Thus, −0.027 is −0.03 rounded to the nearest hundredth.

◻ **Work Practice Problem 16**

The following number line illustrates this rounding.

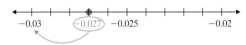

Rounding often occurs with money amounts. Since there are 100 cents in a dollar, each cent is $\frac{1}{100}$ of a dollar. This means that if we want to round to the nearest cent, we round to the nearest hundredth of a dollar.

EXAMPLE 17 The price of a gallon of gasoline in Aimsville is currently $2.1779. Round this to the nearest cent.

Solution:

hundredths place ——┐ ┌—— 7 is greater than 5

$2.17⑦9

Add 1. └— Delete these digits.

Since the digit to the right is greater than 5, we add 1 to the hundredths digit and delete all digits to the right of the hundredths digit.

Thus, $2.1779 rounded to the nearest cent is $2.18.

◻ **Work Practice Problem 17**

✔**Concept Check** 1756.0894 rounded to the nearest ten is

a. 1756.1 **b.** 1760.0894 **c.** 1760 **d.** 1750

EXAMPLE 18 **Determining State Taxable Income**

A high school teacher's taxable income is $41,567.72. The tax tables in the teacher's state use amounts to the nearest dollar. Round the teacher's income to the nearest whole dollar.

Solution: Rounding to the nearest whole dollar means rounding to the ones place.

ones place ——┐ ┌—— 7 is greater than 5

$41,567.72

Add 1. └— Delete these digits.

Thus, the teacher's income rounded to the nearest dollar is $41,568.

◻ **Work Practice Problem 18**

PRACTICE PROBLEM 16

Round −0.072 to the nearest hundredth.

PRACTICE PROBLEM 17

In Cititown, the price of a gallon of gasoline is $2.1589. Round this to the nearest cent.

PRACTICE PROBLEM 18

Water bills in Gotham City are always rounded to the nearest dollar. Lois's water bill was $24.62. Round her bill to the nearest dollar.

Answers
16. −0.07, **17.** $2.16, **18.** $25

✔ **Concept Check Answer**
c

Mental Math

Determine the place value for the digit 7 in each number.

1. 70   **2.** 700   **3.** 0.7   **4.** 0.07

4.1 EXERCISE SET

FOR EXTRA HELP

Student Solutions Manual | PH Math/Tutor Center | CD/Video for Review | MathXL® | MyMathLab

Objective Ⓐ *Write each decimal number in words. See Examples 1 through 3.*

1. 6.52   **2.** 7.59   **3.** 16.23   **4.** −47.65

5. −0.205   **6.** 0.495   **7.** 167.009   **8.** 233.056

9. 200.005   **10.** 5000.02   **11.** 105.6   **12.** 410.3

13. The English Channel Tunnel is 31.04 miles long. (*Source: Railway Directory & Year Book*)

14. The Lake Pontchartrain Causeway bridge over Lake Pontchartrain in Louisiana is approximately 23.87 miles long.

Fill in each check for the described purchase. See Example 4.

15. Your monthly car loan of $321.42 to R. W. Financial

> Your Preprinted Name
> Your Preprinted Address
>
> 60-8124/7233
> 1000613331
> 1407
>
> DATE _____
>
> PAY TO
> THE ORDER OF _____ $ [   ]
>
> _____ DOLLARS
>
> **FIRST STATE BANK**
> OF FARTHINGTON
> FARTHINGTON, IL 64422
>
> MEMO _____
>
> ⑈621497260⑈ 1000613331⑈ 1407

16. Your part of the monthly apartment rent, which is $213.70. You pay this to Amanda Dupre

> Your Preprinted Name
> Your Preprinted Address
>
> 60-8124/7233
> 1000613331
> 1408
>
> DATE _____
>
> PAY TO
> THE ORDER OF _____ $ [   ]
>
> _____ DOLLARS
>
> **FIRST STATE BANK**
> OF FARTHINGTON
> FARTHINGTON, IL 64422
>
> MEMO _____
>
> ⑈621497260⑈ 1000613331⑈ 1408

17. Your cell phone bill of $59.68 to Bell South

Your Preprinted Name Your Preprinted Address	60–8124/7233 1000613331	1409
DATE		
PAY TO THE ORDER OF	$	
	DOLLARS	
FIRST STATE BANK OF FARTHINGTON FARTHINGTON, IL 64422		
MEMO		

⑆621497260⑆ 1000613331⑈ 1409

18. Your grocery bill of $87.49 to Albertsons

Your Preprinted Name Your Preprinted Address	60–8124/7233 1000613331	1410
DATE		
PAY TO THE ORDER OF	$	
	DOLLARS	
FIRST STATE BANK OF FARTHINGTON FARTHINGTON, IL 64422		
MEMO		

⑆621497260⑆ 1000613331⑈ 1410

Objective **B** *Write each decimal number in standard form. See Examples 5 and 6.*

19. Six and five tenths

20. Three and nine tenths

21. Nine and eight hundredths

22. Twelve and six hundredths

23. Negative seven hundred five and six hundred twenty-five thousandths

24. Negative eight hundred four and three hundred ninety-nine thousandths

25. Sixty-four ten-thousandths

26. Thirty-eight ten-thousandths

Objective **C** *Write each decimal as a fraction or a mixed number. Write your answer in simplest form. See Examples 7 through 11.*

27. 0.3   **28.** 0.9   **29.** 0.27   **30.** 0.39   **31.** 0.8   **32.** 0.4

33. −5.47   **34.** −6.3   **35.** 0.048   **36.** 0.082   **37.** 7.008   **38.** 9.005

39. 15.802   **40.** 11.406   **41.** 0.3005   **42.** 0.2006

Objectives **A** **B** **C** **Mixed Practice** *Fill in the chart. The first row is completed for you.*

Decimal Number in Standard Form	In Words	Fraction
0.37	thirty-seven hundredths	$\frac{37}{100}$
43.	eight tenths	
44.	five tenths	
45. 0.077		
46. 0.019		

Objective **D** *Insert* $<$, $>$, *or* $=$ *between each pair of numbers to form a true statement. See Examples 12 through 14.*

47. 0.15   0.16   **48.** 0.12   0.15   **49.** -0.57 -0.54 **50.** -0.59 -0.52

51. 0.098   0.1   **52.** 0.0756   0.2   **53.** 0.54900   0.549   **54.** 0.98400   0.984

55. 167.908   167.980   **56.** 519.3405   519.3054   **57.** -1.0621 -1.07 **58.** -18.1 -18.01

59. -7.052 7.0052   **60.** 0.01 -0.1 **61.** -0.023 -0.024 **62.** -0.562 -0.652

Objective **E** *Round each decimal to the given place value. See Examples 15 through 18.*

63. 0.57, nearest tenth   **64.** 0.54, nearest tenth   **65.** 0.234, nearest hundredth

66. 0.452, nearest hundredth   **67.** 0.5942, nearest thousandth   **68.** 63.4523, nearest thousandth

69. 98,207.23, nearest ten   **70.** 68,934.543, nearest ten   **71.** -17.667, nearest hundredth

72. -0.766, nearest hundredth   **73.** -0.501, nearest tenth   **74.** -0.602, nearest tenth

Round each monetary amount to the nearest cent or dollar as indicated. See Examples 17 through 18.

75. $26.95, to the nearest dollar   **76.** $14,769.52, to the nearest dollar   **77.** $0.1992, to the nearest cent

78. $0.7633, to the nearest cent

Round each number to the given place value.

79. At this writing, the disc of the smallest hard drive was created by Toshiba and measures 2.16 centimeters across. Round this number to the nearest tenth.

2.16 cm or 0.85 in.

80. A large tropical cockroach of the family Dictyoptera is the fastest-moving insect. This insect was clocked at a speed of 3.36 miles per hour. Round this number to the nearest tenth. (*Source:* University of California, Berkeley)

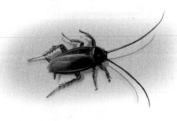

81. During the 2004 Boston Marathon, Catherine Ndereba of Kenya was the first woman to cross the finish line. Her time was 2.4075 hours. Round this time to the nearest hundredth. (*Source:* Boston Athletic Association)

82. The population density of the state of Louisiana is 102.5794 people per square mile. Round this population density to the nearest tenth. (*Source:* U.S. Census Bureau)

83. A used biology textbook is priced at $47.89. Round this price to the nearest dollar.

84. A used office desk is advertised at $19.95 by Drawley's Office Furniture. Round this price to the nearest dollar.

85. The length of a day on Mars is 24.6229 hours. Round this figure to the nearest thousandth. (*Source:* National Space Science Data Center)

86. Venus makes a complete orbit around the Sun every 224.695 days. Round this figure to the nearest whole day. (*Source:* National Space Science Data Center)

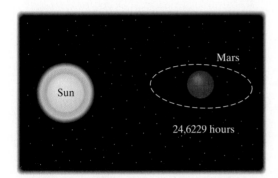

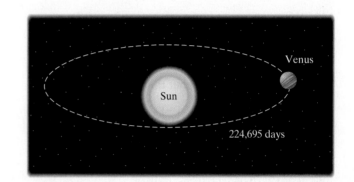

Review

Perform each indicated operation. See Sections 1.3 and 1.4.

87. 3452 + 2314

88. 8945 + 4536

89. 82 − 47

90. 4002 − 3897

Concept Extensions

Solve. See the Concept Check in this section.

91. 2849.1738 rounded to the nearest hundred is
  a. 2849.17
  b. 2800
  c. 2850
  d. 2849.174

92. 146.059 rounded to the nearest ten is
  a. 146.0
  b. 146.1
  c. 140
  d. 150

93. 2849.1738 rounded to the nearest hundredth is
  a. 2849.17
  b. 2800
  c. 2850
  d. 2849.174

94. 146.059 rounded to the nearest tenth is
  a. 146.0
  b. 146.1
  c. 140
  d. 150

95. In your own words, describe how to write a decimal as a fraction or a mixed number.

96. Write 0.00026849576 in words.

97. Write $7\frac{12}{100}$ as a decimal.

98. Write $17\frac{268}{1000}$ as a decimal.

99. Write 0.00026849576 as a fraction.

100. Write a 4-digit number that rounds to 26.3.

101. Write a 5-digit number that rounds to 1.7.

102. Explain how to identify the value of the 9 in the decimal 486.3297.

103. Write a decimal number that is greater than 48.1, but less than 48.2.

104. Which number(s) rounds to 0.26?

0.26559   0.26499   0.25786   0.25186

105. Which number(s) rounds to 0.06?

0.0612   0.066   0.0586   0.0506

 STUDY SKILLS BUILDER

Are You Satisfied with Your Performance on a Particular Quiz or Exam?

If not, don't forget to analyze your quiz or exam and look for common errors. Were most of your errors a result of:

- *Carelessness?* Did you turn in your quiz or exam before the allotted time expired? If so, resolve next time to use the entire time allotted. Any extra time can be spent checking your work.
- *Running out of time?* If so, make a point to better manage your time on your next quiz or exam. Try completing any questions that you are unsure of last and delay checking your work until all questions have been answered.
- *Not understanding a concept?* If so, review that concept and correct your work. Try to understand how this happened so that you make sure it doesn't happen before the next quiz or exam.
- *Test conditions?* When studying for a quiz or exam, make sure you place yourself in conditions similar to test conditions. For example, before your next quiz or exam, use a few sheets of blank paper and take a sample test without the aid of your notes or text.

(See your instructor or use the Chapter Test at the end of each chapter.)

Exercises

1. Have you corrected all your previous quizzes and exams?
2. List any errors you have found common to two or more of your graded papers.
3. Is one of your common errors not understanding a concept? If so, are you making sure you understand all the concepts for the next quiz or exam?
4. Is one of your common errors making careless mistakes? If so, are you now taking all the time allotted to check over your work so that you can minimize the number of careless mistakes?
5. Are you satisfied with your grades thus far on quizzes and tests?
6. If your answer to Exercise 5 is no, are there any more suggestions you can make to your instructor or yourself to help? If so, list them here and share these with your instructor.

4.2 ADDING AND SUBTRACTING DECIMALS

Objectives

A Add Decimals.

B Subtract Decimals.

C Estimate When Adding or Subtracting Decimals.

D Evaluate Expressions with Decimal Replacement Values.

E Solve Problems That Involve Adding or Subtracting Decimals

Objective **A** Adding Decimals

Adding decimals is similar to adding whole numbers. We add digits in corresponding place values from right to left, carrying if necessary. To make sure that digits in corresponding place values are added, we line up the decimal points vertically.

Adding or Subtracting Decimals

Step 1: Write the decimals so that the decimal points line up vertically.

Step 2: Add or subtract as with whole numbers.

Step 3: Place the decimal point in the sum or difference so that it lines up vertically with the decimal points in the problem.

In this section, we will insert zeros in decimals numbers so that place value digits line up neatly. For instance, see Example 1.

EXAMPLE 1 Add: 23.85 + 1.604

Solution: First we line up the decimal points vertically.

```
  23.850   Insert one 0 so that digits line up neatly.
+  1.604
     ↑
line up decimal points
```

Then we add the digits from right to left as for whole numbers.

```
   1
  23.850
+  1.604
  25.454
      └── Place the decimal point in the sum so that all decimal points line up.
```

🔲 **Work Practice Problem 1**

PRACTICE PROBLEM 1

Add.
a. 15.52 + 2.371
b. 20.06 + 17.612
c. 0.125 + 122.8

Helpful Hint

Recall that 0's may be placed after the last digit to the right of the decimal point without changing the value of the decimal. This may be used to help line up place values when adding decimals.

```
   3.2     becomes      3.200   Insert two 0s.
  15.567                15.567
+  0.11               +  0.110   Insert one 0.
                        18.877   Add.
```

Answers
1. a. 17.891, **b.** 37.672, **c.** 122.925

297

PRACTICE PROBLEM 2
Add.
a. $34.567 + 129.43 + 2.8903$
b. $11.21 + 46.013 + 362.526$

EXAMPLE 2 Add: $763.7651 + 22.001 + 43.89$

Solution: First we line up the decimal points.

```
    1 1 1
  763.7651
   22.0010   Insert one 0.
+  43.8900   Insert two 0s.
  829.6561   Add.
```

Work Practice Problem 2

> **Helpful Hint**
> Don't forget that the decimal point in a whole number is after the last digit.

PRACTICE PROBLEM 3
Add: $26.072 + 119$

EXAMPLE 3 Add: $45 + 2.06$

Solution:
```
  45.00   Insert a decimal point and two 0s.
+  2.06   Line up decimal points.
  47.06   Add.
```

Work Practice Problem 3

✔ **Concept Check** What is wrong with the following calculation of the sum of 7.03, 2.008, 19.16, and 3.1415?

```
   7.03
   2.008
  19.16
+ 3.1415
  3.6042
```

PRACTICE PROBLEM 4
Add: $8.1 + (-99.2)$

EXAMPLE 4 Add: $3.62 + (-4.78)$

Solution: Recall from Chapter 2 that to add two numbers with different signs we find the difference of the larger absolute value and the smaller absolute value. The sign of the answer is the same as the sign of the number with the larger absolute value.

```
  4.78
 -3.62
  1.16   Subtract the absolute values.
```

Thus, $3.62 + (-4.78) = -1.16$

The sign of the number with the larger absolute value −4.78 has the larger absolute value.

Work Practice Problem 4

Answers
2. a. 166.8873, b. 419.749,
3. 145.072, 4. −91.1

✔ **Concept Check Answer**
The decimal places are not lined up properly.

Objective B Subtracting Decimals

Subtracting decimals is similar to subtracting whole numbers. We line up digits and subtract from right to left, borrowing when needed.

EXAMPLE 5 Subtract: 3.5 − 0.068. Check your answer.

Solution:
$$
\begin{array}{r}
\overset{9}{\overset{4\ \cancel{10}\ 10}{3.\cancel{5}\cancel{0}\cancel{0}}} \quad \text{Insert two 0s.} \\
- 0.0\,6\,8 \quad \text{Line up decimal points.} \\
\hline
3.4\,3\,2 \quad \text{Subtract.}
\end{array}
$$

Check: Recall that we can check a subtraction problem by adding.

$$
\begin{array}{r}
3.432 \quad \text{Difference} \\
+\,0.068 \quad \text{Subtrahend} \\
\hline
3.500 \quad \text{Minuend}
\end{array}
$$

🔲 **Work Practice Problem 5**

PRACTICE PROBLEM 5

Subtract. Check your answers.
a. 5.8 − 3.92
b. 9.72 − 4.068

EXAMPLE 6 Subtract: 85 − 17.31. Check your answer.

Solution:
$$
\begin{array}{r}
\overset{9}{\overset{7\ 14\ \cancel{10}\ 10}{\cancel{8}\cancel{5}.\cancel{0}\cancel{0}}} \\
- 1\,7.3\,1 \\
\hline
6\,7.6\,9
\end{array}
$$

Check:
$$
\begin{array}{r}
67.69 \quad \text{Difference} \\
+\,17.31 \quad \text{Subtrahend} \\
\hline
85.00 \quad \text{Minuend}
\end{array}
$$

🔲 **Work Practice Problem 6**

PRACTICE PROBLEM 6

Subtract. Check your answers.
a. 53 − 29.31
b. 120 − 68.22

EXAMPLE 7 Subtract 3 from 6.98.

Solution:
$$
\begin{array}{r}
6.98 \\
- 3.00 \quad \text{Insert two 0s.} \\
\hline
3.98
\end{array}
$$

🔲 **Work Practice Problem 7**

PRACTICE PROBLEM 7

Subtract: 18 from 26.99.

EXAMPLE 8 Subtract: −5.8 − 1.7

Solution: Recall from Chapter 2 that to subtract 1.7 we add the opposite of 1.7, or −1.7. Thus

$$-5.8 - 1.7 = -5.8 + (-1.7) \quad \text{To subtract, add the opposite of 1.7 which is } -1.7.$$

Add the absolute values.

$$= -7.5.$$

Use the common negative sign.

🔲 **Work Practice Problem 8**

PRACTICE PROBLEM 8

Subtract: −3.4 − 9.6.

EXAMPLE 9 Subtract: −2.56 − (−4.01)

Solution: $-2.56 - (-4.01) = -2.56 + 4.01$ \quad To subtract, add the opposite of −4.01, which is 4.01.

Subtract the absolute values.

$$= 1.45$$

The answer is (understood) positive since 4.01 has the larger absolute value.

🔲 **Work Practice Problem 9**

PRACTICE PROBLEM 9

Subtract: −1.05 − (−7.23).

Answers
5. a. 1.88, **b.** 5.652, **6. a.** 23.69,
b. 51.78, **7.** 8.99, **8.** −13, **9.** 6.18

Objective C Estimating When Adding or Subtracting Decimals

To help avoid errors, we can also estimate to see if our answer is reasonable when adding or subtracting decimals. Although only one estimate is needed per operation, we show two to show variety.

PRACTICE PROBLEM 10

Add or subtract as indicated. Then estimate to see if the answer is reasonable by rounding the given numbers and adding or subtracting the rounded numbers.

a. 48.1 + 326.97

b. 18.09 − 0.746

EXAMPLE 10 Add or subtract as indicated. Then estimate to see if the answer is reasonable by rounding the given numbers and adding or subtracting the rounded numbers.

a. 27.6 + 519.25

Exact		Estimate 1		Estimate 2
$\overset{1}{27.60}$	rounds to	30		30
+ 519.25	rounds to	+ 500	or	+ 520
546.85		530		550

Since the exact answer is close to either estimate, it is reasonable. (In the first estimate, each number is rounded to the place value of the leftmost digit. In the second estimate, each number is rounded to the nearest ten.)

b. 11.01 − 0.862

Exact		Estimate 1		Estimate 2
$\overset{0\ \ 9\ 10 10}{1\cancel{1}.\cancel{0}\cancel{1}\cancel{0}}$	rounds to	10		11
− 0.862	rounds to	− 1	or	− 1
10.148		9		10

In the first estimate, we rounded the first number to the nearest ten and the second number to the nearest one. In the second estimate, we rounded both numbers to the nearest one. Both estimates show us that our answer is reasonable.

▣ **Work Practice Problem 10**

> **Helpful Hint**
>
> Remember: Estimates are for our convenience to quickly check the reasonableness of an answer.

✔ **Concept Check** Why shouldn't the sum 21.98 + 42.36 be estimated as 30 + 50 = 80?

Objective D Using Decimals as Replacement Values

Let's review evaluating expressions with given replacement values. This time the replacement values are decimals.

EXAMPLE 11 Evaluate $x - y$ for $x = 2.8$ and $y = 0.92$.

Solution: Replace x with 2.8 and y with 0.92 and simplify.

$$x - y = 2.8 - 0.92$$
$$= 1.88$$

$$\begin{array}{r} 2.80 \\ -0.92 \\ \hline 1.88 \end{array}$$

■ **Work Practice Problem 11**

PRACTICE PROBLEM 11

Evaluate $y - z$ for $y = 11.6$ and $z = 10.8$.

Objective E Solving Problems by Adding or Subtracting Decimals

Decimals are very common in real-life problems.

EXAMPLE 12 **Calculating the Cost of Owning an Automobile**

Find the total monthly cost of owning and operating a certain automobile given the expenses shown.

Monthly car payment:	$256.63
Monthly insurance cost:	$47.52
Average gasoline bill per month:	$95.33

Solution:

1. UNDERSTAND. Read and reread the problem. The phrase "total monthly cost" tells us to add.
2. TRANSLATE.

In words:	total monthly cost	is	car payment	plus	insurance cost	plus	gasoline bill
	↓	↓	↓	↓	↓	↓	↓
Translate:	total monthly cost	=	$256.63	+	$47.52	+	$95.33

3. SOLVE: Let's also estimate by rounding each number to the nearest ten.

$$\begin{array}{r} \overset{1\,1\,1}{256.63} \quad \text{rounds to} \quad 260 \\ 47.52 \quad \text{rounds to} \quad 50 \\ + \; 95.33 \quad \text{rounds to} \quad \underline{100} \\ \hline \$399.48 \quad \text{Exact.} \quad\quad 410 \quad \text{Estimate.} \end{array}$$

4. INTERPRET. *Check* your work. Since our estimate is close to our exact answer, our answer is reasonable. *State* your conclusion: The total monthly cost is $399.48.

■ **Work Practice Problem 12**

PRACTICE PROBLEM 12

Find the total monthly cost of owning and operating a certain automobile given the expenses shown.

Monthly car payment:	$536.52
Monthly insurance cost:	$52.68
Average gasoline bill per month:	$87.50

The next bar graph has horizontal bars. To visualize the value represented by a bar, see how far it extends to the right. The value of each bar is labeled and we will study bar graphs further in a later chapter.

EXAMPLE 13 **Comparing Average Heights**

The bar graph shows the current average heights for adults in various countries. How much greater is the average height in Denmark than the average height in the United States?

Continued on next page

Answers
11. 0.8 **12.** $676.70

PRACTICE PROBLEM 13

Use the bar graph in Example 13. How much greater is the average height in the Netherlands than the average height in Czechoslovakia?

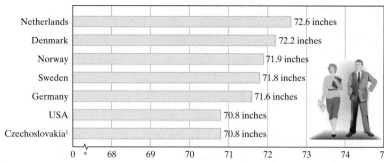

Average Adult Height

Netherlands	72.6 inches
Denmark	72.2 inches
Norway	71.9 inches
Sweden	71.8 inches
Germany	71.6 inches
USA	70.8 inches
Czechoslovakia¹	70.8 inches

0 * 68   69   70   71   72   73   74   75

¹Average for Czech Republic, Slovakia
Source: USA Today, 8/28/97

* The -ᐱ- means that some numbers are purposefully missing on the axis.

Solution:

1. **UNDERSTAND.** Read and reread the problem. Since we want to know "how much greater," we subtract.

2. **TRANSLATE.**

In words:	How much greater	is	Denmark's average height	minus	U.S. average height
	↓	↓	↓	↓	↓
Translate:	How much greater	=	72.2	−	70.8

3. **SOLVE:** We estimate by rounding each number to the nearest whole.

$$
\begin{array}{r}
\overset{1\ \ 12}{7\cancel{2}.\cancel{2}} \quad \text{rounds to} \quad 72 \\
-70.8 \quad \text{rounds to} \quad -71 \\
\hline
1.4 \quad \text{Exact.} \qquad 1 \quad \text{Estimate.}
\end{array}
$$

4. **INTERPRET.** *Check* your work. Since our estimate is close to our exact answer, 1.4 inches is reasonable. *State* your conclusion: The average height in Denmark is 1.4 inches greater than the average U.S. height.

Answer

13. 1.8 in.

🔲 **Work Practice Problem 13**

🖩 **CALCULATOR EXPLORATIONS**

Entering Decimal Numbers

To enter a decimal number, find the key marked ⎡ · ⎤. To enter the number 2.56, for example, press the keys ⎡2⎤ ⎡·⎤ ⎡5⎤ ⎡6⎤. The display will read ⎡ 2.56 ⎤.

Operations on Decimal Numbers

Operations on decimal numbers are performed in the same way as operations on whole or signed numbers. For example, to find 8.625 − 4.29, press the keys ⎡8.625⎤ ⎡−⎤ ⎡4.29⎤ ⎡=⎤ or ⎡ENTER⎤. The display will read ⎡ 4.335 ⎤. (Although entering 8.625, for example, requires pressing more than one key, we group numbers together here for easier reading.)

Use a calculator to perform each indicated operation.

1. 315.782 + 12.96
2. 29.68 + 85.902
3. 6.249 − 1.0076
4. 5.238 − 0.682

5.
$$
\begin{array}{r}
12.555 \\
224.987 \\
5.2 \\
+622.65 \\
\end{array}
$$

6.
$$
\begin{array}{r}
47.006 \\
0.17 \\
313.259 \\
+139.088 \\
\end{array}
$$

Mental Math

Find the sum or difference.

1. 0.3
    + 0.2

2. 0.4
    + 0.5

3. 1.00
    + 0.26

4. 3.00
    + 0.19

5. 7.6
    + 1.3

6. 4.5
    + 3.2

7. 0.9
    − 0.3

8. 0.6
    − 0.2

4.2 EXERCISE SET

Objectives A C Mixed Practice *Add. See Examples 1 through 4, and 10. For those exercises marked, also estimate to see if the answer is reasonable.*

1. 1.3 + 2.2

2. 2.5 + 4.1

3. 5.7 + 1.13

4. 2.31 + 6.4

 5. 24.6 + 2.39 + 0.0678

6. 32.4 + 1.58 + 0.0934

7.   45.023
      3.006
    + 8.403

8.   65.0028
      5.0903
    + 6.9003

9. −2.6 + (−5.97)

10. −18.2 + (−10.8)

11. 15.78 + (−4.62)

12. 6.91 + (−7.03)

13.   234.89
       + 230.67
    Exact: Estimate:

14.   734.89
       + 640.56
    Exact: Estimate:

15.   100.009
          6.08
       +   9.034
    Exact: Estimate:

16.   200.89
          7.49
       + 62.83
    Exact: Estimate:

17. Find the sum of 45.023, 3.006, and 8.403

18. Find the sum of 65.0028, 5.0903, and 6.9003

Objectives B C Mixed Practice *Subtract and check. See Examples 5 through 10. For those exercises marked, also estimate to see if the answer is reasonable.*

19. 8.8 − 2.3

20. 7.6 − 2.1

21. 18 − 2.7

22. 28 − 3.3

 23.   654.9
       − 56.67

24.   863.23
       − 39.453

25. 5.9 − 4.07
    Exact:
    Estimate:

26. 6.4 − 3.04
    Exact:
    Estimate:

27. $923.5 - 61.9$

28. $845.93 - 45.8$

29.
$$\begin{array}{r} 1000 \\ - \ 123.4 \end{array}$$
Exact:

Estimate:

30.
$$\begin{array}{r} 2000 \\ - \ 327.47 \end{array}$$
Exact:

Estimate:

31. $200 - 5.6$

32. $800 - 8.9$

33. $-1.12 - 5.2$

34. $-8.63 - 5.6$

35. $7.7 - 14.1$

36. $10.25 - 21.76$

37. $-2.6 - (-5.7)$

38. $-9.4 - (-10.4)$

39. $3 - 0.0012$

40. $7 - 0.097$

41. Subtract 6.7 from 23.

42. Subtract 9.2 from 45.

Objectives Ⓐ Ⓑ **Mixed Practice** *Perform the indicated operation. See Examples 1 through 10.*

43. $0.9 + 2.2$

44. $0.7 + 3.4$

45. $-6.06 + 0.44$

46. $-5.05 + 0.88$

47. $900.34 - 123.45$

48. $800.74 - 463.98$

49. $50.2 - 600$

50. $40.3 - 700$

51. Subtract 61.9 from 923.5

52. Subtract 45.8 from 845.9

53. Add 100.009 and 6.08 and 9.034

54. Add 200.89 and 7.49 and 62.83

55. $-0.003 + 0.091$

56. $-0.004 + 0.085$

57. $-102.4 - 78.04$

58. $-36.2 - 10.02$

59. $-2.9 - (-1.8)$

60. $-6.5 - (-3.3)$

Objective Ⓓ *Evaluate each expression for $x = 3.6$, $y = 5$, and $z = 0.21$. See Example 11.*

61. $x + z$

62. $y + x$

63. $x - z$

64. $y - z$

65. $y - x + z$

66. $x + y + z$

Objective Ⓔ *Solve. See Examples 12 and 13.*

67. Find the total monthly cost of owning and maintaining a car given the information shown.

Monthly car payment:	$275.36
Monthly insurance cost:	$ 83.00
Average cost of gasoline per month:	$ 81.60
Average maintenance cost per month:	$ 14.75

68. Find the total monthly cost of owning and maintaining a car given the information shown.

Monthly car payment:	$306.42
Monthly insurance cost:	$ 53.50
Average cost of gasoline per month:	$123.00
Average maintenance cost per month:	$ 23.50

69. Gasoline was $2.739 per gallon on one day and $2.879 per gallon the next day. By how much did the price change?

70. A pair of eyeglasses costs a total of $347.89. The frames of the glasses are $97.23. How much do the lenses of the eyeglasses cost?

71. Find the perimeter.

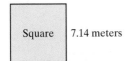

Square   7.14 meters

72. Find the perimeter.

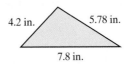

4.2 in.   5.78 in.

7.8 in.

The iPod mini is a miniture version of Apple Computer's popular iPod portable audio player. This mini was introduced in January 2004 with a storage capacity of 4 gigabytes. (This is about 1000 3-minute or 3-megabyte songs.)

73. The top face of the iPod mini shown measures 3.6 inches by 2.0 inches. Find the perimeter of the rectangular face.

74. The face of the larger Apple iPod measures 4.1 inches by 2.4 inches. Find the perimeter of this rectangular face.

Solve.

75. Ann-Margaret Tober bought a book for $32.48. If she paid with two $20 bills, what was her change?

76. Phillip Guillot bought a car part for $18.26. If he paid with two $10 bills, what was his change?

77. The average wind speed at the weather station on Mt. Washington in New Hampshire is 35.2 miles per hour. The highest speed ever recorded at the station is 321.0 miles per hour. How much faster is the highest speed than the average wind speed? (*Source:* National Climatic Data Center)

78. The average annual rainfall in Omaha, Nebraska, is 30.22 inches. The average annual rainfall in New Orleans, Louisiana, is 61.88 inches. On average, how much more rain does New Orleans receive annually than Omaha? (*Source:* National Climatic Data Center)

This bar graph shows the predicted decrease in home video rental revenue for chains such as Blockbuster and Hollywood Video. Use this graph for Exercise 79.

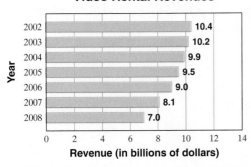

Video Rental Revenues

Year	Revenue
2002	10.4
2003	10.2
2004	9.9
2005	9.5
2006	9.0
2007	8.1
2008	7.0

Revenue (in billions of dollars)

Source: Forrester Research; Note: Many of these years are projections.

79. Find the decrease in video rental revenue from the year 2002 to 2008.

80. It is predicted that home video *sales* (not shown on the bar graph) will increase from $15.3 billion in 2002 to $24.6 billion in 2008. Find the amount of increase.

81. The snowiest city in the United States is Blue Canyon, California, which receives an average of 111.6 more inches of snow than the second-snowiest city. The second-snowiest city in the United States is Marquette, Michigan. Marquette receives an average of 129.2 inches of snow annually. How much snow does Blue Canyon receive on average each year? (*Source:* National Climatic Data Center)

82. The driest city in the world is Aswan, Egypt, which receives an average of only 0.02 inches of rain per year. Yuma, Arizona, is the driest city in the United States. Yuma receives an average of 2.63 more inches of rain each year than Aswan. What is the average annual rainfall in Yuma? (*Source:* National Climatic Data Center)

83. A landscape architect is planning a border for a flower garden that's shaped like a triangle. The sides of the garden measure 12.4 feet, 29.34 feet, and 25.7 feet. Find the amount of border material needed.

84. A contractor needs to buy railing to completely enclose a newly built rectangular deck. If the deck has a length of 15.7 feet and a width of 10.6 feet, find the amount of railing needed.

The following table shows spaceflight information for astronaut James A. Lovell. Use this table to answer Exercises 85 and 86.

Spaceflights of James A. Lovell		
Year	Mission	Duration (in hours)
1965	Gemini 6	330.583
1966	Gemini 12	94.567
1968	Apollo 8	147.0
1970	Apollo 13	142.9
(*Source:* NASA)		

85. Find the total time spent in spaceflight by astronaut James A. Lovell.

86. Find the total time James A. Lovell spent in spaceflight on all Apollo missions.

The bar graph shows the top five chocolate-consuming nations in the world. Use this table to answer Exercises 87 through 91.

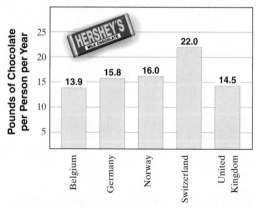

The World's Top Chocolate-Consuming Countries

Source: Hershey Foods Corporation

87. Which country in the table has the greatest chocolate consumption per person?

88. Which country in the table has the least chocolate consumption per person?

89. How much more is the greatest chocolate consumption than the least chocolate consumption shown in the table?

90. How much more chocolate does the average German consume than the average citizen of the United Kingdom?

91. Make a new chart listing the countries and their corresponding chocolate consumptions in order from greatest to least.

Review

Multiply. See Sections 1.6 and 3.3.

92. $23 \cdot 2$

93. $46 \cdot 3$

94. $\left(\dfrac{2}{3}\right)^2$

95. $\left(\dfrac{1}{5}\right)^3$

Concept Extensions

Solve. See the first Concept Check in this section.

96. A friend asks you to check his calculation to the right. Is it correct? If not, explain your friends' error and correct the calculation.

$$
\begin{array}{r}
\overset{1}{9}.2 \\
\overset{1}{8}.63 \\
+\,4.005 \\
\hline
4.960
\end{array}
$$

Find the unknown length in each figure.

△ **97.**

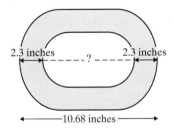

2.3 inches   ?   2.3 inches

10.68 inches

△ **98.**

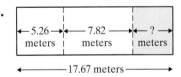

5.26 meters | 7.82 meters | ? meters

17.67 meters

Let's review the values of these common U.S. coins in order to answer the following exercises.

Penny   Nickel   Dime   Quarter

$0.01 $0.05 $0.10 $0.25

Write the value of each group of coins. To do so, it is usually easiest to start with the coin(s) of greatest value and end with the coin(s) of least value.

99.

100.

101. Name the different ways that coins can have a value of $0.17 given that you may use no more than 10 coins.

102. Name the different ways that coin(s) can have a value of $0.25 given that there are no pennies.

103. Why shouldn't the sum

   82.95 + 51.26

be estimated as 90 + 60 = 150?
See the Concept Check in this section.

104. Explain how adding or subtracting decimals is similar to adding or subtracting whole numbers.

105. Laser beams can be used to measure the distance to the moon. One measurement showed the distance to the moon to be 256,435.235 miles. A later measurement showed that the distance is 256,436.012 miles. Find how much farther away the moon is in the second measurement as compared to the first.

4.3 MULTIPLYING DECIMALS AND CIRCUMFERENCE OF A CIRCLE

Objectives

A Multiply Decimals.

B Estimate When Multiplying Decimals.

C Multiply by Powers of 10.

D Evaluate Expressions with Decimal Replacement Values.

E Find the Circumference of a Circle.

F Solve Problems by Multiplying Decimals.

Objective A Multiplying Decimals

Multiplying decimals is similar to multiplying whole numbers. The only difference is that we place a decimal point in the product. To discover where a decimal point is placed in the product, let's multiply 0.6×0.03. We first write each decimal as an equivalent fraction and then multiply.

$$0.6 \times 0.03 = \frac{6}{10} \times \frac{3}{100} = \frac{18}{1000} = 0.018$$

1 decimal place   2 decimal places   3 decimal places

Notice that $1 + 2 = 3$, the number of decimal places in the product. Now let's multiply 0.03×0.002.

$$0.03 \times 0.002 = \frac{3}{100} \times \frac{2}{1000} = \frac{6}{100,000} = 0.00006$$

2 decimal places   3 decimal places   5 decimal places

Again, we see that $2 + 3 = 5$, the number of decimal places in the product.

Instead of writing decimals as fractions each time we want to multiply, we notice a pattern from these examples and state a rule that we can use:

Multiplying Decimals

Step 1: Multiply the decimals as though they are whole numbers.

Step 2: The decimal point in the product is placed so that the number of decimal places in the product is equal to the *sum* of the number of decimal places in the factors.

EXAMPLE 1 Multiply: 23.6×0.78

Solution:

$$
\begin{array}{r}
23.6 \\
\times\, 0.78 \\
\hline
1888 \\
16520 \\
\hline
18.408
\end{array}
$$

23.6   1 decimal place
$\times$ 0.78   2 decimal places

Since $1 + 2 = 3$, insert the decimal point in the product so that there are 3 decimal places.

Work Practice Problem 1

EXAMPLE 2 Multiply: 0.0531×16

Solution:

$$
\begin{array}{r}
0.0531 \\
\times\ \ \ 16 \\
\hline
3186 \\
5310 \\
\hline
0.8496
\end{array}
$$

0.0531   4 decimal places
$\times$ 16   0 decimal places

4 decimal places $(4 + 0 = 4)$

Work Practice Problem 2

PRACTICE PROBLEM 1

Multiply: 45.9×0.42

PRACTICE PROBLEM 2

Multiply: 0.0721×48

Answers
1. 19.278, **2.** 3.4608

309

✔**Concept Check** True or false? The number of decimal places in the product of 0.261 and 0.78 is 6. Explain.

PRACTICE PROBLEM 3

Multiply: $(5.4)(-1.3)$

EXAMPLE 3 Multiply: $(-2.6)(0.8)$

Solution: Recall that the product of a negative number and a positive number is a negative number.

$$(-2.6)(0.8) = -2.08$$

◻ **Work Practice Problem 3**

Objective B Estimating When Multiplying Decimals

Just as for addition and subtraction, we can estimate when multiplying decimals to check the reasonableness of our answer.

PRACTICE PROBLEM 4

Multiply: 30.26×2.98. Then estimate to see whether the answer is reasonable.

EXAMPLE 4 Multiply: 28.06×1.95. Then estimate to see whether the answer is reasonable by rounding each factor, then multiplying the rounded numbers.

Solution:

Exact:	Estimate 1	Estimate 2
28.06	28 Rounded to ones or	30 Rounded to tens
$\times$ 1.95	$\times$ 2	$\times$ 2
14030	56	60
252540		
280600		
54.7170		

The answer 54.7170 is reasonable.

◻ **Work Practice Problem 4**

As shown in Example 4, estimated results will vary depending on what estimates are used. Notice that estimating results is a good way to see whether the decimal point has been correctly placed.

Objective C Multiplying by Powers of 10

There are some patterns that occur when we multiply a number by a power of 10 such as 10, 100, 1000, 10,000, and so on.

$23.6951 \times 10 = 236.951$ Move the decimal point *1 place* to the *right*.
1 zero

$23.6951 \times 100 = 2369.51$ Move the decimal point *2 places* to the *right*.
2 zeros

$23.6951 \times 100,000 = 2,369,510.$ Move the decimal point *5 places* to the *right* (insert a 0).
5 zeros

Answers

3. -7.02, **4.** 90.1748

✔ **Concept Check Answer**

false: 3 decimal places and 2 decimal places means 5 decimal places in the product

Notice that we move the decimal point the same number of places as there are zeros in the power of 10.

Multiplying Decimals by Powers of 10 such as 10, 100, 1000, 10,000 . . .

Move the decimal point to the *right* the same number of places as there are *zeros* in the power of 10.

PRACTICE PROBLEMS 5–7

EXAMPLES Multiply.

5. $7.68 \times 10 = 76.8$ 7.68

6. $23.702 \times 100 = 2370.2$ 23.702

7. $(-76.3)(1000) = -76{,}300$ 76.300

■ **Work Practice Problems 5–7**

Multiply.

5. 23.7×10

6. 203.004×100

7. $(-1.15)(1000)$

There are also powers of 10 that are less than 1. The decimals 0.1, 0.01, 0.001, 0.0001, and so on are examples of powers of 10 less than 1. Notice the pattern when we multiply by these powers of 10:

$569.2 \times 0.1 = 56.92$ Move the decimal point *1 place* to the *left*.
1 decimal place

$569.2 \times 0.01 = 5.692$ Move the decimal point *2 places* to the *left*.
2 decimal places

$569.2 \times 0.0001 = 0.05692$ Move the decimal point *4 places* to the *left* (insert one 0).
4 decimal places

Multiplying Decimals by Powers of 10 such as 0.1, 0.01, 0.001, 0.0001 . . .

Move the decimal point to the *left* the same number of places as there are *decimal places* in the power of 10.

PRACTICE PROBLEMS 8–10

EXAMPLES Multiply.

8. $42.1 \times 0.1 = 4.21$ 42.1

9. $76{,}805 \times 0.01 = 768.05$ 76.805.

10. $(-9.2)(-0.001) = 0.0092$ 0009.2

■ **Work Practice Problems 8–10**

Multiply.

8. 7.62×0.1

9. 1.9×0.01

10. $(-7682)(-0.001)$

Many times we see large numbers written, for example, in the form 297.9 million rather than in the longer standard notation. The next example shows us how to interpret these numbers.

Answers

5. 237, **6.** 20,300.4, **7.** −1150,
8. 0.762, **9.** 0.019, **10.** 7.682

PRACTICE PROBLEM 11

According to the 2000 Census, there were 115.9 million households in the United States. Write this number in standard notation. (*Source:* U.S. Census Bureau)

EXAMPLE 11 At the beginning of 2006, the population of the United States was projected to be 297.9 million. Write this number in standard notation. (*Source:* U.S. Census Bureau)

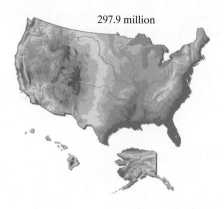

297.9 million

Solution: 297.9 million = 297.9 × 1 million

$$= 297.9 \times 1{,}000{,}000 = 297{,}900{,}000$$

▣ **Work Practice Problem 11**

Objective D Using Decimals as Replacement Values

Now let's practice working with variables.

PRACTICE PROBLEM 12

Evaluate 7*y* for *y* = −0.028.

EXAMPLE 12 Evaluate *xy* for *x* = 2.3 and *y* = 0.44.

Solution: Recall that *xy* means *x* · *y*.

$$xy = (2.3)(0.44)$$

$$\begin{array}{r} 2.3 \\ \times\ 0.44 \\ \hline 92 \\ 920 \\ \hline \end{array}$$

$$= 1.012 \longleftarrow \quad 1.012$$

▣ **Work Practice Problem 12**

Objective E Finding the Circumference of a Circle

Recall that the distance around a polygon is called its **perimeter.** The distance around a circle is given a special name called the **circumference,** and this distance depends on the radius or the diameter of the circle.

Circumference of a Circle

radius

diameter

Circumference = 2 · π · radius   or   Circumference = π · diameter

---

The symbol π is the Greek letter pi, pronounced "pie." It is a number between 3 and 4. The number π rounded to two decimal places is 3.14, and a fraction approximation for π is $\dfrac{22}{7}$.

Answers

11. 115,900,000, **12.** −0.196

EXAMPLE 13 Find the circumference of a circle whose radius is 5 inches. Then use the approximation 3.14 for π to approximate the circumference.

Solution: Circumference $= 2 \cdot \pi \cdot \text{radius}$

$$= 2 \cdot \pi \cdot 5 \text{ inches}$$

$$= 10\pi \text{ inches}$$

5 inches

Next, we replace π with the approximation 3.14.

Circumference $= 10\pi$ inches

("is approximately") $\rightarrow$ $\approx 10(3.14)$ inches

$$= 31.4 \text{ inches}$$

The *exact* circumference or distance around the circle is 10π inches, which is *approximately* 31.4 inches.

▣ **Work Practice Problem 13**

Objective F Solving Problems by Multiplying Decimals

The solutions to many real-life problems are found by multiplying decimals. We continue using our four problem-solving steps to solve such problems.

EXAMPLE 14 Finding the Total Cost of Materials for a Job

A college student is hired to paint a billboard with paint costing $2.49 per quart. If the job requires 3 quarts of paint, what is the total cost of the paint?

Solution:

1. UNDERSTAND. Read and reread the problem. The phrase "total cost" might make us think addition, but since this problem requires repeated addition, let's multiply.

2. TRANSLATE.

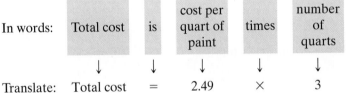

In words:	Total cost	is	cost per quart of paint	times	number of quarts
	↓	↓	↓	↓	↓
Translate:	Total cost	=	2.49	×	3

3. SOLVE. We can estimate to check our calculations. The number 2.49 rounds to 2 and $2 \times 3 = 6$.

$$\begin{array}{r} \overset{1\ 2}{2.49} \\ \times\quad 3 \\ \hline 7.47 \end{array}$$

4. INTERPRET. *Check* your work. Since 7.47 is close to our estimate of 6, our answer is reasonable. *State* your conclusion: The total cost of the paint is $7.47.

▣ **Work Practice Problem 14**

Mental Math

Do not multiply. Just give the number of decimal places in the product. See the Concept Check in this section.

1. 0.46
     × 0.81

2. 57.9
     × 0.36

3. 0.428
     × 0.2

4. 0.0073
     ×   21

5. 0.028
     × 1.36

6. 5.1296
     ×7.3987

4.3 EXERCISE SET

FOR EXTRA HELP

Student Solutions Manual PH Math/Tutor Center CD/Video for Review *Math* XL MathXL® *MyMathLab* MyMathLab

Objectives Ⓐ Ⓑ **Mixed Practice** *Multiply. See Examples 1 through 4. For those exercises marked, also estimate to see if the answer is reasonable.*

1. 0.26×5

2. 0.19×6

 3. 1.2
      ×0.5

4. 6.8
      ×0.3

 5. $(-2.3)(7.65)$

6. $(4.7)(-9.02)$

7. $(-6.89)(-5.7)$

8. $(-6.45)(-2.8)$

9. 5.3×4.2
Exact:
Estimate:

10. 6.2×3.8
Exact:
Estimate:

11. 0.576
      × 0.7

12. 0.971
      × 0.5

13. 1.0047
      ×   8.2
Exact: Estimate:

14. 2.0005
      ×   5.5
Exact: Estimate:

15. 490.2
      ×0.023

16. 300.9
      ×0.032

Objective Ⓒ *Multiply. See Examples 5 through 10.*

17. 6.5×10

18. 7.2×100

19. 6.5×0.1

20. 4.7×0.1

21. $(-7.093)(1000)$

22. $(-1.123)(1000)$

23. 7.093×100

24. 0.5×100

25. $(-9.83)(-0.01)$

26. $(-4.72)(-0.01)$

27. 37.62×0.001

28. 14.3×0.001

Objectives Ⓐ Ⓑ Ⓒ **Mixed Practice** *Multiply. See Examples 1 through 10.*

29. 0.123×0.4

30. 0.216×0.3

 31. $(147.9)(100)$

32. $(345.2)(100)$

33. 8.6×0.15

34. 0.42×5.7

 35. $(937.62)(-0.01)$

36. $(-0.001)(562.01)$

314

37. 562.3×0.001

38. 993.5×0.001

39. $\begin{array}{r} 5.62 \\ \times\ 7.7 \\ \hline \end{array}$

40. $\begin{array}{r} 8.03 \\ \times\ 5.5 \\ \hline \end{array}$

Write each number in standard notation. See Example 11.

41. The storage silos at the main Hershey chocolate factory in Hershey, Pennsylvania, can hold enough cocoa beans to make 5.5 billion Hershey's milk chocolate bars. (*Source:* Hershey Foods Corporation)

42. The total value of works from Pablo Picasso (if sold) is $1.5 billion. (*Source: Top 10 of Everything,* 2005)

43. The Blue Streak is the oldest roller coaster at Cedar Point, an amusement park in Sandusky, Ohio. Since 1964, it has given more than 49.8 million rides. (*Source:* Cedar Fair, L.P.)

44. About 36.4 million American households own at least one dog. (*Source:* American Pet Products Manufacturers Association)

45. The most-visited national park in the United States is the Blue Ridge Parkway in Virginia and North Carolina. An estimated 353 thousand people visited the park each week in 2003. (*Source:* National Park Service)

46. There are 844 thousand places to eat out in the United States. (*Source:* National Restaurant Association)

Objective Ⓓ *Evaluate each expression for $x = 3$, $y = -0.2$, and $z = 5.7$. See Example 12.*

47. xy

48. yz

49. $xz - y$

50. $-5y + z$

Objective Ⓔ *Find the circumference of each circle. Then use the approximation 3.14 for π and approximate each circumference. See Example 13.*

△ **51.**

4 meters

△ **52.**
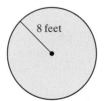
8 feet

△ **53.**

10 centimeters

△ **54.**

22 inches

△ **55.**
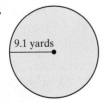
9.1 yards

△ **56.**
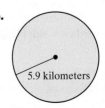
5.9 kilometers

Objectives Ⓔ Ⓕ **Mixed Practice** *Solve. See Examples 13 and 14. For circumference applications find the exact circumference and then use 3.14 for π to approximate the circumference.*

57. A 1-ounce serving of cream cheese contains 6.2 grams of saturated fat. How much saturated fat is in 4 ounces of cream cheese? (*Source: Home and Garden Bulletin No. 72;* U.S. Department of Agriculture)

58. A 3.5-ounce serving of lobster meat contains 0.1 gram of saturated fat. How much saturated fat do 3 servings of lobster meat contain? (*Source:* The National Institute of Health)

59. The average cost of driving a car in 2003 was $0.52 per mile. How much would it have cost to drive a car 8750 miles in 2003? (*Source:* American Automobile Association)

60. In a recent year, a U.S. airline passenger paid $0.1174, on average, to fly 1 mile. How much would it have cost to fly from Atlanta, Georgia, to Minneapolis, Minnesota, a distance of 905 miles? Round to the nearest cent. (*Source:* Air Transport Association of America, Inc.)

△ **61.** In 1893, the first ride called a Ferris wheel was constructed by Washington Gale Ferris. Its diameter was 250 feet. Find its circumference. Give an exact answer and an approximation using 3.14 for π. (*Source: The Handy Science Answer Book,* Visible Ink Press, 1994)

△ **62.** The radius of Earth is approximately 3950 miles. Find the distance around Earth at the equator. Give an exact answer and an approximation using 3.14 for π. (*Hint:* Find the circumference of a circle with radius 3950 miles.)

△ **63.** The London Eye, built for the Millennium celebration in London, resembles a gigantic ferris wheel with a diameter of 135 meters. If Adam Hawn rides the Eye for one revolution, find how far he travels. (Give an exact answer and an approximation using 3.14 for π. (*Source:* Londoneye.com)

△ **64.** The world's longest suspension bridge is the Akashi Kaikyo Bridge in Japan. This bridge has two circular caissons, which are underwater foundations. If the diameter of a caisson is 80 meters, find its circumference. Give an exact answer and an approximation using 3.14 for π. (*Source: Scientific American;* How Things Work Today)

65. A meter is a unit of length in the metric system that is approximately equal to 39.37 inches. Sophia Wagner is 1.65 meters tall. Find her approximate height in inches.

66. The doorway to a room is 2.15 meters tall. Approximate this height in inches. (*Hint:* See Exercise 65.)

67. Jose Severos, an electrician for Central Power and Light, worked 40 hours last week. Calculate his pay before taxes for last week if his hourly wage is $13.88.

68. Maribel Chin, an assembly line worker, worked 20 hours last week. Her hourly rate is $8.52 per hour. Calculate Maribel's pay before taxes.

△ **69. a.** Approximate the circumference of each circle.

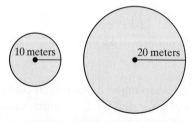

b. If the radius of a circle is doubled, is its corresponding circumference doubled?

△ **70. a.** Approximate the circumference of each circle.

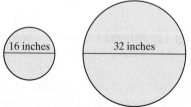

b. If the diameter of a circle is doubled, is its corresponding circumference doubled?

71. Recall that the top face of the Apple iPod mini (see Section 4.2) measures 3.6 inches by 2.0 inches. Find the area of the face of the iPod mini.

72. Recall that the face of the regular Apple iPod measures 4.1 inches by 2.4 inches. Find the area of the face of this iPod.

Review

Divide. See Sections 1.7 and 3.3.

73. $2920 \div 365$

74. $2916 \div 6$

75. $-\dfrac{24}{7} \div \dfrac{8}{21}$

76. $\dfrac{162}{25} \div -\dfrac{9}{75}$

Concept Extensions

Mixed Practice (Sections 4.2, 4.3) *Perform the indicated operations.*

77. $3.6 + 0.04$

78. -3.6×0.04

79. $3.6 - 0.04$

80. $100 - 48.6$

81. -0.221×0.5

82. $7.2 + 0.14 + 98.6$

83. Find how far radio waves travel in 20.6 seconds. (Radio waves travel at a speed of $1.86 \times 100{,}000$ miles per second.)

84. If it takes radio waves approximately 8.3 minutes to travel from the Sun to the Earth, find approximately how far it is from the Sun to the Earth. (*Hint:* See Exercise 83.)

85. In your own words, explain how to find the number of decimal places in a product of decimal numbers.

86. In your own words, explain how to multiply by a power of 10.

87. Write down two decimal numbers whose product will contain 5 decimal places. Without multiplying, explain how you know your answer is correct.

STUDY SKILLS BUILDER

Are You Getting All the Mathematics Help That You Need?

Remember that, in addition to your instructor, there are many places to get help with your mathematics course. For example,

- This text has an accompanying video lesson for every section and worked out solutions to every Chapter Test exercise on video.
- The back of the book contains answers to odd-numbered exercises and selected solutions.
- A student *Solutions Manual* is available that contains worked-out solutions to odd-numbered exercises as well as solutions to every exercise in the Integrated Reviews, Chapter Reviews, Chapter Tests, and Cumulative Reviews.

- Don't forget to check with your instructor for other local resources available to you, such as a tutor center.

Exercises

1. List items you find helpful in the text and all student supplements to this text.
2. List all the campus help that is available to you for this course.
3. List any help (besides the textbook) from Exercises 1 and 2 above that you are using.
4. List any help (besides the textbook) that you feel you should try.
5. Write a goal for yourself that includes trying anything you listed in Exercise 4 during the next week.

4.4 DIVIDING DECIMALS

Objective **A** Dividing Decimals

Dividing decimal numbers is similar to dividing whole numbers. The only difference is that we place a decimal point in the quotient. If the divisor is a whole number, we place the decimal point in the quotient directly above the decimal point in the dividend, and then divide as with whole numbers. Recall that division can be checked by multiplication.

$$
\begin{array}{r}
0.26 \leftarrow \text{quotient} \\
\text{divisor} \rightarrow 32\overline{)8.32} \leftarrow \text{dividend} \\
-64 \\
\hline
1\,92 \\
-1\,92 \\
\hline
0
\end{array}
$$

Check:
$$
\begin{array}{r}
0.26 \quad \text{Quotient} \\
\times \ 32 \quad \text{Divisor} \\
\hline
52 \\
7\,80 \\
\hline
8.32 \quad \text{Dividend}
\end{array}
$$

Dividing by a Whole Number

Step 1: Place the decimal point in the quotient directly above the decimal point in the dividend.

Step 2: Divide as with whole numbers.

PRACTICE PROBLEM 1

Divide: $517.2 \div 6$. Check your answer.

EXAMPLE 1 Divide: $270.2 \div 7$. Check your answer.

Solution:

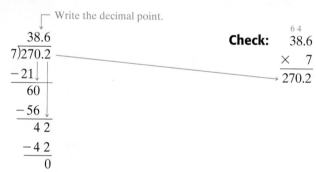

The quotient is 38.6.

◻ **Work Practice Problem 1**

PRACTICE PROBLEM 2

Divide: $26.19 \div 9$. Check your answer.

EXAMPLE 2 Divide: $60.24 \div 8$. Check your answer.

Solution:

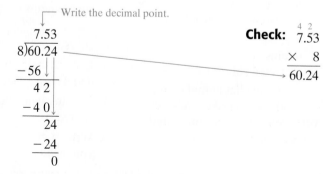

◻ **Work Practice Problem 2**

Answers

1. 86.2, **2.** 2.91

Sometimes to continue dividing we need to insert zeros after the last digit in the dividend.

EXAMPLE 3 Divide: $-5.98 \div 115$

Solution: Recall that a negative number divided by a positive number gives a negative quotient.

$$
\begin{array}{r}
0.052 \\
115\overline{)5.980} \quad \leftarrow \text{Insert one 0.} \\
\underline{-5\,75} \\
230 \\
\underline{-230} \\
0
\end{array}
$$

Thus $-5.98 \div 115 = -0.052$.

◻ Work Practice Problem 3

If the divisor is not a whole number, before we divide we need to move the decimal point to the right until the divisor is a whole number.

$$
\underset{\text{divisor}}{\overset{}{1.5}}\overline{)\underset{\text{dividend}}{64.85}}
$$

To understand how this works, let's rewrite

$1.5\overline{)64.85}$ as $\dfrac{64.85}{1.5}$

and then multiply by 1 in the form of $\dfrac{10}{10}$. We use the form $\dfrac{10}{10}$ so that the denominator (divisor) becomes a whole number.

$$
\frac{64.85}{1.5} = \frac{64.85}{1.5} \cdot 1 = \frac{64.85}{1.5} \cdot \frac{10}{10} = \frac{64.85 \cdot 10}{1.5 \cdot 10} = \frac{648.5}{15}
$$

which can be written as $15.\overline{)648.5}$. Notice that

$1.5\overline{)64.85}$ is equivalent to $15.\overline{)648.5}$

The decimal points in the dividend and the divisor were both moved one place to the right, and the divisor is now a whole number. This procedure is summarized next:

Dividing by a Decimal

Step 1: Move the decimal point in the divisor to the right until the divisor is a whole number.

Step 2: Move the decimal point in the dividend to the right the *same number of places* as the decimal point was moved in Step 1.

Step 3: Divide. Place the decimal point in the quotient directly over the moved decimal point in the dividend.

PRACTICE PROBLEM 4

Divide: 166.88 ÷ 5.6

EXAMPLE 4 Divide: 10.764 ÷ 2.3

Solution: We move the decimal points in the divisor and the dividend one place to the right so that the divisor is a whole number.

$$2.3\overline{)10.764} \qquad \text{becomes} \qquad \begin{array}{r} 4.68 \\ 23\overline{)107.64} \\ -92 \\ \hline 15\,6 \\ -13\,8 \\ \hline 1\,84 \\ -1\,84 \\ \hline 0 \end{array}$$

🔲 **Work Practice Problem 4**

PRACTICE PROBLEM 5

Divide: 1.976 ÷ 0.16

EXAMPLE 5 Divide: 5.264 ÷ 0.32

Solution:

$$0.32\overline{)5.264} \qquad \text{becomes} \qquad \begin{array}{r} 16.45 \\ 32\overline{)526.40} \\ -32 \\ \hline 206 \\ -192 \\ \hline 14\,4 \\ -12\,8 \\ \hline 1\,60 \\ -1\,60 \\ \hline 0 \end{array}$$ Insert one 0.

🔲 **Work Practice Problem 5**

✔ **Concept Check** Is it always true that the number of decimal places in a quotient equals the sum of the decimal places in the dividend and divisor?

PRACTICE PROBLEM 6

Divide 23.4 ÷ 0.57. Round the quotient to the nearest hundredth.

EXAMPLE 6 Divide: 17.5 ÷ 0.48. Round the quotient to the nearest hundredth.

Solution: First we move the decimal points in the divisor and the dividend two places. Then we divide and round the quotient to the nearest hundredth.

hundredths place

$$\begin{array}{r} 36.458 \approx 36.46 \\ 48\overline{)1750.000} \\ -144 \\ \hline 310 \\ -288 \\ \hline 22\,0 \\ -19\,2 \\ \hline 2\,80 \\ -2\,40 \\ \hline 400 \\ -384 \\ \hline 16 \end{array}$$

"is approximately"

When rounding to the nearest hundredth, carry the division process out to one more decimal place, the thousandths place.

🔲 **Work Practice Problem 6**

Objective B Estimating When Dividing Decimals

Just as for addition, subtraction, and multiplication of decimals, we can estimate when dividing decimals to check the reasonableness of our answer.

EXAMPLE 7 Divide: 272.356 ÷ 28.4. Then estimate to see whether the proposed result is reasonable.

Solution:

Exact:	**Estimate 1**		**Estimate 2**

$$
\begin{array}{r}
9.59 \\
284.\overline{)2723.56} \\
-2556 \\
\hline
1675 \\
-1420 \\
\hline
2556 \\
-2556 \\
\hline
0
\end{array}
$$

$$
\begin{array}{r}
9 \\
30\overline{)270}
\end{array}
\quad \text{or} \quad
\begin{array}{r}
10 \\
30\overline{)300}
\end{array}
$$

The estimate is 9 or 10, so 9.59 is reasonable.

■ Work Practice Problem 7

✔ **Concept Check** If a quotient is to be rounded to the nearest thousandth, to what place should the division be carried out? (Assume that the division carries out to your answer.)

Objective C Dividing Decimals by Powers of 10

As with multiplication, there are patterns that occur when we divide decimals by powers of 10 such as 10, 100, 1000, and so on.

$$\frac{569.2}{10} = 56.92 \qquad \text{Move the decimal point } 1 \text{ place to the } left.$$

— 1 zero

$$\frac{569.2}{10,000} = 0.05692 \qquad \text{Move the decimal point } 4 \text{ places to the } left.$$

— 4 zeros

This pattern suggests the following rule:

> ### Dividing Decimals by Powers of 10 such as 10, 100, or 1000
>
> Move the decimal point of the dividend to the *left* the same number of places as there are *zeros* in the power of 10.

PRACTICE PROBLEM 7

Divide: 713.7 ÷ 91.5. Then estimate to see whether the proposed answer is reasonable.

Answer

7. 7.8

✔ **Concept Check Answer**

ten-thousandths place

PRACTICE PROBLEMS 8–9

Divide.

8. $\dfrac{128.3}{1000}$ **9.** $\dfrac{0.56}{10}$

EXAMPLES Divide.

8. $\dfrac{786.1}{1000} = 0.7861$ Move the decimal point *3 places* to the *left*.
↑— 3 zeros

9. $\dfrac{-0.12}{10} = -0.012$ Move the decimal point *1 place* to the *left*. Also, a negative number divided by a positive number is a negative quotient.
↑— 1 zero

■ **Work Practice Problems 8–9**

Objective D Using Decimals as Replacement Values

PRACTICE PROBLEM 10

Evaluate $x \div y$ for $x = 0.035$ and $y = 0.02$.

EXAMPLE 10 Evaluate $x \div y$ for $x = 2.5$ and $y = 0.05$.

Solution: Replace x with 2.5 and y with 0.05.

$$
\begin{array}{ll}
x \div y = 2.5 \div 0.05 & \quad 0.05\overline{)2.5} \quad \text{becomes} \quad 5\overline{)250}\;^{\textstyle 50} \\
\qquad\quad = 50 &
\end{array}
$$

■ **Work Practice Problem 10**

Objective E Solving Problems by Dividing Decimals

Many real-life problems involve dividing decimals.

PRACTICE PROBLEM 11

A bag of fertilizer covers 1250 square feet of lawn. Tim Parker's lawn measures 14,800 square feet. How many bags of fertilizer does he need? If he can buy only whole bags of fertilizer, how many whole bags does he need?

EXAMPLE 11 Calculating Materials Needed for a Job

A gallon of paint covers a 250-square-foot area. If Betty Adkins wishes to paint a wall that measures 1450 square feet, how many gallons of paint does she need? If she can buy only gallon containers of paint, how many gallon containers does she need?

Solution:

1. UNDERSTAND. Read and reread the problem. We need to know how many 250s are in 1450, so we divide.
2. TRANSLATE.

In words:	number of gallons	is	square feet	divided by	square feet per gallon
	↓	↓	↓	↓	↓
Translate:	number of gallons	=	1450	÷	250

3. SOLVE. Let's see if our answer is reasonable by estimating. The dividend 1450 rounds to 1500 and divisor 250 rounds to 300. Then $1500 \div 300 = 5$.

$$
\begin{array}{r}
5.8 \\
250\overline{)1450.0} \\
-1250 \\
\hline
200\ 0 \\
-200\ 0 \\
\hline
0
\end{array}
$$

4. INTERPRET. *Check* your work. Since our estimate is close to our answer of 5, our answer is reasonable. *State* your conclusion: Betty needs 5.8 gallons of paint. If she can buy only gallon containers of paint, she needs 6 gallon containers of paint to complete the job.

Work Practice Problem 11

CALCULATOR EXPLORATIONS

Calculator errors can easily be made by pressing an incorrect key or by not pressing a correct key hard enough. Estimation is a valuable tool that can be used to check calculator results.

EXAMPLE Use estimation to determine whether the calculator result is reasonable or not. (For example, a result that is not reasonable can occur if proper keys are not pressed.)

Simplify: $82.064 \div 23$
Calculator display: 35.68

Solution: Round each number to the nearest 10. Since $80 \div 20 = 4$, the calculator display 35.68 is not reasonable.

Use estimation to determine whether each result is reasonable or not.

1. 102.62×41.8 Result: 428.9516

2. $174.835 \div 47.9$ Result: 3.65

3. $1025.68 - 125.42$ Result: 900.26

4. $562.781 + 2.96$ Result: 858.781

Mental Math

Recall properties of division and simplify.

1. $\dfrac{5.9}{1}$ **2.** $\dfrac{0.7}{0.7}$ **3.** $\dfrac{0}{9.86}$ **4.** $\dfrac{2.36}{0}$

5. $\dfrac{7.261}{7.261}$ **6.** $\dfrac{8.25}{1}$ **7.** $\dfrac{11.1}{0}$ **8.** $\dfrac{0}{89.96}$

4.4 EXERCISE SET

Objectives Ⓐ Ⓑ **Mixed Practice** *Divide. See Examples 1 through 5 and 7. For those exercises marked, also estimate to see if the answer is reasonable.*

1. $3\overline{)13.8}$ **2.** $2\overline{)11.8}$ **3.** $5\overline{)0.47}$ **4.** $6\overline{)0.51}$ **5.** $0.06\overline{)18}$

6. $0.04\overline{)20}$ **7.** $0.82\overline{)4.756}$ **8.** $0.92\overline{)3.312}$ **9.** $5.5\overline{)36.3}$
Exact:
Estimate:
   10. $2.2\overline{)21.78}$
Exact:
Estimate:

11. $6.195 \div 15$ **12.** $8.823 \div 17$ **13.** $-18 \div 0.06$ **14.** $20 \div (-0.04)$ **15.** Divide 4.2 by 0.6.

16. Divide 3.6 by 0.9.   **17.** $0.27\overline{)1.296}$ **18.** $0.34\overline{)2.176}$ **19.** $0.02\overline{)42}$ **20.** $0.03\overline{)24}$

21. $4.756 \div 0.82$ **22.** $3.312 \div 0.92$ **23.** $-36.3 \div -5.5$ **24.** $-21.78 \div -2.2$ **25.** $7.2\overline{)70.56}$
Exact:
Estimate:

26. $6.3\overline{)54.18}$
Exact:
Estimate:
   27. $5.4\overline{)51.84}$ **28.** $7.7\overline{)33.88}$ **29.** $\dfrac{1.215}{0.027}$ **30.** $\dfrac{3.213}{0.051}$

31. $0.25\overline{)13.648}$ **32.** $0.75\overline{)49.866}$ **33.** $3.78\overline{)0.02079}$ **34.** $2.96\overline{)0.01332}$

Divide. Round the quotients as indicated. See Example 6.

35. Divide 429.34 by 2.4 and round the quotient to the nearest whole number.

36. Divide 54.8 by 2.6 and round the quotient to the nearest whole number.

37. Divide 0.549 by 0.023 and round the quotient to the nearest hundredth.

38. Divide 0.0453 by 0.98 and round the quotient to the nearest thousandth.

39. Divide 45.23 by 0.4 and round the quotient to the nearest tenth.

40. Divide 83.32 by 0.063 and round the quotient to the nearest tenth.

Objective C *Divide. See Examples 8 and 9.*

41. $\dfrac{54.982}{100}$ **42.** $\dfrac{342.54}{100}$ **43.** $\dfrac{26.87}{10}$ **44.** $\dfrac{13.49}{10}$ **45.** $12.9 \div (-1000)$ **46.** $13.49 \div (-10,000)$

Objectives A C **Mixed Practice** *Divide. See Examples 1 through 6.*

47. $7\overline{)88.2}$ **48.** $9\overline{)130.5}$ **49.** $\dfrac{13.1}{10}$ **50.** $\dfrac{17.7}{10}$

51. $\dfrac{456.25}{10,000}$ **52.** $\dfrac{986.11}{10,000}$ **53.** $1.239 \div 3$ **54.** $0.54 \div 12$

55. Divide 4.2 by -0.6 **56.** Divide 3.6 by -0.9 **57.** $-1.296 \div 0.27$ **58.** $-2.176 \div 0.34$

59. Divide 42 by 0.02 **60.** Divide 24 by 0.03 **61.** Divide -18 by -0.6

62. Divide 20 by 0.4 **63.** Divide 35 by 0.005 **64.** Divide -35 by -0.0007

65. $-1.104 \div 1.6$ **66.** $-2.156 \div 0.98$ **67.** $-2.4 \div (-100)$

68. $-86.79 \div (-1000)$ **69.** $\dfrac{4.615}{0.071}$ **70.** $\dfrac{23.8}{0.035}$

Objective D *Evaluate each expression for $x = 5.65$, $y = -0.8$, and $z = 4.52$. See Example 10.*

71. $z \div y$ **72.** $z \div x$ **73.** $x \div y$ **74.** $y \div 2$

Objective E *Solve. See Example 11.*

75. Dorren Schmidt pays $73.86 per month to pay back a loan of $1772.64. In how many months will the loan be paid off?

76. Josef Jones is painting the walls of a room. The walls have a total area of 546 square feet. A quart of paint covers 52 square feet. If he must buy paint in whole quarts, how many quarts does he need?

77. The leading monetary winner in men's professional golf in 2003 was Vijay Singh. He earned $7,573,907. Suppose he had earned this working 40 hours per week for a year. Determine his hourly wage to the nearest cent. (*Note:* There are 52 weeks in a year.) (*Source: 2005 World Almanac*)

78. A page of a book contains about 1.5 kilobytes of information. If a computer disk can hold 740 kilobytes of information, how many pages of a book can be stored on one computer disk? Round to the nearest tenth of a page.

79. There are approximately 39.37 inches in 1 meter. How many meters, to the nearest tenth of a meter, are there in 200 inches?

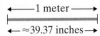
←——1 meter——→
←—≈39.37 inches—→

80. There are 2.54 centimeters in 1 inch. How many inches are there in 50 centimeters? Round to the nearest tenth.

←—— 1 inch ——→
←—— 2.54 cm ——→

81. In the United States, an average child will wear down 730 crayons by his or her tenth birthday. Find the number of boxes of 64 crayons this is equivalent to. Round to the nearest tenth. (*Source:* Binney & Smith Inc.)

82. American farmers receive an average of $238 per 100 chickens. What is the average price per chicken? (*Source:* National Agricultural Statistics Service)

A child is to receive a dose of 0.5 teaspoon of cough medicine every 4 hours. If the bottle contains 4 fluid ounces, answer Exercises 83 through 86.

83. A fluid ounce equals 6 teaspoons. How many teaspoons are in 4 fluid ounces?

84. The bottle of medicine contains how many doses for the child?

85. If the child takes a dose every four hours, how many days will the medicine last?

86. If the child takes a dose every six hours, how many days will the medicine last?

87. Lauren Jackson of the WNBA's Seattle Storm scored a total of 634 points during the 31 basketball games she played in the 2004 regular season. What was the average number of points she scored per game? Round to the nearest hundredth. (*Source:* Women's National Basketball Association)

88. During the 2004 Major League Soccer season, the Metro Stars was the top-scoring team with a total of 47 goals throughout the season. The Metro Stars played 30 games. What was the average number of goals the team scored per game? Round to the nearest hundredth. (*Source:* Major League Soccer)

Review

Write each decimal as a fraction. See Section 4.1.

89. 0.9

90. 0.7

91. 0.05

92. 0.08

Concept Extensions

Mixed Practice (*Sections 4.2, 4.3, 4.4*) *Perform the indicated operation.*

93. $1.278 \div 0.3$

94. 1.278×0.3

95. $1.278 + 0.3$

96. $1.278 - 0.3$

97. $(-8.6)(3.1)$

98. $7.2 + 0.05 + 49.1$

99. $\begin{array}{r} 1000 \\ -\ \ 95.71 \\ \hline \end{array}$

100. $\dfrac{87.2}{-10,000}$

Choose the best estimate.

101. 8.62×41.7
  a. 36
  b. 32
  c. 360
  d. 3.6

102. $1.437 + 20.69$
  a. 34
  b. 22
  c. 3.4
  d. 2.2

103. $78.6 \div 97$
  a. 7.86
  b. 0.786
  c. 786
  d. 7860

104. $302.729 - 28.697$
  a. 270
  b. 20
  c. 27
  d. 300

Recall from Section 1.7 that the average of a list of numbers is their total divided by how many numbers there are in the list. Use this procedure to find the average of the test scores listed in Exercises 105 and 106. If necessary, round to the nearest tenth.

105. 86, 78, 91, 87

106. 56, 75, 80

107. In a recent year, American manufacturers shipped approximately 745.94 million music CDs to retailers. How many music CDs were shipped per week on average? (*Source:* Recording Industry Association of America)

108. The area of a rectangle is 38.7 square feet. If its width is 4.5 feet, find its length.

109. The perimeter of a square is 180.8 centimeters. Find the length of a side.

110. Don Larson is building a horse corral that's shaped like a rectangle with dimensions of 24.28 meters by 15.675 meters. He plans to make a four-wire fence; that is, he will string four wires around the corral. How much wire will he need?

111. When dividing decimals, describe the process you use to place the decimal point in the quotient.

112. In your own words, describe how to quickly divide a number by a power of 10 such as 10, 100, 1000, etc.

To convert wind speeds in miles per hour to knots, divide by 1.15. Use this information and the Saffir-Simpson Hurricane Intensity chart below to answer Exercises 113 through 114. Round to the nearest tenth.

113. The chart gives wind speeds in miles per hour. What is the range of wind speeds for a Category 1 hurricane in knots?

114. What is the range of wind speeds for a Category 4 hurricane in knots?

Saffir-Simpson Hurricane Intensity Scale				
Category	**Wind Speed**	**Barometric Pressure [inches of mercury (Hg)]**	**Storm Surge**	**Damage Potential**
1 (Weak)	75–95 mph	≥ 28.94 in.	4–5 ft	Minimal damage to vegetation
2 (Moderate)	96–110 mph	28.50–28.93 in.	6–8 ft	Moderate damage to houses
3 (Strong)	111–130 mph	27.91–28.49 in.	9–12 ft	Extensive damage to small buildings
4 (Very Strong)	131–155 mph	27.17–27.90 in.	13–18 ft	Extreme structural damage
5 (Devastating)	>155 mph	<27.17 in.	>18 ft	Catastrophic building failures possible

THE BIGGER PICTURE   Operations on Sets of Numbers

Continue your outline from Sections 1.7, 1.9, 2.5, 3.3, and 3.7. Suggestions are once again written to help you complete this part of your outline.

I. Operations on Sets of Numbers

  A. Whole Numbers

    1. Add or Subtract (Sections 1.3, 1.4)

    2. Multiply or Divide (Sections 1.6, 1.7)

    3. Exponent (Section 1.9)

    4. Square Root (Section 1.9)

    5. Order of Operations (Section 1.9)

  B. Integers

    1. Add (Section 2.3)

    2. Subtract (Section 2.4)

    3. Multiply or Divide (Section 2.5)

  C. Fractions

    1. Simplify (Section 3.2)

    2. Multiply (Section 3.3)

    3. Divide (Section 3.3)

    4. Add or Subtract (Sections 3.4, 3.5)

  D. Decimals

    1. Add or Subtract: Line up decimal points.

$$\begin{array}{r} 1.27 \\ +0.6 \\ \hline 1.87 \end{array}$$

2. Multiply:

$$\begin{array}{r} 2.56 \\ \times\ 3.2 \\ \hline 512 \\ 7680 \\ \hline 8.192 \end{array}$$

2.56 — 2 decimal places
× 3.2 — 1 decimal place
$2 + 1 = 3$
8.192 — 3 decimal places

3. Divide:

$$8\overline{)5.\overset{.}{6}} \quad \frac{0.7}{}$$

$$0.6\overline{)0.786} \quad \frac{1.31}{}$$

Perform indicated operations.

1. $3.6 + 8.092 + 10.48$

2. $7 - 3.049$

3. 91.332×100

4. $-\dfrac{68}{10}$

5. $\begin{array}{r} 5.2 \\ \times\ 0.27 \\ \hline \end{array}$

6. $9\overline{)77.94}$

7. $0.35\overline{)0.01785}$

8. $2.3 - (0.4)^2$

9. $\dfrac{8}{15} - \dfrac{2}{5}$

10. $-\dfrac{8}{15} \cdot \dfrac{2}{5}$

Operations on Decimals

Perform the indicated operation.

1. $1.6 + 0.97$

2. $3.2 + 0.85$

3. $9.8 - 0.9$

4. $10.2 - 6.7$

5. $\begin{array}{r} 0.8 \\ \times\, 0.2 \\ \hline \end{array}$

6. $\begin{array}{r} 0.6 \\ \times\, 0.4 \\ \hline \end{array}$

7. $8\overline{)2.16}$

8. $6\overline{)3.12}$

9. $(9.6)(-0.5)$

10. $(-8.7)(-0.7)$

11. $\begin{array}{r} 123.6 \\ -\ 48.04 \\ \hline \end{array}$

12. $\begin{array}{r} 325.2 \\ -\ 36.08 \\ \hline \end{array}$

13. $-25 + 0.026$

14. $0.125 + (-44)$

15. $29.24 \div (-3.4)$

16. $-10.26 \div (-1.9)$

17. -2.8×100

18. 1.6×1000

19. $\begin{array}{r} 96.21 \\ 7.028 \\ +121.7 \\ \hline \end{array}$

20. $\begin{array}{r} 0.268 \\ 1.93 \\ +142.881 \\ \hline \end{array}$

21. $-25.76 \div -46$

22. $-27.09 \div 43$

23. $\begin{array}{r} 12.004 \\ \times\ \ \ 2.3 \\ \hline \end{array}$

24. $\begin{array}{r} 28.006 \\ \times\ \ \ 5.2 \\ \hline \end{array}$

25. Subtract 4.6 from 10

26. Subtract 18 from 0.26

27. $-268.19 - 146.25$

Answers

1. _____
2. _____
3. _____
4. _____
5. _____
6. _____
7. _____
8. _____
9. _____
10. _____
11. _____
12. _____
13. _____
14. _____
15. _____
16. _____
17. _____
18. _____
19. _____
20. _____
21. _____
22. _____
23. _____
24. _____
25. _____
26. _____
27. _____

28. _____

29. _____

30. _____

31. _____

32. _____

33. _____

34. _____

35. _____

36. _____

37. _____

38. _____

28. $-860.18 - 434.85$

29. $\dfrac{2.958}{-0.087}$

30. $\dfrac{-1.708}{0.061}$

31. $160 - 43.19$

32. $120 - 101.21$

33. 15.62×10

34. $15.62 \div 10$

35. $15.62 + 10$

36. $15.62 - 10$

37. According to the federal Nutrition Labeling and Education Act, a food manufacturer may label a food product "Fat Free" if it contains less than 0.5 grams of fat per serving. A new type of cookie contains 0.38 grams of fat per cookie. Can the packaging for this cookie be labeled "Fat Free"? Explain.

38. Estimate the distance in miles between Garden City, Kansas, and Wichita, Kansas, by rounding each given distance to the nearest ten.

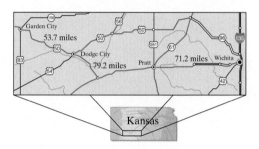

4.5 FRACTIONS, DECIMALS, AND ORDER OF OPERATIONS

Objectives

A Write Fractions as Decimals.

B Compare Fractions and Decimals.

C Simplify Expressions Containing Decimals and Fractions Using Order of Operations

D Evaluate Expressions Given Decimal Replacement Values.

Objective **A** Writing Fractions as Decimals

To write a fraction as a decimal, we interpret the fraction bar to mean division and find the quotient.

Writing Fractions as Decimals

To write a fraction as a decimal, divide the numerator by the denominator.

EXAMPLE 1 Write $\frac{1}{4}$ as a decimal.

Solution: $\frac{1}{4} = 1 \div 4$

$$\begin{array}{r} 0.25 \\ 4\overline{)1.00} \\ -\underline{8} \\ 20 \\ -\underline{20} \\ 0 \end{array}$$

Thus, $\frac{1}{4}$ written as a decimal is 0.25.

■ Work Practice Problem 1

PRACTICE PROBLEM 1

a. Write $\frac{2}{5}$ as a decimal.

b. Write $\frac{9}{40}$ as a decimal.

EXAMPLE 2 Write $-\frac{5}{8}$ as a decimal.

Solution: $-\frac{5}{8} = -(5 \div 8) = -0.625$

$$\begin{array}{r} 0.625 \\ 8\overline{)5.000} \\ -\underline{48} \\ 20 \\ -\underline{16} \\ 40 \\ -\underline{40} \\ 0 \end{array}$$

■ Work Practice Problem 2

PRACTICE PROBLEM 2

Write $-\frac{3}{8}$ as a decimal.

EXAMPLE 3 Write $\frac{2}{3}$ as a decimal.

Solution:
$$\begin{array}{r} 0.666\ldots \\ 3\overline{)2.000} \\ -\underline{1\,8} \\ 20 \\ -\underline{18} \\ 20 \\ -\underline{18} \\ 2 \end{array}$$

This pattern will continue because $\frac{2}{3} = 0.6666\ldots$

Remainder is 2, then 0 is brought down.

Remainder is 2, then 0 is brought down.

Remainder is 2.

PRACTICE PROBLEM 3

a. Write $\frac{5}{6}$ as a decimal.

b. Write $\frac{2}{9}$ as a decimal.

Answers
1. a. 0.4, **b.** 0.225, **2.** −0.375,
3. a. $0.8\overline{3}$, **b.** $0.\overline{2}$

Continued on next page

331

Notice the digit 2 keeps occurring as the remainder. This will continue so that the digit 6 will keep repeating in the quotient. We place a bar over the digit 6 to indicate that it repeats.

$$\frac{2}{3} = 0.666\ldots = 0.\overline{6}$$

We can also write a decimal approximation for $\frac{2}{3}$. For example, $\frac{2}{3}$ rounded to the nearest hundredth is 0.67. This can be written as $\frac{2}{3} \approx 0.67$.

■ **Work Practice Problem 3**

PRACTICE PROBLEM 4

Write $\frac{28}{13}$ as a decimal. Round to the nearest thousandth.

EXAMPLE 4 Write $\frac{22}{7}$ as a decimal. (The fraction $\frac{22}{7}$ is an approximation for π.) Round to the nearest hundredth.

Solution:

$$
\begin{array}{r}
3.142 \approx 3.14 \\
7)\overline{22.000} \\
\underline{-21} \\
1\,0 \\
\underline{-\ 7} \\
30 \\
\underline{-28} \\
20 \\
\underline{-14} \\
6
\end{array}
$$

Carry the division out to the thousandths place.

The fraction $\frac{22}{7}$ in decimal form is approximately 3.14.

■ **Work Practice Problem 4**

PRACTICE PROBLEM 5

Write $3\frac{5}{16}$ as a decimal.

EXAMPLE 5 Write $2\frac{3}{16}$ as a decimal.

Solution:

Option 1. Write the fractional part only as a decimal.

$$\frac{3}{16} \longrightarrow
\begin{array}{r}
0.1875 \\
16)\overline{3.0000} \\
\underline{-1\,6} \\
1\,40 \\
\underline{-1\,28} \\
120 \\
\underline{-112} \\
80 \\
\underline{-\ 80} \\
0
\end{array}
$$

Thus $2\frac{3}{16} = 2.1875$

Option 2. Write $2\frac{3}{16}$ as an improper fraction, and divide.

$$2\frac{3}{16} = \frac{35}{16} \longrightarrow
\begin{array}{r}
2.1875 \\
16)\overline{35.0000} \\
\underline{-32} \\
3\,0 \\
\underline{-1\,6} \\
1\,40 \\
\underline{-1\,28} \\
120 \\
\underline{-112} \\
80 \\
\underline{-\ 80} \\
0
\end{array}
$$

Thus $2\frac{3}{16} = 2.1875$

■ **Work Practice Problem 5**

Answers
4. 2.154,   **5.** 3.3125

Some fractions may be written as decimals using our knowledge of decimals. From Section 4.1, we know that if the denominator of a fraction is 10, 100, 1000, or so on, we can immediately write the fraction as a decimal. For example,

$$\frac{4}{10} = 0.4, \qquad \frac{12}{100} = 0.12, \text{ and so on.}$$

EXAMPLE 6 Write $\frac{4}{5}$ as a decimal.

Solution: Let's write $\frac{4}{5}$ as an equivalent fraction with a denominator of 10.

$$\frac{4}{5} = \frac{4}{5} \cdot \frac{2}{2} = \frac{8}{10} = 0.8$$

■ **Work Practice Problem 6**

PRACTICE PROBLEM 6

Write $\frac{3}{5}$ as a decimal.

EXAMPLE 7 Write $\frac{1}{25}$ as a decimal.

Solution: $\frac{1}{25} = \frac{1}{25} \cdot \frac{4}{4} = \frac{4}{100} = 0.04$

■ **Work Practice Problem 7**

PRACTICE PROBLEM 7

Write $\frac{3}{50}$ as a decimal.

✔ **Concept Check** Suppose you are writing the fraction $\frac{9}{16}$ as a decimal. How do you know you have made a mistake if your answer is 1.735?

Objective B Comparing Decimals and Fractions

Now we can compare decimals and fractions by writing fractions as equivalent decimals.

EXAMPLE 8 Insert $<$, $>$, or $=$ to form a true statement.

$$\frac{1}{8} \qquad 0.12$$

Solution: First we write $\frac{1}{8}$ as an equivalent decimal. Then we compare decimal places.

$$\begin{array}{r} 0.125 \\ 8)\overline{1.000} \\ \underline{-8} \\ 20 \\ \underline{-16} \\ 40 \\ \underline{-40} \\ 0 \end{array}$$

Original numbers	$\frac{1}{8}$	0.12
Decimals	0.125	0.120
Compare	0.125 > 0.12	

Thus, $\qquad \frac{1}{8} > 0.12$

■ **Work Practice Problem 8**

PRACTICE PROBLEM 8

Insert $<$, $>$, or $=$ to form a true statement.

$$\frac{1}{5} \qquad 0.25$$

Answers
6. 0.6, **7.** 0.06, **8.** $<$

✔ **Concept Check Answer**

$\frac{9}{16}$ is less than 1 while 1.735 is greater than 1.

PRACTICE PROBLEM 9

Insert $<$, $>$, or $=$ to form a true statement.

a. $\dfrac{1}{2}$　　0.54　**b.** $0.\overline{4}$　　$\dfrac{4}{9}$

c. $\dfrac{5}{7}$　　0.72

EXAMPLE 9 Insert $<$, $>$, or $=$ to form a true statement.

$$0.\overline{7}\qquad \dfrac{7}{9}$$

Solution: We write $\dfrac{7}{9}$ as a decimal and then compare.

$$\begin{array}{r} 0.77\ldots = 0.\overline{7} \\ 9\overline{)7.00} \\ -6\,3 \\ \hline 70 \\ -63 \\ \hline 7 \end{array}$$

Original numbers	$0.\overline{7}$	$\dfrac{7}{9}$
Decimals	$0.\overline{7}$	$0.\overline{7}$
Compare	$0.\overline{7} = 0.\overline{7}$	

Thus,　$0.\overline{7} = \dfrac{7}{9}$

■ **Work Practice Problem 9**

PRACTICE PROBLEM 10

Write the numbers in order from smallest to largest.

a. $\dfrac{1}{3}, 0.302, \dfrac{3}{8}$　**b.** $1.26, 1\dfrac{1}{4}, 1\dfrac{2}{5}$

c. $0.4, 0.41, \dfrac{5}{7}$

EXAMPLE 10 Write the numbers in order from smallest to largest.

$$\dfrac{9}{20}, \dfrac{4}{9}, 0.456$$

Solution:

Original numbers	$\dfrac{9}{20}$	$\dfrac{4}{9}$	0.456
Decimals	0.450	0.444...	0.456
Compare in order	2nd	1st	3rd

Written in order, we have

1st 2nd 3rd
↓ ↓ ↓
$$\dfrac{4}{9}, \dfrac{9}{20}, 0.456$$

■ **Work Practice Problem 10**

Objective C Simplifying Expressions with Decimals and Fractions

In the remaining examples, we will review the order of operations by simplifying expressions that contain decimals.

Order of Operations

1. Perform all operations within parentheses ( ), brackets [ ], or other grouping symbols such as square roots or fraction bars.
2. Evaluate any expressions with exponents.
3. Multiply or divide in order from left to right.
4. Add or subtract in order from left to right.

Answers

9. a. $<$,　**b.** $=$,　**c.** $<$,

10. a. $0.302, \dfrac{1}{3}, \dfrac{3}{8}$,　**b.** $1\dfrac{1}{4}, 1.26, 1\dfrac{2}{5}$,

c. $0.4, 0.41, \dfrac{5}{7}$

EXAMPLE 11 Simplify: $723.6 \div 1000 \times 10$

Solution: Multiply or divide in order from left to right.

$723.6 \div 1000 \times 10 = 0.7236 \times 10$ Divide.

$= 7.236$ Multiply.

■ Work Practice Problem 11

PRACTICE PROBLEM 11

Simplify: $897.8 \div 100 \times 10$

EXAMPLE 12 Simplify: $-0.5(8.6 - 1.2)$

Solution: According to the order of operations, we simplify inside the parentheses first.

$-0.5(8.6 - 1.2) = -0.5(7.4)$ Subtract.

$= -3.7$ Multiply.

■ Work Practice Problem 12

PRACTICE PROBLEM 12

Simplify: $-8.69(3.2 - 1.8)$

EXAMPLE 13 Simplify: $(-1.3)^2 + 2.4$

Solution: Recall the meaning of an exponent.

$(-1.3)^2 = (-1.3)(-1.3) + 2.4$ Use the definition of an exponent.

$= 1.69 + 2.4$ Multiply. The product of two negative numbers is a positive number

$= 4.09$ Add.

■ Work Practice Problem 13

PRACTICE PROBLEM 13

Simplify: $(-0.7)^2 + 2.1$

EXAMPLE 14 Simplify: $\dfrac{5.68 + (0.9)^2 \div 100}{0.2}$

Solution: First we simplify the numerator of the fraction. Then we divide.

$$\frac{5.68 + (0.9)^2 \div 100}{0.2} = \frac{5.68 + 0.81 \div 100}{0.2} \quad \text{Simplify } (0.9)^2.$$

$$= \frac{5.68 + 0.0081}{0.2} \quad \text{Divide.}$$

$$= \frac{5.6881}{0.2} \quad \text{Add.}$$

$$= 28.4405 \quad \text{Divide.}$$

■ Work Practice Problem 14

PRACTICE PROBLEM 14

Simplify: $\dfrac{20.06 - (1.2)^2 \div 10}{0.02}$

Sometimes real-life problems contain both fractions and decimals. In this section, we solve such problems concerning area. In the next example, we review the area of a triangle.

Answers

11. 89.78,   **12.** −12.166,   **13.** 2.59,

14. 995.8

PRACTICE PROBLEM 15

Find the area of the triangle.

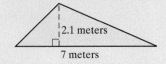

2.1 meters

7 meters

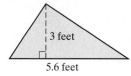 **EXAMPLE 15** The area of a triangle is Area $= \frac{1}{2} \cdot$ base $\cdot$ height. Find the area of the triangle shown.

3 feet

5.6 feet

Solution:

$$\text{Area} = \frac{1}{2} \cdot \text{base} \cdot \text{height}$$

$$= \frac{1}{2} \cdot 5.6 \cdot 3$$

$$= 0.5 \cdot 5.6 \cdot 3 \qquad \text{Write } \frac{1}{2} \text{ as the decimal } 0.5.$$

$$= 8.4$$

The area of the triangle is 8.4 square feet.

Work Practice Problem 15

Objective D Using Decimals as Replacement Values

EXAMPLE 16 Evaluate $-2x + 5$ for $x = 3.8$.

Solution: Replace x with 3.8 in the expression $-2x + 5$ and simplify.

$$-2x + 5 = -2(3.8) + 5 \qquad \text{Replace } x \text{ with 3.8.}$$

$$= -7.6 + 5 \qquad \text{Multiply.}$$

$$= -2.6 \qquad \text{Add.}$$

Work Practice Problem 16

PRACTICE PROBLEM 16

Evaluate $1.7y - 2$ for $y = 2.3$.

Answers

15. 7.35 sq m,   **16.** 1.91

Objective A *Write each number as a decimal. See Examples 1 through 7.*

1. $\dfrac{1}{5}$

2. $\dfrac{1}{20}$

3. $\dfrac{17}{25}$

4. $\dfrac{13}{25}$

5. $\dfrac{3}{4}$

6. $\dfrac{3}{8}$

7. $-\dfrac{2}{25}$

8. $-\dfrac{3}{25}$

9. $\dfrac{6}{5}$

10. $\dfrac{5}{4}$

11. $\dfrac{11}{12}$

12. $\dfrac{5}{12}$

13. $\dfrac{17}{40}$

14. $\dfrac{19}{25}$

15. $\dfrac{9}{20}$

16. $\dfrac{31}{40}$

17. $-\dfrac{1}{3}$

18. $-\dfrac{7}{9}$

19. $\dfrac{7}{16}$

20. $\dfrac{9}{16}$

21. $\dfrac{7}{11}$

22. $\dfrac{9}{11}$

23. $5\dfrac{17}{20}$

24. $4\dfrac{7}{8}$

25. $\dfrac{78}{125}$

26. $\dfrac{159}{375}$

Round each number as indicated. See Example 4.

27. Round your decimal answer to Exercise 17 to the nearest hundredth.

28. Round your decimal answer to Exercise 18 to the nearest hundredth.

29. Round your decimal answer to Exercise 19 to the nearest hundredth.

30. Round your decimal answer to Exercise 20 to the nearest hundredth.

31. Round your decimal answer to Exercise 21 to the nearest tenth.

32. Round your decimal answer to Exercise 22 to the nearest tenth.

Write each fraction as a decimal. If necessary, round to the nearest hundredth. See Examples 1 through 7.

33. During a recent Boston Marathon, $\dfrac{17}{25}$ of the starting runners over the age of 70 finished the race. (*Source:* Boston Athletic Association)

34. About $\dfrac{21}{50}$ of all blood donors have type A blood. (*Source:* American Red Cross Biomedical Services)

35. Of the U.S. mountains that are over 14,000 feet in elevation, $\frac{56}{91}$ are located in Colorado. (*Source:* U.S. Geological Survey)

36. By October 2000, $\frac{29}{46}$ of all individuals who had flown in space were citizens of the United States. (*Source:* Congressional Research Service)

37. The United States contains the greatest fraction of people who use the internet, with about $\frac{67}{94}$ people using it. (*Source:* UCLA Center for Communication Policy)

38. Hungary has the lowest fraction of people using the Internet, with only $\frac{7}{40}$ people using it. (*Source:* UCLA Center for Communication Policy)

Objective B *Insert* $<$, $>$, *or* $=$ *to form a true statement. See Examples 8 and 9.*

39. 0.562 0.569

40. 0.983 0.988

41. 0.215 $\frac{43}{200}$

42. $\frac{29}{40}$ 0.725

43. -0.0932 -0.0923

44. -0.00563 -0.00536

45. $0.\overline{6}$ $\frac{5}{6}$

46. $0.\overline{1}$ $\frac{2}{17}$

47. $\frac{51}{91}$ $0.56\overline{4}$

48. $0.58\overline{3}$ $\frac{6}{11}$

49. $\frac{4}{7}$ 0.14

50. $\frac{5}{9}$ 0.557

51. 1.38 $\frac{18}{13}$

52. 0.372 $\frac{22}{59}$

53. 7.123 $\frac{456}{64}$

54. 12.713 $\frac{89}{7}$

Write the numbers in order from smallest to largest. See Example 10.

55. 0.34, 0.35, 0.32

56. 0.47, 0.42, 0.40

57. 0.49, 0.491, 0.498

58. 0.72, 0.727, 0.728

59. $5.23, \frac{42}{8}, 5.34$

60. $7.56, \frac{67}{9}, 7.562$

61. $\frac{12}{5}, 2.37, \frac{17}{8}$

62. $\frac{29}{16}, 1.75, \frac{59}{32}$

Objective C *Simplify each expression. See Examples 11 through 15.*

63. $(0.4)^2 - 0.1$

64. $(-100)(2.3) - 30$

65. $\frac{1 + 0.8}{-0.6}$

66. $(-0.09)^2 + 1.16$

67. $(-2.3)^2(0.3 + 0.7)$

68. $(8.2)(100) - (8.2)(10)$

69. $(3.1 + 0.7)(2.9 - 0.9)$

70. $\frac{0.707 - 3.19}{13}$

71. $\dfrac{(4.5)^2}{100}$ **72.** $0.9(5.6 - 6.5)$ **73.** $\dfrac{7 + 0.74}{-6}$ **74.** $(1.5)^2 + 0.5$

Find the value of each expression. Give the result as a decimal. See Examples 11 through 15.

75. $\dfrac{1}{5} - 2(7.8)$ **76.** $\dfrac{3}{4} - (9.6)(5)$ **77.** $\dfrac{1}{4}(-9.6 - 5.2)$ **78.** $\dfrac{3}{8}(4.7 - 5.9)$

Find the area of each triangle or rectangle. See Example 15.

△ **79.**

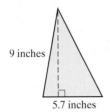

9 inches

5.7 inches

△ **80.**

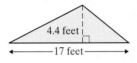

4.4 feet

17 feet

△ **81.**

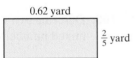

0.62 yard

$\frac{2}{5}$ yard

△ **82.**

1.2 miles

$\frac{7}{8}$ mile

Objective D *Evaluate each expression for* $x = 6$, $y = 0.3$, *and* $z = -2.4$. *See Example 16.*

83. z^2 **84.** y^2 **85.** $x - y$

86. $x - z$ **87.** $4y - z$ **88.** $\dfrac{x}{y} + 2z$

Review

Simplify. See Sections 1.9 and 3.6.

89. $6^2 \cdot 2$ **90.** $4 \cdot 3^4$ **91.** $\left(\dfrac{2}{5}\right)\left(\dfrac{5}{2}\right)^2$ **92.** $\left(\dfrac{2}{3}\right)^2\left(\dfrac{3}{2}\right)^3$

Concept Extensions

Without calculating, describe each number as < 1, $= 1$, *or* > 1. *See the Concept Check in this section.*

93. 1.0 **94.** 1.0000 **95.** 1.00001 **96.** $\dfrac{101}{99}$ **97.** $\dfrac{99}{100}$ **98.** $\dfrac{99}{99}$

In 2004, there were 10,649 commercial radio stations in the United States. The most popular formats are listed in the table along with their counts. Use this graph to answer Exercises 99 through 102.

99. Write the fraction of radio stations with a country music format as a decimal. Round to the nearest thousandth.

100. Write the fraction of radio stations with a news/talk format as a decimal. Round to the nearest hundredth.

101. Estimate, by rounding each number in the table to the nearest hundred, the total number of stations with the top six formats in 2004.

102. Use your estimate from Exercise 101 to write the fraction of radio stations accounted for by the top six formats as a decimal. Round to the nearest hundredth.

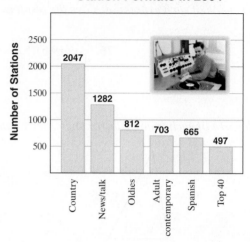

Top Commercial Radio Station Formats in 2004

Format (Total stations: 10,649)

103. Describe 2 ways to determine the larger of two fractions.

104. Describe two ways to write fractions as decimals.

105. Describe two ways to write mixed numbers as decimals.

△ 4.6 SQUARE ROOTS AND THE PYTHAGOREAN THEOREM

Objectives

A Find the Square Root of a Number.

B Approximate Square Roots.

C Use the Pythagorean Theorem.

Objective **A** Finding Square Roots

The square of a number is the number times itself. For example,

The square of 5 is 25 because 5^2 or $5 \cdot 5 = 25$.
The square of -5 is also 25 because $(-5)^2$ or $(-5)(-5) = 25$.

Recall from Chapter 1 that the reverse process of squaring is finding a **square root.** For example,

A square root of 25 is 5 because $\quad^2 = 25$.
A square root of 25 is also $\quad$ because $(-5)^2 = 25$.

Every positive number has two square roots. We see above that the square roots of 25 are 5 and -5.

We use the symbol $\sqrt{\ }$, called a **radical sign,** to indicate the positive square root of a nonnegative number. For example,

$\sqrt{25} = 5$ because $5^2 = 25$ and 5 is positive.
$\sqrt{9} = 3$ because $3^2 = 9$ and 3 is positive.

Square Root of a Number

The square root, $\sqrt{\ }$, of a positive number a is the positive number b whose square is a. In symbols,

$$\sqrt{a} = b, \quad \text{if } b^2 = a$$

Also, $\sqrt{0} = 0$.

> **Helpful Hint**
>
> Remember that the radical sign $\sqrt{\ }$ is used to indicate the **positive square root** of a nonnegative number.

EXAMPLE 1 Find each square root.

a. $\sqrt{49}$ **b.** $\sqrt{1}$ **c.** $\sqrt{81}$

Solution:

a. $\sqrt{49} = 7$ because $7^2 = 49$
b. $\sqrt{1} = 1$ because $1^2 = 1$
c. $\sqrt{81} = 9$ because $9^2 = 81$

▣ **Work Practice Problem 1**

EXAMPLE 2 Find: $\sqrt{\dfrac{1}{36}}$

Solution: $\sqrt{\dfrac{1}{36}} = \dfrac{1}{6}$ because $\dfrac{1}{6} \cdot \dfrac{1}{6} = \dfrac{1}{36}$

▣ **Work Practice Problem 2**

PRACTICE PROBLEM 1

Find each square root.

a. $\sqrt{100}$ **b.** $\sqrt{64}$
c. $\sqrt{121}$ **d.** $\sqrt{0}$

PRACTICE PROBLEM 2

Find: $\sqrt{\dfrac{1}{4}}$

Answers
1. a. 10, **b.** 8, **c.** 11, **d.** 0, **2.** $\dfrac{1}{2}$

341

PRACTICE PROBLEM 3

Find: $\sqrt{\dfrac{9}{16}}$

EXAMPLE 3 Find: $\sqrt{\dfrac{4}{25}}$

Solution: $\sqrt{\dfrac{4}{25}} = \dfrac{2}{5}$ because $\dfrac{2}{5} \cdot \dfrac{2}{5} = \dfrac{4}{25}$

◻ **Work Practice Problem 3**

Objective B Approximating Square Roots

Thus far, we have found square roots of perfect squares. Numbers like $\dfrac{1}{4}$, 36, $\dfrac{4}{25}$, and 1 are called **perfect squares** because their square root is a whole number or a fraction. A square root such as $\sqrt{5}$ cannot be written as a whole number or a fraction since 5 is not a perfect square.

Although $\sqrt{5}$ cannot be written as a whole number or a fraction, it can be approximated by estimating, by using a table (as in Appendix A.6), or by using a calculator.

PRACTICE PROBLEM 4

Use Appendix A.6 or a calculator to approximate the square root of 11 to the nearest thousandth.

EXAMPLE 4 Use an appendix or a calculator to approximate the square root of 43 to the nearest thousandth.

Solution: $\sqrt{43} \approx 6.557$

◻ **Work Practice Problem 4**

Helpful Hint

$\sqrt{43}$ is *approximately* 6.557. This means that if we multiply 6.557 by 6.557, the product is *close* to 43.

$6.557 \times 6.557 = 42.994249$

PRACTICE PROBLEM 5

Approximate $\sqrt{29}$ to the nearest thousandth.

EXAMPLE 5 Approximate $\sqrt{32}$ to the nearest thousandth.

Solution: $\sqrt{32} \approx 5.657$

◻ **Work Practice Problem 5**

Objective C Using the Pythagorean Theorem

One important application of square roots has to do with right triangles. Recall that a **right triangle** is a triangle in which one of the angles is a right angle, or measures 90°. The **hypotenuse** of a right triangle is the side opposite the right angle. The **legs** of a right triangle are the other two sides. These are shown in the following figure. The right angle in the triangle is indicated by the small square drawn in that angle.

The following theorem is true for all right triangles:

Pythagorean Theorem

In any **right triangle,**

$$(\text{leg})^2 + (\text{other leg})^2 = (\text{hypotenuse})^2$$

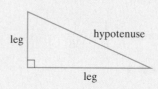

Answers

3. $\dfrac{3}{4}$, **4.** 3.317, **5.** 5.385

Using the Pythagorean theorem, we can use one of the following formulas to find an unknown length of a right triangle:

Finding an Unknown Length of a Right Triangle

$$\text{hypotenuse} = \sqrt{(\text{leg})^2 + (\text{other leg})^2}$$

or

$$\text{leg} = \sqrt{(\text{hypotenuse})^2 - (\text{other leg})^2}$$

EXAMPLE 6 Find the length of the hypotenuse of the given right triangle.

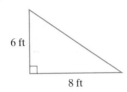

Solution: Since we are finding the hypotenuse, we use the formula

$$\text{hypotenuse} = \sqrt{(\text{leg})^2 + (\text{other leg})^2}$$

Putting the known values into the formula, we have

$$\text{hypotenuse} = \sqrt{(6)^2 + (8)^2} \quad \text{The legs are 6 feet and 8 feet.}$$
$$= \sqrt{36 + 64}$$
$$= \sqrt{100}$$
$$= 10$$

The hypotenuse is 10 feet long.

▥ Work Practice Problem 6

PRACTICE PROBLEM 6

Find the length of the hypotenuse of the given right triangle.

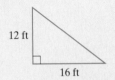

EXAMPLE 7 Approximate the length of the hypotenuse of the given right triangle. Round the length to the nearest whole unit.

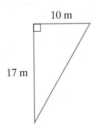

Solution:

$$\text{hypotenuse} = \sqrt{(\text{leg})^2 + (\text{other leg})^2}$$
$$= \sqrt{(17)^2 + (10)^2} \quad \text{The legs are 10 meters and 17 meters.}$$
$$= \sqrt{289 + 100}$$
$$= \sqrt{389}$$
$$\approx 20 \quad \text{From Appendix A.6 or a calculator}$$

The hypotenuse is exactly $\sqrt{389}$ meters, which is approximately 20 meters.

▥ Work Practice Problem 7

PRACTICE PROBLEM 7

Approximate the length of the hypotenuse of the given right triangle. Round to the nearest whole unit.

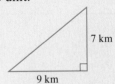

Answers
6. 20 ft, **7.** 11 km

PRACTICE PROBLEM 8

Find the length of the leg in the given right triangle. Give the exact length and a two-decimal-place approximation.

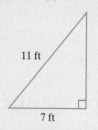

EXAMPLE 8 Find the length of the leg in the given right triangle. Give the exact length and a two-decimal-place approximation.

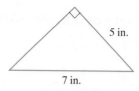

Solution: Notice that the hypotenuse measures 7 inches and the length of one leg measures 5 inches. Since we are looking for the length of the other leg, we use the formula

$$\text{leg} = \sqrt{(\text{hypotenuse})^2 - (\text{other leg})^2}$$

Putting the known values into the formula, we have

$$\text{leg} = \sqrt{(7)^2 - (5)^2} \quad \text{The hypotenuse is 7 inches, and the other leg is 5 inches.}$$
$$= \sqrt{49 - 25}$$
$$= \sqrt{24} \quad \text{Exact answer}$$
$$\approx 4.90 \quad \text{From Appendix A.6 or a calculator}$$

The length of the leg is exactly $\sqrt{24}$ inches, which is approximately 4.90 inches.

⬛ **Work Practice Problem 8**

✔ **Concept Check** The following lists are the lengths of the sides of two triangles. Which set forms a right triangle? Explain.

a. 8, 15, 17   **b.** 24, 30, 40

PRACTICE PROBLEM 9

A football field is a rectangle measuring 100 yards by 53 yards. Draw a diagram and find the length of the diagonal of a football field to the nearest yard.

EXAMPLE 9 **Finding the Diagonal Length of a City Block**

A standard city block is a square that measures 300 feet on a side. Find the length of the diagonal of a city block rounded to the nearest whole foot.

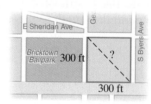

Solution: The diagonal is the hypotenuse of a right triangle, so we use the formula

$$\text{hypotenuse} = \sqrt{(\text{leg})^2 + (\text{other leg})^2}$$

Putting the known values into the formula we have

$$\text{hypotenuse} = \sqrt{(300)^2 + (300)^2} \quad \text{The legs are both 300 feet.}$$
$$= \sqrt{90,000 + 90,000}$$
$$= \sqrt{180,000}$$
$$\approx 424 \quad \text{From Appendix A.6 or a calculator}$$

The length of the diagonal is approximately 424 feet.

⬛ **Work Practice Problem 9**

Answers

8. $\sqrt{72}$ ft ≈ 8.49 ft, **9.** 113 yd

✔ **Concept Check Answers**

set (a) forms a right triangle

Finding Square Roots

To simplify or approximate square roots using a calculator, locate the key marked $\boxed{\sqrt{}}$.

To simplify $\sqrt{64}$, for example, press the keys

$$\boxed{64} \quad \boxed{\sqrt{}} \quad \text{or} \quad \boxed{\sqrt{}} \quad \boxed{64}$$

The display should read $\boxed{\quad 8 \quad}$. Then

$$\sqrt{64} = 8$$

To *approximate* $\sqrt{10}$, press the keys

$$\boxed{10} \quad \boxed{\sqrt{}} \quad \text{or} \quad \boxed{\sqrt{}} \quad \boxed{10}$$

The display should read $\boxed{3.16227766}$. This is an *approximation* for $\sqrt{10}$. A three-decimal-place approximation is

$$\sqrt{10} \approx 3.162$$

Is this answer reasonable? Since 10 is between perfect squares 9 and 16, $\sqrt{10}$ is between $\sqrt{9} = 3$ and $\sqrt{16} = 4$. Our answer is reasonable since 3.162 is between 3 and 4.

Simplify.

1. $\sqrt{1024}$ **2.** $\sqrt{676}$

Approximate each square root. Round each answer to the nearest thousandth.

3. $\sqrt{15}$ **4.** $\sqrt{19}$
5. $\sqrt{97}$ **6.** $\sqrt{56}$

4.6 EXERCISE SET

Objective A *Find each square root. See Examples 1 through 3.*

1. $\sqrt{4}$ **2.** $\sqrt{9}$ **3.** $\sqrt{64}$ **4.** $\sqrt{144}$

5. $\sqrt{\dfrac{1}{81}}$ **6.** $\sqrt{\dfrac{1}{64}}$ **7.** $\sqrt{\dfrac{16}{64}}$ **8.** $\sqrt{\dfrac{36}{81}}$

Objective B *Use Appendix A.6 or a calculator to approximate each square root. Round the square root to the nearest thousandth. See Examples 4 and 5.*

9. $\sqrt{3}$ **10.** $\sqrt{5}$ **11.** $\sqrt{15}$ **12.** $\sqrt{17}$

13. $\sqrt{47}$ **14.** $\sqrt{85}$ **15.** $\sqrt{26}$ **16.** $\sqrt{35}$

Objectives A B Mixed Practice *Find each square root. If necessary, round the square root to the nearest thousandth.*

17. $\sqrt{256}$ **18.** $\sqrt{625}$ **19.** $\sqrt{14}$ **20.** $\sqrt{18}$

21. $\sqrt{\dfrac{49}{144}}$ **22.** $\sqrt{\dfrac{121}{169}}$ **23.** $\sqrt{71}$ **24.** $\sqrt{62}$

Objective **C** *Find the unknown length in each right triangle. If necessary, approximate the length to the nearest thousandth. See Examples 6 through 8.*

25.
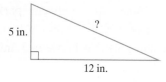
5 in.

?

12 in.

26.
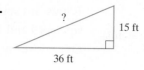
?

15 ft

36 ft

27.
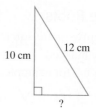
12 cm

10 cm

?

28.
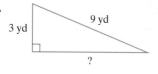
3 yd

9 yd

?

29.
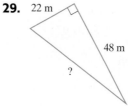
22 m

48 m

?

30.
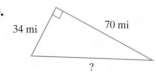
34 mi

70 mi

?

31.
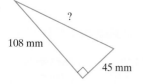
?

108 mm

45 mm

32.
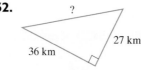
?

27 km

36 km

Sketch each right triangle and find the length of the side not given. If necessary, approximate the length to the nearest thousandth. (Each length is in units.) See Examples 6 through 8.

33. leg = 3, leg = 4

34. leg = 9, leg = 12

35. leg = 5, hypotenuse = 13

36. leg = 6, hypotenuse = 10

37. leg = 10, leg = 14

38. leg = 2, leg = 16

39. leg = 35, leg = 28

40. leg = 30, leg = 15

41. leg = 30, leg = 30

42. leg = 21, leg = 21

43. hypotenuse = 2, leg = 1

44. hypotenuse = 7, leg = 6

45. leg = 7.5, leg = 4

46. leg = 12, leg = 22.5

Solve. See Example 9.

47. A standard city block is a square with each side measuring 100 yards. Find the length of the diagonal of a city block to the nearest hundredth yard.

48. A section of land is a square with each side measuring 1 mile. Find the length of the diagonal of the section of land to the nearest thousandth mile.

49. Find the height of the tree. Round the height to one decimal place.

50. Find the height of the antenna. Round the height to one decimal place.

51. The playing field for football is a rectangle that is 300 feet long by 160 feet wide. Find, to the nearest foot, the length of a straight-line run that started at one corner and went diagonally to end at the opposite corner.

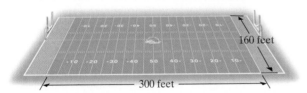

52. A soccer field is in the shape of a rectangle and its dimensions depend on the age of the players. The dimensions of the soccer field below are the minimum dimensions for international play. Find the length of the diagonal of this rectangle. Round answer to the nearest tenth of a yard.

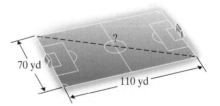

Review

Write each fraction in simplest form. See Section 3.2.

53. $\dfrac{10}{12}$

54. $\dfrac{10}{15}$

55. $\dfrac{24}{60}$

56. $\dfrac{35}{75}$

57. $\dfrac{30}{72}$

58. $\dfrac{18}{30}$

Concept Extensions

Determine what two whole numbers each square root is between without using a calculator or table. Then use a calculator or table to check.

59. $\sqrt{38}$ **60.** $\sqrt{27}$ **61.** $\sqrt{101}$ **62.** $\sqrt{85}$

 63. Without using a calculator, explain how you know that $\sqrt{105}$ is *not* approximately 9.875.

Does the set form the lengths of the sides of a right triangle? See the Concept Check in this section.

64. 25, 60, 65   **65.** 20, 45, 50

STUDY SKILLS BUILDER

Learning New Terms?

By now, you have encountered many new terms. It's never too late to make a list of new terms and review them frequently. Remember that placing these new terms (including page references) on 3 × 5 index cards might help you later when you're preparing for a quiz.

Answer the following.

1. How do new terms stand out in this text so that they can be found?

2. Name one way placing a word and its definition on a 3 × 5 card might be helpful.

CHAPTER 4   Group Activity

Maintaining a Checking Account
(Sections 4.1, 4.2, 4.3, 4.4)

This activity may be completed by working in groups or individually.

A checking account is a convenient way of handling money and paying bills. To open a checking account, the bank or savings and loan association requires a customer to make a deposit. Then the customer receives a checkbook that contains checks, deposit slips, and a register for recording checks written and deposits made. It is important to record all payments and deposits that affect the account. It is also important to keep the checkbook balance current by subtracting checks written and adding deposits made.

About once a month checking customers receive a statement from the bank listing all activity that the account has had in the last month. The statement lists a beginning balance, all checks and deposits, any service charges made against the account, and an ending balance. Because it may take several days for checks that a customer has written to clear the banking system, the check register may list checks that do not appear on the monthly bank statement. These checks are called **outstanding checks.** Deposits that are recorded in the check register but do not appear on the statement are called **deposits in transit.** Because of these differences, it is important to balance, or reconcile, the checkbook against the monthly statement. The steps for doing so are listed below.

Balancing or Reconciling a Checkbook

Step 1: Place a check mark in the checkbook register next to each check and deposit listed on the monthly bank statement. Any entries in the register without a check mark are outstanding checks or deposits in transit.

Step 2: Find the ending checkbook register balance and add to it any outstanding checks and any interest paid on the account.

Step 3: From the total in Step 2, subtract any deposits in transit and any service charges.

Step 4: Compare the amount found in Step 3 with the ending balance listed on the bank statement. If they are the same, the checkbook balances with the bank statement. Be sure to update the check register with service charges and interest.

Step 5: If the checkbook does not balance, recheck the balancing process. Next, make sure that the running checkbook register balance was calculated correctly. Finally, compare the checkbook register with the statement to make sure that each check was recorded for the correct amount.

For the checkbook register and monthly bank statement given:

a. *update the checkbook register*   **b.** *list the outstanding checks and deposits in transit*
c. *balance the checkbook—be sure to update the register with any interest or service fees*

Checkbook Register						Balance
#	**Date**	**Description**	**Payment**	**✔**	**Deposit**	**425.86**
114	4/1	Market Basket	30.27			
115	4/3	May's Texaco	8.50			
	4/4	Cash at ATM	50.00			
116	4/6	UNO Bookstore	121.38			
	4/7	Deposit			100.00	
117	4/9	MasterCard	84.16			
118	4/10	Blockbuster	6.12			
119	4/12	Kroger	18.72			
120	4/14	Parking sticker	18.50			
	4/15	Direct deposit			294.36	
121	4/20	Rent	395.00			
122	4/25	Student fees	20.00			
	4/28	Deposit			75.00	

First National Bank Monthly Statement 4/30		
BEGINNING BALANCE:		425.86
Date	Number	Amount
CHECKS AND ATM WITHDRAWALS		
4/3	114	30.27
4/4	ATM	50.00
4/11	117	84.16
4/13	115	8.50
4/15	119	18.72
4/22	121	395.00
DEPOSITS		
4/7		100.00
4/15	Direct deposit	294.36
SERVICE CHARGES		
Low balance fee		7.50
INTEREST		
Credited 4/30		1.15
ENDING BALANCE:		227.22

Chapter 4 Vocabulary Check

Fill in each blank with one of the words listed below.

vertically	decimal	and	right triangle	hypotenuse
sum	denominator	numerator	square root	legs

1. Like fractional notation, _____ notation is used to denote a part of a whole.

2. To write fractions as decimals, divide the _____ by the _____.

3. To add or subtract decimals, write the decimals so that the decimal points line up _____.

4. When writing decimals in words, write "_____" for the decimal point.

5. When multiplying decimals, the decimal point in the product is placed so that the number of decimal places in the product is equal to the _____ of the number of decimal places in the factors.

6. The _____, $\sqrt{}$, of a positive number a is the positive number b whose square is a.

7. A _____ is a triangle with a right angle. The side opposite the right angle is called the _____, and the other two sides are called _____.

> **Helpful Hint**
>
> Are you preparing for your test? Don't forget to take the Chapter 4 Test on page 358. Then check your answers at the back of the text and use the Chapter Test Prep Video CD to see the fully worked-out solutions to any of the exercises you want to review.

4 Chapter Highlights

DEFINITIONS AND CONCEPTS	**EXAMPLES**
Section 4.1 Introduction to Decimals	

PLACE-VALUE CHART

hundreds	tens	ones	decimal point	tenths	hundredths	thousandths	ten-thousandths	hundred-thousandths
		4	$\uparrow$	2	6	5		
100	10	1		$\dfrac{1}{10}$	$\dfrac{1}{100}$	$\dfrac{1}{1000}$	$\dfrac{1}{10,000}$	$\dfrac{1}{100,000}$

4.265 means

$$4 \cdot 1 + 2 \cdot \frac{1}{10} + 6 \cdot \frac{1}{100} + 5 \cdot \frac{1}{1000}$$

or

$$4 + \frac{2}{10} + \frac{6}{100} + \frac{5}{1000}$$

WRITING (OR READING) A DECIMAL IN WORDS

Step 1. Write the whole number part in words.

Step 2. Write "and" for the decimal point.

Step 3. Write the decimal part in words as though it were a whole number, followed by the place value of the last digit.

A decimal written in words can be written in standard form by reversing the above procedure.

Write 3.08 in words.
Three and eight hundredths

Write "negative four and twenty-one thousandths" in standard form.

$$-4.021$$

DEFINITIONS AND CONCEPTS	**EXAMPLES**

Section 4.1   Introduction to Decimals (*continued*)

TO ROUND DECIMALS TO A PLACE VALUE TO THE RIGHT OF THE DECIMAL POINT

Step 1. Locate the digit to the right of the given place value.

Step 2. If this digit is 5 or greater, add 1 to the digit in the given place value and delete all digits to its right. If this digit is less than 5, delete all digits to the right of the given place value.

Round 86.1256 to the nearest hundredth.

$$\text{hundredths place}$$

Step 1. 86.12⑤6

$$\text{digit to the right}$$

Step 2. Since the digit to the right is 5 or greater, we add 1 to the digit in the hundredths place and delete all digits to its right.

86.1256 rounded to the nearest hundredth is 86.13.

Section 4.2   Adding and Subtracting Decimals

TO ADD OR SUBTRACT DECIMALS

Step 1. Write the decimals so that the decimal points line up vertically.

Step 2. Add or subtract as with whole numbers.

Step 3. Place the decimal point in the sum or difference so that it lines up vertically with the decimal points in the problem.

Add: $4.6 + 0.28$ Subtract: $2.8 - 1.04$

$$\begin{array}{r} 4.60 \\ + 0.28 \\ \hline 4.88 \end{array} \qquad \begin{array}{r} {\scriptstyle 7\ 10} \\ 2.8\!\!\!/0 \\ -1.04 \\ \hline 1.76 \end{array}$$

Section 4.3   Multiplying Decimals and Circumference of a Circle

TO MULTIPLY DECIMALS

Step 1. Multiply the decimals as though they are whole numbers.

Step 2. The decimal point in the product is placed so that the number of decimal places in the product is equal to the *sum* of the number of decimal places in the factors.

The **circumference** of a circle is the distance around the circle.

$C = 2 \cdot \pi \cdot \text{radius}$ or
$C = \pi \cdot \text{diameter}$,

where $\pi \approx 3.14$ or $\dfrac{22}{7}$.

Multiply: 1.48×5.9

$$\begin{array}{r} 1.4\,8 \quad \leftarrow \text{2 decimal places} \\ \times\ 5.9 \quad \leftarrow \text{1 decimal place} \\ \hline 1\,3\,3\,2 \\ 7\,4\,0\,0 \\ \hline 8.7\,3\,2 \quad \leftarrow \text{3 decimal places} \end{array}$$

Find the exact circumference of a circle with radius 5 miles and an approximation by using 3.14 for π.

$$\begin{aligned} C &= 2 \cdot \pi \cdot \text{radius} \\ &= 2 \cdot \pi \cdot 5 \\ &= 10\pi \\ &\approx 10(3.14) \\ &= 31.4 \end{aligned}$$

The circumference is exactly 10π miles and *approximately* 31.4 miles.

DEFINITIONS AND CONCEPTS	EXAMPLES

Section 4.4   Dividing Decimals

To Divide Decimals

Step 1. If the divisor is not a whole number, move the decimal point in the divisor to the right until the divisor is a whole number.

Step 2. Move the decimal point in the dividend to the right the *same number of places* as the decimal point was moved in Step 1.

Step 3. Divide. The decimal point in the quotient is directly over the moved decimal point in the dividend.

Divide: $1.118 \div 2.6$

$$
\begin{array}{r}
0.43 \\
2.6\overline{)1.118} \\
-1\,04 \\
\hline
78 \\
-78 \\
\hline
0
\end{array}
$$

Section 4.5   Fractions, Decimals, and Order of Operations

To **write fractions as decimals,** divide the numerator by the denominator.

Write $\dfrac{3}{8}$ as a decimal.

$$
\begin{array}{r}
0.375 \\
8\overline{)3.000} \\
-2\,4 \\
\hline
60 \\
-56 \\
\hline
40 \\
-40 \\
\hline
0
\end{array}
$$

Order of Operations

1. Perform all operations within parentheses ( ), brackets [ ], or grouping symbols such as square roots or fraction bars.

2. Evaluate any expressions with exponents.

3. Multiply or divide in order from left to right.

4. Add or subtract in order from left to right.

Simplify.

$$
\begin{aligned}
-1.9(12.8 - 4.1) &= -1.9(8.7) \quad \text{Subtract.} \\
&= -16.53 \quad \text{Multiply.}
\end{aligned}
$$

Section 4.6   Square Roots and the Pythagorean Theorem

Square Root of a Number

A **square root** of a number a is a number b whose square is a. We use the radical sign $\sqrt{}$ to name square roots.

$$\sqrt{9} = 3, \ \sqrt{100} = 10, \ \sqrt{1} = 1$$

Pythagorean Theorem

$$(\text{leg})^2 + (\text{other leg})^2 = (\text{hypotenuse})^2$$

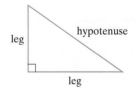

Find the hypotenuse of the given triangle.

$$
\begin{aligned}
\text{hypotenuse} &= \sqrt{(\text{leg})^2 + (\text{other leg})^2} \\
&= \sqrt{(3)^2 + (8)^2} \quad \text{The legs are 3 and 8 inches.} \\
&= \sqrt{9 + 64} \\
&= \sqrt{73} \text{ inches} \\
&\approx 8.5 \text{ inches}
\end{aligned}
$$

DEFINITIONS AND CONCEPTS	EXAMPLES
Section 4.6 Square Roots and the Pythagorean Theorem (*continued*)	

TO FIND AN UNKNOWN LENGTH OF A RIGHT TRIANGLE

$$\text{hypotenuse} = \sqrt{(\text{leg})^2 + (\text{other leg})^2}$$

$$\text{leg} = \sqrt{(\text{hypotenuse})^2 - (\text{other leg})^2}$$

 STUDY SKILLS BUILDER

Are You Prepared for a Test on Chapter 4?

Below I have listed some *common trouble areas* for students in Chapter 4. After studying for your test—but before taking your test—read these.

- Don't forget the order of operations. To simplify $-0.7 + 1.3(5 - 0.1)$, should you add, subtract, or multiply first? First, perform the subtraction within parentheses, then multiply, and finally add.

$$-0.7 + 1.3(5 - 0.1) = -0.7 + 1.3(4.9) \quad \text{Subtract.}$$
$$= -0.7 + 6.37 \quad \text{Multiply.}$$
$$= 5.67 \quad \text{Add.}$$

- If you are having trouble with ordering or operations on decimals, don't forget that you can insert 0s after

the last digit to the right of the decimal point as needed.

Addition	Addition with zeros inserted	Subtraction	Subtraction with zeros inserted
8.1	8.100	7	$\overset{9}{\overset{6\ \cancel{1}0\ 10}{\cancel{7.00}}}$
0.6	0.600	$-\,0.28$	$-\,0.28$
$+\,23.003$	$+\,23.003$		6.72
	31.703		

Place in order from smallest to largest: 0.108, 0.18, 0.0092
If we insert zeros, we have: 0.1080, 0.1800, 0.0092
The decimals in order are: 0.0092, 0.1080, 0.1800 or 0.0092, 0.108, 0.18

---

4 CHAPTER REVIEW

(4.1) *Determine the place value of the number 4 in each decimal.*

1. 23.45

2. 0.000345

Write each decimal in words.

3. −23.45

4. 0.00345

5. 109.23

6. 200.000032

Write each decimal in standard form.

7. Two and fifteen hundredths

8. Negative five hundred three and one hundred two thousandths

9. Sixteen thousand twenty-five and fourteen ten-thousandths

Write each decimal as a fraction or a mixed number.

10. 0.16   **11.** −12.023   **12.** 1.0045   **13.** 0.00231   **14.** 25.25

Insert <, >, *or* = *between each pair of numbers to make a true statement.*

15. 0.49   0.43

16. 0.973   0.9730

17. −402.00032   −402.000032

18. −0.230505   −0.23505

Round each decimal to the given place value.

19. 0.623, nearest tenth

20. 0.9384, nearest hundredth

21. −42.895, nearest hundredth

22. 16.34925, nearest thousandth

23. Every day in America an average of 13,490.5 people get married. Round this number to the nearest hundred.

24. A certain kind of chocolate candy bar contains 10.75 teaspoons of sugar. Convert this number to a mixed number.

(4.2) *Add.*

25. 2.4 + 7.1

26. 3.9 + 1.2

27. −6.4 + (−0.88)

28. −19.02 + 6.98

29. 200.49 + 16.82 + 103.002

30. 0.00236 + 100.45 + 48.29

Subtract.

31. 4.9 − 3.2

32. 5.23 − 2.74

33. −892.1 − 432.4

34. 0.064 − 10.2

35. 100 − 34.98

36. 200 − 0.00198

37. Find the total distance between Grove City and Jerome.

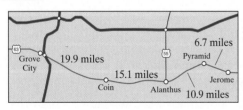

38. Evaluate $x - y$ for $x = 1.2$ and $y = 6.9$.

39. Find the perimeter.

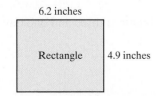

6.2 inches

Rectangle   4.9 inches

40. Find the perimeter.

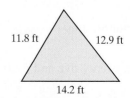

11.8 ft   12.9 ft

14.2 ft

(4.3) *Multiply.*

41. 7.2×10

42. 9.345×1000

43. -34.02×2.3

44. $-839.02 \times (-87.3)$

45. Find the exact circumference of the circle. Then use the approximation 3.14 for π and approximate the circumference.

7 meters

46. A kilometer is approximately 0.625 mile. It is 102 kilometers from Hays to Colby. Write 102 kilometers in miles to the nearest tenth of a mile.

Write each number in standard notation.

47. Saturn is a distance of about 887 million miles from the Sun.

48. The tail of a comet can be over 600 thousand miles long.

(4.4) *Divide. Round the quotient to the nearest thousandth if necessary.*

49. $3\overline{)0.2631}$

50. $20\overline{)316.5}$

51. $-21 \div (-0.3)$

52. $-0.0063 \div 0.03$

53. $0.34\overline{)2.74}$

54. $19.8\overline{)601.92}$

55. $\dfrac{2.67}{100}$

56. $\dfrac{93}{-10}$

57. There are approximately 3.28 feet in 1 meter. Find how many meters are in 24 feet to the nearest tenth of a meter.

$\longleftarrow$ 1 meter $\longrightarrow$

$\longleftarrow \approx$3.28 feet $\longrightarrow$

58. George Strait pays $69.71 per month to pay back a loan of $3136.95. In how many months will the loan be paid off?

(4.5) *Write each fraction as a decimal. Round to the nearest thousandth if necessary.*

59. $\dfrac{4}{5}$

60. $-\dfrac{12}{13}$

61. $2\dfrac{1}{3}$

62. $\dfrac{13}{60}$

Insert $<$, $>$, or $=$ to make a true statement.

63. $0.392 \quad 0.392$

64. $\dfrac{4}{7} \quad 0.625$

65. $0.293 \quad \dfrac{5}{17}$

66. $-0.0231 \quad -0.0221$

Write the numbers in order from smallest to largest.

67. $0.837, 0.839, \dfrac{17}{20}$

68. $\dfrac{3}{7}, 0.42, 0.43$

69. $\dfrac{18}{11}, 1.63, \dfrac{19}{12}$

Simplify each expression.

70. $-7.6 \times 1.9 + 2.5$

71. $(-2.3)^2 - 1.4$

72. $\dfrac{7 + 0.74}{-0.06}$

73. $0.9(6.5 - 5.6)$

74. $\dfrac{(1.5)^2 + 0.5}{0.05}$

75. $0.0726 \div 10 \times 1000$

Find each area.

△ **76.**

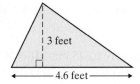

△ **77.**

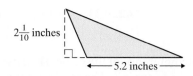

(4.6) *Simplify.*

78. $\sqrt{64}$

79. $\sqrt{144}$

80. $\sqrt{\dfrac{4}{25}}$

81. $\sqrt{\dfrac{1}{100}}$

Find the unknown length of each given right triangle. If necessary, round to the nearest tenth.

82. leg = 12, leg = 5

83. leg = 20, leg = 21

84. leg = 9, hypotenuse = 14

85. leg = 124, hypotenuse = 155

86. A baseball diamond is in the shape of a square and has sides of length 90 feet. Find the distance across the diamond from third base to first base, to the nearest tenth of a foot.

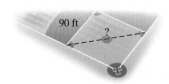

87. Find the height of the building rounded to the nearest tenth.

Mixed Review

88. Write 200.0032 in words.

89. Write negative sixteen thousand twenty-five and fourteen thousandths in standard form.

90. Write 0.00231 as a fraction or a mixed number.

91. Write the numbers $\dfrac{6}{7}, \dfrac{8}{9}, 0.75$ in order from smallest to largest.

Write each fraction as a decimal. Round to the nearest thousandth, if necessary.

92. $-\dfrac{7}{100}$

93. $\dfrac{9}{80}$ (Do not round.)

94. $\dfrac{8935}{175}$

Insert $<, >,$ *or* $=$ *to make a true statement.*

95. -402.000032 -402.00032

96. 0.230505 0.23505

97. $\dfrac{6}{11}$ 0.55

Round each decimal to the given place value.

98. 42.895, nearest hundredth

99. 16.34925, nearest thousandth

Round each money amount to the nearest dollar.

100. $123.46, nearest dollar

101. $3645.52, nearest dollar

Add or subtract as indicated.

102. 3.2 − 4.9

103. 5.23 − 2.74

104. 200.49 + 16.82 + 103.002

105. −0.00236 + (−100.45) + (−48.29)

Multiply or divide as indicated. Round to the nearest thousandth, if necessary.

106.
$$\begin{array}{r} 2.54 \\ \times\ 3.2 \\ \hline \end{array}$$

107. $(-3.45)(2.1)$

108. $0.005\overline{)24.5}$

109. $2.3\overline{)54.98}$

Solve.

△ **110.** Tomaso is going to fertilize his lawn, a rectangle that measures 77.3 feet by 115.9 feet. Approximate the area of the lawn by rounding each measurement to the nearest ten feet.

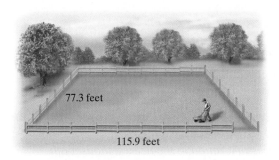

77.3 feet

115.9 feet

111. Estimate the cost of the items to see whether the groceries can be purchased with a $5 bill.

$1.89

$1.07

3 cans for $0.99

Simplify each expression.

112. $\dfrac{(3.2)^2}{100}$

113. $(2.6 + 1.4)(4.5 - 3.6)$

Simplify.

114. $\sqrt{1}$

115. $\sqrt{36}$

116. $\sqrt{\dfrac{16}{81}}$

Find the unknown length of each given right triangle. If necessary, round to the nearest tenth.

117. leg = 66, leg = 56

118. leg = 12, hypotenuse = 24

119. leg = 17, hypotenuse = 51

120. leg = 10, leg = 17

4 CHAPTER TEST

 Use the Chapter Test Prep Video CD to see the fully worked-out solutions to any of the exercises you want to review.

Answers

Write each decimal as indicated.

1. 45.092, in words

2. Three thousand and fifty-nine thousandths, in standard form

Perform each indicated operation. Round the result to the nearest thousandth if necessary.

3. 2.893 + 4.21 + 10.492

4. −47.92 − 3.28

5. 9.83 − 30.25

6. 10.2 × 4.01

7. (−0.00843) ÷ (−0.23)

Round each decimal to the indicated place value.

8. 34.8923, nearest tenth

9. 0.8623, nearest thousandth

Insert <, >, or = between each pair of numbers to form a true statement.

10. 25.0909   25.9090

11. $\frac{4}{9}$ 0.445

Write each decimal as a fraction or a mixed number.

12. 0.345

13. −24.73

Write each fraction as a decimal. If necessary, round to the nearest thousandth.

14. $-\frac{13}{26}$

15. $\frac{16}{17}$

Simplify.

16. $(-0.6)^2 + 1.57$

17. $\frac{0.23 + 1.63}{-0.3}$

18. Subtract 8.6 from 20

Find each square root and simplify. Round to the nearest thousandth if necessary.

19. $\sqrt{49}$

20. $\sqrt{157}$

21. $\sqrt{\frac{64}{100}}$

1. _____

2. _____

3. _____

4. _____

5. _____

6. _____

7. _____

8. _____

9. _____

10. _____

11. _____

12. _____

13. _____

14. _____

15. _____

16. _____

17. _____

18. _____

19. _____

20. _____

21. _____

Solve.

△ **22.** Approximate to the nearest hundredth of a centimeter the length of the missing side of a right triangle with legs of 4 centimeters each.

△ **23.** Find the area.

△ **24.** Find the exact circumference of the circle. Then use the approximation 3.14 for π and approximate the circumference.

9 miles

25. Vivian Thomas is going to put insecticide on her lawn to control grubworms. The lawn is a rectangle that measures 123.8 feet by 80 feet. The amount of insecticide required is 0.02 ounces per square foot.

   a. Find the area of her lawn.

   b. Find how much insecticide Vivian needs to purchase.

26. Find the total distance from Bayette to Center City.

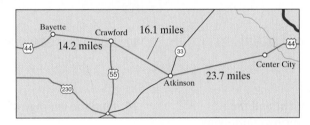

27. At its farthest, Pluto is 4,583 million miles from the Sun. Write this number using standard notation.

22. _____

23. _____

24. _____

25. a. _____

    b. _____

26. _____

27. _____

Write each number in words.

Answers

1. 85

2. 107

3. 126

4. 5026

5. Add: 23 + 136

6. Find the perimeter.

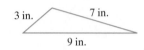

3 in.   7 in.

9 in.

7. Subtract: 543 − 29. Then check by adding.

8. Divide: 3268 ÷ 27

9. Round 278,362 to the nearest thousand.

10. Find all the factors of 30.

11. Multiply: 236 × 86

12. Multiply: 236 × 86 × 0

13. Find each quotient and then check the answer by multiplying.

    a. $1\overline{)8}$

    b. 11 ÷ 1

    c. $\dfrac{9}{9}$

    d. 7 ÷ 7

    e. $\dfrac{10}{1}$

    f. $6\overline{)6}$

14. Find the average of 25, 17, 19, and 39.

15. The Hudson River in New York State is 306 miles long. The Snake River, in the northwestern United States, is 732 miles longer than the Hudson River. How long is the Snake River? (*Source:* U.S. Department of the Interior)

16. Evaluate: $\sqrt{121}$

Answers

1. _____

2. _____

3. _____

4. _____

5. _____

6. _____

7. _____

8. _____

9. _____

10. _____

11. _____

12. _____

13. a. _____

    b. _____

    c. _____

    d. _____

    e. _____

    f. _____

14. _____

15. _____

16. _____

Evaluate.

17. 8^2 **18.** 5^3 **19.** 2^5 **20.** 10^3

21. Evaluate $\dfrac{x - 5y}{y}$ for $x = 21$ and $y = 3$.

22. Evaluate $\dfrac{2a + 4}{c}$ for $a = 7$ and $c = 3$.

23. Find the opposite of each number.
    a. 11   **b.** -2 **c.** 0

24. Find the opposite of each number.
    a. -7 **b.** 4   **c.** -1

25. Add: $-2 + (-21)$

26. Add: $-7 + (-15)$

Find the value of each expression.

27. $5 \cdot 6^2$ **28.** $4 \cdot 2^3$ **29.** -7^2

30. $(-2)^5$ **31.** $(-5)^2$ **32.** -3^2

Write the shaded part as an improper fraction and a mixed number.

33.

34.

35.

36.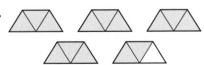

37. Find the prime factorization of 252.

38. Find the difference of 87 and 25.

39. Write $-\dfrac{72}{26}$ in simplest form.

---

17. _____

18. _____

19. _____

20. _____

21. _____

22. _____

23. a. _____

   b. _____

   c. _____

24. a. _____

   b. _____

   c. _____

25. _____

26. _____

27. _____

28. _____

29. _____

30. _____

31. _____

32. _____

33. _____

34. _____

35. _____

36. _____

37. _____

38. _____

39. _____

40. _____

41. _____

42. _____

43. _____

44. _____

45. _____

46. _____

47. _____

48. _____

49. _____

50. _____

40. Write $9\frac{7}{8}$ as an improper fraction.

41. Determine whether $\frac{16}{40}$ and $\frac{10}{25}$ are equivalent.

42. Insert $<$ or $>$ to form a true statement. $\frac{4}{7}$ $\frac{5}{9}$

Multiply.

43. $\frac{2}{3} \cdot \frac{5}{11}$

44. $2\frac{5}{8} \cdot \frac{4}{7}$

45. $\frac{1}{4} \cdot \frac{1}{2}$

46. $7 \cdot 5\frac{2}{7}$

47. Add: $763.7651 + 22.001 + 43.89$

48. Add: $89.27 + 14.361 + 127.2318$

49. Multiply: 23.6×0.78

50. Multiply: 43.8×0.645

5

Ratio, Proportion, and Measurement

Having studied fractions in Chapter 3, we are ready to explore the useful notations of ratio and proportion. Ratio is another name for quotient and is usually written in fraction form. A proportion is an equation with 2 equal ratios.

The Statue of Liberty, standing on Liberty Island in New York City's harbor, is a symbol of freedom and was a gift from the people of France. After the pedestal had been prepared in 1885, the statue arrived dismantled in 214 packing cases of iron framework and copper sheeting and was assembled using rivets. Over a year later it was dedicated by President Grover Cleveland. Throughout this chapter, we explore some of the measurements of the Statue of Liberty.

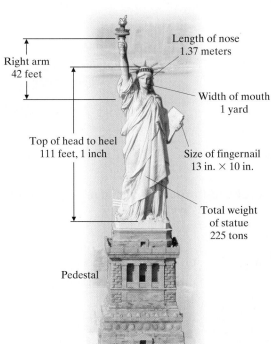

Right arm
42 feet

Top of head to heel
111 feet, 1 inch

Pedestal

Length of nose
1.37 meters

Width of mouth
1 yard

Size of fingernail
13 in. × 10 in.

Total weight
of statue
225 tons

5.1 RATIOS

Objective **A** Writing Ratios as Fractions

A **ratio** is the quotient of two quantities. A ratio, in fact, is no different from a fraction, except that a ratio is sometimes written using notation other than fractional notation. For example, the ratio of 1 to 2 can be written as

$$1 \text{ to } 2 \quad \text{or} \quad \frac{1}{2} \quad \text{or} \quad 1 : 2$$

fractional notation   colon notation

These ratios are all read as, "the ratio of 1 to 2."

✔**Concept Check** How should each ratio be read aloud?

a. $\dfrac{8}{5}$ **b.** $\dfrac{5}{8}$

In this section, we write ratios using fractional notation. If the fraction happens to be an improper fraction, do not write the fraction as a mixed number. Why? The mixed number form is not a ratio or quotient of two quantities.

Writing a Ratio as a Fraction

The order of the quantities is important when writing ratios. To write a ratio as a fraction, write the *first number* of the ratio as the *numerator* of the fraction and the *second number* as the *denominator*.

For example, the ratio of 6 to 11 is $\dfrac{6}{11}$, *not* $\dfrac{11}{6}$.

EXAMPLE 1 Write the ratio of 12 to 17 using fractional notation.

Solution: The ratio is $\dfrac{12}{17}$.

> **Helpful Hint**
> Don't forget that order is important when writing ratios. The ratio $\dfrac{17}{12}$ is *not* the same as the ratio $\dfrac{12}{17}$.

◻ **Work Practice Problem 1**

To simplify a ratio, we just write the fraction in simplest form. Common factors as well as common units can be divided out.

EXAMPLE 2 Write the ratio of $15 to $10 as a fraction in simplest form.

Solution:

$$\frac{\$15}{\$10} = \frac{15}{10} = \frac{3 \cdot \overset{1}{\cancel{5}}}{2 \cdot \underset{1}{\cancel{5}}} = \frac{3}{2}$$

◻ **Work Practice Problem 2**

PRACTICE PROBLEM 1

Write the ratio of 20 to 23 using fractional notation.

PRACTICE PROBLEM 2

Write the ratio of $8 to $6 as a fraction in simplest form.

Answers

1. $\dfrac{20}{23}$, 2. $\dfrac{4}{3}$

✔ **Concept Check Answers**

a. "eight to five,"   **b.** "five to eight"

Helpful
Hint

In the previous example, although $\frac{3}{2} = 1\frac{1}{2}$, a ratio is a quotient of *two* quantities. For that reason, ratios are not written as mixed numbers.

If a ratio contains decimal numbers or mixed numbers, we simplify by writing the ratio as a ratio of whole numbers.

EXAMPLE 3 Write the ratio of 2.6 to 3.1 as a fraction in simplest form.

Solution: The ratio in fraction form is

$$\frac{2.6}{3.1}$$

Now let's clear the ratio of decimals.

$$\frac{2.6}{3.1} = \frac{2.6}{3.1} \cdot 1 = \frac{2.6}{3.1} \cdot \frac{10}{10} = \frac{2.6 \cdot 10}{3.1 \cdot 10} = \frac{26}{31} \quad \text{Simplest form}$$

🔲 **Work Practice Problem 3**

EXAMPLE 4 Write the ratio of $1\frac{1}{5}$ to $2\frac{7}{10}$ as a fraction in simplest form.

Solution: The ratio in fraction form is $\dfrac{1\frac{1}{5}}{2\frac{7}{10}}$.

To simplify, remember that the fraction bar means division.

$$\frac{1\frac{1}{5}}{2\frac{7}{10}} = 1\frac{1}{5} \div 2\frac{7}{10} = \frac{6}{5} \div \frac{27}{10} = \frac{6}{5} \cdot \frac{10}{27} = \frac{6 \cdot 10}{5 \cdot 27} = \frac{2 \cdot \cancel{3} \cdot 2 \cdot \cancel{5}}{\cancel{5} \cdot \cancel{3} \cdot 3 \cdot 3} = \frac{4}{9} \quad \text{Simplest form.}$$

🔲 **Work Practice Problem 4**

EXAMPLE 5 Writing a Ratio from a Circle Graph

The circle graph in the margin shows the part of a car's total mileage that falls into a particular category. Write the ratio of medical miles to total miles as a fraction in simplest form.

Solution:

$$\frac{\text{medical miles}}{\text{total miles}} = \frac{150 \, \cancel{\text{miles}}}{15,000 \, \cancel{\text{miles}}} = \frac{150}{15,000} = \frac{\cancel{150}}{\cancel{150} \cdot 100} = \frac{1}{100}$$

🔲 **Work Practice Problem 5**

PRACTICE PROBLEM 3

Write the ratio of 1.71 to 4.56 as a fraction in simplest form.

PRACTICE PROBLEM 4

Write the ratio of $2\frac{2}{3}$ to $1\frac{13}{15}$ as a fraction in simplest form.

PRACTICE PROBLEM 5

Use the circle graph below to write the ratio of work miles to total miles as a fraction in simplest form.

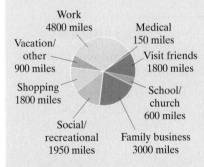

Work
4800 miles

Medical
150 miles

Vacation/
other
900 miles

Visit friends
1800 miles

Shopping
1800 miles

School/
church
600 miles

Social/
recreational
1950 miles

Family business
3000 miles

Total yearly mileage: 15,000

Sources: The American Automobile Manufacturers Association and The National Automobile Dealers Association.

Answers

3. $\frac{3}{8}$, **4.** $\frac{10}{7}$, **5.** $\frac{8}{25}$

△ **PRACTICE PROBLEM 6**

Given the triangle shown:

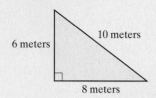

6 meters · 10 meters · 8 meters

a. Find the ratio of the length of the shortest side to the length of the longest side.

b. Find the ratio of the length of the longest side to the perimeter of the triangle.

△ **EXAMPLE 6** Given the rectangle shown:

a. Find the ratio of its width to its length.
b. Find the ratio of its length to its perimeter.

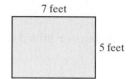

7 feet · 5 feet

Solution:

a. The ratio of its width to its length is

$$\frac{\text{width}}{\text{length}} = \frac{5 \ \text{feet}}{7 \ \text{feet}} = \frac{5}{7}$$

b. Recall that the perimeter of the rectangle is the distance around the rectangle: $7 + 5 + 7 + 5 = 24$ feet. The ratio of its length to its perimeter is

$$\frac{\text{length}}{\text{perimeter}} = \frac{7 \ \text{feet}}{24 \ \text{feet}} = \frac{7}{24}$$

▣ **Work Practice Problem 6**

✔ **Concept Check** Explain why the answer $\frac{7}{5}$ would be incorrect for part (a) of Example 6.

Objective B Writing Rates as Fractions

A special type of ratio is a rate. **Rates** are used to compare *different* kinds of quantities. For example, suppose that a recreational runner can run 3 miles in 33 minutes. If we write this rate as a fraction, we have

$$\frac{3 \ \text{miles}}{33 \ \text{minutes}} = \frac{1 \ \text{mile}}{11 \ \text{minutes}} \quad \text{In simplest form}$$

Helpful Hint

When comparing quantities with different units, write the units as part of the comparison. They do not divide out.

Same Units: $\dfrac{3 \ \text{inches}}{12 \ \text{inches}} = \dfrac{1}{4}$

Different Units: $\dfrac{2 \ \text{miles}}{20 \ \text{minutes}} = \dfrac{1 \ \text{mile}}{10 \ \text{minutes}}$ Units are still written.

PRACTICE PROBLEMS 7–8

Write each rate as a fraction in simplest form.

7. $1680 for 8 weeks

8. 236 miles on 12 gallons of gasoline

Answers

6. a. $\frac{3}{5}$, b. $\frac{5}{12}$, 7. $\frac{\$210}{1 \ \text{wk}}$, 8. $\frac{59 \ \text{mi}}{3 \ \text{gal}}$

✔ **Concept Check Answer**

$\frac{7}{5}$ would be the ratio of the rectangle's length to its width.

EXAMPLES Write each rate as a fraction in simplest form.

7. $2160 for 12 weeks is $\dfrac{2160 \ \text{dollars}}{12 \ \text{weeks}} = \dfrac{180 \ \text{dollars}}{1 \ \text{week}}$

8. 360 miles on 16 gallons of gasoline is $\dfrac{360 \ \text{miles}}{16 \ \text{gallons}} = \dfrac{45 \ \text{miles}}{2 \ \text{gallons}}$

▣ **Work Practice Problems 7–8**

✔ **Concept Check**   True or false? $\dfrac{16 \text{ gallons}}{4 \text{ gallons}}$ is a rate. Explain.

Objective C Finding Unit Rates

A **unit rate** is a rate with a denominator of 1. A familiar example of a unit rate is 55 mph, read as "55 **miles per hour.**" This means 55 miles per 1 hour or

$\dfrac{55 \text{ miles}}{1 \text{ hour}}$ Denominator of 1

Helpful Hint
In this context, the word "per" translates to division.

Writing a Rate as a Unit Rate

To write a rate as a unit rate, divide the numerator of the rate by the denominator.

EXAMPLE 9   Write as a unit rate: $27,000 every 6 months

Solution:

$\dfrac{27,000 \text{ dollars}}{6 \text{ months}}$ $6\overline{)27,000}^{4,500}$

The unit rate is

$\dfrac{4500 \text{ dollars}}{1 \text{ month}}$ or 4500 dollars/month   Read as, "4500 dollars per month."

▦ **Work Practice Problem 9**

EXAMPLE 10   Write as a unit rate: 318.5 miles every 13 gallons of gas

Solution:

$\dfrac{318.5 \text{ miles}}{13 \text{ gallons}}$ $13\overline{)318.5}^{24.5}$

The unit rate is

$\dfrac{24.5 \text{ miles}}{1 \text{ gallon}}$ or 24.5 miles/gallon   Read as, "24.5 miles per gallon."

▦ **Work Practice Problem 10**

Objective D Finding Unit Prices

Rates are used extensively in sports, business, medicine, and science. One of the most common uses of rates is in consumer economics. When a unit rate is "money per item," it is also called a **unit price.**

$$\text{unit price} = \dfrac{\text{price}}{\text{number of units}}$$

PRACTICE PROBLEM 9

Write as a unit rate: 3600 feet every 12 seconds

PRACTICE PROBLEM 10

Write as a unit rate:
52 bushels of fruit from 8 trees

Answers

9. $\dfrac{300 \text{ ft}}{1 \text{ sec}}$ or 300 ft/sec,

10. $\dfrac{6.5 \text{ bushels}}{1 \text{ tree}}$ or 6.5 bushels/tree

✔ **Concept Check Answer**

false; a rate compares different kinds of quantities

PRACTICE PROBLEM 11

Approximate each unit price to decide which is the better buy for a bag of nacho chips: 11 ounces for $2.32 or 16 ounces for $3.59.

EXAMPLE 11 Finding the Best Buy

Approximate each unit price to decide which is the better buy: 4 bars of soap for $0.99 or 5 bars of soap for $1.19.

Solution:

$$\frac{\text{unit}}{\text{price}} = \frac{\text{price}}{\text{no. of units}} = \frac{\$0.99}{4 \text{ bars}} \approx \frac{\$0.25 \text{ per bar}}{\text{of soap}} \qquad \frac{0.247}{4)\overline{0.990}} \approx 0.25$$

("is approximately")

$$\frac{\text{unit}}{\text{price}} = \frac{\text{price}}{\text{no. of units}} = \frac{\$1.19}{5 \text{ bars}} \approx \frac{\$0.24 \text{ per bar}}{\text{of soap}} \qquad \frac{0.238}{5)\overline{1.190}} \approx 0.24$$

Thus, the 5-bar package is the better buy.

Work Practice Problem 11

Answer

11. 11-oz bag

Objective Ⓐ *Write each ratio as a ratio of whole numbers using fractional notation. Write the fraction in simplest form. See Examples 1 through 6.*

1. 16 to 24

2. 25 to 150

3. 7.7 to 10

4. 8.1 to 10

5. 4.63 to 8.21

6. 9.61 to 7.62

7. 9 inches to 12 inches

8. 14 centimeters to 20 centimeters

9. $32 to $100

10. $46 to $102

11. 24 days to 14 days

12. 80 miles to 120 miles

13. $3\dfrac{1}{2}$ to $12\dfrac{1}{4}$

14. $3\dfrac{1}{3}$ to $4\dfrac{1}{6}$

15. $7\dfrac{3}{5}$ hours to $1\dfrac{9}{10}$ hours

16. $25\dfrac{1}{2}$ days to $2\dfrac{5}{6}$ days

Find the ratio described in each exercise as a fraction in simplest form. See Examples 5 and 6.

△ **17.** Find the ratio of the length to the width of a regulation size basketball court.

△ **18.** Find the ratio of the base to the height of the triangular mainsail.

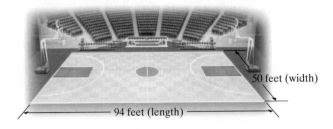

50 feet (width)

94 feet (length)

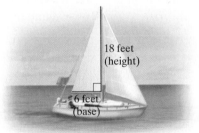

18 feet (height)

6 feet (base)

△ **19.** Find the ratio of the longest side to the perimeter of the right-triangular-shaped billboard.

△ **20.** Find the ratio of the width to the perimeter of the rectangular vegetable garden.

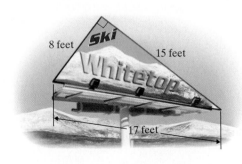

8 feet Ski 15 feet

Whitetop

17 feet

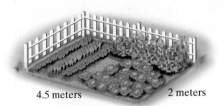

4.5 meters   2 meters

At the Honey Island Parent Teacher Organization meeting one night, there were 125 women and 100 men present.

21. Find the ratio of women to men.

22. Find the ratio of men to the total number of people present.

Blood contains three types of cells: red blood cells, white blood cells, and platelets. For approximately every 600 red blood cells in healthy humans, there are 40 platelets and 1 white blood cell. (Source: American Red Cross Biomedical Services)

23. Write the ratio of red blood cells to platelet cells.

24. Write the ratio of white blood cells to red blood cells.

25. Target stores operate in 49 states. Find the ratio of states without Target stores to states with Target stores. (*Source:* Target Corporation)

26. A total of 32 states have 200 or more public libraries. Find the ratio of states with 200 or more public libraries to states with fewer than 200 public libraries. (*Source:* U.S. Department of Education)

Objective **B** *Write each rate as a fraction in simplest form. See Examples 7 and 8.*

27. 5 shrubs every 15 feet

28. 14 lab tables for 28 students

29. 15 returns for 100 sales

30. 150 graduate students for 8 advisors

31. 8 phone lines for 36 employees

32. 6 laser printers for 28 computers

33. 18 gallons of pesticide for 4 acres of crops

34. 4 inches of rain in 18 hours

Objective **C** *Write each rate as a unit rate. See Examples 9 and 10.*

35. 330 calories in a 3-ounce serving

36. 275 miles in 11 hours

37. A hummingbird moves its wings at a rate of 5400 wingbeats a minute. Write this rate in wingbeats per second.

38. A bat moves its wings at a rate of 1200 wingbeats a minute. Write this rate in wingbeats per second.

39. $1,000,000 lottery winnings paid over 20 years

40. 400,000 library books for 8000 students

41. The state of Arizona has approximately 114,000 square miles of land for 15 counties. (*Source:* U.S. Bureau of the Census)

42. The state of Louisiana has approximately 4,468,800 residents for 64 parishes. (*Note:* Louisiana is the only U.S. state with parishes instead of counties. *Source:* U.S. Bureau of the Census)

43. 12,000 good assembly line products to 40 defective products

44. 5,000,000 lottery tickets for 4 lottery winners

45. On average, it costs $1,165,000 to build 25 Habitat for Humanity houses in the United States. (*Source:* Habitat for Humanity International)

46. The top-grossing concert tour in North America was the 1994 Rolling Stones tour, which grossed $121,200,000 for 60 shows. (*Source:* Pollstar)

47. Greer Krieger can assemble 250 computer boards in an 8-hour shift while Lamont Williams can assemble 402 computer boards in a 12-hour shift.

   a. Find the unit rate of Greer.

   b. Find the unit rate of Lamont.

   c. Who can assemble computer boards faster, Greer or Lamont?

48. Jerry Stein laid 713 bricks in 46 minutes while his associate, Bobby Burns, laid 396 bricks in 30 minutes.

   a. Find the unit rate of Jerry.

   b. Find the unit rate of Bobby.

   c. Who is the faster bricklayer?

For Exercises 49 and 50, round the rates to the nearest tenth.

49. One student drove 400 miles in his car on 14.5 gallons of gasoline. His sister drove 270 miles in her truck on 9.25 gallons of gasoline.

   a. Find the unit rate of the car.
   b. Find the unit rate of the truck.
   c. Which vehicle gets better gas mileage?

50. Charlotte Leal is a grocery scanner who can scan an average of 100 items in 3.5 minutes while her cousin Leo can scan 148 items in 5.5 minutes.

   a. Find the unit rate of Charlotte.
   b. Find the unit rate of Leo.
   c. Who is the faster scanner?

Objective D *Find each unit price and decide which is the better buy. Round to 3 decimal places. Assume that we are comparing different sizes of the same brand. See Example 11.*

51. Crackers:
   $1.19 for 8 ounces
   $1.59 for 12 ounces

52. Pickles:
   $1.89 for 32 ounces
   $0.89 for 18 ounces

53. Frozen orange juice:
   $1.69 for 16 ounces
   $0.69 for 6 ounces

54. Eggs:
   $0.69 for a dozen
   $2.10 for a flat $\left(2\frac{1}{2} \text{ dozen} \right)$

55. Soy sauce:
   12 ounces for $2.29
   8 ounces for $1.49

56. Shampoo:
   20 ounces for $1.89
   32 ounces for $3.19

57. Napkins:
   100 for $0.59
   180 for $0.93

58. Crackers:
   20 ounces for $2.39
   8 ounces for $0.99

Review

Divide. See Section 4.4.

59. $9\overline{)20.7}$

60. $7\overline{)60.2}$

61. $3.7\overline{)0.555}$

62. $4.6\overline{)1.15}$

Concept Extensions

63. Is the ratio $\frac{11}{15}$ the same as the ratio of $\frac{15}{11}$? Explain your answer.

64. Explain why the ratio $\frac{40}{17}$ is incorrect for Exercise 19.

Decide whether each value is a ratio written as a fraction in simplest form. If not, write it as a fraction in simplest form.

65. $\dfrac{6 \text{ inches}}{15 \text{ inches}}$

66. $4\dfrac{1}{2}$

67. A panty hose manufacturing machine will be repaired if the ratio of defective panty hose to good panty hose is at least 1 to 20. A quality control engineer found 10 defective panty hose in a batch of 200. Determine whether the machine should be repaired.

68. A grocer will refuse a shipment of tomatoes if the ratio of bruised tomatoes to the total batch is at least 1 to 10. A sample is found to contain 3 bruised tomatoes and 33 good tomatoes. Determine whether the shipment should be refused.

69. Fill in the table to calculate miles per gallon.

Beginning Odometer Reading	Ending Odometer Reading	Miles Driven	Gallons of Gas Used	Miles per Gallon (round to the nearest tenth)
79,286	79,543		13.4	
79,543	79,895		15.8	
79,895	80,242		16.1	

Find each unit rate.

70. The longest stairway is the service stairway for the Niesenbahn Cable railway near Spiez, Switzerland. It has 11,674 steps and rises to a height of 7759 feet. Find the unit rate of steps per foot rounded to the nearest tenth of a step. (*Source: The Guinness Book of Records*)

71. In the United States, the total number of students enrolled in public schools is 48,000,000. There are 88,300 public schools. Write a unit rate in students per school. Round to the nearest whole. (*Source:* National Center for Education Statistics)

72. Suppose that the amount of a product decreases, say from an 80-ounce container to a 70-ounce container, but the price of the container remains the same. Does the unit price increase or decrease? Explain why.

73. In your own words, define the phrase unit rate.

74. In your own words, define the phrase unit price.

75. Should the rate $\dfrac{3 \text{ lights}}{2 \text{ feet}}$ be written as $\dfrac{3}{2}$? Explain why or why not?

76. Find an item in the grocery store and calculate its unit price.

77. In 2005, 19 states had mandatory helmet laws. (*Source:* Bicycle Helmet Safety Institute)

   a. Find the ratio of states with mandatory helmet laws to total U.S. states.

   b. Find the ratio of states with mandatory helmet laws to states without mandatory helmet laws.

   c. Are your ratios for parts **a** and **b** the same? Explain why or why not.

STUDY SKILLS BUILDER

Is Your Notebook Still Organized?

It's never too late to organize your material in a course. Let's see how you are doing.

1. Are all your graded papers in one place in your math notebook or binder?

2. Flip through the pages of your notebook. Are your notes neat and readable?

3. Are your notes complete with no sections missing?

4. Are important notes marked in some way (like an exclamation point) so that you will know to review them before a quiz or test?

5. Are your assignments complete?

6. Do exercises that have given you trouble have a mark (like a question mark) so that you will remember to talk to your instructor or a tutor about them?

7. Describe your attitude toward this course.

8. List ways your attitude can improve and make a commitment to work on at least one of these during the next week.

5.2 PROPORTIONS

Objective **A** Writing Proportions

A **proportion** is a statement that 2 ratios or rates are equal. For example,

$$\frac{5}{6} = \frac{10}{12}$$

is a proportion. We can read this as, "5 is to 6 as 10 is to 12."

EXAMPLE 1 Write each sentence as a proportion.

a. 12 diamonds is to 15 rubies as 4 diamonds is to 5 rubies.

b. 5 hits is to 9 at bats as 20 hits is to 36 at bats.

Solution:

a. diamonds $\rightarrow$ $\quad \dfrac{12}{15} = \dfrac{4}{5} \quad$ $\leftarrow$ diamonds
rubies $\rightarrow$ $\leftarrow$ rubies

b. hits $\rightarrow$ $\quad \dfrac{5}{9} = \dfrac{20}{36} \quad$ $\leftarrow$ hits
at bats $\rightarrow$ $\leftarrow$ at bats

◻ **Work Practice Problem 1**

PRACTICE PROBLEM 1

Write each sentence as a proportion.

a. 24 right is to 6 wrong as 4 right is to 1 wrong.

b. 32 Cubs fans is to 18 Mets fans as 16 Cubs fans is to 9 Mets fans.

> **Helpful Hint**
>
> Notice in the above examples of proportions that the numerators contain the same units and the denominators contain the same units. In this text, proportions will be written so that this is the case.

Objective **B** Determining Whether Proportions Are True

Like other mathematical statements, a proportion may be either true or false. A proportion is true if its ratios are equal. Since ratios are fractions, one way to determine whether a proportion is true is to write both fractions in simplest form and compare them.

Another way is to compare cross products as we did in Section 3.2.

Using Cross Products to Determine Whether Proportions Are True or False

Cross products

$a \cdot d$ $\dfrac{a}{b} = \dfrac{c}{d}$ $b \cdot c$

If cross products are *equal*, the proportion is *true*.
If $ad = bc$, then the proportion is true.
If cross products are *not equal*, the proportion is *false*.
If $ad \neq bc$, then the proportion is false.

Answers

1. a. $\dfrac{24}{6} = \dfrac{4}{1}$, **b.** $\dfrac{32}{18} = \dfrac{16}{9}$

EXAMPLE 2 Is $\frac{2}{3} = \frac{4}{6}$ a true proportion?

Solution:

Cross products

$2 \cdot 6$ $3 \cdot 4$

$$\frac{2}{3} = \frac{4}{6}$$

$2 \cdot 6 \overset{?}{=} 3 \cdot 4$ Are cross products equal?

$12 = 12$ Equal, so proportion is true.

Since the cross products are equal, the proportion is true.

🔲 **Work Practice Problem 2**

EXAMPLE 3 Is $\frac{4.1}{7} = \frac{2.9}{5}$ a true proportion?

Solution:

Cross products

$4.1 \cdot 5$ $7 \cdot 2.9$

$$\frac{4.1}{7} = \frac{2.9}{5}$$

$4.1 \cdot 5 \overset{?}{=} 7 \cdot 2.9$ Are cross products equal?

$20.5 \neq 20.3$ Not equal, so proportion is false.

Since the cross products are not equal, $\frac{4.1}{7} \neq \frac{2.9}{5}$. The proportion is false.

🔲 **Work Practice Problem 3**

EXAMPLE 4 Is $\dfrac{1\frac{1}{6}}{10\frac{1}{2}} = \dfrac{\frac{1}{2}}{4\frac{1}{2}}$ a true proportion?

Solution:

$$\dfrac{1\frac{1}{6}}{10\frac{1}{2}} = \dfrac{\frac{1}{2}}{4\frac{1}{2}}$$

$1\frac{1}{6} \cdot 4\frac{1}{2} \overset{?}{=} 10\frac{1}{2} \cdot \frac{1}{2}$ Are cross products equal?

$\frac{7}{6} \cdot \frac{9}{2} \overset{?}{=} \frac{21}{2} \cdot \frac{1}{2}$ Write mixed numbers as improper fractions.

$\frac{21}{4} = \frac{21}{4}$ Equal, so proportion is true.

Since the cross products are equal, the proportion is true.

🔲 **Work Practice Problem 4**

✔ **Concept Check** Think about cross products and write the true proportion $\frac{5}{8} = \frac{10}{16}$ in two other ways so that each result is also a true proportion.
(*Note:* There are no units attached in this proportion.)

PRACTICE PROBLEM 2

Is $\frac{3}{6} = \frac{4}{8}$ a true proportion?

PRACTICE PROBLEM 3

Is $\frac{3.6}{6} = \frac{5.4}{8}$ a true proportion?

PRACTICE PROBLEM 4

Is $\dfrac{4\frac{1}{5}}{2\frac{1}{3}} = \dfrac{3\frac{3}{10}}{1\frac{5}{6}}$ a true proportion?

Answers

2. yes, **3.** no, **4.** yes

✔ **Concept Check Answer**

possible answers: $\frac{8}{5} = \frac{16}{10}$ and $\frac{5}{10} = \frac{8}{16}$

Objective C Finding Unknown Numbers in Proportions

When one number of a proportion is unknown, we can use cross products to find the unknown number. For example, to find the unknown number n in the proportion $\frac{n}{30} = \frac{2}{3}$, we first find the cross products.

$$n \cdot 3 \qquad \frac{n}{30} = \frac{2}{3} \qquad 30 \cdot 2 \qquad \text{Find the cross products.}$$

If the proportion is true, then cross products are equal.

$n \cdot 3 = 30 \cdot 2$ Set the cross products equal to each other.

$n \cdot 3 = 60$ Write $2 \cdot 30$ as 60.

To find the unknown number n, we ask ourselves, "What number times 3 is 60?" The number is 20 and can be found by dividing 60 by 3.

$n = \dfrac{60}{3}$ Divide 60 by the number multiplied by n.

$n = 20$ Simplify.

Thus, the unknown number is 20.

To *check,* let's replace n with this value, 20, and verify that a true proportion results.

$\dfrac{20}{30} \overset{?}{=} \dfrac{2}{3}$ ← Replace n with 20.

$$\frac{20}{30} \overset{?}{=} \frac{2}{3}$$

$3 \cdot 20 \overset{?}{=} 2 \cdot 30$

$60 = 60$ Cross products are equal.

Finding an Unknown Value n in a Proportion

Step 1: Set the cross products equal to each other.

Step 2: Divide the number not multiplied by n by the number multiplied by n.

PRACTICE PROBLEM 5

Find the value of the unknown number n.

$$\frac{15}{2} = \frac{60}{n}$$

EXAMPLE 5 Find the value of the unknown number n.

$$\frac{51}{34} = \frac{-3}{n}$$

Solution:

Step 1:

$$\frac{51}{34} = \frac{-3}{n}$$

$51 \cdot n = 34 \cdot -3$ Set cross products equal.

$51 \cdot n = -102$ Multiply.

Step 2:

$n = \dfrac{-102}{51}$ Divide -102 by 51, the number multiplied by n.

$n = -2$ Simplify.

Check: $\dfrac{51}{34} \overset{?}{=} \dfrac{-3}{-2}$ Replace n with its value, -2.

$$\dfrac{51}{34} \overset{?}{=} \dfrac{-3}{-2}$$

$51 \cdot -2 \overset{?}{=} 34 \cdot -3$ Cross products are equal, so the
$-102 = -102$ proportion is true.

■ **Work Practice Problem 5**

EXAMPLE 6 Find the unknown number n.

$$\dfrac{7}{n} = \dfrac{6}{5}$$

Solution:

Step 1:

$$\dfrac{7}{n} = \dfrac{6}{5}$$

$7 \cdot 5 = n \cdot 6$ Set the cross products equal to each other.
$35 = n \cdot 6$ Multiply.

Step 2:

$\dfrac{35}{6} = n$ Divide 35 by 6, the number multiplied by n.

$5\dfrac{5}{6} = n$

Check to see that $5\dfrac{5}{6}$ is the unknown number.

■ **Work Practice Problem 6**

EXAMPLE 7 Find the unknown number n.

$$\dfrac{n}{3} = \dfrac{0.8}{1.5}$$

Solution:

Step 1:

$$\dfrac{n}{3} = \dfrac{0.8}{1.5}$$

$n \cdot 1.5 = 3 \cdot 0.8$ Set the cross products equal to each other.
$n \cdot 1.5 = 2.4$ Multiply.

Step 2:

$n = \dfrac{2.4}{1.5}$ Divide 2.4 by 1.5, the number multiplied by n.

$n = 1.6$ Simplify.

Check to see that 1.6 is the unknown number.

■ **Work Practice Problem 7**

PRACTICE PROBLEM 6

Find the unknown number n.

$$\dfrac{8}{n} = \dfrac{5}{9}$$

PRACTICE PROBLEM 7

Find the unknown number n.

$$\dfrac{n}{6} = \dfrac{0.7}{1.2}$$

Answers

6. $n = 14\dfrac{2}{5}$, **7.** $n = 3.5$

PRACTICE PROBLEM 8

Find the unknown number n.

$$\frac{n}{4\frac{1}{3}} = \frac{4\frac{1}{2}}{1\frac{3}{4}}$$

EXAMPLE 8 Find the unknown number n.

$$\frac{1\frac{2}{3}}{3\frac{1}{4}} = \frac{n}{2\frac{3}{5}}$$

Solution:

Step 1:

$$\frac{1\frac{2}{3}}{3\frac{1}{4}} = \frac{n}{2\frac{3}{5}}$$

$1\frac{2}{3} \cdot 2\frac{3}{5} = 3\frac{1}{4} \cdot n$ Set the cross products equal to each other.

$\frac{13}{3} = 3\frac{1}{4} \cdot n$ Multiply. $1\frac{2}{3} \cdot 2\frac{3}{5} = \frac{5}{3} \cdot \frac{13}{5} = \frac{\overset{1}{\cancel{5}} \cdot 13}{3 \cdot \underset{1}{\cancel{5}}} = \frac{13}{3}$

$\frac{13}{3} = \frac{13}{4} \cdot n$ Write $3\frac{1}{4}$ as $\frac{13}{4}$.

Step 2:

$\frac{13}{3} \div \frac{13}{4} = n$ Divide $\frac{13}{3}$ by $\frac{13}{4}$, the number multiplied by n.

or

$n = \frac{13}{3} \cdot \frac{4}{13} = \frac{4}{3}$ or $1\frac{1}{3}$ Divide by multiplying by the reciprocal.

Check to see that $1\frac{1}{3}$ is the unknown number.

Work Practice Problem 8

Answer

8. $n = 11\frac{1}{7}$

Mental Math

Objective **B** *State whether each proportion is true or false.*

1. $\dfrac{2}{1} = \dfrac{6}{3}$

2. $\dfrac{3}{1} = \dfrac{15}{5}$

3. $\dfrac{1}{2} = \dfrac{3}{5}$

4. $\dfrac{2}{11} = \dfrac{1}{5}$

5. $\dfrac{2}{3} = \dfrac{40}{60}$

6. $\dfrac{3}{4} = \dfrac{6}{8}$

5.2 EXERCISE SET

FOR EXTRA HELP

Student Solutions Manual | PH Math/Tutor Center | CD/Video for Review | Math XL MathXL® | MyMathLab MyMathLab

Objective **A** *Write each sentence as a proportion. See Example 1.*

1. 10 diamonds is to 6 opals as 5 diamonds is to 3 opals.

2. 8 books is to 6 courses as 4 books is to 3 courses.

3. 3 printers is to 12 computers as 1 printer is to 4 computers.

4. 4 hit songs is to 16 releases as 1 hit song is to 4 releases.

5. 6 eagles is to 58 sparrows as 3 eagles is to 29 sparrows.

6. 12 errors is to 8 pages as 1.5 errors is to 1 page.

7. $2\dfrac{1}{4}$ cups of flour is to 24 cookies as $6\dfrac{3}{4}$ cups of flour is to 72 cookies.

8. $1\dfrac{1}{2}$ cups milk is to 10 bagels as $\dfrac{3}{4}$ cup milk is to 5 bagels.

9. 22 vanilla wafers is to 1 cup of cookie crumbs as 55 vanilla wafers is to 2.5 cups of cookie crumbs. (*Source:* Based on data from *Family Circle* magazine)

10. 1 cup of instant rice is to 1.5 cups cooked rice as 1.5 cups of instant rice is to 2.25 cups of cooked rice. (*Source:* Based on data from *Family Circle* magazine)

Objective **B** *Determine whether each proportion is a true proportion. See Examples 2 through 4.*

11. $\dfrac{15}{9} = \dfrac{5}{3}$

12. $\dfrac{8}{6} = \dfrac{20}{15}$

13. $\dfrac{8}{6} = \dfrac{9}{7}$

14. $\dfrac{7}{12} = \dfrac{4}{7}$

15. $\dfrac{9}{36} = \dfrac{2}{8}$

16. $\dfrac{8}{24} = \dfrac{3}{9}$

379

17. $\dfrac{5}{8} = \dfrac{625}{1000}$

18. $\dfrac{30}{50} = \dfrac{600}{1000}$

19. $\dfrac{0.8}{0.3} = \dfrac{0.2}{0.6}$

20. $\dfrac{0.7}{0.4} = \dfrac{0.3}{0.1}$

21. $\dfrac{8}{10} = \dfrac{5.6}{0.7}$

22. $\dfrac{4.2}{8.4} = \dfrac{5}{10}$

23. $\dfrac{\frac{3}{4}}{\frac{4}{3}} = \dfrac{\frac{1}{2}}{\frac{8}{9}}$

24. $\dfrac{\frac{2}{5}}{\frac{2}{7}} = \dfrac{\frac{1}{10}}{\frac{1}{3}}$

25. $\dfrac{2\frac{2}{5}}{\frac{2}{3}} = \dfrac{1\frac{1}{9}}{\frac{1}{4}}$

26. $\dfrac{5\frac{5}{8}}{\frac{5}{3}} = \dfrac{4\frac{1}{2}}{1\frac{1}{5}}$

27. $\dfrac{\frac{4}{5}}{\frac{5}{6}} = \dfrac{\frac{6}{5}}{\frac{5}{9}}$

28. $\dfrac{\frac{6}{7}}{\frac{7}{3}} = \dfrac{\frac{10}{7}}{\frac{7}{5}}$

Objectives Ⓐ Ⓑ **Mixed Practice** *Write each sentence as a proportion. Then determine whether the proportion is a true proportion. See Examples 1 through 4.*

29. eight is to twelve as four is to six

30. six is to eight as nine is to twelve

31. five is to two as thirteen is to five

32. four is to three as seven is to five

33. one and eight tenths is to two as four and five tenths is to five

34. fifteen hundredths is to three as thirty-five hundredths is to seven

35. two thirds is to one fifth as two fifths is to one ninth

36. ten elevenths is to three fourths as one fourth is to one half

Objective Ⓒ *For each proportion, find the unknown number n. See Examples 5 through 8.*

37. $\dfrac{n}{5} = \dfrac{6}{10}$

38. $\dfrac{n}{3} = \dfrac{12}{9}$

39. $\dfrac{-18}{54} = \dfrac{3}{n}$

40. $\dfrac{25}{100} = \dfrac{-7}{n}$

41. $\dfrac{n}{8} = \dfrac{50}{100}$

42. $\dfrac{n}{21} = \dfrac{12}{18}$

43. $\dfrac{8}{15} = \dfrac{n}{6}$

44. $\dfrac{12}{10} = \dfrac{n}{16}$

45. $\dfrac{24}{n} = \dfrac{60}{96}$

46. $\dfrac{26}{n} = \dfrac{28}{49}$

47. $\dfrac{-3.5}{12.5} = \dfrac{-7}{n}$

48. $\dfrac{-0.2}{0.7} = \dfrac{-8}{n}$

49. $\dfrac{0.05}{12} = \dfrac{n}{0.6}$

50. $\dfrac{7.8}{13} = \dfrac{n}{2.6}$

51. $\dfrac{8}{1\frac{1}{3}} = \dfrac{24}{n}$

52. $\dfrac{12}{\frac{3}{4}} = \dfrac{48}{n}$

53. $\dfrac{\frac{1}{3}}{\frac{3}{8}} = \dfrac{\frac{2}{5}}{n}$

54. $\dfrac{\frac{7}{9}}{\frac{8}{27}} = \dfrac{\frac{1}{4}}{n}$

55. $\dfrac{12}{n} = \dfrac{\frac{2}{3}}{\frac{6}{9}}$

56. $\dfrac{24}{n} = \dfrac{\frac{8}{15}}{\frac{5}{9}}$

57. $\dfrac{n}{1\frac{1}{5}} = \dfrac{4\frac{1}{6}}{6\frac{2}{3}}$

58. $\dfrac{n}{3\frac{1}{8}} = \dfrac{7\frac{3}{5}}{2\frac{3}{8}}$

59. $\dfrac{25}{n} = \dfrac{3}{\frac{7}{30}}$

60. $\dfrac{9}{n} = \dfrac{5}{\frac{11}{15}}$

Review

Insert $<$ or $>$ to form a true statement. See Sections 3.7 and 4.1.

61. 8.01   8.1

62. 7.26   7.026

63. $2\frac{1}{2}$ $2\frac{1}{3}$

64. $9\frac{1}{5}$ $9\frac{1}{4}$

65. $5\frac{1}{3}$ $6\frac{2}{3}$

66. $1\frac{1}{2}$ $2\frac{1}{2}$

Concept Extensions

Think about cross products and write each proportion in two other ways so that each result is also a true proportion. See the Concept Check in this section.

67. $\dfrac{9}{15} = \dfrac{3}{5}$

68. $\dfrac{1}{4} = \dfrac{5}{20}$

69. $\dfrac{6}{18} = \dfrac{1}{3}$

70. $\dfrac{2}{7} = \dfrac{4}{14}$

71. If the proportion $\dfrac{a}{b} = \dfrac{c}{d}$ is a true proportion, write two other true proportions using the same letters.

72. Write a true proportion.

73. Explain the difference between a ratio and a proportion.

74. Explain how to find the unknown number in a proportion such as $\dfrac{n}{18} = \dfrac{12}{8}$.

For each proportion, find the unknown number n.

75. $\dfrac{n}{7} = \dfrac{0}{8}$

76. $\dfrac{0}{2} = \dfrac{n}{3.5}$

77. $\dfrac{n}{1150} = \dfrac{588}{483}$

78. $\dfrac{585}{n} = \dfrac{117}{474}$

79. $\dfrac{222}{1515} = \dfrac{37}{n}$

80. $\dfrac{1425}{1062} = \dfrac{n}{177}$

THE BIGGER PICTURE   Operations on Sets of Numbers and Solving Equations

Continue your outline from Sections 1.7, 1.9, 2.5, 3.3, 3.7, and 4.4. Suggestions are once again written to help you complete this part of your outline. Notice that this part of the outline has to do with solving a certain type of equation, proportions.

I. Operations on Sets of Numbers

  A. Whole Numbers

    1. Add or Subtract (Sections 1.3, 1.4)

    2. Multiply or Divide (Sections 1.6, 1.7)

    3. Exponent (Section 1.9)

    4. Square Root (Section 1.9)

    5. Order of Operations (Section 1.9)

  B. Integers

    1. Add (Section 2.3)

    2. Subtract (Section 2.4)

    3. Multiply or Divide (Section 2.5)

  C. Fractions

    1. Simplify (Section 3.2)

    2. Multiply (Section 3.3)

    3. Divide (Section 3.3)

    4. Add or Subtract (Sections 3.4, 3.5)

  D. Decimals

    1. Add or Subtract (Section 4.2)

    2. Multiply (Section 4.3)

    3. Divide (Section 4.4)

II. Solving Equations

  A. Proportions: Set cross products equal to each other. Then solve.

$$\dfrac{14}{3} = \dfrac{2}{n},\ or\ 14 \cdot n = 3 \cdot 2,\ or\ 14 \cdot n = 6,\ or\ n = \dfrac{6}{14} = \dfrac{3}{7}$$

Perform indicated operations.

1. $\dfrac{7}{20} - \dfrac{1}{10}$ **2.** $\dfrac{7}{20} \cdot \dfrac{1}{10}$

3. $\dfrac{7}{20} \div \dfrac{1}{10}$ **4.** $\dfrac{7}{20} + \dfrac{1}{10}$

5. $7.6 + 0.02$ **6.** $7.6(0.02)$

For each proportion, find the unknown number, n.

7. $\dfrac{4}{n} = \dfrac{50}{100}$ **8.** $\dfrac{60}{10} = \dfrac{15}{n}$

9. $\dfrac{n}{0.8} = \dfrac{0.06}{12}$ **10.** $\dfrac{\frac{7}{8}}{\frac{1}{4}} = \dfrac{n}{\frac{5}{6}}$

5.3 PROPORTIONS AND PROBLEM SOLVING

Objective **A** Solving Problems by Writing Proportions

Writing proportions is a powerful tool for solving problems in almost every field, including business, chemistry, biology, health sciences, and engineering, as well as in daily life. Given a specified ratio (or rate) of two quantities, a proportion can be used to determine an unknown quantity.

In this section, we use the same problem solving steps that we have used earlier in this text.

EXAMPLE 1 **Determining Distances from a Map**

On a chamber of commerce map of Abita Springs, 5 miles corresponds to 2 inches. How many miles correspond to 7 inches?

PRACTICE PROBLEM 1

On an architect's blueprint, 1 inch corresponds to 12 feet. How long is a wall represented by a $3\frac{1}{2}$-inch line on the blueprint?

Solution:

1. UNDERSTAND. Read and reread the problem. You may want to draw a diagram.

```
                         between 15 and 20 miles
        15 miles                │
   ┌─────────────────────┐     │ 20 miles
   │ 5 miles │ 5 miles │ 5 miles │ 5 miles │ = a little over 15 miles
   │ 2 inches│ 2 inches│ 2 inches│ 2 inches│ = 7 inches
   └─────────────────────┘        8 inches
           6 inches          │
                        7 inches
```

From the diagram we can see that a reasonable solution should be between 15 and 20 miles.

2. TRANSLATE. We will let n represent our unknown number. Since 5 miles corresponds to 2 inches as n miles corresponds to 7 inches, we have the proportion

   $$\begin{array}{ccc} \text{miles} & \rightarrow & \dfrac{5}{2} = \dfrac{n}{7} & \leftarrow & \text{miles} \\ \text{inches} & \rightarrow & & \leftarrow & \text{inches} \end{array}$$

3. SOLVE: In earlier sections, we estimated to obtain a reasonable answer. Notice we did this in Step 1 above.

   $$\dfrac{5}{2} = \dfrac{n}{7}$$

   $5 \cdot 7 = 2 \cdot n$ Set the cross products equal to each other.

   $35 = 2 \cdot n$ Multiply.

   $\dfrac{35}{2} = n$ Divide 35 by 2, the number multiplied by n.

   $n = 17\dfrac{1}{2}$ or 17.5   Simplify.

4. INTERPRET. *Check* your work. This result is reasonable since it is between 15 and 20 miles. *State* your conclusion: 7 inches corresponds to 17.5 miles.

Answer
1. 42 ft

▨ **Work Practice Problem 1**

We can also solve Example 1 by writing the proportion

$$\frac{2 \text{ inches}}{5 \text{ miles}} = \frac{7 \text{ inches}}{n \text{ miles}}$$

Although other proportions may be used to solve Example 1, we will solve by writing proportions so that the numerators have the same unit measures and the denominators have the same unit measures.

PRACTICE PROBLEM 2

An auto mechanic recommends that 3 ounces of isopropyl alcohol be mixed with a tankful of gas (14 gallons) to increase the octane of the gasoline for better engine performance. At this rate, how many gallons of gas can be treated with a 16-ounce bottle of alcohol?

EXAMPLE 2 **Finding Medicine Dosage**

The standard dose of an antibiotic is 4 cc (cubic centimeters) for every 25 pounds (lb) of body weight. At this rate, find the standard dose for a 140-lb woman.

Solution:

1. UNDERSTAND. Read and reread the problem. You may want to draw a diagram to estimate a reasonable solution.

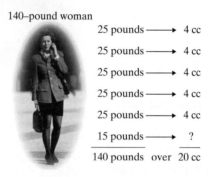

140–pound woman

25 pounds	→	4 cc
25 pounds	→	4 cc
25 pounds	→	4 cc
25 pounds	→	4 cc
25 pounds	→	4 cc
15 pounds	→	?

140 pounds over 20 cc

From the diagram, we can see that a reasonable solution is a little over 20 cc.

2. TRANSLATE. We will let n represent the unknown number. From the problem, we know that 4 cc is to 25 pounds as n cc is to 140 pounds, or

$$\begin{array}{cc} \text{cubic centimeters} \rightarrow & \dfrac{4}{25} = \dfrac{n}{140} \leftarrow \text{cubic centimeters} \\ \text{pounds} \rightarrow & \phantom{\dfrac{4}{25} = \dfrac{n}{140}} \leftarrow \text{pounds} \end{array}$$

3. SOLVE:

$$\frac{4}{25} = \frac{n}{140}$$

$$4 \cdot 140 = 25 \cdot n \qquad \text{Set the cross products equal to each other.}$$

$$560 = 25 \cdot n \qquad \text{Multiply.}$$

$$\frac{560}{25} = n \qquad \text{Divide 560 by 25, the number multiplied by } n.$$

$$n = 22\frac{2}{5} \text{ or } 22.4 \quad \text{Simplify.}$$

4. INTERPRET. *Check* your work. This result is reasonable since it is a little over 20 cc. *State* your conclusion: The standard dose for a 140-lb woman is 22.4 cc.

Work Practice Problem 2

Answer

2. $74\frac{2}{3}$ or $74.\overline{6}$ gal

⚠️ **EXAMPLE 3** **Calculating Supplies Needed to Fertilize a Lawn**

A 50-pound bag of fertilizer covers 2400 square feet of lawn. How many bags of fertilizer are needed to cover a town square containing 15,360 square feet of lawn? Round the answer up to the nearest whole bag.

Solution:

1. UNDERSTAND. Read and reread the problem. Draw a picture.

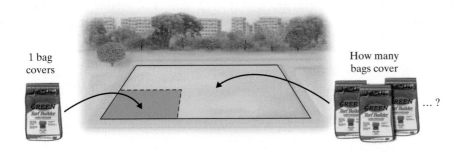

1 bag covers

How many bags cover

... ?

Since one bag covers 2400 square feet, let's see how many 2400's there are in 15,360. We will estimate. The number 15,360 rounded to the nearest thousand is 15,000 and 2400 rounded to the nearest thousand is 2000. Then

$$15{,}000 \div 2000 = 7\frac{1}{2} \text{ or } 7.5.$$

2. TRANSLATE. We'll let n represent the unknown number. From the problem, we know that 1 bag is to 2400 square feet as n bags is to 15,360 square feet.

$$
\begin{array}{ccccc}
\text{bags} & \rightarrow & \dfrac{1}{2400} = \dfrac{n}{15{,}360} & \leftarrow & \text{bags} \\
\text{square feet} & \rightarrow & & \leftarrow & \text{square feet}
\end{array}
$$

Continued on next page

3. SOLVE:

$$\frac{1}{2400} = \frac{n}{15{,}360}$$

$1 \cdot 15{,}360 = 2400 \cdot n$ Set the cross products equal to each other.

$15{,}360 = 2400 \cdot n$ Multiply.

$\dfrac{15{,}360}{2400} = n$ Divide 15,360 by 2400, the number multiplied by n.

$n = 6.4$ Simplify.

4. INTERPRET. *Check* that replacing n with 6.4 makes the proportion true. Is the answer reasonable? Yes, since it's close to $7\frac{1}{2}$ or 7.5. Since we must buy whole bags of fertilizer, 7 bags are needed. *State* your conclusion: To cover 15,360 square feet of lawn, 7 bags are needed.

⬛ Work Practice Problem 3

✔Concept Check You are told that 12 ounces of ground coffee will brew enough coffee to serve 20 people. How could you estimate how much ground coffee will be needed to serve 95 people?

✔ Concept Check Answer

Find how much will be needed for 100 people (20×5) by multiplying 12 ounces by 5, which is 60 ounces.

Objective **A** *Solve. See Examples 1 through 3.*

The ratio of a quarterback's completed passes to attempted passes is 4 to 9.

1. If he attempted 27 passes, find how many passes he completed.

2. If he completed 20 passes, find how many passes he attempted.

It takes Sandra Hallahan 30 minutes to word process and spell check 4 pages.

3. Find how long it takes her to word process and spell check 22 pages.

4. Find how many pages she can word process and spell check in 4.5 hours.

University Law School accepts 2 out of every 7 applicants.

5. If the school accepted 180 students, find how many applications they received.

6. If the school accepted 150 students, find how many applications were received.

On an architect's blueprint, 1 inch corresponds to 8 feet.

7. Find the length of a wall represented by a line $2\frac{7}{8}$ inches long on the blueprint.

8. Find the length of a wall represented by a line $5\frac{1}{4}$ inches on the blueprint.

A human-factors expert recommends that there be at least 9 square feet of floor space in a college classroom for every student in the class.

△ **9.** Find the minimum floor space that 30 students require.

△ **10.** Due to a lack of space, a university converts a 21-by-15-foot conference room into a classroom. Find the maximum number of students the room can accommodate.

A Honda Civic averages 450 miles on a 12-gallon tank of gas.

11. If Dave Smythe runs out of gas in a Honda Civic and AAA comes to his rescue with $1\frac{1}{2}$ gallons of gas, determine how far he can go. Round to the nearest mile.

12. Find how many gallons of gas Denise Wolcott can expect to burn on a 2000-mile vacation trip in a Honda Civic. Round to the nearest gallon.

The scale on an Italian map states that 1 centimeter corresponds to 30 kilometers.

13. Find how far apart Milan and Rome are if their corresponding points on the map are 15 centimeters apart.

14. On the map, a small Italian village is located 0.4 centimeter from the Mediterranean Sea. Find the actual distance.

Milan

Rome

A drink called Sea Breeze Punch is made by mixing 3 parts of grapefruit juice with 4 parts of cranberry juice.

15. Find how much grapefruit juice should be mixed with 32 ounces of cranberry juice.

16. For a party, 6 quarts of grapefruit juice have been purchased to make Sea Breeze Punch. Find how much cranberry juice should be purchased.

A bag of Scott fertilizer covers 3000 square feet of lawn.

△ **17.** Find how many bags of fertilizer should be purchased to cover a rectangular lawn 260 feet by 180 feet.

△ **18.** Find how many bags of fertilizer should be purchased to cover a square lawn measuring 160 feet on each side.

Yearly homeowner property taxes are figured at a rate of $1.45 tax for every $100 of house value.

19. If Janet Blossom pays $2349 in property taxes, find the value of her home.

20. Find the property taxes on a condominium valued at $72,000.

A Cubs baseball player gets 3 hits in every 8 times at bat.

21. If this Cubs player comes up to bat 40 times in the World Series, find how many hits he would be expected to get.

22. At this rate, if he got 12 hits, find how many times he batted.

A survey reveals that 2 out of 3 people prefer Coke to Pepsi.

23. In a room of 40 people, how many people are likely to prefer Coke? Round the answer to the nearest person.

24. In a college class of 36 students, find how many students are likely to prefer Pepsi.

An office uses 5 boxes of envelopes every 3 weeks.

25. Find how long a gross of envelope boxes is likely to last. (A gross of boxes is 144 boxes.) Round to the nearest week.

26. Find how many boxes should be purchased to last a year. Round to the nearest box.

27. The daily supply of oxygen for one person is provided by 625 square feet of lawn. A total of 3750 square feet of lawn would provide the daily supply of oxygen for how many people? (*Source:* Professional Lawn Care Association of America)

28. In the United States, approximately 71 million of the 200 million cars and light trucks in service have driver-side air bags. In a parking lot containing 800 cars and light trucks, how many would be expected to have driver-side air bags? (*Source:* Insurance Institute for Highway Safety)

29. A student would like to estimate the height of the Statue of Liberty in New York City's harbor. The length of the Statue of Liberty's right arm is 42 feet. The student's right arm is 2 feet long and her height is $5\frac{1}{3}$ feet. Use this information to estimate the height of the Statue of Liberty. How close is your estimate to the statue's actual height of 111 feet, 1 inch from heel to top of head? (*Source:* National Park Service)

30. The length of the Statue of Liberty's index finger is 8 feet while the height to the top of the head is about 111 feet. Suppose your measurements are proportionaly the same as this statue and your height is 5 feet.

   a. Use this information to find the proposed length of your index finger. Give an exact measurement and then a decimal rounded to the nearest hundredth.

   b. Measure your index finger and write it as decimal in feet rounded to the nearest hundredth. How close is the length of your index finger to the answer to **a**? Explain why.

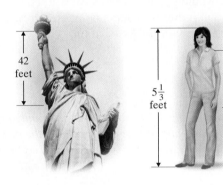

31. There are 72 milligrams of cholesterol in a 3.5 ounce serving of lobster. How much cholesterol is in 5 ounces of lobster? Round to the nearest tenth of a milligram. (*Source:* The National Institute of Health)

32. There are 76 milligrams of cholesterol in a 3-ounce serving of skinless chicken. How much cholesterol is in 8 ounces of chicken? (*Source:* USDA)

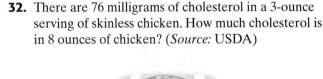

33. Trump World Tower in New York City is 881 feet tall and contains 72 stories. The Empire State Building contains 102 stories. If the Empire State Building has the same number of feet per floor as the Trump World Tower, approximate its height rounded to the nearest foot. (*Source:* skyscrapers.com)

34. Two out of every 5 men blame their poor eating habits on too much fast food. In a room of 40 men, how many would you expect to blame their not eating well on fast food? (*Source:* Healthy Choice Mixed Grills survey)

35. Medication is prescribed in 7 out of every 10 hospital emergency room visits that involve an injury. If a large urban hospital had 620 emergency room visits involving an injury in the past month, how many of these visits would you expect included a prescription for medication? (*Source:* National Center for Health Statistics)

36. Currently in the American population of people aged 65 years old and older, there are 145 women for every 100 men. In a nursing home with 280 male residents over the age of 65, how many female residents over the age of 65 would be expected? (*Source:* U.S. Bureau of the Census)

37. McDonald's four-piece Chicken McNuggets® has 190 calories. How many calories are in a nine-piece Chicken McNuggets? (*Source:* McDonald's Corporation)

38. A small order of McDonald's french fries weighs 68 grams and contains 10 grams of fat. McDonald's sold Super Size® french fries that weighed 176 grams. How many grams of fat were in McDonald's SuperSize french fries? Round to the nearest tenth. (*Source:* McDonald's Corporation)

39. One pound of firmly-packed brown sugar yields $2\frac{1}{4}$ cups. How many pounds of brown sugar will be required in a recipe that calls for 6 cups of firmly packed brown sugar? (*Source:* Based on data from *Family Circle* magazine)

40. One out of 3 American adults has worked in the restaurant industry at some point during his or her life. In an office of 84 workers, how many of these people would you expect to have worked in the restaurant industry at some point? (*Source:* National Restaurant Association)

When making homemade ice cream in a hand-cranked freezer, the tub containing the ice cream mix is surrounded by a brine (water/salt) solution. To freeze the ice cream mix rapidly so that smooth and creamy ice cream results, the brine solution should combine crushed ice and rock salt in a ratio of 5 to 1. Use this for Exercises 41 and 42. (Source: White Mountain Freezers, The Rival Company)

41. A small ice cream freezer requires 12 cups of crushed ice. How much rock salt should be mixed with the ice to create the necessary brine solution?

42. A large ice cream freezer requires $18\frac{3}{4}$ cups of crushed ice. How much rock salt will be needed?

43. The gas/oil ratio for a certain chainsaw is 50 to 1.
  a. How much oil (in gallons) should be mixed with 5 gallons of gasoline?
  b. If 1 gallon equals 128 fluid ounces, write the answer to part **a** in fluid ounces. Round to the nearest whole ounce.

44. The gas/oil ratio for a certain tractor mower is 20 to 1.
  a. How much oil (in gallons) should be mixed with 10 gallons of gas?
  b. If 1 gallon equals 4 quarts, write the answer to part **a** in quarts.

45. The adult daily dosage for a certain medicine is 150 mg (milligrams) of medicine for every 20 pounds of body weight.
  a. At this rate, find the daily dose for a man who weighs 275 pounds.
  b. If the man is to receive 500 mg of this medicine every 8 hours, is he receiving the proper dosage?

46. The adult daily dosage for a certain medicine is 80 mg (milligrams) for every 25 pounds of body weight.
  a. At this rate, find the daily dose for a woman who weighs 190 pounds.
  b. If she is to receive this medicine every 6 hours, find the amount to be given every 6 hours.

Review

Find the prime factorization of each number. See Section 3.2.

47. 15   **48.** 21   **49.** 20   **50.** 24

51. 200   **52.** 300   **53.** 32   **54.** 81

Concept Extensions

As we have seen earlier, proportions are often used in medicine dosage calculations. The exercises below have to do with liquid drug preparations, where the weight of the drug is contained in a volume of solution. The description of mg and ml below will help. We will study metric units further in this chapter.

mg means milligrams (A paper clip weighs about a gram. A milligram is about the weight of $\frac{1}{1000}$ of a paper clip.)

ml means milliliter (A liter is about a quart. A milliliter is about the amount of liquid in $\frac{1}{1000}$ of a quart.)

One way to solve the applications below is to set up the proportion $\frac{\text{mg}}{\text{ml}} = \frac{\text{mg}}{\text{ml}}$.

A solution strength of 15 mg of medicine in 1 ml of solution is available.

55. If a patient needs 12 mg of medicine, how many ml do you administer?

56. If a patient needs 33 mg of medicine, how many ml do you administer?

A solution strength of 8 mg of medicine in 1 ml of solution is available.

57. If a patient needs 10 mg of medicine, how many ml do you administer?

58. If a patient needs 6 mg of medicine, how many ml do you administer?

Estimate the following. See the Concept Check in this section.

59. It takes 1.5 cups of milk to make 11 muffins. Estimate the amount of milk needed to make 8 dozen muffins. Explain your calculation.

60. A favorite chocolate chip recipe calls for $2\frac{1}{2}$ cups of flour to make 2 dozen cookies. Estimate the amount of flour needed to make 50 cookies. Explain your calculation.

A board such as the one pictured below will balance if the following proportion is true:

$$\frac{\text{first weight}}{\text{second distance}} = \frac{\text{second weight}}{\text{first distance}}$$

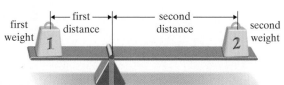

Use this proportion to solve Exercises 61 and 62.

61. Find the distance *n* that will allow the board to balance.

7 feet — *n* feet

40 pounds   60 pounds

62. Find the length *n* needed to lift the weight below.

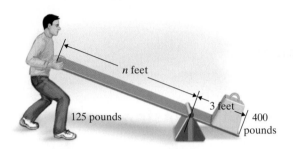

n feet

125 pounds   3 feet   400 pounds

63. Describe a situation in which writing a proportion might solve a problem related to driving a car.

 STUDY SKILLS BUILDER

How Are You Doing?

If you haven't done so yet, take a few moments and think about how you are doing in this course. Are you working toward your goal of successfully completing this course? Is your performance on homework, quizzes, and tests satisfactory? If not, you might want to see your instructor to see if he/she has any suggestions on how you can improve your performance. Reread Section 1.1 for ideas on places to get help with your mathematics course.

Answer the following.

1. List any textbook supplements you are using to help you through this course.

2. List any campus resources you are using to help you through this course.

3. Write a short paragraph describing how you are doing in your mathematics course.

4. If improvement is needed, list ways that you can work toward improving your situation as described in Exercise 3.

Ratio and Proportion

Write each ratio as a ratio of whole numbers using fractional notation. Write the fraction in simplest form.

1. 18 to 20

2. 36 to 100

3. 8.6 to 10

4. 1.6 to 4.6

5. $8.65 to $6.95

6. 7.2 ounces to 8.4 ounces

7. $3\frac{1}{2}$ to 13

8. $1\frac{2}{3}$ to $2\frac{3}{4}$

9. 8 inches to 12 inches

10. 3 hours to 24 hours

Find the ratio described in each problem.

11. The circle graph below shows how the top 20 movies of 2004 were rated. Use this graph to answer the questions.

    a. How many top 20 movies were rated PG-13?

    b. Find the ratio of top 20 PG-13 movies to total movies for that year.

12. Find the ratio of the width to the length of the sign below.

Top 20 Movies of 2004

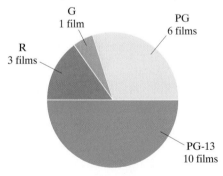

Source: Internet search and Bryan Gay

Write each rate as a fraction in simplest form.

13. 5 offices for every 20 graduate assistants

14. 6 lights every 15 feet

15. 64 computers every 100 households

16. 45 students for every 10 computers

1. _____

2. _____

3. _____

4. _____

5. _____

6. _____

7. _____

8. _____

9. _____

10. _____

11. a. _____

    b. _____

12. _____

13. _____

14. _____

15. _____

16. _____

17. _____

18. _____

19. _____

20. _____

21. _____

22. _____

23. _____

24. _____

25. _____

26. _____

27. _____

28. _____

Write each rate as a unit rate.

17. 165 miles in 3 hours

18. 560 feet in 4 seconds

19. 7524 books for 1254 college students

20. 2002 pounds for 13 adults

Write each unit price, rounded to the nearest hundredth, and decide which is the better buy.

21. Microwave popcorn:
3 packs for $2.39
8 packs for $5.99

22. AA Batteries:
4 for $3.69
10 for $9.89

Determine whether each proportion is true.

23. $\dfrac{7}{4} = \dfrac{5}{3}$

24. $\dfrac{8.2}{2} = \dfrac{16.4}{4}$

Find the unknown number n in each proportion.

25. $\dfrac{5}{3} = \dfrac{40}{n}$

26. $\dfrac{n}{10} = \dfrac{13}{4}$

27. $\dfrac{6}{11} = \dfrac{n}{5}$

28. $\dfrac{21}{n} = \dfrac{7\frac{1}{2}}{3}$

5.4 LENGTH: U.S. AND METRIC SYSTEMS

Objectives

A. Define U.S. Units of Length and Convert from One Unit to Another.

B. Use Mixed Units of Length.

C. Perform Arithmetic Operations on U.S. Units of Length.

D. Define Metric Units of Length and Convert from One Unit to Another.

E. Perform Arithmetic Operations on Metric Units of Length.

Objective A Defining and Converting U.S. System Units of Length

In the United States, two systems of measurement are commonly used. They are the **United States (U.S.), or English, measurement system** and the **metric system.** The U.S. measurement system is familiar to most Americans. Units such as feet, miles, ounces, and gallons are used. However, the metric system is also commonly used in fields such as medicine, sports, international marketing, and certain physical sciences. We are accustomed to buying 2-liter bottles of soft drinks, watching televised coverage of the 100-meter dash at the Olympic Games, or taking a 200-milligram dose of pain reliever.

The U.S. system of measurement uses the **inch, foot, yard,** and **mile** to measure **length.** The following is a summary of equivalencies between units of length:

U.S. Units of Length

$$12 \text{ inches (in.)} = 1 \text{ foot (ft)}$$
$$3 \text{ feet} = 1 \text{ yard (yd)}$$
$$36 \text{ inches} = 1 \text{ yard}$$
$$5280 \text{ feet} = 1 \text{ mile (mi)}$$

To convert from one unit of length to another, we will use **unit fractions.** We define a unit fraction to be a fraction that is equivalent to 1. Examples of unit fractions are as follows:

Unit Fractions

$$\frac{12 \text{ in.}}{1 \text{ ft}} = 1 \text{ or } \frac{1 \text{ ft}}{12 \text{ in.}} = 1 \text{ (since 12 in.} = 1 \text{ ft)}$$

$$\frac{3 \text{ ft}}{1 \text{ yd}} = 1 \text{ or } \frac{1 \text{ yd}}{3 \text{ ft}} = 1 \text{ (since 3 ft} = 1 \text{ yd)}$$

$$\frac{5280 \text{ ft}}{1 \text{ mi}} = 1 \text{ or } \frac{1 \text{ mi}}{5280 \text{ ft}} = 1 \text{ (since 5280 ft} = 1 \text{ mi)}$$

Remember that multiplying a number by 1 does not change the value of the number.

EXAMPLE 1 Convert 8 feet to inches.

Solution: We multiply 8 feet by a unit fraction that uses the equality 12 inches = 1 foot. The unit fraction should be in the form $\frac{\text{units to convert to}}{\text{original units}}$ or in this case $\frac{12 \text{ inches}}{1 \text{ foot}}$. We do this so that like units divide out, as shown.

$$8 \text{ ft} = \frac{8 \text{ ft}}{1} \cdot 1 \qquad \text{Multiply by 1 in the form of } \frac{12 \text{ in.}}{1 \text{ ft}}.$$

$$= \frac{8 \text{ ft}}{1} \cdot \frac{12 \text{ in.}}{1 \text{ ft}}$$

$$= 8 \cdot 12 \text{ in.}$$

$$= 96 \text{ in.} \qquad \text{Multiply.}$$

PRACTICE PROBLEM 1

Convert 5 feet to inches.

Answer

1. 60 in.

Continued on next page

Thus, 8 ft = 96 in., as shown in the diagram:

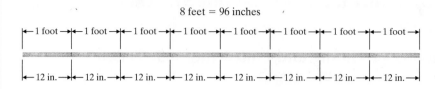

8 feet = 96 inches

■ **Work Practice Problem 1**

PRACTICE PROBLEM 2

Convert 7 yards to feet.

EXAMPLE 2 Convert 7 feet to yards.

Solution: We multiply by a unit fraction that compares 1 yard to 3 feet.

$$7 \text{ ft} = \frac{7 \text{ ft}}{1} \cdot 1$$

$$= \frac{7 \text{ ft}}{1} \cdot \frac{1 \text{ yd}}{3 \text{ ft}} \quad \leftarrow \text{ Units to convert to}$$
$$\qquad\qquad\qquad \leftarrow \text{ Original units}$$

$$= \frac{7}{3} \text{ yd}$$

$$= 2\frac{1}{3} \text{ yd} \qquad \text{Divide.}$$

Thus, $7 \text{ ft} = 2\frac{1}{3} \text{ yd}$, as shown in the diagram.

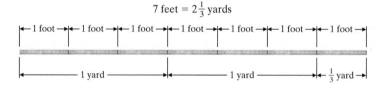

7 feet = $2\frac{1}{3}$ yards

■ **Work Practice Problem 2**

PRACTICE PROBLEM 3

Suppose the bill in the photo measures 18 inches. Convert 18 inches to feet, using decimals.

EXAMPLE 3 Finding Length of Pelican's Bill

The Australian pelican has the longest bill, measuring from 13 to 18.5 inches long. The pelican in the photo has a 15-inch bill. Convert 15 inches to feet, using decimals.

Solution:

$$15 \text{ in.} = \frac{15 \text{ in.}}{1} \cdot \frac{1 \text{ ft}}{12 \text{ in.}} \quad \leftarrow \text{ Units to convert to}$$
$$\qquad\qquad\qquad\qquad \leftarrow \text{ Original units}$$

$$= \frac{15}{12} \text{ ft}$$

$$= \frac{5}{4} \text{ ft} \qquad \text{Simplify } \frac{15}{12}.$$

$$= 1.25 \text{ ft} \qquad \text{Divide.}$$

Thus, 15 in. = 1.25 ft, as shown in the diagram.

15 inches = 1.25 ft

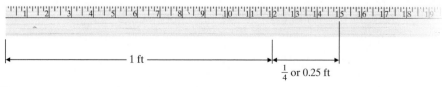

1 ft

$\frac{1}{4}$ or 0.25 ft

■ **Work Practice Problem 3**

Objective B Using Mixed U.S. System Units of Length

Sometimes it is more meaningful to express a measurement of length with mixed units such as 1 ft and 5 in. We usually condense this and write 1 ft 5 in.

In Example 2, we found that 7 feet was the same as $2\frac{1}{3}$ yards. The measurement can also be written as a mixture of yards and feet. That is,

7 ft = _____ yd _____ ft

Because 3 ft = 1 yd, we divide 3 into 7 to see how many whole yards are in 7 feet. The quotient is the number of yards, and the remainder is the number of feet.

$$
\begin{array}{r}
2 \text{ yd } 1 \text{ ft} \\
3\overline{)7} \\
-6 \\
\hline
1
\end{array}
$$

Thus, 7 ft = 2 yd 1 ft, as seen in the diagram:

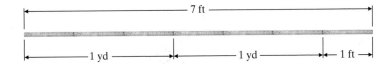

EXAMPLE 4 Convert: 134 in. = _____ ft _____ in.

Solution: Because 12 in. = 1 ft, we divide 12 into 134. The quotient is the number of feet. The remainder is the number of inches. To see why we divide 12 into 134, notice that

$$134 \text{ in.} = \frac{134 \text{ in.}}{1} \cdot \frac{1 \text{ ft}}{12 \text{ in.}} = \frac{134}{12} \text{ ft}$$

$$
\begin{array}{r}
11 \text{ ft } 2 \text{ in.} \\
12\overline{)134} \\
-12 \\
\hline
14 \\
-12 \\
\hline
2
\end{array}
$$

Thus, 134 in. = 11 ft 2 in.

Work Practice Problem 4

EXAMPLE 5 Convert 3 feet 7 inches to inches.

Solution: First, we convert 3 feet to inches. Then we add 7 inches.

$$3 \text{ ft} = \frac{3 \text{ ft}}{1} \cdot \frac{12 \text{ in.}}{1 \text{ ft}} = 36 \text{ in.}$$

Then

$$3 \text{ ft } 7 \text{ in.} = 36 \text{ in.} + 7 \text{ in.} = 43 \text{ in.}$$

Work Practice Problem 5

PRACTICE PROBLEM 4

Convert:
68 in. = _____ ft _____ in.

PRACTICE PROBLEM 5

Convert 5 yards 2 feet to feet.

Answers
4. 5 ft 8 in., **5.** 17 ft

Objective C Performing Operations on U.S. System Units of Length

Finding sums or differences of measurements often involves converting units, as shown in the next example. Just remember that, as usual, only like units can be added or subtracted.

PRACTICE PROBLEM 6

Add 4 ft 8 in. to 8 ft 11 in.

EXAMPLE 6   Add 3 ft 2 in. and 5 ft 11 in.

Solution: To add, we line up the similar units.

$$
\begin{array}{r}
3\ \text{ft}\ \ 2\ \text{in.} \\
+\ 5\ \text{ft}\ 11\ \text{in.} \\
\hline
8\ \text{ft}\ 13\ \text{in.}
\end{array}
$$

Since 13 inches is the same as 1 ft 1 in., we have

$$8\ \text{ft}\ 13\ \text{in.} = 8\ \text{ft} + 1\ \text{ft}\ \ 1\ \text{in.}$$
$$= 9\ \text{ft}\ 1\ \text{in.}$$

🔲 **Work Practice Problem 6**

✔ **Concept Check**   How could you estimate the following sum?

$$
\begin{array}{r}
7\ \text{yd}\ \ 4\ \text{in.} \\
+\ 3\ \text{yd}\ 27\ \text{in.} \\
\hline
\end{array}
$$

PRACTICE PROBLEM 7

A carpenter cuts 1 ft 9 in. from a board of length 5 ft 8 in. Find the remaining length of the board.

EXAMPLE 7   **Finding the Length of a Piece of Rope**

A rope of length 6 yd 1 ft has 2 yd 2 ft cut from one end. Find the length of the remaining rope.

Solution: Subtract 2 yd 2 ft from 6 yd 1 ft.

$$
\begin{array}{rcl}
\text{beginning length} & \rightarrow & 6\ \text{yd}\ 1\ \text{ft} \\
-\quad\quad\text{amount cut} & \rightarrow & -2\ \text{yd}\ 2\ \text{ft} \\
\text{remaining length} & &
\end{array}
$$

We cannot subtract 2 ft from 1 ft, so we borrow 1 yd from the 6 yd. One yard is converted to 3 ft and combined with the 1 ft already there.

Borrow 1 yd = 3 ft

$$5\ \text{yd} + \boxed{1\ \text{yd}}\ \boxed{3\ \text{ft}}$$

$$
\begin{array}{rcl}
\cancel{6\ \text{yd}}\ 1\ \text{ft} & = & 5\ \text{yd}\ 4\ \text{ft} \\
-\ 2\ \text{yd}\ 2\ \text{ft} & = & -2\ \text{yd}\ 2\ \text{ft} \\
\hline
 & & 3\ \text{yd}\ 2\ \text{ft}
\end{array}
$$

The remaining rope is 3 yd 2 ft long.

🔲 **Work Practice Problem 7**

Objective D Defining and Converting Metric System Units of Length

The basic unit of length in the metric system is the **meter.** A meter is slightly longer than a yard. It is approximately 39.37 inches long. Recall that a yard is 36 inches long.

1 yard = 36 inches

1 meter ≈ 39.37 inches

All units of length in the metric system are based on the meter. The following is a summary of the prefixes used in the metric system. Also shown are equivalencies between units of length. Like the decimal system, the metric system uses powers of 10 to define units.

Metric Unit of Length
1 **kilo**meter (km) = 1000 meters (m)
1 **hecto**meter (hm) = 100 m
1 **deka**meter (dam) = 10 m
1 **meter** (m) = 1 m
1 **deci**meter (dm) = 1/10 m or 0.1 m
1 **centi**meter (cm) = 1/100 m or 0.01 m
1 **milli**meter (mm) = 1/1000 m or 0.001 m

The figure below will help you with decimeters, centimeters, and millimeters.

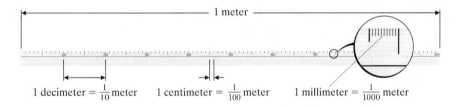

1 decimeter = $\frac{1}{10}$ meter   1 centimeter = $\frac{1}{100}$ meter   1 millimeter = $\frac{1}{1000}$ meter

Helpful Hint

Study the figure above for other equivalencies between metric units of length.

10 decimeters = 1 meter   10 millimeters = 1 centimeter
100 centimeters = 1 meter   10 centimeters = 1 decimeter
1000 millimeters = 1 meter

These same prefixes are used in the metric system for mass and capacity. The most commonly used measurements of length in the metric system are the **meter, millimeter, centimeter,** and **kilometer.**

Being comfortable with the metric units of length means gaining a "feeling" for metric lengths, just as you have a "feeling" for the length of an inch, a foot, and a mile. To help you accomplish this, study the following examples:

A millimeter is about the thickness of a large paper clip.

A centimeter is about the width of a large paper clip.

A meter is slightly longer than a yard.

A kilometer is about two-thirds of a mile.

The length of this book is approximately 27.5 centimeters.

The width of this book is approximately 21.5 centimeters.

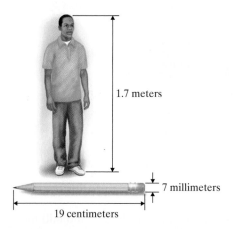

As with the U.S. system of measurement, unit fractions may be used to convert from one unit of length to another. For example, let's convert 1200 meters to kilometers. To do so, we will multiply by 1 in the form of the unit fraction

$$\frac{1 \text{ km}}{1000 \text{ m}} \quad \begin{array}{l}\leftarrow \text{ Units to convert to} \\ \leftarrow \text{ Original units}\end{array}$$

$$1200 \text{ m} = \frac{1200 \text{ m}}{1} \cdot 1 = \frac{1200 \text{ m}}{1} \cdot \overbrace{\frac{1 \text{ km}}{1000 \text{ m}}}^{\text{Unit fraction}} = \frac{1200 \text{ km}}{1000} = 1.2 \text{ km}$$

Thus, 1200 m = 1.2 km as shown in the diagram.

The metric system does, however, have a distinct advantage over the U.S. system of measurement: The ease of converting from one unit of length to another. Since all units of length are powers of 10 of the meter, converting from one unit of length to another is as simple as moving the decimal point. Listing units of length in order from largest to smallest helps to keep track of how many places to move the decimal point when converting.

Let's again convert 1200 meters to kilometers. This time, to convert from meters to kilometers, we move along the chart shown 3 units to the left, from meters to kilometers. This means that we move the decimal point 3 places to the left.

km hm dam **m** dm cm mm

3 units to the left

EXAMPLE 8 Convert 2.3 m to centimeters.

Solution: First we will convert by using a unit fraction.

$$2.3 \text{ m} = \frac{2.3 \text{ m}}{1} \cdot \overbrace{\frac{100 \text{ cm}}{1 \text{ m}}}^{\text{Unit fraction}} = 230 \text{ cm}$$

Now we will convert by listing the units of length in order from left to right and moving from meters to centimeters.

km   hm   dam   **m   dm   cm**   mm

2 units to the right

2.30 m = 230. cm

2 places to the right

With either method, we get 230 cm.

■ **Work Practice Problem 8**

EXAMPLE 9 Convert 450,000 mm to meters.

Solution: We list the units of length in order from left to right and move from millimeters to meters.

km   hm   dam   **m   dm   cm   mm**

3 units to the left

450,000 mm = 450.000 m or 450 m

■ **Work Practice Problem 9**

✔ **Concept Check** What is wrong with the following conversion of 150 cm to meters?

150.00 cm = 15,000 m

Objective E Performing Operations on Metric System Units of Length

To add, subtract, multiply, or divide with metric measurements of length, we write all numbers using the same unit of length and then add, subtract, multiply, or divide as with decimals.

EXAMPLE 10 Subtract 430 m from 1.3 km.

Solution: First we convert both measurements to kilometers or both to meters.

430 m = 0.43 km   or   1.3 km = 1300 m

$$\begin{array}{r} 1.30 \text{ km} \\ - 0.43 \text{ km} \\ \hline 0.87 \text{ km} \end{array} \qquad \begin{array}{r} 1300 \text{ m} \\ - 430 \text{ m} \\ \hline 870 \text{ m} \end{array}$$

The difference is 0.87 km or 870 m.

■ **Work Practice Problem 10**

Mental Math

Convert as indicated.

1. 12 inches to feet

2. 6 feet to yards

3. 24 inches to feet

4. 36 inches to feet

5. 36 inches to yards

6. 2 yards to inches

Determine whether the measurement in each statement is reasonable.

7. The screen of a home television set has a 30-meter diagonal.

8. A window measures 1 meter by 0.5 meter.

9. A drinking glass is made of glass 2 millimeters thick.

10. A paper clip is 4 kilometers long.

11. The distance across the Colorado River is 50 kilometers.

12. A model's hair is 30 centimeters long.

5.4 EXERCISE SET

Objective A *Convert each measurement as indicated. See Examples 1 through 3.*

1. 60 in. to feet

2. 84 in. to feet

3. 12 yd to feet

4. 18 yd to feet

5. 42,240 ft to miles

6. 36,960 ft to miles

7. 102 in. to feet

8. 150 in. to feet

9. 10 ft to yards

10. 25 ft to yards

11. 6.4 mi to feet

12. 3.8 mi to feet

13. 162 in. to yd (Write answer as a decimal.)

14. 7216 yd to mi (Write answer as a decimal.)

15. 3 in. to ft (Write answer as a decimal.)

16. 129 in. to ft (Write answer as a decimal.)

Objective B *Convert each measurement as indicated. See Examples 4 and 5.*

17. 40 ft = _____ yd _____ ft

18. 100 ft = _____ yd _____ ft

19. 41 in. = _____ ft _____ in.

20. 75 in. = _____ ft _____ in.

21. 10,000 ft = _____ mi _____ ft

22. 25,000 ft = _____ mi _____ ft

23. 5 ft 2 in. = _____ in.

24. 4 ft 11 in. = _____ in.

25. 7 yd 2 ft = _____ ft

26. 7 yd 1 ft = _____ ft

27. 2 yd 1 ft = _____ in.

28. 1 yd 2 ft = _____ in.

Objective **C** *Perform each indicated operation. Simplify the result if possible. See Examples 6 and 7.*

29. 5 ft 8 in. + 6 ft 7 in.

30. 9 ft 10 in. + 8 ft 4 in.

31. 12 yd 2 ft + 9 yd 2 ft

32. 16 yd 2 ft + 8 yd 1 ft

33. 24 ft 8 in. − 16 ft 3 in.

34. 15 ft 5 in. − 8 ft 2 in.

35. 16 ft 3 in. − 10 ft 9 in.

36. 14 ft 8 in. − 3 ft 11 in.

37. 6 ft 8 in. ÷ 2

38. 26 ft 10 in. ÷ 2

39. 12 yd 2 ft × 4

40. 15 yd 1 ft × 8

Objective **D** *Convert as indicated. See Examples 8 and 9.*

41. 40 m to centimeters

42. 18 m to centimeters

43. 40 mm to centimeters

44. 18 mm to centimeters

45. 300 m to kilometers

46. 400 m to kilometers

47. 1400 mm to meters

48. 6400 mm to meters

49. 1500 cm to meters

50. 6400 cm to meters

51. 0.42 km to centimeters

52. 0.95 km to centimeters

53. 7 km to meters

54. 5 km to meters

55. 8.3 cm to millimeters

56. 4.6 cm to millimeters

57. 20.1 mm to decimeters

58. 140.2 mm to decimeters

59. 0.04 m to millimeters

60. 0.2 m to millimeters

Objective **E** *Perform each indicated operation. See Example 10.*

61. 8.6 m + 0.34 m

62. 14.1 cm + 3.96 cm

63. 2.9 m + 40 mm

64. 30 cm + 8.9 m

65. 24.8 mm − 1.19 cm

66. 45.3 m − 2.16 dam

67. 15 km − 2360 m

68. 14 cm − 15 mm

69. 18.3 m × 3

70. 14.1 m × 4

71. 6.2 km ÷ 4

72. 9.6 m ÷ 5

Objectives Ⓐ Ⓒ Ⓓ Ⓔ **Mixed Practice** *Solve. Remember to insert units when writing your answers. For Exercises 73 through 82, complete the charts.*

		Yards	Feet	Inches
73.	Chrysler Building in New York City		1046	
74.	4-story building			792
75.	Python length		35	
76.	Ostrich height			108

Complete the chart.

		Meters	Millimeters	Kilometers	Centimeters
77.	Length of elephant	5			
78.	Height of grizzly bear	3			
79.	Tennis ball diameter				6.5
80.	Golf ball diameter				4.6
81.	Distance from London to Paris			342	
82.	Distance from Houston to Dallas			396	

83. The National Zoo maintains a small patch of bamboo, which it grows as a food supply for its pandas. Two weeks ago, the bamboo was 6 ft 10 in. tall. Since then, the bamboo has grown 3 ft 8 in. How tall is the bamboo now?

84. While exploring in the Marianas Trench, a submarine probe was lowered to a point 1 mile 1400 feet below the ocean's surface. Later it was lowered an additional 1 mile 4000 feet below this point. How far is the probe below the surface of the Pacific?

85. The length of one of the Statue of Liberty's hands is 16 ft 5 in. One of the Statue's eyes is 2 ft 6 in. across. How much longer is a hand than the width of an eye? (*Source:* National Park Service)

86. The width of the Statue of Liberty's head from ear to ear is 10 ft. The height of the Statue's head from chin to cranium is 17 ft 3 in. How much taller is the Statue's head than its width? (*Source:* National Park Service)

87. A 3.4-m rope is attached to a 5.8-m rope. However, when the ropes are tied, 8 cm of length is lost to form the knot. What is the length of the tied ropes?

88. A 2.15-m-long sash cord has become frayed at both ends so that 1 cm is trimmed from each end. How long is the remaining cord?

89. The ice on a pond is 5.33 cm thick. For safe skating, the owner of the pond insists that it must be 80 mm thick. How much thicker must the ice be before skating is allowed?

90. The sediment on the bottom of the Towamencin Creek is normally 14 cm thick, but the recent flood washed away 22 mm of sediment. How thick is it now?

91. The Amana Corporation stacks up its microwave ovens in a distribution warehouse. Each stack is 1 ft 9 in. wide. How far from the wall would 9 of these stacks extend?

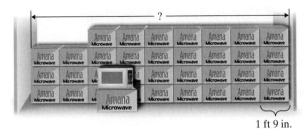

1 ft 9 in.

92. The highway commission is installing concrete sound barriers along a highway. Each barrier is 1 yd 2 ft long. Find the total length of 25 barriers placed end to end.

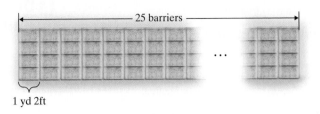

1 yd 2ft

93. A logging firm needs to cut a 67-m-long redwood log into 20 equal pieces before loading it onto a truck for shipment. How long will each piece be?

94. An 18.3-m-tall flagpole is mounted on a 65-cm-high pedestal. How far is the top of the flagpole from the ground?

95. The world's longest Coca-Cola truck is in Sweden and is 79 feet long. How many *yards* long are 4 of these trucks? (*Source: Coca-Cola Today*)

△ **96.** The world's largest Coca-Cola sign is in Arica, Chile. It is in the shape of a rectangle whose length is $133\frac{1}{3}$ yards and whose width is 131 feet. Find the area of the sign in square feet. (*Source: Coca-Cola Today*) (*Hint:* Recall that area of a rectangle is the product: length times width.)

Review

Write each decimal as a fraction and each fraction as a decimal. See Section 4.1.

97. 0.21   **98.** 0.86   **99.** $\frac{13}{100}$ **100.** $\frac{47}{100}$ **101.** $\frac{1}{4}$ **102.** $\frac{3}{20}$

Concept Extensions

Estimate each sum or difference. See the Concept Check in this section.

103. 5 yd 2 in.
        + 7 yd 30 in.

104. 45 ft 1 in.
        − 10 ft 11 in.

105. Using a unit other than the foot, write a length that is equivalent to 4 feet. (*Hint:* There are many possibilities.)

106. Using a unit other than the meter, write a length that is equivalent to 7 meters. (*Hint:* There are many possibilities.)

107. To convert from meters to centimeters, the decimal point is moved two places to the right. Explain how this relates to the fact that the prefix *centi* means $\frac{1}{100}$.

108. Explain why conversions in the metric system are easier to make than conversions in the U.S. system of measurement.

Objectives

A Define U.S. Units of Weight and Convert from One Unit to Another.

B Perform Arithmetic Operations on Units of Weight.

C Define Metric Units of Mass and Convert from One Unit to Another.

D Perform Arithmetic Operations on Units of Mass.

Objective A Defining and Converting U.S. System Units of Weight

Whenever we talk about how heavy an object is, we are concerned with the object's **weight.** We discuss weight when we refer to a 12-ounce box of Rice Krispies, a 15-pound tabby cat, or a barge hauling 24 tons of garbage.

12 ounces

15 pounds

24 tons of garbage

The most common units of weight in the U.S. measurement system are the **ounce,** the **pound,** and the **ton.** The following is a summary of equivalencies between units of weight:

U.S. Units of Weight	Unit Fractions
16 ounces (oz) = 1 pound (lb)	$\dfrac{16\ \text{oz}}{1\ \text{lb}} = \dfrac{1\ \text{lb}}{16\ \text{oz}} = 1$
2000 pounds = 1 ton	$\dfrac{2000\ \text{lb}}{1\ \text{ton}} = \dfrac{1\ \text{ton}}{2000\ \text{lb}} = 1$

✔**Concept Check** If you were describing the weight of a fully-loaded semi-trailer, which type of unit would you use: ounce, pound, or ton? Why?

Unit fractions that equal 1 are used to convert between units of weight in the U.S. system. When converting using unit fractions, recall that the numerator of a unit fraction should contain the units we are converting to and the denominator should contain the original units.

PRACTICE PROBLEM 1

Convert 4500 pounds to tons.

EXAMPLE 1 Convert 9000 pounds to tons.

Solution: We multiply 9000 lb by a unit fraction that uses the equality

2000 pounds = 1 ton.

Remember, the unit fraction should be $\dfrac{\text{units to convert to}}{\text{original units}}$ or $\dfrac{1\ \text{ton}}{2000\ \text{lb}}$.

Answer

1. $2\dfrac{1}{4}$ tons

✔ **Concept Check Answer**

ton

$$9000 \text{ lb} = \frac{9000 \text{ lb}}{1} \cdot 1 = \frac{9000 \text{ lb}}{1} \cdot \frac{1 \text{ ton}}{2000 \text{ lb}} = \frac{9000 \text{ tons}}{2000} = \frac{9}{2} \text{ tons or } 4\frac{1}{2} \text{ tons}$$

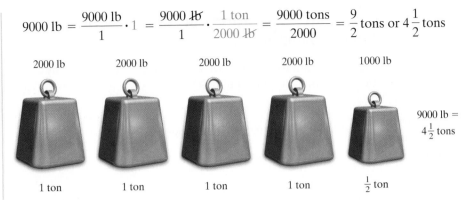

| 2000 lb | 2000 lb | 2000 lb | 2000 lb | 1000 lb |
| 1 ton | 1 ton | 1 ton | 1 ton | $\frac{1}{2}$ ton |

$9000 \text{ lb} = 4\frac{1}{2} \text{ tons}$

Work Practice Problem 1

EXAMPLE 2 Convert 3 pounds to ounces.

Solution: We multiply by the unit fraction $\frac{16 \text{ oz}}{1 \text{ lb}}$ to convert from pounds to ounces.

$$3 \text{ lb} = \frac{3 \text{ lb}}{1} \cdot 1 = \frac{3 \text{ lb}}{1} \cdot \frac{16 \text{ oz}}{1 \text{ lb}} = 3 \cdot 16 \text{ oz} = 48 \text{ oz}$$

1 pound   1 pound   1 pound
16 ounces 16 ounces 16 ounces

3 lb = 48 oz

Work Practice Problem 2

As with length, it is sometimes useful to simplify a measurement of weight by writing it in terms of mixed units.

EXAMPLE 3 Convert: 33 ounces = _____ lb _____ oz

Solution: Because 16 oz = 1 lb, divide 16 into 33 to see how many pounds are in 33 ounces. The quotient is the number of pounds, and the remainder is the number of ounces. To see why we divide 16 into 33, notice that

$$33 \text{ oz} = 33 \text{ oz} \cdot \frac{1 \text{ lb}}{16 \text{ oz}} = \frac{33}{16} \text{ lb}$$

```
      2 lb 1 oz
16)33
  -32
    1
```

Thus, 33 ounces is the same as 2 lb 1 oz.

16 ounces 16 ounces 1 ounce
1 pound   1 pound   1 ounce

33 oz = 2 lb 1 oz

Work Practice Problem 3

PRACTICE PROBLEM 2
Convert 56 ounces to pounds.

PRACTICE PROBLEM 3
Convert:
45 ounces = _____ lb _____ oz

Answers
2. $3\frac{1}{2}$ lb, 3. 2 lb 13 oz

Objective B Performing Operations on U.S. System Units of Weight

Performing arithmetic operations on units of weight works the same way as performing arithmetic operations on units of length.

PRACTICE PROBLEM 4

Subtract 5 tons 1200 lb from 8 tons 100 lb.

EXAMPLE 4 Subtract 3 tons 1350 lb from 8 tons 1000 lb.

Solution: To subtract, we line up similar units.

$$
\begin{array}{r}
8 \text{ tons } 1000 \text{ lb} \\
- 3 \text{ tons } 1350 \text{ lb} \\
\end{array}
$$

Since we cannot subtract 1350 lb from 1000 lb, we borrow 1 ton from the 8 tons. To do so, we write 1 ton as 2000 lb and combine it with the 1000 lb.

7 tons + (1 ton) 2000 lb

$$
\begin{array}{r}
8 \text{ tons } 1000 \text{ lb} \\
- 3 \text{ tons } 1350 \text{ lb} \\
\end{array}
\quad
\begin{array}{c}
= \\
= \\
\end{array}
\quad
\begin{array}{r}
7 \text{ tons } 3000 \text{ lb} \\
- 3 \text{ tons } 1350 \text{ lb} \\
\hline
4 \text{ tons } 1650 \text{ lb} \\
\end{array}
$$

To check, see that the sum of 4 tons 1650 lb and 3 tons 1350 lb is 8 tons 1000 lb.

🖳 **Work Practice Problem 4**

PRACTICE PROBLEM 5

A 5-lb 14-oz batch of cookies is packed into a 6-oz container before it is mailed. Find the total weight.

EXAMPLE 5 Finding the Weight of a Child

Bryan weighed 8 lb 8 oz at birth. By the time he was 1 year old, he had gained 11 lb 14 oz. Find his weight at age 1 year.

Solution:

$$
\begin{array}{lll}
\text{birth weight} & \rightarrow & 8 \text{ lb } 8 \text{ oz} \\
+ \text{ weight gained} & \rightarrow & + 11 \text{ lb } 14 \text{ oz} \\
\hline
\text{total weight} & \rightarrow & 19 \text{ lb } 22 \text{ oz} \\
\end{array}
$$

Since 22 oz equals 1 lb 6 oz,

$$
\begin{aligned}
19 \text{ lb } 22 \text{ oz} &= 19 \text{ lb} + 1 \text{ lb } 6 \text{ oz} \\
&= 20 \text{ lb } 6 \text{ oz}
\end{aligned}
$$

Bryan weighed 20 lb 6 oz on his first birthday.

🖳 **Work Practice Problem 5**

Objective C Defining and Converting Metric System Units of Mass

In scientific and technical areas, a careful distinction is made between **weight** and **mass. Weight** is really a measure of the pull of gravity. The farther from Earth an object gets, the less it weighs. However, **mass** is a measure of the amount of substance in the object and does not change. Astronauts orbiting Earth weigh much less than they weigh on Earth, but they have the same mass in orbit as they do on Earth. Here on Earth weight and mass are the same, so either term may be used.

Answers

4. 2 tons 900 lb, **5.** 6 lb 4 oz

The basic unit of mass in the metric system is the **gram.** It is defined as the mass of water contained in a cube 1 centimeter (cm) on each side.

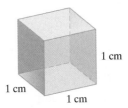

The following examples may help you get a feeling for metric masses:

A tablet contains 200 milligrams of ibuprofen.

A large paper clip weighs approximately 1 gram.

A box of crackers weighs 453 grams.

A kilogram is slightly over 2 pounds. An adult woman may weigh 60 kilograms.

The prefixes for units of mass in the metric system are the same as for units of length, as shown in the following table:

Metric Unit of Mass
1 **kilo**gram (kg) = 1000 grams (g)
1 **hecto**gram (hg) = 100 g
1 **deka**gram (dag) = 10 g
1 gram (g) = 1 g
1 **deci**gram (dg) = 1/10 g or 0.1 g
1 **centi**gram (cg) = 1/100 g or 0.01 g
1 **milli**gram (mg) = 1/1000 g or 0.001 g

✔**Concept Check** True or false? A decigram is larger than a dekagram. Explain.

The **milligram,** the **gram,** and the **kilogram** are the three most commonly used units of mass in the metric system.

As with lengths, all units of mass are powers of 10 of the gram, so converting from one unit of mass to another involves moving only the decimal point. To convert from one unit of mass to another in the metric system, list the units of mass in order from largest to smallest.

Let's convert 4300 milligrams to grams. To convert from milligrams to grams, we move along the list 3 units to the left.

kg   hg   dag   **g**   dg   cg   **mg**

3 units to the left

This means that we move the decimal point 3 places to the left to convert from milligrams to grams.

$$4300 \text{ mg} = 4.3 \text{ g}$$

Don't forget, the same conversion can be done with unit fractions.

$$4300 \text{ mg} = \frac{4300 \text{ mg}}{1} \cdot 1 = \frac{4300 \text{ mg}}{1} \cdot \frac{0.001 \text{ g}}{1 \text{ mg}}$$
$$= 4300 \cdot 0.001 \text{ g}$$
$$= 4.3 \text{ g} \quad \text{To multiply by 0.001, move the decimal point 3 places to the left.}$$

To see that this is reasonable, study the diagram:

Thus, $4300 \text{ mg} = 4.3 \text{ g}$

PRACTICE PROBLEM 6

Convert 3.41 g to milligrams.

EXAMPLE 6 Convert 3.2 kg to grams.

Solution: First we convert by using a unit fraction.

$$3.2 \text{ kg} = 3.2 \text{ kg} \cdot 1 = 3.2 \text{ kg} \cdot \overbrace{\frac{1000 \text{ g}}{1 \text{ kg}}}^{\text{Unit fraction}} = 3200 \text{ g}$$

Now let's list the units of mass in order from left to right and move from kilograms to grams.

kg   hg   dag   g   dg   cg   mg

3 units to the right

$$3.200 \text{ kg} = 3200. \text{ g}$$

3 places to the right

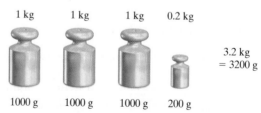

Work Practice Problem 6

Answer

6. 3410 mg

EXAMPLE 7 Convert 2.35 cg to grams.

Solution: We list the units of mass in a chart and move from centigrams to grams.

kg   hg   dag   g   dg   cg   mg

2 units to the left

02.35 cg = 0.0235 g

2 places to the left

■ **Work Practice Problem 7**

Objective D Performing Operations on Metric System Units of Mass

Arithmetic operations can be performed with metric units of mass just as we performed operations with metric units of length. We convert each number to the same unit of mass and add, subtract, multiply, or divide as with decimals.

EXAMPLE 8 Subtract 5.4 dg from 1.6 g.

Solution: We convert both numbers to decigrams or to grams before subtracting.

5.4 dg = 0.54 g   or   1.6 g = 16 dg

$$\begin{array}{r} 1.60 \text{ g} \\ - 0.54 \text{ g} \\ \hline 1.06 \text{ g} \end{array} \qquad \begin{array}{r} 16.0 \text{ dg} \\ - 5.4 \text{ dg} \\ \hline 10.6 \text{ dg} \end{array}$$

The difference is 1.06 g or 10.6 dg.

■ **Work Practice Problem 8**

PRACTICE PROBLEM 7

Convert 56.2 cg to grams.

PRACTICE PROBLEM 8

Subtract 3.1 dg from 2.5 g.

Answers

7. 0.562 g,   **8.** 2.19 g or 21.9 dg

Mental Math

Convert.

1. 16 ounces to pounds

2. 32 ounces to pounds

3. 1 ton to pounds

4. 3 tons to pounds

5. 1 pound to ounces

6. 3 pounds to ounces

7. 2000 pounds to tons

8. 4000 pounds to tons

Determine whether the measurement in each statement is reasonable.

9. The doctor prescribed a pill containing 2 kg of medication.

10. A full-grown cat weighs approximately 15 g.

11. A bag of flour weighs 4.5 kg.

12. A staple weighs 15 mg.

13. A professor weighs less than 150 g.

14. A car weighs 2000 mg.

5.5 EXERCISE SET

FOR EXTRA HELP
Student Solutions Manual PH Math/Tutor Center CD/Video for Review Math XL MathXL® MyMathLab MyMathLab

Objective A *Convert as indicated. See Examples 1 through 3.*

1. 2 pounds to ounces

2. 5 pounds to ounces

3. 5 tons to pounds

4. 7 tons to pounds

5. 12,000 pounds to tons

6. 32,000 pounds to tons

 7. 60 ounces to pounds

8. 90 ounces to pounds

9. 3500 pounds to tons

10. 11,000 pounds to tons

11. 16.25 pounds to ounces

12. 14.5 pounds to ounces

 13. 4.9 tons to pounds

14. 8.3 tons to pounds

15. $4\frac{3}{4}$ pounds to ounces

16. $9\frac{1}{8}$ pounds to ounces

17. 2950 pounds to the nearest tenth of a ton

18. 51 ounces to the nearest tenth of a pound

19. $\frac{4}{5}$ oz to pounds

20. $\frac{1}{4}$ oz to pounds

21. $5\frac{3}{4}$ lb to ounces

22. $2\frac{1}{4}$ lb to ounces

23. 10 lb 1 oz to ounces

24. 7 lb 6 oz to ounces

25. 89 oz to _____ lb _____ oz

26. 100 oz = _____ lb _____ oz

Objective **B** *Perform each indicated operation. See Examples 4 and 5.*

27. 34 lb 12 oz + 18 lb 14 oz

28. 6 lb 10 oz + 10 lb 8 oz

29. 6 tons 1540 lb + 2 tons 850 lb

30. 2 tons 1575 lb + 1 ton 480 lb

31. 5 tons 1050 lb − 2 tons 875 lb

32. 4 tons 850 lb − 1 ton 260 lb

33. 12 lb 4 oz − 3 lb 9 oz

34. 45 lb 6 oz − 26 lb 10 oz

35. 5 lb 3 oz × 6

36. 2 lb 5 oz × 5

37. 6 tons 1500 lb ÷ 5

38. 5 tons 400 lb ÷ 4

Objective **C** *Convert as indicated. See Examples 6 and 7.*

39. 500 g to kilograms

40. 650 g to kilograms

41. 4 g to milligrams

42. 9 g to milligrams

43. 25 kg to grams

44. 18 kg to grams

45. 48 mg to grams

46. 112 mg to grams

47. 6.3 g to kilograms

48. 4.9 g to kilograms

49. 15.14 g to milligrams

50. 16.23 g to milligrams

51. 4.01 kg to grams

52. 3.16 kg to grams

53. 35 hg to centigrams

54. 4.26 cg to dekagrams

Objective **D** *Perform each indicated operation. See Example 8.*

55. 3.8 mg + 9.7 mg

56. 41.6 g + 9.8 g

57. 205 mg + 5.61 g

58. 2.1 g + 153 mg

59. 9 g − 7150 mg

60. 4 kg − 2410 g

61. 1.61 kg − 250 g

62. 6.13 g − 418 mg

63. 5.2 kg × 2.6   **64.** 4.8 kg × 9.3   **65.** 17 kg ÷ 8   **66.** 8.25 g ÷ 6

Objectives Ⓐ Ⓑ Ⓒ Ⓓ **Mixed Practice** *Solve. Remember to insert units when writing your answers. For Exercises 67 through 74, complete the chart.*

	Object	Tons	Pounds	Ounces
67.	Statue of Liberty—weight of copper sheeting	100		
68.	Statue of Liberty—weight of steel	125		
69.	A 12-inch cube of osmium (heaviest metal)		1,345	
70.	A 12-inch cube of lithium (lightest metal)		32	

	Object	Grams	Kilograms	Milligrams	Centigrams
71.	Capsule of Amoxicillin (Antibiotic)			500	
72.	Tablet of Topamax (Epilepsy and Migraine uses)			25	
73.	A six-year-old boy		21		
74.	A golf ball	45			

75. A can of 7-Up weighs 336 grams. Find the weight in kilograms of 24 cans.

76. Guy Green normally weighs 73 kg, but he lost 2800 grams after being sick with the flu. Find Guy's new weight.

77. Sudafed is a decongestant that comes in two strengths. Regular strength contains 60 mg of medication. Extra strength contains 0.09 g of medication. How much extra medication is in the extra-strength tablet?

78. A small can of Planters sunflower seeds weighs 177 g. If each can contains 6 servings, find the weight of one serving.

79. Doris Johnson has two open containers of Uncle Ben's rice. If she combines 1 lb 10 oz from one container with 3 lb 14 oz from the other container, how much total rice does she have?

80. Dru Mizel maintains the records of the amount of coal delivered to his department in the steel mill. In January, 3 tons 1500 lb were delivered. In February, 2 tons 1200 lb were delivered. Find the total amount delivered in these two months.

81. Carla Hamtini was amazed when she grew a 28 lb 10 oz zucchini in her garden, but later she learned that the heaviest zucchini ever grown weighed 64 lb 8 oz in Llanharry, Wales, by B. Lavery in 1990. How far below the record weight was Carla's zucchini? (*Source: The Guinness Book of Records*)

82. The heaviest baby born in good health weighed an incredible 22 lb 8 oz. He was born in Italy in September, 1955. How much heavier is this than a 7 lb 12 oz baby? (*Source: The Guinness Book of Records*)

83. Tim Caucutt's doctor recommends that Tim limit his daily intake of sodium to 0.6 gram. A one-ounce serving of Cheerios with $\frac{1}{2}$ cup of fortified skim milk contains 350 mg of sodium. How much more sodium can Tim have after he eats a bowl of Cheerios for breakfast, assuming he intends to follow the doctor's orders?

84. A large bottle of Hire's Root Beer weighs 1900 grams. If a carton contains 6 large bottles of root beer, find the weight in kilograms of 5 cartons.

85. Three milligrams of preservatives are added to a 0.5-kg box of dried fruit. How many milligrams of preservatives are in 3 cartons of dried fruit if each carton contains 16 boxes?

86. One box of Swiss Miss Cocoa Mix weighs 0.385 kg, but 39 grams of this weight is the packaging. Find the actual weight of the cocoa in 8 boxes.

87. A carton of 12 boxes of Quaker Oats Oatmeal weighs 6.432 kg. Each box includes 26 grams of packaging material. What is the actual weight of the oatmeal in the carton?

88. The supermarket prepares hamburger in 85-gram market packages. When Leo Gonzalas gets home, he divides the package in half before refrigerating the meat. How much will each package weigh?

89. The Shop 'n Bag supermarket chain ships hamburger meat by placing 10 packages of hamburger in a box, with each package weighing 3 lb 4 oz. How much will 4 boxes of hamburger weigh?

90. The Quaker Oats Company ships its 1-lb 2-oz boxes of oatmeal in cartons containing 12 boxes of oatmeal. How much will 3 such cartons weigh?

91. A carton of Del Monte Pineapple weighs 55 lb 4 oz, but 2 lb 8 oz of this weight is due to packaging. Subtract the weight of the packaging to find the actual weight of the pineapple in 4 cartons.

92. The Hormel Corporation ships cartons of canned ham weighing 43 lb 2 oz each. Of this weight, 3 lb 4 oz is due to packaging. Find the actual weight of the ham found in 3 cartons.

Review

Write each fraction as a decimal. See Section 4.5.

93. $\frac{4}{25}$

94. $\frac{3}{5}$

95. $\frac{7}{8}$

96. $\frac{3}{16}$

Concept Extensions

97. Use a unit other than centigram and write a mass that is equivalent to 25 centigrams. (*Hint:* There are many possibilities.)

98. Use a unit other than pound and write a weight that is equivalent to 4000 pounds. (*Hint:* There are many possibilities.)

True or False? See the Concept Check in this section.

99. A kilogram is larger than a gram.

100. A decigram is larger than a milligram.

101. Why is the decimal point moved to the right when grams are converted to milligrams?

102. To change 8 pounds to ounces, multiply by 16. Why is this the correct procedure?

STUDY SKILLS BUILDER

How Are Your Homework Assignments Going?

Remember that it is important to keep up with homework. Why? Many concepts in mathematics build on each other. Often, your understanding of a day's lecture depends on an understanding of the previous day's material.

To complete a homework assignment, remember these 4 things:

- Attempt all of it.
- Check it.
- Correct it.
- If needed, ask questions about it.

Take a moment and review your completed homework assignments. Answer the exercises below based on this review.

1. Approximate the fraction of your homework you have attempted.
2. Approximate the fraction of your homework you have checked (if possible).
3. If you are able to check your homework, have you corrected it when errors have been found?
4. When working homework, if you do not understand a concept, what do you personally do?

5.6 CAPACITY: U.S. AND METRIC SYSTEMS

Objective A Defining and Converting U.S. System Units of Capacity

Units of **capacity** are generally used to measure liquids. The number of gallons of gasoline needed to fill a gas tank in a car, the number of cups of water needed in a bread recipe, and the number of quarts of milk sold each day at a supermarket are all examples of using units of capacity. The following summary shows equivalencies between units of capacity:

> ### U.S. Units of Capacity
>
> 8 fluid ounces (fl oz) = 1 cup (c)
> 2 cups = 1 pint (pt)
> 2 pints = 1 quart (qt)
> 4 quarts = 1 gallon (gal)

Just as with units of length and weight, we can form unit fractions to convert between different units of capacity. For instance,

$$\frac{2 \text{ c}}{1 \text{ pt}} = \frac{1 \text{ pt}}{2 \text{ c}} = 1 \quad \text{and} \quad \frac{2 \text{ pt}}{1 \text{ qt}} = \frac{1 \text{ qt}}{2 \text{ pt}} = 1$$

EXAMPLE 1 Convert 9 quarts to gallons.

Solution: We multiply by the unit fraction $\frac{1 \text{ gal}}{4 \text{ qt}}$.

$$9 \text{ qt} = \frac{9 \text{ qt}}{1} \cdot 1$$

$$= \frac{9 \text{ qt}}{1} \cdot \frac{1 \text{ gal}}{4 \text{ qt}}$$

$$= \frac{9 \text{ gal}}{4}$$

$$= 2\frac{1}{4} \text{ gal}$$

Thus, 9 quarts is the same as $2\frac{1}{4}$ gallons, as shown in the diagram:

1 gallon	1 gallon	$\frac{1}{4}$ gallon

9 quarts
$= 2\frac{1}{4}$ gal

■ **Work Practice Problem 1**

Objectives

A Define U.S. Units of Capacity and Convert from One Unit to Another.

B Perform Arithmetic Operations on U.S. Units of Capacity.

C Define Metric Units of Capacity and Convert from One Unit to Another.

D Perform Arithmetic Operations on Metric Units of Capacity.

PRACTICE PROBLEM 1

Convert 43 pints to quarts.

Answer

1. $21\frac{1}{2}$ qt

PRACTICE PROBLEM 2

Convert 26 quarts to cups.

EXAMPLE 2 Convert 14 cups to quarts.

Solution: Our equivalency table contains no direct conversion from cups to quarts. However, from this table we know that

$$1 \text{ qt} = 2 \text{ pt} = \frac{2 \text{ pt}}{1} \cdot 1 = \frac{2 \text{ pt}}{1} \cdot \frac{2 \text{ c}}{1 \text{ pt}} = 4 \text{ c}$$

so 1 qt = 4 c. Now we have the unit fraction $\frac{1 \text{ qt}}{4 \text{ c}}$. Thus,

$$14 \text{ c} = \frac{14 \text{ c}}{1} \cdot 1 = \frac{14 \text{ c}}{1} \cdot \frac{1 \text{ qt}}{4 \text{ c}} = \frac{14 \text{ qt}}{4} = \frac{7}{2} \text{ qt} \quad \text{or} \quad 3\frac{1}{2} \text{ qt}$$

1 quart + 1 quart + 1 quart + ½ quart = 14 cups = $3\frac{1}{2}$ qt

Work Practice Problem 2

✔ **Concept Check** If 50 cups are converted to quarts, will the equivalent number of quarts be less than or greater than 50? Explain.

Objective B Performing Operations on U.S. System Units of Capacity

As is true of units of length and weight, units of capacity can be added, subtracted, multiplied, and divided.

PRACTICE PROBLEM 3

Subtract 2 qt from 1 gal 1 qt.

EXAMPLE 3 Subtract 3 qt from 4 gal 2 qt.

Solution: To subtract, we line up similar units.

```
  4 gal 2 qt
−       3 qt
```

We cannot subtract 3 qt from 2 qt. We need to borrow 1 gallon from the 4 gallons, convert it to 4 quarts, and then combine it with the 2 quarts.

```
3 gal + (1 gal) 4 qt
  4 gal 2 qt   =    3 gal 6 qt
−       3 qt   =  −       3 qt
                    3 gal 3 qt
```

To check, see that the sum of 3 gal 3 qt and 3 qt is 4 gal 2 qt.

Work Practice Problem 3

PRACTICE PROBLEM 4

A large oil drum contains 15 gal 3 qt of oil. How much will be in the drum if an additional 4 gal 3 qt of oil is poured into it?

EXAMPLE 4 Finding the Amount of Water in an Aquarium

An aquarium contains 6 gal 3 qt of water. If 2 gal 2 qt of water is added, what is the total amount of water in the aquarium?

Solution:
```
beginning water  →    6 gal 3 qt
+   water added  →  + 2 gal 2 qt
    total water  →    8 gal 5 qt
```

Answers

2. 104 c, **3.** 3 qt, **4.** 20 gal 2 qt

✔ **Concept Check Answer**

less than 50

Since 5 qt = 1 gal 1 qt, we have

$$= \overbrace{8 \text{ gal}}^{8 \text{ gal}} + \overbrace{1 \text{ gal } 1 \text{ qt}}^{5 \text{ qt}}$$
$$= 9 \text{ gal } 1 \text{ qt}$$

The total amount of water is 9 gal 1 qt.

Work Practice Problem 4

Objective C Defining and Converting Metric System Units of Capacity

Thus far, we know that the basic unit of length in the metric system is the meter and that the basic unit of mass in the metric system is the gram. What is the basic unit of capacity? The **liter.** By definition, a **liter** is the capacity or volume of a cube measuring 10 centimeters on each side.

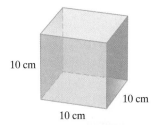

10 cm
10 cm
10 cm

The following examples may help you get a feeling for metric capacities:

One liter of liquid is slightly more than one quart.

1 quart   1 liter

Many soft drinks are packaged in 2-liter bottles.

The metric system was designed to be a consistent system. Once again, the prefixes for metric units of capacity are the same as for metric units of length and mass, as summarized in the following table:

Metric Unit of Capacity
1 **kilo**liter (kl) = 1000 liters (L)
1 **hecto**liter (hl) = 100 L
1 **deka**liter (dal) = 10 L
1 liter (L) = 1 L
1 **deci**liter (dl) = 1/10 L or 0.1 L
1 **centi**liter (cl) = 1/100 L or 0.01 L
1 **milli**liter (ml) = 1/1000 L or 0.001 L

The **milliliter** and the **liter** are the two most commonly used metric units of capacity.

Converting from one unit of capacity to another involves multiplying by powers of 10 or moving the decimal point to the left or to the right. Listing units of capacity in order from largest to smallest helps to keep track of how many places to move the decimal point when converting.

Let's convert 2.6 liters to milliliters. To convert from liters to milliliters, we move along the chart 3 units to the right.

kl   hl   dal   **L**   dl   cl   **ml**

3 units to the right

This means that we move the decimal point 3 places to the right to convert from liters to milliliters.

2.600 L = 2600. ml

This same conversion can be done with unit fractions.

$$2.6 \text{ L} = \frac{2.6 \text{ L}}{1} \cdot 1$$

$$= \frac{2.6 \text{ L}}{1} \cdot \frac{1000 \text{ ml}}{1 \text{ L}}$$

$$= 2.6 \cdot 1000 \text{ ml}$$

$$= 2600 \text{ ml} \quad \text{To multiply by 1000, move the decimal point 3 places to the right.}$$

To visualize the result, study the diagram below:

2.6 L

1000 ml   1000 ml   600 ml = 2600 ml

Thus, 2.6 L = 2600 ml.

PRACTICE PROBLEM 5

Convert 2100 ml to liters.

EXAMPLE 5   Convert 3210 ml to liters.

Solution: Let's use the unit fraction method first.

Unit fraction

$$3210 \text{ ml} = \frac{3210 \text{ ml}}{1} \cdot 1 = 3210 \text{ ml} \cdot \frac{1 \text{ L}}{1000 \text{ ml}} = 3.21 \text{ L}$$

Now let's list the unit measures in order from left to right and move from milliliters to liters.

kl   hl   dal   L   dl   cl   ml

3 units to the left

3210 ml = 3.210 L, the same results as before and shown below in the diagram.

3 places to the left

1000 ml   1000 ml   1000 ml

210 ml

3210 ml

1 L   1 L   1 L   0.210 L = 3.210 L

Answer

5. 2.1 L

■ **Work Practice Problem 5**

EXAMPLE 6 Convert 0.185 dl to milliliters.

Solution: We list the unit measures in order from left to right and move from deciliters to milliliters.

kl	hl	dal	L	dl	cl	ml

2 units to the right

0.185 dl = 18.5 ml

2 places to the right

Work Practice Problem 6

Objective D Performing Operations on Metric System Units of Capacity

As was true for length and weight, arithmetic operations involving metric units of capacity can also be performed. Make sure that the metric units of capacity are the same before adding, subtracting, multiplying, or dividing.

EXAMPLE 7 Add 2400 ml to 8.9 L.

Solution: We must convert both to liters or both to milliliters before adding the capacities together.

$$2400 \text{ ml} = 2.4 \text{ L} \qquad \text{or} \qquad 8.9 \text{ L} = 8900 \text{ ml}$$

$$
\begin{array}{r}
2.4 \text{ L} \\
+ \ 8.9 \text{ L} \\
\hline
11.3 \text{ L}
\end{array}
\qquad
\begin{array}{r}
2400 \text{ ml} \\
+ \ 8900 \text{ ml} \\
\hline
11{,}300 \text{ ml}
\end{array}
$$

The total is 11.3 L or 11,300 ml. They both represent the same capacity.

Work Practice Problem 7

✔ **Concept Check** How could you estimate the following operation? Subtract 950 ml from 7.5 L.

EXAMPLE 8 Finding the Amount of Medication a Person Has Received

A patient hooked up to an IV unit in the hospital is to receive 12.5 ml of medication every hour. How much medication does the patient receive in 3.5 hours?

Solution: We multiply 12.5 ml by 3.5.

$$
\begin{array}{rl}
\text{medication per hour} \rightarrow & 12.5 \text{ ml} \\
\times \qquad \qquad \text{hours} \rightarrow & \times \ 3.5 \\
\hline
\text{total medication} & 625 \\
& 3750 \\
\hline
& 43.75 \text{ ml}
\end{array}
$$

The patient receives 43.75 ml of medication.

Work Practice Problem 8

PRACTICE PROBLEM 6
Convert 2.13 dal to liters.

PRACTICE PROBLEM 7
Add 1250 ml to 2.9 L.

PRACTICE PROBLEM 8
If 28.6 L of water can be pumped every minute, how much water can be pumped in 85 minutes?

Answers
6. 21.3 L, **7.** 4150 ml or 4.15 L,
8. 2431 L

✔ **Concept Check Answer**
950 ml = 0.95 L; round 0.95 to 1;
7.5 − 1 = 6.5 L

Mental Math

Convert as indicated.

1. 2 c to pints

2. 4 c to pints

3. 4 qt to gallons

4. 8 qt to gallons

5. 2 pt to quarts

6. 6 pt to quarts

7. 8 fl oz to cups

8. 24 fl oz to cups

9. 1 pt to cups

10. 3 pt to cups

11. 1 gal to quarts

12. 2 gal to quarts

Determine whether the measurement in each statement is reasonable.

13. Clair took a dose of 2 L of cough medicine to cure her cough.

14. John drank 250 ml of milk for lunch.

15. Jeannie likes to relax in a tub filled with 3000 ml of hot water.

16. Sarah pumped 20 L of gasoline into her car yesterday.

5.6 EXERCISE SET

Objective A *Convert each measurement as indicated. See Examples 1 and 2.*

1. 32 fluid ounces to cups

2. 16 quarts to gallons

3. 8 quarts to pints

4. 9 pints to quarts

5. 10 quarts to gallons

6. 15 cups to pints

 7. 80 fluid ounces to pints

8. 18 pints to gallons

9. 2 quarts to cups

10. 3 pints to fluid ounces

11. 120 fluid ounces to quarts

12. 20 cups to gallons

13. 6 gallons to fluid ounces

14. 5 quarts to cups

15. $4\frac{1}{2}$ pints to cups

16. $6\frac{1}{2}$ gallons to quarts

17. 5 gal 3 qt to quarts   **18.** 4 gal 1 qt to quarts   **19.** $\frac{1}{2}$ cup to pint   **20.** $\frac{1}{2}$ pint to quarts

21. 58 qt = _____ gal _____ qt

22. 70 qt = _____ gal _____ qt

23. 39 pt = _____ gal _____ qt _____ pt

24. 29 pt = _____ gal _____ qt _____ pt

25. $2\frac{3}{4}$ gallons to pints

26. $3\frac{1}{4}$ quarts to cups

Objective B *Perform each indicated operation. See Examples 3 and 4.*

27. 4 gal 3 qt + 5 gal 2 qt   **28.** 2 gal 3 qt + 8 gal 3 qt   **29.** 1 c 5 fl oz + 2 c 7 fl oz

30. 2 c 3 fl oz + 2 c 6 fl oz   **31.** 3 gal − 1 gal 3 qt   **32.** 2 pt − 1 pt 1 c

33. 3 gal 1 qt − 1 qt 1 pt   **34.** 3 qt 1 c − 1 c 4 fl oz   **35.** 1 pt 1 c × 3

36. 1 qt 1 pt × 2   **37.** 8 gal 2 qt × 2   **38.** 6 gal 1 pt × 2

39. 9 gal 2 qt ÷ 2   **40.** 5 gal 6 fl oz ÷ 2

Objective C *Convert as indicated. See Examples 5 and 6.*

41. 5 L to milliliters   **42.** 8 L to milliliters   **43.** 4500 ml to liters   **44.** 3100 ml to liters

45. 3.2 L to centiliters   **46.** 1.7 L to centiliters   **47.** 410 L to kiloliters   **48.** 250 L to kiloliters

49. 64 ml to liters   **50.** 39 ml to liters   **51.** 0.16 kl to liters   **52.** 0.48 kl to liters

53. 3.6 L to milliliters   **54.** 1.9 L to milliliters   **55.** 0.16 L to kiloliters   **56.** 0.127 L to kiloliters

Objective **D** *Perform each indicated operation. See Examples 7 and 8.*

57. 2.9 L + 19.6 L

58. 18.5 L + 4.6 L

59. 2700 ml + 1.8 L

60. 4.6 L + 1600 ml

61. 8.6 L − 190 ml

62. 4.8 L − 283 ml

63. 11,400 ml − 0.8 L

64. 6850 ml − 0.3 L

65. 480 ml × 8

66. 290 ml × 6

67. 81.2 L ÷ 0.5

68. 5.4 L ÷ 3.6

Objectives **A** **B** **C** **D** **Mixed Practice** *Solve. Remember to insert units when writing your answers. For Exercises 69 through 72, complete the chart.*

	Capacity	Cups	Gallons	Quarts	Pints
69.	An average-size bath of water		21		
70.	A dairy cow's daily milk yield				38
71.	Your kidneys filter about this amount of blood every minute	4			
72.	The amount of water needed in a punch recipe	2			

73. Mike Schaferkotter drank 410 ml of Mountain Dew from a 2-liter bottle. How much Mountain Dew remains in the bottle?

74. The Werners' Volvo has a 54.5-L gas tank. Only 3.8 liters of gasoline still remain in the tank. How much is needed to fill it?

75. Margie Phitts added 354 ml of Prestone dry gas to the 18.6 L of gasoline in her car's tank. Find the total amount of gasoline in the tank.

76. Chris Peckaitis wishes to share a 2-L bottle of Coca Cola equally with 7 of his friends. How much will each person get?

77. Can 5 pt 1 c of fruit punch and 2 pt 1 c of ginger ale be poured into a 1-gal container without it overflowing?

78. Three cups of prepared Jell-O are poured into 6 dessert dishes. How many fluid ounces of Jell-O are in each dish?

79. Stanley Fisher paid $14 to fill his car with 44.3 liters of gasoline. Find the price per liter of gasoline to the nearest thousandth of a dollar.

80. A student carelessly misread the scale on a cylinder in the chemistry lab and added 40 cl of water to a mixture instead of 40 ml. Find the excess amount of water.

Review

Write each fraction in simplest form. See Section 3.2.

81. $\dfrac{20}{25}$

82. $\dfrac{75}{100}$

83. $\dfrac{27}{45}$

84. $\dfrac{56}{60}$

85. $\dfrac{72}{80}$

86. $\dfrac{18}{20}$

Concept Extensions

Solve. See the Concept Checks in this section.

87. If 70 pints are converted to gallons, will the equivalent number of gallons be less than or greater than 70? Explain why.

88. If 30 gallons are converted to quarts, will the equivalent number of quarts be less than or greater than 30? Explain why.

89. Explain how to estimate the following operation: Add 986 ml to 6.9 L.

90. Find the number of fluid ounces in 1 gallon.

91. Explain how to borrow in order to subtract 1 gal 2 qt from 3 gal 1 qt.

A cubic centimeter (cc) is the amount of space that a volume of 1 ml occupies. Because of this, we will say that 1 cc = 1 ml.

A common syringe is one with a capacity of 3 cc. Use the diagram and give the measurement indicated by each arrow.

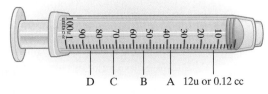

92. A

93. B

94. C

95. D

In order to measure small dosages, such as for insulin, u-100 syringes are used. For these syringes, 1 cc has been divided into 100 equal units (u). Use the diagram and give the measurement indicated by each arrow in units (u) and then cubic centimeters. Use 100 u = 1 cc *and round to the nearest hundredth.*

96. A

97. B

98. C

99. D

5.7 CONVERSIONS BETWEEN THE U.S. AND METRIC SYSTEMS

Objective Ⓐ Converting Between the U.S. and Metric Systems

The metric system probably had its beginnings in France in the 1600s, but it was the Metric Act of 1866 that made the use of this system legal (but not mandatory) in the United States. Other laws have followed that allow for a slow, but deliberate, transfer to the modernized metric system. In April, 2001, for example, the U.S. Stock Exchanges completed their change to decimal trading instead of fractions. By the end of 2009, all products sold in Europe (with some exceptions) will be required to have only metric units on their labels. (*Source:* U.S. Metric Association and National Institute of Standards and Technology)

You may be surprised at the number of everyday items we use that are already manufactured in metric units. We easily recognize 1L and 2L soda bottles, but what about the following?

Pencil leads (0.5 mm or 0.7 mm)

Camera film (35 mm)

Sporting events (5 km or 10 km races)

Medicines (500 mg capsules)

Labels on retail goods (dual-labeled since 1994)

Since the United States has not completely converted to the metric system, we need to practice converting from one system to the other. Below is a table of mostly approximate conversions.

Length:

metric	U.S. System
1 m	≈ 1.09 yd
1 m	≈ 3.28 ft
1 km	≈ 0.62 mi
2.54 cm	= 1 in.
0.30 m	≈ 1 ft
1.61 km	≈ 1 mi

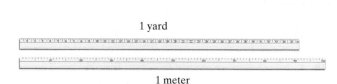

1 yard

1 meter

Capacity:

metric	U.S. System
1 L	≈ 1.06 qt
1 L	≈ 0.26 gal
3.79 L	≈ 1 gal
0.95 L	≈ 1 qt
29.57 ml	≈ 1 fl oz

1 quart   1 liter

Weight (mass):

metric	U.S. System
1 kg	≈ 2.20 lb
1 g	≈ 0.04 oz
0.45 kg	≈ 1 lb
28.35 g	≈ 1 oz

1 pound   1 kilogram

There are many ways to perform these metric to U.S. Conversions. We will do so by using unit fractions.

EXAMPLE 1 Compact Discs

Compact discs are 12 centimeters in diameter. Convert this length to inches. Round the result to two decimal places. (*Source: usByte.com*)

Solution: From our length conversion table, we know that 2.54 cm = 1 in. This fact gives us two unit fractions: $\dfrac{2.54 \text{ cm}}{1 \text{ in.}}$ and $\dfrac{1 \text{ in.}}{2.54 \text{ cm}}$. We use the unit fraction with cm in the denominator so that these units divide out.

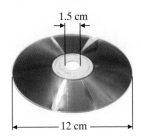

1.5 cm

12 cm

$$12 \text{ cm} = \frac{12 \text{ cm}}{1} \cdot 1 = \frac{12 \cancel{\text{ cm}}}{1} \cdot \overbrace{\frac{1 \text{ in.}}{2.54 \cancel{\text{ cm}}}}^{\text{Unit fraction}} \quad \begin{array}{l} \leftarrow \text{ Units to convert to} \\ \leftarrow \text{ Original units} \end{array}$$

$$= \frac{12 \text{ in.}}{2.54}$$

$$\approx 4.72 \text{ in.} \quad \text{Divide.}$$

Thus, the diameter of a compact disc is exactly 12 cm or approximately 4.72 inches. For a dimension this size, you can use a ruler to check. Another method is to approximate. Our result, 4.72 in., is close to 5 inches. Since 1 in. is about 2.5 cm, then 5 in. is about 5(2.5 cm) = 12.5 cm, which is close to 12 cm.

▣ **Work Practice Problem 1**

EXAMPLE 2 Liver

The liver is your largest internal organ. It weighs about 3.5 pounds in a grown man. Convert this weight to kilograms. Round to the nearest tenth. (*Source: Some Body!* by Dr. Pete Rowan)

Solution: $3.5 \text{ lb} \approx \dfrac{3.5 \cancel{\text{ lb}}}{1} \cdot \overbrace{\dfrac{0.45 \text{ kg}}{1 \cancel{\text{ lb}}}}^{\text{Unit fraction}} = 3.5(0.45 \text{ kg}) \approx 1.6 \text{ kg}$

Thus 3.5 pounds are approximately 1.6 kilograms. From the table of conversions, we know that 1 kg ≈ 2.2 lb. So that 0.5 kg ≈ 1.1 lb and adding, we have 1.5 kg ≈ 3.3 lb. Our result is reasonable.

▣ **Work Practice Problem 2**

PRACTICE PROBLEM 3

Convert 237 ml to fluid ounces. Round to the nearest whole fluid ounce.

EXAMPLE 3 Postage Stamp

Australia converted to the metric system in 1973. In that year, four postage stamps were issued to publicize this conversion. One such stamp is shown below. Let's check the mathematics on the stamp by converting 7 fluid ounces to milliliters. Round to the nearest hundred.

Solution: $7 \text{ fl oz} \approx \dfrac{7 \text{ fl oz}}{1} \cdot \overbrace{\dfrac{29.57 \text{ ml}}{1 \text{ fl oz}}}^{\text{Unit fraction}} = 7(29.57 \text{ ml}) = 206.99 \text{ ml}$

Rounded to the nearest hundred, $7 \text{ fl oz} \approx 200 \text{ ml}$.

■ **Work Practice Problem 3**

Answer

3. 8 fl oz

5.7 EXERCISE SET

FOR EXTRA HELP

 Student Solutions Manual

PH Math/Tutor Center

 CD/Video for Review

 MathXL® MathXL

MyMathLab MyMathLab

Note: Because approximations are used, your answers may vary slightly from the answers given in the back of the book.

Objective A *Convert as indicated. If necessary, round answers to two decimal places. See Examples 1 through 3.*

1. 578 milliliters to fluid ounces

2. 5 liters to quarts

3. 86 inches to centimeters

4. 86 miles to kilometers

5. 1000 grams to ounces

6. 100 kilograms to pounds

7. 93 kilometers to miles

8. 9.8 meters to feet

9. 14.5 liters to gallons

10. 150 milliliters to fluid ounces

11. 30 pounds to kilograms

12. 15 ounces to grams

Fill in the chart. Give exact answers or round to 1 decimal place.

		Meters	Yards	Centimeters	Feet	Inches
13.	The Height of a Woman				5	
14.	Statue of Liberty Length of Nose	1.37				
15.	Leaning Tower of Pisa		60			
16.	Blue Whale		36			

Solve. If necessary, round answers to two decimal places. See Examples 1 through 3.

17. The balance beam for female gymnasts is 10 centimeters wide. Convert this width to inches.

18. In men's gymnastics, the rings are 250 centimeters from the floor. Convert this height to inches, then to feet.

19. The speed limit is 70 miles per hour. Convert this to kilometers per hour.

20. The speed limit is 40 kilometers per hour. Convert this to miles per hour.

21. Ibuprofen comes in 200 milligram tablets. Convert this to ounces. (Round your answer to this exercise to 3 decimal places.)

22. Vitamin C tablets come in 500 milligram caplets. Convert this to ounces.

23. A stone is a unit in the British customary system. Use the conversion: 14 pounds = 1 stone to check the equivalencies in this 1973 Australian stamp. Is 100 kilograms approximately 15 stone 10 pounds?

24. Convert 5 feet 11 inches to centimeters and check the conversion on this 1973 Australian stamp. Is it correct?

25. You find two soda sizes at the store. One is 12 fluid ounces and the other is 380 milliliters. Which is larger?

26. A punch recipe calls for 2 gallons of pineapple juice. You have 8 liters of pineapple juice. Do you have enough for the recipe?

27. A $3\frac{1}{2}$-inch diskette is not really $3\frac{1}{2}$ inches. To find its actual width, convert this measurement to centimeters, then to millimeters. Round the result to the nearest ten.

28. The average two-year-old is 84 centimeters tall. Convert this to feet and inches.

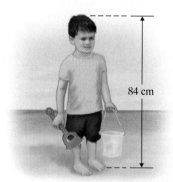

29. For an average adult, the weight of a right lung is greater than the weight of a left lung. If the right lung weighs 1.5 pounds and the left lung weighs 1.25 pounds, find the difference in grams. (*Source: Some Body!*)

30. The skin of an average adult weighs 9 pounds and is the heaviest organ. Find the weight in grams. (*Source: Some Body!*)

31. A fast sneeze has been clocked at about 167 kilometers per hour. Convert this to miles per hour. Round to the nearest whole.

32. A Boeing 747 has a cruising speed of about 980 kilometers per hour. Convert this to miles per hour. Round to the nearest whole.

33. The General Sherman giant sequoia tree has a diameter of about 8 meters at its base. Convert this to feet. (*Source: Fantastic Book of Comparisions*)

34. The largest crater on the near side of the moon is Billy Crater. It has a diameter of 303 kilometers. Convert this to miles. (*Source: Fantastic Book of Comparisions*)

35. The total length of the track on a CD is about 4.5 kilometers. Convert this to miles. Round to the nearest whole mile.

36. The distance between Mackinaw City, Michigan, and Cheyenne, Wyoming, is 2079 kilometers. Convert this to miles. Round to the nearest whole mile.

37. A doctor orders a dosage of 5 ml of medicine every 4 hours for 1 week. How many fluid ounces of medicine should be purchased? Round up to the next whole fluid ounce.

38. A doctor orders a dosage of 12 ml of medicine every 6 hours for 10 days. How many fluid ounces of medicine should be purchased? Round up to the next whole fluid ounce.

Without actually converting, choose the most reasonable answer.

39. A twin mattress has a width of about _____.
  a. 1 m   **b.** 100 m
  c. 10 m   **d.** 1000 m

40. A pie plate has a diameter of about _____.
  a. 22 m   **b.** 22 km
  c. 22 cm   **d.** 22 g

41. A liter has _____ capacity than a quart.
  a. less   **b.** greater   **c.** the same

42. A foot is _____ a meter.
  a. shorter than   **b.** longer than
  c. the same length as

43. A kilogram weighs _____ a pound.
  a. the same as   **b.** less than
  c. greater than

44. A football field is 100 yards, which is about _____.
  a. 9 m   **b.** 90 m
  c. 900 m   **d.** 9000 m

45. An $8\frac{1}{2}$ ounce glass of water has a capacity of about _____.
  a. 250 L   **b.** 25 L
  c. 2.5 L   **d.** 250 ml

46. A 5-gallon gasoline can has a capacity of about _____.
  a. 19 L   **b.** 1.9 L
  c. 19 ml   **d.** 1.9 ml

47. The weight of an average man is about _____.
  a. 700 kg   **b.** 7 kg
  c. 0.7 kg   **d.** 70 kg

48. The weight of a pill is about _____.
  a. 200 kg   **b.** 20 kg
  c. 2 kg   **d.** 200 mg

Review

Perform the indicated operations. See Section 1.9.

49. $6 \cdot 4 + 5 \div 1$

50. $10 \div 2 + 9(8)$

51. $\dfrac{10 + 8}{10 - 8}$

52. $\dfrac{14 + 1}{5(3)}$

53. $3 + 5(19 - 17) - 8$

54. $1 + 4(19 - 9) + 5$

55. $3[(1 + 5) \cdot (8 - 6)]$

56. $5[(18 - 8) - 9]$

Concept Extensions

Body surface area (BSA) is often used to calculate dosages for some drugs. BSA is calculated in square meters using a person's weight and height.

$$\text{BSA} = \sqrt{\frac{(\text{weight in kg}) \times (\text{height in cm})}{3600}}$$

For Exercises 57 through 62, calculate the BSA for each person. Round to the nearest hundredth. You will need to use the square root key on your calculator.

57. An adult whose height is 182 cm and weight is 90 kg.

58. An adult whose height is 157 cm and weight is 63 kg.

59. A child whose height is 40 in. and weight is 50 kg. (*Hint:* Don't forget to first convert inches to centimeters)

60. A child whose height is 26 in. and weight is 13 kg.

61. An adult whose height is 60 in. and weight is 150 lb.

62. An adult whose height is 69 in. and weight is 172 lb.

Solve.

63. Suppose the adult from Exercise 57 is to receive a drug that has a recommended dosage range of 10–12 mg per sq meter. Find the dosage range for the adult.

64. Suppose the child from Exercise 60 is to receive a drug that has a recommended dosage of 30 mg per sq meter. Find the dosage for the child.

65. A handball court is a rectangle that measures 20 meters by 40 meters. Find its area in square meters and square feet.

66. A backpack measures 16 inches by 13 inches by 5 inches. Find the volume of a box with these dimensions. Find the volume in cubic inches and cubic centimeters. Round the cubic centimeters to the nearest whole cubic centimeter.

CHAPTER 5   Group Activity

Sections 5.1–5.7

Consumer Price Index

Do you remember when the regular price of a candy bar was 5¢, 10¢, or 25¢? It is certainly difficult to find a candy bar for that price these days. The reason is inflation: the tendency for the price of a given product to increase over time. Businesses and government agencies use the Consumer Price Index (CPI) to track inflation. The CPI measures the change in prices over time of basic consumer goods and services.

The CPI is very useful for comparing the prices of fixed items in various years. For instance, suppose an insurance company customer submits a claim for the theft of a fishing boat purchased in 1975. Because the customer's policy includes replacement cost coverage, the insurance company must calculate how much it would cost to replace the boat at the time of the theft. (Let's assume the theft took place in 2003.) The customer has a receipt for the boat showing that it cost $598 in 1975. The insurance company can use the following proportion to calculate the replacement cost:

$$\frac{\text{price in earlier year}}{\text{price in later year}} = \frac{\text{CPI value in earlier year}}{\text{CPI value in later year}}$$

Because the CPI value is 53.8 for 1975 and 184.0 for 2003, the insurance company would use the following proportion for this situation. (We will let n represent the unknown price in 2003).

$$\frac{\text{price in 1975}}{\text{price in 2003}} = \frac{\text{CPI value in 1975}}{\text{CPI value in 2003}}$$

$$\frac{598}{n} = \frac{53.8}{184.0}$$

$$53.8 \cdot n = 598(184.0)$$

$$53.8 \cdot n = 110{,}032$$

$$\frac{53.8 \cdot n}{53.8} = \frac{110{,}032}{53.8}$$

$$n \approx 2045$$

The replacement cost of the fishing boat at 2003 prices is $2045.

Critical Thinking

1. What trends do you see in the CPI values in the table? Do you think these trends make sense? Explain.

2. A piece of jewelry cost $800 in 1985. What is its 2000 replacement value?

3. In 2000, the cost of a loaf of bread was about $1.89. What would an equivalent loaf of bread cost in 1950?

4. Suppose a couple purchased a house for $22,000 in 1920. At what price could they have expected to sell the house in 1990?

5. An original Ford Model T cost about $850 in 1915. What is the equivalent cost of a Model T in 2000 dollars?

Consumer Price Index	
Year	**CPI**
1915	10.1
1920	20.0
1925	17.5
1930	16.7
1935	13.7
1940	14.0
1945	18.0
1950	24.1
1955	26.8
1960	29.6
1965	31.5
1970	38.8
1975	53.8
1980	82.4
1985	107.6
1990	130.7
1995	152.4
1997	160.5
1998	163.0
1999	166.6
2000	172.2
2001	177.1
2002	179.9
2003	184.0

(*Source:* Bureau of Labor Statistics, U.S. Department of Labor)

Chapter 5 Vocabulary Check

Fill in each blank with one of the words or phrases listed below.

not equal	equal	cross products	rate	mass	unit fractions	unit rate

ratio	unit price	proportion	meter	liter	weight

1. A _____ is the quotient of two numbers. It can be written as a fraction, using a colon, or using the word *to*.

2. $\dfrac{x}{2} = \dfrac{7}{16}$ is an example of a _____.

3. A _____ is a rate with a denominator of 1.

4. A _____ is a "money per item" unit rate.

5. A _____ is used to compare different kinds of quantities.

6. In the proportion $\dfrac{x}{2} = \dfrac{7}{16}$, $x \cdot 16$ and $2 \cdot 7$ are called _____.

7. If cross products are _____ the proportion is true.

8. If cross products are _____ the proportion is false.

9. _____ is a measure of the pull of gravity.

10. _____ is a measure of the amount of substance in an object. This measure does not change.

11. The basic unit of length in the metric system is the _____.

12. To convert from one unit of length to another, _____ may be used.

13. The _____ is the basic unit of capacity in the metric system.

> **Helpful Hint**
>
> Are you preparing for your test? Don't forget to take the Chapter 5 Test on page 443. Then check your answers at the back of the text and use the Chapter Test Prep Video CD to see the fully worked-out solutions to any of the exercises you want to review.

5 Chapter Highlights

DEFINITIONS AND CONCEPTS	EXAMPLES
Section 5.1 Ratios	
A **ratio** is the quotient of two quantities.	The ratio of 3 to 4 can be written as $\dfrac{3}{4}$ or $3{:}4$ ↑ fraction notation ↑ colon notation
Rates are used to compare different kinds of quantities.	Write the rate 12 spikes every 8 inches as a fraction in simplest form. $\dfrac{12 \text{ spikes}}{8 \text{ inches}} = \dfrac{3 \text{ spikes}}{2 \text{ inches}}$
A **unit rate** is a rate with a denominator of 1.	Write as a unit rate: 117 miles on 5 gallons of gas $\dfrac{117 \text{ miles}}{5 \text{ gallons}} = \dfrac{23.4 \text{ miles}}{1 \text{ gallon}}$ or 23.4 miles per gallon or 23.4 miles/gallon
A **unit price** is a "money per item" unit rate.	Write as a unit price: $5.88 for 42 ounces of detergent $\dfrac{\$5.88}{42 \text{ ounces}} = \dfrac{\$0.14}{1 \text{ ounce}} = \$0.14$ per ounce

DEFINITIONS AND CONCEPTS	**EXAMPLES**

Section 5.2   Proportions

A **proportion** is a statement that two ratios or rates are equal.

USING CROSS PRODUCTS TO DETERMINE WHETHER PROPORTIONS ARE TRUE OR FALSE

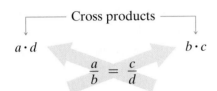

Cross products

$$a \cdot d \qquad \frac{a}{b} = \frac{c}{d} \qquad b \cdot c$$

If cross products are equal, the proportion is true.
If $ad = bc$, then the proportion is true.
If cross products are not equal, the proportion is false.
If $ad \neq bc$, then the proportion is false.

FINDING AN UNKNOWN VALUE *N* IN A PROPORTION

Step 1. Set the cross products equal to each other.

Step 2. Divide the number not multiplied by n by the number multiplied by n.

$\dfrac{1}{2} = \dfrac{4}{8}$ is a proportion.

Is $\dfrac{6}{10} = \dfrac{9}{15}$ a true proportion?

Cross products

$$6 \cdot 15 \qquad \frac{6}{10} = \frac{9}{15} \qquad 10 \cdot 9$$

$6 \cdot 15 \stackrel{?}{=} 10 \cdot 9$ Are cross products equal?
$90 = 90$

Since cross products are equal, the proportion is a true proportion.

Find n: $\dfrac{n}{7} = \dfrac{5}{8}$

Step 1.

$$\frac{n}{7} = \frac{5}{8}$$

$n \cdot 8 = 7 \cdot 5$ Set the cross products equal to each other.
$n \cdot 8 = 35$ Multiply.

Step 2.

$n = \dfrac{35}{8}$ Divide 35 by 8, the number multiplied by n.

$n = 4\dfrac{3}{8}$

Section 5.3   Proportions and Problem Solving

Given a specified ratio (or rate) of two quantities, a proportion can be used to determine an unknown quantity.

On a map, 50 miles corresponds to 3 inches. How many miles correspond to 10 inches?

1. UNDERSTAND. Read and reread the problem.

2. TRANSLATE. We let n represent the unknown number. We are given that 50 miles is to 3 inches as n miles is to 10 inches.

miles $\rightarrow$ $\dfrac{50}{3} = \dfrac{n}{10}$ $\leftarrow$ miles
inches $\rightarrow$ $\phantom{\dfrac{50}{3}}$ $\phantom{\dfrac{n}{10}}$ $\leftarrow$ inches

DEFINITIONS AND CONCEPTS	**EXAMPLES**

Section 5.3   Proportions and Problem Solving

	3. SOLVE:

$$\frac{50}{3} = \frac{n}{10}$$

$50 \cdot 10 = 3 \cdot n$ Set the cross products equal to each other.

$500 = 3 \cdot n$ Multiply.

$\dfrac{500}{3} = n$ Divide 500 by 3, the number multiplied by n.

$n = 166\dfrac{2}{3}$

4. INTERPRET. *Check* your work. *State* your conclusion:

On the map, $166\dfrac{2}{3}$ miles corresponds to 10 inches.

Section 5.4   Length: U.S. and Metric Systems

To convert from one unit of length to another, multiply by a **unit fraction** in the form

$$\frac{\text{units to convert to}}{\text{original units}}.$$

LENGTH: U.S. SYSTEM OF MEASUREMENT

12 inches (in.) = 1 foot (ft)

3 feet = 1 yard (yd)

5280 feet = 1 mile (mi)

The basic unit of length in the metric system is the **meter.** A meter is slightly longer than a yard.

LENGTH: METRIC SYSTEM OF MEASUREMENT

Metric Unit of Length
1 **kilo**meter (km) = 1000 meters (m)
1 **hecto**meter (hm) = 100 m
1 **deka**meter (dam) = 10 m
1 meter (m) = 1 m
1 **deci**meter (dm) = 1/10 m or 0.1 m
1 **centi**meter (cm) = 1/100 m or 0.01 m
1 **milli**meter (mm) = 1/1000 m or 0.001 m

$$\frac{12 \text{ inches}}{1 \text{ foot}}, \frac{1 \text{ foot}}{12 \text{ inches}}, \frac{3 \text{ feet}}{1 \text{ yard}}$$

Convert 6 feet to inches.

$$6 \text{ ft} = \frac{6 \text{ ft}}{1} \cdot 1$$

$$= \frac{6 \text{ ft}}{1} \cdot \frac{12 \text{ in.}}{1 \text{ ft}} \quad \begin{array}{l} \leftarrow \text{ units to convert to} \\ \leftarrow \text{ original units} \end{array}$$

$$= 6 \cdot 12 \text{ in.}$$

$$= 72 \text{ in.}$$

Convert 3650 centimeters to meters.

$$3650 \text{ cm} = 3650 \text{ cm} \cdot 1$$

$$= \frac{3650 \text{ cm}}{1} \cdot \frac{0.01 \text{ m}}{1 \text{ cm}} = 36.5 \text{ m}$$

or

km   hm   dam   m   dm   cm   mm

2 units to the left

3650 cm = 36.5 m

2 places to the left

DEFINITIONS AND CONCEPTS	**EXAMPLES**

Section 5.5   Weight and Mass: U.S. and Metric Systems

Weight is really a measure of the pull of gravity. **Mass** is a measure of the amount of substance in an object and does not change.	Convert 5 pounds to ounces. $$5 \text{ lb} = 5 \text{ lb} \cdot 1 = \frac{5 \text{ lb}}{1} \cdot \frac{16 \text{ oz}}{1 \text{ lb}} = 80 \text{ oz}$$

WEIGHT: U.S. SYSTEM OF MEASUREMENT

$$16 \text{ ounces (oz)} = 1 \text{ pound (1b)}$$

$$2000 \text{ pounds} = 1 \text{ ton}$$

A **gram** is the basic unit of mass in the metric system. It is the mass of water contained in a cube 1 centimeter on each side. A paper clip weighs about 1 gram.

Convert 260 grams to kilograms.

$$260 \text{ g} = \frac{260 \text{ g}}{1} \cdot 1 = \frac{260 \text{ g}}{1} \cdot \frac{1 \text{ kg}}{1000 \text{ g}} = 0.26 \text{ kg}$$

or

MASS: METRIC SYSTEM OF MEASUREMENT

Metric Unit of Mass
1 kilogram (kg) = 1000 grams (g)
1 hectogram (hg) = 100 g
1 dekagram (dag) = 10 g
1 gram (g) = 1 g
1 decigram (dg) = 1/10 g or 0.1 g
1 centigram (cg) = 1/100 g or 0.01 g
1 milligram (mg) = 1/1000 g or 0.001 g

kg hg dag g dg cg mg

3 units to the left

260 g = 0.260 kg

3 places to the left

Section 5.6   Capacity: U.S. and Metric Systems

CAPACITY: U.S. SYSTEM OF MEASUREMENT

$$8 \text{ fluid ounces (fl oz)} = 1 \text{ cup (c)}$$

$$2 \text{ cups} = 1 \text{ pint (pt)}$$

$$2 \text{ pints} = 1 \text{ quart (qt)}$$

$$4 \text{ quarts} = 1 \text{ gallon (gal)}$$

Convert 5 pints to gallons.

$$1 \text{ gal} = 4 \text{ qt} = 8 \text{ pt}$$

$$5 \text{ pt} = 5 \text{ pt} \cdot 1 = \frac{5 \text{ pt}}{1} \cdot \frac{1 \text{ gal}}{8 \text{ pt}} = \frac{5}{8} \text{ gal}$$

The **liter** is the basic unit of capacity in the metric system. It is the capacity or volume of a cube measuring 10 centimeters on each side. A liter of liquid is slightly more than 1 quart.

Convert 1.5 liters to milliliters.

$$1.5 \text{ L} = \frac{1.5 \text{ L}}{1} \cdot 1 = \frac{1.5 \text{ L}}{1} \cdot \frac{1000 \text{ ml}}{1 \text{ L}} = 1500 \text{ ml}$$

or

CAPACITY: METRIC SYSTEM OF MEASUREMENT

Metric Unit of Capacity
1 kiloliter (kl) = 1000 liters (L)
1 hectoliter (hl) = 100 L
1 dekaliter (dal) = 10 L
1 liter (L) = 1 L
1 deciliter (dl) = 1/10 L or 0.1 L
1 centiliter (cl) = 1/100 L or 0.01 L
1 milliliter (ml) = 1/1000 L or 0.001 L

kl hl dal L dl cl ml

3 units to the right

1.500 L = 1500 ml

3 places to the right

DEFINITIONS AND CONCEPTS	EXAMPLES
Section 5.7 Conversions Between the U.S. and Metric Systems	

To convert between systems, use approximate unit fractions from Section 5.7.	Convert 7 feet to meters. $$7 \text{ ft} \approx \frac{7 \text{ ft}}{1} \cdot \frac{0.30 \text{ m}}{1 \text{ ft}} = 2.1 \text{ m}$$ Convert 8 liters to quarts. $$8 \text{ L} \approx \frac{8 \text{ L}}{1} \cdot \frac{1.06 \text{ qt}}{1 \text{ L}} = 8.48 \text{ qt}$$ Convert 363 grams to ounces. $$363 \text{ g} \approx \frac{363 \text{ g}}{1} \cdot \frac{0.04 \text{ oz}}{1 \text{ g}} = 14.52 \text{ oz}$$

5 CHAPTER REVIEW

(5.1) *Write each ratio as a fraction in simplest form.*

1. 23 to 37

2. $121 to $143

3. 4.25 yards to 8.75 yards

4. $2\frac{1}{4}$ to $4\frac{3}{8}$

The circle graph below shows how the top 20 movies (or films) of 2004 were rated. Use this graph to answer the questions.

Top 20 Movies of 2004

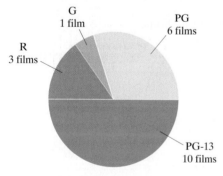

Source: Internet search and Bryan Gay

5. a. How many top 20 movies were rated PG?

   b. Find the ratio of top 20 PG-rated movies to total movies for that year.

6. a. How many top 20 movies were rated R?

   b. Find the ratio of top 20 R-rated movies to total movies for that year.

Write each rate as a fraction in simplest form.

7. 8 stillborn births to 1000 live births

8. 6 professors for 20 graduate research assistants

438

Write each rate as a unit rate.

9. $6.96 for 4 diskettes

10. 8 gallons of pesticide for 6 acres of crops

11. $234 for books for 5 college courses

12. 104 bushels of fruit from 8 trees

Find each unit price and decide which is the better buy. Round to 3 decimal places. Assume that we are comparing different sizes of the same brand.

13. Taco sauce: 8 ounces for $0.99 or 12 ounces for $1.69

14. Peanut butter: 18 ounces for $1.49 or 28 ounces for $2.39

(5.2) *Write each sentence as a proportion.*

15. 16 sandwiches is to 8 players as 2 sandwiches is to 1 player.

16. 12 tires is to 3 cars as 4 tires is to 1 car.

Determine whether each proportion is true.

17. $\dfrac{21}{8} = \dfrac{14}{6}$

18. $\dfrac{3.75}{3} = \dfrac{7.5}{6}$

Find the unknown number n in each proportion.

19. $\dfrac{n}{6} = \dfrac{15}{18}$

20. $\dfrac{n}{9} = \dfrac{5}{3}$

21. $\dfrac{8}{\frac{3}{2}} = \dfrac{n}{6}$

22. $\dfrac{8}{5} = \dfrac{9}{n}$

23. $\dfrac{27}{\frac{9}{4}} = \dfrac{n}{5}$

24. $\dfrac{6}{\frac{5}{2}} = \dfrac{n}{3}$

25. $\dfrac{0.4}{n} = \dfrac{2}{4.7}$

26. $\dfrac{n}{4\frac{1}{2}} = \dfrac{2\frac{1}{10}}{8\frac{2}{5}}$

(5.3) *Solve.*

The ratio of a quarterback's completed passes to attempted passes is 3 to 7.

27. If he attempts 32 passes, find how many passes he completed. Round to the nearest whole pass.

28. If he completed 15 passes, find how many passes he attempted.

One bag of pesticide covers 4000 square feet of garden.

△ **29.** Find how many bags of pesticide should be purchased to cover a rectangular garden that is 180 feet by 175 feet.

△ **30.** Find how many bags of pesticide should be purchased to cover a square garden that is 250 feet on each side.

On an architect's blueprint, 1 inch = 12 feet.

31. Find the length of a wall represented by a $3\frac{3}{8}$-inch line on the blueprint.

32. If an exterior wall is 99 feet long, find how long the blueprint measurement should be.

(5.4) *Convert.*

33. 108 in. to feet

34. $\frac{1}{2}$ yd to inches

35. 52 ft = _____ yd _____ ft

36. 46 in. = _____ ft _____ in.

37. 42 m to centimeters

38. 2.31 m to kilometers

Perform each indicated operation.

39. 4 yd 2 ft + 16 yd 2 ft

40. 12 ft 1 in. − 4 ft 8 in.

41. 8 cm + 15 mm

42. 19.6 km ÷ 8

Solve.

43. The local ambulance corps plans to award 20 framed certificates of valor to some of its outstanding members. If each frame requires 6 ft 4 in. of framing material, how much material is needed for all the frames?

△ **44.** The college has ordered that NO SMOKING signs be placed above the doorway of each classroom. Each sign is 0.8 m long and 30 cm wide. Find the area of each sign. (*Hint:* Recall that the area of a rectangle = width · length.)

0.8 meter

30 centimeters

(5.5) *Convert.*

45. 66 oz to pounds

46. 2.3 tons to pounds

47. 52 oz = _____ lb _____ oz.

48. 10,300 lb = _____ tons _____ lb

49. 27 mg to grams

50. 40 kg to grams

Perform each indicated operation.

51. 6 lb 5 oz − 2 lb 12 oz

52. 8 lb 6 oz × 4

Solve.

53. Donshay Berry ordered 1 lb 12 oz of soft-center candies and 2 lb 8 oz of chewy-center candies for his party. Find the total weight of the candy ordered.

54. Eight friends spent a weekend in the Poconos tapping maple trees and preparing 9.3 kg of maple syrup. Find the weight each friend receives if they share the syrup equally.

(5.6) *Convert.*

55. 3 qt 1 pt to pints

56. 18 quarts to cups

57. 9 pt = _____ qt _____ pt

58. 15 qt = _____ gal _____ qt

59. 3.8 L to milliliters

60. 4.2 ml to deciliters

Perform each indicated operation.

61. 1 qt 1 pt + 3 qt 1 pt

62. 0.946 L − 210 ml

Solve.

63. Each bottle of Kiwi liquid shoe polish holds 85 ml of the polish. Find the number of liters of shoe polish contained in 8 boxes if each box contains 16 bottles.

64. Ivan Miller wants to pour three separate containers of saline solution into a single vat with a capacity of 10 liters. Will 6 liters of solution in the first container combined with 1300 milliliters in the second container and 2.6 liters in the third container fit into the larger vat?

(5.7) *Note: Because approximations are used in this section, your answers may vary slightly from the answers given in the back of the book.*

Convert as indicated. If necessary, round to two decimal places.

65. 7 meters to feet

66. 11.5 yards to meters

67. 17.5 liters to gallons

68. 7.8 liters to quarts

69. 15 ounces to grams

70. 23 pounds to kilograms

71. A 100-meter dash is being held today. How many yards is this?

72. If a person weighs 82 kilograms, how many pounds is this?

73. How many quarts are contained in a 3-liter bottle of cola?

74. A compact disc is 1.2 mm thick. Find the height (in inches) of 50 discs.

Mixed Review

Write each ratio as a fraction in simplest form.

75. 15 to 25

76. 6 pints to 48 pints

Write each rate as a fraction in simplest form.

77. 2 teachers for 18 students

78. 6 nurses for 24 patients

Write each rate as a unit rate.

79. 136 miles in 4 hours

80. 12 gallons of milk from 6 cows

Find each unit price and decide which is the better buy. Round to 3 decimal places. Assume that we are comparing different sizes of the same brand.

81. cold medicine:
$4.94 for 4 oz.
$9.98 for 8 oz.

80. juice:
12 oz for $0.65.
64 oz for $2.98.

Write each sentence as a proportion.

83. 2 cups of cookie dough is to 30 cookies as 4 cups of cookie dough is to 60 cookies

84. 5 nickels is to 3 dollars as 20 nickels is to 12 dollars

Find the unknown number n in each proportion.

85. $\dfrac{3}{n} = \dfrac{15}{8}$

86. $\dfrac{5}{4} = \dfrac{n}{20}$

Convert the following.

87. 2.5 mi to feet

88. 129 in. to feet

89. 8200 lb = _____ tons _____ lb

90. 5 m to centimeters

91. 1400 mg to grams

92. 286 mm to kilometers

Perform the indicated operations and simplify.

93. 9.3 km − 183 m

94. 6 gal 1 qt + 2 gal 1 qt

Use the Chapter Test Prep Video CD to see the fully worked-out solutions to any of the exercises you want to review.

Write each ratio or rate as a fraction in simplest form.

1. $75 to $10

2. 9 inches of rain in 30 days

3. 8.6 to 10

4. $5\frac{7}{8}$ to $9\frac{3}{4}$

5. The world's largest yacht, the Octopus, measures in at 414 feet long. A Boeing 747-400 jumbo jet measures 231 feet long. Find the ratio of the length of the Octopus to the length of a 747–400. (*Source: Power & Motoryacht* magazine)

231 ft

414 ft

Find each unit rate.

6. 650 kilometers in 8 hours

7. 140 students for 5 teachers

8. QR10 (Quest for Curiosity) is the world's first bipedal robot capable of running (moving with both legs off the ground at the same time) at a rate of 108 inches each 12 seconds. (*Source: Guinness World Records*)

QRIO

Find each unit price and decide which is the better buy.

9. Steak sauce:
8 ounces for $1.19
12 ounces for $1.89

Determine whether the proportion is true.

10. $\frac{28}{16} = \frac{14}{8}$

Find the unknown number n in each proportion.

11. $\frac{n}{3} = \frac{15}{9}$

12. $\frac{8}{n} = \frac{11}{6}$

13. $\frac{-1.5}{5} = \frac{2.4}{n}$

14. $\frac{n}{2\frac{5}{8}} = \frac{1\frac{1}{6}}{3\frac{1}{2}}$

1. _____

2. _____

3. _____

4. _____

5. _____

6. _____

7. _____

8. _____

9. _____

10. _____

11. _____

12. _____

13. _____

14. _____

Solve.

15. On an architect's drawing, 2 inches corresponds to 9 feet. Find the length of a home represented by a line that is 11 inches long.

16. If a car can be driven 80 miles in 3 hours, how long will it take to travel 100 miles?

17. The standard dose of medicine for a dog is 10 grams for every 15 pounds of body weight. What is the standard dose for a dog that weighs 80 pounds?

Convert.

18. 280 in. = _____ ft _____ in.

19. $2\frac{1}{2}$ gal to quarts

20. 30 oz to pounds

21. 40 mg to grams

22. 3.6 cm to millimeters

23. 0.83 L to milliliters

Perform each indicated operation.

24. 8 lb 6 oz − 4 lb 9 oz

25. 5 gal 2 qt ÷ 2

26. 1.8 km + 456 m

Convert. Round to the nearest tenth of a degree, if necessary.

27. The sugar maples in front of Bette MacMillan's house are 8.4 meters tall. Because they interfere with the phone lines, the telephone company plans to remove the top third of the trees. How tall will the maples be after they are shortened?

28. A total of 15 gal 1 qt of oil has been removed from a 20-gallon drum. How much oil still remains in the container?

29. The engineer in charge of bridge construction said that the span of a certain bridge would be 88 m. But the actual construction required it to be 340 cm longer. Find the span of the bridge, in meters.

30. If 2 ft 9 in. of material is used to manufacture one scarf, how much material is needed for 6 scarves?

31. The Vietnam Veterans Memorial, inscribed with the names of 58,226 deceased and missing U.S. soldiers from the Vietnam War, is located on the National Mall in Washington, D.C. This memorial is formed from two straight sections of wall that meet at an angle at the center of the monument. Each wall is 246 ft 9 in. long. What is the total length of the Vietnam Veterans Memorial's wall? (*Source:* National Park Service)

32. Each panel making up the wall of the Vietnam Veterans Memorial is 101.6 cm wide. There are a total of 148 panels making up the wall. What is the total length of the wall in meters? (*Source:* National Park Service)

33. A 5-kilometer race is being held today. How many miles is this?

15. _____

16. _____

17. _____

18. _____

19. _____

20. _____

21. _____

22. _____

23. _____

24. _____

25. _____

26. _____

27. _____

28. _____

29. _____

30. _____

31. _____

32. _____

33. _____

1. Subtract. Check each answer by adding.
   a. $12 - 9$
   b. $11 - 6$
   c. $5 - 5$
   d. $7 - 0$

2. Multiply
   a. $20 \cdot 0$
   b. $20 \cdot 1$
   c. $0 \cdot 20$
   d. $1 \cdot 20$

3. Round 248,982 to the nearest hundred.

4. Round 248,982 to the nearest thousand.

5. Multiply:
   a. $\begin{array}{r} 25 \\ \times\ 8 \\ \hline \end{array}$
   b. $\begin{array}{r} 246 \\ \times\ 5 \\ \hline \end{array}$

6. Divide: $10,468 \div 28$

7. The director of a learning lab at a local community college is working on next year's budget. Thirty-three new DVD players are needed at a cost of $187 each. What is the total cost of these DVD players?

8. A study is being conducted for erecting soundproof walls along the interstate of a metropolitan area. The following feet of walls are part of the proposal. Find their total: 4800 feet, 3270 feet, 2761 feet, 5760 feet.

9. Find the prime factorization of 80.

10. Find $\sqrt{64}$.

11. Write $\dfrac{12}{20}$ in simplest form.

12. Find $9^2 \cdot \sqrt{9}$.

Multiply.

13. $-\dfrac{1}{4} \cdot \dfrac{1}{2}$

14. $3\dfrac{3}{8} \cdot 4\dfrac{5}{9}$

15. $\dfrac{6}{13} \cdot \dfrac{26}{30}$

16. $\dfrac{2}{11} \cdot \dfrac{5}{8} \cdot \dfrac{22}{27}$

Perform the indicated operation and simplify.

17. $\dfrac{2}{7} + \dfrac{3}{7}$

18. $\dfrac{26}{30} - \dfrac{7}{30}$

19. $\dfrac{7}{8} + \dfrac{6}{8} + \dfrac{3}{8}$

20. $\dfrac{7}{10} - \dfrac{3}{10} + \dfrac{4}{10}$

21. Find the LCM of 7 and 14.

22. Add: $\dfrac{17}{25} + \dfrac{3}{10}$

Answers

1. a. _____
   b. _____
   c. _____
   d. _____
2. a. _____ b. _____
   c. _____ d. _____
3. _____
4. _____
5. a. _____
   b. _____
6. _____
7. _____
8. _____
9. _____
10. _____
11. _____
12. _____
13. _____
14. _____
15. _____
16. _____
17. _____
18. _____
19. _____
20. _____
21. _____
22. _____

23. _____

24. _____

25. _____

26. _____

27. _____

28. _____

29. _____

30. _____

31. _____

32. _____

33. _____

34. _____

35. _____

36. _____

37. _____

38. _____

39. _____

40. _____

41. _____

42. _____

43. _____

44. _____

45. _____

46. _____

47. _____

48. _____

49. _____

50. _____

23. Write an equivalent fraction with the indicated denominator. $\dfrac{1}{2} = \dfrac{}{14}$

24. Determine whether these fractions are equivalent.

$$\dfrac{10}{55}, \quad \dfrac{6}{33}$$

25. Subtract: $\dfrac{2}{3} - \dfrac{10}{11}$

26. Subtract: $17\dfrac{5}{24} - 9\dfrac{5}{9}$

27. A flight from Tucson to Phoenix, Arizona, requires $\dfrac{5}{12}$ of an hour. If the plane has been flying $\dfrac{1}{4}$ of an hour, find how much time remains before landing.

28. Simplify: $80 \div 8 \cdot 2 + 7$

29. Add: $2\dfrac{1}{3} + 5\dfrac{3}{8}$

30. Find the average of $\dfrac{3}{5}, \dfrac{4}{9}$, and $\dfrac{11}{15}$.

31. Insert $<$ or $>$ to form a true statement.

$$\dfrac{3}{4} \quad \dfrac{9}{11}$$

32. Multiply: $28{,}000 \times 500$

33. Write the decimal -5.82 in words.

34. Write "seventy-five thousandths" in standard form.

35. Round 736.2359 to the nearest tenth.

36. Round 736.2359 to the nearest thousandth.

37. Add: $23.85 + 1.604$

38. Subtract: $700 - 18.76$

39. Multiply: 0.0531×16

40. Write $\dfrac{3}{8}$ as a decimal.

41. Divide: $-5.98 \div 115$

42. Write 7.9 as an improper fraction.

43. Simplify: $-0.5(8.6 - 1.2)$

44. Find the unknown number n.
$$\dfrac{n}{4} = \dfrac{12}{16}$$

45. Write the numbers in order from smallest to largest.

$$\dfrac{9}{20}, \dfrac{4}{9}, 0.456$$

46. Write the rate as a unit rate.

700 meters in 5 seconds

Write each ratio as a fraction in simplest form.

47. The ratio of $15 to $10

48. The ratio of 7 to 21

49. The ratio of 2.6 to 3.1

50. The ratio of 900 to 9000

6

Percent

This chapter is devoted to percent, a concept used virtually every day in ordinary and business life. Understanding percent and using it efficiently depends on understanding ratios because a percent is a ratio whose denominator is 100. We present techniques to write percents as fractions and as decimals and then solve problems relating to sales tax, commission, discounts, interest, and other real-life situations that use percents.

The Nutrition Labeling and Education Act (NLEA) was signed into law on November 8, 1990. It requires food manufacturers to include nutrition information on their product labels. The NLEA provides specific guidelines concerning the use of terms such as "low fat," or "high fiber." Labels contain information about portion sizes, vitamins and minerals, and sodium, fat, and cholesterol content of foods. The result of this important legislation is to help consumers make more informed and healthier food choices. In Exercises 13 through 16 of Section 6.4, we will determine what percent of some foods' total calories is from fat.

Nutrition Facts

Serving Size 18 crackers (29g)
Servings Per Container About 9

Amount Per Serving

Calories 120 Calories from Fat 35

	% Daily Value*
Total Fat 4g	**6%**
Saturated Fat 0.5g	**3%**
Polyunsaturated Fat 0g	
Monounsaturated Fat 1.5g	
Cholesterol 0mg	**0%**
Sodium 220mg	**9%**
Total Carbohydrate 21g	**7%**
Dietary Fiber 2g	**7%**
Sugars 3g	
Protein 2g	

Vitamin A 0% • Vitamin C 0%

Calcium 2% • Iron 4%

Phosphorus 10%

6.1 PERCENTS, DECIMALS, AND FRACTIONS

Objective **A** Understanding Percent

The word **percent** comes from the Latin phrase *per centum*, which means **"per 100."** For example, 53% (percent) means 53 per 100. In the square below, 53 of the 100 squares are shaded. Thus, 53% of the figure is shaded.

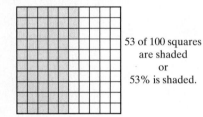

53 of 100 squares
are shaded
or
53% is shaded.

Since 53% means 53 per 100, 53% is the ratio of 53 to 100, or $\dfrac{53}{100}$.

$$53\% = \dfrac{53}{100}$$

Also,

$$7\% = \dfrac{7}{100} \qquad \text{7 parts per 100 parts}$$

$$73\% = \dfrac{73}{100} \qquad \text{73 parts per 100 parts}$$

$$109\% = \dfrac{109}{100} \qquad \text{109 parts per 100 parts}$$

Percent

Percent means **per one hundred.** The "%" symbol is used to denote percent.

Percent is used in a variety of everyday situations. For example:

- The interest rate is 5.7%.
- 50.5% of U.S. homes have Internet access.
- The store is having a 25%-off sale.
- 78% of us trust our local fire department.
- The enrollment in community colleges has increased 141% in the last 30 years.

PRACTICE PROBLEM 1

Of 100 students in a club, 23 are freshmen. What percent of the students are freshmen?

Answer

1. 23%

EXAMPLE 1

In a survey of 100 people, 17 people drive blue cars. What percent of people drive blue cars?

Solution: Since 17 people out of 100 drive blue cars, the fraction is $\dfrac{17}{100}$. Then

$$\dfrac{17}{100} = 17\%$$

▧ **Work Practice Problem 1**

EXAMPLE 2 46 out of every 100 college students live at home. What percent of students live at home? (*Source:* Independent Insurance Agents of America)

Solution:

$$\frac{46}{100} = 46\%$$

 Work Practice Problem 2

Objective **B** Writing Percents as Decimals and Fractions

Since percent means "per hundred," we have that

$$1\% = \frac{1}{100} = 0.01$$

In other words, the percent symbol means "per hundred" or, equivalently, "$\frac{1}{100}$" or "0.01." Thus

Write 87% as a fraction: $87\% = 87 \times \frac{1}{100} = \frac{87}{100}$

or

Write 87% as a decimal: $87\% = 87 \times (0.01) = 0.87$

Of course, we know that the end results are the same, that is,

$$\frac{87}{100} = 0.87$$

The above gives us two options for converting percents. We can replace the percent symbol, %, by $\frac{1}{100}$ or 0.01 and then multiply.

For consistency, when we
- convert from a percent to a *decimal,* we will drop the % symbol and multiply by 0.01.
- convert from a percent to a *fraction,* we will drop the % symbol and multiply by $\frac{1}{100}$.

Let's practice writing percents as decimals, then writing percents as fractions.

Writing a Percent as a Decimal

Replace the percent symbol with its decimal equivalent, 0.01; then multiply.

$$43\% = 43(0.01) = 0.43$$

Helpful Hint

If it helps, think of writing a percent as a decimal by

Percent → | Remove the % symbol and move decimal point 2 places to the left | → Decimal

PRACTICE PROBLEM 2

29 out of 100 executives are in their forties. What percent of executives are in their forties?

Answer
2. 29%

450

PRACTICE PROBLEMS 3–7

Write each percent as a decimal.

3. 89%   **4.** 2.7%

5. 150%   **6.** 0.69%

7. 500%

EXAMPLES   Write each percent as a decimal.

3. $23\% = 23(0.01) = 0.23$ Replace the percent symbol with 0.01, then multiply.

4. $4.6\% = 4.6(0.01) = 0.046$ Replace the percent symbol with 0.01. Then multiply.

5. $190\% = 190(0.01) = 1.90 \text{ or } 1.9$

6. $0.74\% = 0.74(0.01) = 0.0074$

7. $100\% = 100(0.01) = 1.00 \text{ or } 1$

> **Helpful Hint**
> We just learned that
> $100\% = 1$

Work Practice Problems 3–7

✔ **Concept Check**   Why is it incorrect to write the percent 0.033% as 3.3 in decimal form?

Now let's write percents as fractions.

Writing a Percent as a Fraction

Replace the percent symbol with its fraction equivalent, $\frac{1}{100}$; then multiply. Don't forget to simplify the fraction if possible.

$$43\% = 43 \cdot \frac{1}{100} = \frac{43}{100}$$

PRACTICE PROBLEMS 8–12

Write each percent as a fraction or mixed number in simplest form.

8. 25%

9. 2.3%

10. 175%

11. $66\frac{2}{3}\%$

12. 8%

EXAMPLES   Write each percent as a fraction or mixed number in simplest form.

8. $40\% = 40 \cdot \frac{1}{100} = \frac{40}{100} = \frac{2 \cdot \cancel{20}^{1}}{5 \cdot \cancel{20}_{1}} = \frac{2}{5}$

9. $1.9\% = 1.9 \cdot \frac{1}{100} = \frac{1.9}{100}$. We don't want the numerator of the fraction to contain a decimal, so we multiply by 1 in the form of $\frac{10}{10}$.

$$= \frac{1.9}{100} \cdot \frac{10}{10} = \frac{1.9 \cdot 10}{100 \cdot 10} = \frac{19}{1000}$$

10. $125\% = 125 \cdot \frac{1}{100} = \frac{125}{100} = \frac{5 \cdot \cancel{25}^{1}}{4 \cdot \cancel{25}_{1}} = \frac{5}{4} \text{ or } 1\frac{1}{4}$

11. $33\frac{1}{3}\% = 33\frac{1}{3} \cdot \frac{1}{100} = \frac{100}{3} \cdot \frac{1}{100} = \frac{\cancel{100}^{1} \cdot 1}{3 \cdot \cancel{100}_{1}} = \frac{1}{3}$

      → Write as an improper fraction.

> **Helpful Hint**
> Just as in Example 7, we confirm that $100\% = 1$

12. $100\% = 100 \cdot \frac{1}{100} = \frac{100}{100} = 1$

Work Practice Problems 8–12

Answers

3. 0.89,   **4.** 0.027,   **5.** 1.5,   **6.** 0.0069,

7. 5,   **8.** $\frac{1}{4}$,   **9.** $\frac{23}{1000}$,   **10.** $\frac{7}{4}$ or $1\frac{3}{4}$,

11. $\frac{2}{3}$,   **12.** $\frac{2}{25}$

✔ **Concept Check Answer**

To write a percent as a decimal, the decimal point should be moved two places to the left, not to the right. So the correct answer is 0.00033.

Objective C Writing Decimals or Fractions as Percents

To write a decimal or fraction as a percent, we use the result of Examples 7 or 12 on the previous page. In these examples, we found that $1 = 100\%$.

Write 0.38 as a percent: $0.38 = 0.38(1) = 0.38(100\%) = 38.\%$

Write $\frac{1}{4}$ as a percent: $\frac{1}{4} = \frac{1}{4}(1) = \frac{1}{4} \cdot 100\% = \frac{100}{4}\% = 25\%$

First, let's practice writing decimals as percents.

Writing a Decimal as a Percent

Multiply by 1 in the form of 100%.

$$0.27 = 0.27(100\%) = 27.\%$$

Helpful Hint

If it helps, think of writing a decimal as a percent by reversing the steps in the Helpful Hint on page 449.

Percent ← | Move the decimal point 2 places to the right and attach a % symbol. | ← Decimal

---

EXAMPLES Write each decimal as a percent.

13. $0.65 = 0.65(100\%) = 65.\%$ or 65% Multiply by 100%.

14. $1.25 = 1.25(100\%) = 125.\%$ or 125%

15. $0.012 = 0.012(100\%) = 001.2\%$ or 1.2%

16. $0.6 = 0.6(100\%) = 060.\%$ or 60%

Helpful Hint
A zero was inserted as a placeholder.

 Work Practice Problems 13–16

✔ **Concept Check** Why is it incorrect to write the decimal 0.0345 as 34.5% in percent form?

Now let's write fractions as percents.

Writing a Fraction as a Percent

Multiply by 1 in the form of 100%.

$$\frac{1}{8} = \frac{1}{8} \cdot 100\% = \frac{1}{8} \cdot \frac{100}{1}\% = \frac{100}{8}\% = 12\frac{1}{2}\% \text{ or } 12.5\%$$

Helpful Hint

From Example 12, we know that

$$100\% = 1$$

Recall that when we multiply a number by 1, we are not changing the value of that number. This means that when we multiply a number by 100%, we are not changing its value but rather writing the number as an equivalent percent.

PRACTICE PROBLEMS 13–16

Write each decimal as a percent.

13. 0.19   **14.** 1.75
15. 0.044   **16.** 0.7

Answers
13. 19%,   **14.** 175%,   **15.** 4.4%,
16. 70%

✔ **Concept Check Answer**

To change a decimal to a percent, multiply by 100%, or move the decimal point *only* two places to the right. So the correct answer is 3.45%.

Write each fraction or mixed number as a percent.

17. $\frac{1}{2}$ **18.** $\frac{7}{40}$ **19.** $2\frac{1}{4}$

EXAMPLES Write each fraction or mixed number as a percent.

17. $\frac{9}{20} = \frac{9}{20} \cdot 100\% = \frac{9}{20} \cdot \frac{100}{1}\% = \frac{900}{20}\% = 45\%$

18. $\frac{2}{3} = \frac{2}{3} \cdot 100\% = \frac{2}{3} \cdot \frac{100}{1}\% = \frac{200}{3}\% = 66\frac{2}{3}\%$

19. $1\frac{1}{2} = \frac{3}{2} \cdot 100\% = \frac{3}{2} \cdot \frac{100}{1}\% = \frac{300}{2}\% = 150\%$

> **Helpful Hint**
> $\frac{200}{3} = 66.\overline{6}$. Thus, another way to write $\frac{200}{3}\%$ is $66.\overline{6}\%$.

◻ **Work Practice Problems 17–19**

✔ **Concept Check** Which digit in the percent 76.4582% represents

a. A tenth percent?

c. A hundredth percent?

b. A thousandth percent?

d. A whole percent?

PRACTICE PROBLEM 20

Write $\frac{3}{17}$ as a percent. Round to the nearest hundredth percent.

EXAMPLE 20 Write $\frac{1}{12}$ as a percent. Round to the nearest hundredth percent.

Solution:

"approximately"

$$\frac{1}{12} = \frac{1}{12} \cdot 100\% = \frac{1}{12} \cdot \frac{100\%}{1} = \frac{100}{12}\% \approx 8.33\%$$

$$\begin{array}{r} 8.333 \approx 8.33 \\ 12\overline{)100.000} \\ -96 \\ \hline 4\,0 \\ -3\,6 \\ \hline 40 \\ -36 \\ \hline 40 \\ -36 \\ \hline 4 \end{array}$$

Thus, $\frac{1}{12}$ is approximately 8.33%.

◻ **Work Practice Problem 20**

Objective D Converting Percents, Decimals, and Fractions

Let's summarize what we have learned so far about percents, decimals, and fractions:

> ### Summary of Converting Percents, Decimals, and Fractions
>
> - *To write a percent as a decimal,* replace the % symbol with its decimal equivalent, 0.01; then multiply.
> - *To write a percent as a fraction,* replace the % symbol with its fraction equivalent, $\frac{1}{100}$; then multiply.
> - *To write a decimal or fraction as a percent,* multiply by 100%.

If we let p represent a number, below we summarize using symbols.

Write a percent as a decimal:	Write a percent as a fraction:	Write a number as a percent:
$p\% = p(0.01)$	$p\% = p \cdot \dfrac{1}{100}$	$p = p \cdot 100\%$

EXAMPLE 21 17.8% of automobile thefts in the continental United States occur in the Midwest. Write this percent as a decimal and as a fraction. (*Source:* The American Automobile Manufacturers Association)

Solution:

As a decimal: $17.8\% = 17.8(0.01) = 0.178.$

As a fraction: $17.8\% = 17.8 \cdot \dfrac{1}{100} = \dfrac{17.8}{100} = \dfrac{17.8}{100} \cdot \dfrac{10}{10} = \dfrac{178}{1000} = \dfrac{\overset{1}{\cancel{2}} \cdot 89}{\underset{1}{\cancel{2}} \cdot 500} = \dfrac{89}{500}.$

Thus, 17.8% written as a decimal is 0.178, and written as a fraction is $\dfrac{89}{500}$.

▶ **Work Practice Problem 21**

EXAMPLE 22 An advertisement for a stereo system reads "$\dfrac{1}{4}$ off." What percent off is this?

Solution: Write $\dfrac{1}{4}$ as a percent.

$$\frac{1}{4} = \frac{1}{4} \cdot 100\% = \frac{1}{4} \cdot \frac{100\%}{1} = \frac{100}{4}\% = 25\%$$

Thus, "$\dfrac{1}{4}$ off" is the same as "25% off."

▶ **Work Practice Problem 22**

Note: It is helpful to know a few basic percent conversions. Appendix A.4 contains a handy reference of percent, decimal, and fraction equivalencies.

Also, Appendix A.5 shows how to find common percents of a number.

PRACTICE PROBLEM 21

A family decides to spend no more than 22.5% of its monthly income on rent. Write 22.5% as a decimal and as a fraction.

PRACTICE PROBLEM 22

Provincetown's budget for waste disposal increased by $1\dfrac{1}{4}$ times over the budget from last year. What percent increase is this?

Answers

21. $0.225, \dfrac{9}{40}$,   **22.** 125%

Mental Math

Write each fraction as a percent.

1. $\dfrac{13}{100}$

2. $\dfrac{92}{100}$

3. $\dfrac{87}{100}$

4. $\dfrac{71}{100}$

5. $\dfrac{1}{100}$

6. $\dfrac{2}{100}$

6.1 EXERCISE SET

FOR EXTRA HELP

Student Solutions Manual   PH Math/Tutor Center   CD/Video for Review   MathXL® MathXL®   MyMathLab MyMathLab

Objective A *Solve. See Examples 1 and 2.*

1. A basketball player makes 81 out of 100 attempted free throws. What percent of free throws was made?

2. In a survey of 100 people, 54 preferred chocolate syrup on their ice cream. What percent preferred chocolate syrup?

Adults were asked what type of cookie was their favorite. The circle graph below shows the average results for every 100 people. Use this graph to answer Exercises 3 through 6. See Examples 1 and 2.

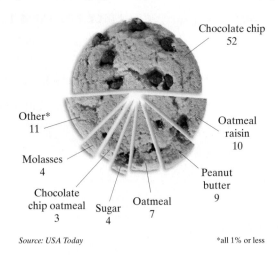

Chocolate chip
52

Other*
11

Oatmeal raisin
10

Molasses
4

Peanut butter
9

Chocolate chip oatmeal
3

Sugar
4

Oatmeal
7

Source: USA Today   *all 1% or less

3. What percent preferred peanut butter cookies?

4. What percent preferred oatmeal raisin cookies?

5. What type of cookie was preferred by most adults? What percent preferred this type of cookie?

6. What two types of cookies were preferred by the same number of adults? What percent preferred each type?

Objective B *Write each percent as a decimal. See Examples 3 through 7.*

7. 48%

8. 64%

9. 6%

10. 9%

11. 100%

12. 136%

13. 61.3%

14. 52.7%

15. 2.8%

16. 1.7%

17. 0.6%

18. 0.9%

19. 300%

20. 700%

21. 32.58%

22. 72.18%

Write each percent as a fraction or mixed number in simplest form. See Examples 8 through 12.

23. 12%

24. 24%

25. 4%

26. 2%

27. 4.5%

28. 7.5%   **29.** 175%   **30.** 250%   **31.** 6.25%   **32.** 3.75%

33. $10\frac{1}{3}\%$ **34.** $7\frac{3}{4}\%$ **35.** $22\frac{3}{8}\%$ **36.** $15\frac{5}{8}\%$

Objective **C** *Write each decimal as a percent. See Examples 13 through 16.*

37. 0.003   **38.** 0.006   **39.** 0.22   **40.** 0.45   **41.** 5.3

42. 1.6   **43.** 0.056   **44.** 0.027   **45.** 0.3328   **46.** 0.1115

47. 3.00   **48.** 5.00   **49.** 0.7   **50.** 0.8

Objective **C** *Write each fraction or mixed number as a percent. See Examples 17 through 19.*

51. $\frac{7}{10}$ **52.** $\frac{3}{10}$ **53.** $\frac{2}{5}$ **54.** $\frac{4}{5}$ **55.** $\frac{17}{50}$

56. $\frac{47}{50}$ **57.** $\frac{3}{8}$ **58.** $\frac{5}{16}$ **59.** $\frac{7}{9}$ **60.** $\frac{1}{3}$

61. $2\frac{1}{2}$ **62.** $2\frac{1}{5}$ **63.** $1\frac{9}{10}$ **64.** $2\frac{7}{10}$

Write each fraction as a percent. Round to the nearest hundredth percent. See Example 20.

65. $\frac{7}{11}$ **66.** $\frac{5}{12}$ **67.** $\frac{4}{15}$ **68.** $\frac{10}{11}$

Objective **D** *Complete each table. See Examples 21 and 22.*

69.

Percent	Decimal	Fraction
35%		
		$\frac{1}{5}$
	0.5	
70%		
		$\frac{3}{8}$

70.

Percent	Decimal	Fraction
50%		
		$\frac{2}{5}$
	0.25	
12.5%		
		$\frac{5}{8}$
		$\frac{7}{50}$

71.

Percent	Decimal	Fraction
40%		
	0.235	
		$\frac{4}{5}$
$33\frac{1}{3}\%$		
		$\frac{7}{8}$
7.5%		

72.

Percent	Decimal	Fraction
	0.525	
		$\frac{3}{4}$
$66\frac{2}{3}\%$		
		$\frac{5}{6}$
100%		

73.

Percent	Decimal	Fraction
200%		
	2.8	
705%		
		$4\frac{27}{50}$

74.

Percent	Decimal	Fraction
800%		
	3.2	
608%		
		$9\frac{13}{50}$

Solve. See Examples 21 and 22.

75. Approximately 14.8% of new luxury cars are silver, making silver the most popular new vehicle color for that class. Write this percent as a decimal and a fraction. (*Source:* Ward's Communications)

76. In 1950, the United States produced 75.7% of all motor vehicles made worldwide. Write this percent as a decimal and a fraction. (*Source:* American Automobile Manufacturers Association)

77. At this writing, 23% of Americans surveyed are in favor of abolishing the penny. Write this percent as a decimal and a fraction.

78. 52% of Americans say that their ideal family size is fewer than three children. Write this percent as a decimal and a fraction. (*Source:* Gallup)

In Exercises 79 through 82, you are asked to write each percent in this circle graph as a decimal and a fraction.

World Population by Continent

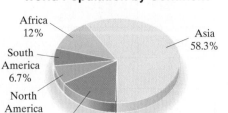

Africa 12%
South America 6.7%
North America 7.1%
Europe 15.5%
Australia 0.4%
Asia 58.3%

79. Australia: 0.4%

80. Asia: 58.3%

81. Africa: 12%

82. North America: 7.1%

Review

Find the value of n. See Section 5.2.

83. $3 \cdot n = 45$ **84.** $2 \cdot n = 16$ **85.** $6 \cdot n = 72$ **86.** $5 \cdot n = 35$

Concept Extensions

Solve. See the Concept Check in this section.

87. Given the percent 52.8647%, round as indicated.
   a. Round to a tenth of a percent.
   b. Round to a hundredth of a percent.

88. Given the percent 0.5269%, round as indicated.
   a. Round to a tenth of a percent.
   b. Round to a hundredth of a percent.

89. Which of the following are correct?
   a. 6.5% = 0.65   **b.** 7.8% = 0.078
   c. 120% = 0.12   **d.** 0.35% = 0.0035

90. Which of the following are correct?
   a. 0.231 = 23.1%   **b.** 5.12 = 0.0512%
   c. 3.2 = 320%   **d.** 0.0175 = 0.175%

Recall that 1 = 100%. This means that 1 whole is 100%. Use this for Exercises 91 through 92. (Source: Some Body by Dr. Pete Rowen)

91. The four blood types are A, B, O, and AB. (Each blood type can also be further classified as Rh-positive or Rh-negative depending upon whether your blood contains protein or not.) Given the percent blood types for the U.S. below, calculate the percent of U.S. population with AB blood type.

92. The top four components of bone are below. Find the missing percent.
   1. Minerals—45%
   2. Living tissue—30%
   3. Water—20%
   4. Other—?

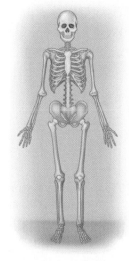

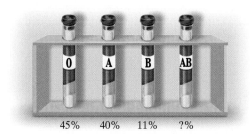

45%   40%   11%   ?%

What percent of the figure is shaded?

93.

94.

Fill in the blanks.

95. A fraction written as a percent is greater than 100% when the numerator is _____ than the denominator. (greater/less)

96. A decimal written as a percent is less than 100% when the decimal is _____ than 1. (greater/less)

Write each fraction as a decimal and then write each decimal as a percent. Round the decimal to three decimal places (nearest thousandth) and the percent to the nearest tenth of a percent.

97. $\dfrac{21}{79}$

98. $\dfrac{56}{102}$

The bar graph shows the predicted fastest-growing occupations. Use this graph for Exercises 99 through 102.

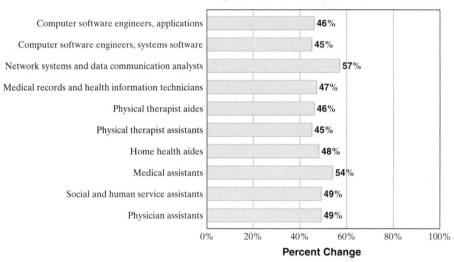

Fastest-Growing Occupations 2002–2012

Occupation	Percent Change
Computer software engineers, applications	46%
Computer software engineers, systems software	45%
Network systems and data communication analysts	57%
Medical records and health information technicians	47%
Physical therapist aides	46%
Physical therapist assistants	45%
Home health aides	48%
Medical assistants	54%
Social and human service assistants	49%
Physician assistants	49%

Source: Bureau of Labor Statistics

99. What occupation is predicted to be the fastest growing?

100. What occupation is predicted to be the second fastest growing?

101. Write the percent change for physician assistants as a decimal.

102. Write the percent change for medical assistants as a decimal.

103. In your own words, explain how to write a percent as a decimal.

104. In your own words, explain how to write a decimal as a percent.

 STUDY SKILLS BUILDER

Are You Satisfied with Your Performance in This Course thus Far?

To see if there is room for improvement, answer these questions:

1. Am I attending all classes and arriving on time?

2. Am I working and checking my homework assignments on time?

3. Am I getting help (from my instructor or a campus learning resource lab) when I need it?

4. In addition to my instructor, am I using the text supplements that might help me?

5. Am I satisfied with my performance on quizzes and exams?

If you answered no to any of these questions, read or reread Section 1.1 for suggestions in these areas. Also, you might want to contact your instructor for additional feedback.

6.2 SOLVING PERCENT PROBLEMS USING EQUATIONS

Objectives

A Write Percent Problems as Equations.

B Solve Percent Problems

Note: Sections 6.2 and 6.3 introduce two methods for solving percent problems. It is not necessary that you study both sections. You may want to check with your instructor for further advice.

Throughout this text, we have written mathematical statements such as $3 + 10 = 13$, or area = length · width. These statements are called "equations." An **equation** is a mathematical statement that contains an equal sign. To solve percent problems in this section, we translate the problems into such mathematical statements, or equations.

Objective **A** Writing Percent Problems as Equations

Recognizing key words in a percent problem is helpful in writing the problem as an equation. Three key words in the statement of a percent problem and their meanings are as follows:

of means **multiplication** (·)

is means **equals** (=)

what (or some equivalent) means **the unknown number**

In our examples, we let the letter n stand for the unknown number.

> **Helpful Hint**
> Any letter of the alphabet can be used to represent the unknown number. In this section, we use the letter n.

EXAMPLE 1 Translate to an equation.

5 is what percent of 20?

Solution: 5 is what percent of 20?

$$5 = n \cdot 20$$

Work Practice Problem 1

> **Helpful Hint**
> Remember that an equation is simply a mathematical statement that contains an equal sign (=).
> $$5 = n \cdot 20$$
> ↑
> equal sign

EXAMPLE 2 Translate to an equation.

1.2 is 30% of what number?

Solution: 1.2 is 30% of what number?

$$1.2 = 30\% \cdot n$$

Work Practice Problem 2

PRACTICE PROBLEM 1

Translate: 6 is what percent of 24?

PRACTICE PROBLEM 2

Translate: 1.8 is 20% of what number?

Answers

1. $6 = n \cdot 24$, **2.** $1.8 = 20\% \cdot n$

459

PRACTICE PROBLEM 3

Translate: What number is 40% of 3.6?

PRACTICE PROBLEMS 4–6

Translate each to an equation.
4. 42% of 50 is what number?
5. 15% of what number is 9?
6. What percent of 150 is 90?

EXAMPLE 3 Translate to an equation.

What number is 25% of 0.008?

Solution: What number is 25% of 0.008?

$$n = 25\% \cdot 0.008$$

Work Practice Problem 3

EXAMPLES Translate each of the following to an equation:

4. 38% of 200 is what number?

$$38\% \cdot 200 = n$$

5. 40% of what number is 80?

$$40\% \cdot n = 80$$

6. What percent of 85 is 34?

$$n \cdot 85 = 34$$

Work Practice Problems 4–6

✔**Concept Check** In the equation $2 \cdot n = 10$, what step should be taken to solve the equation for n?

Objective **B** Solving Percent Problems

You may have noticed by now that each percent problem has contained three numbers—in our examples, two are known and one is unknown. Each of these numbers is given a special name.

15%   of   60   is   9

$$\underset{\substack{15\% \\ \text{percent}}}{15\%} \cdot \underset{\substack{60 \\ \text{base}}}{60} = \underset{\substack{9 \\ \text{amount}}}{9}$$

We call this equation the **percent equation.**

Percent Equation

percent · base = amount

Helpful Hint

Notice that the percent equation given above is a true statement. To see this, simplify the left side as shown:

$$15\% \cdot 60 = 9$$
$$0.15 \cdot 60 = 9 \quad \text{Write 15\% as 0.15.}$$
$$9 = 9 \quad \text{Multiply.}$$

The statement $9 = 9$ is true.

Answers

3. $n = 40\% \cdot 3.6$, 4. $42\% \cdot 50 = n$,
5. $15\% \cdot n = 9$, 6. $n \cdot 150 = 90$

✔ Concept Check Answer

If $2 \cdot n = 10$, then $n = \dfrac{10}{2}$, or $n = 5$.

After a percent problem has been written as a percent equation, we can use the equation to find the unknown number. This is called **solving** the equation.

Solving Percent Equations for the Amount

EXAMPLE 7

What number is 35% of 40?

Solution:

$n = 35\% \cdot 40$ Translate to an equation.

$n = 0.35 \cdot 40$ Write 35% as 0.35.

$n = 14$ Multiply $0.35 \cdot 40 = 14$.

Thus, 14 is 35% of 40.

💻 **Work Practice Problem 7**

PRACTICE PROBLEM 7
What number is 20% of 85?

Helpful Hint   When solving a percent equation, write the percent as a decimal (or fraction).

EXAMPLE 8

85% of 300 is what number?

Solution:

$85\% \cdot 300 = n$ Translate to an equation.

$0.85 \cdot 300 = n$ Write 85% as 0.85.

$255 = n$ Multiply $0.85 \cdot 300 = 255$.

Thus, 85% of 300 is 255.

💻 **Work Practice Problem 8**

PRACTICE PROBLEM 8
90% of 150 is what number?

Solving Percent Equations for the Base

EXAMPLE 9

12% of what number is 0.6?

Solution:

$12\% \cdot n = 0.6$ Translate to an equation.

$0.12 \cdot n = 0.6$ Write 12% as 0.12.

Recall from Section 5.2 that if "0.12 times some number is 0.6," then the number is 0.6 divided by 0.12.

$n = \dfrac{0.6}{0.12}$ Divide 0.6 by 0.12, the number multiplied by n.

$n = 5$

Thus, 12% of 5 is 0.6.

💻 **Work Practice Problem 9**

PRACTICE PROBLEM 9
15% of what number is 1.2?

Answers
7. 17, **8.** 135, **9.** 8

PRACTICE PROBLEM 10

27 is $4\frac{1}{2}$ % of what number?

EXAMPLE 10

$$13 \quad \text{is} \quad 6\frac{1}{2}\% \quad \text{of} \quad \text{what number?}$$

Solution:

$$13 = 6\frac{1}{2}\% \cdot n \quad \text{Translate to an equation.}$$

$$13 = 0.065 \cdot n \quad 6\frac{1}{2}\% = 6.5\% = 0.065.$$

$$\frac{13}{0.065} = n \quad \text{Divide 13 by 0.065, the number multiplied by } n.$$

$$200 = n$$

Thus, 13 is $6\frac{1}{2}\%$ of 200.

■ **Work Practice Problem 10**

Solving Percent Equations for Percent

EXAMPLE 11

$$\text{What percent} \quad \text{of} \quad 12 \quad \text{is} \quad 9?$$

Solution:

$$n \cdot 12 = 9 \quad \text{Translate to an equation.}$$

$$n = \frac{9}{12} \quad \text{Divide 9 by 12, the number multiplied by } n.$$

$$n = 0.75$$

Next, since we are looking for percent, we write 0.75 as a percent.

$$n = 75\%$$

So, 75% of 12 is 9.

■ **Work Practice Problem 11**

PRACTICE PROBLEM 11

What percent of 80 is 8?

> **Helpful Hint**
> If your unknown in the percent equation is the percent, don't forget to convert your answer to a percent.

PRACTICE PROBLEM 12

35 is what percent of 25?

EXAMPLE 12

$$78 \quad \text{is} \quad \text{What percent} \quad \text{of} \quad 65?$$

Solution:

$$78 = n \cdot 65 \quad \text{Translate to an equation.}$$

$$\frac{78}{65} = n \quad \text{Divide 78 by 65, the number multiplied by } n.$$

$$1.2 = n$$

$$120\% = n \quad \text{Write 1.2 as a percent.}$$

So, 78 is 120% of 65.

■ **Work Practice Problem 12**

Answers

10. 600, **11.** 10%, **12.** 140%

Concept Check Consider these problems

1. 75% of 50 =

a. 50
b. a number greater than 50
c. a number less than 50

2. 40% of a number is 10. Is the number

a. 10
b. less than 10
c. greater than 10?

3. 800 is 120% of what number? Is the number

a. 800
b. less than 800
c. greater than 800?

> **Helpful Hint**
>
> Use the following to see if your answers are reasonable.
>
> $$(100\%) \text{ of a number} = \text{the number}$$
>
> $$\begin{pmatrix} \text{a percent} \\ \text{greater than} \\ 100\% \end{pmatrix} \text{ of a number} = \begin{matrix} \text{a number larger} \\ \text{than the original number} \end{matrix}$$
>
> $$\begin{pmatrix} \text{a percent} \\ \text{less than } 100\% \end{pmatrix} \text{ of a number} = \begin{matrix} \text{a number less} \\ \text{than the original number} \end{matrix}$$

✔ **Concept Check Answers**

1. c, **2.** c, **3.** b

Mental Math

Identify the percent, the base, and the amount in each equation. Recall that percent · base = amount.

1. $42\% \cdot 50 = 21$

2. $30\% \cdot 65 = 19.5$

3. $107.5 = 125\% \cdot 86$

4. $99 = 110\% \cdot 90$

6.2 EXERCISE SET

Objective A *Translate each to an equation. Do not solve. See Examples 1 through 6.*

1. 15% of 72 is what number?

2. 72% of 63 is what number?

3. 30% of what number is 80?

4. 50% of what number is 8?

5. 1.9 is 40% of what number?

6. 0.5 is 20% of what number?

7. What percent of 90 is 20?

8. 4.5 is what percent of 45?

9. What number is 9% of 43?

10. What number is 25% of 55?

Objective B *Solve. See Examples 7 and 8.*

11. 10% of 35 is what number?

12. 25% of 60 is what number?

13. What number is 14% of 52?

14. What number is 30% of 17?

Solve. See Examples 9 and 10.

15. 5% of what number is 30?

16. 25% of what number is 25?

17. 1.2 is 12% of what number?

18. 0.22 is 44% of what number?

Solve. See Examples 11 and 12.

19. What percent of 60 is 66?

20. What percent of 20 is 30?

21. 16 is what percent of 50?

22. 27 is what percent of 50?

Objectives A B Mixed Practice *Solve. See Examples 1 through 12.*

23. 0.1 is 10% of what number?

24. 0.5 is 5% of what number?

25. 125% of 36 is what number?

26. 200% of 13.5 is what number?

27. 82.5 is $16\frac{1}{2}\%$ of what number?

28. 7.2 is $6\frac{1}{4}\%$ of what number?

29. 126 is what percent of 31.5?

30. 264 is what percent of 33?

31. What number is 42% of 60?

32. What number is 36% of 80?

33. What percent of 150 is 67.5?

34. What percent of 105 is 88.2?

35. 120% of what number is 42?

36. 160% of what number is 40?

37. 2.4% of 26 is what number?

38. 4.8% of 32 is what number?

39. What percent of 600 is 3?

40. What percent of 500 is 2?

41. 6.67 is 4.6% of what number?

42. 9.75 is 7.5% of what number?

43. 1575 is what percent of 2500?

44. 2520 is what percent of 3500?

Review

Find the value of n in each proportion. See Section 5.2.

45. $\dfrac{27}{n} = \dfrac{9}{10}$

46. $\dfrac{35}{n} = \dfrac{7}{5}$

47. $\dfrac{n}{5} = \dfrac{8}{11}$

48. $\dfrac{n}{3} = \dfrac{6}{13}$

Write each phrase as a proportion.

49. 17 is to 12 as n is to 20

50. 20 is to 25 as n is to 10

51. 8 is to 9 as 14 is to n

52. 5 is to 6 as 15 is to n

Concept Extensions

For each equation, determine the next step taken to find the value of n. See the first Concept Check in this section.

53. $5 \cdot n = 32$
    a. $n = 5 \cdot 32$ **b.** $n = \dfrac{5}{32}$ **c.** $n = \dfrac{32}{5}$ **d.** none of these

54. $n = 0.7 \cdot 12$
    a. $n = 8.4$ **b.** $n = \dfrac{12}{0.7}$ **c.** $n = \dfrac{0.7}{12}$ **d.** none of these

55. $0.06 = n \cdot 7$
    a. $n = 0.06 \cdot 7$ **b.** $n = \dfrac{0.06}{7}$ **c.** $n = \dfrac{7}{0.06}$ **d.** none of these

56. Write a word statement for the equation $20\% \cdot n = 18.6$. Use the phrase "some number" for "n".

57. Write a word statement for the equation $n = 33\frac{1}{3}\% \cdot 24$. Use the phrase "some number" for "n".

For each exercise, determine whether the percent, n, is (a) 100%, (b) greater than 100%, or (c) less than 100%. See the last Concept Check in this section.

58. $n\%$ of 20 is 30

59. $n\%$ of 98 is 98

60. $n\%$ of 120 is 85

For each exercise, determine whether the number, n, is (a) equal to 45, (b) greater than 45, or (c) less than 45.

61. 55% of 45 is n

62. 230% of 45 is n

63. 100% of 45 is n

64. 30% of n is 45

65. 100% of n is 45

66. 180% of n is 45

Solve.

67. In your own words, explain how to solve a percent equation.

68. Write a percent problem that uses the percent 50%.

69. 1.5% of 45,775 is what number?

70. What percent of 75,528 is 27,945.36?

71. 22,113 is 180% of what number?

THE BIGGER PICTURE   Operations on Sets of Numbers and Solving Equations

Continue your outline from Sections 1.7, 1.9, 2.5, 3.3, 3.7, 4.4, and 5.2. Suggestions are once again written to help you complete this part of your outline. Notice that this part of the outline has to do with solving equations.

I. Operations on Sets of Numbers
  A. Whole Numbers
    1. Add or Subtract (Sections 1.3, 1.4)
    2. Multiply or Divide (Sections 1.6, 1.7)
    3. Exponent (Section 1.9)
    4. Square Root (Section 1.9)
    5. Order of Operations (Section 1.9)
  B. Integers
    1. Add (Section 2.3)
    2. Subtract (Section 2.4)
    3. Multiply or Divide (Section 2.5)
  C. Fractions
    1. Simplify (Section 3.2)
    2. Multiply (Section 3.3)
    3. Divide (Section 3.3)
    4. Add or Subtract (Sections 3.4, 3.5)
  D. Decimals
    1. Add or Subtract (Section 4.2)
    2. Multiply (Section 4.3)
    3. Divide (Section 4.4)

II. Solving Equations
  A. Proportions (Section 5.2)
  B. Percent Problems
    1. Solved by Equations: Remember that "of" means multiplication and "is" means equals.

    12% of some number is 6 translates to

    $$12\% \cdot n = 6 \ or \ 0.12 \cdot n = 6 \ or \ n = \frac{6}{0.12} \ or \ n = 50$$

Perform the indicated operations.

1. $\dfrac{2}{9} + \dfrac{1}{5}$

2. $42 \div 2 \cdot 3$

3. $-0.03(0.7)$

4. $\sqrt{49} + \sqrt{1}$

Solve.

5. $\dfrac{3}{8} = \dfrac{n}{128}$

6. $\dfrac{7.2}{n} = \dfrac{36}{8}$

7. 215 is what percent of 86?

8. 95% of 48 is what number?

9. 4.2 is what percent of 15?

10. 93.6 is 52% of what number?

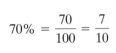 6.3 SOLVING PERCENT PROBLEMS USING PROPORTIONS

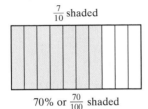

There is more than one method that can be used to solve percent problems. (See the note at the beginning of Section 6.2.) In the last section, we used the percent equation. In this section, we will use proportions.

Objective Ⓐ Writing Percent Problems as Proportions

To understand the proportion method, recall that 70% means the ratio of 70 to 100, or $\frac{70}{100}$.

$$70\% = \frac{70}{100} = \frac{7}{10}$$

$\frac{7}{10}$ shaded

70% or $\frac{70}{100}$ shaded

Since the ratio $\frac{70}{100}$ is equal to the ratio $\frac{7}{10}$, we have the proportion

$$\frac{7}{10} = \frac{70}{100}.$$

We call this proportion the "percent proportion." In general, we can name the parts of this proportion as follows:

Percent Proportion

$$\frac{\text{amount}}{\text{base}} = \frac{\text{percent}}{100} \quad \leftarrow \text{always 100}$$

or

$$\begin{array}{c} \text{amount} \rightarrow \\ \text{base} \rightarrow \end{array} \frac{a}{b} = \frac{p}{100} \quad \leftarrow \text{percent}$$

When we translate percent problems to proportions, the **percent,** p, can be identified by looking for the symbol % or the word *percent*. The **base,** b, usually follows the word *of*. The **amount,** a, is the part compared to the whole.

 Helpful Hint

Part of Proportion	How It's Identified
Percent	% or percent
Base	Appears after *of*
Amount	Part compared to whole

PRACTICE PROBLEM 1

Translate to a proportion.
15% of what number is 55?

PRACTICE PROBLEM 2

Translate to a proportion.
35 is what percent of 70?

PRACTICE PROBLEM 3

Translate to a proportion.
What number is 25% of 68?

PRACTICE PROBLEM 4

Translate to a proportion.
520 is 65% of what number?

EXAMPLE 1 Translate to a proportion.

12% of what number is 47?

Solution:

| percent | base
It appears
after the
word *of*. | amount
It is the part
compared to
the whole. |

$$\text{amount} \rightarrow \frac{47}{b} = \frac{12}{100} \leftarrow \text{percent}$$
$$\text{base} \rightarrow$$

◻ **Work Practice Problem 1**

EXAMPLE 2 Translate to a proportion.

101 is what percent of 200?

Solution:

| amount
It is the
part compared
to the whole. | percent | base
It appears
after the word
of. |

$$\text{amount} \rightarrow \frac{101}{200} = \frac{p}{100} \leftarrow \text{percent}$$
$$\text{base} \rightarrow$$

◻ **Work Practice Problem 2**

EXAMPLE 3 Translate to a proportion.

What number is 90% of 45?

Solution:

| amount
It is the
part compared
to the whole. | percent | base
It appears
after the
word *of*. |

$$\text{amount} \rightarrow \frac{a}{45} = \frac{90}{100} \leftarrow \text{percent}$$
$$\text{base} \rightarrow$$

◻ **Work Practice Problem 3**

EXAMPLE 4 Translate to a proportion.

238 is 40% of what number?

Solution: amount   percent   base

$$\frac{238}{b} = \frac{40}{100}$$

◻ **Work Practice Problem 4**

Answers

1. $\frac{55}{b} = \frac{15}{100}$, 2. $\frac{35}{70} = \frac{p}{100}$,

3. $\frac{a}{68} = \frac{25}{100}$, 4. $\frac{520}{b} = \frac{65}{100}$

EXAMPLE 5 Translate to a proportion.

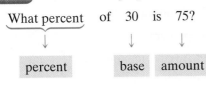

$$\frac{75}{30} = \frac{p}{100}$$

Work Practice Problem 5

EXAMPLE 6 Translate to a proportion.

$$\frac{a}{105} = \frac{45}{100}$$

Work Practice Problem 6

Objective B Solving Percent Problems

The proportions that we have written in this section contain three values that can change: the percent, the base, and the amount. If any two of these values are known, we can find the third (the unknown value). To do this, we write a percent proportion and find the unknown value as we did in Section 5.2.

EXAMPLE 7 Solving Percent Proportions for the Amount

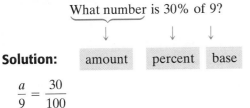

$$\frac{a}{9} = \frac{30}{100}$$

To solve, we set cross products equal to each other.

$$\frac{a}{9} \diagup\hspace{-1.1em}\diagdown \frac{30}{100}$$

$a \cdot 100 = 9 \cdot 30$ Set cross products equal.

$a \cdot 100 = 270$ Multiply.

Recall from Section 5.2 that if "some number times 100 is 270," then the number is 270 divided by 100.

$a = \dfrac{270}{100}$ Divide 270 by 100, the number multiplied by a.

$a = 2.7$ Simplify.

Thus, 2.7 is 30% of 9.

Work Practice Problem 7

PRACTICE PROBLEM 5

Translate to a proportion.
What percent of 50 is 65?

PRACTICE PROBLEM 6

Translate to a proportion.
36% of 80 is what number?

PRACTICE PROBLEM 7

What number is 8% of 120?

Helpful Hint   The proportion in Example 7 contains the ratio $\dfrac{30}{100}$. A ratio in a proportion may be simplified before solving the proportion. The unknown number in both

$\dfrac{a}{9} = \dfrac{30}{100}$ and $\dfrac{a}{9} = \dfrac{3}{10}$ is 2.7

Answers

5. $\dfrac{65}{50} = \dfrac{p}{100}$, **6.** $\dfrac{a}{80} = \dfrac{36}{100}$,

7. 9.6

✔**Concept Check** Consider the statement "78 is what percent of 350?"
Which part of the percent proportion is unknown?

a. the amount   **b.** the base   **c.** the percent

Consider another statement: "14 is 10% of some number."
Which part of the percent proportion is unknown?

a. the amount   **b.** the base   **c.** the percent

PRACTICE PROBLEM 8

75% of what number is 60?

> **EXAMPLE 8** **Solving Percent Problems for the Base**
>
>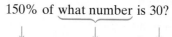
> 150% of what number is 30?
>
> **Solution:**   percent   base   amount
>
> $\dfrac{30}{b} = \dfrac{150}{100}$ Write the proportion.
>
> $\dfrac{30}{b} = \dfrac{3}{2}$ Write $\dfrac{150}{100}$ as $\dfrac{3}{2}$.
>
> $30 \cdot 2 = b \cdot 3$ Set cross products equal.
>
> $60 = b \cdot 3$ Multiply.
>
> $\dfrac{60}{3} = b$ Divide 60 by 3, the number multiplied by b.
>
> $20 = b$ Simplify.
>
> Thus, 150% of 20 is 30.
>
> ▢ **Work Practice Problem 8**

✔**Concept Check** When solving a percent problem by using a proportion, describe how you can check the result.

PRACTICE PROBLEM 9

15.2 is 5% of what number?

> **EXAMPLE 9**
>
> 20.8   is   40%   of   what number?
>
> **Solution:**   amount   percent   base
>
> $\dfrac{20.8}{b} = \dfrac{40}{100}$ or $\dfrac{20.8}{b} = \dfrac{2}{5}$ Write the proportion and simplify $\dfrac{40}{100}$.
>
> $20.8 \cdot 5 = b \cdot 2$ Set cross products equal.
>
> $104 = b \cdot 2$ Multiply.
>
> $\dfrac{104}{2} = b$ Divide 104 by 2, the number multiplied by b.
>
> $52 = b$ Simplify.
>
> So, 20.8 is 40% of 52.
>
> ▢ **Work Practice Problem 9**

Answers

8. 80, **9.** 304

✔ **Concept Check Answers**

c, b;
By putting the result into the proportion
and checking that the proportion is true

Copyright 2007 Pearson Education Inc

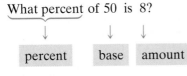 **Solving Percent Problems for the Percent**

What percent of 50 is 8?

Solution: percent   base   amount

$$\frac{8}{50} = \frac{p}{100} \quad \text{or} \quad \frac{4}{25} = \frac{p}{100} \qquad \text{Write the proportion and simplify } \frac{8}{50}.$$

$$4 \cdot 100 = 25 \cdot p \qquad \text{Set cross products equal.}$$

$$400 = 25 \cdot p \qquad \text{Multiply.}$$

$$\frac{400}{25} = p \qquad \text{Divide 400 by 25, the number multiplied by } p.$$

$$16 = p \qquad \text{Simplify.}$$

So, 16% of 50 is 8.

📖 **Work Practice Problem 10**

Helpful Hint

Recall from our percent proportion that this number already is a percent. Just keep the number as is and attach a % symbol.

EXAMPLE 11

504 is what percent of 360?

Solution: amount   percent   base

$$\frac{504}{360} = \frac{p}{100}$$

Let's choose not to simplify the ratio $\frac{504}{360}$.

$$504 \cdot 100 = 360 \cdot p \qquad \text{Set cross products equal.}$$

$$50{,}400 = 360 \cdot p \qquad \text{Multiply.}$$

$$\frac{50{,}400}{360} = p \qquad \text{Divide 50,400 by 360, the number multiplied by } p.$$

$$140 = p \qquad \text{Simplify.}$$

Notice that by choosing not to simplify $\frac{504}{360}$, we had larger numbers in our equation. Either way, we find that 504 is 140% of 360.

📖 **Work Practice Problem 11**

You may have noticed the following while working examples.

Helpful Hint

Use the following to see whether your answers are reasonable.

100% of a number = the number

$$\left(\begin{array}{c} \text{a percent} \\ \text{greater than} \\ 100\% \end{array} \right) \text{of a number} = \begin{array}{c} \text{a number larger} \\ \text{than the original number} \end{array}$$

$$\left(\begin{array}{c} \text{a percent} \\ \text{less than 100\%} \end{array} \right) \text{of a number} = \begin{array}{c} \text{a number less} \\ \text{than the original number} \end{array}$$

Mental Math

Identify the amount, the base, and the percent in each equation. Recall that $\dfrac{amount}{base} = \dfrac{percent}{100}$.

1. $\dfrac{12.6}{42} = \dfrac{30}{100}$

2. $\dfrac{201}{300} = \dfrac{67}{100}$

3. $\dfrac{20}{100} = \dfrac{102}{510}$

4. $\dfrac{40}{100} = \dfrac{248}{620}$

6.3 EXERCISE SET

Objective Ⓐ *Translate each to a proportion. Do not solve. See Examples 1 through 6.*

1. 32% of 65 is what number?

2. 92% of 30 is what number?

3. What number is 19% of 130?

4. What number is 5% of 125?

5. 2.3 is 58% of what number?

6. 1.2 is 47% of what number?

7. 40% of what number is 75?

8. 520 is 85% of what number?

9. What percent of 200 is 70?

10. 8.2 is what percent of 82?

Objective Ⓑ *Solve. See Example 7.*

11. 10% of 55 is what number?

12. 25% of 84 is what number?

13. What number is 18% of 105?

14. What number is 40% of 29?

Solve. See Examples 8 and 9.

15. 15% of what number is 60?

16. 75% of what number is 75?

17. 7.8 is 78% of what number?

18. 1.1 is 44% of what number?

Solve. See Examples 10 and 11.

19. 105 is what percent of 84?

20. 77 is what percent of 44?

21. 14 is what percent of 50?

22. 37 is what percent of 50?

Objectives **A** **B** **Mixed Practice** *Solve. See Examples 1 through 11.*

23. 2.9 is 10% of what number?

24. 6.2 is 5% of what number?

25. 2.4% of 80 is what number?

26. 6.5% of 120 is what number?

27. 160 is 16% of what number?

28. 30 is 6% of what number?

29. 348.6 is what percent of 166?

30. 262.4 is what percent of 82?

31. What number is 89% of 62?

32. What number is 53% of 130?

33. What percent of 8 is 3.6?

34. What percent of 5 is 1.6?

35. 140% of what number is 119?

36. 170% of what number is 221?

37. 1.8% of 48 is what number?

38. 7.8% of 24 is what number?

39. What percent of 500 is 3?

40. What percent of 800 is 4?

41. 3.5 is 2.5% of what number?

42. 9.18 is 6.8% of what number?

43. 2486 is what percent of 2200?

44. 9310 is what percent of 3800?

Review

Add or subtract the fractions. See Sections 3.4, 3.5, and 3.7.

45. $-\dfrac{11}{16} + \left(-\dfrac{3}{16}\right)$

46. $\dfrac{7}{12} - \dfrac{5}{8}$

47. $3\dfrac{1}{2} - \dfrac{11}{30}$

48. $2\dfrac{2}{3} + 4\dfrac{1}{2}$

Add or subtract the decimals. See Section 4.2.

49. $\begin{array}{r} 0.41 \\ + 0.29 \\ \hline \end{array}$

50. $\begin{array}{r} 10.78 \\ 4.3 \\ + 0.21 \\ \hline \end{array}$

51. $\begin{array}{r} 2.38 \\ - 0.19 \\ \hline \end{array}$

52. $\begin{array}{r} 16.37 \\ - 2.61 \\ \hline \end{array}$

Concept Extensions

53. Write a word statement for the proportion $\dfrac{n}{28} = \dfrac{25}{100}$. Use the phrase "the number" for "*n*."

Solve. See the Concept Checks in this section.

Suppose you have finished solving three percent problems using proportions that you set up correctly. Check each answer to see if each makes the proportion a true proportion. If any proportion is not true, solve it to find the correct solution.

54. $\dfrac{a}{64} = \dfrac{25}{100}$
Is the amount equal to 17?

55. $\dfrac{520}{b} = \dfrac{65}{100}$
Is the base equal to 800?

56. $\dfrac{36}{12} = \dfrac{p}{100}$
Is the percent equal to 50 (50%)?

57. Write a percent statement that translates to
$$\frac{16}{80} = \frac{20}{100}$$

 58. In your own words, explain how to use a proportion to solve a percent problem.

Solve. Round to the nearest tenth, if necessary.

59. What number is 22.3% of 53,862?

60. What percent of 110,736 is 88,542?

61. 8652 is 119% of what number?

 THE BIGGER PICTURE Operations on Sets of Numbers and Solving Equations

Continue your outline from Sections 1.7, 1.9, 2.5, 3.3, 3.7, 4.4, and 5.2. (If you did not cover Section 6.2, pay no attention to the part of the outline numbered II.B.1.) Suggestions are once again written to help you complete this part of your outline. Notice that this part of the outline has to do with solving equations.

I. Operations on Sets of Numbers

  A. Whole Numbers

    1. Add or Subtract (Sections 1.3, 1.4)

    2. Multiply or Divide (Sections 1.6, 1.7)

    3. Exponent (Section 1.9)

    4. Square Root (Section 1.9)

    5. Order of Operations (Section 1.9)

  B. Integers

    1. Add (Section 2.3)

    2. Subtract (Section 2.4)

    3. Multiply or Divide (Section 2.5)

  C. Fractions

    1. Simplify (Section 3.2)

    2. Multiply (Section 3.3)

    3. Divide (Section 3.3)

    4. Add or Subtract (Sections 3.4, 3.5)

  D. Decimals

    1. Add or Subtract (Section 4.2)

    2. Multiply (Section 4.3)

    3. Divide (Section 4.4)

II. Solving Equations

  A. Proportions (Section 5.2)

  B. Percent Problems

    1. Solved by Equations (Section 6.2—you may not have covered this section)

    2. Solved by Proportions: Remember that percent, p, is identified by % or percent,

    base, b, usually appears after "of" and

    amount, a, is the part compared to the whole.

    12% of some number is 6 translates to

$$\frac{6}{b} = \frac{12}{100} \text{ or } 6 \cdot 100 = b \cdot 12 \text{ or } \frac{600}{12} = b \text{ or } 50 = b$$

Perform the indicated operations.

1. $\dfrac{2}{9} + \dfrac{1}{5}$

2. $42 \div 2 \cdot 3$

3. $-0.03\,(0.7)$

4. $\sqrt{49} + \sqrt{1}$

Solve.

5. $\dfrac{3}{8} = \dfrac{n}{128}$

6. $\dfrac{7.2}{n} = \dfrac{36}{8}$

7. 215 is what percent of 86?

8. 95% of 48 is what number?

9. 4.2 is what percent of 15?

10. 93.6 is 52% of what number?

Percent and Percent Problems

Write each number as a percent.

1. 0.12

2. 0.68

3. $\frac{1}{8}$

4. $\frac{5}{2}$

5. 5.2

6. 8

7. $\frac{3}{50}$

8. $\frac{11}{25}$

9. $7\frac{1}{2}$

10. $3\frac{1}{4}$

11. 0.03

12. 0.05

Write each percent as a decimal.

13. 65%

14. 31%

15. 8%

16. 7%

17. 142%

18. 400%

19. 2.9%

20. 6.6%

Write each percent as a decimal and as a fraction or mixed number in simplest form.
(If necessary when writing as a decimal, round to the nearest thousandth.)

21. 3%

22. 5%

23. 5.25%

24. 12.75%

25. 38%   **26.** 45%   **27.** $12\frac{1}{3}\%$ **28.** $16\frac{2}{3}\%$

25. _____

26. _____

27. _____

Solve each percent problem.

28. _____

29. 12% of 70 is what number?   **30.** 36 is 36% of what number?

29. _____

30. _____

31. 212.5 is 85% of what number?   **32.** 66 is what percent of 55?

31. _____

32. _____

33. 23.8 is what percent of 85?   **34.** 38% of 200 is what number?

33. _____

34. _____

35. _____

35. What number is 25% of 44?   **36.** What percent of 99 is 128.7?

36. _____

37. _____

37. What percent of 250 is 215?   **38.** What number is 45% of 84?

38. _____

39. _____

39. 42% of what number is 63?   **40.** 95% of what number is 58.9?

40. _____

6.4 APPLICATIONS OF PERCENT

Objectives

A Solve Applications Involving Percent.

B Find Percent Increase and Percent Decrease.

Objective **A** Solving Applications Involving Percent

Percent is used in a variety of everyday situations. The next examples show just a few ways that percent occurs in real-life settings. (Each of these examples shows two ways of solving these problems. If you studied Section 6.2 only, see *Method 1*. If you studied Section 6.3 only, see *Method 2*.)

EXAMPLE 1 Finding Percent of Nursing Schools with Increases in Enrollment

There is a world wide shortage of nurses that is projected to be 20% below requirements by 2020. Until 2001, there has also been a continual decline in enrollment in nursing schools. That has recently changed.

In 2003, 2178 of the total 2593 nursing schools in the U.S. had an increase in applications or enrollment. What percent of nursing schools had an increase? Round to the nearest whole percent. (*Source:* CNN and *Nurse Week*)

Solution: *Method 1.* First, we state the problem in words.

In words: 2178   is   what percent   of   2593?

Translate: 2178   = n ·   2593

Next, solve for n.

$$\frac{2178}{2593} = n \quad \text{Divide 2178 by 2593, the number multiplied by } n.$$

$$0.84 \approx n \quad \text{Divide and round to the nearest hundredth.}$$

$$84\% \approx n \quad \text{Write as a percent.}$$

In 2003, about 84% of nursing schools had an increase in applications or enrollment.

Method 2.

In words: 2178   is   what percent   of   2593?

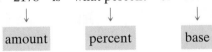
amount   percent   base

Translate: amount → $\dfrac{2178}{2593} = \dfrac{p}{100}$ ← percent
             base →

Next, solve for p.

$$2178 \cdot 100 = 2593 \cdot p \quad \text{Set cross products equal.}$$

$$217{,}800 = 2593 \cdot p \quad \text{Multiply.}$$

$$\frac{217{,}800}{2593} = p \quad \text{Divide 217,800 by 2593, the number multiplied by } p.$$

$$84 \approx p$$

In 2003, about 84% of nursing schools had an increase in applications or enrollment.

Work Practice Problem 1

PRACTICE PROBLEM 1

There are 106 nursing schools in Ohio. Of these schools, 61 offer RN (registered nurse) degrees. What percent of nursing schools in Ohio offer RN degrees? Round to the nearest whole percent.

Answer
1. 58%

477

PRACTICE PROBLEM 2

The freshmen class of 775 students is 31% of all students at Euclid University. How many students go to Euclid University?

EXAMPLE 2 Finding the Base Number of Absences

Mr. Buccaran, the principal at Slidell High School, counted 31 freshmen absent during a particular day. If this is 4% of the total number of freshmen, how many freshmen are there at Slidell High School?

Solution: *Method 1.* First we state the problem in words; then we translate.

In words: 31   is   4%   of   what number?

Translate: 31   =   4%   · n

Next, we solve for n.

$31 = 0.04 \cdot n$ Write 4% as a decimal.

$\dfrac{31}{0.04} = n$ Divide 31 by 0.04, the number multiplied by n.

$775 = n$ Simplify.

There are 775 freshmen at Slidell High School.

Method 2. First we state the problem in words; then we translate.

In words: 31   is   4%   of   what number?

amount   percent   base

Translate: amount → $\dfrac{31}{b}$ = $\dfrac{4}{100}$ ← percent
base →

Next, we solve for b.

$31 \cdot 100 = b \cdot 4$ Set cross products equal.

$3100 = b \cdot 4$ Multiply.

$\dfrac{3100}{4} = b$ Divide 3100 by 4, the number multiplied by b.

$775 = b$ Simplify.

There are 775 freshmen at Slidell High School.

▣ **Work Practice Problem 2**

PRACTICE PROBLEM 3

The nutrition label below is from a can of cashews. Find what percent of total calories are from fat. Round to the nearest tenth of a percent.

Nutrition Facts

Serving Size $\frac{1}{4}$ cup (33g)
Servings Per Container About 9

Amount Per Serving

Calories 190 **Calories from Fat** 130

	% Daily Value
Total Fat 16g	**24%**
Saturated Fat 3g	**16%**
Cholesterol 0mg	**0%**
Sodium 135mg	**6%**
Total Carbohydrate 9g	**3%**
Dietary Fiber 1g	**5%**
Sugars 2g	
Protein 5g	

Vitamin A 0% • Vitamin C 0%
Calcium 0% • Iron 8%

EXAMPLE 3 Finding Nutrition Label Percents

Standardized nutrition labels like the one shown at the right have been on foods since 1994. It is recommended that no more than 30% of your calorie intake be from fat. Find what percent of the total calories shown are fat.

Solution: *Method 1.*

In words: 10   is   what percent   of   80?

Translate: 10   = n ·   80

Nutrition Facts

Serving Size 1 pouch (20g)
Servings Per Container 6

Amount Per Serving

Calories	80
Calories from fat	10

	% Daily Value*
Total Fat 1g	**2%**
Sodium 45mg	**2%**
Total Carbohydrate 17g	**6%**
Sugars 9g	
Protein 0g	
Vitamin C	25%

Not a significant source of saturated fat, cholesterol, dietary fiber, vitamin A, calcium and iron.

*Percent Daily Values are based on a 2,000 calorie diet.

Fruit snacks nutrition label

Answers

2. 2500, **3.** 68.4%

Next, we solve for *n*.

$$\frac{10}{80} = n \quad \text{Divide 10 by 80, the number multiplied by } n.$$

$$0.125 = n \quad \text{Simplify.}$$

$$12.5\% = n \quad \text{Write 0.125 as a percent.}$$

12.5% of this food's total calories are from fat.

Method 2.
In words: 10 is what percent of 80?

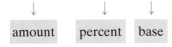

amount   percent   base

Translate: amount → $\dfrac{10}{80} = \dfrac{p}{100}$ ← percent
 base →

Next, we solve for *p*.

$$10 \cdot 100 = 80 \cdot p \quad \text{Set cross products equal.}$$

$$1000 = 80 \cdot p \quad \text{Multiply.}$$

$$\frac{1000}{80} = p \quad \text{Divide 1000 by 80, the number multiplied by } p.$$

$$12.5 = p \quad \text{Simplify.}$$

12.5% of this food's total calories are from fat.

■ **Work Practice Problem 3**

EXAMPLE 4 **Finding the Base Increase in Population**

The state of Nevada had the largest percent increase in population, about 66%, from the 1990 census to the 2000 census. In 1990, the population of Nevada was about 1202 thousand.

a. Find the increase in population from 1990 to 2000.
b. Find the population of Nevada in 2000.

(*Source:* U.S. Census Bureau)

Solution: *Method 1.*   First we find the increase in population.

In words: What number is 66% of 1202?

Translate: *n*   = 66% · 1202
Next, we solve for *n*.

$$n = 0.66 \cdot 1202 \quad \text{Write 66\% as a decimal.}$$

$$n = 793.32 \quad \text{Multiply.}$$

Continued on next page

PRACTICE PROBLEM 4

The state of Arizona had the second-largest percent increase in population, 40%, from the 1990 census to the 2000 census. In 1990, the population of Arizona was about 3665 thousand. (*Source:* U.S. Census Bureau)

a. Find the increase in population from 1990 to 2000.

b. Find the population of Arizona in 2000.

Answers
4. a. 1466 thousand, **b.** 5131 thousand

The increase in population is 793.32 thousand. This means that the

$$\begin{matrix} \text{Nevada} \\ \text{population} \\ \text{in 2000} \end{matrix} = \begin{matrix} \text{Population} \\ \text{in 1990} \end{matrix} + \begin{matrix} \text{Increase} \\ \text{in population} \end{matrix}$$

$$= 1202 \text{ thousand} + 793.32 \text{ thousand}$$

$$= 1995.32 \text{ thousand}$$

Method 2. First we find the increase in population.

In words: What number is 66% of 1202?

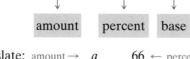

amount   percent   base

Translate: $\begin{matrix} \text{amount} \rightarrow \\ \text{base} \rightarrow \end{matrix} \dfrac{a}{1202} = \dfrac{66}{100} \leftarrow \text{percent}$

Next, we solve for a.

$a \cdot 100 = 1202 \cdot 66$ Set cross products equal.

$a \cdot 100 = 79{,}332$ Multiply.

$a = \dfrac{79{,}332}{100}$ Divide 79,332 by 100, the number multiplied by a.

$a = 793.32$ Simplify.

The increase in population is 793.32 thousand. This means that the population of Nevada in 2000 was

$$\begin{matrix} \text{Nevada} \\ \text{population} \\ \text{in 2000} \end{matrix} = \begin{matrix} \text{Population} \\ \text{in 1990} \end{matrix} + \begin{matrix} \text{Increase} \\ \text{in population} \end{matrix}$$

$$= 1202 \text{ thousand} + 793.32 \text{ thousand}$$

$$= 1995.32 \text{ thousand}$$

■ **Work Practice Problem 4**

Objective **B** Finding Percent Increase and Percent Decrease

We often use percents to show how much an amount has increased or decreased.

Suppose that the population of a town is 10,000 people and then it increases by 2000 people. The **percent of increase** is

$\begin{matrix} \text{amount of increase} \rightarrow \\ \text{original amount} \rightarrow \end{matrix} \dfrac{2000}{10{,}000} = 0.2 = 20\%$

In general, we have the following.

Percent of Increase

$$\text{percent of increase} = \frac{\text{amount of increase}}{\text{original amount}}$$

Then write the quotient as a percent.

EXAMPLE 5 Finding Percent Increase

The number of applications for a mathematics scholarship at Yale increased from 34 to 45 in one year. What is the percent increase? Round to the nearest whole percent.

Solution: First we find the amount of increase by subtracting the original number of applicants from the new number of applicants.

$$\text{amount of increase} = 45 - 34 = 11$$

The amount of increase is 11 applicants. To find the percent of increase,

$$\text{percent of increase} = \frac{\text{amount of increase}}{\text{original amount}} = \frac{11}{34} \approx 0.32 = 32\%$$

The number of applications increased by about 32%.

▢ **Work Practice Problem 5**

✔ Concept Check A student is calculating the percent increase in enrollment from 180 students one year to 200 students the next year. Explain what is wrong with the following calculations:

$$\begin{array}{l}\text{Amount} \\ \text{of increase}\end{array} = 200 - 180 = 20$$

$$\begin{array}{l}\text{Percent of} \\ \text{increase}\end{array} = \frac{20}{200} = 0.1 = 10\%$$

Suppose that your income was $300 a week and then it decreased by $30. The **percent of decrease** is

$$\begin{array}{l}\text{amount of decrease} \rightarrow \\ \text{original amount} \rightarrow\end{array} \frac{\$30}{\$300} = 0.1 = 10\%$$

Percent of Decrease

$$\text{percent of decrease} = \frac{\text{amount of decrease}}{\text{original amount}}$$

Then write the quotient as a percent.

EXAMPLE 6 Finding Percent Decrease

In response to a decrease in sales, a company with 1500 employees reduces the number of employees to 1230. What is the percent decrease?

Solution: First we find the amount of decrease by subtracting 1230 from 1500.

$$\text{amount of decrease} = 1500 - 1230 = 270$$

The amount of decrease is 270. To find the percent of decrease,

$$\begin{array}{l}\text{percent of} \\ \text{decrease}\end{array} = \frac{\text{amount of decrease}}{\text{original amount}} = \frac{270}{1500} = 0.18 = 18\%$$

The number of employees decreased by 18%.

▢ **Work Practice Problem 6**

PRACTICE PROBLEM 5

The number of people attending the local play, *Peter Pan,* increased from 285 on Friday to 333 on Saturday. Find the percent increase in attendance. Round to the nearest tenth of a percent.

Helpful Hint Make sure that this number is the original number and not the new number.

PRACTICE PROBLEM 6

A town with a population of 20,200 in 1995 decreased to 18,483 in 2005. What was the percent decrease?

Answers

5. 16.8%, **6.** 8.5%

✔ **Concept Check Answer**

To find the percent of increase, you have to divide the amount of increase (20) by the original amount (180).

6.4 EXERCISE SET

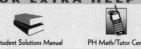

Student Solutions Manual　PH Math/Tutor Center　CD/Video for Review　MathXL®　MyMathLab

Objective A *Solve. See Examples 1 and 2.*

1. An inspector found 24 defective bolts during an inspection. If this is 1.5% of the total number of bolts inspected, how many bolts were inspected?

2. A day care worker found 28 children absent one day during an epidemic of chicken pox. If this was 35% of the total number of children attending the day care center, how many children attend this day care center?

3. 18% of Frank's wages are withheld for income tax. Find the amount withheld from Frank's wages of $3680 per month.

4. The Hodder family paid 20% of the purchase price of a $75,000 home as a down payment. Determine the amount of the down payment.

5. Vera Faciane earns $2000 per month and budgets $300 per month for food. What percent of her monthly income is spent on food?

6. Last year, Mai Toberlan bought a share of stock for $83. She was paid a dividend of $4.15. Determine what percent of the stock price is the dividend.

7. A manufacturer of electronic components expects 1.04% of its products to be defective. Determine the number of defective components expected in a batch of 28,350 components. Round to the nearest whole component.

8. An owner of a repair service company estimates that for every 40 hours a repairperson is on the job, he can bill for only 78% of the hours. The remaining hours, the repairperson is idle or driving to or from a job. Determine the number of hours per 40-hour week the owner can bill for a repairperson.

9. Of the 535 members of the 108th U.S. Congress, 73 have attended a community college. What percent of the members of the 108th Congress is this? Round to the nearest tenth of a percent. (*Source: American Association of Community Colleges*)

10. The Los Angeles County courts excused 775,130 prospective jurors from jury duty in a recent year. This represented 28% of all juror qualification affidavits sent out that year. How many juror qualification affidavits were sent out that year? Round to the nearest whole affidavit. (*Source:* Los Angeles Superior Court)

11. There are about 98,400 female dental hygienists registered in the United States. If this represents about 98.3% of the nation's dental hygienists, find the approximate number of dental hygienists in the United States. Round to the nearest whole. (*Source:* The American Dental Hygienists' Association)

12. 31.6% of all households in the United States own at least one pet dog. There are 11,250 households in Anytown. How many of these households would you expect own a dog? (*Source:* American Veterinary Medical Association)

For each food described, find what percent of total calories is from fat. If necessary, round to the nearest tenth of a percent. See Example 3.

13. Ranch dressing serving size of 2 tablespoons

	Calories
Total	40
From fat	20

14. Unsweetened cocoa powder serving size of 1 tablespoon

	Calories
Total	20
From fat	5

15.

Nutrition Facts

Serving Size 18 crackers (29g)
Servings Per Container About 9

Amount Per Serving

Calories 120 Calories from Fat 35

	% Daily Value*
Total Fat 4g	**6%**
Saturated Fat 0.5g	**3%**
Polyunsaturated Fat 0g	
Monounsaturated Fat 1.5g	
Cholesterol 0mg	**0%**
Sodium 220mg	**9%**
Total Carbohydrate 21g	**7%**
Dietary Fiber 2g	**7%**
Sugars 3g	
Protein 2g	

Vitamin A 0% • Vitamin C 0%

Calcium 2% • Iron 4%

Phosphorus 10%

Snack Crackers

16.

Nutrition Facts

Serving Size 28 crackers (31g)
Servings Per Container About 6

Amount Per Serving

Calories 130 Calories from Fat 35

	% Daily Value*
Total Fat 4g	**6%**
Saturated Fat 2g	**10%**
Polyunsaturated Fat 1g	
Monounsaturated Fat 1g	
Cholesterol 0mg	**0%**
Sodium 470mg	**20%**
Total Carbohydrate 23g	**8%**
Dietary Fiber 1g	**4%**
Sugars 4g	
Protein 2g	

Vitamin A 0% • Vitamin C 0%

Calcium 0% • Iron 2%

Snack Crackers

Solve. Round money amounts to the nearest cent and all other amounts to the nearest tenth. See Example 4.

17. Ace Furniture Company currently produces 6200 chairs per month. If production decreases by 8%, find the decrease and the new number of chairs produced each month.

18. The enrollment at a local college decreased by 5% over last year's enrollment of 7640. Find the decrease in enrollment and the current enrollment.

19. By carefully planning their meals, a family was able to decrease their weekly grocery bill by 20%. Their weekly grocery bill used to be $170. What is their new weekly grocery bill?

20. The profit of Ramone Company last year was $175,000. This year's profit decreased by 11%. Find this year's profit.

21. A car manufacturer announced that next year the price of a certain model of car would increase by 4.5%. This year the price is $19,286. Find the increase in price and the new price.

22. A union contract calls for a 6.5% salary increase for all employees. Determine the increase and the new salary that a worker currently making $38,500 under this contract can expect.

23. From 2002 to 2012, the number of people employed as physician assistants in the United States is expected to increase by 49%. The number of people employed as physician assistants in 2002 was 63,000. Find the predicted number of physician assistants in 2012. (*Source:* Bureau of Labor Statistics)

24. The state of North Dakota had the smallest percent increase in population, 0.5%, from the 1990 census to the 2000 census. In 1990, the population of North Dakota was 638,800. What was the population of North Dakota in 2000? (*Source:* U.S. Census Bureau)

North Dakota

25. The population of Americans aged 65 and older was 35 million in 2000. That population is projected to increase by 80% by 2025. Find the increase and the projected 2025 population. (*Source:* Bureau of the Census)

26. From 2000 to 2010, the number of masters degrees awarded to women is projected to increase by 8.3%. The number of women who received masters degrees in 2000 was 265,000. Find the predicted number of women to be awarded masters degrees in 2010. (*Source:* U.S. National Center for Education Statistics)

Objective B *Find the amount of increase and the percent increase. See Example 5.*

	Original Amount	New Amount	Amount of Increase	Percent Increase
27.	40	50		
28.	10	15		
29.	85	187		
30.	78	351		

Find the amount of decrease and the percent decrease. See Example 6.

	Original Amount	New Amount	Amount of Decrease	Percent Decrease
31.	8	6		
32.	25	20		
33.	160	40		
34.	200	162		

Solve. Round percents to the nearest tenth, if necessary. See Examples 5 and 6.

35. There are 150 calories in a cup of whole milk and only 84 in a cup of skim milk. In switching to skim milk, find the percent decrease in number of calories per cup.

36. In reaction to a slow economy, the number of employees at a soup company decreased from 530 to 477. What was the percent decrease in the number of employees?

37. By changing his driving routines, Alan Miller increased his car's rate of miles per gallon from 19.5 to 23.7. Find the percent increase.

38. John Smith decided to decrease the number of calories in his diet from 3250 to 2100. Find the percent decrease.

39. The number of cable TV systems recently decreased from 10,845 to 10,700. Find the percent decrease.

40. Before taking a typing course, Geoffry Landers could type 32 words per minute. By the end of the course, he was able to type 76 words per minute. Find the percent increase.

41. In 1940, the average size of a U.S. farm was 174 acres. By 2003, the average size of a U.S. farm had increased to 441 acres. What was the percent increase? (*Source:* National Agricultural Statistics Service)

42. In 1995, 272.6 million recorded music cassettes were shipped to retailers in the United States. By 2000, this number had decreased to 76.0 million cassettes. What was the percent decrease? (*Source:* Recording Industry Association of America)

43. In 1994, approximately 16,000,000 Americans subscribed to cellular phone service. By 2003, this number had increased to about 159,000,000 American subscribers. What was the percent increase? (*Source:* Network World, Inc.)

44. In 1970, there were 1754 deaths from boating accidents in the United States. By 2003, the number of deaths from boating accidents had decreased to 703. What was the percent decrease? (*Source:* U.S. Coast Guard)

45. In 1994, approximately 16,000 occupational therapy assistants and aides were employed in the United States. According to one survey, by 2005, this number is expected to increase to 29,000 assistants and aides. What is the percent increase? (*Source:* Bureau of Labor Statistics)

46. In 1994, approximately 206,000 medical assistants were employed in the United States. By 2005, this number is expected to increase to 327,000 medical assistants. What is the percent increase? (*Source:* Bureau of Labor Statistics)

47. In 1999, discarded electronics, including obsolete computer equipment, accounted for 75,000 tons of solid waste per year in Massachusetts. By 2006, discarded electronic waste is expected to increase to 300,000 tons of waste per year in the state. Find the percent increase. (*Source:* Massachusetts Department of Environmental Protection)

48. The average soft-drink size has increased from 13.1 oz to 19.9 oz over the past two decades. Find the percent increase. (*Source:* University of North Carolina at Chapel Hill, *Journal for American Medicine*)

49. The population of Tokyo is expected to decrease from 127,333 thousand in 2004 to 99,887 thousand in 2050. Find the percent decrease. (*Source:* International Programs Center, Bureau of the Census, U.S. Dept. of Commerce)

50. In 2002, approximately 394,000 computer application software engineers were employed in the United States. By 2012, this number is expected to increase to 573,000. What is the percent increase? (*Source:* Bureau of Labor Statistics)

Review

Perform each indicated operation. See Sections 4.2 and 4.3.

51. $\begin{array}{r} 0.12 \\ \times\ \ 38 \\ \hline \end{array}$

52. $\begin{array}{r} 42 \\ \times 0.7 \\ \hline \end{array}$

53. $9.20 + 1.98$

54. $46 + 7.89$

55. $78 - 19.46$

56. $64.80 - 10.72$

Concept Extensions

57. If a number is increased by 100%, how does the increased number compare with the original number? Explain your answer.

58. In your own words, explain what is wrong with the following statement. "Last year we had 80 students attend. This year we have a 50% increase or a total of 160 students attend."

59. Explain what errors were made by each student when solving percent of increase or decrease problems and then correct the errors. *"The population of a certain rural town was 150 in 1980, 180 in 1990, and 150 in 2000."*

   a. Find the percent of increase in population from 1980 to 1990.

   Miranda's solution: Percent of increase $= \dfrac{30}{180} = 0.1\overline{6} \approx 16.7\%$

   b. Find the percent of decrease in population from 1990 to 2000.

   Jeremy's solution: Percent of decrease $= \dfrac{30}{150} = 0.20 = 20\%$

   c. The percent of increase from 1980 to 1990 is the same as the percent of decrease from 1990 to 2000. True or false.

   Chris's answer: True because they had the same amount of increase as the amount of decrease.

6.5 PERCENT AND PROBLEM SOLVING: SALES TAX, COMMISSION, AND DISCOUNT

Objective **A** Calculating Sales Tax and Total Price

Percents are frequently used in the retail trade. For example, most states charge a tax on certain items when purchased. This tax is called a **sales tax,** and retail stores collect it for the state. Sales tax is almost always stated as a percent of the purchase price.

A 6% sales tax rate on a purchase of a $10 item gives a sales tax of

sales tax = 6% of $10 = 0.06 · $10.00 = $0.60

The total price to the customer would be

$$\underbrace{\text{purchase price}}_{\downarrow} \text{ plus } \underbrace{\text{sales tax}}_{\downarrow}$$

$$\$10.00 \quad + \quad \$0.60 = \$10.60$$

This example suggests the following equations:

Sales Tax and Total Price

sales tax = tax rate · purchase price

total price = purchase price + sales tax

In this section we round dollar amounts to the nearest cent.

EXAMPLE 1 Finding Sales Tax and Purchase Price

Find the sales tax and the total price on the purchase of an $85.50 trench coat in a city where the sales tax rate is 7.5%.

Solution: The purchase price is $85.50 and the tax rate is 7.5%.

$$\underbrace{\text{sales tax}}_{\downarrow} = \underbrace{\text{tax rate}}_{\downarrow} \cdot \underbrace{\text{purchase price}}_{\swarrow}$$

sales tax = 7.5% · $85.50

= 0.075 · $85.5   Write 7.5% as a decimal.

≈ $6.41   Rounded to the nearest cent.

Thus, the sales tax is $6.41. Next find the total price.

$$\underbrace{\text{total price}}_{\downarrow} = \underbrace{\text{purchase price}}_{\swarrow} + \underbrace{\text{sales tax}}_{\swarrow}$$

total price = $85.50 + $6.41

= $91.91

The sales tax on $85.50 is $6.41, and the total price is $91.91.

■ **Work Practice Problem 1**

PRACTICE PROBLEM 1

If the sales tax rate is 6%, what is the sales tax and the total amount due on a $29.90 Goodgrip tire?

Answer

1. tax: $1.79; total: $31.69

PRACTICE PROBLEM 2

The sales tax on a $13,500 automobile is $1080. Find the sales tax rate.

✔**Concept Check** The purchase price of a textbook is $50 and sales tax is 10%. If you are told by the cashier that the total price is $75, how can you tell that a mistake has been made?

EXAMPLE 2 **Finding a Sales Tax Rate**

The sales tax on a $300 printer is $22.50. Find the sales tax rate.

Solution: Let r represent the unknown sales tax rate. Then

$$\underbrace{\text{sales tax}} \; = \; \underbrace{\text{tax rate}} \; \cdot \; \underbrace{\text{purchase price}}$$

$$\$22.50 = r \cdot \$300$$

$$\frac{22.50}{300} = r \quad \text{Divide 22.50 by 300, the number multiplied by } r.$$

$$0.075 = r \quad \text{Simplify.}$$

$$7.5\% = r \quad \text{Write 0.075 as a percent.}$$

The sales tax rate is 7.5%.

▪ **Work Practice Problem 2**

Objective B **Calculating Commissions**

A **wage** is payment for performing work. Hourly wage, commissions, and salary are some of the ways wages can be paid. Many people who work in sales are paid a commission. An employee who is paid a **commission** is paid a percent of his or her total sales.

Commission

$$\text{commission} = \text{commission rate} \cdot \text{sales}$$

EXAMPLE 3 **Finding the Amount of Commission**

Sherry Souter, a real estate broker for Wealth Investments, sold a house for $114,000 last week. If her commission is 1.5% of the selling price of the home, find the amount of her commission.

Solution:

commission	=	commission rate	·	sales	
commission	=	1.5%	·	$114,000	
	=	0.015	·	$114,000	Write 1.5% as 0.015.
	=	$1710			Multiply.

PRACTICE PROBLEM 3

Mr. Olsen is a sales representative for Miko Copiers. Last month he sold $37,632 worth of copy equipment and supplies. What is his commission for the month if he is paid a commission of 6.6% of his total sales for the month?

Answers
2. 8%, **3.** $2483.71

✔ **Concept Check Answer**

Since $10\% = \frac{1}{10}$, the sales tax is $\frac{\$50}{10} = \$5$. The total price should have been $55.

Her commission on the house is $1710.

⬛ **Work Practice Problem 3**

EXAMPLE 4 **Finding a Commission Rate**

A salesperson earned $1560 for selling $13,000 worth of television and stereo systems. Find the commission rate.

Solution: Let r stand for the unknown commission rate. Then

$$\text{commission} = \text{commission rate} \cdot \text{sales}$$

$$\$1560 = r \cdot \$13,000$$

$$\frac{1560}{13,000} = r \quad \text{Divide 1560 by 13,000, the number multiplied by } r.$$

$$0.12 = r \quad \text{Simplify.}$$

$$12\% = r \quad \text{Write 0.12 as a percent.}$$

The commission rate is 12%.

⬛ **Work Practice Problem 4**

Objective **C** **Calculating Discount and Sale Price**

Suppose that an item that normally sells for $40 is on sale for 25% off. This means that the **original price** of $40 is reduced, or **discounted,** by 25% of $40, or $10. The **discount rate** is 25%, the **amount of discount** is $10, and the **sale price** is $40 − $10, or $30. Study the diagram below to visualize these terms.

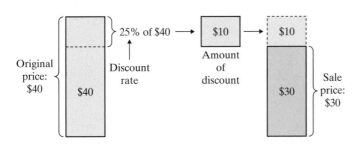

PRACTICE PROBLEM 4

A salesperson earns $1290 for selling $8600 worth of appliances. Find the commission rate.

Answer
4. 15%

To calculate discounts and sale prices, we can use the following equations:

Discount and Sale Price

amount of discount = discount rate · original price

sale price = original price − amount of discount

PRACTICE PROBLEM 5

A Panasonic TV is advertised on sale for 15% off the regular price of $700. Find the discount and the sale price.

EXAMPLE 5 Finding a Discount and a Sale Price

A speaker that normally sells for $65 is on sale for 25% off. What is the discount and what is the sale price?

Solution: First we find the discount.

amount of discount	=	discount rate	·	original price

amount of discount = 25% · $65

= 0.25 · $65   Write 25% as 0.25.

= $16.25   Multiply.

The discount is $16.25. Next, find the sale price.

sale price	=	original price	−	discount

sale price = $65 − $16.25

= $48.75   Subtract.

The sale price is $48.75.

⬛ **Work Practice Problem 5**

Answer

5. $105; $595

Objective **A** *Solve. See Examples 1 and 2.*

1. What is the sales tax on a suit priced at $150 if the sales tax rate is 5%?

2. If the sales tax rate is 6%, find the sales tax on a microwave oven priced at $188.

3. The purchase price of a camcorder is $799. What is the total price if the sales tax rate is 7.5%?

4. A stereo system has a purchase price of $426. What is the total price if the sales tax rate is 8%?

5. A chair and ottoman have a purchase price of $600. If the sales tax on this purchase is $57, find the sales tax rate.

6. The sales tax on the purchase of a $2500 computer is $162.50. Find the sales tax rate.

7. The sales tax on a table saw is $10.20.

   a. What is the purchase price of the table saw (before tax) if the sales tax rate is 8.5%?

   b. Find the total price of the table saw.

8. The sales tax on a one-half-carat diamond ring is $76.

   a. Find the purchase price of the ring (before tax) if the sales tax rate is 9.5%.

   b. Find the total price of the ring.

9. A gold and diamond bracelet sells for $1800. Find the total price if the sales tax rate is 6.5%.

10. The purchase price of a personal computer is $1890. If the sales tax rate is 8%, what is the total price?

11. The sales tax on the purchase of a truck is $920. If the tax rate is 8%, find the purchase price of the truck.

12. The sales tax on the purchase of a desk is $27.50. If the tax rate is 5%, find the purchase price of the desk.

13. The sales tax is $98.70 on a stereo sound system purchase of $1645. Find the sales tax rate.

14. The sales tax is $103.50 on a necklace purchase of $1150. Find the sales tax rate.

15. A cell phone costs $90 and a battery recharger costs $15. What is the total price for purchasing these items if the sales tax rate is 7%?

16. Ms. Warner bought a blouse for $35, a skirt for $55, and a blazer for $95. Find the total price she paid, given a sales tax rate of 6.5%.

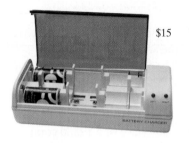 $15  $90

Objective **B** *Solve. See Examples 3 and 4.*

17. Jane Moreschi, a sales representative for a large furniture warehouse, is paid a commission rate of 4%. Find her commission if she sold $1,236,856 worth of furniture last year.

18. Rosie Davis-Smith is a beauty consultant for a home cosmetic business. She is paid a commission rate of 4.8%. Find her commission if she sold $1638 in cosmetics last month.

19. A salesperson earned a commission of $1380.40 for selling $9860 worth of paper products. Find the commission rate.

20. A salesperson earned a commission of $3575 for selling $32,500 worth of books to various bookstores. Find the commission rate.

21. How much commission will Jack Pruet make on the sale of a $125,900 house if he receives 1.5% of the selling price?

22. Frankie Lopez sold $9638 of jewelry this week. Find her commission for the week if she receives a commission rate of 5.6%.

23. A real estate agent earned a commission of $2565 for selling a house. If his rate is 3%, find the selling price of the house.

24. A salesperson earned $1750 for selling fertilizer. If her commission rate is 7%, find the selling price of the fertilizer.

Objective **C** *Find the amount of discount and the sale price. See Example 5.*

	Original Price	Discount Rate	Amount of Discount	Sale Price
25.	$68	10%		
26.	$47	20%		
27.	$96.50	50%		
28.	$110.60	40%		
29.	$215	35%		
30.	$370	25%		
31.	$21,700	15%		
32.	$17,800	12%		

33. A $300 fax machine is on sale for 15% off. Find the discount and the sale price.

34. A $2000 designer dress is on sale for 30% off. Find the discount and the sale price.

Objectives **A** **B** **Mixed Practice** Complete each table.

	Purchase Price	Tax Rate	Sales Tax	Total Price
35.	$586	9%		
36.	$243	8%		
37.	$82	5.5%		
38.	$65	8.4%		

	Sale	Commission Rate	Commission
39.	$235,800	3%	
40.	$195,450	5%	
41.	$17,900		$1432
42.	$25,600		$2304

Review

Multiply. See Sections 4.3 and 4.5.

43. $2000 \cdot 0.3 \cdot 2$

44. $500 \cdot 0.08 \cdot 3$

45. $400 \cdot 0.03 \cdot 11$

46. $1000 \cdot 0.05 \cdot 5$

47. $600 \cdot 0.04 \cdot \dfrac{2}{3}$

48. $6000 \cdot 0.06 \cdot \dfrac{3}{4}$

Concept Extensions

Solve. See the Concept Check in this section.

49. Your purchase price is $68 and the sales tax rate is 9.5%. Round each amount and use the rounded amounts to estimate the total price. Choose the best estimate.

  a. $105   **b.** $58   **c.** $93   **d.** $77

50. Your purchase price is $200 and the tax rate is 10%. Choose the best estimate of the total price.

  a. $190   **b.** $210   **c.** $220   **d.** $300

One very useful application of percent is mentally calculating a tip. Recall that to find 10% of a number, simply move the decimal point one place to the left. To find 20% of a number, just double 10% of the number. To find 15% of a number, find 10% and then add to that number half of the 10% amount. Mentally fill in the chart below. To do so, start by rounding the bill amount to the nearest dollar.

Tipping Chart			
Bill Amount	**10%**	**15%**	**20%**
51. $40.21			
52. $15.89			
53. $72.17			
54. $9.33			

55. Suppose that the original price of a shirt is $50. Which is better, a 60% discount or a discount of 30% followed by a discount of 35% of the reduced price? Explain your answer.

56. Which is better, a 30% discount followed by an additional 25% off or a 20% discount followed by an additional 40% off? To see, suppose an item costs $100 and calculate each discounted price. Explain your answer.

57. A diamond necklace sells for $24,966. If the tax rate is 7.5%, find the total price.

58. A house recently sold for $562,560. The commission rate on the sale is 5.5%. If the real estate agent is to receive 60% of the commission, find the amount received by the agent.

STUDY SKILLS BUILDER

Are You Familiar with Your Textbook Supplements?

Below is a review of some of the student supplements available for additional study. Check to see if you are using the ones most helpful to you.

- Chapter Test Prep Videos on CD. This material is found with your textbook and is fully explained there. The CD contains video clip solutions to the Chapter Test exercises in this text and are excellent help when studying for chapter tests.

- Lecture Videos on CD-ROM. These video segments are keyed to each section of the text. The material is presented by me, Elayn Martin-Gay, and I have placed a 🔘 by the exercises in the text that I have worked on the video.

- The *Student Solutions Manual*. This contains worked out solutions to odd-numbered exercises as well as every exercise in the Integrated Reviews, Chapter Reviews, Chapter Tests, and Cumulative Reviews.

- Prentice Hall Tutor Center. Mathematic questions may be phoned, faxed, or emailed to this center.

- MyMathLab, MathXL, and Interact Math. These are computer and Internet tutorials. This supplement may already be available to you somewhere on campus, for example at your local learning resource lab. Take a moment and find the name and location of any such lab on campus.

　　As usual, your instructor is your best source of information.

Let's see how you are doing with textbook supplements.

1. Name one way the Lecture Videos can be helpful to you.

2. Name one way the Chapter Test Prep Video can help you prepare for a chapter test.

3. List any textbook supplements that you have found useful.

4. Have you located and visited a learning resource lab located on your campus?

5. List the textbook supplements that are currently housed in your campus' learning resource lab.

6.6 PERCENT AND PROBLEM SOLVING: INTEREST

Objective A Calculating Simple Interest

Interest is money charged for using other people's money. When you borrow money, you pay interest. When you loan or invest money, you earn interest. The money borrowed, loaned, or invested is called the **principal amount,** or simply **principal.** Interest is normally stated in terms of a percent of the principal for a given period of time. The **interest rate** is the percent used in computing the interest. Unless stated otherwise, *the rate is understood to be per year.* When the interest is computed on the original principal, it is called **simple interest.** Simple interest is calculated using the following equation:

Simple Interest

$$\text{simple interest} = \text{principal} \cdot \text{rate} \cdot \text{time}$$

where the rate is understood to be per year and time is in years.

EXAMPLE 1 Finding Simple Interest

Find the simple interest after 2 years on $500 at an interest rate of 12%.

Solution: In this example, the principal is $500, the rate is 12%, and the time is 2 years.

simple interest	=	principal	·	rate	·	time	
↓		↓		↓		↓	
simple interest	=	$500	·	12%	·	2	
	=	$500	·	0.12	·	2	Write 12% as 0.12.
	=	$120					Multiply.

The simple interest is $120.

Work Practice Problem 1

If time is not given in years, we need to convert the given time to years.

EXAMPLE 2 Finding Simple Interest

Ivan Borski borrowed $2400 at 10% simple interest for 8 months to buy a used Chevy S-10. Find the simple interest he paid.

Solution: Since there are 12 months in a year, we first find what part of a year 8 months is.

$$8 \text{ months} = \frac{8}{12} \text{ year} = \frac{2}{3} \text{ year}$$

Now we find the simple interest.

simple interest	=	principal	·	rate	·	time
↓		↓		↓		↓
simple interest	=	$2400	·	10%	·	$\frac{2}{3}$
	=	$2400	·	0.10	·	$\frac{2}{3}$
	=	$160				

The interest on Ivan's loan is $160.

Work Practice Problem 2

PRACTICE PROBLEM 1

Find the simple interest after 3 years on $750 at an interest rate of 8%.

PRACTICE PROBLEM 2

Juanita Lopez borrowed $800 for 9 months at a simple interest rate of 20%. How much interest did she pay?

Answers
1. $180, **2.** $120

495

When money is borrowed, the borrower pays the original amount borrowed, or the principal, as well as the interest. When money is invested, the investor receives the original amount invested, or the principal, as well as the interest. In either case, the **total amount** is the sum of the principal and the interest.

Finding the Total Amount of a Loan or Investment

total amount (paid or received) = principal + interest

PRACTICE PROBLEM 3

If $500 is borrowed at a simple interest rate of 12% for 6 months, find the total amount paid.

EXAMPLE 3 **Finding the Total Amount of an Investment**

An accountant invested $2000 at a simple interest rate of 10% for 2 years. What total amount of money will she have from her investment in 2 years?

Solution: First we find her interest.

$$\text{simple interest} = \text{principal} \cdot \text{rate} \cdot \text{time}$$

$$\text{simple interest} = \$2000 \cdot 10\% \cdot 2$$
$$= \$2000 \cdot 0.10 \cdot 2$$
$$= \$400$$

The interest is $400.

Next, we add the interest to the principal.

$$\text{total amount} = \text{principal} + \text{interest}$$

$$\text{total amount} = \$2000 + \$400$$
$$= \$2400$$

After 2 years, she will have a total amount of $2400.

▢ **Work Practice Problem 3**

✔ **Concept Check** Which investment would earn more interest: an amount of money invested at 8% interest for 2 years, or the same amount of money invested at 8% for 3 years? Explain.

Objective B Calculating Compound Interest

Recall that simple interest depends on the original principal only. Another type of interest is compound interest. **Compound interest** is computed on not only the principal, but also on the interest already earned in previous compounding periods. Compound interest is used more often than simple interest.

Let's see how compound interest differs from simple interest. Suppose that $2000 is invested at 7% interest **compounded annually** for 3 years. This means that interest is added to the principal at the end of each year and that next year's interest is computed on this new amount. In this section, we round dollar amounts to the nearest cent.

Answer

3. $530

✔ **Concept Check Answer**

8% for 3 years. Since the interest rate is the same, the longer you keep the money invested, the more interest you earn.

	Amount at Beginning of Year	Principal	•	Rate	•	Time	= Interest	Amount at End of Year
1st year	$2000	$2000	•	0.07	•	1	= $140	$2000 + 140 = $2140
2nd year	$2140	$2140	•	0.07	•	1	= $149.80	$2140 + 149.80 = $2289.80
3rd year	$2289.80	$2289.80	•	0.07	•	1	= $160.29	$2289.80 + 160.29 = $2450.09

The compound interest earned can be found by

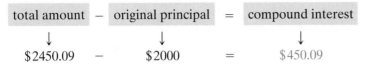

total amount − original principal = compound interest
↓   ↓   ↓
$2450.09   − $2000   = $450.09

The simple interest earned would have been

principal · rate · time = interest
↓   ↓   ↓   ↓
$2000   ·   0.07 ·   3   = $420

Since compound interest earns "interest on interest," compound interest earns more than simple interest.

Computing compound interest using the method above can be tedious. We can use a **compound interest table** or a calculator to compute interest more quickly. The compound interest table in this textbook is found in Appendix A.7. This table gives the total compound interest and principal paid on $1 for given rates and numbers of years. Then we can use the following equation to find the total amount of interest and principal:

Finding Total Amounts with Compound Interest

total amount = original principal · compound interest factor (from table)

As mentioned above, the compound interest factor can also be found by using a calculator. See the Calculator Explorations box at the end of this section for instructions.

EXAMPLE 4 **Finding Total Amount Received on an Investment**

$4000 is invested at 8% compounded semiannually for 10 years. Find the total amount at the end of 10 years.

Solution: Look in Appendix A.7. The compound interest factor for 10 years at 8% in the Compounded Semiannually section is 2.19112.

total amount = original principal · compound interest factor
↓   ↓   ↓
total amount = $4000   ·   2.19112
              = $8764.48

Therefore, the total amount at the end of 10 years is $8764.48.

🔲 **Work Practice Problem 4**

EXAMPLE 5 **Finding Compound Interest Earned**

In Example 4 we found that the total amount for $4000 invested at 8% compounded semiannually for 10 years is $8764.48. Find the compound interest earned.

Solution:

interest earned = total amount − original principal
↓   ↓   ↓
interest earned = $8764.48   − $4000
                 = $4764.48

The compound interest earned is $4764.48.

🔲 **Work Practice Problem 5**

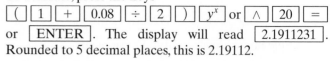

CALCULATOR EXPLORATIONS   Compound Interest Factor

A compound interest factor may be found by using your calculator and evaluating the formula

$$\text{compound interest factor} = \left(1 + \frac{r}{n}\right)^{nt}$$

where r is the interest rate, t is the time in years, and n is the number of times compounded per year. For example, we stated earlier that the compound interest factor for 10 years at 8% compounded semiannually is 2.19112. Let's find this factor by evaluating the compound interest factor formula when $r = 8\%$ or 0.08, $t = 10$, and $n = 2$ (compounded semiannually means 2 times per year). Thus,

$$\text{compound interest factor} = \left(1 + \frac{0.08}{2}\right)^{2 \cdot 10}$$

$$\text{or } \left(1 + \frac{0.08}{2}\right)^{20}$$

To evaluate, press the keys

$$\boxed{(} \ \boxed{1} \ \boxed{+} \ \boxed{0.08} \ \boxed{\div} \ \boxed{2} \ \boxed{)} \ \boxed{y^x} \text{ or } \boxed{\wedge} \ \boxed{20} \ \boxed{=}$$

or $\boxed{\text{ENTER}}$. The display will read $\boxed{2.1911231}$. Rounded to 5 decimal places, this is 2.19112.

Find the compound interest factors. Use the table in the Appendix A.7 to check your answers.

1. 5 years, 9%, compounded quarterly

2. 15 years, 14%, compounded daily

3. 20 years, 11%, compounded annually

4. 1 year, 7%, compounded semiannually

5. Find the total amount after 4 years when $500 is invested at 6% compounded quarterly.

6. Find the total amount for 19 years when $2500 is invested at 5% compounded daily.

Objective A *Find the simple interest. See Examples 1 and 2.*

	Principal	Rate	Time
1.	$200	8%	2 years
3.	$160	11.5%	4 years
5.	$5000	10%	$1\frac{1}{2}$ years
7.	$375	18%	6 months
9.	$2500	16%	21 months

	Principal	Rate	Time
2.	$800	9%	3 years
4.	$950	12.5%	5 years
6.	$1500	14%	$2\frac{1}{4}$ years
8.	$775	15%	8 months
10.	$1000	10%	18 months

Solve. See Examples 1 through 3.

11. A company borrows $62,500 for 2 years at a simple interest of 12.5% to buy an airplane. Find the total amount paid on the loan.

12. $65,000 is borrowed to buy a house. If the simple interest rate on the 30-year loan is 10.25%, find the total amount paid on the loan.

13. A money market fund advertises a simple interest rate of 9%. Find the total amount received on an investment of $5000 for 15 months.

14. The Real Service Company takes out a 270-day (9-month) short-term, simple interest loan of $4500 to finance the purchase of some new equipment. If the interest rate is 14%, find the total amount that the company pays back.

15. Marsha Waide borrows $8500 and agrees to pay it back in 4 years. If the simple interest rate is 12%, find the total amount she pays back.

16. Ms. Lapchinski gives her 18-year-old daughter a graduation gift of $2000. If this money is invested at 8% simple interest for 5 years, find the total amount.

Objective B *Find the total amount in each compound interest account. See Example 4.*

17. $6150 is compounded semiannually at a rate of 14% for 15 years.

18. $2060 is compounded annually at a rate of 15% for 10 years.

19. $1560 is compounded daily at a rate of 8% for 5 years.

20. $1450 is compounded quarterly at a rate of 10% for 15 years.

21. $10,000 is compounded semiannually at a rate of 9% for 20 years.

22. $3500 is compounded daily at a rate of 8% for 10 years.

Find the total amount of compound interest earned. See Example 5.

23. $2675 is compounded annually at a rate of 9% for 1 year.

24. $6375 is compounded semiannually at a rate of 10% for 1 year.

25. $2000 is compounded annually at a rate of 8% for 5 years.

26. $2000 is compounded semiannually at a rate of 8% for 5 years.

27. $2000 is compounded quarterly at a rate of 8% for 5 years.

28. $2000 is compounded daily at a rate of 8% for 5 years.

Review

Find the perimeter of each figure. See Section 1.3.

△ **29.**

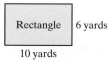
Rectangle 6 yards
10 yards

△ **30.**

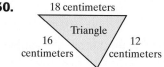
18 centimeters
Triangle
16 centimeters   12 centimeters

△ **31.**

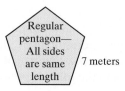
Regular pentagon— All sides are same length   7 meters

△ **32.**

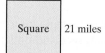
Square 21 miles

Concept Extensions

33. Explain how to look up a compound interest factor in the compound interest table.

34. Explain how to find the amount of interest in a compounded account.

35. Compare the following accounts: Account 1: $1000 is invested for 10 years at a simple interest rate of 6%. Account 2: $1000 is compounded semiannually at a rate of 6% for 10 years. Discuss how the interest is computed for each account. Determine which account earns more interest. Why?

CHAPTER 6   Group Activity

Sections 6.1, 6.6

How Much Can You Afford for a House?

When a home buyer takes out a mortgage to buy a house, the loan is generally repaid on a monthly basis with a monthly mortgage payment. (Some banks also offer bi-weekly payment programs.) An important consideration in choosing a house is the amount of the monthly payment. Usually, the amount that a home buyer can afford to make as a monthly payment will dictate the house purchase price that can be afforded.

The first step in deciding how much can be afforded for a house is finding out how much income the household has each month before taxes. The Mortgage Bankers Association of American (MBAA) suggests that the monthly mortgage payment be between 25% and 28% of the total monthly income. If other long-term debts exist (such as car or education loans and long-term credit card debt repayment), the MBAA further recommends that the total of housing costs and other monthly debt payments not exceed 36% of the total monthly income.

Once the size of the monthly payment that can be afforded has been found, a mortgage payment calculator can be used to work backward to estimate the mortgage amount that will give that desired monthly payment. For example, the Interest.com Web site includes a mortgage payment calculator at http://www.interest.com/calculators/monthlypayment.shtml. (Alternatively, visit www.interest.com and navigate to "Use our mortgage calculators.") Look for the calculator to calculate the monthly payment for a particular mortgage loan. With this mortgage payment calculator, the user can input the interest rate (as a percent), the term of the loan (in years), and total home loan amount (in dollars). This information is then used to calculate the associated monthly payment. To work backward with this mortgage payment calculator to find the total loan amount that can be afforded:

- Enter the interest rate that is likely for your loan and the term of the loan in which you are interested.

- Then make a guess (perhaps $100,000?) for the total home loan amount that can be afforded.
- Have the mortgage calculator calculate the monthly payment.
- If the monthly payment that is calculated is higher than the range that can be afforded, repeat the calculation using the same interest rate and loan term but a lower value for the total home loan amount.
- If the monthly payment that is calculated is lower than the range that can be afforded, repeat the calculation using the same interest rate and loan term but a higher value for the total home loan amount.
- Repeat these calculations methodically until a monthly payment is obtained that is in the range that can be afforded. The initial principal value that gave this monthly payment amount is an estimate of the mortgage amount that can be afforded to buy a home.

Group Activity

1. Research current interest rates on 30-year mortgages.
2. Use the method described above to find the size of mortgages that can be afforded by households with the following total monthly incomes before taxes. (Assume in each case that the household has no other debts.) Use a loan term of 30 years and a current interest rate on a 30-year mortgage.

   a. $3000   **b.** $3500   **c.** $4000
   d. $4500   **e.** $5000   **f.** $5500

3. Create a table of your results.

Chapter 6 Vocabulary Check

Fill in each blank with one of the words or phrases listed below.

percent	of	amount	100%	compound interest
base	is	0.01	$\frac{1}{100}$	

1. In a mathematical statement, _____ usually means "multiplication."

2. In a mathematical statement, _____ means "equals."

3. _____ means "per hundred."

4. _____ is computed not only on the principal, but also on interest already earned in previous compounding periods.

5. In the percent proportion $\dfrac{\rule{3cm}{0.4pt}}{\rule{3cm}{0.4pt}} = \dfrac{\text{percent}}{100}$.

6. To write a decimal or fraction as a percent, multiply by _____.

7. The decimal equivalent of the % symbol is _____.

8. The fraction equivalent of the % symbol is _____.

Helpful Hint

Are you preparing for your test? Don't forget to take the Chapter 6 Test on page 509. Then check your answers at the back of the text and use the Chapter Test Prep Video CD to see the fully worked-out solutions to any of the exercises you want to review.

6 Chapter Highlights

DEFINITIONS AND CONCEPTS	EXAMPLES
Section 6.1 Percents, Decimals, and Fractions	

Percent means "per hundred." The % symbol denotes percent.	$51\% = \dfrac{51}{100}$ 51 per 100 $7\% = \dfrac{7}{100}$ 7 per 100
To write a percent as a decimal, replace the % symbol with its decimal equivalent, 0.01, and multiply. **To write a decimal as a percent,** multiply by 100%.	$32\% = 32(0.01) = 0.32$ $0.08 = 0.08(100\%) = 08.\% = 8\%$
To write a percent as a fraction, replace the % symbol with its fraction equivalent, $\dfrac{1}{100}$, and multiply. **To write a fraction as a percent,** multiply by 100%.	$25\% = 25 \cdot \dfrac{1}{100} = \dfrac{25}{100} = \dfrac{\overset{1}{\cancel{25}}}{4 \cdot \cancel{25}} = \dfrac{1}{4}$ $\dfrac{1}{6} = \dfrac{1}{6} \cdot 100\% = \dfrac{1}{6} \cdot \dfrac{100}{1}\% = \dfrac{100}{6}\% = 16\dfrac{2}{3}\%$

DEFINITIONS AND CONCEPTS	**EXAMPLES**

Section 6.2   Solving Percent Problems Using Equations

Three key words in the statement of a percent problem are

of, which means **multiplication** ($\cdot$)

is, which means **equals** ($=$)

what (or some equivalent word or phrase), which stands for **the unknown number**

Solve:

$$
\begin{array}{ccccc}
6 & \text{is} & 12\% & \text{of} & \text{what number?} \\
\downarrow & \downarrow & \downarrow & \downarrow & \downarrow \\
6 & = & 12\% & \cdot & n \\
6 & = & 0.12 & \cdot & n
\end{array}
$$ Write 12% as a decimal.

$$\frac{6}{0.12} = n$$ Divide 6 by 0.12, the number multiplied by n.

$$50 = n$$

Thus, 6 is 12% of 50.

Section 6.3   Solving Percent Problems Using Proportions

PERCENT PROPORTION

$$\frac{\text{amount}}{\text{base}} = \frac{\text{percent}}{100} \leftarrow \text{always 100}$$

or

$$\begin{array}{c} \text{amount} \rightarrow \\ \text{base} \rightarrow \end{array} \frac{a}{b} = \frac{p}{100} \leftarrow \text{percent}$$

Solve:

20.4 is what percent of 85?

$$
\begin{array}{ccc}
\downarrow & \downarrow & \downarrow \\
\boxed{\text{amount}} & \boxed{\text{percent}} & \boxed{\text{base}}
\end{array}
$$

$$\begin{array}{c} \text{amount} \rightarrow \\ \text{base} \rightarrow \end{array} \frac{20.4}{85} = \frac{p}{100} \leftarrow \text{percent}$$

$$20.4 \cdot 100 = 85 \cdot p \quad \text{Set cross products equal.}$$

$$2040 = 85 \cdot p \quad \text{Multiply.}$$

$$\frac{2040}{85} = p \quad \text{Divide 2040 by 85, the number multiplied by } p.$$

$$24 = p \quad \text{Simplify.}$$

Thus, 20.4 is 24% of 85.

Section 6.4   Applications of Percent

PERCENT OF INCREASE

$$\text{percent of increase} = \frac{\text{amount of increase}}{\text{original amount}}$$

PERCENT OF DECREASE

$$\text{percent of decrease} = \frac{\text{amount of decrease}}{\text{original amount}}$$

A town with a population of 16,480 decreased to 13,870 over a 12-year period. Find the percent decrease. Round to the nearest whole percent.

$$\text{amount of decrease} = 16{,}480 - 13{,}870$$

$$= 2610$$

$$\text{percent of decrease} = \frac{\text{amount of decrease}}{\text{original amount}}$$

$$= \frac{2610}{16{,}480} \approx 0.16$$

$$= 16\%$$

The town's population decreased by 16%.

Section 6.5   Percent and Problem Solving: Sales Tax, Commission, and Discount

SALES TAX AND TOTAL PRICE

$$\text{sales tax} = \text{sales tax rate} \cdot \text{purchase price}$$

$$\text{total price} = \text{purchase price} + \text{sales tax}$$

Find the sales tax and the total price of a purchase of $42 if the sales tax rate is 9%.

$$
\begin{array}{ccccc}
\boxed{\text{sales tax}} & = & \boxed{\text{sales tax rate}} & \cdot & \boxed{\text{purchase price}} \\
\downarrow & & \downarrow & & \downarrow \\
\text{sales tax} & = & 9\% & \cdot & \$42
\end{array}
$$

$$= 0.09 \cdot \$42$$

$$= \$3.78$$

continued

DEFINITIONS AND CONCEPTS	EXAMPLES

Section 6.5   Percent and Problem Solving: Sales Tax, Commission, and Discount (*continued*)

The total price is

$$\text{total price} = \text{purchase price} + \text{sales tax}$$

$$\text{total price} = \$42 + \$3.78$$
$$= \$45.78$$

COMMISSION

$$\text{commission} = \text{commission rate} \cdot \text{total sales}$$

A salesperson earns a commission of 3%. Find the commission from sales of $12,500 worth of appliances.

$$\text{commission} = \text{commission rate} \cdot \text{sales}$$

$$\text{commission} = 3\% \cdot \$12,500$$
$$= 0.03 \cdot 12,500$$
$$= \$375$$

DISCOUNT AND SALE PRICE

$$\text{amount of discount} = \text{discount rate} \cdot \text{original price}$$
$$\text{sale price} = \text{original price} - \text{amount of discount}$$

A suit is priced at $320 and is on sale today for 25% off. What is the sale price?

$$\text{amount of discount} = \text{discount rate} \cdot \text{original price}$$

$$\text{amount of discount} = 25\% \cdot \$320$$

$$= 0.25 \cdot 320$$
$$= \$80$$

$$\text{sale price} = \text{original price} - \text{amount of discount}$$

$$\text{sale price} = \$320 - \$80$$
$$= \$240$$

The sale price is $240.

Section 6.6   Percent and Problem Solving: Interest

SIMPLE INTEREST

$$\text{interest} = \text{principal} \cdot \text{rate} \cdot \text{time}$$

where the rate is understood to be per year.

Find the simple interest after 3 years on $800 at an interest rate of 5%.

$$\text{interest} = \text{principal} \cdot \text{rate} \cdot \text{time}$$

$$\text{interest} = \$800 \cdot 5\% \cdot 3$$
$$= \$800 \cdot 0.05 \cdot 3 \quad \text{Write 5\% as 0.05.}$$
$$= \$120 \quad \text{Multiply.}$$

The interest is $120.

Compound interest is computed not only on the principal, but also on interest already earned in previous compounding periods. (See Appendix A.7.)

$$\text{total amount} = \text{original principal} \cdot \begin{array}{c} \text{compound} \\ \text{interest} \\ \text{factor} \end{array}$$

$800 is invested at 5% compounded quarterly for 10 years. Find the total amount at the end of 10 years.

$$\text{total amount} = \text{original principal} \cdot \begin{array}{c} \text{compound} \\ \text{interest} \\ \text{factor} \end{array}$$

$$\text{total amount} = \$800 \cdot 1.64362$$
$$\approx \$1314.90$$

Are You Prepared for a Test on Chapter 6?

Below I have listed some *common trouble areas* for students in Chapter 6. After studying for your test—but before taking your test—read these.

- Can you convert from percents to fractions or decimals and from fractions or decimals to percents?

  Percent to decimal: $7.5\% = 7.5(0.01) = 0.075$

  Percent to fraction: $11\% = 11 \cdot \dfrac{1}{100} = \dfrac{11}{100}$

  Decimal to percent: $0.36 = 0.36(100\%) = 36\%$

Fraction to percent: $\dfrac{6}{7} = \dfrac{6}{7} \cdot 100\% = \dfrac{6}{7} \cdot \dfrac{100}{1}\%$

$= \dfrac{600}{7}\% = 85\dfrac{5}{7}\%$

- Do you remember how to find percent increase or percent decrease? The number of CDs increased from 40 to 48. Find the percent increase.

$\dfrac{\text{percent}}{\text{increase}} = \dfrac{\text{increase}}{\text{original number}} = \dfrac{8}{40} = 0.20 = 20\%$

6 CHAPTER REVIEW

(6.1) *Solve.*

1. In a survey of 100 adults, 37 preferred pepperoni on their pizzas. What percent preferred pepperoni?

2. A basketball player made 77 out 100 attempted free throws. What percent of free throws was made?

Write each percent as a decimal.

3. 83%

4. 75%

5. 73.5%

6. 1.5%

7. 125%

8. 145%

9. 0.5%

10. 0.7%

11. 200%

12. 400%

13. 26.25%

14. 85.34%

Write each decimal as a percent.

15. 2.6

16. 0.055

17. 0.35

18. 1.02

19. 0.725

20. 0.252

21. 0.076

22. 0.085

23. 0.71

24. 0.65

25. 4

26. 9

Write each percent as a fraction or mixed number in simplest form.

27. 1%

28. 10%

29. 25%

30. 8.5%

31. 10.2%

32. $16\frac{2}{3}\%$

33. $33\frac{1}{3}\%$

34. 110%

Write each fraction or mixed number as a percent.

35. $\frac{1}{5}$

36. $\frac{7}{10}$

37. $\frac{5}{6}$

38. $1\frac{2}{3}$

39. $1\frac{1}{4}$

40. $\frac{3}{5}$

41. $\frac{1}{16}$

42. $\frac{5}{8}$

(6.2) *Translate each to an equation and solve.*

43. 1250 is 1.25% of what number?

44. What number is $33\frac{1}{3}\%$ of 24,000?

45. 124.2 is what percent of 540?

46. 22.9 is 20% of what number?

47. What number is 40% of 7500?

48. 693 is what percent of 462?

(6.3) *Translate each to a proportion and solve.*

49. 104.5 is 25% of what number?

50. 16.5 is 5.5% of what number?

51. What number is 36% of 180?

52. 63 is what percent of 35?

53. 93.5 is what percent of 85?

54. What number is 33% of 500?

(6.4) *Solve.*

55. In a survey of 2000 people, it was found that 1320 have a microwave oven. Find the percent of people who own microwaves.

56. Of the 12,360 freshmen entering County College, 2000 are enrolled in basic college mathematics. Find the percent of entering freshmen who are enrolled in basic college mathematics. Round to the nearest whole percent.

57. The number of violent crimes in a city decreased from 675 to 534. Find the percent decrease. Round to the nearest tenth of a percent.

58. The current charge for dumping waste in a local landfill is $16 per cubic foot. To cover new environmental costs, the charge will increase to $33 per cubic foot. Find the percent increase.

59. This year the fund drive for a charity collected $215,000. Next year, a 4% decrease is expected. Find how much is expected to be collected in next year's drive.

60. A local union negotiated a new contract that increases the hourly pay 15% over last year's pay. The old hourly rate was $11.50. Find the new hourly rate rounded to the nearest cent.

(6.5) *Solve.*

61. If the sales tax rate is 5.5%, what is the total amount charged for a $250 coat?

62. Find the sales tax paid on a $25.50 purchase if the sales tax rate is 4.5%.

63. Russ James is a sales representative for a chemical company and is paid a commission rate of 5% on all sales. Find his commission if he sold $100,000 worth of chemicals last month.

64. Carol Sell is a sales clerk in a clothing store. She receives a commission of 7.5% on all sales. Find her commission for the week if her sales for the week were $4005. Round to the nearest cent.

65. A $3000 mink coat is on sale for 30% off. Find the discount and the sale price.

66. A $90 calculator is on sale for 10% off. Find the discount and the sale price.

(6.6) *Solve.*

67. Find the simple interest due on $4000 loaned for 4 months at 12% interest.

68. Find the simple interest due on $6500 loaned for 3 months at 20%.

69. Find the total amount in an account if $5500 is compounded annually at 12% for 15 years.

70. Find the total amount in an account if $6000 is compounded semiannually at 11% for 10 years.

71. Find the compound interest earned if $100 is compounded quarterly at 12% for 5 years.

72. Find the compound interest earned if $1000 is compounded quarterly at 18% for 20 years.

Mixed Review

Write each percent as a decimal.

73. 3.8%

74. 24.5%

75. 0.9%

Write each decimal as a percent.

76. 0.54

77. 95.2

78. 0.3

Write each percent as a fraction or mixed number in simplest form.

79. 47%

80. $6\frac{2}{5}\%$

81. 5.6%

Write each fraction or mixed number as a percent.

82. $\frac{3}{8}$

83. $\frac{2}{13}$

84. $\frac{6}{5}$

Translate each into an equation and solve.

85. 43 is 16% of what number?

86. 27.5 is what percent of 25?

87. What number is 36% of 1968?

88. 67 is what percent of 50?

Translate each into a proportion and solve.

89. 75 is what percent of 25?

90. What number is 16% of 240?

91. 28 is 5% of what number?

92. 52 is what percent of 16?

Solve.

93. The total number of cans in a soft drink machine is 300. If 78 soft drinks have been sold, find the percent of soft drink cans that have been sold.

94. A home valued at $96,950 last year has lost 7% of its value this year. Find the loss in value.

95. A dinette set sells for $568.00. If the sales tax rate is 8.75%, find the purchase price of the dinette set.

96. The original price of a video game is $23.00. It is on sale for 15% off. What is the amount of the discount?

97. A candy salesman makes a commission of $1.60 from each case of candy he sells. If a case of candy costs $12.80, what is his rate of commission?

98. Find the total amount due on a 6 month loan of $1400 at a simple interest rate of 13%.

99. Find the total amount due on a loan of $5,500 for 9 years at 12.5% simple interest.

6 CHAPTER TEST

 Use the Chapter Test Prep Video CD to see the fully worked-out solutions to any of the exercises you want to review.

Answers

Write each percent as a decimal.

1. 85%   **2.** 500%   **3.** 0.8%

Write each decimal as a percent.

4. 0.056   **5.** 6.1   **6.** 0.39

Write each percent as a fraction or mixed number in simplest form.

7. 120%   **8.** 38.5%   **9.** 0.2%

Write each fraction or mixed number as a percent.

10. $\frac{11}{20}$ **11.** $\frac{3}{8}$ **12.** $1\frac{5}{9}$

Solve.

13. What number is 42% of 80?   **14.** 0.6% of what number is 7.5?

15. 567 is what percent of 756?

1. _____

2. _____

3. _____

4. _____

5. _____

6. _____

7. _____

8. _____

9. _____

10. _____

11. _____

12. _____

13. _____

14. _____

15. _____

16. _____

17. _____

18. _____

19. _____

20. _____

21. _____

22. _____

23. _____

24. _____

25. _____

Solve. Round all dollar amounts to the nearest cent.

16. An alloy is 12% copper. How much copper is contained in 320 pounds of this alloy?

17. A farmer in Nebraska estimates that 20% of his potential crop, or $11,350, has been lost to a hard freeze. Find the total value of his potential crop.

18. If the local sales tax rate is 1.25%, find the total amount charged for a stereo system priced at $354.

19. A town's population increased from 25,200 to 26,460. Find the percent increase.

20. A $120 framed picture is on sale for 15% off. Find the discount and the sale price.

21. Randy Nguyen is paid a commission rate of 4% on all sales. Find Randy's commission if his sales were $9875.

22. A sales tax of $1.53 is added to an item's price of $152.99. Find the sales tax rate. Round to the nearest whole percent.

23. Find the simple interest earned on $2000 saved for $3\frac{1}{2}$ years at an interest rate of 9.25%.

24. $1365 is compounded annually at 8%. Find the total amount in the account after 5 years.

25. A couple borrowed $400 from a bank at 13.5% for 6 months for car repairs. Find the total amount due the bank at the end of the 6-month period.

1. How many cases can be filled with 9900 cans of jalapeños if each case holds 48 cans? How many cans will be left over? Will there be enough cases to fill an order for 200 cases?

2. Multiply: 409×76

3. Write each fraction as a mixed number or a whole number.

   a. $\dfrac{30}{7}$ **b.** $\dfrac{16}{15}$ **c.** $\dfrac{84}{6}$

4. Write each mixed number as an improper fraction.

   a. $2\dfrac{5}{7}$ **b.** $10\dfrac{1}{10}$ **c.** $5\dfrac{3}{8}$

5. Write $-\dfrac{10}{27}$ in simplest form.

6. Find the average of 28, 34, and 70.

7. Multiply and simplify: $\dfrac{23}{32} \cdot \dfrac{4}{7}$

8. Round 76,498 to the nearest ten.

9. Divide and simplify: $\dfrac{2}{5} \div \dfrac{1}{2}$

10. Write the shaded part of the figure as an improper fraction and as a mixed number.

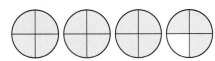

11. Find the perimeter of the rectangle.

   $\frac{2}{15}$ inch

   $\frac{4}{15}$ inch

12. Find $2 \cdot 5^2$

13. Find the LCM of 12 and 20.

14. Subtract $\dfrac{7}{9}$ from $\dfrac{10}{9}$.

15. Add: $\dfrac{2}{5} + \dfrac{4}{15}$

16. Find $\dfrac{2}{3}$ of 510.

17. Subtract: $7\dfrac{3}{14} - 3\dfrac{6}{7}$

18. Simplify: $9 \cdot \sqrt{25} - 6 \cdot \sqrt{4}$

Perform each indicated operation.

19. $\dfrac{3}{4} \div 5$

20. $20\dfrac{4}{5} + 12\dfrac{7}{8}$

21. $\left(-\dfrac{1}{4}\right)^2$

22. $1\dfrac{7}{8} \cdot 3\dfrac{2}{5}$

Answers

1. _____

2. _____

3. a. _____

   b. _____

   c. _____

4. a. _____

   b. _____

   c. _____

5. _____

6. _____

7. _____

8. _____

9. _____

10. _____

11. _____

12. _____

13. _____

14. _____

15. _____

16. _____

17. _____

18. _____

19. _____

20. _____

21. _____

22. _____

Write each fraction as a decimal.

23. $-\dfrac{5}{8}$

24. $\dfrac{9}{100}$

25. $\dfrac{22}{7}$ (Round to the nearest hundredth.)

26. $\dfrac{48}{10,000}$

27. The price of a gallon of gasoline in Aimsville is currently $2.1779. Round this to the nearest cent.

28. Subtract: $38 - 10.06$

29. Add: $763.7651 + 22.001 + 43.89$

30. 12.483×100

31. Multiply: 23.6×0.78

32. 76.3×1000

Divide.

33. $\dfrac{786.1}{1000}$

34. $0.5\overline{)0.638}$

35. $\dfrac{0.12}{10}$

36. $0.23\overline{)11.6495}$

37. Simplify: $723.6 \div 1000 \times 10$

38. Simplify: $\dfrac{3.19 - 0.707}{13}$

39. Write $\dfrac{1}{4}$ as a decimal.

40. Write $\dfrac{5}{9}$ as a decimal. Give an exact answer and a three-decimal-place approximation.

41. Is $\dfrac{4.1}{7} = \dfrac{2.9}{5}$ a true proportion?

42. Find each unit rate and decide on the better buy.

$0.93 for 18 flour tortillas

$1.40 for 24 flour tortillas

43. On a chamber of commerce map of Abita Springs, 5 miles corresponds to 2 inches. How many miles correspond to 7 inches?

44. Write each percent as a decimal.

a. 7%   **b.** 200%   **c.** 0.5%

45. Translate to an equation: What number is 25% of 0.008?

46. Write $\dfrac{3}{8}$ as a percent.

Sidebar answer blanks:

23. \
24. \
25. \
26. \
27. \
28. \
29. \
30. \
31. \
32. \
33. \
34. \
35. \
36. \
37. \
38. \
39. \
40. \
41. \
42. \
43. \
44. a. \
b. \
c. \
45. \
46.

7

Statistics and Probability

We often need to make decisions based on known statistics or the probability of an event occurring. For example, we decide whether or not to bring an umbrella to work based on the probability of rain. We choose an investment based on its mean, or average, return. We can predict which football team will win based on the trend in its previous wins and losses. This chapter reviews presenting data in a usable form on a graph and the basic ideas of statistics and probability.

A tornado is a violent, whirling column of air that is often spawned by the unstable weather conditions that occur during thunderstorms. Although tornadoes are capable of sustaining wind speeds of 250 to more than 300 mph, most tornadoes have wind speeds under 110 mph. The average forward speed of a tornado is 30 mph, but some tornadoes have been known to travel over land at speeds up to 70 mph. The path of a tornado can extend anywhere from a few feet to 100 miles long. Each year in the United States, an average of 800 tornadoes occur, causing an average of 80 deaths. The deadliest tornado in the United States was the Tri-State Tornado Outbreak on March 18, 1925, which killed 689 people and injured over 2000 more in Missouri, Illinois, and Indiana. In Exercises 19–24, Section 7.1, and the Chapter Highlights for Section 7.2, we will see how graphs can be used to summarize data about tornadoes.

7.1 READING PICTOGRAPHS, BAR GRAPHS, HISTOGRAMS, AND LINE GRAPHS

Often data is presented visually in a graph. In this section, we practice reading several kinds of graphs including pictographs, bar graphs, and line graphs.

Objective **A** Reading Pictographs

A **pictograph** such as the one below is a graph in which pictures or symbols are used. This type of graph contains a key that explains the meaning of the symbol used. An advantage of using a pictograph to display information is that comparisons can easily be made. A disadvantage of using a pictograph is that it is often hard to tell what fractional part of a symbol is shown. For example, in the pictograph below, Sweden shows a part of a symbol, but it's hard to read with any accuracy what fractional part of a symbol is shown.

PRACTICE PROBLEM 1

Use the pictograph shown in Example 1 to answer the following questions:

a. Approximate the amount of nuclear energy that was generated in Japan.

b. Approximate the total nuclear energy generated in Japan and Russia.

> **EXAMPLE 1** Calculating Nuclear Energy Generated

The following pictograph shows the approximate amount of nuclear energy generated by selected countries in the year 2002. Use this pictograph to answer the questions.

**Nuclear Energy Generated
by Selected Countries** (2002)

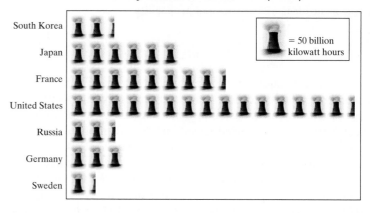

Source: Energy Information Administration

a. Approximate the amount of nuclear energy that was generated in Germany.

b. Approximate how much more nuclear energy was generated in France than in Germany.

Solution:

a. Germany corresponds to 3 symbols, and each symbol represents 50 billion kilowatt hours of energy. This means that Germany generated approximately $3 \cdot (50 \text{ billion})$ or 150 billion kilowatt hours of energy.

b. France shows $5\frac{1}{2}$ more symbols than Germany. This means that France generated $5\frac{1}{2} \cdot (50 \text{ billion})$ or 275 billion more kilowatt hours of nuclear energy than Germany.

Work Practice Problem 1

Answers

1. a. 300 billion kilowatt hours,
b. 425 billion kilowatt hours

Objective **B** **Reading Bar Graphs**

Another way to visually present data is with a **bar graph.** Bar graphs can appear with vertical bars or horizontal bars. Although we have studied bar graphs in previous sections, we now practice reading the height of the bars contained in a bar graph. An advantage to using bar graphs is that a scale is usually included for greater accuracy. Care must be taken when reading bar graphs, as well as other types of graphs—they may be misleading, as shown later in this section.

EXAMPLE 2 **Finding Number of Endangered Species**

The following bar graph shows the number of endangered species in the U.S. in 2001. Use this graph to answer the questions.

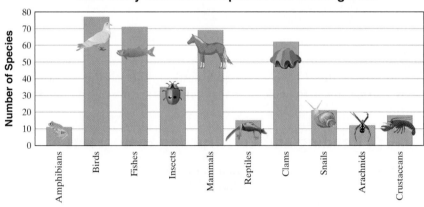

How Many U.S. Animal Species Are Endangered?

Source: U.S. Fish and Wildlife Service

a. Approximate the number of endangered species that are reptiles.

b. Which category has the most endangered species?

Solution:

a. To approximate the number of endangered species that are reptiles, we go to the top of the bar that represents reptiles. From the top of this bar, we move horizontally to the left until the scale is reached. We read the height of the bar on the scale as approximately 15. There are approximately 15 reptile species that are endangered, as shown.

b. The most endangered species is represented by the tallest (longest) bar. The tallest bar corresponds to birds.

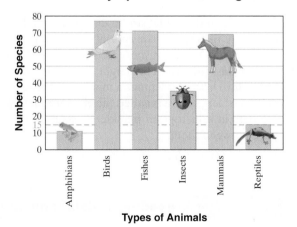

How Many Species Are Endangered?

Source: U.S. Fish and Wildlife Service

■ **Work Practice Problem 2**

PRACTICE PROBLEM 2

Use the bar graph in Example 2 to answer the following questions:

a. Approximate the number of endangered species that are insects.

b. Which category shows the fewest endangered species?

Answers
2. a. 35,   **b.** amphibians

As mentioned previously, graphs can be misleading. Both graphs below show the same information, but with different scales. Special care should be taken when forming conclusions from the appearance of a graph.

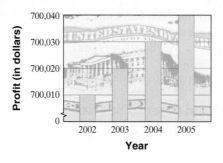

Are profits shown in the graphs above greatly increasing, or are they remaining about the same?

Helpful Hint

Notice the $\succ$ symbol on each vertical scale on the previous graphs. Remember that this symbol alerts us that numbers are missing on that scale.

Objective **C** Reading and Constructing Histograms

Suppose that the test scores of 36 students are summarized in the table below:

Student Scores	Frequency (Number of Students)
40–49	1
50–59	3
60–69	2
70–79	10
80–89	12
90–99	8

The results in the table can be displayed in a histogram. A **histogram** is a special bar graph. The width of each bar represents a range of numbers called a **class interval.** The height of each bar corresponds to how many times a number in the class interval occurred and is called the **class frequency.** The bars in a histogram lie side by side with no space between them.

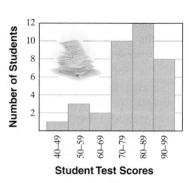

Student Test Scores

PRACTICE PROBLEM 3

Use the histogram on the right to determine how many students scored 70–79 on the test.

Answer

3. 10

EXAMPLE 3 **Reading a Histogram on Student Test Scores**

Use the preceding histogram to determine how many students scored 50–59 on the test.

Solution: We find the bar representing 50–59. The height of this bar is 3, which means 3 students scored 50–59 on the test.

◻ **Work Practice Problem 3**

EXAMPLE 4 **Reading a Histogram on Student Test Scores**

Use the preceding histogram to determine how many students scored 80 or above on the test.

Solution: We see that two different bars fit this description. There are 12 students who scored 80–89 and 8 students who scored 90–99. The sum of these two categories is 12 + 8 or 20 students. Thus, 20 students scored 80 or above on the test.

■ **Work Practice Problem 4**

Now we will look at a way to construct histograms.

The daily high temperatures for 1 month in New Orleans, Louisiana, are recorded in the following list:

85°	90°	95°	89°	88°	94°
87°	90°	95°	92°	95°	94°
82°	92°	96°	91°	94°	92°
89°	89°	90°	93°	95°	91°
88°	90°	88°	86°	93°	89°

The data in this list have not been organized and can be hard to interpret. One way to organize the data is to place it in a **frequency distribution table.** We will do this in Example 5.

EXAMPLE 5 **Completing a Frequency Distribution on Temperature**

Complete the frequency distribution table for the preceding temperature data.

Solution: Go through the data and place a tally mark in the second column of the table next to the class interval. Then count the tally marks and write each total in the third column of the table.

Class Intervals (Temperatures)	Tally	Class Frequency (Number of Days)
82°–84°	I	1
85°–87°	III	3
88°–90°	⊞⊞ I	11
91°–93°	⊞ II	7
94°–96°	⊞ III	8

■ **Work Practice Problem 5**

EXAMPLE 6 **Constructing a Histogram**

Construct a histogram from the frequency distribution table in Example 5.

Solution:

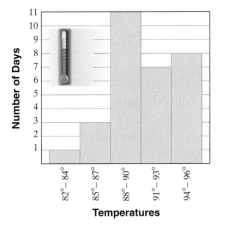

■ **Work Practice Problem 6**

PRACTICE PROBLEM 4

Use the histogram from Example 3 to determine how many students scored less than 60 on the test.

PRACTICE PROBLEM 5

Complete the frequency distribution table for the data below. Each number represents a credit card owner's unpaid balance for one month.

0	53	89	125
265	161	37	76
62	201	136	42

Class Intervals (Credit Card Balances)	Tally	Class Frequency (Number of Months)
$0–$49	____	____
$50–$99	____	____
$100–$149	____	____
$150–$199	____	____
$200–$249	____	____
$250–$299	____	____

PRACTICE PROBLEM 6

Construct a histogram from the frequency distribution table above.

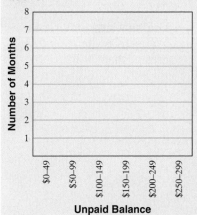

Answers

4. 4

5.

Tally	Class Frequency (Number of Months)
III	3
IIII	4
II	2
I	1
I	1
I	1

6.

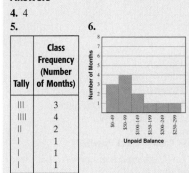

✔ **Concept Check**   Which of the following sets of data is better suited to representation by a histogram? Explain.

Set 1		Set 2	
Grade on Final	# of Students	Section Number	Avg. Grade on Final
51–60	12	150	78
61–70	18	151	83
71–80	29	152	87
81–90	23	153	73
91–100	25		

Objective D Reading Line Graphs

Another common way to display information with a graph is by using a **line graph.** An advantage of a line graph is that it can be used to visualize relationships between two quantities. A line graph can also be very useful in showing a change over time.

EXAMPLE 7 Reading Temperatures from Line Graph

The following line graph shows the average daily temperature for each month for Omaha, Nebraska. Use this graph to answer the questions below.

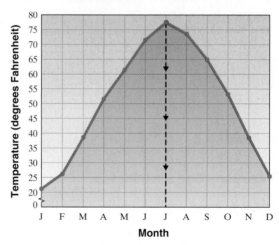

Average Daily Temperature for Omaha, Nebraska

Source: National Climatic Data Center

a. During what month is the average daily temperature the highest?

b. During what month, from July through December, is the average daily temperature 65°F?

c. During what months is the average daily temperature less than 30°F?

Solution:

a. The month with the highest temperature corresponds to the highest point. This is the red point shown on the graph above. We follow this highest point downward to the horizontal month scale and see that this point corresponds to July.

PRACTICE PROBLEM 7

Use the temperature graph in Example 7 to answer the following questions:

a. During what month is the average daily temperature the lowest?

b. During what month is the average daily temperature 25°F?

c. During what months is the average daily temperature greater than 70°F?

Answers

7. a. January,   **b.** December,
c. June, July, and August

✔ **Concept Check Answer**

Set 1; the grades are arranged in range of scores.

11. Approximate the number of ounces of chicken consumed per week in 1998.

12. Approximate the number of ounces of chicken consumed per week in 2004.

13. In what year(s) was the number of ounces of chicken consumed per week greater than 21 ounces?

14. In what year(s) was the number of ounces of chicken consumed per week 21 ounces or less?

15. What was the increase in average chicken consumption from 1995 to 2004?

16. What was the increase in average chicken consumption from 1998 to 2004?

17. Suppose that you need to represent 17 ounces on this pictograph. How many symbols represent 17 ounces?

18. Describe a trend in eating habits shown by this graph.

Objective **B** *The following bar graph shows the average number of people killed by tornadoes during the months of the year. Use this graph to answer Exercises 19 through 24. See Example 2.*

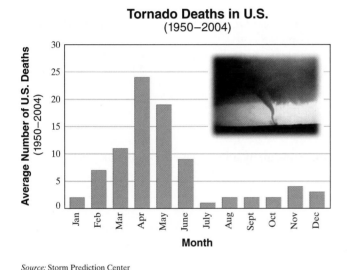

Tornado Deaths in U.S.
(1950–2004)

Source: Storm Prediction Center

19. In which month(s) did the most tornado-related deaths occur?

20. In which month(s) did the fewest tornado-related deaths occur?

21. Approximate the average number of tornado-related deaths that occurred in May.

22. Approximate the average number of tornado-related deaths that occurred in April.

23. In which month(s) did more than 5 deaths occur?

24. In which month(s) did more than 15 deaths occur?

The following horizontal bar graph shows the 2004 population of the world's largest agglomerations (cities plus their suburbs). Use this graph to answer Exercises 25 through 32. See Example 2.

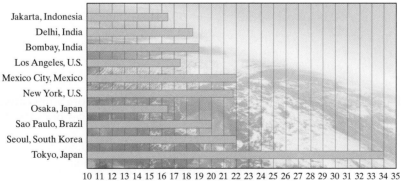

World's Largest Agglomerations

Source: Thomas Brinkhoff: *The Principal Agglomerations of the World,*
http://www.citypopulation.de, 8/17/2004

25. Estimate the population of Delhi, India.

26. Estimate the population of Seoul, South Korea.

27. Name the city with the largest population and estimate its population.

28. Name the city whose population is between 17 and 18 million and estimate its population.

29. Name the city in the United States with the largest population and estimate its population.

30. Name the city in the graph with the smallest population and estimate its population.

31. How much larger is the population of Tokyo than the population of Sao Paulo?

32. How much larger is the population of Mexico City than the population of Bombay?

Objective **C** *The following histogram shows the number of miles that each adult, from a survey of 100 adults, drives per week. Use this histogram to answer Exercises 33 through 42. See Examples 3 and 4.*

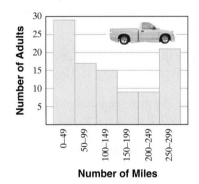

33. How many adults drive 100–149 miles per week?

34. How many adults drive 200–249 miles per week?

35. How many adults drive fewer than 150 miles per week?

36. How many adults drive 200 miles or more per week?

37. How many adults drive 100–199 miles per week?

38. How many adults drive 150–249 miles per week?

39. How many more adults drive 250–299 miles per week than 200–249 miles per week?

40. How many more adults drive 0–49 miles per week than 50–99 miles per week?

41. What is the ratio of adults who drive 150–199 miles per week to the total number of adults surveyed?

42. What is the ratio of adults who drive 50–99 miles per week to the total number of adults surveyed?

The following histogram shows the projected ages of householders for the year 2010. Use this histogram to answer Exercises 43 through 50. For Exercises 45 through 48, estimate to the nearest whole million. See Examples 3 and 4.

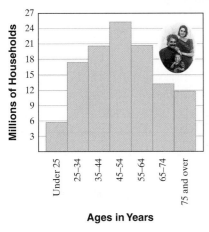

Ages in Years

Source: U.S. Bureau of the Census, *Current Population Reports*

43. The most householders will be in what age range?

44. The least number of householders will be in what age range?

45. How many householders will be 55–64 years old?

46. How many householders will be 35–44 years old?

47. How many householders will be 44 years old or younger?

48. How many householders will be 55 years old or older?

49. Which bar represents the household you expect to be in during the year 2010?

50. How many more householders will be 45–54 years old than 55–64 years old?

The following list shows the golf scores for an amateur golfer. Use this list to complete the frequency distribution table to the right. See Example 5.

78	84	91	93	97
97	95	85	95	96
101	89	92	89	100

	Class Intervals (Scores)	Tally	Class Frequency (Number of Games)
51.	70–79		
52.	80–89		
53.	90–99		
54.	100–109		

Twenty-five people in a survey were asked to give their current checking account balances. Use the balances shown in the following list to complete the frequency distribution table to the right. See Example 5.

$53	$105	$162	$443	$109
$468	$47	$259	$316	$228
$207	$357	$15	$301	$75
$86	$77	$512	$219	$100
$192	$288	$352	$166	$292

	Class Intervals (Account Balances)	Tally	Class Frequency (Number of People)
55.	$0–$99		
56.	$100–$199		
57.	$200–$299		
58.	$300–$399		
59.	$400–$499		
60.	$500–$599		

61. Use the frequency distribution table from Exercises 51 through 54 to construct a histogram. See Example 6.

Golf Scores

62. Use the frequency distribution table from Exercises 55 through 60 to construct a histogram. See Example 6.

Account Balances

Objective D *The following line graph shows the World Cup goals per game average during the years shown. Use this graph to answer Exercises 63 through 70. See Example 7.*

63. Find the average number of goals per game in 1994.

64. Find the average number of goals per game in 2002.

65. During what year shown was the average number of goals per game the highest?

66. During what year shown was the average number of goals per game the lowest?

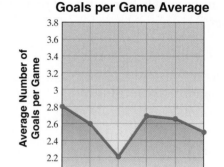

**World Cup
Goals per Game Average**

Source: Soccer America Magazine

67. Between 1998 and 2002, did the average number of goals per game increase or decrease?

68. Between 1990 and 1994, did the average number of goals per game increase or decrease?

69. During what year(s) was the average goals per game less than 2.5?

70. During what year(s) was the average goals per game greater than 2.6?

Review

Find each percent. See Sections 6.2 and 6.3.

71. 30% of 12

72. 45% of 120

73. 10% of 62

74. 95% of 50

Write each fraction as a percent. See Section 6.1.

75. $\frac{1}{4}$

76. $\frac{2}{5}$

77. $\frac{17}{50}$

78. $\frac{9}{10}$

Concept Extensions

The following double-line graph shows temperature highs and lows for a week. Use this graph to answer Exercises 79 through 84.

79. What was the high temperature reading on Thursday?

80. What was the low temperature reading on Thursday?

81. What day was the temperature the lowest? What was this low temperature?

82. What day of the week was the temperature the highest? What was this high temperature?

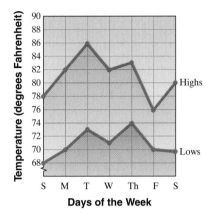

83. On what day of the week was the difference between the high temperature and the low temperature the greatest? What was this difference in temperature?

84. On what day of the week was the difference between the high temperature and the low temperature the least? What was this difference in temperature?

85. True or false? With a bar graph, the width of the bar is just as important as the height of the bar. Explain your answer.

7.2 READING CIRCLE GRAPHS

Objective **A** Reading Circle Graphs

In Section 6.1, the following **circle graph** was shown. This particular graph shows the average favorite cookie for every 100 people.

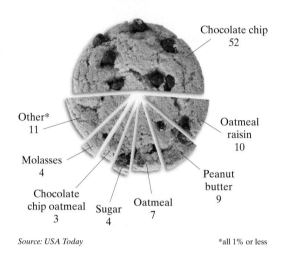

Chocolate chip
52

Oatmeal
raisin
10

Peanut
butter
9

Oatmeal
7

Sugar
4

Chocolate
chip oatmeal
3

Molasses
4

Other*
11

Source: USA Today   *all 1% or less

Each sector of the graph (shaped like a piece of pie) shows a category and the relative size of the category. In other words, the most popular cookie is the chocolate chip cookie, and it is represented by the largest sector.

PRACTICE PROBLEM 1

Find the ratio of people preferring oatmeal raisin cookies to total people. Write the ratio as a fraction in simplest form.

EXAMPLE 1 Find the ratio of people preferring chocolate chip cookies to total people. Write the ratio as a fraction in simplest form.

Solution: The ratio is

$$\frac{\text{people preferring chocolate chip}}{\text{total people}} = \frac{52}{100} = \frac{13}{25}$$

▢ **Work Practice Problem 1**

A circle graph is often used to show percents in different categories, with the whole circle representing 100%.

PRACTICE PROBLEM 2

Using the circle graph shown in Example 2, determine the percent of Americans that have two or more working computers at home.

EXAMPLE 2 Using a Circle Graph

The following circle graph shows the percent of Americans with various numbers of working computers at home. Using the circle graph shown, determine the percent of Americans that have one or more working computers at home.

Number of Working Computers at Home

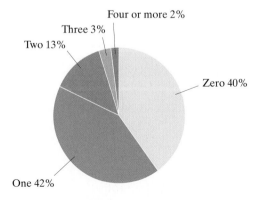

Four or more 2%

Three 3%

Two 13%

Zero 40%

One 42%

Source: UCLA Center for Communication Policy

Answers

1. $\frac{1}{10}$,   **2.** 18%

526

Solution: To find this percent, we add the percents corresponding to one, two, three, and four or more working computers at home. The percent of Americans that have one or more working computers at home is

$$42\% + 13\% + 3\% + 2\% = 60\%$$

▣ **Work Practice Problem 2**

> **Helpful Hint**
>
> Since a circle graph represents a whole, the percents should add to 100% or 1. Notice this is true for Example 2.

EXAMPLE 3 **Finding Percent of Population**

In 2005, the population of the United States was approximately 295,500,000. Using the circle graph from Example 2, find the number of Americans that have no working computers at home.

Solution: We use the percent equation.

amount	=	percent	·	base

$$\text{amount} = 0.40 \cdot 295{,}500{,}000$$
$$= 0.40(295{,}500{,}000) = 118{,}200{,}000$$

Thus, 118,200,000 Americans have no working computer at home.

▣ **Work Practice Problem 3**

✔ **Concept Check** Can the following data be represented by a circle graph? Why or why not?

Responses to the Question, "In Which Activities Are You Involved?"	
Intramural sports	60%
On-campus job	42%
Fraternity/sorority	27%
Academic clubs	21%
Music programs	14%

Objective B Drawing Circle Graphs

To draw a circle graph, we use the fact that a whole circle contains 360° (degrees).

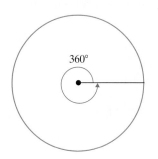

360°

PRACTICE PROBLEM 3

Using the circle graph from Example 2, find the number of Americans that have four or more working computers at home.

Answer
3. 5,910,000 Americans

✔ **Concept Check Answer**
no; the percents add up to more than 100%

PRACTICE PROBLEM 4

Use the data shown to draw a circle graph.

Freshmen	30%
Sophomores	27%
Juniors	25%
Seniors	18%

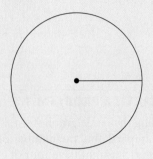

EXAMPLE 4 **Drawing Circle Graph for U.S. Armed Forces Personnel**

The following table shows the percent of U.S. armed forces personnel that are in each branch of service. (*Source:* U.S. Department of Defense)

Branch of Service	Percent
Army	33
Navy	27
Marine Corps	12
Air Force	25
Coast Guard	3

Draw a circle graph showing this data.

Solution: First we find the number of degrees in each sector representing each branch of service. Remember that the whole circle contains 360°. (We will round degrees to the nearest whole.)

Sector	Degrees in Each Sector
Army	$33\% \times 360° = 0.33 \times 360° = 118.8° \approx 119°$
Navy	$27\% \times 360° = 0.27 \times 360° = 97.2° \approx 97°$
Marine Corps	$12\% \times 360° = 0.12 \times 360° = 43.2° \approx 43°$
Air Force	$25\% \times 360° = 0.25 \times 360° = 90° = 90°$
Coast Guard	$3\% \times 360° = 0.03 \times 360° = 10.8° \approx 11°$

Next we draw a circle and mark its center. Then we draw a line from the center of the circle to the circle itself.

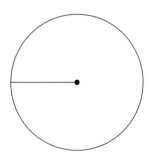

To construct the sectors, we will use a **protractor.** We place the hole in the protractor over the center of the circle. Then we adjust the protractor so that 0° on the protractor is aligned with the line that we drew.

It makes no difference which sector we draw first. To construct the "Army" sector, we find 119° on the protractor and mark our circle. Then we remove the protractor and use this mark to draw a second line from the center to the circle itself.

Answer

4.

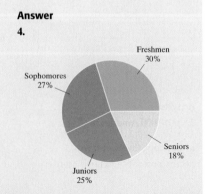

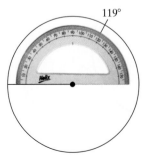

119°

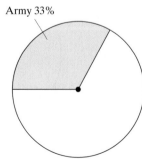

Army 33%

To construct the "Navy" sector, we follow the same procedure as above, except that we line up 0° with the second line we drew and mark the protractor at 97°.

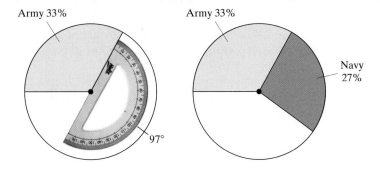

We continue in this manner until the circle graph is complete.

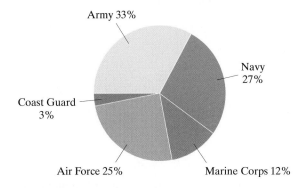

🔲 **Work Practice Problem 4**

✔**Concept Check** True or false? The larger a sector in a circle graph, the larger the percent of the total it represents. Explain your answer.

7.2 EXERCISE SET

Objective Ⓐ *The following circle graph is a result of surveying 700 college students. They were asked where they live while attending college. Use this graph to answer Exercises 1 through 6. Write all ratios as fractions in simplest form. See Example 1.*

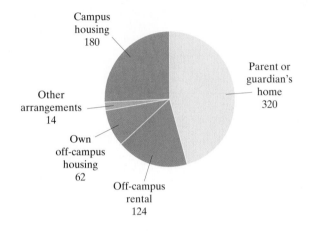

1. Where do most of these college students live?

2. Besides the category "Other Arrangements," where do least of these college students live?

3. Find the ratio of students living in campus housing to total students.

4. Find the ratio of students living in off-campus rentals to total students.

5. Find the ratio of students living in campus housing to students living in a parent or guardian's home.

6. Find the ratio of students living in off-campus rentals to students living in a parent or guardian's home.

The following circle graph shows the percent of the land area of the continents of Earth. Use this graph for Exercises 7 through 14. See Examples 2 and 3.

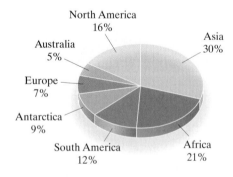

Source: National Geographic Society

7. Which continent is the largest?

8. Which continent is the smallest?

9. What percent of the land on Earth is accounted for by Asia and Europe together?

10. What percent of the land on Earth is accounted for by North and South America?

The total amount of land on Earth is approximately 57,000,000 square miles. Use the graph to find the area of the continents given in Exercises 11 through 14.

11. Asia   **12.** South America   **13.** Australia   **14.** Europe

The following circle graph shows the percent of the types of books available at Midway Memorial Library. Use this graph for Exercises 15 through 24. See Examples 2 and 3.

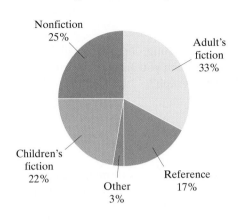

15. What percent of books are classified as some type of fiction?

16. What percent of books are nonfiction or reference?

17. What is the second-largest category of books?

18. What is the third-largest category of books?

If this library has 125,600 books, find how many books are in each category given in Exercises 19 through 24.

19. Nonfiction

20. Reference

21. Children's fiction

22. Adult's fiction

23. Reference or other

24. Nonfiction or other

Objective B *Draw a circle graph to represent the information given in each table. See Example 4.*

25.

2004 Light Vehicle Sales by Vehicle Origin	
Country of Origin	**Percent**
United States	58
Asia	36
Europe	6
(*Source:* Ward's AutoInfoBank)	

26.

Number of Times the "Are We There Yet?" Question Is Asked to Parents During Road Trips:	
Never	20%
Once	11%
2–5 times	36%
6–10 times	14%
More than 10 times	19%
(*Source:* KRC Research for Goodyear Tire & Rubber Co.)	

Review

Write the prime factorization of each number. See Section 3.2.

27. 20   **28.** 25   **29.** 40   **30.** 16   **31.** 85   **32.** 105

Concept Extensions

The following circle graph shows the relative sizes of the great oceans.

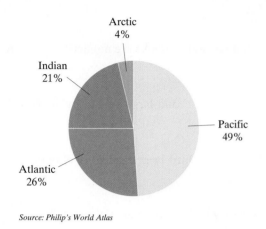

Arctic
4%

Indian
21%

Pacific
49%

Atlantic
26%

Source: Philip's World Atlas

33. Without calculating, determine which ocean is the largest. How can you answer this question by looking at the circle graph?

34. Without calculating, determine which ocean is the smallest. How can you answer this question by looking at the circle graph?

These oceans together make up 264,489,800 square kilometers of the Earth's surface. Find the square kilometers for each ocean.

35. Pacific Ocean   **36.** Atlantic Ocean   **37.** Indian Ocean   **38.** Arctic Ocean

Answer the question. See the Concept Check in this section.

39. True or false? The smaller a sector in a circle graph, the smaller the percent of the total it represents.

40. Can the data below be represented by a circle graph?

Type of Ice Cream Preferred:	
Vanilla	50%
Chocolate	46%

Explain.

INTEGRATED REVIEW Sections 7.1–7.2

Reading Graphs

The following pictograph shows the average number of pounds of beef and veal consumed per person per year in the United States. Use this graph to answer Exercises 1 through 4.

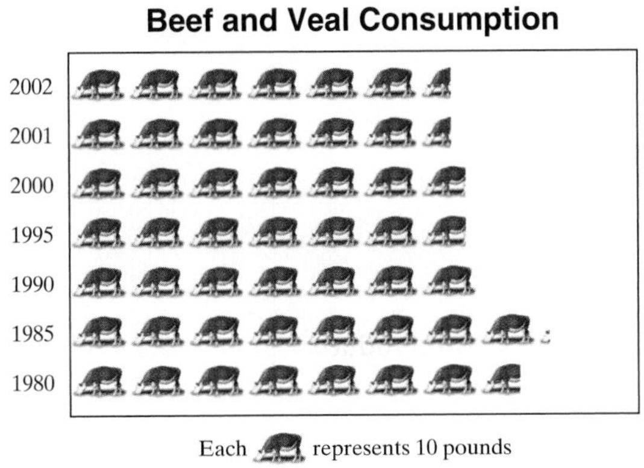

Beef and Veal Consumption
2002
2001
2000
1995
1990
1985
1980
Each represents 10 pounds

Source: U.S. Department of Agriculture

1. Approximate the number of pounds of beef and veal consumed per person in 1995.

2. Approximate the number of pounds of beef and veal consumed per person in 1980.

3. How much more beef was consumed in 1980 than in 2002?

4. In what year(s) was the number of pounds consumed the least?

The following bar graph shows the highest U.S. dams. Use this graph to answer Exercises 5 through 8.

5. Name the U.S. dam with the greatest height and estimate its height.

6. Name the U.S. dam whose height is between 625 and 650 feet and estimate its height.

7. Estimate how much higher the Hoover Dam is than the Glen Canyon Dam.

8. How many U.S. dams have heights over 700 feet?

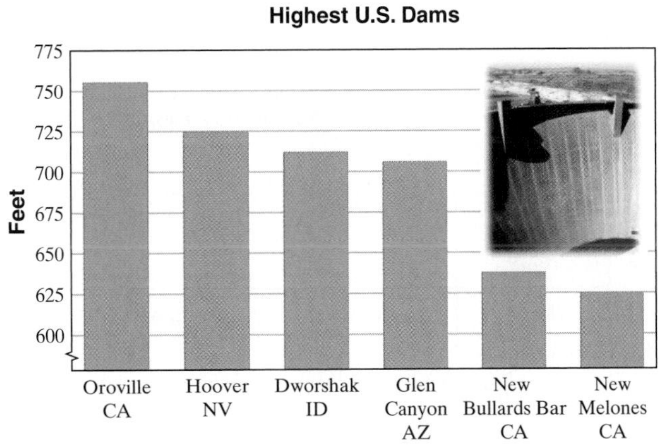

Highest U.S. Dams
Feet
775
750
725
700
675
650
625
600
Oroville CA
Hoover NV
Dworshak ID
Glen Canyon AZ
New Bullards Bar CA
New Melones CA

Source: Committee on Register of Dams

The following line graph shows the daily high temperatures for 1 week in Annapolis, Maryland. Use this graph to answer Exercises 9 through 12.

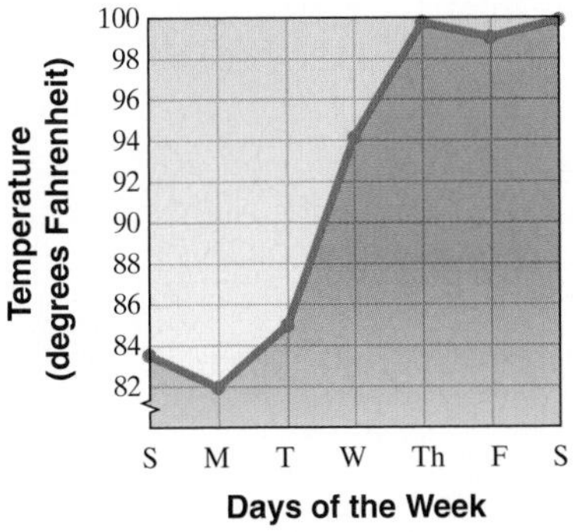

Temperature (degrees Fahrenheit)
100
98
96
94
92
90
88
86
84
82
S M T W Th F S
Days of the Week

9. Name the day(s) of the week with the highest temperature and give that high temperature.

10. Name the day(s) of the week with the lowest temperature and give that low temperature.

11. On what days of the week was the temperature less than 90° Fahrenheit?

12. On what days of the week was the temperature greater than 90° Fahrenheit?

Answers

1. ______
2. ______
3. ______
4. ______
5. ______
6. ______
7. ______
8. ______
9. ______
10. ______
11. ______
12. ______

13. _____

14. _____

15. _____

16. _____

17. see table

18. see table

19. see table

20. see table

21. see table

22. see graph

The following circle graph shows the type of beverage milk consumed in the United States. Use this graph for Exercises 13 through 16. If a store in Kerrville, Texas, sells 200 quart containers of milk per week, estimate how many quart containers are sold in each category below.

Types of Beverage Milk Consumed

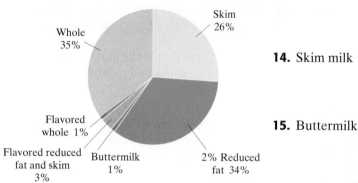

Source: U.S. Department of Agriculture

13. Whole milk

14. Skim milk

15. Buttermilk

16. Flavored reduced fat and skim milk

The following list shows weekly quiz scores for a student in basic college mathematics. Use this list to complete the frequency distribution table.

50	80	71	83	86
67	89	93	88	97
	53	90		
75	80	78	93	99

	Class Intervals (Scores)	Tally	Class Frequency (Number of Quizzes)
17.	50–59		
18.	60–69		
19.	70–79		
20.	80–89		
21.	90–99		

22. Use the table from Exercises 17 through 21 to construct a histogram.

7.3 MEAN, MEDIAN, AND MODE

Objective A Finding the Mean

Sometimes we want to summarize data by displaying them in a graph, but sometimes it is also desirable to be able to describe a set of data, or a set of numbers, by a single "middle" number. Three such **measures of central tendency** are the **mean,** the **median,** and the **mode.**

The most common measure of central tendency is the mean (sometimes called the "arithmetic mean" or the "average"). Recall that we first introduced finding the average of a list of numbers in Section 1.7.

The **mean (average)** of a set of number items is the sum of the items divided by the number of items.

$$\text{mean} = \frac{\text{sum of items}}{\text{number of items}}$$

EXAMPLE 1 Finding the Mean Time in an Experiment

Seven students in a psychology class conducted an experiment on mazes. Each student was given a pencil and asked to successfully complete the same maze. The timed results are below:

Student	Ann	Thanh	Carlos	Jesse	Melinda	Ramzi	Dayni
Time (Seconds)	13.2	11.8	10.7	16.2	15.9	13.8	18.5

a. Who completed the maze in the shortest time? Who completed the maze in the longest time?

b. Find the mean time.

c. How many students took longer than the mean time? How many students took shorter than the mean time?

Solution:

a. Carlos completed the maze in 10.7 seconds, the shortest time. Dayni completed the maze in 18.5 seconds, the longest time.

b. To find the mean (or average), we find the sum of the number items and divide by 7, the number of items.

$$\text{mean} = \frac{13.2 + 11.8 + 10.7 + 16.2 + 15.9 + 13.8 + 18.5}{7}$$

$$= \frac{100.1}{7} = 14.3$$

c. Three students, Jesse, Melinda, and Dayni, had times longer than the mean time. Four students, Ann, Thanh, Carlos, and Ramzi, had times shorter than the mean time.

Work Practice Problem 1

✔ **Concept Check** Estimate the mean of the following set of data:

5, 10, 10, 10, 10, 15

Often in college, the calculation of a **grade point average** (GPA) is a **weighted mean** and is calculated as shown in Example 2.

PRACTICE PROBLEM 1

Find the mean of the following test scores: 77, 85, 86, 91, and 88.

Answer
1. 85.4

✔ **Concept Check Answer**
10

PRACTICE PROBLEM 2

Find the grade point average if the following grades were earned in one semester.

Grade	Credit Hours
A	2
C	4
B	5
D	2
A	2

EXAMPLE 2 **Calculating Grade Point Average (GPA)**

The following grades were earned by a student during one semester. Find the student's grade point average.

Course	Grade	Credit Hours
College mathematics	A	3
Biology	B	3
English	A	3
PE	C	1
Social studies	D	2

Solution: To calculate the grade point average, we need to know the point values for the different possible grades. The point values of grades commonly used in colleges and universities are given below:

A: 4, B: 3, C: 2, D: 1, F: 0

Now, to find the grade point average, we multiply the number of credit hours for each course by the point value of each grade. The grade point average is the sum of these products divided by the sum of the credit hours.

Course	Grade	Point Value of Grade	Credit Hours	Point Value · Credit Hours
College mathematics	A	4	3	12
Biology	B	3	3	9
English	A	4	3	12
PE	C	2	1	2
Social studies	D	1	2	2
			Totals: 12	37

$$\text{grade point average} = \frac{37}{12} \approx 3.08 \text{ rounded to two decimal places}$$

The student earned a grade point average of 3.08.

▣ **Work Practice Problem 2**

Objective **B** **Finding the Median**

You may have noticed that a very low number or a very high number can affect the mean of a list of numbers. Because of this, you may sometimes want to use another measure of central tendency. A second measure of central tendency is called the **median.** The median of a list of numbers is not affected by a low or high number in the list.

The **median** of a set of numbers in numerical order is the middle number. If the number of items is odd, the median is the middle number. If the number of items is even, the median is the mean of the two middle numbers.

EXAMPLE 3 Find the median of the following list of numbers:

25, 54, 56, 57, 60, 71, 98

Solution: Because this list is in numerical order, the median is the middle number, 57.

▣ **Work Practice Problem 3**

PRACTICE PROBLEM 3

Find the median of the list of numbers: 7, 9, 13, 23, 24, 35, 38, 41, 43

Answers

2. 2.73, **3.** 24

EXAMPLE 4 Find the median of the following list of scores: 67, 91, 75, 86, 55, 91

Solution: First we list the scores in numerical order and then find the middle number.

55, 67, 75, 86, 91, 91

Since there is an even number of scores, there are two middle numbers, 75 and 86. The median is the mean of the two middle numbers.

$$\text{median} = \frac{75 + 86}{2} = 80.5$$

The median is 80.5.

🔲 **Work Practice Problem 4**

Helpful Hint Don't forget to write the numbers in order from smallest to largest before finding the median.

Objective C Finding the Mode

The last common measure of central tendency is called the **mode.**

The **mode** of a set of numbers is the number that occurs most often. (It is possible for a set of numbers to have more than one mode or to have no mode.)

EXAMPLE 5 Find the mode of the list of numbers:

11, 14, 14, 16, 31, 56, 65, 77, 77, 78, 79

Solution: There are two numbers that occur the most often. They are 14 and 77. This list of numbers has two modes, 14 and 77.

🔲 **Work Practice Problem 5**

EXAMPLE 6 Find the median and the mode of the following set of numbers. These numbers were high temperatures for 14 consecutive days in a city in Montana.

76, 80, 85, 86, 89, 87, 82, 77, 76, 79, 82, 89, 89, 92

Solution: First we write the numbers in numerical order.

76, 76, 77, 79, 80, 82, 82, 85, 86, 87, 89, 89, 89, 92

Since there is an even number of items, the median is the mean of the two middle numbers, 82 and 85.

$$\text{median} = \frac{82 + 85}{2} = 83.5$$

The mode is 89, since 89 occurs most often.

🔲 **Work Practice Problem 6**

✔**Concept Check** True or false? Every set of numbers *must* have a mean, median, and mode. Explain your answer.

Helpful Hint Don't forget that it is possible for a list of numbers to have no mode. For example, the list

2, 4, 5, 6, 8, 9

has no mode. There is no number or numbers that occur more often than the others.

Mental Math

State the mean for each list of numbers.

1. 3, 5

2. 10, 20

3. 1, 3, 5

4. 7, 7, 7

7.3 EXERCISE SET

FOR EXTRA HELP

 Student Solutions Manual

 PH Math/Tutor Center

 CD/Video for Review

Math XL
MathXL®

MyMathLab
MyMathLab

Objectives **A** **B** **C** **Mixed Practice** *For each set of numbers, find the mean, the median, and the mode. If necessary, round the mean to one decimal place. See Examples 1 and 3 through 6.*

1. 21, 28, 16, 42, 38

2. 42, 35, 36, 40, 50

3. 7.6, 8.2, 8.2, 9.6, 5.7, 9.1

4. 4.9, 7.1, 6.8, 6.8, 5.3, 4.9

5. 0.2, 0.3, 0.5, 0.6, 0.6, 0.9, 0.2, 0.7, 1.1

6. 0.6, 0.6, 0.8, 0.4, 0.5, 0.3, 0.7, 0.8, 0.1

7. 231, 543, 601, 293, 588, 109, 334, 268

8. 451, 356, 478, 776, 892, 500, 467, 780

The eight tallest buildings in the world are listed in the following table. Use this table to answer Exercises 9 through 12. If necessary, round results to one decimal place. See Examples 1 and 3 through 6.

9. Find the mean height of the five tallest buildings.

10. Find the median height of the five tallest buildings.

11. Find the median height of the eight tallest buildings.

12. Find the mean height of the eight tallest buildings.

Building	Height (in Feet)
Petronas Tower 1, Kuala Lumpur	1483
Petronas Tower 2, Kuala Lumpur	1483
Sears Tower, Chicago	1450
Jin Mao Building, Shanghai	1381
Citic Plaza, Guangzhou	1283
Shun Hing Square, Shenzhen	1260
Empire State Building, New York	1250
Central Plaza, Hong Kong	1227
(*Source:* Council on Tall Buildings and Urban Habitat)	

13. Given the building heights, explain how you know, without calculating, that the answer to Exercise 10 is more than the answer to Exercise 11.

14. Given the building heights, explain how you know, without calculating, that the answer to Exercise 12 is less than the answer to Exercise 9.

For Exercises 15 through 18, the grades are given for a student for a particular semester. Find the grade point average. If necessary, round the grade point average to the nearest hundredth. See Example 2.

15.

Grade	Credit Hours
B	3
C	3
A	4
C	4

16.

Grade	Credit Hours
D	1
F	1
C	4
B	5

17.

Grade	Credit Hours
A	3
A	3
B	4
B	1
B	2

18.

Grade	Credit Hours
B	2
B	2
A	3
C	3
B	3

During an experiment, the following times (in seconds) were recorded:

7.8, 6.9, 7.5, 4.7, 6.9, 7.0

19. Find the mean. Round to the nearest tenth.

20. Find the median.

21. Find the mode.

In a mathematics class, the following test scores were recorded for a student: 86, 95, 91, 74, 77, 85.

22. Find the mean. Round to the nearest hundredth.

23. Find the median.

24. Find the mode.

The following pulse rates were recorded for a group of 15 students: 78, 80, 66, 68, 71, 64, 82, 71, 70, 65, 70, 75, 77, 86, 72.

25. Find the mean.

26. Find the median.

27. Find the mode.

28. How many rates were higher than the mean?

29. How many rates were lower than the mean?

Review

Write each fraction in simplest form. See Section 3.2.

30. $\frac{12}{20}$

31. $\frac{6}{18}$

32. $\frac{4}{36}$

33. $\frac{18}{30}$

34. $\frac{35}{100}$

35. $\frac{55}{75}$

Concept Extensions

Find the missing numbers in each set of numbers.

36. 16, 18, _____, _____, _____. The mode is 21. The median is 20.

37. _____, _____, _____, 40, _____. The mode is 35. The median is 37. The mean is 38.

38. Write a list of numbers for which you feel the median would be a better measure of central tendency than the mean.

STUDY SKILLS BUILDER

Tips for Studying for an Exam

To prepare for an exam, try the following study techniques.

- Start the study process days before your exam.
- Make sure that you are up-to-date on your assignments.
- If there is a topic that you are unsure of, use one of the many resources that are available to you. For example,

    See your instructor.

    Visit a learning resource center on campus.

    Read the textbook material and examples on the topic.

    View a video on the topic.

- Reread your notes and carefully review the Chapter Highlights at the end of any chapter.
- Work the review exercises at the end of the chapter. Check your answers and correct any mistakes. If you have trouble, use a resource listed above.
- Find a quiet place to take the Chapter Test found at the end of the chapter. Do not use any resources when taking this sample test. This way, you will have a clear indication of how prepared you are for your exam.

Check your answers and make sure that you correct any missed exercises.

- Get lots of rest the night before the exam. It's hard to show how well you know the material if your brain is foggy from lack of sleep.

Good luck and keep a positive attitude.

Let's see how you did on your last exam.

1. How many days before your last exam did you start studying?

2. Were you up-to-date on your assignments at that time or did you need to catch up on assignments?

3. List the most helpful text supplement (if you used one).

4. List the most helpful campus supplement (if you used one).

5. List your process for preparing for a mathematics test.

6. Was this process helpful? In other words, were you satisfied with your performance on your exam?

7. If not, what changes can you make in your process that will make it more helpful to you?

7.4 COUNTING AND INTRODUCTION TO PROBABILITY

Objective **A** Using a Tree Diagram

In our daily conversations, we often talk about the likelihood or the **probability** of a given result occurring. For example:

The *chance* of thundershowers is 70 percent.

What are the *odds* that the Saints will go to the Super Bowl?

What is the *probability* that you will finish cleaning your room today?

Each of these chance happenings—thundershowers, the New Orleans Saints playing in the Super Bowl, and cleaning your room today—is called an **experiment.** The possible results of an experiment are called **outcomes.** For example, flipping a coin is an experiment, and the possible outcomes are heads (H) or tails (T).

One way to picture the outcomes of an experiment is to draw a **tree diagram.** Each outcome is shown on a separate branch. For example, the outcomes of flipping a coin are

Heads   Tails

EXAMPLE 1 Draw a tree diagram for tossing a coin twice. Then use the diagram to find the number of possible outcomes.

Solution: There are 4 possible outcomes when tossing a coin twice.

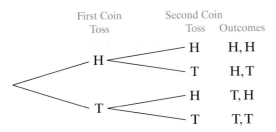

First Coin Toss   Second Coin Toss   Outcomes

H   H   H, H

H   T   H, T

T   H   T, H

T   T   T, T

◻ **Work Practice Problem 1**

PRACTICE PROBLEM 1

Draw a tree diagram for tossing a coin three times. Then use the diagram to find the number of possible outcomes.

Answer

1.

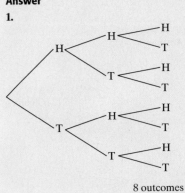

8 outcomes

PRACTICE PROBLEM 2

Draw a tree diagram for an experiment consisting of tossing a coin and then rolling a die. Then use the diagram to find the number of possible outcomes.

EXAMPLE 2 Draw a tree diagram for an experiment consisting of rolling a die and then tossing a coin. Then use the diagram to find the number of possible outcomes.

Die

Solution: Recall that a die has six sides and that each side represents a number, 1 through 6.

Roll a Die	Toss a coin	Outcomes
1	H	1, H
	T	1, T
2	H	2, H
	T	2, T
3	H	3, H
	T	3, T
4	H	4, H
	T	4, T
5	H	5, H
	T	5, T
6	H	6, H
	T	6, T

There are 12 possible outcomes for rolling a die and then tossing a coin.

💻 **Work Practice Problem 2**

Any number of outcomes considered together are called an **event.** For example, when tossing a coin twice, H, H is an event. The event is tossing heads first and tossing heads second. Another event would be tossing tails first and then heads (T, H), and so on.

Objective B Finding the Probability of an Event

As we mentioned earlier, the **probability of an event is a measure of the chance or likelihood of it occurring.** For example, if a coin is tossed, what is the probability that heads occurs? Since one of two equally likely possible outcomes is heads, the probability is $\frac{1}{2}$.

The Probability of an Event

$$\text{probability of an event} = \frac{\text{number of ways that the event can occur}}{\text{number of possible outcomes}}$$

Answer

2.

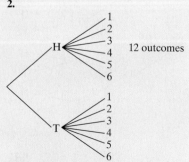

12 outcomes

🗨️ **Helpful Hint**

Note from the definition of probability that the probability of an event is always between 0 and 1, inclusive (i.e., including 0 and 1). A probability of 0 means that an event won't occur, and a probability of 1 means that an event is certain to occur.

EXAMPLE 3 If a coin is tossed twice, find the probability of tossing heads and then heads (H, H).

Solution: 1 way the event can occur

$$\text{H, T,} \quad \overbrace{\text{H, H,}} \quad \text{T, H,} \quad \text{T, T}$$

4 possible outcomes

$$\text{probability} = \frac{1}{4} \quad \begin{array}{l}\text{Number of ways the event can occur}\\ \text{Number of possible outcomes}\end{array}$$

The probability of tossing heads and then heads is $\frac{1}{4}$.

Work Practice Problem 3

PRACTICE PROBLEM 3

If a coin is tossed three times, find the probability of tossing heads, then tails, then tails (H, T, T).

EXAMPLE 4 If a die is rolled one time, find the probability of rolling a 3 or a 4.

Solution: Recall that there are 6 possible outcomes when rolling a die.

2 ways that the event can occur

$$\text{possible outcomes:} \quad \underline{1, \quad 2, \quad 3, \quad 4, \quad 5, \quad 6}$$

6 possible outcomes

$$\text{probability of a 3 or a 4} = \frac{2}{6} \quad \begin{array}{l}\text{Number of ways the event can occur}\\ \text{Number of possible outcomes}\end{array}$$
$$= \frac{1}{3} \quad \text{Simplest form}$$

Work Practice Problem 4

PRACTICE PROBLEM 4

If a die is rolled one time, find the probability of rolling a 1 or a 2.

✔**Concept Check** Suppose you have calculated a probability of $\frac{11}{9}$. How do you know that you have made an error in your calculation?

EXAMPLE 5 Find the probability of choosing a red marble from a box containing 1 red, 1 yellow, and 2 blue marbles.

Solution: 1 way that event can occur

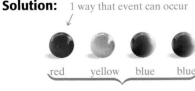

red   yellow   blue   blue

4 possible outcomes

$$\text{probability} = \frac{1}{4}$$

Work Practice Problem 5

PRACTICE PROBLEM 5

Use the diagram from Example 5 and find the probability of choosing a blue marble from the box.

Answers

3. $\frac{1}{8}$, 4. $\frac{1}{3}$, 5. $\frac{1}{2}$

✔ **Concept Check Answer**

The number of ways an event can occur can't be larger than the number of possible outcomes.

Mental Math

If a coin is tossed once, find the probability of each event.

1. The coin lands heads up.

2. The coin lands tails up.

If the spinner shown is spun once, find the probability of each event.

3. The spinner stops on red.

4. The spinner stops on blue.

Objective A *Draw a tree diagram for each experiment. Then use the diagram to find the number of possible outcomes. See Examples 1 and 2.*

1. Choosing a vowel (a, e, i, o, u) and then a number (1, 2, or 3)

2. Choosing a number (1 or 2) and then a vowel (a, e, i, o, u)

3. Spinning Spinner A once

4. Spinning Spinner B once

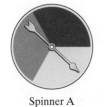

Spinner A

Spinner B

5. Spinning Spinner B twice

6. Spinning Spinner A twice

7. Spinning Spinner A and then Spinner B

8. Spinning Spinner B and then Spinner A

 9. Tossing a coin and then spinning Spinner B

10. Tossing a coin and then spinning Spinner A

Objective **B** *If a single die is tossed once, find the probability of each event. See Examples 3 through 5.*

11. A 5

12. A 7

13. A 1 or a 4

14. A 2 or a 3

15. An even number

16. An odd number

17. A number greater than 1

18. A number less than 5

Suppose the spinner shown is spun once. Find the probability of each event. See Examples 3 through 5.

19. The result of the spin is 2.

20. The result of the spin is 3.

21. The result of a spin is 1, 2, or 3.

22. The result of a spin is not 3.

23. The result of the spin is an odd number.

24. The result of the spin is an even number.

If a single choice is made from the bag of marbles shown, find the probability of each event. See Examples 3 through 5.

25. A red marble is chosen.

26. A blue marble is chosen.

27. A yellow marble is chosen.

28. A green marble is chosen.

29. A blue or red marble is chosen.

30. A red or yellow marble is chosen.

A new drug is being tested that is supposed to lower blood pressure. This drug was given to 200 people and the results are below.

Lower Blood Pressure	Higher Blood Pressure	Blood Pressure Not Changed
152	38	10

31. If a person is testing this drug, what is the probability that their blood pressure will be higher?

32. If a person is testing this drug, what is the probability that their blood pressure will be lower?

33. If a person is testing this drug, what is the probability that their blood pressure will not change?

34. What is the sum of the answers to Exercises 31, 32, and 33? In your own words, explain why.

Review

Perform each indicated operation. See Sections 3.3 and 3.5.

35. $\dfrac{1}{2} + \dfrac{1}{3}$ **36.** $\dfrac{7}{10} - \dfrac{2}{5}$ **37.** $\dfrac{1}{2} \cdot \dfrac{1}{3}$ **38.** $\dfrac{7}{10} \div \dfrac{2}{5}$ **39.** $5 \div \dfrac{3}{4}$ **40.** $\dfrac{3}{5} \cdot 10$

Concept Extensions

Recall that a deck of cards contains 52 cards. These cards consist of four suits (hearts, spades, clubs, and diamonds) of each of the following: 2, 3, 4, 5, 6, 7, 8, 9, 10, jack, queen, king, and ace. If a card is chosen from a deck of cards, find the probability of each event.

41. The king of hearts   **42.** The 10 of spades

43. A king   **44.** A 10

45. A heart   **46.** A club

47. A red card   **48.** A king or queen

Two dice are tossed. Find the probability of each sum of the dice. (Hint: Draw a tree diagram of the possibilities of two tosses of a die, and then find the sum of the numbers on each branch.)

49. A sum of 4   **50.** A sum of 11   **51.** A sum of 13   **52.** A sum of 2

Solve. See the Concept Check in this section.

53. In your own words, explain why the probability of an event cannot be greater than 1.

54. In your own words, explain when the probability of an event is 0.

CHAPTER 7   Group Activity

Sections 7.1, 7.3

This activity may be completed by working in groups or individually.

How often have you read an article in a newspaper or in a magazine that included results from a survey or poll? Surveys seem to have become very popular ways of getting feedback on anything from a political candidate, to a new product, to services offered by a health club. In this activity, you will conduct a survey and analyze the results.

1. Conduct a survey of 30 students in one of your classes. Ask each student to report his or her age.

2. Classify each age according to the following categories: under 20, 20 to 24, 25 to 29, 30 to 39, 40 to 49, and 50 or over. Tally the number of your survey respondents that fall into each category. Make a bar graph of your results. What does this graph tell you about the ages of your survey respondents?

3. Find the average age of your survey respondents.

4. Find the median age of your survey respondents.

5. Find the mode of the ages of your survey respondents.

6. Compare the mean, median, and mode of your age data. Are these measures similar? Which is largest? Which is smallest? If there is a noticeable difference between any of these measures, can you explain why?

Chapter 7 Vocabulary Check

Fill in each blank with one of the words or phrases listed below.

outcomes	bar	experiment	mean	tree diagram
pictograph	line	class interval	median	probability
histogram	circle	class frequency	mode	

1. A _____ graph presents data using vertical or horizontal bars.

2. The _____ of a set of number items is $\dfrac{\text{sum of items}}{\text{number of items}}$.

3. The possible results of an experiment are the _____.

4. A _____ is a graph in which pictures or symbols are used to visually present data.

5. The _____ of a set of numbers is the number that occurs most often.

6. A _____ graph displays information with a line that connects data points.

7. The _____ of an ordered set of numbers is the middle number.

8. A _____ is one way to picture and count outcomes.

9. An _____ is an activity being considered, such as tossing a coin or rolling a die.

10. In a _____ graph, each section (shaped like a piece of pie) shows a category and the relative size of the category.

11. The _____ of an event is $\dfrac{\substack{\text{number of ways that} \\ \text{the event can occur}}}{\substack{\text{number of possible} \\ \text{outcomes}}}$.

12. A _____ is a special bar graph in which the width of each bar represents a _____ and the height of each bar represents the _____.

Helpful Hint

Are you preparing for your test? Don't forget to take the Chapter Test on page 556. Then check your answers at the back of your text and use the Chapter Test Prep Video CD to see the fully worked-out solutions to any of the exercises you want to review.

7 Chapter Highlights

DEFINITIONS AND CONCEPTS	EXAMPLES
Section 7.1 Reading Pictographs, Bar Graphs, Histograms, and Line Graphs	

A **pictograph** is a graph in which pictures or symbols are used to visually present data.

A **line graph** displays information with a line that connects data points.

A **bar graph** presents data using vertical or horizontal bars.

The bar graph on the right shows the number of acres of wheat harvested in 1996 for leading states.

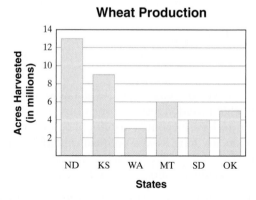

Wheat Production

Source: U.S. Department of Agriculture

1. Approximately how many acres of wheat were harvested in Kansas?

   9,000,000 acres

DEFINITIONS AND CONCEPTS	**EXAMPLES**

Section 7.1   Reading Pictographs, Bar Graphs, Histograms, and Line Graphs (*continued*)

A **histogram** is a special bar graph in which the width of each bar represents a **class interval** and the height of each bar represents the **class frequency.** The histogram on the right shows student quiz scores.	**2.** About how many more acres of wheat were harvested in North Dakota than South Dakota? 13 million $-$ 4 million 9 million or 9,000,000 acres 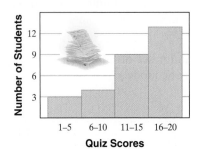 **1.** How many students received a score of 6–10? 4 students **2.** How many students received a score of 11–20? 9 + 13 = 22 students

Section 7.2   Reading Circle Graphs

In a **circle graph,** each section (shaped like a piece of pie) shows a category and the relative size of the category. The circle graph on the right classifies tornadoes by wind speed.	**Tornado Wind Speeds** 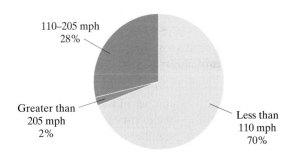 *Source:* National Oceanic and Atmospheric Administration **1.** What percent of tornadoes have wind speeds of 110 mph or greater? 28% + 2% = 30% **2.** If there were 1235 tornadoes in the United States in 1995, how many of these might we expect to have had wind speeds less than 110 mph? Find 70% of 1235. $70\%(1235) = 0.70(1235) = 864.5 \approx 865$ Around 865 tornadoes would be expected to have had wind speeds of less than 110 mph.

DEFINITIONS AND CONCEPTS	**EXAMPLES**
Section 7.3 Mean, Median, and Mode	

The **mean** (or **average**) of a set of number items is $$\text{mean} = \frac{\text{sum of items}}{\text{number of items}}$$	Find the mean, median, and mode of the following set of numbers: 33, 35, 35, 43, 68, 68 $$\text{mean} = \frac{33 + 35 + 35 + 43 + 68 + 68}{6} = 47$$
The **median** of a set of numbers in numerical order is the middle number. If the number of items is even, the median is the mean of the two middle numbers.	The median is the mean of the two middle numbers, 35 and 43 $$\text{median} = \frac{35 + 43}{2} = 39$$
The **mode** of a set of numbers is the number that occurs most often. (A set of numbers may have no mode or more than one mode.)	There are two modes because there are two numbers that occur twice: 35 and 68

Section 7.4 Counting and Introduction to Probability	

An **experiment** is an activity being considered, such as tossing a coin or rolling a die. The possible results of an experiment are the **outcomes.** A **tree diagram** is one way to picture and count outcomes.	Draw a tree diagram for tossing a coin and then choosing a number from 1 to 4. 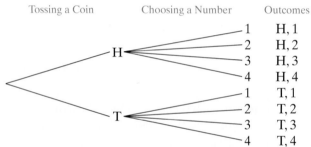
Any number of outcomes considered together is called an **event.** The **probability** of an event is a measure of the chance or likelihood of it occurring. $$\begin{array}{l}\text{probability of}\\ \text{an event}\end{array} = \frac{\begin{array}{c}\text{number of ways that}\\ \text{the event can occur}\end{array}}{\begin{array}{c}\text{number of possible}\\ \text{outcomes}\end{array}}$$	Find the probability of tossing a coin twice and tails occurring each time. 1 way the event can occur HH, HT, TH, TT 4 possible outcomes $$\text{probability} = \frac{1}{4}$$

STUDY SKILLS BUILDER

Are You Prepared for a Test on Chapter 7?

Below I have listed some *common trouble areas* for students in Chapter 7. After studying for your test—but before taking your test—read these.

- Do you remember that a set of numbers can have no mode, 1 mode, or even more than 1 mode?

  2, 5, 8, 9   no mode

  2, 2, 8, 9   mode: 2

  2, 2, 3, 3, 5, 7, 7   mode: 2, 3, 7

- Do you remember how to find the median of an even-numbered set of numbers?

  2, 5, 8, 9 $\dfrac{5 + 8}{2} = 6.5$ The median is the average of the two "middle" numbers.

- Don't forget that the probability of an event is always between 0 and 1 inclusive (including 0 and 1).

- What is the probability of an event that won't occur? 0

- What is the probability of an event that is certain to occur? 1

CHAPTER REVIEW

(7.1) *The following pictograph shows the number of new homes constructed in 2003, by region. Use this graph to answer Exercises 1 through 6.*

2003 Housing Starts by Region of United States

Northeast	🏠🏠🏠🏠
Midwest	🏠🏠🏠🏠🏠🏠🏠🏠🏠🏠
South	🏠🏠🏠🏠🏠🏠🏠🏠🏠🏠🏠🏠🏠🏠🏠🏠🏠🏠
West	🏠🏠🏠🏠🏠🏠🏠🏠🏠🏠🏠

Each 🏠 represents 50,000 homes

Source: U.S. Census Bureau

1. How many housing starts were there in the Midwest in 2003?

2. How many housing starts were there in the Northeast in 2003?

3. Find the total housing starts in the Midwest and Northeast.

4. How many more housing starts were in the South than in the West?

5. Which region(s) had 400,000 or more housing starts?

6. Which region(s) had fewer than 400,000 housing starts?

The following bar graph shows the percent of persons age 25 or over who completed four or more years of college. Use this graph to answer Exercises 7 through 10.

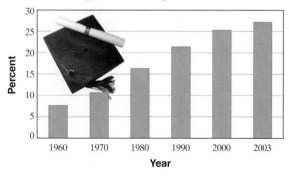

Source: U.S. Census Bureau

7. Approximate the percent of persons who completed four or more years of college in 1960.

8. What year shown had the greatest percent of persons completing four or more years of college?

9. What years shown had 15% or more of persons completing four or more years of college?

10. Describe any patterns you notice in this graph.

The following line graph shows the average price of a 30-second television advertisement during the Super Bowl for the years shown. Use this graph to answer Exercises 11 through 15.

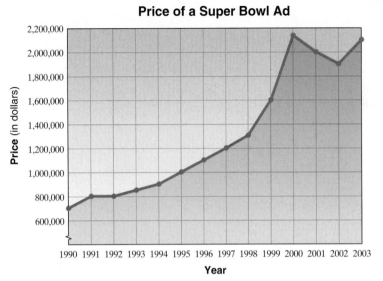

Price of a Super Bowl Ad

Sources: Nielsen Media Research and *Advertising Age* research

11. Approximate the price of a Super Bowl ad in 2003.

12. Approximate the price of a Super Bowl ad in 1997.

13. Between which two years did the price of a Super Bowl ad *not* increase?

14. Between which two years did the price of a Super Bowl ad increase the most?

15. During which years was the price of a Super Bowl ad *less than* $1,000,000?

The following histogram shows the hours worked per week by the employees of Southern Star Furniture. Use this histogram to answer Exercises 16 through 19.

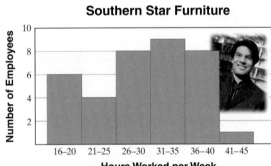

Southern Star Furniture

16. How many employees work 21–25 hours per week?

17. How many employees work 41–45 hours per week?

18. How many employees work 36 hours or more per week?

19. How many employees work 30 hours or less per week?

Following is a list of monthly record high temperatures for New Orleans, Louisiana. Use this list to complete the frequency distribution table below.

83	96	101	92
85	100	92	102
89	101	87	84

	Class Intervals (Temperatures)	Tally	Class Frequency (Number of Months)
20.	80°–89°		
21.	90°–99°		
22.	100°–109°		

23. Use the table from Exercises 20, 21, and 22 to draw a histogram.

Record Highs

Temperatures

(7.2) *The following circle graph shows a family's $4000 monthly budget. Use this graph to answer Exercises 24 through 30. Write all ratios as fractions in simplest form.*

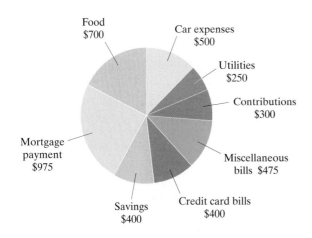

24. What is the largest budget item?

25. What is the smallest budget item?

26. How much money is budgeted for the mortgage payment and utilities?

27. How much money is budgeted for savings and contributions?

28. Find the ratio of the mortgage payment to the total monthly budget.

29. Find the ratio of food to the total monthly budget.

30. Find the ratio of car expenses to food.

The following circle graph shows the percent of the 50 states with various rural interstate highway speed limits in 2000. Use this graph to determine the number of states with each speed limit in Exercises 31 through 34.

Percent of States with Rural Interstate Highway Speed Limit

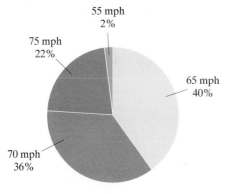

Source: Insurance Institute for Highway Safety

31. How many states had a rural interstate highway speed limit of 65 mph?

32. How many states had a rural interstate highway speed limit of 75 mph?

33. How many states had a rural interstate highway speed limit of 55 mph?

34. How many states had a rural interstate highway speed limit of 70 mph or 75 mph?

(7.3) *Find the mean, median, and any mode(s) for each list of numbers. If necessary, round to the nearest tenth.*

35. 13, 23, 33, 14, 6

36. 45, 86, 21, 60, 86, 64, 45

37. 14,000, 20,000, 12,000, 20,000, 36,000, 45,000

38. 560, 620, 123, 400, 410, 300, 400, 780, 430, 450

For Exercises 39 and 40, the grades are given for a student for a particular semester. Find each grade point average. If necessary, round the grade point average to the nearest hundredth.

39.

Grade	Credit Hours
A	3
A	3
C	2
B	3
C	1

40.

Grade	Credit Hours
B	3
B	4
C	2
D	2
B	3

(7.4) *Draw a tree diagram for each experiment. Then use the diagram to determine the number of outcomes.*

Spinner 1

Spinner 2

41. Tossing a coin and then spinning Spinner 1

42. Spinning Spinner 2 and then tossing a coin

43. Spinning Spinner 1 twice

44. Spinning Spinner 2 twice

45. Spinning Spinner 1 and then Spinner 2

Find the probability of each event.

46. Rolling a 4 on a die

47. Rolling a 3 on a die

48. Spinning a 4 on the spinner

49. Spinning a 3 on the spinner

50. Spinning either a 1, 3, or 5 on the spinner

51. Spinning either a 2 or a 4 on the spinner

52. Rolling an even number on a die

53. Rolling a number greater than 3 on a die

Mixed Review

Find the mean, median, and any mode(s) for each list of numbers. If needed round answers to two decimal places.

54. 73, 82, 95, 68, 54

55. 25, 27, 32, 98, 62

56. 750, 500, 427, 322, 500, 225

57. 952, 327, 566, 814, 327, 729

Given a bag containing 2 red marbles, 2 blue marbles, 3 yellow marbles, and 1 green marble, find the following:

58. The probability of choosing a blue marble from the bag

59. The probability of choosing a yellow marble from the bag

60. The probability of choosing a red marble from the bag

61. The probability of choosing a green marble from the bag

7 CHAPTER TEST

Remember to use the Chapter Test Prep Video CD to see the fully worked-out solutions to any of the exercises you want to review.

The following pictograph shows the money collected each week from a wrapping paper fundraiser. Use this graph to answer Exercises 1 through 3.

1. _____

Weekly Wrapping Paper Sales

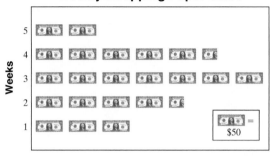

2. _____

1. How much money was collected during the second week?

2. During which week was the most money collected? How much money was collected during that week?

3. What was the total money collected for the fundraiser?

The bar graph shows the normal monthly precipitation in centimeters for Chicago, Illinois. Use this graph to answer Exercises 4 through 6.

3. _____

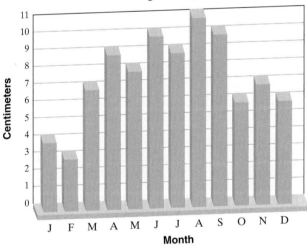

Source: U.S. National Oceanic and Atmospheric Administration, *Climatography of the United States*, No. 81

4. _____

4. During which month(s) does Chicago normally have more than 9 centimeters of precipitation?

5. _____

5. During which month does Chicago normally have the least amount of precipitation? How much precipitation occurs during that month?

6. During which month(s) does 7 centimeters of precipitation normally occur?

6. _____

7. Use the information in the table to draw a bar graph. Clearly label each bar.

Countries with the Highest Newspaper Circulations	
Country	Average Daily Circulation (in millions)
Japan	72
US	56
China	50
India	31
Germany	24
Russia	24
UK	19

(*Source:* World Association of Newspapers)

Countries with the Highest Newspaper Circulations

7. see graph

The following line graph shows the annual inflation rate in the United States for the years 1990–2003. Use this graph to answer Exercises 8 through 10.

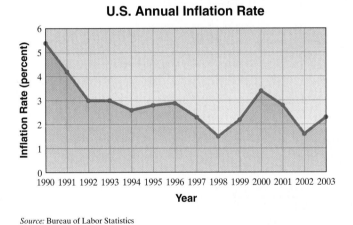

Source: Bureau of Labor Statistics

8. Approximate the annual inflation rate in 2002.

9. During which of the years shown was the inflation rate greater than 3%?

10. During which sets of years was the inflation rate increasing?

8. _____

9. _____

10. _____

The result of a survey of 200 people is shown in the following circle graph. Each person was asked to tell his or her favorite type of music. Use this graph to answer Exercises 11 and 12.

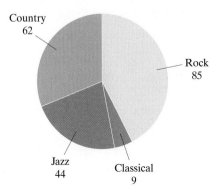

11. Find the ratio of those who prefer rock music to the total number surveyed.

12. Find the ratio of those who prefer country music to those who prefer jazz.

11. _____

12. _____

13. _____

The following circle graph shows the U.S. labor force employment by industry for 2000. There were approximately 132,000,000 people employed by these industries in the United States in 2000. Use the graph to find how many people were employed by the industries given in Exercises 13 and 14.

U.S. Labor Force Employment by Industry

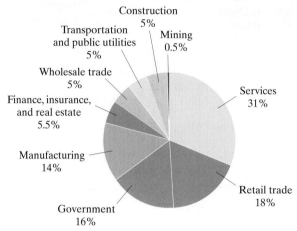

Source: Bureau of Labor Statistics

14. _____

13. Services

14. Government

A professor measures the heights of the students in her class. The results are shown in the following histogram. Use this histogram to answer Exercises 15 and 16.

15. _____

Student Heights

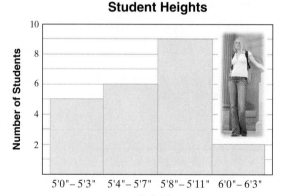

15. How many students are 5′8″–5′11″ tall?

16. How many students are 5′7″ or shorter?

16. _____

17. The history test scores of 25 students are shown below. Use these scores to complete the frequency distribution table.

70	86	81	65	92
43	72	85	69	97
82	51	75	50	68
88	83	85	77	99
77	63	59	84	90

Class Intervals (Scores)	Tally	Class Frequency (Number of Students)
40–49		
50–59		
60–69		
70–79		
80–89		
90–99		

17. see table

18. Use the results of Exercise 17 to draw a histogram.

Scores

Find the mean, median, and mode of each list of numbers.

19. 26, 32, 42, 43, 49

20. 8, 10, 16, 16, 14, 12, 12, 13

19. _____

20. _____

Find the grade point average. If necessary, round to the nearest hundredth.

21. _____

21.

Grade	Credit Hours
A	3
B	3
C	3
B	4
A	1

22. Draw a tree diagram for the experiment of spinning the spinner twice. State the number of outcomes.

23. Draw a tree diagram for the experiment of tossing a coin twice. State the number of outcomes.

22. _____

Suppose that the numbers 1 to 10 are each written on a scrap of paper and placed in a bag. You then select one number from the bag.

24. What is the probability of choosing a 6 from the bag?

25. What is the probability of choosing a 3 or a 4 from the bag?

23. _____

24. _____

25. _____

Answers

1. Write 106,052,447 in words.

2. Write 276,004 in words.

△ **3.** Find the perimeter of the polygon shown.

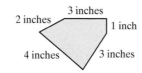

4. Find the perimeter of the rectangle shown.

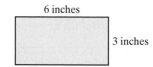

1. _____

2. _____

3. _____

4. _____

5. Subtract: $900 - 174$. Check by adding.

6. Subtract: $17{,}801 - 8216$ Check by adding.

5. _____

6. _____

7. Round 248,982 to the nearest hundred.

8. Round 844,497 to the nearest thousand.

7. _____

8. _____

9. Multiply: 25×8

10. Multiply: 395×74

9. _____

10. _____

11. Divide and check: $1872 \div 9$

12. Divide and check: $3956 \div 46$

11. _____

12. _____

13. Simplify: $2 \cdot 4 - 3 \div 3$

14. Simplify: $8 \cdot 4 + 9 \div 3$

13. _____

14. _____

15. Evaluate $x^2 + z - 3$ for $x = 5$ and $z = 4$.

16. Evaluate $2a^2 + 5 - c$ for $a = 2$ and $c = 3$.

15. _____

16. _____

17. a. _____

  b. _____

  c. _____

17. Insert $<$ or $>$ between each pair of numbers to make a true statement.

a. -7 7
b. 0 -4
c. -9 -11

18. Insert $<$ or $>$ to make a true statement.

a. -14 0
b. $-(-7)$ -8

18. a. _____

  b. _____

19. _____

19. Add using a number line: $5 + (-2)$

20. Add using a number line: $-3 + (-4)$

20. _____

21. _____

22. _____

Add.

21. $-5 + (-1)$

22. $3 + (-7)$

23. $2 + 6$

24. $21 + 15 + (-19)$

Subtract.

25. $-4 - 10$

26. $-2 - 3$

27. $6 - (-5)$

28. $19 - (-10)$

29. $-11 - (-7)$

30. $-16 - (-13)$

Divide.

31. $\dfrac{-12}{6}$

32. $\dfrac{-30}{-5}$

33. $-20 \div (-4)$

34. $26 \div (-2)$

35. $\dfrac{48}{-3}$

36. $\dfrac{-120}{12}$

37. Add: $1\dfrac{4}{5} + 4 + 2\dfrac{1}{2}$

38. Multiply: $5\dfrac{1}{3} \cdot 2\dfrac{1}{8}$

Write each rate as a fraction in simplest form.

39. $2160 for 12 weeks

40. 340 miles every 5 hours

41. Convert 7 feet to yards.

42. Convert 2.5 tons to pounds.

43. Convert 2.35 cg to grams.

44. Convert 106 cm to millimeters.

45. Find $\sqrt{\dfrac{1}{36}}$.

46. Find: $\sqrt{\dfrac{1}{25}}$

47. Find the mode of the list of numbers:
11, 14, 14, 16, 31, 56, 65, 77, 77, 78, 79

48. Find the median of the numbers in Exercise 47.

49. If a coin is tossed twice, find the probability of tossing heads and then heads.

50. A bag contains 3 red marbles and 2 blue marbles. Find the probability of choosing a red marble.

23.	_____
24.	_____
25.	_____
26.	_____
27.	_____
28.	_____
29.	_____
30.	_____
31.	_____
32.	_____
33.	_____
34.	_____
35.	_____
36.	_____
37.	_____
38.	_____
39.	_____
40.	_____
41.	_____
42.	_____
43.	_____
44.	_____
45.	_____
46.	_____
47.	_____
48.	_____
49.	_____
50.	_____

8

Introduction to Algebra

In this chapter we continue making the transition from arithmetic to algebra. Recall that in algebra, letters are used to stand for unknown quantities. Using variables is a very powerful tool for solving problems that cannot be solved with arithmetic alone. This chapter introduces simplifying algebraic expressions, and solving variable equations.

The double-line graph given shows the projected shortage of registered nurses. The red line shows the expected demand for nurses while the blue line shows the expected supply of nurses. Since the red line is above the blue line, we project there to be a shortage of nurses, since red is above blue. In Exercises 39 and 40 of Section 8.5, we calculate the actual shortage in percent and number of nurses for a few particular years.

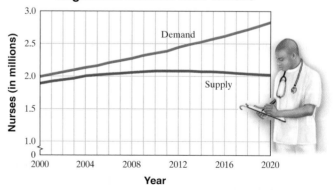

National Supply and Demand Projections for Full-Time Equivalent Registered Nurses: 2000 to 2020

Source: Bureau of Health Professions, RN Supply and Demand Projections

8.1 VARIABLE EXPRESSIONS

Objectives

Objective A Evaluating Algebraic Expressions

Recall from Section 2.1 that a combination of numbers, letters (variables), and operation symbols is called an **algebraic expression** or simply an **expression.** For example,

$$3 + x, \quad 5 \cdot y, \quad \text{and} \quad 2 \cdot z - 1 + x$$

are expressions.

If two variables or a number and a variable are next to each other, with no operation sign between them, the indicated operation is multiplication. For example,

$$2x \quad \text{means} \quad 2 \cdot x$$

and

$$xy \text{ or } x(y) \quad \text{means} \quad x \cdot y$$

Also, the meaning of an exponent remains the same when the base is a variable. For example,

$$x^2 = \underbrace{x \cdot x}_{\text{2 factors of } x} \quad \text{and} \quad y^5 = \underbrace{y \cdot y \cdot y \cdot y \cdot y}_{\text{5 factors of } y}$$

Throughout this text, we have practiced replacing a variable in an expression by a number and then finding the value of the expression. Remember that this is called **evaluating the expression.** Let's review this process. When finding the value of an expression, don't forget to follow the order of operations.

EXAMPLE 1 Evaluate: $2x + y$ when $x = 8$ and $y = -7$

Solution: Replace x with 8 and y with -7 in $2x + y$.

$$\begin{aligned} 2x + y &= 2 \cdot 8 + (-7) && \text{Replace } x \text{ with 8 and } y \text{ with } -7. \\ &= 16 + (-7) && \text{Multiply first because of the order of operations.} \\ &= 9 && \text{Add.} \end{aligned}$$

⬛ **Work Practice Problem 1**

EXAMPLE 2 Evaluate: $\dfrac{3m - 2n}{-2q}$ when $m = 8$, $n = 4$, and $q = 1$

Solution:

$$\begin{aligned} \frac{3m - 2n}{-2q} &= \frac{3 \cdot 8 - 2 \cdot 4}{-2 \cdot 1} && \text{Replace } m \text{ with 8}, n \text{ with 4, and } q \text{ with 1.} \\ &= \frac{24 - 8}{-2} && \text{Multiply.} \\ &= \frac{16}{-2} && \text{Subtract in the numerator.} \\ &= -8 && \text{Divide.} \end{aligned}$$

⬛ **Work Practice Problem 2**

Objectives

A Evaluate Algebraic Expressions for Given Replacement Values for the Variables.

B Use Properties of Numbers to Combine Like Terms.

C Use Properties of Numbers to Multiply Expressions.

PRACTICE PROBLEM 1

Evaluate: $5x - y$ when $x = 2$ and $y = -3$

PRACTICE PROBLEM 2

Evaluate: $\dfrac{5r - 2s}{-3q}$ when $r = 3$, $s = 3$, and $q = 1$

Answers
1. 13, **2.** -3

563

PRACTICE PROBLEM 3

Evaluate: $13 - (3a + 8)$ when $a = -2$

EXAMPLE 3 Evaluate: $8 - (6a - 5)$ when $a = -3$

Solution:

$$
\begin{aligned}
8 - (6a - 5) &= 8 - (6 \cdot (-3) - 5) && \text{Replace } a \text{ with } -3. \\
&= 8 - (-18 - 5) && \text{Multiply.} \\
&= 8 - (-23) && \text{Simplify inside the parentheses.} \\
&= 8 + 23 \\
&= 31 && \text{Add.}
\end{aligned}
$$

■ **Work Practice Problem 3**

PRACTICE PROBLEM 4

Evaluate: $a^2 - 0.7b$ when $a = 6$ and $b = -2$

EXAMPLE 4 Evaluate: $x^3 - 1.1y$ when $x = 4$ and $y = -1$

Solution:

$$
\begin{aligned}
x^3 - 1.1y &= 4^3 - 1.1(-1) && \text{Replace } x \text{ with 4 and } y \text{ with } -1. \\
&= 64 - 1.1(-1) && \text{Evaluate } 4^3. \\
&= 64 - (-1.1) && \text{Multiply.} \\
&= 64 + 1.1 \\
&= 65.1 && \text{Add.}
\end{aligned}
$$

■ **Work Practice Problem 4**

Objective B Combining Like Terms

The addends of an algebraic expression are called the **terms** of the expression.

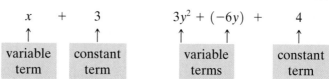

A term that is only a number has a special name. It is called a **constant term,** or simply a **constant.** A term that contains a variable is called a **variable term.**

x	$+$	3		$3y^2 + (-6y) +$		4
↑		↑		↑	↑	↑
variable term		constant term		variable terms		constant term

The number factor of a variable term is called the **numerical coefficient.** A numerical coefficient of 1 is usually not written.

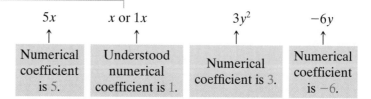

Helpful Hint

Recall that $1 \cdot$ any number = that number. This means that

$1 \cdot x = x$ or that $1x = x$.

Thus x can always be replaced by $1x$ or $1 \cdot x$.

Terms with the same variable factors, except that they may have different numerical coefficients, are called **like terms.**

Like Terms	Unlike Terms
$3x, \dfrac{1}{2}x$	$5x, x^2$
$-6y, 2y, y$	$7x, 7y$

Answers

3. 11,   **4.** 37.4

A sum or difference of like terms can be simplified using the **distributive property.** Recall from Section 1.6 that the distributive property says that multiplication distributes over addition (and subtraction). Using variables, we can write the distributive property as follows:

$$\overset{\frown}{(a + b)}c = ac + bc.$$

If we write the right side of the equation first, then the left side, we have the following:

Distributive Property

If a, b, and c are numbers, then

$$ac + bc = (a + b)c$$

Also,

$$ac - bc = (a - b)c$$

The distributive property guarantees that, no matter what number x is, $7x + 5x$ (for example) has the same value as $(7 + 5)x$, or $12x$. We then have that

$$7x + 5x = (7 + 5)x = 12x$$

This is an example of **combining like terms.** An algebraic expression is **simplified** when all like terms have been combined.

EXAMPLE 5 Simplify each expression by combining like terms.

a. $3x + 2x$ **b.** $y - 7y$

Solution: We add or subtract like terms.

a. $3x + 2x = (3 + 2)x$
$$= 5x$$

Understood 1

b. $y - 7y = 1y - 7y$
$$= (1 - 7)y$$
$$= -6y$$

◻ **Work Practice Problem 5**

The commutative and associative properties of addition and multiplication can also help us simplify expressions. We presented these properties in Sections 1.3 and 1.6 and state them again using variables.

Properties of Addition and Multiplication

If a, b, and c are numbers, then

$a + b = b + a$ Commutative property of addition

$a \cdot b = b \cdot a$ Commutative property of multiplication

That is, the **order** of adding or multiplying two numbers can be changed without changing their sum or product.

$(a + b) + c = a + (b + c)$ Associative property of addition

$(a \cdot b) \cdot c = a \cdot (b \cdot c)$ Associative property of multiplication

That is, the **grouping** of numbers in addition or multiplication can be changed without changing their sum or product.

PRACTICE PROBLEM 5

Simplify each expression by combining like terms.

a. $8m - 11m$

b. $5a + a$

Answers

5. a. $-3m$, **b.** $6a$

PRACTICE PROBLEM 6

Simplify: $8m + 5 + m - 4$

Helpful Hint

- The commutative properties say the order of adding or multiplying two numbers can be changed without changing sum or product.
- The associative properties say grouping numbers when adding or multiplying can be changed without changing sum or product.
- This is not true for subtraction or division.

PRACTICE PROBLEMS 7–10

Simplify each expression by combining like terms.

7. $7y + 11y - 8$
8. $2y - 6 + y + 7y$
9. $3.7x + 5 - 4.2x + 15$
10. $-9y + 2 - 4y - 8x + 12 - x$

PRACTICE PROBLEMS 11–12

Multiply.

11. $7(8a)$
12. $-5(9x)$

PRACTICE PROBLEM 13

Use the distributive property to multiply: $7(y + 2)$

Answers

6. $9m + 1$,   7. $18y - 8$,   8. $10y - 6$,
9. $-0.5x + 20$,   10. $-13y - 9x + 14$
11. $56a$,   12. $-45x$,   13. $7y + 14$

✔ **Concept Check Answer**

did not distribute the 8

EXAMPLE 6   Simplify: $2y - 6 + 4y + 8$

Solution: We begin by writing subtraction as the addition of opposites.

$$\begin{aligned}
2y - 6 + 4y + 8 &= 2y + (-6) + 4y + 8 \\
&= 2y + 4y + (-6) + 8 \quad \text{Apply the commutative property of addition.} \\
&= (2 + 4)y + (-6) + 8 \quad \text{Apply the distributive property.} \\
&= 6y + 2 \quad \text{Simplify.}
\end{aligned}$$

▣ **Work Practice Problem 6**

EXAMPLES   Simplify each expression by combining like terms.

7. $6x + 2x - 5 = 8x - 5$
8. $\begin{aligned}4x + 3 - 5x + 2x &= 4x - 5x + 2x + 3 \\ &= 1x + 3 \quad \text{or} \quad x + 3\end{aligned}$
9. $\begin{aligned}1.2y + 10 - 5.7y - 9 &= 1.2y - 5.7y + 10 - 9 \\ &= -4.5y + 1\end{aligned}$
10. $2x - 5 + 3y + 4x - 10y + 11 = 6x - 7y + 6$

▣ **Work Practice Problems 7–10**

Objective C Multiplying Expressions

We can also use properties of numbers to multiply expressions such as $3(2x)$. By the associative property of multiplication, we can write the product $3(2x)$ as $(3 \cdot 2)x$, which simplifies to $6x$.

EXAMPLES   Multiply.

11. $\begin{aligned}5(3y) &= (5 \cdot 3)y \quad \text{Apply the associative property of multiplication.} \\ &= 15y \quad \text{Multiply.}\end{aligned}$
12. $\begin{aligned}-2(4x) &= (-2 \cdot 4)x \quad \text{Apply the associative property of multiplication.} \\ &= -8x \quad \text{Multiply.}\end{aligned}$

▣ **Work Practice Problems 11–12**

We can use the distributive property to combine like terms, which we have done, and also to multiply expressions such as $2(3 + x)$. By the distributive property, we have that

$$\begin{aligned}
2(3 + x) &= 2 \cdot 3 + 2 \cdot x \quad \text{Apply the distributive property.} \\
&= 6 + 2x \quad \text{Multiply.}
\end{aligned}$$

EXAMPLE 13   Use the distributive property to multiply: $6(x + 4)$

Solution: By the distributive property,

$$\begin{aligned}
6(x + 4) &= 6 \cdot x + 6 \cdot 4 \quad \text{Apply the distributive property.} \\
&= 6x + 24 \quad \text{Multiply.}
\end{aligned}$$

▣ **Work Practice Problem 13**

✔ **Concept Check**   What's wrong with the following?

$$8(a - b) = 8a - b$$

EXAMPLE 14 Multiply: $-3(5a + 2)$

Solution: By the distributive property,

$-3(5a + 2) = -3(5a) + (-3)(2)$ Apply the distributive property.

$= (-3 \cdot 5)a + (-6)$ Apply the associative property. Also, write $(-3)(2)$ as -6.

$= -15a - 6$ Multiply.

■ **Work Practice Problem 14**

PRACTICE PROBLEM 14

Multiply: $4(7a - 5)$

To simplify expressions containing parentheses, we first use the distributive property and multiply.

EXAMPLE 15 Simplify: $2(3 + 7x) - 15$

Solution: First we use the distributive property to remove parentheses.

$2(3 + 7x) - 15 = 2(3) + 2(7x) - 15$ Apply the distributive property.

$= 6 + 14x - 15$ Multiply.

$= 14x + (-9)$ or $14x - 9$ Combine like terms.

■ **Work Practice Problem 15**

PRACTICE PROBLEM 15

Simplify: $5(2y - 3) - 8$

> **Helpful Hint**
> 2 is *not* distributed to the -15 since it is not within the parentheses.

EXAMPLE 16 Simplify: $-2(x - 5) + 4(2x + 2)$

Solution: First we use the distributive property to remove parentheses.

$-2(x - 5) + 4(2x + 2) = -2(x) - (-2)(5) + 4(2x) + 4(2)$ Apply the distributive property.

$= -2x + 10 + 8x + 8$ Multiply.

$= 6x + 18$ Combine like terms.

■ **Work Practice Problem 16**

PRACTICE PROBLEM 16

Simplify:
$-7(x - 1) + 5(2x + 3)$

EXAMPLE 17 Finding the Area of a Deck

Find the area of the rectangular deck.

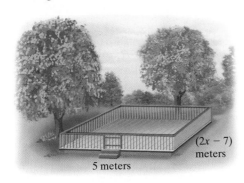

$(2x - 7)$ meters

5 meters

Solution: Recall how to find the area of a rectangle.

$A = l \cdot w$

$= 5(2x - 7)$ Let length = 5 and width = $(2x - 7)$.

$= 10x - 35$ Multiply.

The area is $(10x - 35)$ square meters.

■ **Work Practice Problem 17**

PRACTICE PROBLEM 17

Find the area of the rectangular garden.

$(12y + 9)$ yards

3 yards

Answers
14. $28a - 20$, **15.** $10y - 23$,
16. $3x + 22$, **17.** $(36y + 27)$ sq yd

Mental Math

Identify each pair of terms as like terms or unlike terms.

1. $5x$ and $5y$

2. $-3a$ and $-3b$

3. x and $-2x$

4. $7y$ and y

5. $-5n$ and $6n^2$

6. $4m^2$ and $2m$

7. $8b$ and $-6b$

8. $12a$ and $-11a$

8.1 EXERCISE SET

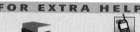

Objective A *Evaluate each expression when $x = -2$, $y = 5$, and $z = -3$. See Examples 1 through 4.*

1. $3 + 2z$

2. $7 + 3z$

3. $-y - z$

4. $-y - x$

5. $z - x + y$

6. $x + y - z$

7. $3x - z$

8. $y + 5z$

9. $8 - (5y - 7)$

10. $5 + (2x - 1)$

11. $y^3 - 4x$

12. $y^2 - 2z$

13. $\dfrac{6xy}{4}$

14. $\dfrac{8yz}{15}$

15. $\dfrac{2y - 2}{x}$

16. $\dfrac{6 + 3x}{z}$

17. $\dfrac{x + 2y}{2z}$

18. $\dfrac{2z - y}{3x}$

19. $\dfrac{5x}{y} - 10$

20. $7 - \dfrac{3y}{z}$

21. $\dfrac{xz}{y} + \dfrac{3}{10}$

22. $\dfrac{x}{yz} + \dfrac{31}{30}$

23. $|x| - |y| - 7.6$

24. $|z| - |y| - 12.7$

Objective B *Simplify each expression by combining like terms. See Examples 5 through 10.*

25. $3x + 5x$

26. $8y + 3y$

27. $5n - 9n$

28. $7z - 10z$

29. $4c + c - 7c$

30. $5b - 8b - b$

31. $5x - 7x + x - 3x$

32. $8y + y - 2y - y$

33. $4a + 3a + 6a - 8$

34. $5b - 4b + b - 15$

35. $1.7x + 3.4 - 2.6x + 7.8$

36. $-8.6y + 1.3 - 2.9y - 14.7$

37. $3x + 7 - x - 14$

38. $9x - 6 + x - 10$

39. $4x + 5y + 2 - y - 9x - 7$

40. $a + 4b + 3 - 7a - 5b - 10$

41. $\dfrac{5}{6} - \dfrac{7}{12}x - \dfrac{1}{3} - \dfrac{3}{10}x$

42. $-\dfrac{2}{5} + \dfrac{4}{9}y - \dfrac{4}{15} + \dfrac{1}{6}y$

43. $-5m - 2.3m + 11 + 2.5m - 15.1$ **44.** $-13n - 4.8n + 13 + 6.9n - 13.6$

Objective **C** *Multiply. See Examples 11 through 14.*

45. $6(5x)$

46. $4(4x)$

47. $-2(11y)$

48. $-3(21z)$

49. $-0.6(7a)$

50. $-0.4(9a)$

51. $\dfrac{2}{3}(-6a)$

52. $\dfrac{3}{4}(-8a)$

53. $2(y + 2)$

54. $3(x + 1)$

55. $5(3a - 8)$

56. $4(5y - 6)$

57. $-4(3x + 7)$

58. $-8(8y + 10)$

59. $1.2(5x - 0.1)$

60. $3.1(7x - 0.3)$

61. $\dfrac{1}{2}(-8x - 3)$

62. $\dfrac{1}{5}(-20x - 7)$

Simplify each expression. Use the distributive property to remove parentheses first. See Examples 15 and 16.

63. $2(x + 4) - 17$

64. $5(6 + y) - 2$

65. $4(6n - 5) + 3n$

66. $3(5 - 2b) - 4b$

67. $3 + 6(w + 2) + w$

68. $8z + 5(6 + z) + 20$

69. $-2(3x + 1) - 5(x - 2)$

70. $-3(5x - 2) - 2(3x + 1)$

Objectives **A** **B** **C** **Mixed Practice** *Solve. See Example 17.*

71. Find the area of a rectangular movie screen that is 50 feet long and 40 feet high. Use $A = lw$.

72. Find the area of a 60-meter by 25-meter rectangular swimming pool. Use $A = lw$.

73. A decorator wishes to put a wallpaper border around a rectangular room that measures 14 feet by 18 feet. Find the room's perimeter. Use $P = 2l + 2w$.

74. How much fencing will a rancher need for a rectangular cattle lot that measures 80 feet by 120 feet? Use $P = 2l + 2w$.

75. How much interest will $3000 in a passbook savings account earn in 2 years at Money Bank, which pays 6% simple interest? Use $I = prt$.

76. How much interest will a $12,000 certificate of deposit earn in 1 year at a rate of 8% simple interest? Use $I = prt$.

△ **77.** Find the area of the figure. Use $A = s^2$.

Square | 4y centimeters

△ **78.** Find the area of the figure. Use $A = lw$.

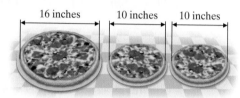
12 feet | $(x + 3)$ feet | Rectangle

79. Find the area of a circular braided rug with a radius of 5 feet. Use $A = \pi r^2$ and $\pi \approx 3.14$.

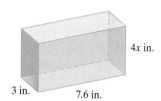
5 feet

80. Mario's Pizza sells one 16″ cheese pizza or two 10″ cheese pizzas for $9.99. Which deal gives you more pizza? Use $A = \pi r^2$ with $\pi \approx 3.14$.

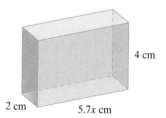
16 inches | 10 inches | 10 inches

81. Find the perimeter of a triangular garden that measures 5 feet by x feet by $(2x + 1)$ feet. Use $P = a + b + c$.

82. Find the perimeter of a triangular picture frame that measures x inches by x inches by $(x - 14)$ inches. Use $P = a + b + c$.

83. Convert Paris, France's, low temperature of $-5°C$ to Fahrenheit. Use $F = \dfrac{9}{5}C + 32$.

84. Convert Nome, Alaska's, 18°F high temperature to Celsius. Use $C = \dfrac{5}{9}(F - 32)$.

Exercises 85 through 88 have to do with volume. Volume is a measure of the space of a solid. It is measured in cubic units and we will study volume further in Chapter 9.

85. Find the volume of a box that measures 12 inches by 6 inches by 4 inches. Use $V = lwh$.

86. How many cubic meters does a space shuttle cargo compartment have if its dimensions are 8 meters long by 4 meters wide by 3 meters high? Use $V = lwh$.

87. Find the volume. Use $V = lwh$.

4x in.
3 in.   7.6 in.

88. Find the volume. Use $V = lwh$.

4 cm
2 cm   5.7x cm

Review

Perform each indicated operation. See Sections 2.3 and 2.4.

89. $-13 + 10$ **90.** $-7 - (-4)$ **91.** $-4 - (-12)$ **92.** $-15 + 23$ **93.** $-4 + 4$ **94.** $8 + (-8)$

Concept Extensions

If the expression on the left side of the equal sign is equivalent to the right, write "correct." If not, write "incorrect" and then write an expression that is equivalent to the left side. See the Concept Check in this section.

95. $5(3x - 2) = 15x - 2$

96. $2(xy) = 2x \cdot 2y$

97. $7x - (x + 2) = 7x - x - 2$

98. $4(y - 3) + 11 = 4y - 6 + 11$

Review commutative, associative, and distributive properties. Then identify which property allows us to write the equivalent expression on the right side of the equal sign.

99. $6(2x - 3) + 5 = 12x - 18 + 5$

100. $9 + 7x + (-2) = 7x + 9 + (-2)$

101. $-7 + (4 + y) = (-7 + 4) + y$

102. $(x + y) + 11 = 11 + (x + y)$

103. If x is a whole number, which expression is the largest: $2x, 5x,$ or $\frac{1}{3}x$? Explain your answer.

104. If x is a whole number, which expression is the smallest: $2x, 5x,$ or $\frac{1}{3}x$? Explain your answer.

Find the area of each figure.

△ **105.**

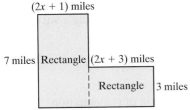

$(2x + 1)$ miles

7 miles | Rectangle | $(2x + 3)$ miles

Rectangle | 3 miles

△ **106.**

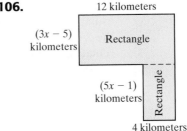

12 kilometers

$(3x - 5)$ kilometers | Rectangle

$(5x - 1)$ kilometers | Rectangle

4 kilometers

To appraise the value of a large tree in landscaping, the trunk area is used. The trunk area A is calculated with the formula $A = 0.7854d^2$, where d is the diameter of the tree.

107. The national champion Western red cedar tree is located in Olympic National Park, Washington. Its trunk has a diameter of 242 inches. Use the formula to find the trunk area of this tree. Round your result to the nearest tenth. (*Source: American Forests*)

108. The national champion sugar pine tree is located in Dorrington, California. Its trunk has a diameter of 141 inches. Use the formula to find the trunk area of this tree. Round your result to the nearest tenth. (*Source: American Forests*)

Simplify.

109. $9684q - 686 - 4860q + 12{,}960$

110. $76(268x + 592) - 2960$

Objectives

A Determine Whether a Given Number Is a Solution of an Equation.

B Use the Addition Property of Equality to Solve Equations.

8.2 SOLVING EQUATIONS: THE ADDITION PROPERTY

Frequently in this book we have written statements like $7 + 4 = 11$ or Area = length · width. Each of these statements is called an **equation.** An equation is of the form

expression = expression

An equation can be labeled as

$$\underbrace{x + 7}_{\text{left side}} = \underset{\text{right side}}{10}$$

equal sign

Objective **A** Determining Whether a Number Is a Solution

When an equation contains a variable, finding which values of the variable make an equation a true statement is called **solving** an equation for the variable. A **solution** of an equation is a value for the variable that makes an equation a true statement. For example, 2 is a solution of the equation $x + 5 = 7$ since replacing x with 2 results in the *true* statement $2 + 5 = 7$. Similarly, 3 is not a solution of $x + 5 = 7$ since replacing x with 3 results in the *false* statement $3 + 5 = 7$.

PRACTICE PROBLEM 1

Determine whether 4 is a solution of the equation $3(y - 6) = 6$.

EXAMPLE 1 Determine whether 6 is a solution of the equation $4(x - 3) = 12$.

Solution: We replace x with 6 in the equation.

$$4(x - 3) = 12$$
$$\downarrow$$
$$4(6 - 3) \overset{?}{=} 12 \quad \text{Replace } x \text{ with 6.}$$
$$4(3) \overset{?}{=} 12$$
$$12 \overset{?}{=} 12 \quad \text{True}$$

Since $12 = 12$ is a true statement, 6 *is* a solution of the equation.

Work Practice Problem 1

PRACTICE PROBLEM 2

Determine whether -2 is a solution of the equation $-4x - 3 = 5$.

EXAMPLE 2 Determine whether -1 is a solution of the equation $3y + 1 = 3$.

Solution:

$$3y + 1 = 3$$
$$3(-1) + 1 \overset{?}{=} 3$$
$$-3 + 1 \overset{?}{=} 3$$
$$-2 \overset{?}{=} 3 \quad \text{False}$$

Since $-2 = 3$ is false, -1 is *not* a solution of the equation.

Work Practice Problem 2

Answers

1. no, **2.** yes

Objective B Using the Addition Property to Solve Equations

To solve an equation, we use properties of equality to write simpler equations, all equivalent to the original equation, until the final equation has the form

$x =$ **number** or **number** $= x$

Equivalent equations have the same solution, so the word "number" above represents the solution of the original equation. The first property of equality to help us write simpler, equivalent, equations is the **addition property of equality.**

Addition Property of Equality

Let a, b, and c represent numbers. Then

$a = b$	Also, $a = b$
and $a + c = b + c$	and $a - c = b - c$
are equivalent equations.	are equivalent equations.

In other words, the same number may be added to or subtracted from both sides of an equation without changing the solution of the equation.

A good way to visualize a true equation is to picture a balanced scale. Since it is balanced, each side of the scale weighs the same amount. Similarly, in a true equation the expressions on each side have the same value. Picturing our balanced scale, if we add the same weight to each side, the scale remains balanced.

EXAMPLE 3 Solve: $x - 2 = 1$ for x.

Solution: To solve the equation for x, we need to rewrite the equation in the form $x =$ number. In other words, our goal is to get x alone on one side of the equation. To do so, we add 2 to both sides of the equation.

$x - 2 = 1$
$x - 2 + 2 = 1 + 2$ Add 2 to both sides of the equation.
$x + 0 = 3$ Replace $-2 + 2$ with 0.
$x = 3$ Simplify by replacing $x + 0$ with x.

Check: To check, we replace x with 3 in the *original* equation.

$x - 2 = 1$ Original equation
$3 - 2 \stackrel{?}{=} 1$ Replace x with 3.
$1 \stackrel{?}{=} 1$ True

Since $1 = 1$ is a true statement, 3 is the solution of the equation.

■ **Work Practice Problem 3**

Helpful Hint

Note that it is always a good idea to check the solution in the *original* equation to see that it makes the equation a true statement.

PRACTICE PROBLEM 3

Solve the equation for y: $y - 5 = -3$

Answer

3. 2

Let's visualize how we used the addition property of equality to solve the equation in Example 3. Picture the original equation, $x - 2 = 1$, as a balanced scale. The left side of the equation has the same value as the right side.

If the same weight is added to each side of a scale, the scale remains balanced. Likewise, if the same number is added to each side of an equation, the left side continues to have the same value as the right side.

PRACTICE PROBLEM 4

Solve: $-1 = z + 9$

EXAMPLE 4 Solve: $-8 = x + 1$

Solution: To get x alone on one side of the equation, we subtract 1 from both sides of the equation.

$$-8 = x + 1$$
$$-8 - 1 = x + 1 - 1 \quad \text{Subtract 1 from both sides.}$$
$$-9 = x + 0 \quad \text{Replace } 1 - 1 \text{ with } 0.$$
$$-9 = x \quad \text{Simplify.}$$

Check:

$$-8 = x + 1$$
$$-8 \overset{?}{=} -9 + 1 \quad \text{Replace } x \text{ with } -9.$$
$$-8 \overset{?}{=} -8 \quad \text{True}$$

The solution is -9.

Work Practice Problem 4

Helpful Hint

Remember that we can get the variable alone on either side of the equation. For example, the equations $x = 2$ and $2 = x$ both have the solution of 2.

PRACTICE PROBLEM 5

Solve: $x - 2.6 = -1.8 - 5.9$

EXAMPLE 5 Solve: $y - 1.2 = -3.2 - 6.6$

Solution: First we simplify the right side of the equation.

$$y - 1.2 = -3.2 - 6.6$$
$$y - 1.2 = -9.8$$

Next, we get y alone on the left side by adding 1.2 to both sides of the equation.

$$y - 1.2 + 1.2 = -9.8 + 1.2 \quad \text{Add 1.2 to both sides.}$$
$$y = -8.6 \quad \text{Simplify.}$$

Check to see that -8.6 is the solution.

Work Practice Problem 5

Answers

4. -10,   5. -5.1

✔**Concept Check** What number should be added to or subtracted from both sides of the equation in order to solve the equation $-3.75 = y + 2.1$?

EXAMPLE 6 Solve: $5x + 2 - 4x = 7 - 9$

Solution: First we simplify each side of the equation separately.

$$5x + 2 - 4x = 7 - 9$$
$$\underbrace{5x - 4x}_{} + 2 = \underbrace{7 - 9}_{}$$
$$1x + 2 = -2$$

To get x alone on the left side, we subtract 2 from both sides.

$$1x + 2 - 2 = -2 - 2$$
$$1x = -4 \text{ or } x = -4$$

Check to verify that -4 is the solution.

📖 **Work Practice Problem 6**

EXAMPLE 7 Solve: $\dfrac{7}{8} = y - \dfrac{1}{2}$

Solution: We use the addition property of equality to add $\dfrac{1}{2}$ to both sides.

$$\frac{7}{8} = y - \frac{1}{2}$$
$$\frac{7}{8} + \frac{1}{2} = y - \frac{1}{2} + \frac{1}{2} \qquad \text{Add } \frac{1}{2} \text{ to both sides.}$$
$$\frac{7}{8} + \frac{4}{8} = y \qquad\qquad\quad \text{Simplify.}$$
$$\frac{11}{8} = y \qquad\qquad\qquad \text{Simplify.}$$

Check to see that $\dfrac{11}{8}$ is the solution. (Although $\dfrac{11}{8} = 1\dfrac{3}{8}$, we will leave solutions as improper fractions.)

📖 **Work Practice Problem 7**

Recall that the addition property of equality allows us to add or subtract the same number to or from both sides of an equation. Let's see how adding the same number to both sides of an equation also allows us to subtract the same number from both sides. To do so, let's add $(-c)$ to both sides of $a = b$. Then we have

$$a + (-c) = b + (-c)$$

which is the same as $a - c = b - c$, and there we have it.

PRACTICE PROBLEM 6
Solve:
$-6y + 1 + 7y = 6 - 11$

PRACTICE PROBLEM 7
Solve: $\dfrac{2}{3} = x - \dfrac{4}{9}$

Answers

6. -6, **7.** $\dfrac{10}{9}$

✔ **Concept Check Answer**
subtract 2.1 from both sides

Mental Math

Solve each equation.

1. $x - 2 = 0$ **2.** $x - 5 = 0$ **3.** $x + 1 = 0$ **4.** $x + 6 = 0$

8.2 EXERCISE SET

FOR EXTRA HELP

Student Solutions Manual   PH Math/Tutor Center   CD/Video for Review   Math XL MathXL®   MyMathLab MyMathLab

Objective A *Decide whether the given number is a solution of the given equation. See Examples 1 and 2.*

1. Is 10 a solution of $x - 8 = 2$?

2. Is 9 a solution of $y - 2 = 7$?

3. Is -5 a solution of $x + 12 = 17$?

4. Is -7 a solution of $a + 23 = -16$?

5. Is -8 a solution of $-9f = 64 - f$?

6. Is -6 a solution of $-3k = 12 - k$?

7. Is 3 a solution of $5(c - 5) = -10$?

8. Is 1 a solution of $2(b - 3) = 10$?

Objective B *Solve. Check each solution. See Examples 3 through 7.*

9. $a + 5 = 23$ **10.** $f + 4 = -6$ **11.** $d - 9 = -17$

12. $s - 7 = 15$ **13.** $7 = y - 2$ **14.** $1 = y + 7$

15. $-12 = x + 4$ **16.** $-10 = z - 15$ **17.** $x + \dfrac{1}{2} = \dfrac{7}{2}$

18. $x + \dfrac{1}{3} = \dfrac{4}{3}$ **19.** $y - \dfrac{3}{4} = -\dfrac{5}{8}$ **20.** $y - \dfrac{5}{6} = -\dfrac{11}{12}$

21. $x - 3 = -1 + 4$ **22.** $y - 8 = -5 - 1$ **23.** $-7 + 10 = m - 5$

24. $1 - 8 = n + 2$ **25.** $x - 0.6 = 4.7$ **26.** $y - 1.2 = 7.5$

576

27. $-2 - 3 = -4 + x$

28. $7 - (-10) = x - 5$

29. $y + 2.3 = -9.2 - 8.6$

30. $x + 4.7 = -7.5 - 3.4$

31. $-8x + 4 + 9x = -1 + 7$

32. $3x - 2x + 5 = 5 - 2$

33. $5 + (-12) = 5x - 7 - 4x$

34. $11 + (-15) = 6x - 4 - 5x$

35. $7x + 14 - 6x = -4 + (-10)$

36. $-10x + 11x + 5 = -9 + (-5)$

Review

Perform each indicated operation. See Section 3.3.

37. $\dfrac{-7}{-7}$

38. $\dfrac{4.2}{4.2}$

39. $\dfrac{1}{3} \cdot 3$

40. $\dfrac{1}{5} \cdot 5$

41. $-\dfrac{2}{3} \cdot -\dfrac{3}{2}$

42. $-\dfrac{7}{2} \cdot -\dfrac{2}{7}$

Concept Extensions

What number should be added to or subtracted from both sides of each equation in order to solve the equation?

43. $\dfrac{2}{3} + x = \dfrac{1}{12}$

44. $12.5 = -3.75 + x$

45. $-\dfrac{1}{7} = -\dfrac{4}{5} + x$

46. $9.1 = 5.9 + x$

47. In your own words, explain what is meant by the phrase "a number is a solution of an equation."

48. In your own words, explain how to check a possible solution of an equation.

Solve.

49. $x - 76,862 = 86,102$

50. $-968 + 432 = 86y - 508 - 85y$

A football team's total offense T is found by adding the total passing yardage P to the total rushing yardage R: T = P + R.

51. During the 2003 football season, the Atlanta Falcons' total offense was 4357 yards. The Falcons' passing yardage for the season was 2408 yards. How many yards did the Falcons gain by rushing during the season? (*Source:* National Football League)

52. During the 2003 football season, the Miami Dolphins' total offense was 4609 yards. The Dolphins' rushing yardage for the season was 1817 yards. How many yards did the Dolphins gain by passing during the season? (*Source:* National Football League)

In accounting, a company's annual net income I can be computed using the relation I = R − E, where R is the company's total revenues for the year and E is the company's total expenses for the year.

53. At the end of fiscal year 2004, Best Buy had a net income of $705,000,000. During the year, Best Buy had total revenues of $24,547,000,000. What was Best Buy's total expenses for the year? (*Source:* Best Buy Co., Inc.)

54. At the end of fiscal year 2003, Kodak had a net income of $265,000,000. During the year, Kodak had total expenses of $13,317,000,000. What was Kodak's total revenues for the year? (*Source:* Eastman Kodak Company)

STUDY SKILLS BUILDER

Are You Preparing for Your Final Exam?

To prepare for your final exam, try the following study techniques:

- Review the material that you will be responsible for on your exam. This includes material from your textbook, your notebook, and any handouts from your instructor.

- Review any formulas that you may need to memorize.

- Check to see if your instructor or mathematics department will be conducting a final exam review.

- Check with your instructor to see whether final exams from previous semesters/quarters are available to students for review.

- Use your previously taken exams as a practice final exam. To do so, rewrite the test questions in mixed order on blank sheets of paper. This will help you prepare for exam conditions.

- If you are unsure of a few concepts, see your instructor or visit a learning lab for assistance. Also, view the video segment of any troublesome sections.

- If you need further exercises to work, try the Cumulative Reviews at the end of the chapters.

Once again, good luck! I hope you have enjoyed this textbook and your mathematics course.

8.3 SOLVING EQUATIONS: THE MULTIPLICATION PROPERTY

Objective

A Use the Multiplication Property to Solve Equations.

Objective A Using the Multiplication Property to Solve Equations

Although the addition property of equality is a powerful tool for helping us solve equations, it cannot help us solve all types of equations. For example, it cannot help us solve an equation such as $2x = 6$. To solve this equation, we use a second property of equality called the **multiplication property of equality.**

Multiplication Property of Equality

Let a, b, and c represent numbers and let $c \neq 0$. Then

$a = b$	Also, $a = b$
and $a \cdot c = b \cdot c$	and $\dfrac{a}{c} = \dfrac{b}{c}$
are equivalent equations.	are equivalent equations.

In other words, both sides of an equation may be multiplied or divided by the same nonzero number without changing the solution of the equation.

Picturing again our balanced scale, if we multiply or divide the weight on each side by the same nonzero number, the scale (or equation) remains balanced.

To solve $2x = 6$ for x, we use the multiplication property of equality to divide both sides of the equation by 2, and simplify as follows:

$$2x = 6$$
$$\frac{2x}{2} = \frac{6}{2} \quad \text{Divide both sides by 2.}$$
$$\frac{2}{2} \cdot x = 3$$
$$1 \cdot x = 3 \quad \text{Simplify.}$$
$$x = 3$$

EXAMPLE 1 Solve: $-5x = 15$

Solution: To get x by itself, we divide both sides by -5.

$$-5x = 15 \quad \text{Original equation}$$
$$\frac{-5x}{-5} = \frac{15}{-5}$$
$$\frac{-5}{-5} \cdot x = \frac{15}{-5} \quad \text{Divide both sides by } -5$$
$$1 \cdot x = -3 \quad \text{Simplify.}$$
$$x = -3$$

PRACTICE PROBLEM 1

Solve: $-3y = 18$

Answer
1. -6

Continued on next page

Check: To check, we replace x with -3 in the original equation.

$$-5x = 15 \quad \text{Original equation}$$
$$-5(-3) \stackrel{?}{=} 15 \quad \text{Let } x = -3.$$
$$15 \stackrel{?}{=} 15 \quad \text{True}$$

The solution is -3.

🔲 **Work Practice Problem 1**

PRACTICE PROBLEM 2

Solve: $-16 = 8x$

EXAMPLE 2 Solve: $-8 = 2y$

Solution: To get y alone, we divide both sides of the equation by 2.

$$-8 = 2y$$
$$\frac{-8}{2} = \frac{2y}{2} \quad \text{Divide both sides by 2.}$$
$$-4 = 1 \cdot y \quad \text{or} \quad y = -4$$

Check to see that -4 is the solution.

🔲 **Work Practice Problem 2**

PRACTICE PROBLEM 3

Solve: $-0.3y = -27$

EXAMPLE 3 Solve: $-1.2x = -36$

Solution: We divide both sides of the equation by the coefficient of x, which is -1.2.

$$-1.2x = -36$$
$$\frac{-1.2x}{-1.2} = \frac{-36}{-1.2}$$
$$1 \cdot x = 30$$
$$x = 30$$

Check to see that 30 is the solution.

🔲 **Work Practice Problem 3**

PRACTICE PROBLEM 4

Solve: $\frac{5}{7}b = 25$

EXAMPLE 4 Solve: $\frac{3}{5}a = 9$

Solution: Recall that the product of a number and its reciprocal is 1. To get a alone then, we multiply both sides by $\frac{5}{3}$, the reciprocal of $\frac{3}{5}$.

$$\frac{3}{5}a = 9$$
$$\frac{5}{3} \cdot \frac{3}{5}a = \frac{5}{3} \cdot 9 \quad \text{Multiply both sides by } \frac{5}{3}.$$
$$1 \cdot a = \frac{5 \cdot \overset{3}{\cancel{9}}}{\cancel{3} \cdot 1} \quad \text{Multiply.}$$
$$a = 15 \quad \text{Simplify.}$$

Answers

2. -2, **3.** 90, **4.** 35

Copyright 2007 Pearson Education Inc

Check: To check, we replace a with 15 in the original equation.

$$\frac{3}{5}a = 9 \quad \text{Original equation}$$

$$\frac{3}{5} \cdot 15 \overset{?}{=} 9 \quad \text{Replace } a \text{ with 15.}$$

$$\frac{3 \cdot \overset{3}{\cancel{15}}}{\underset{1}{\cancel{5}} \cdot 1} \overset{?}{=} 9 \quad \text{Multiply.}$$

$$9 \overset{?}{=} 9 \quad \text{True}$$

Since $9 = 9$ is true, 15 is the solution of $\frac{3}{5}a = 9$.

▣ **Work Practice Problem 4**

EXAMPLE 5 Solve: $-\frac{1}{4}x = \frac{1}{8}$

Solution: We multiply both sides of the equation by $-\frac{4}{1}$, the reciprocal of $-\frac{1}{4}$.

$$-\frac{1}{4}x = \frac{1}{8}$$

$$-\frac{4}{1} \cdot -\frac{1}{4}x = -\frac{4}{1} \cdot \frac{1}{8} \quad \text{Multiply both sides by } -\frac{4}{1}.$$

$$1 \cdot x = -\frac{\overset{1}{\cancel{4}} \cdot 1}{1 \cdot \underset{2}{\cancel{8}}} \quad \text{Multiply.}$$

$$x = -\frac{1}{2} \quad \text{Simplify.}$$

Check to see that $-\frac{1}{2}$ is the solution.

▣ **Work Practice Problem 5**

✔**Concept Check** Which operation is appropriate for solving each of the following equations, addition or division?

a. $6 = -4x$
b. $6 = x - 4$

We often need to simplify one or both sides of an equation before applying the properties of equality to get the variable alone.

EXAMPLE 6 Solve: $3y - 7y = 12$

Solution: First we combine like terms.

$$3y - 7y = 12$$

$$-4y = 12 \quad \text{Combine like terms.}$$

$$\frac{-4y}{-4} = \frac{12}{-4} \quad \text{Divide both sides by } -4.$$

$$y = -3 \quad \text{Simplify.}$$

Continued on next page

PRACTICE PROBLEM 5

Solve: $-\frac{7}{10}x = \frac{2}{5}$

PRACTICE PROBLEM 6

Solve: $2m - 4m = 10$

Answers

5. $-\frac{4}{7}$, **6.** -5

✔ **Concept Check Answers**
a. division, **b.** addition

Check: We replace y with -3.

$$3y - 7y = 12$$

$$3(-3) - 7(-3) \stackrel{?}{=} 12$$

$$-9 + 21 \stackrel{?}{=} 12$$

$$12 \stackrel{?}{=} 12 \quad \text{True}$$

The solution is -3.

◼ **Work Practice Problem 6**

PRACTICE PROBLEM 7

Solve: $-3a + 2a = -8 + 6$

EXAMPLE 7 Solve: $-2z + z = 11 - 5$

Solution: We simplify both sides of the equation first.

$$-2z + z = 11 - 5$$

$$-1z = 6 \qquad \text{Combine like terms.}$$

$$\frac{-1z}{-1} = \frac{6}{-1} \qquad \text{Divide both sides by } -1.$$

$$z = -6 \qquad \text{Simplify.}$$

Check to see that -6 is the solution.

◼ **Work Practice Problem 7**

Answer

7. 2

8.3 EXERCISE SET

Objective *Solve. See Examples 1 through 5.*

1. $5x = 20$ **2.** $6y = 48$ **3.** $-3z = 12$ **4.** $-2x = 26$ **5.** $0.4y = -12$ **6.** $0.8x = -8$

7. $2z = -34$ **8.** $7y = -21$ **9.** $-0.3x = -15$ **10.** $-0.4z = -16$ **11.** $10 = \dfrac{2}{5}x$ **12.** $27 = \dfrac{3}{7}x$

13. $\dfrac{1}{6}y = -5$ **14.** $\dfrac{1}{8}y = -3$ **15.** $\dfrac{5}{6}x = \dfrac{5}{18}$ **16.** $\dfrac{4}{7}y = \dfrac{8}{21}$ **17.** $-\dfrac{2}{9}z = \dfrac{4}{27}$ **18.** $-\dfrac{3}{4}v = \dfrac{9}{14}$

Solve. First combine any like terms on each side of the equation. See Examples 6 and 7.

19. $2w - 12w = 40$ **20.** $-8y + y = 35$ **21.** $16 = 10t - 8t$ **22.** $100 = 15y - 5y$

23. $2z = 1.2 + 1.4$ **24.** $3x = 1.1 + 0.7$ **25.** $4 - 10 = -3z$ **26.** $12 - 20 = -4x$

Mixed Practice *Solve. See Examples 1 through 7.*

27. $-7x = 0$ **28.** $-20y = 0$ **29.** $0.4 = -8z$ **30.** $0.5 = -20x$

31. $\dfrac{8}{5}t = -\dfrac{3}{8}$ **32.** $\dfrac{7}{4}r = -\dfrac{2}{7}$ **33.** $-\dfrac{3}{5}x = -\dfrac{6}{15}$ **34.** $-\dfrac{6}{7}y = -\dfrac{1}{14}$

35. $-3.6 = -0.9u + 0.3u$ **36.** $-5.4 = -1.4y + 1.3y$ **37.** $5 - 5 = 2x + 7x$

38. $12 + (-12) = 7x + 8x$ **39.** $-42 + 20 = -2x + 13x$ **40.** $-4y + 9y = -20 + 15$

41. $-3x - 3x = 50 - 2$

42. $5y - 9y = -14 + (-14)$

43. $23x - 25x = 7 - 9$

44. $6x - 8x = 12 - 22$

45. $\frac{1}{4}x - \frac{5}{8}x = 20 - 47$

46. $\frac{1}{2}x - \frac{4}{5}x = 10 - 19$

Review

Evaluate each expression when $x = 5$. See Section 8.1.

47. $3x + 10$

48. $40x$

49. $\frac{x - 3}{2}$

50. $7x - 20$

51. $\frac{3x + 5}{x - 7}$

52. $\frac{2x - 1}{x - 8}$

Concept Extensions

What operation is appropriate for solving each equation: addition or division? See the Concept Check in this section.

53. $12 = x - 5$

54. $12 = -5x$

55. $-7x = 21$

56. $-7 + x = 21$

57. Why does the multiplication property of equality not allow us to divide both sides of an equation by zero?

58. Is the equation $-x = 6$ solved for the variable? Explain why or why not.

59. Solve: $-0.025x = 91.2$

60. Solve: $3.6y = -1.259 - 3.277$

The equation $d = r \cdot t$ describes the relationship between distance d in miles, rate r in miles per hour, and time t in hours. If necessary, round answers to the nearest tenth.

61. The distance between New Orleans, Louisiana, and Memphis, Tennessee by road is 390 miles. How long will it take to drive from New Orleans to Memphis if the driver maintains a speed of 60 miles per hour? (*Source:* 2005 *World Almanac*)

62. The distance between Boston, Massachusetts, and Milwaukee, Wisconsin, by road is 1050 miles. How long will it take to drive from Boston to Milwaukee if the driver maintains a speed of 55 miles per hour? (*Source:* 2005 *World Almanac*)

63. The distance between Cleveland, Ohio, and Indianapolis, Indiana, by road is 294 miles. At what speed should a driver drive if he or she would like to make the trip in 5 hours? (*Source:* 2005 *World Almanac*)

64. The distance between St. Louis, Missouri, and Minneapolis, Minnesota, by road is 552 miles. If it took 9 hours to drive from St. Louis to Minneapolis, what was the driver's average speed? (*Source:* 2005 *World Almanac*)

Expressions and Equations

Evaluate each expression when x = −1 and y = 3.

1. $y - x$

2. $\dfrac{8y}{4x}$

3. $5x + 2y$

4. $\dfrac{y^2 + x}{2x}$

Simplify each expression by combining like terms.

5. $7x + x$

6. $6y - 10y$

7. $2a + 5a - 9a - 2$

8. $3x - y + 4 - 5x + 4y - 11$

Multiply. Simplify if possible.

9. $-5(4x)$

10. $5(y + 2)$

11. $3(x + 5) - 3$

12. $-4(x - 1) + 3(5x + 4)$

Find the area.

 13.

| Rectangle | 3 meters |

(4x − 2) meters

△ **14.**

Square

5y inches

Solve and check.

15. $x + 7 = 20$

16. $-11 = x - 2$

17. $n - \dfrac{2}{5} = \dfrac{3}{10}$

18. $-7y = 0$

19. $12 = 11x - 14x$

20. $\dfrac{3}{5}x = 15$

21. $x - 1.2 = -4.5 + 2.3$

22. $8y + 7y = -45$

23. $6 - (-5) = x + 5$

24. $-0.2m = -1.6$

25. $-\dfrac{2}{3}n = \dfrac{6}{11}$

26. $11x = 55$

Answers

1. _____
2. _____
3. _____
4. _____
5. _____
6. _____
7. _____
8. _____
9. _____
10. _____
11. _____
12. _____
13. _____
14. _____
15. _____
16. _____
17. _____
18. _____
19. _____
20. _____
21. _____
22. _____
23. _____
24. _____
25. _____
26. _____

8.4 SOLVING EQUATIONS USING ADDITION AND MULTIPLICATION PROPERTIES

Objective **A** Solving Equations Using Addition and Multiplication Properties

We will now solve equations using more than one property of equality. To solve an equation such as $2x - 6 = 18$, we will first get the variable term $2x$ alone on one side of the equation.

PRACTICE PROBLEM 1

Solve: $5y - 8 = 17$

EXAMPLE 1 Solve: $2x - 6 = 18$

Solution: We start by adding 6 to both sides to get the variable term $2x$ alone.

$$2x - 6 = 18$$
$$2x - 6 + 6 = 18 + 6 \quad \text{Add 6 to both sides.}$$
$$2x = 24 \quad \text{Simplify.}$$

To finish solving, we divide both sides by 2.

$$\frac{2x}{2} = \frac{24}{2} \quad \text{Divide both sides by 2.}$$
$$1 \cdot x = 12 \quad \text{Simplify.}$$
$$x = 12$$

Check:

$$2x - 6 = 18$$
$$2(12) - 6 \stackrel{?}{=} 18 \quad \text{Replace } x \text{ with 12 and simplify.}$$
$$24 - 6 \stackrel{?}{=} 18$$
$$18 \stackrel{?}{=} 18 \quad \text{True}$$

The solution is 12.

■ **Work Practice Problem 1**

PRACTICE PROBLEM 2

Solve: $10 - y = 45$

EXAMPLE 2 Solve: $20 - x = 21$

Solution: First we get the variable term alone on one side of the equation.

$$20 - x = 21$$
$$20 - x - 20 = 21 - 20 \quad \text{Subtract 20 from both sides.}$$
$$-1x = 1 \quad \text{Simplify. Recall that } -x \text{ means } -1x.$$
$$\frac{-1x}{-1} = \frac{1}{-1} \quad \text{Divide both sides by } -1.$$
$$1 \cdot x = -1 \quad \text{Simplify.}$$
$$x = -1$$

Check:

$$20 - x = 21$$
$$20 - (-1) \stackrel{?}{=} 21$$
$$21 \stackrel{?}{=} 21 \quad \text{True}$$

The solution is -1.

■ **Work Practice Problem 2**

Answers

1. 5, 2. -35

586

EXAMPLE 3 Solve: $1 = \frac{2}{3}x + 7$

Solution: Subtract 7 from both sides to get the variable term alone.

$$1 - 7 = \frac{2}{3}x + 7 - 7 \quad \text{Subtract 7 from both sides.}$$

$$-6 = \frac{2}{3}x \quad \text{Simplify.}$$

$$\frac{3}{2} \cdot -6 = \frac{3}{2} \cdot \frac{2}{3}x \quad \text{Multiply both sides by } \frac{3}{2}.$$

$$\frac{3 \cdot \overset{-3}{\cancel{-6}}}{\underset{1}{\cancel{2}} \cdot 1} = 1 \cdot x \quad \text{Simplify.}$$

$$-9 = x \quad \text{Simplify.}$$

Check to see that the solution is -9.

Helpful Hint Don't forget that we can get the variable alone on either side of the equation.

◾ **Work Practice Problem 3**

If an equation contains variable terms on both sides, we use the addition property of equality to get all the variable terms on one side and all the constants, or numbers, on the other side.

EXAMPLE 4 Solve: $3a - 6 = a + 4$

Solution:

$$3a - 6 = a + 4$$

$$3a - 6 + 6 = a + 4 + 6 \quad \text{Add 6 to both sides.}$$

$$3a = a + 10 \quad \text{Simplify.}$$

$$3a - a = a + 10 - a \quad \text{Subtract } a \text{ from both sides.}$$

$$2a = 10 \quad \text{Simplify.}$$

$$\frac{2a}{2} = \frac{10}{2} \quad \text{Divide both sides by 2.}$$

$$a = 5 \quad \text{Simplify.}$$

Check to see that the solution is 5.

◾ **Work Practice Problem 4**

EXAMPLE 5 Solve: $7x + 3.2 = 4x - 1.6$

Solution:

$$7x + 3.2 = 4x - 1.6$$

$$7x + 3.2 - 3.2 = 4x - 1.6 - 3.2 \quad \text{Subtract 3.2 from both sides.}$$

$$7x = 4x - 4.8 \quad \text{Simplify.}$$

$$7x - 4x = 4x - 4.8 - 4x \quad \text{Subtract } 4x \text{ from both sides.}$$

$$3x = -4.8 \quad \text{Simplify.}$$

$$\frac{3x}{3} = -\frac{4.8}{3} \quad \text{Divide both sides by 3.}$$

$$x = -1.6 \quad \text{Simplify.}$$

Check to see that -1.6 is the solution.

◾ **Work Practice Problem 5**

PRACTICE PROBLEM 3

Solve: $11 = \frac{3}{4}y + 20$

PRACTICE PROBLEM 4

Solve: $9x - 12 = x + 4$

PRACTICE PROBLEM 5

Solve: $8x + 4.2 = 10x - 11.6$

Answers

3. -12, **4.** 2, **5.** 7.9

Objective B Solving Equations Containing Parentheses

If an equation contains parentheses, we must first use the distributive property to remove them.

PRACTICE PROBLEM 6

Solve: $6(a - 5) = 7a - 13$

EXAMPLE 6 Solve: $7(x - 2) = 9x - 6$

Solution: First we apply the distributive property.

$$7(x - 2) = 9x - 6$$
$$7x - 14 = 9x - 6 \quad \text{Apply the distributive property.}$$

Next, we move variable terms to one side of the equation and constants to the other side.

$$7x - 14 - 9x = 9x - 6 - 9x \quad \text{Subtract } 9x \text{ from both sides.}$$
$$-2x - 14 = -6 \quad \text{Simplify.}$$
$$-2x - 14 + 14 = -6 + 14 \quad \text{Add 14 to both sides.}$$
$$-2x = 8 \quad \text{Simplify.}$$
$$\frac{-2x}{-2} = \frac{8}{-2} \quad \text{Divide both sides by } -2.$$
$$x = -4 \quad \text{Simplify.}$$

Check to see that -4 is the solution.

■ **Work Practice Problem 6**

You may want to use the steps below to solve equations.

Steps for Solving an Equation

Step 1: If parentheses are present, use the distributive property.

Step 2: Combine any like terms on each side of the equation.

Step 3: Use the addition property of equality to rewrite the equation so that variable terms are on one side of the equation and constant terms are on the other side.

Step 4: Use the multiplication property of equality to divide both sides by the numerical coefficient of the variable to solve for.

Step 5: Check the solution in the *original equation*.

PRACTICE PROBLEM 7

Solve: $4(2x - 3) + 4 = 0$

EXAMPLE 7 Solve: $3(2x - 6) + 6 = 0$

Solution:

$$3(2x - 6) + 6 = 0$$

Step 1: $\quad 6x - 18 + 6 = 0 \quad \text{Apply the distributive property.}$

Step 2: $\quad 6x - 12 = 0 \quad \text{Combine like terms on the left side of the equation.}$

Step 3: $\quad 6x - 12 + 12 = 0 + 12 \quad \text{Add 12 to both sides.}$

$$6x = 12 \quad \text{Simplify.}$$

Step 4: $\quad \dfrac{6x}{6} = \dfrac{12}{6} \quad \text{Divide both sides by 6.}$

$$x = 2 \quad \text{Simplify.}$$

Check:

Step 5: $3(2x - 6) + 6 = 0$

$3(2 \cdot 2 - 6) + 6 \overset{?}{=} 0$

$3(4 - 6) + 6 \overset{?}{=} 0$

$3(-2) + 6 \overset{?}{=} 0$

$-6 + 6 \overset{?}{=} 0$

$0 \overset{?}{=} 0$ True

The solution is 2.

■ **Work Practice Problem 7**

Objective C Writing Sentences as Equations

Next, we practice translating sentences into equations. Below are key words and phrases that translate to an equal sign: (*Note:* For a review of key words and phrases that translate to addition, subtraction, multiplication, and divisions, see Sections 1.8 and 2.1.)

Key Words or Phrases	Examples	Symbols
equals	3 equals 2 plus 1	$3 = 2 + 1$
gives	the quotient of 10 and −5 gives −2	$\dfrac{10}{-5} = -2$
is/was	17 minus 12 is 5	$17 - 12 = 5$
yields	11 plus 2 yields 13	$11 + 2 = 13$
amounts to	twice −15 amounts to −30	$2(-15) = -30$
is equal to	−24 is equal to 2 times −12	$-24 = 2(-12)$

EXAMPLE 8 Translate each sentence into an equation.

a. The product of 7 and 6 is 42.

b. Twice the sum of 3 and 5 is equal to 16.

c. The quotient of −45 and 5 yields −9.

Solution:

a. In words: the product of 7 and 6   is   42

Translate: $7 \cdot 6 \quad = \quad 42$

b. In words: twice   the sum of 3 and 5   is equal to   16

Translate: $2 \quad (3 + 5) \quad = \quad 16$

c. In words: the quotient of −45 and 5   yields   −9

Translate: $\dfrac{-45}{5} \quad = \quad -9$

■ **Work Practice Problem 8**

PRACTICE PROBLEM 8

Translate each sentence into an equation.

a. The difference of 110 and 80 is 30.

b. The product of 3 and the sum of −9 and 11 amounts to 6.

c. The quotient of 24 and −6 yields −4.

Answers

8. a. $110 - 80 = 30$,

b. $3(-9 + 11) = 6$, **c.** $\dfrac{24}{-6} = -4$

CALCULATOR EXPLORATIONS Checking Equations

A calculator can be used to check possible solutions of equations. To do this, replace the variable by the possible solution and evaluate each side of the equation separately. For example, to see whether 7 is a solution of the equation $52x = 15x + 259$, replace x with 7 and use your calculator to evaluate each side separately.

Equation: $52x = 15x + 259$
$52 \cdot 7 \stackrel{?}{=} 15 \cdot 7 + 259$ *Replace x with 7.*

Evaluate left side: $\boxed{52}$ $\boxed{\times}$ $\boxed{7}$ $\boxed{=}$ or $\boxed{\text{ENTER}}$.
Display: $\boxed{364}$.

Evaluate right side: $\boxed{15}$ $\boxed{\times}$ $\boxed{7}$ $\boxed{+}$ $\boxed{259}$ $\boxed{=}$
or $\boxed{\text{ENTER}}$. Display: $\boxed{364}$.

Since the left side equals the right side, 7 is a solution of the equation $52x = 15x + 259$.

Use a calculator to determine whether the numbers given are solutions of each equation.

1. $76(x - 25) = -988$;   12
2. $-47x + 862 = -783$;   35
3. $x + 562 = 3x + 900$; -170
4. $55(x + 10) = 75x + 910$; -18
5. $29x - 1034 = 61x - 362$; -21
6. $-38x + 205 = 25x + 120$;   25

8.4 EXERCISE SET

FOR EXTRA HELP

Student Solutions Manual   PH Math/Tutor Center   CD/Video for Review   MathXL®   MyMathLab

Objective A *Solve each equation. See Examples 1 through 5.*

1. $2x - 6 = 0$
2. $3y - 12 = 0$
3. $3n + 3.6 = 9.3$
4. $4z + 0.8 = 5.2$

5. $6 - n = 10$
6. $7 - y = 9$
7. $-\frac{2}{5}x + 19 = -21$
8. $-\frac{3}{7}y - 14 = 7$

9. $1.7 = 2y + 9.5$
10. $-5.1 = 3x + 2.4$
11. $2n + 8 = 0$
12. $8w + 40 = 0$

13. $3x - 7 = 4x + 5$
14. $7x - 1 = 8x + 4$
 15. $10x + 15 = 6x + 3$
16. $5x - 3 = 2x - 18$

17. $9 - 3x = 14 + 2x$
18. $4 - 7m = -3m + 4$
19. $-1.4x - 2 = -1.2x + 7$ **20.** $5.7y + 14 = 5.4y - 10$

Objective B *Solve each equation. See Examples 6 and 7.*

21. $3(x - 1) = 12$
22. $2(x + 5) = -8$
 23. $-2(y + 4) = 2$

24. $-1(y + 3) = 10$
25. $35 - 17 = 3(x - 2)$
26. $22 - 42 = 4(x - 1)$

27. $2(y - 3) = y - 6$
28. $3(z + 2) = 5z + 6$
29. $2t - 1 = 3(t + 7)$

30. $-4 + 3c = 4(c + 2)$
31. $3(5c + 1) - 12 = 13c + 3$
32. $4(3t + 4) - 20 = 3 + 5t$

590

Copyright 2007 Pearson Education, Inc.

Objectives Ⓐ Ⓑ **Mixed Practice** *Solve. See Examples 1 through 7.*

33. $3r + 4 = 19$

34. $5m + 1 = 46$

35. $2x - 1 = -7$

36. $3t - 2 = -11$

37. $8 - t = 3$

38. $6 - x = 4$

39. $7 = 4c - 1$

40. $9 = 2b - 5$

41. $9a + 29 = -7$

42. $10 + 4v = -6$

43. $0 = 4x + 4$

44. $0 = 5y + 5$

45. $11(x - 2) = 22$

46. $5(a - 4) = 20$

47. $5x - 2 = -8 - 4$

48. $7y - 3 = -10 - 14$

49. $-3c + 1 - 4c = -20$

50. $-b + 5 - b = -7$

51. $3(x - 5) = -7 - 11$

52. $4(x - 2) = -20 - 4$

53. $-5 + 7k = -13 + 8k$

54. $-7 + 9d = -17 + 10d$

55. $4x + 3 = 2x + 11$

56. $6y - 8 = 3y + 7$

57. $-8(n + 2) + 17 = -6n - 5$

58. $-10(x + 1) + 2 = -x + 10$

59. $\frac{3}{8}x + 14 = \frac{5}{8}x - 2$

60. $\frac{2}{7}x - 9 = \frac{5}{7}x - 15$

61. $10 + 5(z - 2) = -4z + 1$

62. $20 + 4(w - 5) = 5 - 2w$

63. $\frac{5}{8}a = \frac{1}{8}a + \frac{3}{4}$

64. $\frac{4}{9}a = \frac{1}{9}a + \frac{5}{6}$

65. $7(6 + w) = 6(w - 2)$

66. $6(5 + c) = 5(c - 4)$

67. $3 + 2(2n - 5) = 1$

68. $5 + 4(3x - 2) = 21$

69. $2(3z - 2) - 2(5 - 2z) = 4$

70. $2(3w + 7) - 4(5 - 2w) = 6$

Objective Ⓒ *Write each sentence as an equation. See Example 8.*

71. The sum of -42 and 16 is -26.

72. The difference of -30 and 10 equals -40.

73. The product of -5 and -29 gives 145.

74. The quotient of -16 and 2 yields -8.

75. Three times the difference of -14 and 2 amounts to -48.

76. The product of -2 and the sum of 3 and 12 is -30.

77. The quotient of 100 and twice 50 is equal to 1.

78. Seventeen subtracted from -12 equals -29.

Review

The following bar graph shows the estimated number of U.S. federal individual income tax returns that will be filed electronically during the years shown. Electronically filed returns include Telefile and online returns. Use this graph to answer Exercises 79 through 82. See Section 7.1.

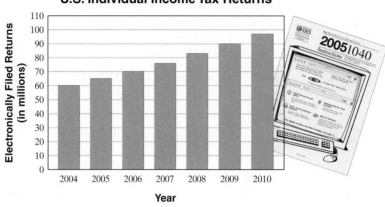

Total Electronically Filed
U.S. Individual Income Tax Returns

Source: IRS Compliance Research Division

79. Approximate the number of electronically filed returns estimated for 2010.

80. Approximate the number of electronically filed returns estimated for 2008.

81. By how much is the number of electronically filed returns expected to increase from 2006 to 2009?

82. Describe any trends shown in this graph.

Concept Extensions

Using the steps for solving an equation, choose the next operation for solving the given equation.

83. $2x - 5 = -7$
    a. Add 7 to both sides.
    b. Add 5 to both sides.
    c. Divide both sides by 2.

84. $3x + 2x = -x - 4$
    a. Add 4 to both sides.
    b. Subtract $2x$ from both sides.
    c. Add $3x$ and $2x$.

85. $-3x = -1.2$
    a. Divide both sides by -3.
    b. Add 1.2 to both sides.
    c. Add $3x$ to both sides.

86. $9 - 5x = 15$
    a. Divide both sides by -5.
    b. Subtract 15 from both sides.
    c. Subtract 9 from both sides.

87. A classmate shows you his steps for solving the given equation. His solution does not check, but he is unable to find the error. Check this solution, find the error, and correct it.

$$2(3x - 5) = 5x - 7$$
$$6x - 5 = 5x - 7$$
$$6x - 5 + 5 = 5x - 7 + 5$$
$$6x = 5x - 2$$
$$6x - 5x = 5x - 2 - 5x$$
$$x = -2$$

The equation $C = \dfrac{5}{9}(F - 32)$ gives the relationship between Celsius temperatures C and Fahrenheit temperatures F.

88. The highest recorded temperature in Australia occurred in January 1960 at Oodnadatta, South Australia. The temperature reached 50.7°C. Use the given equation to convert this temperature to degrees Fahrenheit. (*Source:* World Weather Centre at Perth)

89. The highest recorded temperature in Africa occurred in September 1922 at Al'Aziziyah, Libya. The temperature reached 57.8°C. Use the given equation to convert this temperature to degrees Fahrenheit. (*Source:* World Weather Centre at Perth)

90. The lowest recorded temperature in Australia occurred in June 1994 at Charlotte Pass, New South Wales. The temperature plummeted to −23.0°C. Use the given equation to convert this temperature to degrees Fahrenheit. (*Source:* World Weather Centre at Perth)

91. The lowest recorded temperature in North America occurred in February 1947 at Snag, Canada. The temperature plummeted to −63.0°C. Use the given equation to convert this temperature to degrees Fahrenheit. (*Source:* World Weather Centre at Perth)

 THE BIGGER PICTURE Operations on Sets of Numbers and Solving Equations

Continue your outline from Sections 1.7, 1.9, 2.5, 3.3, 3.7, 4.4, 5.2, and 6.2 or 6.3. Suggestions are once again written to help you complete this part of your outline. Notice that this part of the outline has to do once again with solving equations.

I. Operations on Sets of Numbers

   A. Whole Numbers

      1. **Add or Subtract** (Sections 1.3, 1.4)

      2. **Multiply or Divide** (Sections 1.6, 1.7)

      3. **Exponent** (Section 1.9)

      4. **Square Root** (Section 1.9)

      5. **Order of Operations** (Section 1.9)

   B. Integers

      1. **Add** (Section 2.3)

      2. **Subtract** (Section 2.4)

      3. **Multiply or Divide** (Section 2.5)

   C. Fractions

      1. **Simplify** (Section 3.2)

      2. **Multiply** (Section 3.3)

      3. **Divide** (Section 3.3)

      4. **Add or Subtract** (Sections 3.4, 3.5)

   D. Decimals

      1. **Add or Subtract** (Section 4.2)

      2. **Multiply** (Section 4.3)

      3. **Divide** (Section 4.4)

II. Solving Equations

   A. **Proportions** (Section 5.2)

   B. **Percent Problems**

      1. **Solved by Equations** (Section 6.2)

      2. **Solved by Proportions** (Section 6.3)

C. Equations in General: Simplify both sides of the equation by removing parentheses and combining any like terms. Then use the Addition Property to write variable terms on one side, constants (or numbers) on the other side. Then use the Multiplication Property to solve for the variable by dividing both sides of the equation by the coefficient of the variable.

Solve: $2(x - 5) = 80$

$$2x - 10 = 80 \qquad \text{Use the distributive property.}$$
$$2x - 10 + 10 = 80 + 10 \qquad \text{Add 10 to both sides.}$$
$$2x = 90 \qquad \text{Simplify.}$$
$$\frac{2x}{2} = \frac{90}{2} \qquad \text{Divide both sides by 2.}$$
$$x = 45 \qquad \text{Simplify.}$$

Solve.

1. $-8x = 40$

2. $x - 14 = -3$

3. $\dfrac{2}{5}x = -14$

4. $5y + 7 - 4y - 10 = 100$

5. $\dfrac{2}{3} = \dfrac{50}{n}$

6. $8x + 9 = -79$

7. 15% of 76 is what number?

8. What percent of 130 is 195?

9. $4x - 5 = 2x - 17$

10. $3 + 5(2n - 4) = 10$

8.5 EQUATIONS AND PROBLEM SOLVING

Objective **A** Writing Sentences as Equations

Now that we have practiced solving equations for a variable, we can extend considerably our problem-solving skills. We begin by writing sentences as equations using the following key words and phrases as a guide:

Addition	Subtraction	Multiplication	Division	Equal Sign
sum	difference	product	quotient	equals
plus	minus	times	divided by	gives
added to	subtracted from	multiply	into	is/was
more than	less than	twice	per	yields
increased by	decreased by	of		amounts to
total	less	double		is equal to

Notice that these sentences contain unknown numbers, which we will represent with x.

PRACTICE PROBLEM 1

Write each sentence as an equation. Use x to represent "a number."

a. Five times a number is 20.

b. The sum of a number and -5 yields 14.

c. Ten subtracted from a number amounts to -23.

d. Five times the difference of a number and 7 is equal to -8.

e. The quotient of triple a number and 5 gives 1.

EXAMPLE 1 Write each sentence as an equation. Use x to represent "a number."

a. Nine increased by a number is 5.

b. Twice a number equals -10.

c. A number minus 6 amounts to 168.

d. Three times the sum of a number and 5 is -30.

e. The quotient of twice a number and 8 is equal to 2.

Solution:

a. In words:

nine	increased by	a number	is	5
↓	↓	↓	↓	↓

Translate: 9 $+$ x $=$ 5

b. In words:

twice a number	equals	-10
↓	↓	↓

Translate: $2x$ $=$ -10

c. In words:

a number	minus	6	amounts to	168
↓	↓	↓	↓	↓

Translate: x $-$ 6 $=$ 168

d. In words:

three times	the sum of a number and 5	is	-30
↓	↓	↓	↓

Translate: 3 $(x + 5)$ $=$ -30

e. In words:

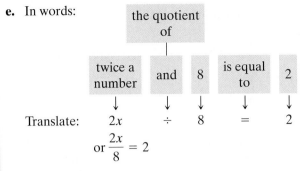

Translate: $2x \div 8 = 2$

or $\dfrac{2x}{8} = 2$

◼ **Work Practice Problem 1**

Objective B Using Problem-Solving Steps to Solve Problems

Our main purpose for studying arithmetic and algebra is to solve problems. The same problem-solving steps that have been used throughout this text are used in this section also. Those steps are next.

Problem-Solving Steps

1. UNDERSTAND the problem. During this step, become comfortable with the problem. Some ways of doing this are as follows:
   - Read and reread the problem.
   - Construct a drawing.
   - Propose a solution and check. Pay careful attention to how you check your proposed solution. This will help when writing an equation to model the problem.
   - Choose a variable to represent the unknown. Use this variable to represent any other unknowns.

2. TRANSLATE the problem into an equation.

3. SOLVE the equation.

4. INTERPRET the results: *Check* the proposed solution in the stated problem and *state* your conclusion.

The first problem that we solve consists of finding an unknown number.

EXAMPLE 2 Finding an Unknown Number

Twice a number plus 3 is the same as the number minus 6. Find the unknown number.

Solution:

1. UNDERSTAND the problem. To do so, we read and reread the problem.
   Let's propose a solution to help us understand. Suppose the unknown number is 5. Twice this number plus 3 is $2 \cdot 5 + 3$ or 13. Is this the same as the number minus 6, or $5 - 6$, or -1? Since 13 is not the same as -1, we know that 5 is not the solution. However, remember that the purpose of proposing a solution is not to guess correctly, but to better understand the problem.
   Now let's choose a variable to represent the unknown. Let's let

   x = unknown number

2. TRANSLATE the problem into an equation.

   In words:

twice a number	plus 3	is the same as	the number minus 6
↓	↓	↓	↓

   Translate: $2x$ $+ 3$ $=$ $x - 6$ *Continued on next page*

PRACTICE PROBLEM 2

Translate "The difference of a number and 2 equals 6 added to three times the number" into an equation and solve.

Answer

2. $x - 2 = 6 + 3x, -4$

3. SOLVE the equation. To solve the equation, we first subtract x from both sides.

$$2x + 3 = x - 6$$

$$2x + 3 - x = x - 6 - x$$

$$x + 3 = -6 \qquad \text{Simplify.}$$

$$x + 3 - 3 = -6 - 3 \qquad \text{Subtract 3 from both sides.}$$

$$x = -9 \qquad \text{Simplify.}$$

4. INTERPRET the results. First, *Check* the proposed solution in the stated problem. Twice "−9" is −18 and −18 + 3 is −15. This is equal to the number minus 6, or "−9" − 6, or −15. Then *state* your conclusion: The unknown number is −9.

▣ **Work Practice Problem 2**

✔ **Concept Check**　Suppose you have solved an equation involving perimeter to find the length of a rectangular table. Explain why you would want to recheck your math if you obtain the result of −5.

EXAMPLE 3　Determining Voter Counts

In the 2002 Senate election in West Virginia, incumbent John D. Rockefeller IV received 114,379 *more* votes than his challenger, Jay Wolfe. If a total of 436,183 votes were cast, find how many votes John D. Rockefeller IV received. (*Source: World Almanac*)

Solution:

1. UNDERSTAND the problem. We read and reread the problem.

   Let's propose and check a solution to help us better understand the problem. Suppose the challenger received 200,000 votes. Since Rockefeller received 114,379 *more* votes, he then received 200,000 + 114,379 = 314,379 votes. With these numbers, the total votes cast were 200,000 (challenger) + 314,379 (Rockefeller) = 514,379 votes. This is more than 436,183, the total votes cast, so we are incorrect. Not only do we now have a better understanding of the problem, but we know Wolfe received fewer than 200,000 votes since our proposed solution led to a total that was too big. Now let's choose a variable to represent an unknown. Then use this variable to represent any other unknown quantities. Let

   x = the number of challenger votes

   Then

   $x + 114,379$ = the number of incumbent votes
   since he received 114,379 more votes

2. TRANSLATE the problem into an equation.

   In words:

challenger votes	+	incumbent votes	=	total votes
↓		↓		↓

   Translate:　　　x　　　+　$x + 114,379$　=　436,183

3. SOLVE the equation:

$$x + x + 114,379 = 436,183$$

$$2x + 114,379 = 436,183 \qquad \text{Combine like terms.}$$

$$2x + 114,379 - 114,379 = 436,183 - 114,379 \qquad \text{Subtract 114,379 from both sides.}$$

$$2x = 321,804 \qquad \text{Simplify.}$$

$$\frac{2x}{2} = \frac{321,804}{2} \qquad \text{Divide both sides by 2.}$$

$$x = 160,902 \qquad \text{Simplify.}$$

PRACTICE PROBLEM 3

At a recent U.S./Japan summit meeting, 121 delegates attended. If the United States sent 19 more delegates than Japan, find how many the United States sent.

West Virginia

Answer

3. 70 delegates

✔ **Concept Check Answer**

length cannot be negative

4. INTERPRET the results. First *Check* the proposed solution in the stated problem. Since x represents the number of votes the challenger received, the challenger received 160,902 votes. The incumbent received $x + 114,379 = 160,902 + 114,379 = 275,281$ votes. To check, notice that the total number of challenger votes and incumbent votes is $160,902 + 275,281 = 436,183$ votes, the given total of votes cast. Also, 275,281 is 114,379 more votes than 160,902, so the solution checks. Then, *state* your conclusion: The incumbent, John D. Rockefeller IV, received 275,281 votes.

🖳 **Work Practice Problem 3**

EXAMPLE 4 **Calculating Separate Costs**

Leo Leal sold a used computer system and software for $2100, receiving four times as much money for the computer system as for the software. Find the price of each.

Solution:

1. UNDERSTAND the problem. We read and reread the problem. Then we choose a variable to represent an unknown. We use this variable to represent any other unknown quantities. We let

x = the software price

$4x$ = the computer system price

2. TRANSLATE the problem into an equation.

In words:

software price	and	computer price	is	2100
↓	↓	↓	↓	↓

Translate:　x　$+$　$4x$　$=$　2100

3. SOLVE the equation:

$$x + 4x = 2100$$
$$5x = 2100 \quad \text{Combine like terms.}$$
$$\frac{5x}{5} = \frac{2100}{5} \quad \text{Divide both sides by 5.}$$
$$x = 420 \quad \text{Simplify.}$$

4. INTERPRET the results. *Check* the proposed solution in the stated problem. The software sold for $420. The computer system sold for $4x = 4(\$420) = \$1680$. Since $\$420 + \$1680 = \$2100$, the total price, and $1680 is four times $420, the solution checks. *State* your conclusion: The software sold for $420, and the computer system sold for $1680.

🖳 **Work Practice Problem 4**

PRACTICE PROBLEM 4

A woman's $21,000 estate is to be divided so that her husband receives twice as much as her son. How much will each receive?

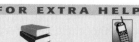
Objective A *Write each sentence as an equation. Use x to represent "a number." See Example 1.*

1. A number added to −5 is −7.

2. Five subtracted from a number equals 10.

3. Three times a number yields 27.

4. The quotient of 8 and a number is −2.

5. A number subtracted from −20 amounts to 104.

6. Two added to twice a number gives −14.

7. Twice a number gives 108.

8. Five times a number is equal to −75.

9. The product of 5 and the sum of −3 and a number is −20.

10. Twice the sum of −17 and a number is −14.

Objective B *Translate each to an equation. Then solve the equation. See Example 2.*

11. Three times a number, added to 9 is 33. Find the number.

12. Twice a number, subtracted from 60 is 20. Find the number.

13. The sum of 3, 4, and a number amounts to 16. Find the number.

14. The sum of 7, 9, and a number is 40. Find the number.

15. The difference of a number and 3 is equal to the quotient of 10 and 5. Find the number.

16. Eight decreased by a number equals the quotient of 15 and 5. Find the number.

17. Thirty less a number is equal to the product of 3 and the sum of the number and 6. Find the number.

18. The product of a number and 3 is twice the sum of that number and 5. Find the number.

19. 40 subtracted from five times a number is 8 more than the number. Find the number.

20. Five times the sum of a number and 2 is 11 less than the number times 8. Find the number.

21. Three times the difference of some number and 5 amounts to the quotient of 108 and 12. Find the number.

22. Seven times the difference of some number and 1 gives the quotient of 70 and 10. Find the number.

23. The product of 4 and a number is the same as 30 less twice that same number. Find the number.

24. Twice a number equals 25 less triple that same number. Find the number.

Solve. See Examples 3 and 4.

25. In the 2004 presidential election, George W. Bush received 34 more electoral votes than John Kerry. If a total of 538 electoral votes were cast for the two candidates, find how many votes each candidate received. (*Source:* Voter News Service)

26. Based on the 2000 Census, California has 21 more electoral votes for president than Texas. If the total number of electoral votes for these two states is 89, find the number for each state. (*Source: The World Almanac* 2005)

27. Bamboo and Pacific Kelp, a kind of sea weed, are two fast-growing plants. Bamboo grows twice as fast as kelp. If in one day both can grow a total of 54 inches, find how many inches each plant can grow in one day.

28. Norway has had three times as many rulers as Liechtenstein. If the total rulers for both countries is 56, find the number of rulers for Norway and the number for Liechtenstein.

Norway   Liechtenstein

Bamboo   Kelp

29. The country with the most universities[*] is India, followed by the United States. If India has 2649 more universities than the United States and their combined total is 14,165, find the number of universities in India and the number in the United States [[*] Includes all further education establishments. (*Source:* The Top 10 of Everything)]

30. The average life expectancy for a man is 34 years longer than the life expectancy for a polar bear. If the total of these life expectancies is 110 years, find the life expectancy of each.

31. A Nintendo Gamecube and several games are sold for $600. The cost of the games is 3 times as much as the cost of the Gamecube alone. Find the cost of the Gamecube and the cost of the games.

32. Disneyland®, in Anaheim, California, has 12 more rides than its neighboring sister park, Disney's California Adventure, which opened in 2001. Together, the two parks have 36 rides. How many rides does each park have? (*Source:* The Walt Disney Company)

33. The two NCAA stadiums with the largest capacities are Michigan Stadium (Univ. of Michigan) and Neyland Stadium (Univ. of Tennessee). Michigan Stadium has a capacity of 4647 more than Neyland. If the combined capacity for the two stadiums is 210,355, find the capacity for each stadium. (*Source:* National Collegiate Athletic Association)

34. An NHRA top fuel dragster has a top speed of 95 mph faster than an Indy Racing League car. If the combined top speeds for these two cars is 565 mph, find the top speed of each car. (*Source:* USA Today)

35. California contains the largest state population of native Americans. This population is three times the native American population of Washington state. If the total of these two populations is 412 thousand find the native American population in each of these two states. (*Source:* U.S. Census Bureau)

36. In 2020, China is projected to be the country with the greatest number of visiting tourists. This number is twice the number of tourists projected for Spain. If the total number of tourists for these two countries is projected to be 210 million, find the number projected for each. (*Source: The State of the World Atlas* by Dan Smith)

37. A crow will eat five more ounces of food a day than a finch. If together they eat 13 ounces of food, find how many ounces of food the crow consumes and how many ounces of food the finch consumes.

38. A Toyota Camry is traveling twice as fast as a Dodge truck. If their combined speed is 105 miles per hour, find the speed of the car and the speed of the truck.

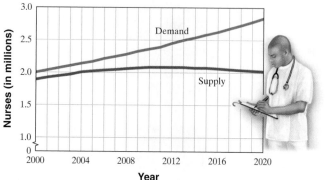

39. In 2020, the shortage of nurses is projected to be 533,201 more nurses than the shortage in 2010. If the total number of nurse shortages for these two years is 1,083,631, find the nurse shortage for each year.

40. The percent shortage of nurses in 2019 is predicted to be three times the percent shortage in 2007. If the total percent shortages for these two years is 36%, find the percent shortage in 2007 and the percent shortage in 2019.

National Supply and Demand Projections for Registered Nurses: 2000 to 2020

Source: Bureau of Health Professions, RN Supply and Demand Projections

41. Anthony Tedesco sold his used mountain bike and accessories for $270. If he received five times as much money for the bike as he did for the accessories, find how much money he received for the bike.

42. A tractor and a plow attachment are worth $1200. The tractor is worth seven times as much money as the plow. Find the value of the tractor and the value of the plow.

43. During the 2004 Women's NCAA Division I basketball championship game, the Connecticut Huskies scored 9 more points than the Tennessee Lady Volunteers. Together, both teams scored a total of 131 points. How many points did the 2004 Champion Connecticut Huskies score during this game? (*Source:* National Collegiate Athletic Association)

44. During the 2004 Men's NCAA Division I basketball championship game, the Connecticut Huskies scored 9 fewer points than the Georgia Tech Yellow Jackets. Together, both teams scored a total of 155 points. How many points did the 2004 Champion Georgia Tech Yellow Jackets score during this game? (*Source:* National Collegiate Athletic Association)

Review

Round each number to the given place value. See Section 1.5.

45. 586 to the nearest ten

46. 82 to the nearest ten

47. 1026 to the nearest hundred

48. 52,333 to the nearest thousand

49. 2986 to the nearest thousand

50. 101,552 to the nearest hundred

Concept Extensions

51. Solve Example 3 again, but this time let x be the number of incumbent votes. Did you get the same results? Explain why or why not.

In real estate, a house's selling price P is found by adding the real estate agent's commission C to the amount A that the seller of the house receives: $P = A + C$.

52. Brianna Morley's house sold for $230,000. Her real estate agent received a commission of $13,800. How much did Brianna receive? (*Hint:* Substitute the known values into the equation, then solve the equation for the remaining unknown.)

53. Duncan Bostic plans to use a real estate agent to sell his house. He hopes to sell the house for $165,000 and keep $156,750 of that. If everything goes as he has planned, how much will his real estate agent receive as a commission?

In retailing, the retail price P of an item can be computed using the equation $P = C + M$, where C is the wholesale cost of the item and M is the amount of markup.

54. The retail price of a computer system is $999 after a markup of $450. What is the wholesale cost of the computer system? (*Hint:* Substitute the known values into the equation, then solve the equation for the remaining unknown.)

55. Slidell Feed and Seed sells a bag of cat food for $12. If the store paid $7 for the cat food, what is the markup on the cat food?

CHAPTER 8   Group Activity

Sections 8.1–8.4

Modeling Equation Solving with Addition and Subtraction

We can use positive counters ● and negative counters ● to help us model the equation-solving process. We also need to use an object that represents a variable. We use small slips of paper with the variable name written on them.

Recall that taking a ● and ● together creates a neutral or zero pair. After a neutral pair has been formed, it can be removed from or added to an equation model without changing the overall value. We also need to remember that we can add or remove the same number of positive or negative counters from both sides of an equation without changing the overall value.

We can represent the equation $x + 5 = 2$ as follows:

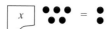

To get the variable by itself, we must remove 5 black counters from both sides of the model. Because there are only 2 counters on the right side, we must add 5 negative counters to both sides of the model. Then we can remove neutral pairs: 5 from the left side and 2 from the right side.

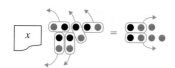

We are left with the following model, which represents the solution, $x = -3$.

$$\boxed{x} \quad = \quad ●\ ●\ ●$$

Similarly, we can represent the equation $x - 4 = -6$ as follows:

$$\boxed{x} \quad ●●\ ●● \quad = \quad ●●●\ ●●●$$

To get the variable by itself, we must remove 4 red counters from both sides of the model

$$\boxed{x} \quad ●●\ ●● \quad = \quad ●●●\ ●●●$$

We are left with the following model, which represents the solution, $x = -2$.

$$\boxed{x} \quad = \quad ●\ ●$$

Use the counter model to solve each equation.

1. $x - 3 = -7$ **2.** $x - 1 = -9$

3. $x + 2 = 8$ **4.** $x + 4 = 5$

5. $x + 8 = 3$ **6.** $x - 5 = -1$

7. $x - 2 = 1$ **8.** $x - 5 = 10$

9. $x + 3 = -7$ **10.** $x + 8 = -2$

Chapter 8 Vocabulary Check

Fill in each blank with one of the words or phrases listed below.

variable	simplified	algebraic expression
terms	combined	evaluating the expression
like	numerical coefficient	

1. An algebraic expression is _____ when all like terms have been _____ .
2. Terms that are exactly the same, except that they may have different numerical coefficients, are called _____ terms.
3. A letter used to represent a number is called a _____ .
4. A combination of operations on variables and numbers is called an _____ .
5. The addends of an algebraic expression are called the _____ of the expression.
6. The number factor of a variable term is called the _____ .
7. Replacing a variable in an expression by a number and then finding the value of the expression is called _____ for the variable.

Helpful Hint

Are you preparing for your test? Don't forget to take the Chapter 8 Test on page 610. Then check your answers at the back of the text and use the Chapter Test Prep Video CD to see the fully worked-out solutions to any of the exercises you want to review.

Chapter Highlights

DEFINITIONS AND CONCEPTS	EXAMPLES
Section 8.1 Variable Expressions	

A letter used to represent a number is called a **variable.** A combination of numbers, letters (variables), and operation symbols is called an **algebraic expression,** or **expression.**	x, y, z, a, b $3 + x, 7y, x^3 + y - 10$
Replacing a variable in an expression by a number and then finding the value of the expression is called **evaluating the expression.**	Evaluate: $2x + y$ when $x = 22$ and $y = 4$ $2x + y = 2 \cdot 22 + 4$ Replace x with 22 and y with 4. $ = 44 + 4$ Multiply. $ = 48$ Add.
The addends of an algebraic expression are called the **terms** of the expression.	$5x^2 + (-4x) + (-2)$ ⎯⎯ 3 terms
The number factor of a variable term is called the **numerical coefficient.**	**Term** **Numerical Coefficient** $7x$ 7 $-6y$ -6 x or $1x$ 1
Terms that are exactly the same, except that they may have different numerical coefficients, are called **like terms.**	$5x + 11x = (5 + 11)x = 16x$ like terms $y - 6y = (1 - 6)y = -5y$

continued

DEFINITIONS AND CONCEPTS	EXAMPLES

Section 8.1   Variable Expressions (*continued*)

An algebraic expression is **simplified** when all like terms have been **combined.**

Use the distributive property to multiply an algebraic expression by a term.

Simplify:

$$-4(x + 2) + 3(5x - 7)$$
$$= -4(x) + (-4)(2) + 3(5x) - 3(7)$$
$$= -4x + (-8) + 15x - (21)$$
$$= -4x + 15x + (-8) + (-21)$$
$$= 11x + (-29) \quad \text{or} \quad 11x - 29$$

Section 8.2   Solving Equations: The Addition Property

ADDITION PROPERTY OF EQUALITY

Let a, b, and c represent numbers. Then

$a = b$	Also, $a = b$
and $a + c = b + c$	and $a - c = b - c$
are equivalent equations.	are equivalent equations.

In other words, the same number may be added to or subtracted from both sides of an equation without changing the solution of the equation.

Solve for x:

$$x + 8 = 2 + (-1)$$
$$x + 8 = 1$$
$$x + 8 - 8 = 1 - 8 \qquad \text{Subtract 8 from both sides.}$$
$$x = -7 \qquad \text{Simplify.}$$

The solution is -7.

Section 8.3   Solving Equations: The Multiplication Property

MULTIPLICATION PROPERTY OF EQUALITY

Let a, b, and c represent numbers and let $c \neq 0$. Then

$a = b$	Also, $a = b$
and $a \cdot c = b \cdot c$	and $\dfrac{a}{c} = \dfrac{b}{c}$
are equivalent equations.	are equivalent equations.

In other words, both sides of an equation may be multiplied or divided by the same nonzero number without changing the solution of the equation.

Solve: $-7x = 42$

$$\frac{-7x}{-7} = \frac{42}{-7} \quad \text{Divide both sides by } -7.$$
$$x = -6 \quad \text{Simplify.}$$

Solve: $\dfrac{2}{3}x = -10$

$$\frac{\overset{1}{\cancel{3}}}{\underset{1}{\cancel{2}}} \cdot \frac{\overset{1}{\cancel{2}}}{\underset{1}{\cancel{3}}}x = \frac{3}{2} \cdot -10 \quad \text{Multiply both sides by } \frac{3}{2}.$$
$$x = -15 \quad \text{Simplify.}$$

Section 8.4   Solving Equations Using Addition and Multiplication Properties

STEPS FOR SOLVING AN EQUATION

Step 1. If parentheses are present, use the distributive property.

Step 2. Combine any like terms on each side of the equation.

Step 3. Use the addition property of equality to rewrite the equation so that variable terms are on one side of the equation and constant terms are on the other side.

Step 4. Use the multiplication property of equality to divide both sides by the numerical coefficient of the variable to solve.

Step 5. Check the solution in the *original equation.*

Solve for x: $5(3x - 1) + 15 = -5$

Step 1. $15x - 5 + 15 = -5$ Apply the distributive property.

Step 2. $15x + 10 = -5$ Combine like terms.

Step 3. $15x + 10 - 10 = -5 - 10$ Subtract 10 from both sides.

$$15x = -15$$

Step 4. $\dfrac{15x}{15} = \dfrac{-15}{15}$ Divide both sides by 15.

$$x = -1$$

Step 5.   Check to see that -1 is the solution.

DEFINITIONS AND CONCEPTS	**EXAMPLES**

Section 8.5   Equations and Problem Solving

PROBLEM-SOLVING STEPS

1. UNDERSTAND the problem. Some ways of doing this are

Read and reread the problem.

Construct a drawing.

Choose a variable to represent an unknown in the problem.

2. TRANSLATE the problem into an equation.

3. SOLVE the equation.

4. INTERPRET the results. *Check* the proposed solution in the stated problem and *state* your conclusion.

The incubation period for a golden eagle is three times the incubation period for a hummingbird. If the total of their incubation periods is 60 days, find the incubation period for each bird. (*Source: Wildlife Fact File,* International Masters Publishers)

1. UNDERSTAND the problem. Then choose a variable to represent an unknown. Let

x = incubation period of a hummingbird

$3x$ = incubation period of a golden eagle

2. TRANSLATE.

incubation of hummingbird	+	incubation of golden eagle	is	60
$\downarrow$		$\downarrow$	$\downarrow$	$\downarrow$
x	+	$3x$	=	60

3. SOLVE:

$$x + 3x = 60$$
$$4x = 60$$
$$\frac{\overset{1}{\cancel{4}}x}{\underset{1}{\cancel{4}}} = \frac{60}{4}$$
$$x = 15$$

4. INTERPRET the solution in the stated problem. The incubation period for a hummingbird is 15 days. The incubation period for a golden eagle is $3x = 3 \cdot 15 = 45$ days.

Since 15 days + 45 days = 60 days and 45 is 3(15), the solution checks.

State your conclusion: The incubation period for a hummingbird is 15 days. The incubation period for a golden eagle is 45 days.

Are You Prepared for a Test on Chapter 8?

Below I have listed some *common trouble areas* for students in Chapter 8. After studying for your test, but before taking your test, read these.

- Be careful when evaluating expressions. For example, evaluate $3x - y$ when $x = -2$ and $y = -3$.

$$3x - y = 3(-2) - (-3) \quad \text{Let } x = -2 \text{ and } y = -3.$$
$$= -6 - (-3) \quad \text{Multiply.}$$
$$= -6 + 3$$
$$= -3 \quad \text{Add.}$$

- Remember the distributive property.

$$5(4x - 3) + 2 = 5 \cdot 4x - 5 \cdot 3 + 2 \quad \text{Use the distributive property.}$$
$$= 20x - 15 + 2 \quad \text{Simplify.}$$
$$= 20x - 13 \quad \text{Combine like terms.}$$

- Don't forget the steps for solving a linear equation.

$$2(3x - 2) + 16 = 6$$
$$6x - 4 + 16 = 6 \quad \text{Apply the distributive property.}$$
$$6x + 12 = 6 \quad \text{Combine like terms.}$$
$$6x + 12 - 12 = 6 - 12 \quad \text{Subtract 12 from both sides.}$$
$$6x = -6 \quad \text{Simplify.}$$
$$\frac{6x}{6} = \frac{-6}{6} \quad \text{Divide both sides by 6.}$$
$$1 \cdot x = -1 \quad \text{Simplify.}$$
$$x = -1$$

Remember: This is simply a checklist of common trouble areas. For a review of Chapter 8 see the Highlights and Chapter Review at the end of this chapter.

---

8 CHAPTER REVIEW

(8.1) *Evaluate each expression when $x = 5$, $y = 0$, and $z = -2$.*

1. $z^3 + 9$

2. $4z - 3$

3. $\dfrac{5x + 3}{y}$

4. $\dfrac{y}{5z}$

5. $6.3 - (3x - 20)$

6. $\dfrac{4y - 11x}{3z}$

△ **7.** Find the volume of a storage cube whose sides measure 2 feet. Use $V = s^3$.

2 feet

△ **8.** Find the volume of a wooden crate in the shape of a cube 4 feet on each side. Use $V = s^3$.

4 feet

9. Lamar deposited his $5000 bonus into an account paying 6% annual interest. How much interest will he earn in 6 years? Use $I = prt$.

10. Jennifer Lewis borrowed $2000 from her grandmother and agreed to pay her 5% simple interest. How much interest will she owe after 3 years? Use $I = prt$.

Simplify each expression by combining like terms.

11. $-6x - 9x$

12. $\dfrac{2}{3}x - \dfrac{9}{10}x$

13. $2y - 10 - 8y$

14. $8a + a - 7 - 15a$

15. $y + 3 - 9y - 1$

16. $1.7x - 3.2 + 2.9x - 8.7$

Multiply.

17. $-2(4y)$

18. $3(5y - 8)$

Simplify.

19. $7x + 3(x - 4) + x$

20. $4(x - 7) + 21$

21. $3(5a - 2) + 10(-2a + 1)$

22. $6y + 3 + 2(3y - 6)$

Find the area of each figure.

△ **23.**

(2x − 1) yards

3 yards | Rectangle

△ **24.**

5y meters

Square

(8.2)

25. Is 4 a solution of $5(2 - x) = -10$?

26. Is 0 a solution of $6y + 2 = 23 + 4y$?

Solve.

27. $z - 5 = -7$

28. $x + 1 = 8$

29. $x + \dfrac{7}{8} = \dfrac{3}{8}$

30. $y + \dfrac{4}{11} = -\dfrac{2}{11}$

31. $n + 18 = 10 - (-2)$

32. $15 = 8x + 35 - 7x$

33. $m - 3.9 = -2.6$

34. $z - 4.6 = -2.2$

(8.3) *Solve.*

35. $-3y = -21$

36. $-8x = 72$

37. $-5n = -5$

38. $-3a = 15$

39. $\dfrac{2}{3}x = -\dfrac{8}{15}$

40. $-\dfrac{7}{8}y = 21$

41. $-1.2x = 144$

42. $-0.8y = -10.4$

43. $-5x = 100 - 120$

44. $18 - 30 = -4x$

(8.4) *Solve.*

45. $3x - 4 = 11$

46. $6y + 1 = 73$

47. $-\dfrac{5}{9}x + 23 = -12$

48. $-\dfrac{2}{3}x - 11 = \dfrac{2}{3}x - 55$

49. $6.8 + 4y = -2.2$

50. $-9.6 + 5y = -3.1$

51. $2x + 7 = 6x - 1$

52. $5x - 18 = -4x + 36$

53. $5(n - 3) = 7 + 3n$

54. $7(2 + x) = 4x - 1$

55. $2(4n - 11) + 8 = 5n + 4$

56. $3(5x - 6) + 9 = 13x + 7$

Write each sentence as an equation.

57. The difference of 20 and -8 is 28.

58. The product of -5 and the sum of -2 and 6 yields -20.

59. The quotient of -75 and the sum of 5 and 20 is equal to -3.

60. Nineteen subtracted from -2 amounts to -21.

(8.5) *Write each sentence as an equation. Use x to represent "a number."*

61. A number increased by 8 is 40.

62. Twelve subtracted from twice a number is 10.

Solve.

63. Five times a number subtracted from 40 is the same as three times the number. Find the number.

64. The product of a number and 3 is twice the difference of that number and 8. Find the number.

65. In an election between the incumbent and a challenger, the incumbent received 11,206 more votes than the challenger. If a total of 18,298 votes were cast, find the number of votes for each candidate.

66. Rajiv Puri has twice as many cassette tapes as he has compact discs. Find the number of CDs if he has a total of 126 music recordings.

Mixed Review

Evaluate each expression when $x = 4$, $y = -3$, and $z = 5$.

67. $18 - (9 - 5x)$

68. $\dfrac{z}{100} + \dfrac{y}{10}$

Simplify.

69. $9x - 20x$

70. $-5(7x)$

71. $12x + 5(2x - 3) - 4$

72. $-7(x + 6) - 2(x - 5)$

73. Is 3 a solution of $4y + 2 - 6y = 5 + 7$?

74. Is 7 a solution of $4(z - 8) + 12 = 8$?

Solve.

75. $c - 5 = -13 + 7$

76. $7x + 5 - 6x = -20$

77. $-7x + 3x = -50 - 2$

78. $-x + 8x = -38 - 4$

79. $14 - y = -3$

80. $7 - z = 0$

81. $9x + 12 - 8x = -6 + (-4)$

82. $-17x + 14 + 20x - 2x = 5 - (-3)$

83. $\dfrac{4}{9}x = -\dfrac{1}{3}$

84. $-\dfrac{5}{24}x = \dfrac{5}{6}$

85. $2y + 6y = 24 - 8$

86. $13x - 7x = -4 - 12$

87. $\dfrac{2}{3}x - 12 = -4$

88. $\dfrac{7}{8}x + 5 = -2$

89. $-5z + 3z - 7 = 8z - 7$

90. $4x - 3 + 6x = 5x - 3$

91. Three times a number added to twelve is 27. Find the number.

92. Twice the sum of a number and four is ten. Find the number.

CHAPTER TEST

Remember to use the Chapter Test Prep Video CD to see the fully worked-out solutions to any of the exercises you want to review.

Answers

1. _____

2. _____

3. _____

4. _____

5. _____

6. _____

7. _____

8. _____

9. _____

10. _____

11. _____

12. _____

13. _____

1. Evaluate: $\dfrac{3x - 5}{2y}$ when $x = 7$ and $y = -8$

2. Simplify $7x - 5 - 12x + 10$ by combining like terms.

3. Multiply: $-2(3y + 7)$

4. Simplify: $5(3z + 2) - z - 18$

△ **5.** Write a product that represents the area of the rectangle. Then multiply.

4 meters

| Rectangle | $(3x - 1)$ meters |

Solve.

6. $x - 17 = -10$

7. $y + \dfrac{3}{4} = \dfrac{1}{4}$

8. $-4x = 48$

9. $-\dfrac{5}{8}x = -25$

10. $5x + 12 - 4x - 14 = 22$

11. $2 - c + 2c = 5$

12. $3x - 5 = -11$

13. $-4x + 7 = 15$

610

14. $3.6 - 2x = -5.4$

15. $12 = 3(4 + 2y)$

16. $5x - 2 = x - 10$

17. $10y - 1 = 7y + 21$

18. $6 + 2(3n - 1) = 28$

19. $4(5x + 3) = 2(7x + 6)$

Solve.

△ **20.** A lawn is in the shape of a trapezoid with a height of 60 feet and bases of 70 feet and 130 feet. Find the area of the lawn. Use

$$A = \frac{1}{2} \cdot h \cdot (B + b).$$

△ **21.** If the height of a triangularly shaped jib sail is 12 feet and its base is 5 feet, find the area of the sail. Use

$$A = \frac{1}{2} \cdot b \cdot h.$$

22. The difference of three times a number and five times the same number is 4. Find the number.

23. In a championship basketball game, Paula Zimmerman made twice as many points as Maria Kaminsky. If the total number of points made by both women was 51, find how many points Paula made.

24. In a 10-kilometer race, there are 112 more men entered than women. Find the number of women runners if the total number of runners in the race is 600.

14. _____

15. _____

16. _____

17. _____

18. _____

19. _____

20. _____

21. _____

22. _____

23. _____

24. _____

Answers

1. Find the place value of the digit 4 in the whole number 48,761.

2. Write 2036 in words.

3. Add: 34,285 + 149,761

4. Find the average of 56, 18, and 43.

△ **5.** Find the perimeter of the polygon shown.

6. Subtract 8 from 25.

2 inches
3 inches
1 inch
4 inches
3 inches

7. The governor's salary in the state of Alabama was recently increased by $1706. If the old salary was $94,655, find the new salary. (*Source: The World Almanac and Book of Facts,* 2003 and 2005)

8. Find $\sqrt{25}$.

9. Subtract: 7826 − 505
Check by adding.

10. Find 8^2.

11. The graph below shows the ratings of Best Picture nominees since PG-13 was introduced in 1984. On this graph, each bar represents a different rating, and the height of each bar represents the number of Best Picture nominees for that rating. (*Source:* Academy of Motion Picture Arts and Sciences; Internet Movie Database)

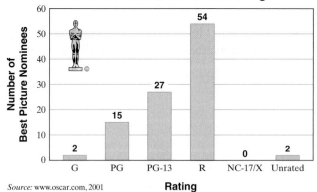

Best Picture Nominee Ratings

Source: www.oscar.com, 2001

a. Which rating did most Best Picture nominees have?

b. Find the total number of Best Picture nominees that were rated G, PG, or PG-13.

12. Evaluate: $\left(-\dfrac{1}{2}\right)^3$

Answers

1. _____

2. _____

3. _____

4. _____

5. _____

6. _____

7. _____

8. _____

9. _____

10. _____

11. a. _____

b. _____

12. _____

Simplify.

13. $-(-4)$ **14.** $-|20|$ **15.** $-|-5|$ **16.** $|0|$

Add.

17. $-2 + (-21)$ **18.** $-8.2 + 4.6$

19. $(-3) + 4 + (-11)$ **20.** $\dfrac{2}{5} + \left(-\dfrac{3}{10}\right)$

Subtract.

21. $8 - 15$ **22.** $4.6 - (-1.2)$

23. $-4 - (-5)$ **24.** $\dfrac{7}{10} - \dfrac{23}{24}$

Multiply.

25. $-2(-5)$ **26.** $-8(1.2)$

27. $(-1)(-2)(-3)(-4)$ **28.** $-2\dfrac{2}{9}\left(1\dfrac{4}{5}\right)$

29. Simplify: $(-3) \cdot |-5| - (-2) + 4^2$ **30.** Solve: $4x - 7.1 = 3x + 2.6$

31. Multiply: 0.0531×16 **32.** Multiply: 0.0531×1000

33. Given the rectangle shown: **34.** Add: $\dfrac{5}{12} + \dfrac{2}{9}$

7 feet

5 feet

   a. Find the ratio of its width to its length.
   b. Find the ratio of its length to its
      perimeter.

13. _____

14. _____

15. _____

16. _____

17. _____

18. _____

19. _____

20. _____

21. _____

22. _____

23. _____

24. _____

25. _____

26. _____

27. _____

28. _____

29. _____

30. _____

31. _____

32. _____

33. a. _____

    b. _____

34. _____

35. _____

36. _____

37. _____

38. _____

39. _____

40. _____

41. _____

42. _____

43. _____

44. _____

45. _____

46. _____

47. _____

48. _____

49. _____

50. _____

51. _____

52. _____

53. _____

54. _____

35. 12% of what number is 0.6?

36. Multiply: $\dfrac{7}{8} \cdot \dfrac{2}{3}$

37. What percent of 12 is 9?

38. Divide: $1\dfrac{4}{5} \div 2\dfrac{3}{10}$

39. Convert 3 pounds to ounces.

40. Round 23,781 to the nearest thousand.

41. Add 2400 ml to 8.9 L.

42. Round 0.02351 to the nearest thousandth.

43. Is $\dfrac{1\frac{1}{6}}{10\frac{1}{2}} = \dfrac{\frac{1}{2}}{4\frac{1}{2}}$ a true proportion?

44. Is $\dfrac{7.8}{3} = \dfrac{5.2}{2}$ a true proportion?

45. The standard dose of an antibiotic is 4 cc (cubic centimeters) for every 25 pounds (lb) of body weight. At this rate, find the standard dose for a 140-lb woman.

46. On a certain map, 2 inches represents 75 miles. How many miles are represented by 7 inches?

Write each percent as a decimal.

47. 4.6%

48. 452%

Write each percent as a fraction in simplest form.

49. $33\dfrac{1}{3}\%$

50. 27%

51. Translate to an equation: Five is what percent of 20?

52. Translate to a proportion: Five is what percent of 20?

53. Find the sales tax and the total price on the purchase of an $85.50 trench coat in a city where the sales tax rate is 7.5%.

54. A salesperson makes a 7% commission rate on her total sales. If her total sales are $23,000, what is her commission?

55. The following bar graph shows the number of endangered species in 2001. Use this graph to answer the questions.

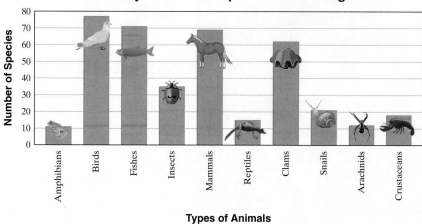

How Many U.S. Animal Species Are Endangered?

Source: U.S. Fish and Wildlife Service

a. Approximate the number of endangered species that are reptiles.
b. Which category has the most endangered species?

56. Find the mean, median, and mode of 1, 7, 8, 10, 11, 11.

55. a. _____

b. _____

56. _____

9

Geometry

The word *geometry* is formed from the Greek words *geo*, meaning Earth, and *metron*, meaning measure. Geometry literally means to measure the Earth. In this chapter we learn about various geometric figures and their properties such as perimeter, area, and volume. Knowledge of geometry can help us solve practical problems in real-life situations. For instance, knowing certain measures of a circular swimming pool allows us to calculate how much water it can hold.

Modern soccer may have its origins as far back as 3000 years ago. Although soccer (called football in England) was originally banned in England for its vulgarity, perhaps Eton College had the earliest known rules of the game in 1815. Today soccer is undisputed as the most watched and played sport. This past World Cup was watched by 33 billion people around the world.

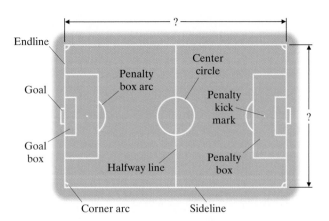

Dimensions of soccer playing fields are determined by many factors, including the ages of the players. In Exercises 69, 70, Section 9.3, and 37, 38, Section 9.5, we calculate the perimeter and area of various-sized fields.

△ **9.1** LINES AND ANGLES

Objective **A** Identifying Lines, Line Segments, Rays, and Angles

Let's begin with a review of two important concepts—space and plane.

Space extends in all directions indefinitely. Examples of objects in space are houses, grains of salt, bushes, your *Basic College Mathematics with Early Integers* textbook, and you.

A **plane** is a flat surface that extends indefinitely. Surfaces like a plane are a classroom floor or a blackboard or whiteboard.

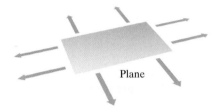

Plane

The most basic concept of geometry is the idea of a point in space. A **point** has no length, no width, and no height, but it does have location. We represent a point by a dot, and we usually label points with capital letters.

Point *P*

A **line** is a set of points extending indefinitely in two directions. A line has no width or height, but it does have length. We can name a line by any two of its points or by a single lowercase letter. A **line segment** is a piece of a line with two endpoints.

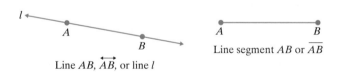

Line *AB*, $\overleftrightarrow{AB}$, or line *l*   Line segment *AB* or $\overline{AB}$

A **ray** is a part of a line with one endpoint. A ray extends indefinitely in one direction. An **angle** is made up of two rays that share the same endpoint. The common endpoint is called the **vertex.**

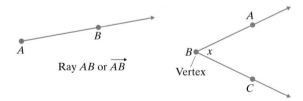

Ray *AB* or $\overrightarrow{AB}$ Vertex

The angle in the figure above can be named

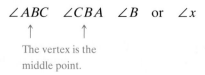

∠*ABC*   ∠*CBA*   ∠*B*   or   ∠*x*

The vertex is the middle point.

Rays *BA* and *BC* are **sides** of the angle.

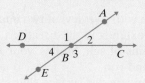

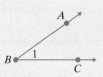

> ### Naming an Angle
>
> When there is no confusion as to what angle is being named, you may use the vertex alone.
>
> Name of ∠B is all right.   Name of ∠B is *not* all right.
> There is no confusion. ∠B means ∠1.   There is confusion. Does ∠B mean
> ∠1, ∠2, ∠3, or ∠4?

PRACTICE PROBLEM 1

Identify each figure as a line, a ray, a line segment, or an angle. Then name the figure using the given points.

a.   **b.**

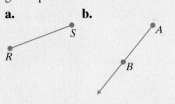

c.   **d.**

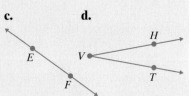

PRACTICE PROBLEM 2

Use the figure in Example 2 to list other ways to name ∠z.

EXAMPLE 1 Identify each figure as a line, a ray, a line segment, or an angle. Then name the figure using the given points.

a.   **b.**

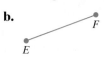

c.   **d.**

Solution:

Figure (a) extends indefinitely in two directions. It is line CD or $\overleftrightarrow{CD}$.
Figure (b) has two endpoints. It is line segment EF or $\overline{EF}$.
Figure (c) has two rays with a common endpoint. It is ∠MNO, ∠ONM, or ∠N.
Figure (d) is part of a line with one endpoint. It is ray PT or $\overrightarrow{PT}$.

▣ **Work Practice Problem 1**

EXAMPLE 2 List other ways to name ∠y.

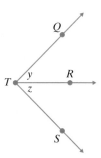

Solution: Two other ways to name ∠y are ∠QTR and ∠RTQ. We may *not* use the vertex alone to name this angle because three different angles have T as their vertex.

▣ **Work Practice Problem 2**

Answers

1. **a.** line segment; line segment RS or $\overline{RS}$, **b.** ray; ray AB or $\overrightarrow{AB}$, **c.** line; line EF or $\overleftrightarrow{EF}$, **d.** angle; ∠TVH, or ∠HVT or ∠V,
2. ∠RTS, ∠STR

Objective B Classifying Angles as Acute, Right, Obtuse, or Straight

An angle can be measured in **degrees.** The symbol for degrees is a small, raised circle, °. There are 360° in a full revolution, or a full circle.

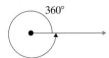

$\frac{1}{2}$ of a revolution measures $\frac{1}{2}(360°) = 180°$. An angle that measures 180° is called a **straight angle.**

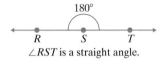

∠RST is a straight angle.

$\frac{1}{4}$ of a revolution measures $\frac{1}{4}(360°) = 90°$. An angle that measures 90° is called a **right angle.** The symbol ∟ is used to denote a right angle.

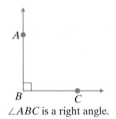

∠ABC is a right angle.

An angle whose measure is between 0° and 90° is called an **acute angle.**

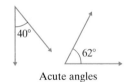

Acute angles

An angle whose measure is between 90° and 180° is called an **obtuse angle.**

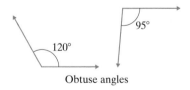

Obtuse angles

EXAMPLE 3 Classify each angle as acute, right, obtuse, or straight.

a.

b.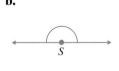

c. **d.**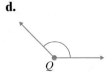

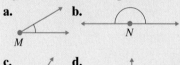

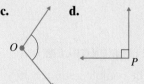

PRACTICE PROBLEM 3

Classify each angle as acute, right, obtuse, or straight.

Answers
3. **a.** acute, **b.** straight, **c.** obtuse, **d.** right

Continued on next page

Solution:

a. ∠R is a right angle, denoted by ⌐.

b. ∠S is a straight angle.

c. ∠T is an acute angle. It measures between 0° and 90°.

d. ∠Q is an obtuse angle. It measures between 90° and 180°.

▣ **Work Practice Problem 3**

Let's look at ∠B below, whose measure is 62°.

There is a shorthand notation for writing the measure of this angle. To write "The measure of ∠B is 62°," we can write,

$$m\angle B = 62°.$$

By the way, note that ∠B is an acute angle because $m\angle B$ is between 0° and 90°.

Objective **C** Identifying Complementary and Supplementary Angles

Two angles that have a sum of 90° are called **complementary angles.** We say that each angle is the **complement** of the other.

∠R and ∠S are complementary angles because

$$m\angle R + m\angle S = 60° + 30° = 90°$$

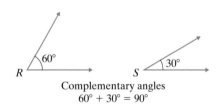

Complementary angles
60° + 30° = 90°

Two angles that have a sum of 180° are called **supplementary angles.** We say that each angle is the **supplement** of the other.

∠M and ∠N are supplementary angles because

$$m\angle M + m\angle N = 125° + 55° = 180°$$

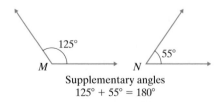

Supplementary angles
125° + 55° = 180°

PRACTICE PROBLEM 4

Find the complement of a 36° angle.

EXAMPLE 4 Find the complement of a 48° angle.

Solution: Two angles that have a sum of 90° are complementary. This means that the complement of an angle that measures 48° is an angle that measures 90° − 48° = 42°.

▣ **Work Practice Problem 4**

Answer

4. 54°

EXAMPLE 5 Find the supplement of a 107° angle.

Solution: Two angles that have a sum of 180° are supplementary. This means that the supplement of an angle that measures 107° is an angle that measures 180° − 107° = 73°.

▣ **Work Practice Problem 5**

✔**Concept Check** True or false? The supplement of a 38° angle is 52°. Explain.

Objective ▣ Finding Measures of Angles

Measures of angles can be added or subtracted to find measures of related angles.

EXAMPLE 6 Find the measure of ∠x.

Solution: $m\angle x = m\angle QTS - m\angle RTS$
$= 87° - 52°$
$= 35°$

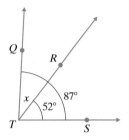

▣ **Work Practice Problem 6**

Two lines in a plane can be either parallel or intersecting. **Parallel lines** never meet. **Intersecting lines** meet at a point. The symbol ‖ is used to indicate "is parallel to." For example, in the figure $p\|q$.

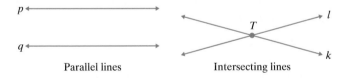

Parallel lines   Intersecting lines

Some intersecting lines are perpendicular. Two lines are **perpendicular** if they form right angles when they intersect. The symbol ⊥ is used to denote "is perpendicular to." For example, in the figure below, $n \perp m$.

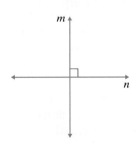

Perpendicular lines

When two lines intersect, four angles are formed. Two angles that are opposite each other are called **vertical angles.** Vertical angles have the same measure. Two angles that share a common side are called **adjacent angles.** Adjacent angles formed by intersecting lines are supplementary. That is, they have a sum of 180°.

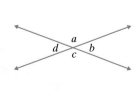

Vertical angles:
∠a and ∠c
∠d and ∠b

Adjacent angles:
∠a and ∠b
∠b and ∠c
∠c and ∠d
∠d and ∠a

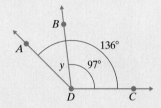
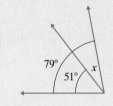

Here are a few real-life examples of the lines we just discussed.

Parallel lines

Vertical angles

Perpendicular lines

PRACTICE PROBLEM 7

Find the measure of $\angle a$, $\angle b$, and $\angle c$.

EXAMPLE 7 Find the measure of $\angle x$, $\angle y$, and $\angle z$ if the measure of $\angle t$ is 42°.

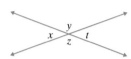

Solution: Since $\angle t$ and $\angle x$ are vertical angles, they have the same measure, so $\angle x$ measures 42°.

Since $\angle t$ and $\angle y$ are adjacent angles, their measures have a sum of 180°. So $\angle y$ measures $180° - 42° = 138°$.

Since $\angle y$ and $\angle z$ are vertical angles, they have the same measure. So $\angle z$ measures 138°.

■ **Work Practice Problem 7**

A line that intersects two or more lines at different points is called a **transversal.** Line l is a transversal that intersects lines m and n. The eight angles formed have special names. Some of these names are:

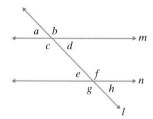

Corresponding angles: $\angle a$ and $\angle e$, $\angle c$ and $\angle g$, $\angle b$ and $\angle f$, $\angle d$ and $\angle h$

Alternate interior angles: $\angle c$ and $\angle f$, $\angle d$ and $\angle e$

When two lines cut by a transversal are *parallel,* the following are true:

Parallel Lines Cut by a Transversal

If two parallel lines are cut by a transversal, then the measures of **corresponding angles are equal** and the measures of the **alternate interior angles are equal.**

PRACTICE PROBLEM 8

Given that $m \parallel n$ and that the measure of $\angle w = 40°$, find the measures of all the angles shown.

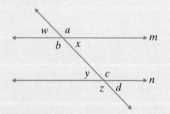

EXAMPLE 8 Given that $m \parallel n$ and that the measure of $\angle w$ is 100°, find the measures of $\angle x$, $\angle y$, and $\angle z$.

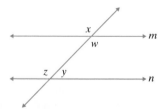

Solution:

$m\angle x = 100°$. $\quad$ $\angle x$ and $\angle w$ are vertical angles.

$m\angle z = 100°$. $\quad$ $\angle x$ and $\angle z$ are corresponding angles.

$m\angle y = 180° - 100° = 80°$. $\quad$ $\angle z$ and $\angle y$ are supplementary angles.

■ **Work Practice Problem 8**

Answers
7. $m\angle a = 112°; m\angle b = 68°$;
 $m\angle c = 68°$,
8. $m\angle x = 40°; m\angle y = 40°$;
 $m\angle z = 140°; m\angle a = 140°$;
 $m\angle b = 140°$; $m\angle c = 140°$;
 $m\angle d = 40°$

Objective A *Identify each figure as a line, a ray, a line segment, or an angle. Then name the figure using the given points. See Example 1.*

1.
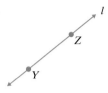

2.

3.

4.

5.

6.

7.

8.

Objective B *Fill in each blank. See Example 3.*

9. A right angle has a measure of _____.

10. A straight angle has a measure of _____.

11. An acute angle measures between _____ and _____.

12. An obtuse angle measures between _____ and _____.

Classify each angle as acute, right, obtuse, or straight. See Example 3.

13.

14.

15.

16.
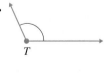

17.

18.

19.

20.

Objective **C** *Find each complementary or supplementary angle as indicated. See Examples 4 and 5.*

21. Find the complement of a 17° angle.

22. Find the complement of an 87° angle.

23. Find the supplement of a 17° angle.

24. Find the supplement of an 87° angle.

25. Find the complement of a 58° angle.

26. Find the complement of a 22° angle.

27. Find the supplement of a 105° angle.

28. Find the supplement of a 155° angle.

29. Identify the pairs of complementary angles.

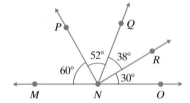

30. Identify the pairs of complementary angles.

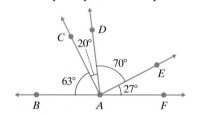

31. Identify the pairs of supplementary angles.

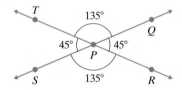

32. Identify the pairs of supplementary angles.

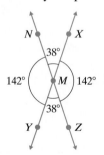

Objective **D** *Find the measure of ∠x in each figure. See Example 6.*

33.

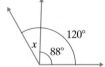

34.

35.

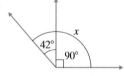

36.

Find the measures of angles x, y, and z in each figure. See Examples 7 and 8.

37.

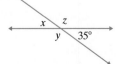

38.

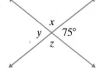

39.

40.

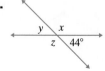

41. $m \parallel n$

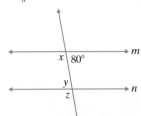

42. $m \parallel n$

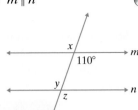

43. $m \parallel n$

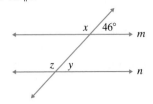

44. $m \parallel n$

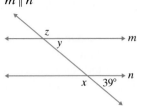

Objectives Ⓐ Ⓓ **Mixed Practice** *Find two other ways of naming each angle. See Example 2.*

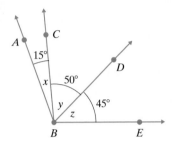

45. $\angle x$

46. $\angle y$

47. $\angle z$

48. $\angle ABE$ (just name one other way)

Find the measure of each angle in the figure above.

49. $\angle ABC$

50. $\angle EBD$

51. $\angle CBD$

52. $\angle CBA$

53. $\angle DBA$

54. $\angle EBC$

55. $\angle CBE$

56. $\angle ABE$

Review

Perform each indicated operation. See Sections 3.3, 3.5, and 3.7.

57. $\dfrac{7}{8} + \dfrac{1}{4}$

58. $\dfrac{7}{8} - \dfrac{1}{4}$

59. $\dfrac{7}{8} \cdot \dfrac{1}{4}$

60. $\dfrac{7}{8} \div \dfrac{1}{4}$

61. $3\dfrac{1}{3} - 2\dfrac{1}{2}$

62. $3\dfrac{1}{3} + 2\dfrac{1}{2}$

63. $3\dfrac{1}{3} \div 2\dfrac{1}{2}$

64. $3\dfrac{1}{3} \cdot 2\dfrac{1}{2}$

Concept Extensions

65. The angle between the two walls of the Vietnam Veterans Memorial in Washington, D.C., is 125.2°. Find the supplement of this angle. (*Source:* National Park Service)

66. The faces of Khafre's Pyramid at Giza, Egypt, are inclined at an angle of 53.13°. Find the complement of this angle. (*Source:* PBS *NOVA* Online)

Answer true or false for Exercises 67 through 70. See the Concept Check in this section.

67. The complement of a 100° angle is an 80° angle.

68. It is possible to find the complement of a 120° angle.

69. It is possible to find the supplement of a 120° angle.

70. The supplement of a 5° angle is a 175° angle.

71. If lines m and n are parallel, find the measures of angles a through e.

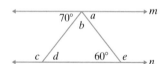

72. In your own words, describe how to find the complement and the supplement of a given angle.

73. Find two complementary angles with the same measure.

74. Can two supplementary angles both be acute? Explain why or why not.

In order to prepare for the sections ahead in this chapter, we first review plane figures and solids.

Objective Ⓐ **Identifying Plane Figures**

Recall from Section 9.1 that a **plane** is a flat surface that extends indefinitely.

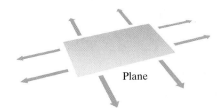

Plane

A **plane figure** is a figure that lies on a plane. Plane figures, like planes, have length and width but no thickness or depth.

A **polygon** is a closed plane figure that basically consists of three or more line segments that meet at their end points.

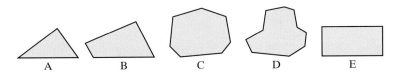

A **regular polygon** is one whose sides are all the same length and whose angles are the same measure.

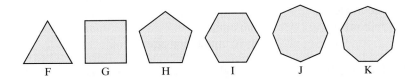

A polygon is named according to the number of its sides.

Polygons		
Number of Sides	**Name**	**Figure Examples**
3	Triangle	A, F
4	Quadrilateral	B, E, G
5	Pentagon	H
6	Hexagon	I
7	Heptagon	C
8	Octagon	J
9	Nonagon	K
10	Decagon	D

Some triangles and quadrilaterals are given special names, so let's study these polygons further. We begin with triangles.

The sum of the measures of the angles of a triangle is 180°.

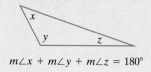

$$m\angle x + m\angle y + m\angle z = 180°$$

Find the measure of $\angle x$.

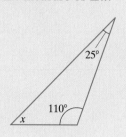

EXAMPLE 1 Find the measure of $\angle a$.

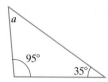

Solution: Since the sum of the measures of the three angles is 180°, we have

measure of $\angle a$, or $m\angle a = 180° - 95° - 35° = 50°$

To check, see that $95° + 35° + 50° = 180°$.

⬛ **Work Practice Problem 1**

We can classify triangles according to the lengths of their sides. (We will use tick marks to denote the sides and angles of a figure that are equal.)

 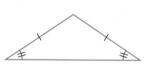 

Equilateral triangle

All three sides are the same length. Also, all three angles have the same measure.

Isosceles triangle

Two sides are the same length. Also, the angles opposite the equal sides have equal measure.

Scalene triangle

No sides are the same length. No angles have the same measure.

One other important type of triangle is a right triangle. A **right triangle** is a triangle with a right angle. The side opposite the right angle is called the **hypotenuse,** and the other two sides are called **legs.**

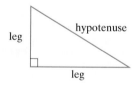

Find the measure of $\angle y$.

EXAMPLE 2 Find the measure of $\angle b$.

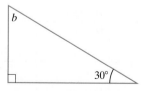

Solution: We know that the measure of the right angle, ⌐, is 90°. Since the sum of the measures of the angles is 180°, we have

measure of $\angle b$, or $m\angle b = 180° - 90° - 30° = 60°$

⬛ **Work Practice Problem 2**

Answers

1. 45°, **2.** 65°

Helpful Hint

From the previous example, can you see that in a right triangle, the sum of the other two acute angles is 90°? This is because

$$90° \ + \ 90° \ = \ 180°$$

| right angle's measure | sum of other two angles' measures | sum of angles' measures |

Now we review some special quadrilaterals. A **parallelogram** is a special quadrilateral with opposite sides parallel and equal in length.

A **rectangle** is a special **parallelogram** that has four right angles.

A **square** is a special **rectangle** that has all four sides equal in length.

A **rhombus** is a special **parallelogram** that has all four sides equal in length.

A **trapezoid** is a quadrilateral with exactly one pair of opposite sides parallel.

parallel sides

✔ **Concept Check** True or false? All quadrilaterals are parallelograms. Explain.

In addition to triangles, quadrilaterals, and other polygons, circles are also plane figures. A **circle** is a plane figure that consists of all points that are the same fixed distance from a point c. The point c is called the **center** of the circle. A **radius** of a circle is the distance from the center of the circle to any point on the circle. A **diameter** of a circle is the distance across the circle passing through the center. Notice that the diameter is twice the radius, and the radius is half the diameter.

radius
center
diameter

✔ **Concept Check Answer**
false

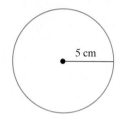

$$\text{diameter} = 2 \cdot \text{radius} \qquad \text{radius} = \frac{\text{diameter}}{2}$$

$$d = 2 \cdot r \qquad\qquad r = \frac{d}{2}$$

PRACTICE PROBLEM 3

Find the radius of the circle.

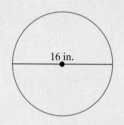

16 in.

EXAMPLE 3 Find the diameter of the circle.

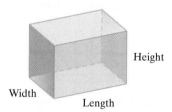

5 cm

Solution: The diameter is twice the radius.

$$d = 2 \cdot r$$
$$d = 2 \cdot 5 \text{ cm} = 10 \text{ cm}$$

The diameter is 10 centimeters.

◼ **Work Practice Problem 3**

Objective **B** Identifying Solid Figures

Recall from Section 9.1 that space extends in all directions indefinitely.

A **solid** is a figure that lies in space. Solids have length, width, and height or depth.

A **rectangular solid** is a solid that consists of six sides, or faces, all of which are rectangles.

Height

Width

Length

A **cube** is a rectangular solid whose six sides are squares.

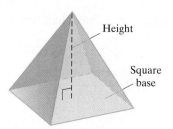

A **pyramid** is shown below. The pyramids we will study have square bases and heights that are perpendicular to their base.

Height

Square base

Answer

3. 8 in.

A **sphere** consists of all points in space that are the same distance from a point c. The point c is called the **center** of the sphere. A **radius** of a sphere is the distance from the center to any point on the sphere. A **diameter** of a sphere is the distance across the sphere passing through the center.

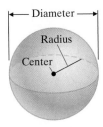

The radius and diameter of a sphere are related in the same way as the radius and diameter of a circle.

$$d = 2 \cdot r \quad \text{or} \quad r = \frac{d}{2}$$

EXAMPLE 4 Find the radius of the sphere.

Solution: The radius is half the diameter.

$$r = \frac{d}{2}$$

$$r = \frac{36 \text{ feet}}{2} = 18 \text{ feet}$$

The radius is 18 feet.

Work Practice Problem 4

The **cylinders** we will study have bases that are in the shape of circles and heights that are perpendicular to their base.

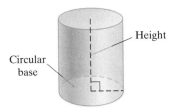

The **cones** we will study have bases that are circles and heights that are perpendicular to their base.

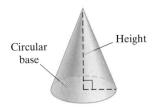

PRACTICE PROBLEM 4

Find the diameter of the sphere.

Identify each polygon. See the table at the beginning of this section.

1.

2.

3.

4.

5.

6.

7.

8.

Objective **A** *Classify each triangle as equilateral, isosceles, or scalene. Also identify any triangles that are also right triangles.*

9.

10.

11.

12.

13.

14.

Find the measure of $\angle x$ in each figure. See Examples 1 and 2.

15.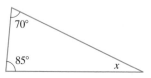

70°
85°
x

16.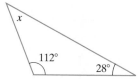

x
112°
28°

17.

95°
72°
x

18.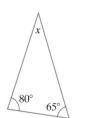

x
80°
65°

19.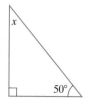

x
50°

20.

x
20°

632

Fill in each blank.

21. Twice the radius of a circle is its _____.

22. A rectangle with all four sides equal is a _____.

23. A parallelogram with four right angles is a _____.

24. Half the diameter of a circle is its _____.

25. A quadrilateral with opposite sides parallel is a _____.

26. A quadrilateral with exactly one pair of opposite sides parallel is a _____.

27. The side opposite the right angle of a right triangle is called the _____.

28. A triangle with no equal sides is a _____.

Find the unknown diameter or radius in each figure. See Example 3.

29.

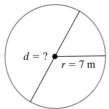

$d = ?$
$r = 7$ m

30.

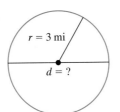

$r = 3$ mi
$d = ?$

31.

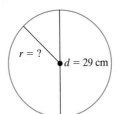

$r = ?$
$d = 29$ cm

32.

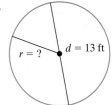

$r = ?$
$d = 13$ ft

33.

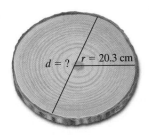

$d = ?$ $r = 20.3$ cm

34.

$d = ?$
$r = 7.8$ in.

35.

$d = 72$ in.
$r = ?$

Largest pumpkin pie (*Source: Guinness World Records*)

36.

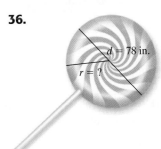

$d = 78$ in.
$r = ?$

Largest lollipop (*Source: Guinness World Records*)

Objective B *Identify each solid.*

37.

38.

39.

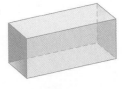

40.

41.

42.

Identify the shape of each item.

43.

44.

45.

46.

47.

48.

49.

50.

Find each unknown radius or diameter. See Example 4.

51. The radius of a sphere is 7.4 inches. Find its diameter.

7.4 in.

52. The radius of a sphere is 5.8 meters. Find its diameter.

5.8 m

53. Find the radius of the sphere.

← *d* = 26 miles →

54. Find the radius of the sphere.

← *d* = 78 cm →

55. Saturn has a radius of approximately 36,184 miles. What is its diameter?

56. A sphere-shaped wasp nest found in Japan had a radius of approximately 15 inches. What was its diameter? (*Source: Guinness World Records*)

Review

Perform each indicated operation. See Sections 1.3, 1.6, 4.2, and 4.3.

57. $2(18) + 2(36)$

58. $4(87)$

59. $4(3.14)$

60. $2(7.8) + 2(9.6)$

Concept Extensions

Determine whether each statement is true or false. See the Concept Check in this section.

61. A square is also a rhombus.

62. A square is also a regular polygon.

63. A rectangle is also a parallelogram.

64. A trapezoid is also a parallelogram.

65. A pentagon is also a quadrilateral.

66. A rhombus is also a parallelogram.

67. Is an isosceles right triangle possible? If so, draw one.

68. The following demonstration is credited to the mathematician Pascal, who is said to have developed it as a young boy.

   Cut a triangle from a piece of paper. The length of the sides and the size of the angles is unimportant. Tear the points off the triangle as shown.

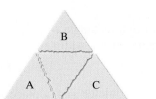

Place the points of the triangle together. Notice that a straight line is formed. What was Pascal trying to show?

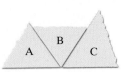

69. In your own words, explain whether a parallelogram is also a rhombus.

PRACTICE PROBLEM 1

a. Find the perimeter of the rectangle.

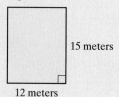

15 meters

12 meters

b. Find the perimeter of the rectangular lot shown below:

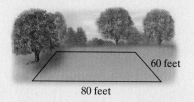

60 feet

80 feet

PRACTICE PROBLEM 2

Find the perimeter of a rectangle with a length of 22 centimeters and a width of 10 centimeters.

Answers
1. a. 54 m, **b.** 280 ft, **2.** 64 cm

636

9.3 PERIMETER

Objective **A** Using Formulas to Find Perimeters

Recall from Section 1.3 that the perimeter of a polygon is the distance around the polygon. This means that the perimeter of a polygon is the sum of the lengths of its sides.

EXAMPLE 1 Find the perimeter of the rectangle below.

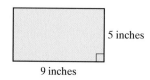

5 inches

9 inches

Solution:

$$\text{perimeter} = 9 \text{ inches} + 9 \text{ inches} + 5 \text{ inches} + 5 \text{ inches}$$
$$= 28 \text{ inches}$$

☐ **Work Practice Problem 1**

Notice that the perimeter of the rectangle in Example 1 can be written as $2 \cdot (9 \text{ inches}) + 2 \cdot (5 \text{ inches})$.

↑   ↑
length   width

In general, we can say that the perimeter of a rectangle is always

$$2 \cdot \text{length} + 2 \cdot \text{width}$$

As we have just seen, the perimeter of some special figures such as rectangles form patterns. These patterns are given as **formulas.** The formula for the perimeter of a rectangle is shown next:

Perimeter of a Rectangle

$$\text{perimeter} = 2 \cdot \text{length} + 2 \cdot \text{width}$$

In symbols, this can be written as

$$P = 2 \cdot l + 2 \cdot w$$

length

width   width

length

EXAMPLE 2 Find the perimeter of a rectangle with a length of 11 inches and a width of 3 inches.

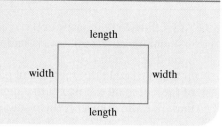

11 in.

3 in.

Solution: We use the formula for perimeter and replace the letters by their known lengths.

$$P = 2 \cdot l + 2 \cdot w$$
$$= 2 \cdot 11 \text{ in.} + 2 \cdot 3 \text{ in.} \quad \text{Replace } l \text{ with 11 in. and } w \text{ with 3 in.}$$
$$= 22 \text{ in.} + 6 \text{ in.}$$
$$= 28 \text{ in.}$$

The perimeter is 28 inches.

☐ **Work Practice Problem 2**

Recall that a square is a special rectangle with all four sides the same length. The formula for the perimeter of a square is shown next:

Perimeter of a Square

$$\text{Perimeter} = \text{side} + \text{side} + \text{side} + \text{side}$$
$$= 4 \cdot \text{side}$$

In symbols,

$$P = 4 \cdot s$$

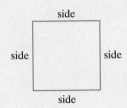

EXAMPLE 3 **Finding the Perimeter of a Field**

How much fencing is needed to enclose a square field 50 yards on a side?

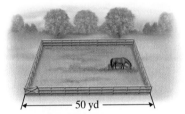

50 yd

Solution: To find the amount of fencing needed, we find the distance around, or perimeter. The formula for the perimeter of a square is $P = 4 \cdot s$. We use this formula and replace s by 50 yards.

$$P = 4 \cdot s$$
$$= 4 \cdot 50 \text{ yd}$$
$$= 200 \text{ yd}$$

The amount of fencing needed is 200 yards.

■ **Work Practice Problem 3**

The formula for the perimeter of a triangle with sides of lengths a, b, and c is given next:

Perimeter of a Triangle

$$\text{Perimeter} = \text{side } a + \text{side } b + \text{side } c$$

In symbols,

$$P = a + b + c$$

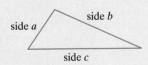

side a side b

side c

PRACTICE PROBLEM 3

Find the perimeter of a square tabletop if each side is 5 feet long.

5 feet

5 feet

Answer

3. 20 ft

PRACTICE PROBLEM 4

Find the perimeter of a triangle if the sides are 5 centimeters, 9 centimeters, and 7 centimeters in length.

EXAMPLE 4 Find the perimeter of a triangle if the sides are 3 inches, 7 inches, and 6 inches.

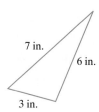

Solution: The formula for the perimeter is $P = a + b + c$, where a, b, and c are the lengths of the sides. Thus,

$$P = a + b + c$$
$$= 3 \text{ in.} + 7 \text{ in.} + 6 \text{ in.}$$
$$= 16 \text{ in.}$$

The perimeter of the triangle is 16 inches.

▣ **Work Practice Problem 4**

Recall that to find the perimeter of other polygons, we find the sum of the lengths of their sides.

PRACTICE PROBLEM 5

Find the perimeter of the trapezoid shown.

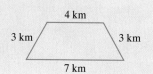

EXAMPLE 5 Find the perimeter of the trapezoid shown below:

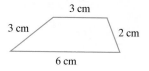

Solution: To find the perimeter, we find the sum of the lengths of its sides.

perimeter = 3 cm + 2 cm + 6 cm + 3 cm = 14 cm

The perimeter is 14 centimeters.

▣ **Work Practice Problem 5**

PRACTICE PROBLEM 6

Find the perimeter of the room shown.

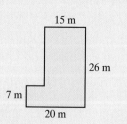

EXAMPLE 6 **Finding the Perimeter of a Room**

Find the perimeter of the room shown below:

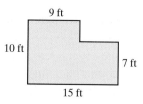

Solution: To find the perimeter of the room, we first need to find the lengths of all sides of the room.

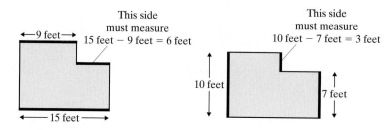

Answers

4. 21 cm, **5.** 17 km, **6.** 92 m

Now that we know the measures of all sides of the room, we can add the measures to find the perimeter.

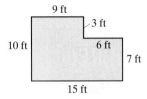

$$\text{perimeter} = 10 \text{ ft} + 9 \text{ ft} + 3 \text{ ft} + 6 \text{ ft} + 7 \text{ ft} + 15 \text{ ft}$$
$$= 50 \text{ ft}$$

The perimeter of the room is 50 feet.

▣ **Work Practice Problem 6**

EXAMPLE 7 **Calculating the Cost of Baseboard**

A rectangular room measures 10 feet by 12 feet. Find the cost to install new base-board around the room if the cost of the baseboard is $0.66 per foot.

Solution: First we find the perimeter of the room.

$$P = 2 \cdot l + 2 \cdot w$$
$$= 2 \cdot 12 \text{ ft} + 2 \cdot 10 \text{ ft} \quad \text{Replace } l \text{ with 12 feet and } w \text{ with 10 feet.}$$
$$= 24 \text{ ft} + 20 \text{ ft}$$
$$= 44 \text{ ft}$$

The cost of the baseboard is

$$\text{cost} = \$0.66 \cdot 44 \text{ ft} = 29.04$$

The cost of the baseboard is $29.04.

▣ **Work Practice Problem 7**

Objective B Using Formulas to Find Circumferences

Recall from Section 4.3 that the distance around a circle is called the **circumference.** This distance depends on the radius or the diameter of the circle.

   The formulas for circumference are shown next:

Circumference of a Circle

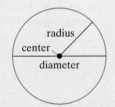

Circumference = $2 \cdot \pi \cdot$ radius   or   Circumference = $\pi \cdot$ diameter
In symbols,

$$C = 2 \cdot \pi \cdot r \quad \text{or} \quad C = \pi \cdot d,$$

where $\pi \approx 3.14 \quad \text{or} \quad \pi \approx \dfrac{22}{7}$.

PRACTICE PROBLEM 7

A rectangular lot measures 60 feet by 120 feet. Find the cost to install fencing around the lot if the cost of fencing is $1.90 per foot.

Answer
7. $684

To better understand circumference and π(pi), try the following experiment. Take any can and measure its circumference and its diameter.

The can in the figure above has a circumference of 23.5 centimeters and a diameter of 7.5 centimeters. Now divide the circumference by the diameter.

$$\frac{\text{circumference}}{\text{diameter}} = \frac{23.5 \text{ cm}}{7.5 \text{ cm}} \approx 3.13$$

Try this with other sizes of cylinders and circles—you should always get a number close to 3.1. The exact ratio of circumference to diameter is π. (Recall that $\pi \approx 3.14$ or $\approx \frac{22}{7}$.)

PRACTICE PROBLEM 8

a. An irrigation device waters a circular region with a diameter of 20 yards. Find the exact circumference of the watered region, then use $\pi \approx 3.14$ to give an approximation.

b. A manufacturer of clocks is designing a new model. To help the designer calculate the cost of materials to make the new clock, calculate the circumference of a clock with a face diameter of 12 inches. Give an exact circumference; then use $\pi \approx 3.14$ to approximate.

Answers

8. a. exactly 20π yd ≈ 62.8 yd,
b. exactly 12π in. ≈ 37.68 in.

✔ Concept Check Answer

a square with side length 5 in.

EXAMPLE 8 Finding Circumference of Spa

Mary Catherine Dooley plans to install a border of new tiling around the circumference of her circular spa. If her spa has a diameter of 14 feet, find its exact circumference. Then use the approximation 3.14 for π to approximate the circumference.

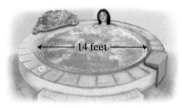

14 feet

Solution: Because we are given the diameter, we use the formula $C = \pi \cdot d$.

$$C = \pi \cdot d$$
$$= \pi \cdot 14 \text{ ft} \quad \text{\small Replace } d \text{ with 14 feet.}$$
$$= 14\pi \text{ ft}$$

The circumference of the spa is *exactly* 14π feet. By replacing π with the *approximation* 3.14, we find that the circumference is *approximately* 14 feet · 3.14 = 43.96 feet.

Work Practice Problem 8

✔ Concept Check The distance around which figure is greater: a square with side length 5 inches or a circle with radius 3 inches?

Objective **A** *Find the perimeter of each figure. See Examples 1 through 6.*

1.

Rectangle — 15 ft, 17 ft

2.

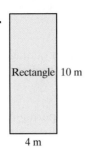

Rectangle — 10 m, 4 m

3.

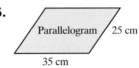

Parallelogram — 25 cm, 35 cm

4.

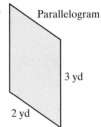

Parallelogram — 3 yd, 2 yd

5.

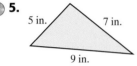

5 in., 7 in., 9 in.

6.

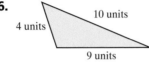

10 units, 4 units, 9 units

7.

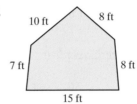

10 ft, 8 ft, 7 ft, 8 ft, 15 ft

8.

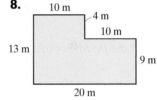

10 m, 4 m, 10 m, 13 m, 20 m, 9 m

Find the perimeter of each regular polygon.

9.

4 inches

10.

8 m

11.

21 cm

12.

15 yd

Solve. See Examples 1 through 7.

13. A polygon has sides of length 5 feet, 3 feet, 2 feet, 7 feet, and 4 feet. Find its perimeter.

14. A triangle has sides of length 8 inches, 12 inches, and 10 inches. Find its perimeter.

15. Baseboard is to be installed in a square room that measures 15 feet on one side. Find how much baseboard is needed.

16. Find how much fencing is needed to enclose a rectangular rose garden 85 feet by 15 feet.

17. If a football field is 53 yards wide and 120 yards long, what is the perimeter?

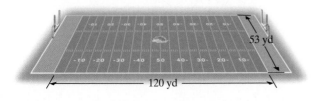

53 yd

120 yd

18. A stop sign has eight equal sides of length 12 inches. Find its perimeter.

641

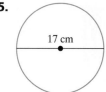 **19.** A metal strip is being installed around a workbench that is 8 feet long and 3 feet wide. Find how much stripping is needed.

20. Find how much fencing is needed to enclose a rectangular garden 70 feet by 21 feet.

21. If the stripping in Exercise 19 costs $3 per foot, find the total cost of the stripping.

22. If the fencing in Exercise 20 costs $2 per foot, find the total cost of the fencing.

23. A regular hexagon has a side length of 6 inches. Find its perimeter.

24. A regular pentagon has a side length of 14 meters. Find its perimeter.

25. Find the perimeter of the top of a square compact disc case if the length of one side is 7 inches.

26. Find the perimeter of a square ceramic tile with a side of length 5 inches.

27. A rectangular room measures 6 feet by 8 feet. Find the cost of installing a strip of wallpaper around the room if the wallpaper costs $0.86 per foot.

28. A rectangular house measures 75 feet by 60 feet. Find the cost of installing gutters around the house if the cost is $2.36 per foot.

Find the perimeter of each figure. See Example 6.

29.

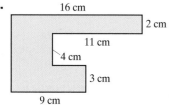

30.

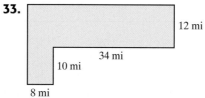

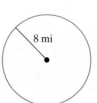 **31.**

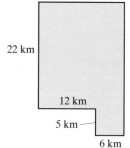

32.

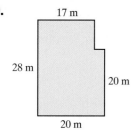

33.

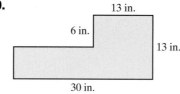

34.

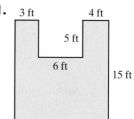

Objective **B** *Find the circumference of each circle. Give the exact circumference and then an approximation. Use* $\pi \approx 3.14$. *See Example 8.*

35.

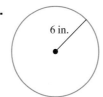

36.

37.

38.

50 ft

39.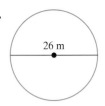

26 m

40.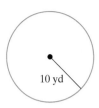

10 yd

41. A circular fountain has a radius of 5 feet. Approximate the distance around the fountain. Use $\frac{22}{7}$ for π.

42. A circular walkway has a radius of 40 meters. Approximate the distance around the walkway. Use 3.14 for π.

43. Meteor Crater, near Winslow, Arizona, is 4000 feet in diameter. Approximate the distance around the crater. Use 3.14 for π. (*Source: The Handy Science Answer Book*)

44. The largest pearl, the *Pearl of Lao-tze*, has a diameter of $5\frac{1}{2}$ inches. Approximate the distance around the pearl. Use $\frac{22}{7}$ for π. (*Source: The Guinness Book of Records*)

Objectives Ⓐ Ⓑ **Mixed Practice** *Find the distance around each figure. For circles, give the exact circumference and then an approximation. Use $\pi \approx 3.14$.*

45.

9 mi
4.7 mi
6 mi
11 mi

46.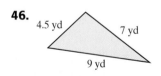

4.5 yd
7 yd
9 yd

47.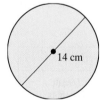

14 cm

48.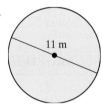

11 m

49.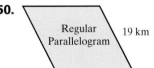

Regular Pentagon
8 mm

50.

Regular Parallelogram
19 km

51.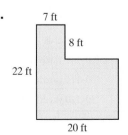

7 ft
8 ft
22 ft
20 ft

52.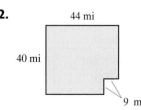

44 mi
40 mi
9 mi

Review

Simplify. See Section 1.9.

53. $5 + 6 \cdot 3$ **54.** $25 - 3 \cdot 7$ **55.** $(20 - 16) \div 4$ **56.** $6 \cdot (8 + 2)$

57. $(18 + 8) - (12 + 4)$ **58.** $72 \div (2 \cdot 6)$ **59.** $(72 \div 2) \cdot 6$ **60.** $4^1 \cdot (2^3 - 8)$

Concept Extensions

Recall from Section 1.6 that area measures the amount of surface of a region. Given the following situations, tell whether you are more likely to be concerned with area or perimeter.

61. ordering fencing to fence a yard

62. ordering grass seed to plant in a yard

63. buying carpet to install in a room

64. buying gutters to install on a house

65. ordering paint to paint a wall

66. ordering baseboards to install in a room

67. buying a wallpaper border to go on the walls around a room

68. buying fertilizer for your yard

There are a number of factors that determine the dimensions of a rectangular soccer field. Use the table below to answer Exercises 69 and 70.

Soccer Field Width and Length		
Age	Width Min–Max	Length Min–Max
Under 6/7:	15–20 yards	25–30 yards
Under 8:	20–25 yards	30–40 yards
Under 9:	30–35 yards	40–50 yards
Under 10:	40–50 yards	60–70 yards
Under 11:	40–50 yards	70–80 yards
Under 12:	40–55 yards	100–105 yards
Under 13:	50–60 yards	100–110 yards
International:	70–80 yards	110–120 yards

69. a. Find the minimum length and width of a soccer field for 8-year-old children. (Carefully consider the age.)

  b. Find the perimeter of this field.

70. a. Find the maximum length and width of a soccer field for 12-year-old children.

  b. Find the perimeter of this field.

Solve. See the Concept Check in this section. Choose the figure that has greater distance around.

71. a. A square with side length 3 inches
    b. A circle with diameter 4 inches

72. a. A circle with diameter 7 inches
    b. A square with side length 7 inches

73. a. Find the circumference of each circle. Approximate the circumference by using 3.14 for π.

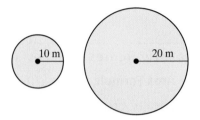

b. If the radius of a circle is doubled, is its corresponding circumference doubled?

74. a. Find the circumference of each circle. Approximate the circumference by using 3.14 for π.

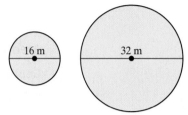

b. If the diameter of a circle is doubled, is its corresponding circumference doubled?

75. Find the perimeter of the skating rink.

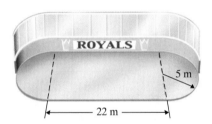

76. In your own words, explain how to find the perimeter of any polygon.

77. The perimeter of this rectangle is 30 feet. Find its width.

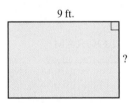

Find the perimeter. Round your results to the nearest tenth.

78.

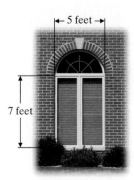

79.

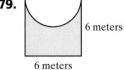

9.4 AREA

Objective A Finding Area of Geometric Figures

Recall that area measures the amount of surface of a region. Thus far, we know how to find the area of a rectangle and a square. These formulas, as well as formulas for finding the areas of other common geometric figures, are given next:

Area Formulas of Common Geometric Figures

Geometric Figure	Area Formula
RECTANGLE 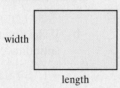	Area of a rectangle: **Area = length · width** $A = lw$
SQUARE 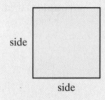	Area of a square: **Area = side · side** $A = s \cdot s = s^2$
TRIANGLE 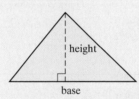	Area of a triangle: **Area $= \dfrac{1}{2} \cdot$ base · height** $A = \dfrac{1}{2} \cdot b \cdot h$
PARALLELOGRAM 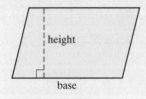	Area of a parallelogram: **Area = base · height** $A = b \cdot h$
TRAPEZOID 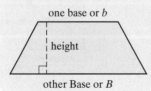	Area of a trapezoid: **Area $= \dfrac{1}{2} \cdot$ (one base + other Base) · height** $A = \dfrac{1}{2} \cdot (b + B) \cdot h$

Use these formulas for the following examples.

Helpful Hint

Area is always measured in square units.

EXAMPLE 1 Find the area of the triangle.

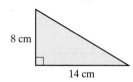

8 cm

14 cm

Solution: $A = \frac{1}{2} \cdot b \cdot h$

$\qquad = \frac{1}{2} \cdot 14 \text{ cm} \cdot 8 \text{ cm}$

$\qquad = \frac{\overset{1}{\cancel{2}} \cdot 7 \cdot 8}{\underset{1}{\cancel{2}}} \text{ sq cm}$

$\qquad = 56 \text{ square cm}$

Helpful Hint

You may see 56 sq cm, for example, written with the notation 56 cm². Both of these notations mean the same quantity.

The area is 56 square centimeters.

■ **Work Practice Problem 1**

EXAMPLE 2 Find the area of the parallelogram.

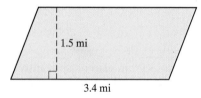

1.5 mi

3.4 mi

Solution:

$A = b \cdot h$

$\qquad = 3.4 \text{ miles} \cdot 1.5 \text{ miles}$

$\qquad = 5.1 \text{ square miles}$

The area is 5.1 square miles.

■ **Work Practice Problem 2**

Helpful Hint

When finding the area of figures, be sure all measurements are changed to the same unit before calculations are made.

EXAMPLE 3 Find the area of the figure.

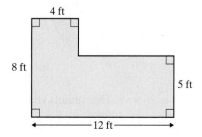

4 ft

8 ft

5 ft

12 ft

Continued on next page

PRACTICE PROBLEM 1

Find the area of the triangle.

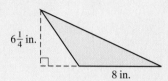

$6\frac{1}{4}$ in.

8 in.

PRACTICE PROBLEM 2

Find the area of the square.

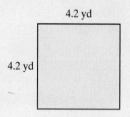

4.2 yd

4.2 yd

PRACTICE PROBLEM 3

Find the area of the figure.

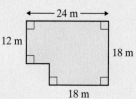

24 m

12 m

18 m

18 m

Answers

1. 25 sq in., **2.** 17.64 sq yd,

3. 396 sq m

Solution: Split the figure into two rectangles. To find the area of the figure, we find the sum of the areas of the two rectangles.

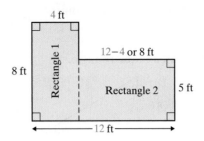

Area of Rectangle 1 $= l \cdot w$

$\qquad = 8 \text{ feet} \cdot 4 \text{ feet}$

$\qquad = 32 \text{ square feet}$

Notice that the length of Rectangle 2 is 12 feet $-$ 4 feet, or 8 feet.

Area of Rectangle 2 $= l \cdot w$

$\qquad = 8 \text{ feet} \cdot 5 \text{ feet}$

$\qquad = 40 \text{ square feet}$

Area of the Figure $=$ Area of Rectangle 1 $+$ Area of Rectangle 2

$\qquad = 32 \text{ square feet} + 40 \text{ square feet}$

$\qquad = 72 \text{ square feet}$

■ **Work Practice Problem 3**

Helpful Hint

The figure in Example 3 can also be split into two rectangles as shown:

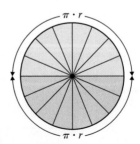

To better understand the formula for area of a circle, try the following. Cut a circle into many pieces as shown:

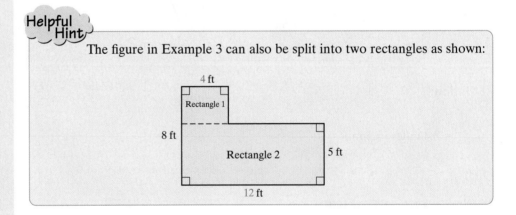

The circumference of a circle is $2 \cdot \pi \cdot r$. This means that the circumference of half a circle is half of $2 \cdot \pi \cdot r$, or $\pi \cdot r$.

Then unfold the two halves of the circle and place them together as shown:

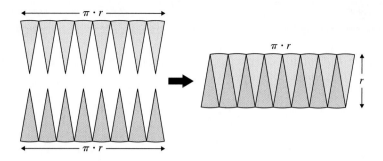

The figure on the right is almost a parallelogram with a base of $\pi \cdot r$ and a height of r. The area is

$$A = \boxed{\text{base}} \cdot \boxed{\text{height}}$$

$$= (\pi \cdot r) \cdot \quad r$$

$$= \pi \cdot r^2$$

This is the formula for area of a circle.

Area Formula of a Circle

CIRCLE

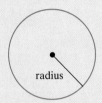

radius

Area of a circle:

Area $= \pi \cdot (\mathbf{radius})^2$

$\quad A = \pi \cdot r^2$

(A fraction approximation for π is $\dfrac{22}{7}$.)

(A decimal approximation for π is 3.14.)

EXAMPLE 4 Find the area of a circle with a radius of 3 feet. Find the exact area and an approximation. Use 3.14 as an approximation for π.

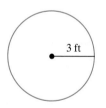

3 ft

Solution: We let $r = 3$ ft and use the formula.

$A = \pi \cdot r^2$

$\quad = \pi \cdot (3 \text{ ft})^2$

$\quad = \pi \cdot 9$ square ft, or $9 \cdot \pi$ square ft

To approximate this area, we substitute 3.14 for π.

$9 \cdot \pi$ square feet $\approx 9 \cdot 3.14$ square feet

$\qquad\qquad\qquad = 28.26$ square feet

The *exact* area of the circle is 9π square feet, which is *approximately* 28.26 square feet.

🔲 **Work Practice Problem 4**

✔**Concept Check** Use diagrams to decide which figure would have a larger area: a circle of diameter 10 inches or a square 10 inches long on each side.

PRACTICE PROBLEM 4

Find the area of the given circle. Find the exact area and an approximation. Use 3.14 as an approximation for π.

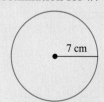

7 cm

Answer

4. 49π sq cm ≈ 153.86 sq cm

✔ **Concept Check Answer**

a square 10 in. long on each side

Objective 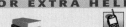 *Find the area of the geometric figure. If the figure is a circle, give an exact area and then use the given* **approximation** *for π to approximate the area. See Examples 1 through 4.*

1.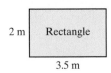
2 m · Rectangle · 3.5 m

2.
2.75 ft · Rectangle · 7 ft

3.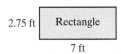
3 yd · $6\frac{1}{2}$ yd

4.
5 ft · $4\frac{1}{2}$ ft

5.
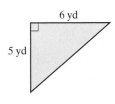
6 yd · 5 yd

6.
5 ft · 7 ft

7. Use 3.14 for π.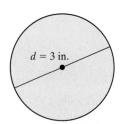
d = 3 in.

8. Use $\frac{22}{7}$ for π.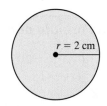
r = 2 cm

9.

Square · 4.2 ft

10.

Square · 2.6 m

11.
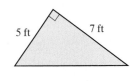
5 m · Trapezoid · 4 m · 9 m

12.
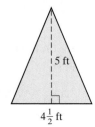
Trapezoid · 6 in. · 5 in. · $8\frac{1}{2}$ in.

13.
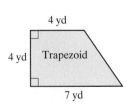
4 yd · 4 yd · Trapezoid · 7 yd

14.
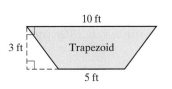
10 ft · 3 ft · Trapezoid · 5 ft

15.
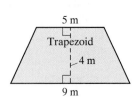
7 ft · Parallelogram · $5\frac{1}{4}$ ft

16.
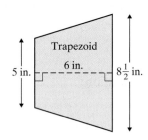
Parallelogram · $4\frac{1}{4}$ cm · 3 cm

17.

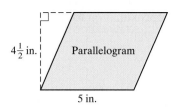

$4\frac{1}{2}$ in.   Parallelogram

5 in.

18.

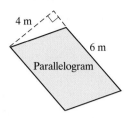

4 m

6 m

Parallelogram

19.

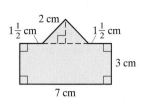

2 cm

$1\frac{1}{2}$ cm $1\frac{1}{2}$ cm

3 cm

7 cm

20.

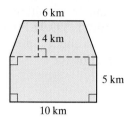

6 km

4 km

5 km

10 km

21.

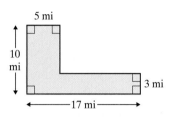

5 mi

10 mi

3 mi

17 mi

22.

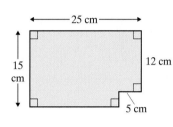

25 cm

15 cm

12 cm

5 cm

23.

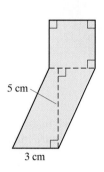

5 cm

3 cm

24.

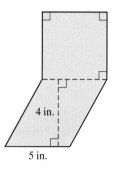

4 in.

5 in.

25. Use $\frac{22}{7}$ for π.

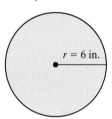

$r = 6$ in.

26. Use 3.14 for π.

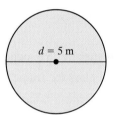

$d = 5$ m

Solve. See Examples 1 through 4.

27. A $10\frac{1}{2}$-foot by 16-foot concrete wall is to be built using concrete blocks. Find the area of the wall.

28. The floor of Terry's attic is 24 feet by 35 feet. Find how many square feet of insulation are needed to cover the attic floor.

29. The world's largest flag measures 505 feet by 225 feet. It's the U.S. "Super flag" owned by "Ski" Demski of Long Beach, California. Find its area. (*Source: Guinness World Records,* 2005)

30. The longest illuminated sign is in Ramat Gan, Israel, and measures 197 feet by 66 feet. Find its area. (*Source: The Guinness Book of Records*)

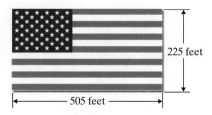

225 feet

505 feet

31. Paul Revere's Pizza in the USA will bake and deliver a pizza with a 4-foot diameter. This pizza is called the "Ultimate Party Pizza" and its current price is $99.99. Find the exact area of the top of the pizza and an approximation. Use 3.14 as an approximation for π.

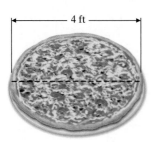

32. The face of a watch has a diameter of 2 centimeters. What is its area? Find the exact area and an approximation. Use 3.14 as an approximation for π.

33. One side of a concrete block measures 8 inches by 16 inches. Find the area of the side in square inches. Find the area in square feet (144 sq in. = 1 sq ft).

34. A standard *double* roll of wallpaper is $6\frac{5}{6}$ feet wide and 33 feet long. Find the area of the *double* roll.

35. A picture frame measures 20 inches by $25\frac{1}{2}$ inches. Find how many square inches of glass the frame requires.

36. A mat to go under a tablecloth is made to fit a round dining table with a 4-foot diameter. Approximate how many square feet of mat there are. Use 3.14 as an approximation for π.

37. A drapery panel measures 6 feet by 7 feet. Find how many square feet of material are needed for *four* panels.

38. A page in this book measures 27.5 centimeters by 20.5 centimeters. Find its area.

39. Find how many square feet of land are in the plot shown:

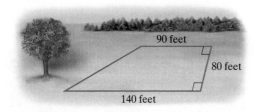

40. For Gerald Gomez to determine how much grass seed he needs to buy, he must know the size of his yard. Use the drawing to determine how many square feet are in his yard.

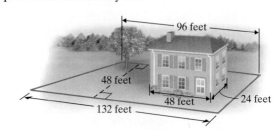

41. The shaded part of the roof shown is in the shape of a trapezoid and needs to be shingled. The number of packages of shingles to buy depends on the area. Use the dimensions given to find the area of the shaded part of the roof to the nearest whole square foot.

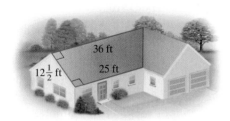

42. The end of the building shaded in the drawing is to be bricked. The number of bricks to buy depends on the area.

a. Find the area.

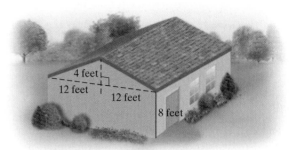

b. If the side area of each brick (including mortar room) is $\frac{1}{6}$ square ft, find the number of bricks needed to buy.

Review

Find the perimeter or circumference of each geometric figure. See Section 9.3.

43. Give an exact circumference and an approximation. Use 3.14 for π.

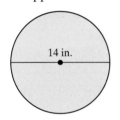

44.

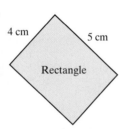

45.

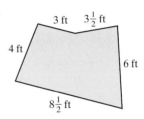

46.

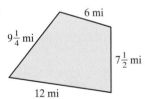

47.

48.

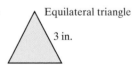

Concept Extensions

49. A pizza restaurant recently advertised two specials. The first special was a 12-inch diameter pizza for $10. The second special was two 8-inch diameter pizzas for $9. Determine the better buy. (*Hint:* First compare the areas of the pizzas in the two specials and then find a price per square inch for the pizzas in both specials.)

50. Find the approximate area of the state of Utah.

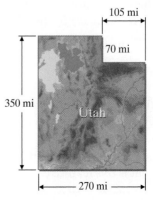

51. Find the area of a rectangle that measures 2 *feet* by 8 *inches*. Give the area in square feet and in square inches.

52. In your own words, explain why perimeter is measured in units and area is measured in square units. (*Hint:* See Section 1.6 for an introduction on the meaning of area.)

53. Find the area of the shaded region. Use the approximation 3.14 for π.

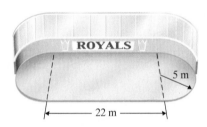

6 in.

54. Estimate the cost of a piece of carpet for a rectangular room 10 feet by 15 feet. The cost of the carpet is $6.50 per yard.

55. The largest pumpkin pie was made and served in Windsor, California. The pie had a diameter of 72 inches. Find the exact area of the top of the pie and an approximation. Use $\pi \approx 3.14$. (*Source: Guinness World Records*)

56. The largest lollipop was made in Gränna, Sweden. It had a diameter of 78 inches. Find the exact area of a face of the lollipop and an approximation. Use $\pi \approx 3.14$. (*Source: Guinness World Records*)

Find the area of each figure. If needed, use $\pi \approx 3.14$ and round results to the nearest tenth.

57. Find the skating area.

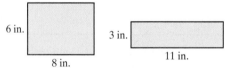

ROYALS

5 m

22 m

58.

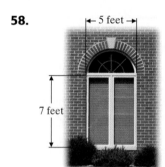

5 feet

7 feet

59. Do two rectangles with the same perimeter have the same area? To see, find the perimeter and the area of each rectangle.

6 in.

8 in.

3 in.

11 in.

 STUDY SKILLS BUILDER

How Well Do You Know Your Textbook?

Let's check to see whether you are familiar with your textbook yet. Remember, for help, see Section 1.1 in this text.

1. What does the 🔘 icon mean?

2. What does the ✎ icon mean?

3. What does the △ icon mean?

4. Where can you find a review for each chapter? What answers to this review can be found in the back of your text?

5. Each chapter contains an overview of the chapter along with examples. What is this feature called?

6. Each chapter contains a review of vocabulary. What is this feature called?

7. There are free CDs in your text. What content is contained on these CDs?

8. What is the location of the section that is entirely devoted to study skills?

9. There are Practice Problems that are contained in the margin of the text. What are they and how can they be used?

Objective A Finding Volume and Surface Area of Solids

A convex solid is a set of points, *S*, not all in one plane, such that for any two points *A* and *B* in *S*, all points between *A* and *B* are also in *S*. In this section, we will find the volume and surface area of special types of solids called polyhedrons. A solid formed by the intersection of a finite number of planes is called a **polyhedron.** The box below is an example of a polyhedron.

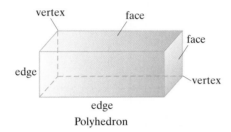

vertex   face

face

edge

vertex

edge

Polyhedron

Each of the plane regions of the polyhedron is called a **face** of the polyhedron. If the intersection of two faces is a line segment, this line segment is an **edge** of the polyhedron. The intersections of the edges are the **vertices** of the polyhedron.

Volume is a measure of the space of a region. The volume of a box or can, for example, is the amount of space inside. Volume can be used to describe the amount of juice in a pitcher or the amount of concrete needed to pour a foundation for a house.

The volume of a solid is the number of **cubic units** in the solid. A cubic centimeter and a cubic inch are illustrated.

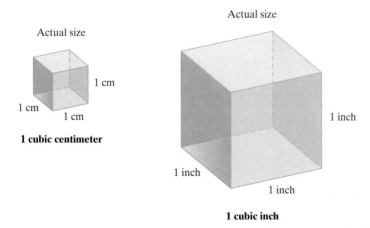

Actual size

1 cm

1 cm   1 cm

1 cubic centimeter

Actual size

1 inch

1 inch

1 inch

1 cubic inch

The **surface area** of a polyhedron is the sum of the areas of the faces of the polyhedron. For example, each face of the cube to the left above has an area of 1 square centimeter. Since there are 6 faces of the cube, the sum of the areas of the faces is 6 square centimeters. Surface area can be used to describe the amount of material needed to cover a solid. Surface area is measured in square units.

Formulas for finding the volumes, V, and surface areas, SA, of some common solids are given next.

Volume and Surface Area Formulas of Common Solids	
Solid	**Formulas**
RECTANGULAR SOLID	$V = lwh$ $SA = 2lh + 2wh + 2lw$ where h = height, w = width, l = length
CUBE	$V = s^3$ $SA = 6s^2$ where s = side
SPHERE	$V = \dfrac{4}{3}\pi r^3$ $SA = 4\pi r^2$ where r = radius
CIRCULAR CYLINDER	$V = \pi r^2 h$ $SA = 2\pi rh + 2\pi r^2$ where h = height, r = radius
CONE	$V = \dfrac{1}{3}\pi r^2 h$ $SA = \pi r\sqrt{r^2 + h^2} + \pi r^2$ where h = height, r = radius
SQUARE-BASED PYRAMID	$V = \dfrac{1}{3}s^2 h$ $SA = B + \dfrac{1}{2}pl$ where B = area of base; p = perimeter of base, h = height, s = side, l = slant height

EXAMPLE 1 Find the volume and surface area of a rectangular box that is 12 inches long, 6 inches wide, and 3 inches high.

3 in.

6 in.   12 in.

Solution: Let $h = 3$ in., $l = 12$ in., and $w = 6$ in.

$$V = lwh$$

$$V = 12 \text{ inches} \cdot 6 \text{ inches} \cdot 3 \text{ inches} = 216 \text{ cubic inches}$$

The volume of the rectangular box is 216 cubic inches.

$$SA = 2lh + 2wh + 2lw$$
$$= 2(12 \text{ in.})(3 \text{ in.}) + 2(6 \text{ in.})(3 \text{ in.}) + 2(12 \text{ in.})(6 \text{ in.})$$
$$= 72 \text{ sq in.} + 36 \text{ sq in.} + 144 \text{ sq in.}$$
$$= 252 \text{ sq in.}$$

The surface area of rectangular box is 252 square inches.

📗 **Work Practice Problem 1**

✔**Concept Check** Juan is calculating the volume of the following rectangular solid. Find the error in his calculation.

~~Volume $= l + w + h$~~
~~$= 14 \text{ cm} + 8 \text{ cm} + 5 \text{ cm}$~~
~~$= 27 \text{ cu cm}$~~

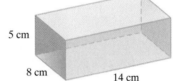

5 cm

8 cm   14 cm

EXAMPLE 2 Find the volume and surface area of a ball of radius 2 inches. Give the exact volume and surface area. Then use the approximation $\frac{22}{7}$ for π.

2 in.

Solution:

$$V = \frac{4}{3}\pi r^3 \qquad \text{Formula for volume of a sphere.}$$

$$V = \frac{4}{3} \cdot \pi (2 \text{ in.})^3 \qquad \text{Let } r = 2 \text{ inches.}$$

$$= \frac{32}{3}\pi \text{ cu in.} \qquad \text{Exact volume.}$$

$$\approx \frac{32}{3} \cdot \frac{22}{7} \text{ cu in.} \qquad \text{Approximate } \pi \text{ with } \frac{22}{7}.$$

$$= \frac{704}{21} \text{ or } 33\frac{11}{21} \text{ cu in.} \qquad \text{Approximate volume.}$$

Continued on next page

PRACTICE PROBLEM 1

Find the volume and surface area of a rectangular box that is 5 feet long, 2 feet wide, and 4 feet deep.

PRACTICE PROBLEM 2

Find the volume and surface area of a ball of radius $\frac{1}{2}$ centimeter. Give the exact volume and surface area. Then use $\frac{22}{7}$ for π.

Answers

1. $V = 40$ cu ft; $SA = 76$ sq ft,

2. $V = \frac{1}{6}\pi$ cu cm $\approx \frac{11}{21}$ cu cm;
   $SA = \pi$ sq cm $\approx 3\frac{1}{7}$ sq cm

✔ **Concept Check Answer**

Volume $= l \cdot w \cdot h$
$= 14 \cdot 8 \cdot 5$
$= 560$ cu cm

The volume of the sphere is exactly $\frac{32}{3}\pi$ cubic inches or approximately $33\frac{11}{21}$ cubic inches.

$$SA = 4\pi r^2 \qquad \text{Formula for surface area.}$$

$$SA = 4 \cdot \pi(2\,\text{in.})^2 \qquad \text{Let } r = 2 \text{ inches.}$$

$$= 16\pi \,\text{sq in.} \qquad \text{Exact surface area.}$$

$$\approx 16 \cdot \frac{22}{7}\,\text{sq in.} \qquad \text{Approximate } \pi \text{ with } \frac{22}{7}.$$

$$= \frac{352}{7} \text{ or } 50\frac{2}{7}\,\text{sq in.} \qquad \text{Approximate surface area.}$$

The surface area of the sphere is exactly 16π square inches or approximately $50\frac{2}{7}$ square inches.

🖳 **Work Practice Problem 2**

PRACTICE PROBLEM 3

Approximate the volume of a cylinder of radius 5 inches and height 7 inches. Use 3.14 for π. Give an exact answer and an approximate answer.

EXAMPLE 3 Approximate the volume of a can that has a $3\frac{1}{2}$-inch radius and a height of 6 inches. Use $\frac{22}{7}$ for π. Give an exact volume and an approximate volume.

$3\frac{1}{2}$ in.

6 in.

Solution: Using the formula for a circular cylinder, we have

$$V = \pi \cdot r^2 \cdot h \qquad 3\frac{1}{2} = \frac{7}{2}$$

$$= \pi \cdot \left(\frac{7}{2}\,\text{in.}\right)^2 \cdot 6\,\text{in.}$$

$$= \pi \cdot \frac{49}{4}\,\text{sq in.} \cdot 6\,\text{in.}$$

$$= \frac{\pi \cdot 49 \cdot \overset{1}{\cancel{2}} \cdot 3}{\underset{1}{\cancel{2}} \cdot 2}\,\text{cu in.}$$

$$= 73\frac{1}{2}\pi \,\text{cu in. or } 73.5\pi \,\text{cu in.}$$

This is the exact volume. To approximate the volume, use the approximation $\frac{22}{7}$ for π.

$$V = 73\frac{1}{2}\pi \text{ or } \frac{147}{2} \cdot \frac{22}{7}\,\text{cu in.} \qquad \text{Replace } \pi \text{ with } \frac{22}{7}.$$

$$= \frac{21 \cdot \overset{1}{\cancel{7}} \cdot \overset{1}{\cancel{2}} \cdot 11}{\underset{1}{\cancel{2}} \cdot \underset{1}{\cancel{7}}}\,\text{cu in.}$$

$$= 231 \text{ cubic in.}$$

The volume is approximately 231 cubic inches.

🖳 **Work Practice Problem 3**

Answer

3. 175π cu in. ≈ 549.5 cu in.

EXAMPLE 4 Approximate the volume of a cone that has a height of 14 centimeters and a radius of 3 centimeters. Use 3.14 for π. Give an exact answer and an approximate answer.

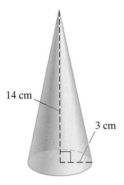

14 cm

3 cm

Solution: Using the formula for volume of a cone, we have

$$V = \frac{1}{3} \cdot \pi \cdot r^2 \cdot h$$

$$= \frac{1}{3} \cdot \pi \cdot (3 \text{ cm})^2 \cdot 14 \text{ cm} \quad \text{Replace } r \text{ with 3 cm and } h \text{ with 14 cm.}$$

$$= 42\pi \text{ cu cm}$$

Thus, 42π cubic centimeters is the exact volume. To approximate the volume, use the approximation 3.14 for π.

$$V \approx 42 \cdot 3.14 \text{ cu cm} \quad \text{Replace } \pi \text{ with 3.14.}$$

$$= 131.88 \text{ cu cm}$$

The volume is approximately 131.88 cubic centimeters.

▣ **Work Practice Problem 4**

PRACTICE PROBLEM 4

Find the volume of a square-based pyramid that has a 3-meter side and a height of 5.1 meters.

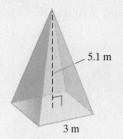

5.1 m

3 m

Answer

4. 15.3 cu m

9.5 EXERCISE SET

FOR EXTRA HELP

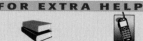

Student Solutions Manual PH Math/Tutor Center CD/Video for Review Math XL MathXL® MyMathLab MyMathLab

Objective **A** *Find the volume and surface area of each solid. See Examples 1 through 4. For formulas containing π, give an exact area and then approximate using* $\frac{22}{7}$ *for* π.

1.

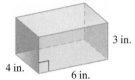

3 in.
4 in.
6 in.

2.

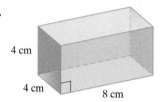

4 cm
4 cm
8 cm

3.

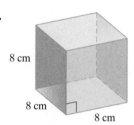

8 cm
8 cm
8 cm

4.

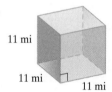

11 mi
11 mi
11 mi

5.

3 yd
2 yd

6.

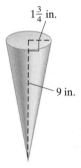

$1\frac{3}{4}$ in.
9 in.

7.

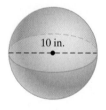

10 in.

8.

3 mi

9. Find the volume only.

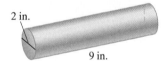

2 in.
9 in.

10. Find the volume only.

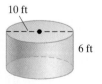

10 ft
6 ft

11. Find the volume only.

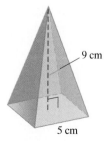

9 cm
5 cm

12. Find the volume only.

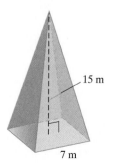

15 m
7 m

660

Copyright 2007 Pearson Education, Inc.

Solve.

13. Find the volume of a cube with edges of $1\frac{1}{3}$ inches.

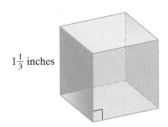

$1\frac{1}{3}$ inches

14. A water storage tank is in the shape of a cone with the pointed end down. If the radius is 14 feet and the depth of the tank is 15 feet, approximate the volume of the tank in cubic feet. Use $\frac{22}{7}$ for π.

14 ft

15 ft

15. Find the volume and surface area of a rectangular box 2 feet by 1.4 feet by 3 feet.

16. Find the volume and surface area of a box in the shape of a cube that is 5 feet on each side.

17. Find the volume of a pyramid with a square base 5 inches on a side and a height of $1\frac{3}{10}$ inches.

18. Approximate to the nearest hundredth the volume of a sphere with a radius of 2 centimeters. Use 3.14 for π.

19. A paperweight is in the shape of a square-based pyramid 20 centimeters tall. If an edge of the base is 12 centimeters, find the volume of the paperweight.

20. A birdbath is made in the shape of a hemisphere (half-sphere). If its radius is 10 inches, approximate the volume. Use $\frac{22}{7}$ for π.

10 in.

21. Find the exact volume and surface area of a sphere with a radius of 7 inches.

22. A tank is in the shape of a cylinder 8 feet tall and 3 feet in radius. Find the exact volume and surface area of the tank.

23. Find the volume of a rectangular block of ice 2 feet by $2\frac{1}{2}$ feet by $1\frac{1}{2}$ feet.

24. Find the capacity (volume in cubic feet) of a rectangular ice chest with inside measurements of 3 feet by $1\frac{1}{2}$ feet by $1\frac{3}{4}$ feet.

25. An ice cream cone with a 4-centimeter diameter and 3-centimeter depth is filled exactly level with the top of the cone. Approximate how much ice cream (in cubic centimeters) is in the cone. Use $\frac{22}{7}$ for π.

26. A child's toy is in the shape of a square-based pyramid 10 inches tall. If an edge of the base is 7 inches, find the volume of the toy.

27. Ball lightning is a rare form of lightning in which a moving white or colored luminous sphere is seen. It can last from a few seconds to a few minutes and travels at about walking pace. An average sphere size is 6 inches in diameter. Find the exact volume of a sphere with this diameter and then approximate the volume using 3.14 for π.

28. A monkey ball tree produces large green fruit in the shape of spheres. These fruits are approximately 4 inches (or 10 centimeters) in diameter and have a coarse surface. Find the exact volume of a sphere with diameter 4 inches and then approximate the volume using 3.14 for π. (Round to the nearest tenth.)

Review

Evaluate. See Section 1.9.

29. 5^2

30. 7^2

31. 3^2

32. 20^2

33. $1^2 + 2^2$

34. $5^2 + 3^2$

35. $4^2 + 2^2$

36. $1^2 + 6^2$

There are a number of factors that determine the dimensions of a rectangular soccer field. Use the table below to answer Exercises 37 and 38. See Section 9.4.

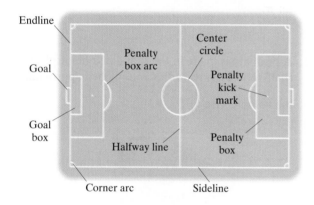

Soccer Field Width and Length		
Age	Width Min–Max	Length Min–Max
Under 6/7:	15–20 yards	25–30 yards
Under 8:	20–25 yards	30–40 yards
Under 9:	30–35 yards	40–50 yards
Under 10:	40–50 yards	60–70 yards
Under 11:	40–50 yards	70–80 yards
Under 12:	40–55 yards	100–105 yards
Under 13:	50–60 yards	100–110 yards
International:	70–80 yards	110–120 yards

37. a. Find the minimum length and width of a soccer field for 9-year-old children. (Carefully consider the age.)

   b. Find the area of this field.

38. a. Find the maximum length and width of a soccer field for 11-year-old children.

   b. Find the area of this field.

Concept Extensions

39. The Great Pyramid of Khufu at Giza is the tallest of the ancient Egyptian pyramids. Its original height was 146.5 meters. The length of each side of its square base was originally 230 meters. Find the volume of the Great Pyramid of Khufu as it was originally built. Round to the nearest whole cubic meter. (*Source:* PBS *NOVA* Online)

40. The second-tallest pyramid at Giza is Khafre's Pyramid. Its original height was 471 feet. The length of each side of its square base was originally 704 feet. Find the volume of Khafre's Pyramid as it was originally built. (*Source:* PBS *NOVA* Online)

41. Menkaure's Pyramid, the shortest of the three Great Pyramids at Giza, was originally 65.5 meters tall. Each of the sides of its square base was originally 344 meters long. What was the volume of Menkaure's Pyramid as it was originally built? Round to the nearest whole cubic meter. (*Source:* PBS *NOVA* Online)

42. Due to factors such as weathering and loss of outer stones, the Great Pyramid of Khufu now stands only 137 meters tall. Its square base is now only 227 meters on a side. Find the current volume of the Great Pyramid of Khufu to the nearest whole cubic meter. How much has its volume decreased since it was built? See Exercise 39 for comparison. (*Source:* PBS *NOVA* Online)

43. The centerpiece of the New England Aquarium in Boston is its Giant Ocean Tank. This exhibit is a four-story cylindrical saltwater tank containing sharks, sea turtles, stingrays, and tropical fish. The radius of the tank is 16.3 feet and its height is 32 feet (assuming that a story is 8 feet). What is the volume of the Giant Ocean Tank? Use $\pi \approx 3.14$ and round to the nearest tenth of a cubic foot. (*Source:* New England Aquarium)

44. Except for service dogs for guests with disabilities, Walt Disney World does not allow pets in its parks or hotels. However, the resort does make pet-boarding services available to guests. The pet-care kennels at Walt Disney World offer three different sizes of indoor kennels. Of these, the smaller two kennels measure

a. 2′1″ by 1′8″ by 1′7″ and
b. 1′1″ by 2′ by 8″

What is the volume of each kennel rounded to the nearest cubic foot? Which is larger? (*Source:* Walt Disney World Resort)

45. Can you compute the volume of a rectangle? Why or why not?

46. Find the volume of the figure below. Give an exact measure and then a whole number approximation.

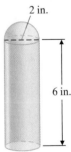

2 in.

6 in.

Geometry Concepts

1. _____

2. _____

3. _____

4. _____

5. _____

6. _____

7. _____

8. _____

9. _____

10. _____

11. _____

12. _____

13. _____

14. _____

15. _____

16. _____

△ **1.** Find the supplement and the complement of a 27° angle.

Find the measures of angles x, y, and z in each figure.

2.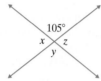

3. $m \| n$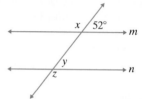

4. Find the measure of $\angle x$.

5. Find the diameter.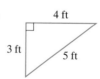

2.3 in.

6. Find the radius.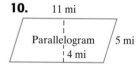

$8\frac{1}{2}$ in.

For Exercises 7 through 11, find the perimeter (or circumference) and area of each figure. For the circle give an exact circumference and area. Then use $\pi \approx 3.14$ to approximate each. Don't forget to attach correct units.

7.

Square | 5 m

8.

4 ft

3 ft

5 ft

9.

5 cm

10.

11 mi

Parallelogram | 5 mi

4 mi

11.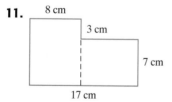

8 cm

3 cm

7 cm

17 cm

12. The smallest cathedral is in High-landville, Missouri. The rectangular floor of the cathedral measures 14 feet by 17 feet. Find its perimeter and its area. (*Source: The Guinness Book of Records*)

Find the volume of each solid. Don't forget to attach correct units. For Exercises 13 and 14, find the surface area, also.

13. A cube with edges of 4 inches each.

14. A rectangular box 2 feet by 3 feet by 5.1 feet.

15. A pyramid with a square base 10 centimeters on a side and a height of 12 centimeters.

16. A sphere with a diameter of 3 miles. Give the exact volume and then use $\pi \approx \frac{22}{7}$ to approximate.

9.6 CONGRUENT AND SIMILAR TRIANGLES

Objectives

A Decide Whether Two Triangles Are Congruent.

B Find the Ratio of Corresponding Sides in Similar Triangles.

C Find Unknown Lengths of Sides in Similar Triangles.

Objective **A** Deciding Whether Two Triangles Are Congruent

Two triangles are **congruent** when they have the same shape and the same size. In congruent triangles, the measures of corresponding angles are equal and the lengths of corresponding sides are equal. The following triangles are congruent:

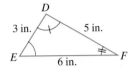

Since these triangles are congruent, the measures of corresponding angles are equal.

    Angles with equal measure: $\angle A$ and $\angle D$, $\angle B$ and $\angle E$, $\angle C$ and $\angle F$

Also, the lengths of corresponding sides are equal.

    Equal corresponding sides: $\overline{AB}$ and $\overline{DE}$, $\overline{BC}$ and $\overline{EF}$, $\overline{CA}$ and $\overline{FD}$

    Any one of the following may be used to determine whether two triangles are congruent:

Congruent Triangles

Angle-Side-Angle (ASA)

If the measures of two angles of a triangle equal the measures of two angles of another triangle, and the lengths of the sides between each pair of angles are equal, the triangles are congruent.

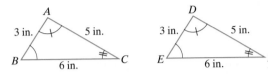

For example, these two triangles are congruent by Angle-Side-Angle.

Side-Side-Side (SSS)

If the lengths of the three sides of a triangle equal the lengths of the corresponding sides of another triangle, the triangles are congruent.

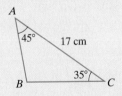 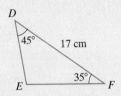

For example, these two triangles are congruent by Side-Side-Side.

(continued)

Congruent Triangles (continued)

Side-Angle-Side (SAS)

If the lengths of two sides of a triangle equal the lengths of corresponding sides of another triangle, and the measures of the angles between each pair of sides are equal, the triangles are congruent.

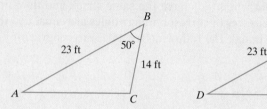

For example, these two triangles are congruent by Side-Angle-Side.

PRACTICE PROBLEM 1

a. Determine whether triangle *MNO* is congruent to triangle *RQS*.

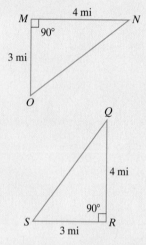

b. Determine whether triangle *GHI* is congruent to triangle *JKL*.

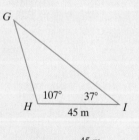

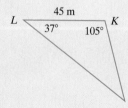

Answers

1. a. congruent, **b.** not congruent

EXAMPLE 1 Determine whether triangle *ABC* is congruent to triangle *DEF*.

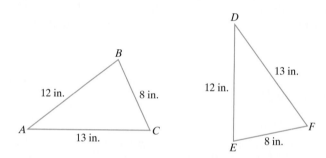

Solution: Since the lengths of all three sides of triangle *ABC* equal the lengths of all three sides of triangle *DEF*, the triangles are congruent.

Work Practice Problem 1

In Example 1, notice that as soon as we know that the two triangles are congruent, we know that all three corresponding angles are congruent.

Objective B Finding the Ratios of Corresponding Sides in Similar Triangles

Two triangles are **similar** when they have the same shape but not necessarily the same size. In similar triangles, the measures of corresponding angles are equal and corresponding sides are in proportion. The following triangles are similar:

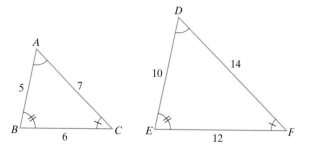

Since these triangles are similar, the measures of corresponding angles are equal.

Angles with equal measure: $\angle A$ and $\angle D$, $\angle B$ and $\angle E$, $\angle C$ and $\angle F$. Also, the lengths of corresponding sides are in proportion.

Sides in proportion: $\dfrac{AB}{DE} = \dfrac{BC}{EF} = \dfrac{CA}{FD}$ or, in this particular case,

$$\frac{AB}{DE} = \frac{5}{10} = \frac{1}{2},\ \frac{BC}{EF} = \frac{6}{12} = \frac{1}{2},\ \frac{CA}{FD} = \frac{7}{14} = \frac{1}{2}$$

The ratio of corresponding sides is $\dfrac{1}{2}$.

EXAMPLE 2 Find the ratio of corresponding sides for the similar triangles *ABC* and *DEF*.

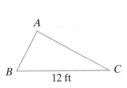
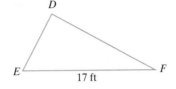

Solution: We are given the lengths of two corresponding sides. Their ratio is

$$\frac{12\ \text{feet}}{17\ \text{feet}} = \frac{12}{17}$$

🔲 **Work Practice Problem 2**

Objective C Finding Unknown Lengths of Sides in Similar Triangles

Because the ratios of lengths of corresponding sides are equal, we can use proportions to find unknown lengths in similar triangles.

EXAMPLE 3 Given that the triangles are similar, find the missing length *n*.

Solution: Since the triangles are similar, corresponding sides are in proportion. Thus, the ratio of 2 to 3 is the same as the ratio of 10 to *n*, or

$$\frac{2}{3} = \frac{10}{n}$$

To find the unknown length *n*, we set cross products equal.

$$\frac{2}{3} \diagup\!\!\!\!\diagdown \frac{10}{n}$$

$2 \cdot n = 3 \cdot 10$ Set cross products equal.
$2 \cdot n = 30$ Multiply.
$n = \dfrac{30}{2}$ Divide 30 by 2, the number multiplied by *n*.
$n = 15$

The missing length is 15 units.

🔲 **Work Practice Problem 3**

PRACTICE PROBLEM 2

Find the ratio of corresponding sides for the similar triangles *QRS* and *XYZ*.

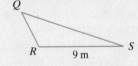
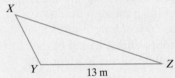

PRACTICE PROBLEM 3

Given that the triangles are similar, find the missing length *n*.

a.

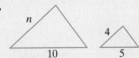

b.

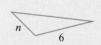

Answers

2. $\dfrac{9}{13}$, **3. a.** $n = 8$, **b.** $n = \dfrac{10}{3}$

or $3\dfrac{1}{3}$

✔**Concept Check** The following two triangles are similar. Which vertices of the first triangle appear to correspond to which vertices of the second triangle?

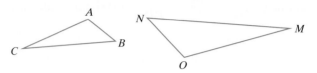

Many applications involve a diagram containing similar triangles. Surveyors, astronomers, and many other professionals continually use similar triangles in their work.

PRACTICE PROBLEM 4

Tammy Shultz, a firefighter, needs to estimate the height of a burning building. She estimates the length of her shadow to be 8 feet long and the length of the building's shadow to be 60 feet long. Find the approximate height of the building if she is 5 feet tall.

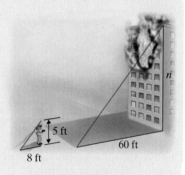

EXAMPLE 4 **Finding the Height of a Tree**

Mel Rose is a 6-foot-tall park ranger who needs to know the height of a particular tree. He measures the shadow of the tree to be 69 feet long when his own shadow is 9 feet long. Find the height of the tree.

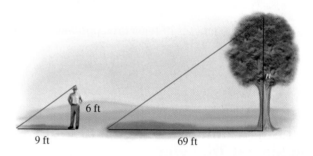

Solution:

1. UNDERSTAND. Read and reread the problem. Notice that the triangle formed by the Sun's rays, Mel, and his shadow is similar to the triangle formed by the Sun's rays, the tree, and its shadow.

2. TRANSLATE. Write a proportion from the similar triangles formed.

$$\underbrace{\frac{\text{Mel's height}}{\text{height of tree}}}_{} \quad \overset{\rightarrow}{\rightarrow} \quad \frac{6}{n} = \frac{9}{69} \quad \overset{\leftarrow}{\leftarrow} \quad \underbrace{\frac{\text{length of Mel's shadow}}{\text{length of tree's shadow}}}_{}$$

$$\text{or } \frac{6}{n} = \frac{3}{23} \quad \text{Simplify } \frac{9}{69}. \text{ (ratio in lowest terms)}$$

3. SOLVE for n:

$$\frac{6}{n} \diagup\!\!\!\!\diagdown \frac{3}{23}$$

$$6 \cdot 23 = n \cdot 3 \quad \text{Set cross products equal.}$$
$$138 = n \cdot 3 \quad \text{Multiply.}$$
$$\frac{138}{3} = n \quad \text{Divide 138 by 3, the number multiplied by } n.$$
$$46 = n$$

4. INTERPRET. *Check* to see that replacing n with 46 in the proportion makes the proportion true. *State* your conclusion: The height of the tree is 46 feet.

■ **Work Practice Problem 4**

Answer

4. approximately 37.5 ft

✔ **Concept Check Answer**

A corresponds to *O*; *B* corresponds to *N*; *C* corresponds to *M*

Mental Math

Each pair of triangles is similar. Name the congruent angles and the corresponding sides that are proportional.

1.

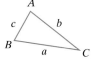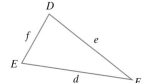

2.

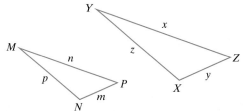

Objective **A** *Determine whether each pair of triangles is congruent. See Example 1.*

1.

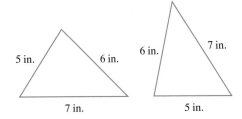

2.

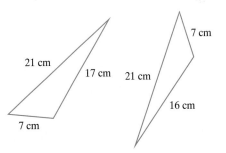

3.

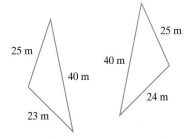

4.

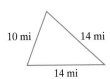

5.

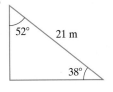

6.

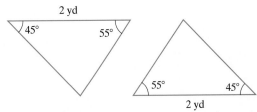

669

7.

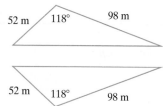

8.

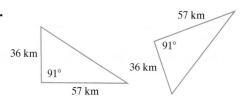

Objective **B** *Find each ratio of the corresponding sides of the given similar triangles. See Example 2.*

9.

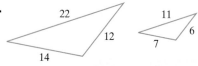

10.

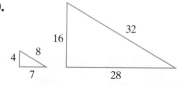

11.

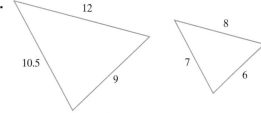

12.

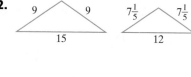

Objective **C** *Given that the pairs of triangles are similar, find the length of the side labeled n. See Example 3.*

13.

14.

15.

16.

17.

18.

19.

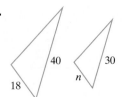

20.

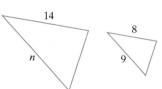

21.

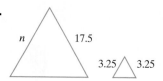

22.

23.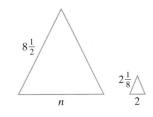

24.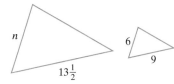

25.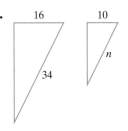

26.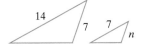

27.

28.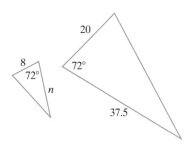

Solve. See Example 4.

29. Given the following diagram, approximate the height of the Bank One Tower in Oklahoma City, OK. (*Source: The World Almanac,* 2005)

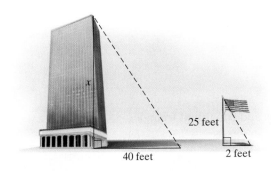

30. The tallest tree standing today is a redwood located in the Humboldt Redwoods State Park near Ukiah, California. Given the following diagram, approximate its height. (*Source: Guinness World Records,* 2005)

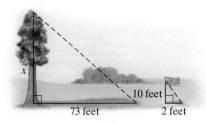

31. Samantha Black, a 5-foot-tall park ranger, needs to know the height of a tree. She notices that when the shadow of the tree is 48 feet long, her shadow is 4 feet long. Find the height of the tree.

32. Lloyd White, a firefighter, needs to estimate the height of a burning building. He estimates the length of his shadow to be 9 feet long and the length of the building's shadow to be 75 feet long. Find the approximate height of the building if he is 6 feet tall.

33. If a 30-foot tree casts an 18-foot shadow, find the length of the shadow cast by a 24-foot tree.

34. If a 24-foot flagpole casts a 32-foot shadow, find the length of the shadow cast by a 44-foot antenna. Round to the nearest tenth.

35. A triangular park is planned and waiting to be approved by the city zoning commission. A drawing of the park shows sides of length 5 inches, $7\frac{1}{2}$ inches and $10\frac{5}{8}$ inches. If the scale on the drawing is $\frac{1}{4}$ in. = 10 ft, find the actual proposed dimensions of the park.

36. Ben and Joyce Lander draw a triangular deck on their house plans. Joyce measures sides of the deck drawing on the plans to be 3 inches, $4\frac{1}{2}$ inches, and 6 inches. If the scale on the drawing is $\frac{1}{4}$ in. = 1 foot, find the lengths of the sides of the deck they want built.

Review

Find the average of each list of numbers. See Section 1.7.

37. 14, 17, 21, 18

38. 87, 84, 93

39. 76, 79, 88

40. 7, 8, 4, 6, 3, 8

Concept Extensions

41. The print area on a particular page measures 7 inches by 9 inches. A printing shop is to copy the page and reduce the print area so that its length is 5 inches. What will its width be? Will the print now fit on a 3-by-5-inch index card?

Given that the pairs of triangles are similar, find the length of the side labeled n. Round your results to 1 decimal place.

42.

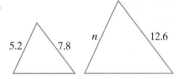

43.

44. In your own words, describe any differences in similar triangles and congruent triangles.

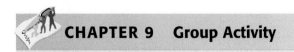

CHAPTER 9   Group Activity

The Cost of Road Signs

Sections 9.1, 9.2, 9.4

There are nearly 4 million miles of streets and roads in the United States. With streets, roads, and highways come the need for traffic control, guidance, warning, and regulation. Road signs perform many of these tasks. Just in our routine travels, we see a wide variety of road signs every day. Think how many road signs must exist on the 4 million miles of roads in the United States. Have you ever wondered how much signs like these cost?

The cost of a road sign generally depends on the type of sign. Costs for several types of signs and signposts are listed in the table. Examples of various types of signs are shown below.

Road Sign Costs	
Type of Sign	**Cost**
Regulatory, warning, marker	$15–$18 per square foot
Large guide	$20–$25 per square foot
Type of Post	**Cost**
U-channel	$125–$200 each
Square tube	$10–$15 per foot
Steel breakaway posts	$15–$25 per foot

The cost of a sign is based on its area. For diamond, square, or rectangular signs, the area is found by multiplying the length (in feet) times the width (in feet). Then the area is multiplied by the cost per square foot. For signs with irregular shapes, costs are generally figured *as if* the sign were a rectangle, multiplying the height and width at the tallest and widest parts of the sign.

Group Activity

Locate four different kinds of road signs on or near your campus. Measure the dimensions of each sign, including the height of the post on which it is mounted. Using the cost data given in the table, find the minimum and maximum costs of each sign, including its post. Summarize your results in a table, and include a sketch of each sign.

Regulatory   Warning   Marker   Large Guide   Posts

U-channel

Square tube

Steel breakaway posts

Chapter 9 Vocabulary Check

Fill in each blank with one of the words or phrases listed below.

transversal	line segment	obtuse	straight	adjacent
right	volume	area	legs	acute
right triangle	perimeter	hypotenuse	vertical	supplementary
similar	congruent	ray	angle	line
complementary	vertex			

1. A _____ is a triangle with a right angle. The side opposite the right angle is called the _____, and the other two sides are called _____.
2. A _____ is a piece of a line with two endpoints.
3. Two angles that have a sum of 90° are called _____ angles.
4. A _____ is a set of points extending indefinitely in two directions.
5. The _____ of a polygon is the distance around the polygon.
6. An _____ is made up of two rays that share the same endpoint. The common endpoint is called the _____.
7. _____ triangles have the same shape and the same size.
8. _____ measures the amount of surface of a region.
9. A _____ is a part of a line with one endpoint. A ray extends indefinitely in one direction.
10. _____ triangles have exactly the same shape but not necessarily the same size.
11. A line that intersects two or more lines at different points is called a _____.
12. An angle that measures 180° is called a _____ angle.
13. The measure of the space of a solid is called its _____.
14. When two lines intersect, four angles are formed. Two of these angles that are opposite each other are called _____ angles.
15. Two of these angles from Exercise 14 that share a common side are called _____ angles.
16. An angle whose measure is between 90° and 180° is called an _____ angle.
17. An angle that measures 90° is called a _____ angle.
18. An angle whose measure is between 0° and 90° is called an _____ angle.
19. Two angles that have a sum of 180° are called _____ angles.

> **Helpful Hint**
>
> Are you preparing for your test? Don't forget to take the Chapter 9 Test on page 685. Then check your answers at the back of the text and use the Chapter Test Prep Video CD to see the fully worked-out solutions to any of the exercises you want to review.

9 Chapter Highlights

DEFINITIONS AND CONCEPTS	EXAMPLES
Section 9.1 Lines and Angles	
A **line** is a set of points extending indefinitely in two directions. A line has no width or height, but it does have length. We name a line by any two of its points.	Line AB or $\overleftrightarrow{AB}$

DEFINITIONS AND CONCEPTS	**EXAMPLES**
Section 9.1 Lines and Angles (*continued*)	

A **line segment** is a piece of a line with two endpoints.

Line segment AB or $\overline{AB}$

A **ray** is a part of a line with one endpoint. A ray extends indefinitely in one direction.

Ray AB or $\overrightarrow{AB}$

An **angle** is made up of two rays that share the same endpoint. The common endpoint is called the **vertex.**

An angle that measures 180° is called a **straight angle.**

$\angle RST$ is a straight angle.

An angle that measures 90° is called a **right angle.** The symbol ∟ is used to denote a right angle.

$\angle ABC$ is a right angle.

An angle whose measure is between 0° and 90° is called an **acute angle.**

Acute angles

An angle whose measure is between 90° and 180° is called an **obtuse angle.**

Obtuse angles

Two angles that have a sum of 90° are called **complementary angles.** We say that each angle is the **complement** of the other.

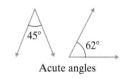

Complementary angles
60° + 30° = 90°

Two angles that have a sum of 180° are called **supplementary angles.** We say that each angle is the **supplement** of the other.

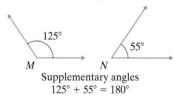

Supplementary angles
125° + 55° = 180°

continued

DEFINITIONS AND CONCEPTS	**EXAMPLES**
Section 9.1 Lines and Angles (*continued*)	

When two lines intersect, four angles are formed. Two of these angles that are opposite each other are called **vertical angles.** Vertical angles have the same measure. Two of these angles that share a common side are called **adjacent angles.** Adjacent angles formed by intersecting lines are supplementary. A line that intersects two or more lines at different points is called a **transversal.** Line *l* is a transversal that intersects lines *m* and *n*. The eight angles formed have special names. Some of these names are: Corresponding angles: $\angle a$ and $\angle e$, $\angle c$ and $\angle g$, $\angle b$ and $\angle f$, $\angle d$ and $\angle h$ Alternate interior angles: $\angle c$ and $\angle f$, $\angle d$ and $\angle e$ **PARALLEL LINES CUT BY A TRANSVERSAL** If two parallel lines are cut by a transversal, then the measures of **corresponding angles are equal** and the measures of **alternate interior angles are equal.**	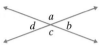 Vertical angles: $\angle a$ and $\angle c$ $\angle d$ and $\angle b$ Adjacent angles: $\angle a$ and $\angle b$ $\angle b$ and $\angle c$ $\angle c$ and $\angle d$ $\angle d$ and $\angle a$ 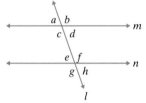

| **Section 9.2   Plane Figures and Solids** ||

The **sum of the measures** of the angles of a triangle is $180°$.	Find the measure of $\angle x$. The measure of $\angle x = 180° - 85° - 45° = 50°$
A **right triangle** is a triangle with a right angle. The side opposite the right angle is called the **hypotenuse,** and the other two sides are called **legs.**	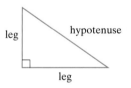
For a circle or a sphere:  $$\text{diameter} = 2 \cdot \text{radius}$$ $$d = 2 \cdot r$$ $$\text{radius} = \frac{\text{diameter}}{2}$$ $$r = \frac{d}{2}$$	Find the diameter of the circle. $d = 2 \cdot r$ $\quad = 2 \cdot 6 \text{ feet} = 12 \text{ feet}$

DEFINITIONS AND CONCEPTS	**EXAMPLES**

Section 9.3   Perimeter

PERIMETER FORMULAS

Rectangle:

$$P = 2 \cdot l + 2 \cdot w$$

Square:

$$P = 4 \cdot s$$

Triangle:

$$P = a + b + c$$

Circumference of a Circle:

$$C = 2 \cdot \pi \cdot r \quad \text{or} \quad C = \pi \cdot d,$$

where $\pi \approx 3.14$ or $\pi \approx \dfrac{22}{7}$

Find the perimeter of the rectangle with length 28 meters and width 15 meters.

$$\begin{aligned} P &= 2 \cdot l + 2 \cdot w \\ &= 2 \cdot 28 \text{ m} + 2 \cdot 15 \text{ m} \\ &= 56 \text{ m} + 30 \text{ m} \\ &= 86 \text{ m} \end{aligned}$$

The perimeter is 86 meters.

Section 9.4   Area

AREA FORMULAS

Rectangle:

$$A = l \cdot w$$

Square:

$$A = s^2$$

Triangle:

$$A = \frac{1}{2} \cdot b \cdot h$$

Parallelogram:

$$A = b \cdot h$$

Trapezoid:

$$A = \frac{1}{2} \cdot (b + B) \cdot h$$

Circle:

$$A = \pi \cdot r^2$$

Find the area of the square with side length 8 centimeters.

$$\begin{aligned} A &= s^2 \\ &= (8 \text{ cm})^2 \\ &= 64 \text{ square centimeters} \end{aligned}$$

The area of the square is 64 square centimeters.

Section 9.5   Volume and Surface Area

VOLUME FORMULAS

Rectangular Solid:

$$V = l \cdot w \cdot h$$

Cube:

$$V = s^3$$

Sphere:

$$V = \frac{4}{3} \cdot \pi \cdot r^3$$

SURFACE AREA FORMULAS

See page 655.

Find the volume of the sphere. Use $\dfrac{22}{7}$ for π.

4 in.

continued

DEFINITIONS AND CONCEPTS	**EXAMPLES**
Section 9.5 Volume and Surface Area (*continued*)	

Right Circular Cylinder: $$V = \pi \cdot r^2 \cdot h$$ **Cone:** $$V = \frac{1}{3} \cdot \pi \cdot r^2 \cdot h$$ **Square-Based Pyramid:** $$V = \frac{1}{3} \cdot s^2 \cdot h$$	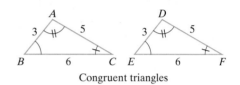 $$V = \frac{4}{3} \cdot \pi \cdot r^3$$ $$\approx \frac{4}{3} \cdot \frac{22}{7} \cdot (4 \text{ inches})^3$$ $$= \frac{4 \cdot 22 \cdot 64}{3 \cdot 7} \text{ cubic inches}$$ $$= \frac{5632}{21} \quad \text{or} \quad 268\frac{4}{21} \text{ cubic inches}$$

Section 9.6 Congruent and Similar Triangles	

Congruent triangles have the same shape and the same size. Corresponding angles are equal, and corresponding sides are equal.	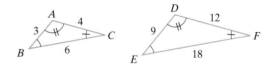 Congruent triangles
Similar triangles have exactly the same shape but not necessarily the same size. Corresponding angles are equal, and the ratios of the lengths of corresponding sides are equal.	$$\frac{AB}{DE} = \frac{3}{9} = \frac{1}{3}, \frac{BC}{EF} = \frac{6}{18} = \frac{1}{3},$$ $$\frac{CA}{FD} = \frac{4}{12} = \frac{1}{3}$$

STUDY SKILLS BUILDER

Are You Prepared for a Test on Chapter 9?

Listed below are some common trouble areas for students in Chapter 9. After studying for your test—but before taking your test—read these.

- Don't forget the difference between complementary and supplementary angles.

  Complementary angles have a sum of 90°.

  Supplementary angles have a sum of 180°.

  The complement of a 15° angle measures $90° - 15° = 75°$.

  The supplement of a 15° angle measures $180° - 15° = 165°$.

- Remember: Perimeter is measured in units.

  Area is measured in square units.

  Volume is measured in cubic units.

Perimeter	**Area**	**Volume**

10 units	6 square units	12 cubic units

Remember: This is simply a checklist of common trouble areas. For a review of Chapter 9, see the Highlights and Chapter Review at the end of this chapter.

9 CHAPTER REVIEW

(9.1) *Classify each angle as acute, right, obtuse, or straight.*

1.

2.

3. *C*

4.

5. Find the complement of a 25° angle.

6. Find the supplement of a 105° angle.

Find the measure of angle x in each figure.

7.

8.

9.
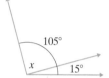

10.

11. Identify the pairs of supplementary angles.

12. Identify the pairs of complementary angles.
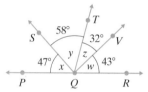

Find the measures of angles x, y, and z in each figure.

13.
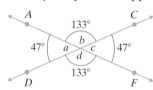

14.
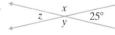

15. Given that $m \parallel n$.
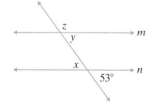

16. Given that $m \parallel n$.
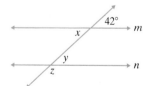

(9.2) *Find the measure of $\angle x$ in each figure.*

17.

18.

19.

20.

Find the unknown diameter or radius as indicated.

21.
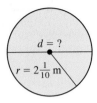
$d = ?$
$r = 2\frac{1}{10}$ m

22.

$d = 14$ ft
$r = ?$

23.

$d = 19$ m
$r = ?$

24.
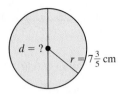
$d = ?$
$r = 7\frac{3}{5}$ cm

Identify each solid.

25.

26.

27.

28.

Find the unknown radius or diameter as indicated.

29. The radius of a sphere is 9 inches. Find its diameter.

30. The diameter of a sphere is 4.7 meters. Find its radius.

Identify each regular polygon.

31.

32.

Identify each triangle as equilateral, isosceles, or scalene. Also identify any triangle that is a right triangle.

33.

34.

(9.3) *Find the perimeter of each figure.*

35.
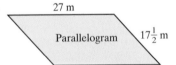
27 m
Parallelogram
$17\frac{1}{2}$ m

36.
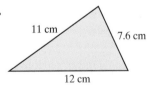
11 cm
7.6 cm
12 cm

37.
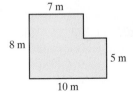
7 m
8 m
5 m
10 m

38.
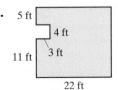
5 ft
4 ft
11 ft
3 ft
22 ft

Solve.

39. Find the perimeter of a rectangular sign that measures 6 feet by 10 feet.

40. Find the perimeter of a town square that measures 110 feet on a side.

Find the circumference of each circle. Use $\pi \approx 3.14$.

41.

1.7 in.

42.

5 yd

(9.4) *Find the area of each figure. For the circles, find the exact area and then use $\pi \approx 3.14$ to approximate the area.*

43.
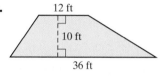
12 ft
10 ft
36 ft

44.
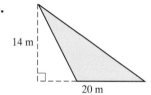
14 m
20 m

45.
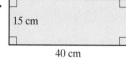
15 cm
40 cm

46.
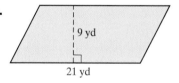
9 yd
21 yd

47.

7 ft

48.
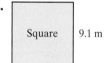
Square   9.1 m

49.
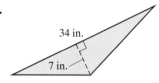
34 in.
7 in.

50.
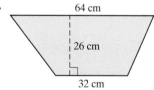
64 cm
26 cm
32 cm

51.
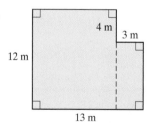
4 m
3 m
12 m
13 m

52. The amount of sealer necessary to seal a driveway depends on the area. Find the area of a rectangular driveway 36 feet by 12 feet.

53. Find how much carpet is necessary to cover the floor of the room shown.

10 feet
13 feet

(9.5) *Find the volume and surface area of the solids in Exercises 54 and 55. For Exercises 56 and 57, give an exact volume and an approximation.*

54.

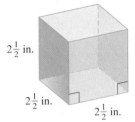

$2\frac{1}{2}$ in.

$2\frac{1}{2}$ in.

$2\frac{1}{2}$ in.

55.

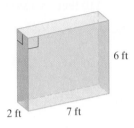

6 ft

2 ft   7 ft

56. Use $\pi \approx 3.14$.

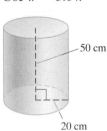

50 cm

20 cm

57. Use $\pi \approx \frac{22}{7}$.

$\frac{1}{2}$ km

58. Find the volume of a pyramid with a square base 2 feet on a side and a height of 2 feet.

59. Approximate the volume of a tin can 8 inches high and 3.5 inches in radius. Use 3.14 for π.

60. A chest has 3 drawers. If each drawer has inside measurements of $2\frac{1}{2}$ feet by $1\frac{1}{2}$ feet by $\frac{2}{3}$ foot, find the total volume of the 3 drawers.

61. A cylindrical canister for a shop vacuum is 2 feet tall and 1 foot in *diameter*. Find its exact volume.

(9.6) *Given that the pairs of triangles are similar, find the unknown length n.*

62.

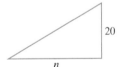

20   8

15

n

63.

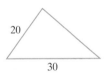

20   n

30   20

64.

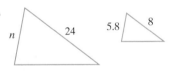

n 24   5.8   8

Solve.

65. A housepainter needs to estimate the height of a condominium. He estimates the length of his shadow to be 7 feet long and the length of the building's shadow to be 42 feet long. Find the approximate height of the building if the house-painter is $5\frac{1}{2}$ feet tall.

66. Santa's elves are making a triangular sail for a toy sailboat. The toy sail is to be the same shape as a real sailboat's sail. Use the following diagram to find the unknown lengths x and y.

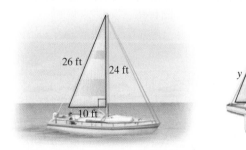

26 ft   24 ft y 2 in.

10 ft x

Mixed Review

Find the following.

67. Find the supplement of a 72° angle.

68. Find the complement of a 1° angle.

Find the measure of angle x in each figure.

69.

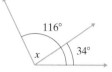

70.

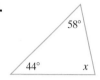

71.

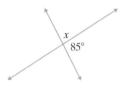

72.

Find the unknown diameter or radius as indicated.

73.

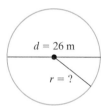

74.

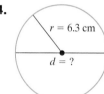

Find the perimeter of each figure.

75.

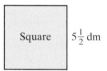

76.

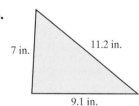

77.

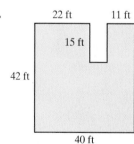

Find the area of each figure. For the circle, find the exact area and then use $\pi = 3.14$ to approximate the area.

78.

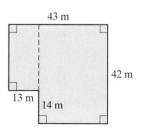

79.

Find the volume of each solid.

80. Give an approximation using $\frac{22}{7}$ for π.

81. Find the surface area, also.

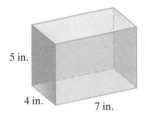

Solve.

82. Find the volume of air in a rectangular room 15 feet by 12 feet with a 7-foot ceiling.

83. A mover has two boxes left for packing. Both are cubical, one 3 feet on a side and the other 1.2 feet on a side. Find their combined volume.

Given that the pairs of triangles are similar, find the unknown length n.

84.

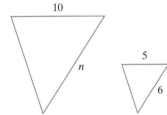

85.

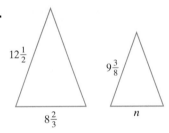

9 CHAPTER TEST

Use the Chapter Test Prep Video CD to see the fully worked-out solutions to any of the exercises you want to review.

1. Find the complement of a 78° angle.

2. Find the supplement of a 124° angle.

3. Find the measure of ∠x.

Find the measure of x, y, and z in each figure.

4.

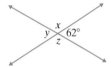

5. Given: m ∥ n.

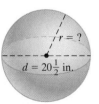

Find the unknown diameter or radius as indicated.

6.

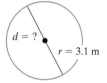

7.

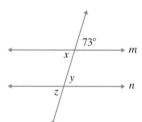

8. Find the measure of ∠x.

Find the perimeter (or circumference) and area of each figure. For the circle, give the exact value and then use π ≈ 3.14 for an approximation.

9.

9 in.

10.

Rectangle   5.3 yd

7 yd

11.

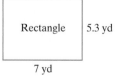

6 in.

11 in.

7 in.

23 in.

Answers

1. _____

2. _____

3. _____

4. _____

5. _____

6. _____

7. _____

8. _____

9. _____

10. _____

11. _____

685

12. _____

13. _____

14. _____

15. _____

16. _____

17. _____

18. _____

19. _____

Find the volume of each solid. For the cylinder, use $\pi \approx \dfrac{22}{7}$.

12.

5 in.

2 in.

13. Find the surface, also

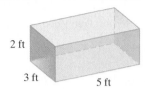

2 ft

3 ft   5 ft

Solve.

14. Find the perimeter of a square photo with a side length of 4 inches.

15. How much soil is needed to fill a rectangular hole 3 feet by 3 feet by 2 feet?

16. Find how much baseboard is needed to go around a rectangular room that measures 18 feet by 13 feet. If baseboard costs $1.87 per foot, also calculate the total cost needed for materials.

17. Vivian Thomas is going to put insecticide on her lawn to control grubworms. The lawn is a rectangle measuring 123.8 feet by 80 feet. The amount of insecticide required is 0.02 ounces per square foot. Find how much insecticide Vivian needs to purchase.

18. Given that the following triangles are similar, find the missing length n.

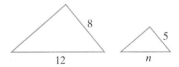

8

12

5

n

19. Tamara Watford, a surveyor, needs to estimate the height of a tower. She estimates the length of her shadow to be 4 feet long and the length of the tower's shadow to be 48 feet long. Find the approximate height of the tower if she is $5\dfrac{3}{4}$ feet tall.

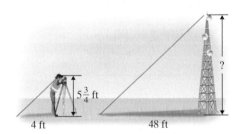

$5\frac{3}{4}$ ft

4 ft   48 ft

?

Chapters 1–9

1. Write the decimal -5.82 in words.

2. Add: $\dfrac{7}{11} + \dfrac{1}{6}$

3. Round 736.2359 to the nearest tenth.

4. Round 736.2359 to the nearest hundred.

5. Add: $45 + 2.06$

6. Divide: $-3\dfrac{1}{3} \div 1\dfrac{5}{6}$

Multiply.

7. 7.68×10

8. $\dfrac{7}{11} \cdot \dfrac{1}{6}$

9. $(-76.3)(1000)$

10. $5\dfrac{1}{2} \cdot 2\dfrac{1}{11}$

11. Divide: $270.2 \div 7$. Check your answer.

12. Divide: $\dfrac{56.7}{100}$

13. Simplify: $-0.5(8.6 - 1.2)$

14. Simplify: $\dfrac{5 + 2(8 - 3)}{30 \div 6 \cdot 5}$

15. Insert $<$, $>$, or $=$ to form a true statement. $\dfrac{1}{8}$ 0.12

16. Insert $<$, $>$, or $=$ to form a true statement. $\dfrac{3}{4}$ $\dfrac{13}{16}$

17. Write the ratio of 2.6 to 3.1 as a fraction in simplest form.

18. Find: $\dfrac{2}{9} + \dfrac{7}{15} - \dfrac{1}{3}$

19. Is $\dfrac{2}{3} = \dfrac{4}{6}$ a true proportion?

20. Solve for x: $\dfrac{7}{8} = \dfrac{x}{20}$

21. In a survey of 100 people, 17 people drive blue cars. What percent drive blue cars?

22. Solve for x: $4x - 7x = -30$

Answers

1. _____

2. _____

3. _____

4. _____

5. _____

6. _____

7. _____

8. _____

9. _____

10. _____

11. _____

12. _____

13. _____

14. _____

15. _____

16. _____

17. _____

18. _____

19. _____

20. _____

21. _____

22. _____

Write each percent as a fraction or mixed number in simplest form.

23. 1.9%   **24.** 26%   **25.** 125%   **26.** 560%

27. 85% of 300 is what number?   **28.** What percent of 16 is 2.4?

29. 20.8 is 40% of what number?   **30.** Find: $\left(7 - \sqrt{16}\right)^2$

31. Mr. Buccaran, the principal at Slidell High School, counted 31 freshmen absent during a particular day. If this is 4% of the total number of freshmen, how many freshmen are there at Slidell High School?

32. Flooring tiles cost $90 for a box with 40 tiles. Each tile is 1 square foot. Find the unit price in dollars per square foot.

33. Sherry Souter, a real estate broker for Wealth Investments, sold a house for $114,000 last week. If her commission is 1.5% of the selling price of the home, find the amount of her commission.

34. A student can complete 7 exercises in 6 minutes. At this rate, how many exercises can be completed in 30 minutes?

35. Convert 8 feet to inches.

36. 100 inches = _____ yd _____ ft _____ in.

37. Convert 3.2 kilograms to grams.   **38.** Convert 70 mm to meters.

39. Subtract 3 quarts from 4 gallons 2 quarts.   **40.** Write seventy thousand, fifty-two in standard form.

41. Find the measure of $\angle a$.

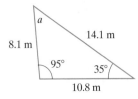

42. Find the perimeter of the triangle in Exercise 41.

43. Find the perimeter of the rectangle below:

44. Solve for x: $7(x - 2) = 9x - 6$

45. Find $\sqrt{\dfrac{4}{25}}$.   **46.** Find $\sqrt{\dfrac{9}{16}}$.

23. _____

24. _____

25. _____

26. _____

27. _____

28. _____

29. _____

30. _____

31. _____

32. _____

33. _____

34. _____

35. _____

36. _____

37. _____

38. _____

39. _____

40. _____

41. _____

42. _____

43. _____

44. _____

45. _____

46. _____

A.1 ADDITION TABLE AND ONE HUNDRED ADDITION FACTS

+	0	1	2	3	4	5	6	7	8	9
0	0	1	2	3	4	5	6	7	8	9
1	1	2	3	4	5	6	7	8	9	10
2	2	3	4	5	6	7	8	9	10	11
3	3	4	5	6	7	8	9	10	11	12
4	4	5	6	7	8	9	10	11	12	13
5	5	6	7	8	9	10	11	12	13	14
6	6	7	8	9	10	11	12	13	14	15
7	7	8	9	10	11	12	13	14	15	16
8	8	9	10	11	12	13	14	15	16	17
9	9	10	11	12	13	14	15	16	17	18

One Hundred Addition Facts

Knowledge of the basic addition facts found above is an important prerequisite for a course in prealgebra. Study the table above and then perform the additions. Check your answers either by comparing them with those found in the back-of-the-book answer section or by using the table. Review any facts that you missed.

1. $\begin{array}{r} 1 \\ +4 \\ \hline \end{array}$ **2.** $\begin{array}{r} 5 \\ +6 \\ \hline \end{array}$ **3.** $\begin{array}{r} 2 \\ +3 \\ \hline \end{array}$ **4.** $\begin{array}{r} 7 \\ +8 \\ \hline \end{array}$ **5.** $\begin{array}{r} 3 \\ +9 \\ \hline \end{array}$ **6.** $\begin{array}{r} 6 \\ +1 \\ \hline \end{array}$

7. $\begin{array}{r} 4 \\ +4 \\ \hline \end{array}$ **8.** $\begin{array}{r} 0 \\ +6 \\ \hline \end{array}$ **9.** $\begin{array}{r} 9 \\ +5 \\ \hline \end{array}$ **10.** $\begin{array}{r} 8 \\ +2 \\ \hline \end{array}$ **11.** $\begin{array}{r} 5 \\ +7 \\ \hline \end{array}$ **12.** $\begin{array}{r} 3 \\ +2 \\ \hline \end{array}$

13. $\begin{array}{r} 5 \\ +5 \\ \hline \end{array}$ **14.** $\begin{array}{r} 1 \\ +1 \\ \hline \end{array}$ **15.** $\begin{array}{r} 8 \\ +1 \\ \hline \end{array}$ **16.** $\begin{array}{r} 6 \\ +6 \\ \hline \end{array}$ **17.** $\begin{array}{r} 2 \\ +9 \\ \hline \end{array}$ **18.** $\begin{array}{r} 3 \\ +5 \\ \hline \end{array}$

19. $\begin{array}{r} 9 \\ +9 \\ \hline \end{array}$ **20.** $\begin{array}{r} 5 \\ +2 \\ \hline \end{array}$ **21.** $\begin{array}{r} 6 \\ +4 \\ \hline \end{array}$ **22.** $\begin{array}{r} 0 \\ +0 \\ \hline \end{array}$ **23.** $\begin{array}{r} 1 \\ +9 \\ \hline \end{array}$ **24.** $\begin{array}{r} 3 \\ +7 \\ \hline \end{array}$

25. 9
     +8

26. 0
     +8

27. 4
     +9

28. 3
     +0

29. 7
     +5

30. 8
     +9

31. 9
     +7

32. 2
     +6

33. 4
     +3

34. 8
     +5

35. 3
     +1

36. 0
     +3

37. 7
     +1

38. 3
     +4

39. 8
     +0

40. 6
     +3

41. 2
     +4

42. 0
     +9

43. 8
     +8

44. 5
     +3

45. 3
     +6

46. 6
     +9

47. 4
     +8

48. 0
     +1

49. 2
     +5

50. 6
     +0

51. 2
     +0

52. 4
     +2

53. 8
     +3

54. 7
     +4

55. 1
     +7

56. 4
     +6

57. 0
     +5

58. 9
     +1

59. 8
     +6

60. 5
     +1

61. 6
     +7

62. 4
     +0

63. 1
     +6

64. 4
     +5

65. 0
     +7

66. 5
     +8

67. 7
     +6

68. 7
     +0

69. 4
     +1

70. 5
     +4

71. 0
     +4

72. 1
     +2

73. 7
     +9

74. 3
     +8

75. 7
     +7

76. 9
     +4

77. 1
     +0

78. 4
     +7

79. 2
     +2

80. 1
     +3

81. 2
     +8

82. 5
     +9

83. 6
     +2

84. 9
     +6

85. 5
     +0

86. 8
     +7

87. 7
     +3

88. 0
     +2

89. 9
     +2

90. 3
     +3

91. 9
     +3

92. 1
     +5

93. 2
     +7

94. 6
     +5

95. 7
     +2

96. 1
     +8

97. 6
     +8

98. 8
     +4

99. 9
     +0

100. 2
      +1

A.2 MULTIPLICATION TABLE AND ONE HUNDRED MULTIPLICATION FACTS

×	1	2	3	4	5	6	7	8	9
1	1	2	3	4	5	6	7	8	9
2	2	4	6	8	10	12	14	16	18
3	3	6	9	12	15	18	21	24	27
4	4	8	12	16	20	24	28	32	36
5	5	10	15	20	25	30	35	40	45
6	6	12	18	24	30	36	42	48	54
7	7	14	21	28	35	42	49	56	63
8	8	16	24	32	40	48	56	64	72
9	9	18	27	36	45	54	63	72	81

One Hundred Multiplication Facts

Knowledge of the basic multiplication facts found above is an important prerequisite for a course in prealgebra. Study the table above and then perform the multiplications. Check your answers either by comparing them with those found in the back-of-the-book answer section or by using the table. Review any facts that you missed.

1. $\begin{array}{r} 1 \\ \times\,1 \\ \hline \end{array}$ **2.** $\begin{array}{r} 5 \\ \times\,7 \\ \hline \end{array}$ **3.** $\begin{array}{r} 7 \\ \times\,8 \\ \hline \end{array}$ **4.** $\begin{array}{r} 3 \\ \times\,3 \\ \hline \end{array}$ **5.** $\begin{array}{r} 8 \\ \times\,4 \\ \hline \end{array}$ **6.** $\begin{array}{r} 9 \\ \times\,5 \\ \hline \end{array}$

7. $\begin{array}{r} 4 \\ \times\,7 \\ \hline \end{array}$ **8.** $\begin{array}{r} 7 \\ \times\,1 \\ \hline \end{array}$ **9.** $\begin{array}{r} 2 \\ \times\,2 \\ \hline \end{array}$ **10.** $\begin{array}{r} 0 \\ \times\,5 \\ \hline \end{array}$ **11.** $\begin{array}{r} 9 \\ \times\,7 \\ \hline \end{array}$ **12.** $\begin{array}{r} 8 \\ \times\,8 \\ \hline \end{array}$

13. $\begin{array}{r} 3 \\ \times\,2 \\ \hline \end{array}$ **14.** $\begin{array}{r} 6 \\ \times\,0 \\ \hline \end{array}$ **15.** $\begin{array}{r} 5 \\ \times\,6 \\ \hline \end{array}$ **16.** $\begin{array}{r} 2 \\ \times\,5 \\ \hline \end{array}$ **17.** $\begin{array}{r} 4 \\ \times\,6 \\ \hline \end{array}$ **18.** $\begin{array}{r} 0 \\ \times\,7 \\ \hline \end{array}$

19. $\begin{array}{r} 6 \\ \times\,3 \\ \hline \end{array}$ **20.** $\begin{array}{r} 8 \\ \times\,9 \\ \hline \end{array}$ **21.** $\begin{array}{r} 5 \\ \times\,8 \\ \hline \end{array}$ **22.** $\begin{array}{r} 7 \\ \times\,2 \\ \hline \end{array}$ **23.** $\begin{array}{r} 4 \\ \times\,8 \\ \hline \end{array}$ **24.** $\begin{array}{r} 1 \\ \times\,2 \\ \hline \end{array}$

25. $\begin{array}{r} 9 \\ \times\,6 \\ \hline \end{array}$ **26.** $\begin{array}{r} 3 \\ \times\,1 \\ \hline \end{array}$ **27.** $\begin{array}{r} 8 \\ \times\,7 \\ \hline \end{array}$ **28.** $\begin{array}{r} 2 \\ \times\,8 \\ \hline \end{array}$ **29.** $\begin{array}{r} 6 \\ \times\,9 \\ \hline \end{array}$ **30.** $\begin{array}{r} 5 \\ \times\,5 \\ \hline \end{array}$

31. $\begin{array}{r} 2 \\ \times\,1 \\ \hline \end{array}$ **32.** $\begin{array}{r} 8 \\ \times\,0 \\ \hline \end{array}$ **33.** $\begin{array}{r} 4 \\ \times\,9 \\ \hline \end{array}$ **34.** $\begin{array}{r} 8 \\ \times\,3 \\ \hline \end{array}$ **35.** $\begin{array}{r} 6 \\ \times\,2 \\ \hline \end{array}$ **36.** $\begin{array}{r} 4 \\ \times\,5 \\ \hline \end{array}$

37. $\begin{array}{r} 9 \\ \times\,4 \\ \hline \end{array}$ **38.** $\begin{array}{r} 2 \\ \times\,9 \\ \hline \end{array}$ **39.** $\begin{array}{r} 3 \\ \times\,4 \\ \hline \end{array}$ **40.** $\begin{array}{r} 1 \\ \times\,6 \\ \hline \end{array}$ **41.** $\begin{array}{r} 8 \\ \times\,6 \\ \hline \end{array}$ **42.** $\begin{array}{r} 9 \\ \times\,8 \\ \hline \end{array}$

43. $\begin{array}{r} 1 \\ \times\,8 \\ \hline \end{array}$ **44.** $\begin{array}{r} 5 \\ \times\,1 \\ \hline \end{array}$ **45.** $\begin{array}{r} 9 \\ \times\,0 \\ \hline \end{array}$ **46.** $\begin{array}{r} 7 \\ \times\,4 \\ \hline \end{array}$ **47.** $\begin{array}{r} 9 \\ \times\,3 \\ \hline \end{array}$ **48.** $\begin{array}{r} 0 \\ \times\,3 \\ \hline \end{array}$

49. $\begin{array}{r} 3 \\ \times\,5 \\ \hline \end{array}$ **50.** $\begin{array}{r} 6 \\ \times\,8 \\ \hline \end{array}$ **51.** $\begin{array}{r} 5 \\ \times\,9 \\ \hline \end{array}$ **52.** $\begin{array}{r} 2 \\ \times\,6 \\ \hline \end{array}$ **53.** $\begin{array}{r} 1 \\ \times\,0 \\ \hline \end{array}$ **54.** $\begin{array}{r} 3 \\ \times\,9 \\ \hline \end{array}$

55. $\begin{array}{r} 9 \\ \times\,9 \\ \hline \end{array}$ **56.** $\begin{array}{r} 5 \\ \times\,4 \\ \hline \end{array}$ **57.** $\begin{array}{r} 0 \\ \times\,6 \\ \hline \end{array}$ **58.** $\begin{array}{r} 1 \\ \times\,9 \\ \hline \end{array}$ **59.** $\begin{array}{r} 5 \\ \times\,0 \\ \hline \end{array}$ **60.** $\begin{array}{r} 6 \\ \times\,1 \\ \hline \end{array}$

61. $\begin{array}{r} 9 \\ \times\,2 \\ \hline \end{array}$ **62.** $\begin{array}{r} 1 \\ \times\,7 \\ \hline \end{array}$ **63.** $\begin{array}{r} 1 \\ \times\,3 \\ \hline \end{array}$ **64.** $\begin{array}{r} 7 \\ \times\,3 \\ \hline \end{array}$ **65.** $\begin{array}{r} 6 \\ \times\,6 \\ \hline \end{array}$ **66.** $\begin{array}{r} 4 \\ \times\,0 \\ \hline \end{array}$

67. $\begin{array}{r} 7 \\ \times\,9 \\ \hline \end{array}$ **68.** $\begin{array}{r} 4 \\ \times\,3 \\ \hline \end{array}$ **69.** $\begin{array}{r} 7 \\ \times\,5 \\ \hline \end{array}$ **70.** $\begin{array}{r} 2 \\ \times\,0 \\ \hline \end{array}$ **71.** $\begin{array}{r} 6 \\ \times\,7 \\ \hline \end{array}$ **72.** $\begin{array}{r} 0 \\ \times\,8 \\ \hline \end{array}$

73. $\begin{array}{r} 8 \\ \times\,5 \\ \hline \end{array}$ **74.** $\begin{array}{r} 2 \\ \times\,4 \\ \hline \end{array}$ **75.** $\begin{array}{r} 0 \\ \times\,1 \\ \hline \end{array}$ **76.** $\begin{array}{r} 3 \\ \times\,8 \\ \hline \end{array}$ **77.** $\begin{array}{r} 9 \\ \times\,1 \\ \hline \end{array}$ **78.** $\begin{array}{r} 7 \\ \times\,0 \\ \hline \end{array}$

79. $\begin{array}{r} 5 \\ \times\,3 \\ \hline \end{array}$ **80.** $\begin{array}{r} 4 \\ \times\,4 \\ \hline \end{array}$ **81.** $\begin{array}{r} 1 \\ \times\,5 \\ \hline \end{array}$ **82.** $\begin{array}{r} 6 \\ \times\,5 \\ \hline \end{array}$ **83.** $\begin{array}{r} 3 \\ \times\,0 \\ \hline \end{array}$ **84.** $\begin{array}{r} 1 \\ \times\,4 \\ \hline \end{array}$

85. $\begin{array}{r} 3 \\ \times\,7 \\ \hline \end{array}$ **86.** $\begin{array}{r} 4 \\ \times\,2 \\ \hline \end{array}$ **87.** $\begin{array}{r} 0 \\ \times\,2 \\ \hline \end{array}$ **88.** $\begin{array}{r} 7 \\ \times\,7 \\ \hline \end{array}$ **89.** $\begin{array}{r} 8 \\ \times\,2 \\ \hline \end{array}$ **90.** $\begin{array}{r} 6 \\ \times\,4 \\ \hline \end{array}$

91. $\begin{array}{r} 0 \\ \times\,0 \\ \hline \end{array}$ **92.** $\begin{array}{r} 2 \\ \times\,7 \\ \hline \end{array}$ **93.** $\begin{array}{r} 4 \\ \times\,1 \\ \hline \end{array}$ **94.** $\begin{array}{r} 0 \\ \times\,4 \\ \hline \end{array}$ **95.** $\begin{array}{r} 2 \\ \times\,3 \\ \hline \end{array}$ **96.** $\begin{array}{r} 8 \\ \times\,1 \\ \hline \end{array}$

97. $\begin{array}{r} 3 \\ \times\,6 \\ \hline \end{array}$ **98.** $\begin{array}{r} 5 \\ \times\,2 \\ \hline \end{array}$ **99.** $\begin{array}{r} 0 \\ \times\,9 \\ \hline \end{array}$ **100.** $\begin{array}{r} 7 \\ \times\,6 \\ \hline \end{array}$

Plane Figures Have Length and Width but No Thickness or Depth		
Name	**Description**	**Figure**
Polygon	Union of three or more coplanar line segments that intersect with each other only at each endpoint, with each endpoint shared by two segments.	
Triangle	Polygon with three sides (sum of measures of three angles is 180°).	
Scalene Triangle	Triangle with no sides of equal length.	
Isosceles Triangle	Triangle with two sides of equal length.	
Equilateral Triangle	Triangle with all sides of equal length.	
Right Triangle	Triangle that contains a right angle.	leg hypotenuse / leg
Quadrilateral	Polygon with four sides (sum of measures of four angles is 360°).	
Trapezoid	Quadrilateral with exactly one pair of opposite sides parallel.	base / leg parallel sides leg / base
Isosceles Trapezoid	Trapezoid with legs of equal length.	
Parallelogram	Quadrilateral with both pairs of opposite sides parallel.	
Rhombus	Parallelogram with all sides of equal length.	

(Continued)

Plane Figures Have Length and Width but No Thickness or Depth (continued)		
Name	**Description**	**Figure**
Rectangle	Parallelogram with four right angles.	
Square	Rectangle with all sides of equal length.	
Circle	All points in a plane the same distance from a fixed point called the **center.**	radius / center / diameter

Solid Figures Have Length, Width, and Height or Depth		
Name	**Description**	**Figure**
Rectangular Solid	A solid with six sides, all of which are rectangles.	
Cube	A rectangular solid whose six sides are squares.	
Sphere	All points the same distance from a fixed point, called the **center.**	radius / center
Right Circular Cylinder	A cylinder having two circular bases that are perpendicular to its altitude.	
Right Circular Cone	A cone with a circular base that is perpendicular to its altitude.	

A.4 TABLE OF PERCENTS, DECIMALS, AND FRACTION EQUIVALENTS

Percent	Decimal	Fraction
1%	0.01	$\frac{1}{100}$
5%	0.05	$\frac{1}{20}$
10%	0.1	$\frac{1}{10}$
12.5% or $12\frac{1}{2}$%	0.125	$\frac{1}{8}$
$16.\overline{6}$% or $16\frac{2}{3}$%	$0.1\overline{6}$	$\frac{1}{6}$
20%	0.2	$\frac{1}{5}$
25%	0.25	$\frac{1}{4}$
30%	0.3	$\frac{3}{10}$
$33.\overline{3}$% or $33\frac{1}{3}$%	$0.\overline{3}$	$\frac{1}{3}$
37.5% or $37\frac{1}{2}$%	0.375	$\frac{3}{8}$
40%	0.4	$\frac{2}{5}$
50%	0.5	$\frac{1}{2}$
60%	0.6	$\frac{3}{5}$
62.5% or $62\frac{1}{2}$%	0.625	$\frac{5}{8}$
$66.\overline{6}$% or $66\frac{2}{3}$%	$0.\overline{6}$	$\frac{2}{3}$
70%	0.7	$\frac{7}{10}$
75%	0.75	$\frac{3}{4}$
80%	0.8	$\frac{4}{5}$
$83.\overline{3}$% or $83\frac{1}{3}$%	$0.8\overline{3}$	$\frac{5}{6}$
87.5% or $87\frac{1}{2}$%	0.875	$\frac{7}{8}$
90%	0.9	$\frac{9}{10}$
100%	1.0	1
110%	1.1	$1\frac{1}{10}$
125%	1.25	$1\frac{1}{4}$
$133.\overline{3}$% or $133\frac{1}{3}$%	$1.\overline{3}$	$1\frac{1}{3}$
150%	1.5	$1\frac{1}{2}$
$166.\overline{6}$% or $166\frac{2}{3}$%	$1.\overline{6}$	$1\frac{2}{3}$
175%	1.75	$1\frac{3}{4}$
200%	2.0	2

Common Percent Equivalences*	Shortcut Method for Finding Percent	Example
$1\% = 0.01 \left(\text{or } \frac{1}{100}\right)$	To find 1% of a number, multiply by 0.01. To do so, move the decimal point 2 places to the left.	1% of 210 is 2.10 or 2.1. 1% of 1500 is 15. 1% of 8.6 is 0.086.
$10\% = 0.1 \left(\text{or } \frac{1}{10}\right)$	To find 10% of a number, multiply by 0.1, or move the decimal point of the number one place to the left.	10% of 140 is 14. 10% of 30 is 3. 10% of 17.6 is 1.76.
$25\% = \frac{1}{4}$	To find 25% of a number, find $\frac{1}{4}$ of the number, or divide the number by 4.	25% of 20 is $\frac{20}{4}$ or 5. 25% of 8 is 2. 25% of 10 is $\frac{10}{4}$ or $2\frac{1}{2}$.
$50\% = \frac{1}{2}$	To find 50% of a number, find $\frac{1}{2}$ of the number, or divide the number by 2.	50% of 64 is $\frac{64}{2}$ or 32. 50% of 1000 is 500. 50% of 9 is $\frac{9}{2}$ or $4\frac{1}{2}$.
$100\% = 1$	To find 100% of a number, multiply the number by 1. In other words, 100% of a number is the number.	100% of 98 is 98. 100% of 1407 is 1407. 100% of 18.4 is 18.4.
$200\% = 2$	To find 200% of a number, multiply the number by 2.	200% of 31 is $31 \cdot 2$ or 62. 200% of 750 is 1500. 200% of 6.5 is 13.

*See Appendix A.4.

A.6 TABLE OF SQUARES AND SQUARE ROOTS

n	n²	√n	n	n²	√n
1	1	1.000	51	2601	7.141
2	4	1.414	52	2704	7.211
3	9	1.732	53	2809	7.280
4	16	2.000	54	2916	7.348
5	25	2.236	55	3025	7.416
6	36	2.449	56	3136	7.483
7	49	2.646	57	3249	7.550
8	64	2.828	58	3364	7.616
9	81	3.000	59	3481	7.681
10	100	3.162	60	3600	7.746
11	121	3.317	61	3721	7.810
12	144	3.464	62	3844	7.874
13	169	3.606	63	3969	7.937
14	196	3.742	64	4096	8.000
15	225	3.873	65	4225	8.062
16	256	4.000	66	4356	8.124
17	289	4.123	67	4489	8.185
18	324	4.243	68	4624	8.246
19	361	4.359	69	4761	8.307
20	400	4.472	70	4900	8.367
21	441	4.583	71	5041	8.426
22	484	4.690	72	5184	8.485
23	529	4.796	73	5329	8.544
24	576	4.899	74	5476	8.602
25	625	5.000	75	5625	8.660
26	676	5.099	76	5776	8.718
27	729	5.196	77	5929	8.775
28	784	5.292	78	6084	8.832
29	841	5.385	79	6241	8.888
30	900	5.477	80	6400	8.944
31	961	5.568	81	6561	9.000
32	1024	5.657	82	6724	9.055
33	1089	5.745	83	6889	9.110
34	1156	5.831	84	7056	9.165
35	1225	5.916	85	7225	9.220
36	1296	6.000	86	7396	9.274
37	1369	6.083	87	7569	9.327
38	1444	6.164	88	7744	9.381
39	1521	6.245	89	7921	9.434
40	1600	6.325	90	8100	9.487
41	1681	6.403	91	8281	9.539
42	1764	6.481	92	8464	9.592
43	1849	6.557	93	8649	9.644
44	1936	6.633	94	8836	9.695
45	2025	6.708	95	9025	9.747
46	2116	6.782	96	9216	9.798
47	2209	6.856	97	9409	9.849
48	2304	6.928	98	9604	9.899
49	2401	7.000	99	9801	9.950
50	2500	7.071	100	10,000	10.000

A.7 COMPOUND INTEREST TABLE

Compounded Annually

	5%	6%	7%	8%	9%	10%	11%	12%	13%	14%	15%	16%	17%	18%
1 year	1.05000	1.06000	1.07000	1.08000	1.09000	1.10000	1.11000	1.12000	1.13000	1.14000	1.15000	1.16000	1.17000	1.18000
5 years	1.27628	1.33823	1.40255	1.46933	1.53862	1.61051	1.68506	1.76234	1.84244	1.92541	2.01136	2.10034	2.19245	2.28776
10 years	1.62889	1.79085	1.96715	2.15892	2.36736	2.59374	2.83942	3.10585	3.39457	3.70722	4.04556	4.41144	4.80683	5.23384
15 years	2.07893	2.39656	2.75903	3.17217	3.64248	4.17725	4.78459	5.47357	6.25427	7.13794	8.13706	9.26552	10.53872	11.97375
20 years	2.65330	3.20714	3.86968	4.66096	5.60441	6.72750	8.06231	9.64629	11.52309	13.74349	16.36654	19.46076	23.10560	27.39303

Compounded Semiannually

	5%	6%	7%	8%	9%	10%	11%	12%	13%	14%	15%	16%	17%	18%
1 year	1.05063	1.06090	1.07123	1.08160	1.09203	1.10250	1.11303	1.12360	1.13423	1.14490	1.15563	1.16640	1.17723	1.18810
5 years	1.28008	1.34392	1.41060	1.48024	1.55297	1.62889	1.70814	1.79085	1.87714	1.96715	2.06103	2.15892	2.26098	2.36736
10 years	1.63862	1.80611	1.98979	2.19112	2.41171	2.65330	2.91776	3.20714	3.52365	3.86968	4.24785	4.66096	5.11205	5.60441
15 years	2.09757	2.42726	2.80679	3.24340	3.74532	4.32194	4.98395	5.74349	6.61437	7.61226	8.75496	10.06266	11.55825	13.26768
20 years	2.68506	3.26204	3.95926	4.80102	5.81636	7.03999	8.51331	10.28572	12.41607	14.97446	18.04424	21.72452	26.13302	31.40942

Compounded Quarterly

	5%	6%	7%	8%	9%	10%	11%	12%	13%	14%	15%	16%	17%	18%
1 year	1.05095	1.06136	1.07186	1.08243	1.09308	1.10381	1.11462	1.12551	1.13648	1.14752	1.15865	1.16986	1.18115	1.19252
5 years	1.28204	1.34686	1.41478	1.48595	1.56051	1.63862	1.72043	1.80611	1.89584	1.98979	2.08815	2.19112	2.29891	2.41171
10 years	1.64362	1.81402	2.00160	2.20804	2.43519	2.68506	2.95987	3.26204	3.59420	3.95926	4.36038	4.80102	5.28497	5.81636
15 years	2.10718	2.44322	2.83182	3.28103	3.80013	4.39979	5.09225	5.89160	6.81402	7.87809	9.10513	10.51963	12.14965	14.02741
20 years	2.70148	3.29066	4.00639	4.87544	5.93015	7.20957	8.76085	10.64089	12.91828	15.67574	19.01290	23.04980	27.93091	33.83010

Compounded Daily

	5%	6%	7%	8%	9%	10%	11%	12%	13%	14%	15%	16%	17%	18%
1 year	1.05127	1.06183	1.07250	1.08328	1.09416	1.10516	1.11626	1.12747	1.13880	1.15024	1.16180	1.17347	1.18526	1.19716
5 years	1.28400	1.34983	1.41902	1.49176	1.56823	1.64861	1.73311	1.82194	1.91532	2.01348	2.11667	2.22515	2.33918	2.45906
10 years	1.64866	1.82203	2.01362	2.22535	2.45933	2.71791	3.00367	3.31946	3.66845	4.05411	4.48031	4.95130	5.47178	6.04696
15 years	2.11689	2.45942	2.85736	3.31968	3.85678	4.48077	5.20569	6.04786	7.02625	8.16288	9.48335	11.01738	12.79950	14.86983
20 years	2.71810	3.31979	4.05466	4.95216	6.04831	7.38703	9.02202	11.01883	13.45751	16.43582	20.07316	24.51533	29.94039	36.56577

The Bigger Picture

To see the sections that formed this outline, see Sections 1.7, 1.9, 2.5, 3.3, 3.7, 4.4, 5.2, 6.2, 6.3, and 8.4.

I. Operations on Sets of Numbers

A. Whole Numbers

1. Add or Subtract:

$$\begin{array}{r} 14 \\ +\ 39 \\ \hline 53 \end{array} \qquad \begin{array}{r} 300 \\ -\ 27 \\ \hline 273 \end{array}$$

2. Multiply or Divide:

$$\begin{array}{r} 238 \\ \times\ 47 \\ \hline 1666 \\ 9520 \\ \hline 11{,}186 \end{array} \qquad \begin{array}{r} 127\ \text{R2} \\ 7\overline{)891} \\ -7 \\ \hline 19 \\ -14 \\ \hline 51 \\ -49 \\ \hline 2 \end{array}$$

3. Exponent:

4 factors of 3

$$3^4 = \overbrace{3 \cdot 3 \cdot 3 \cdot 3} = 81$$

4. Square Root:

$\sqrt{25} = 5$ *because* $5 \cdot 5 = 25$ and 5 is a positive number.

5. Order of Operations:

$$\begin{aligned} 24 \div 3 \cdot 2 - (2 + 8) &= 24 \div 3 \cdot 2 - (10) &&\text{Simplify within parentheses.} \\ &= 8 \cdot 2 - 10 &&\text{Multiply or divide from left to right.} \\ &= 16 - 10 &&\text{Multiply or divide from left to right.} \\ &= 6 &&\text{Add or subtract from left to right.} \end{aligned}$$

B. Integers

1. Add: $-5 + (-2) = -7$ Adding like signs.

Add absolute value. Attach the common sign.

$-5 + 2 = -3$ Adding unlike signs.

Subtract absolute values. Attach the sign of the number with the larger absolute value.

2. Subtract: Add the first number to the opposite of the second number.

$$7 - 10 = 7 + (-10) = -3$$

3. Multiply or Divide: Multiply or divide as usual. If the signs of the two numbers are the same, the answer is positive. If the signs of the two numbers are different, the answer is negative.

$$-5 \cdot 5 = -25, \quad \frac{-32}{-8} = 4$$

C. Fractions

1. Simplify: Factor the numerator and denominator. Then divide out factors of 1 by dividing out common factors in the numerator and denominator.

Simplify: $\dfrac{20}{28} = \dfrac{4 \cdot 5}{4 \cdot 7} = \dfrac{5}{7}$

2. Multiply: Numerator times numerator over denominator times denominator.

$$\frac{5}{9} \cdot \frac{2}{7} = \frac{10}{63}$$

3. Divide: First fraction times the reciprocal of the second fraction.

$$\frac{2}{11} \div \frac{3}{4} = \frac{2}{11} \cdot \frac{4}{3} = \frac{8}{33}$$

4. Add or Subtract: Must have same denominators. If not, find the LCD, and write each fraction as an equivalent fraction with the LCD as denominator.

$$\frac{2}{5} + \frac{1}{15} = \frac{2}{5} \cdot \frac{3}{3} + \frac{1}{15} = \frac{6}{15} + \frac{1}{15} = \frac{7}{15}$$

D. Decimals

1. Add or Subtract: Line up decimal points.

$$\begin{array}{r} 1.27 \\ + \ 0.6 \\ \hline 1.87 \end{array}$$

2. Multiply:

$$\begin{array}{r} 2.56 \\ \times \ 3.2 \\ \hline 512 \\ 768 \\ \hline 8.192 \end{array}$$

2.56 — 2 decimal places
× 3.2 — 1 decimal place
2 + 1 = 3
8.192 — 3 decimal places

3. Divide: $8\overline{)5.6}$ gives 0.7 $0.6\overline{)0.786}$ gives 1.31

II. Solving Equations

A. Proportions: Set cross products equal to each other. Then solve.

$$\frac{14}{3} = \frac{2}{n}, \text{ or } 14 \cdot n = 3 \cdot 2, \text{ or } 14 \cdot n = 6, \text{ or } n = \frac{6}{14} = \frac{3}{7}$$

B. Percent Problems

1. Solved by Equations: Remember that "of" means multiplication and "is" means equals.

"12% of some number is 6" translates to

$$12\% \cdot n = 6 \text{ or } 0.12 \cdot n = 6 \text{ or } n = \frac{6}{0.12} \text{ or } n = 50$$

2. Solved by Proportions: Remember that percent, p, is identified by % or percent, base, b, usually appears after "of" and amount, a, is the part compared to the whole.

"12% of some number is 6" translates to

$$\frac{6}{b} = \frac{12}{100} \text{ or } 6 \cdot 100 = b \cdot 12 \text{ or } \frac{600}{12} = b \text{ or } 50 = b$$

C. Equations in General: Simplify both sides of the equation by removing parentheses and adding any like terms. Then use the Addition Property to write variable terms on one side, constants (or numbers) on the other side. Then use the Multiplication Property to solve for the variable by dividing both sides of the equation by the coefficient of the variable.

Solve: $2(x - 5) = 80$

$$\begin{aligned} 2x - 10 &= 80 && \text{Use the distributive property.} \\ 2x - 10 + 10 &= 80 + 10 && \text{Add 10 to both sides.} \\ 2x &= 90 && \text{Simplify.} \\ \frac{2x}{2} &= \frac{90}{2} && \text{Divide both sides by 2.} \\ x &= 45 && \text{Simplify.} \end{aligned}$$

C Exponents and Polynomials

C.1 ADDING AND SUBTRACTING POLYNOMIALS

Objectives

A Add Polynomials.

B Subtract Polynomials.

C Evaluate Polynomials at Given Replacement Values.

Before we add and subtract polynomials, let's first review some definitions presented in Section 8.1. Recall that the *addends* of an algebraic expression are the *terms* of the expression.

Expression

$$3x + 5$$

2 terms

$$7y^2 + (-6y) + 4$$

3 terms

Also, recall that *like terms* can be added or subtracted by using the distributive property. For example,

$$7x + 3x = (7 + 3)x = 10x$$

Objective **A** Adding Polynomials

Some terms are also **monomials.** A term is a monomial if the term contains only whole-number exponents and no variable in the denominator.

Monomials	Not Monomials	
$3x^2$	$\dfrac{2}{y}$	Variable in denominator
$-\dfrac{1}{2}a^2bc^3$	$-2x^{-5}$	Not a whole number exponent
7		

A monomial or a sum and/or difference of monomials is called a **polynomial.**

Polynomial

A **polynomial** is a monomial or a sum and/or difference of monomials.

Examples of Polynomials

$$5x^3 - 6x^2 + 2x + 10, \quad -1.2y^3 + 0.7y, \quad z, \quad \frac{1}{3}r - \frac{1}{2}, \quad 0$$

Some polynomials are given special names depending on their number of terms.

Types of Polynomials

A **monomial** is a polynomial with exactly one term.
A **binomial** is a polynomial with exactly two terms.
A **trinomial** is a polynomial with exactly three terms.

Below are examples of monomials, binomials, and trinomials. Each of these examples is also a polynomial.

Polynomials			
Monomials	**Binomials**	**Trinomials**	**More Than Three Terms**
z	$x + 2$	$x^2 - 2x + 1$	$5x^3 - 6x^2 + 2x - 10$
4	$\dfrac{1}{3}r - \dfrac{1}{2}$	$y^5 + 3y^2 - 1.7$	$t^7 - t^5 + t^3 - t + 1$
$0.2x^2$	$-1.2y^3 + 0.7y$	$-a^3 + 2a^2 - 5a$	$z^8 - z^4 + 3z^2 - 2z$

To add polynomials, we use the commutative and associative properties to rearrange and group like terms. Then, we combine like terms.

Adding Polynomials

To add polynomials, combine like terms.

PRACTICE PROBLEM 1

Add: $(2y + 7) + (9y - 14)$

EXAMPLE 1 Add: $(3x - 1) + (-6x + 2)$

Solution:

$$
\begin{aligned}
(3x - 1) + (-6x + 2) &= (3x - 6x) + (-1 + 2) && \text{Group like terms.}\\
&= (-3x) + (1) && \text{Combine like terms.}\\
&= -3x + 1
\end{aligned}
$$

▢ **Work Practice Problem 1**

PRACTICE PROBLEM 2

Add:
$(5x^2 + 4x - 3) + (x^2 - 6x)$

EXAMPLE 2 Add: $(9y^2 - 6y) + (7y^2 + 10y + 2)$

Solution:

$$
\begin{aligned}
(9y^2 - 6y) + (7y^2 + 10y + 2) &= 9y^2 + 7y^2 - 6y + 10y + 2 && \text{Group like terms.}\\
&= 16y^2 + 4y + 2
\end{aligned}
$$

▢ **Work Practice Problem 2**

PRACTICE PROBLEM 3

Find the sum of
$(7z^2 - 4.2z + 11)$ and
$(-9z^2 - 1.9z + 4)$.

EXAMPLE 3 Find the sum of $(-y^2 + 2y + 1.7)$ and $(12y^2 - 6y - 3.6)$.

Solution: Recall that "sum" means addition.

$$
\begin{aligned}
&(-y^2 + 2y + 1.7) + (12y^2 - 6y - 3.6)\\
&= \underbrace{-y^2 + 12y^2}_{} + \underbrace{2y - 6y}_{} + \underbrace{1.7 - 3.6}_{} && \text{Group like terms.}\\
&= 11y^2 - 4y - 1.9 && \text{Combine like terms.}
\end{aligned}
$$

▢ **Work Practice Problem 3**

Polynomials can also be added vertically. To do this, line up like terms underneath one another. Let's vertically add the polynomials in Example 3.

Answers

1. $11y - 7$, **2.** $6x^2 - 2x - 3$,
3. $-2z^2 - 6.1z + 15$

EXAMPLE 4 Find the sum of $(-y^2 + 2y + 1.7)$ and $(12y^2 - 6y - 3.6)$. Use a vertical format.

Solution: Line up like terms underneath one another.

$$\begin{array}{r} -y^2 + 2y + 1.7 \\ +12y^2 - 6y - 3.6 \\ \hline 11y^2 - 4y - 1.9 \end{array}$$

☐ **Work Practice Problem 4**

Notice that we are finding the same sum in Example 4 as in Example 3. Of course, the results are the same.

Objective B Subtracting Polynomials

To subtract one polynomial from another, recall how we subtract numbers. To subtract a number, we add its opposite: $a - b = a + (-b)$.

For example,

$$7 - 10 = 7 + (-10)$$
$$= -3$$

To subtract a polynomial, we also add its opposite. Just as the opposite of 3 is -3, the opposite of $(2x^2 - 5x + 1)$ is $-(2x^2 - 5x + 1)$. Let's practice simplifying the opposite of a polynomial.

EXAMPLE 5 Simplify: $-(2x^2 - 5x + 1)$

Solution: Rewrite $-(2x^2 - 5x + 1)$ as $-1(2x^2 - 5x + 1)$ and use the distributive property.

$$-(2x^2 - 5x + 1) = -1(2x^2 - 5x + 1)$$
$$= -1(2x^2) + (-1)(-5x) + (-1)(1)$$
$$= -2x^2 + 5x - 1$$

☐ **Work Practice Problem 5**

Notice the result of Example 5.

$$-(2x^2 - 5x + 1) = -2x^2 + 5x - 1$$

This means that **the opposite of a polynomial can be found by changing the signs of the terms of the polynomial.** This leads to the following.

Subtracting Polynomials

To subtract polynomials, change the signs of the terms of the polynomial being subtracted, then add.

EXAMPLE 6 Subtract: $(5a + 7) - (2a - 10)$

Solution:

$$(5a + 7) - (2a - 10) = (5a + 7) + (-2a + 10) \quad \text{Add the opposite of } 2a - 10.$$
$$= 5a - 2a + 7 + 10 \quad \text{Group like terms.}$$
$$= 3a + 17$$

☐ **Work Practice Problem 6**

PRACTICE PROBLEM 4

Add the polynomials in Practice Problem 3 vertically.

PRACTICE PROBLEM 5

Simplify: $-(7y^2 + 4y - 6)$

PRACTICE PROBLEM 6

Subtract:
$(3b - 2) - (7b + 23)$

Answers
4. same as 3, **5.** $-7y^2 - 4y + 6$,
6. $-4b - 25$

PRACTICE PROBLEM 7

Subtract:
$(11x^2 + 7x + 2) - (15x^2 + 4x)$

PRACTICE PROBLEM 8

Subtract $(3x^2 - 12x)$ from $(-4x^2 + 20x + 17)$.

PRACTICE PROBLEM 9

Subtract $(3x^2 - 12x)$ from $(-4x^2 + 20x + 17)$. Use a vertical format.

PRACTICE PROBLEM 10

Find the value of the polynomial $2y^3 + y^2 - 6$ when $y = 3$.

EXAMPLE 7   Subtract: $(8x^2 - 4x + 1) - (10x^2 + 4)$

Solution:

$(8x^2 - 4x + 1) - (10x^2 + 4) = (8x^2 - 4x + 1) + (-10x^2 - 4)$ ← Add the opposite of $10x^2 + 4$.

$\qquad = 8x^2 - 10x^2 - 4x + 1 - 4$ ← Group like terms.

$\qquad = -2x^2 - 4x - 3$

▣ **Work Practice Problem 7**

EXAMPLE 8   Subtract $(-6z^2 - 2z + 13)$ from $(4z^2 - 20z)$.

Solution: Be careful when arranging the polynomials in this example.

$(4z^2 - 20z) - (-6z^2 - 2z + 13) = (4z^2 - 20z) + (6z^2 + 2z - 13)$

$\qquad = 4z^2 + 6z^2 - 20z + 2z - 13$ ← Group like terms.

$\qquad = 10z^2 - 18z - 13$

▣ **Work Practice Problem 8**

✔ **Concept Check**   Find and explain the error in the following subtraction.

$(3x^2 + 4) - (x^2 - 3x)$
$= (3x^2 + 4) + (-x^2 - 3x)$
$= 3x^2 - x^2 - 3x + 4$
$= 2x^2 - 3x + 4$

Just as with adding polynomials, we can subtract polynomials using a vertical format. Let's subtract the polynomials in Example 8 using a vertical format.

EXAMPLE 9   Subtract $(-6z^2 - 2z + 13)$ from $(4z^2 - 20z)$. Use a vertical format.

Solution: Line up like terms underneath one another.

$$\begin{array}{r} 4z^2 - 20z \\ -(-6z^2 - 2z + 13) \\ \hline \end{array} \qquad \begin{array}{r} 4z^2 - 20z \\ +6z^2 + 2z - 13 \\ \hline 10z^2 - 18z - 13 \end{array}$$

▣ **Work Practice Problem 9**

Objective C Evaluating Polynomials

Polynomials have different values depending on the replacement values for the variables.

EXAMPLE 10   Find the value of the polynomial $3t^3 - 2t + 5$ when $t = 1$.

Solution: Replace t with 1 and simplify.

$3t^3 - 2t + 5 = 3(1)^3 - 2(1) + 5$ Let $t = 1$.

$\qquad = 3(1) - 2 + 5$ $(1)^3 = 1$.

$\qquad = 3 - 2 + 5$

$\qquad = 6$

The value of $3t^3 - 2t + 5$ when $t = 1$ is 6.

▣ **Work Practice Problem 10**

Many real-world applications are modeled by polynomials.

EXAMPLE 11 Finding the Height of an Object

An object is dropped from the top of an 800-foot-tall building. Its height at time t seconds is given by the polynomial $-16t^2 + 800$. Find the height of the object when $t = 1$ second and when $t = 3$ seconds.

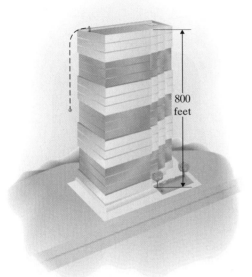

Solution: To find each height, we evaluate the polynomial when $t = 1$ and when $t = 3$.

$$-16t^2 + 800 = -16(1)^2 + 800$$
$$= -16 + 800$$
$$= 784$$

The height of the object at 1 second is 784 feet.

$$-16t^2 + 800 = -16(3)^2 + 800$$
$$= -16(9) + 800$$
$$= -144 + 800$$
$$= 656$$

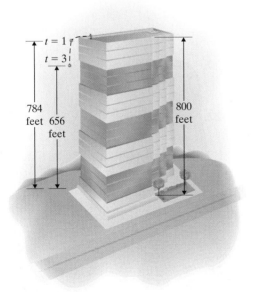

The height of the object at 3 seconds is 656 feet.

🖥 **Work Practice Problem 11**

PRACTICE PROBLEM 11

An object is dropped from the top of a 530-foot cliff. Its height in feet at time t seconds is given by the polynomial $-16t^2 + 530$. Find the height of the object when $t = 1$ second and when $t = 4$ seconds.

Helpful Hint Don't forget to insert units, if appropriate.

Answer
11. 514 feet; 274 feet

Objective A *Add the polynomials. See Examples 1 through 4.*

1. $(2x + 3) + (-7x - 27)$

2. $(9y - 16) + (-43y + 16)$

3. $(-4z^2 - 6z + 1) + (-5z^2 + 4z + 5)$

4. $(17a^2 - 6a + 3) + (16a^2 - 6a - 10)$

5. $(12y - 20) + (9y^2 + 13y - 20)$

6. $(5x^2 - 6) + (-3x^2 + 17x - 2)$

7. $(4.3a^4 + 5) + (-8.6a^4 - 2a^2 + 4)$

8. $(-12.7z^3 - 14z) + (-8.9z^3 + 12z + 2)$

Objective B *Subtract the polynomials. See Examples 5 through 9.*

9. $(5a - 6) - (a + 2)$

10. $(12b + 7) - (-b - 5)$

11. $(3x^2 - 2x + 1) - (5x^2 - 6x)$

12. $(-9z^2 + 6z + 2) - (3z^2 + 1)$

13. $(10y^2 - 7) - (20y^3 - 2y^2 - 3)$

14. $(11x^3 + 15x - 9) - (-x^3 + 10x^2 - 9)$

15. Subtract $(3x - 4)$ from $(2x + 12)$.

16. Subtract $(6a + 1)$ from $(-7a + 7)$.

17. Subtract $(5y^2 + 4y - 6)$ from $(13y^2 - 6y - 14)$.

18. Subtract $(16x^2 - x + 1)$ from $(12x^2 - 3x - 12)$.

Objectives A B Mixed Practice *Perform each indicated operation. See Examples 1 through 9.*

19. $(25x - 5) + (-20x - 7)$

20. $(14x + 2) + (-7x - 1)$

21. $(4y + 4) - (3y + 8)$

22. $(6z - 3) - (8z + 5)$

23. $(9x^2 - 6) + (-5x^2 + x - 10)$

24. $(12a^2 - 4a - 4) + (-5a - 5)$

25. $(10x + 4.5) + (-x - 8.6)$

26. $(20x - 0.8) + (x + 1.2)$

27. $(12a - 5) - (-3a + 2)$

28. $(8t + 9) - (-2t + 6)$

29. $(21y - 4.6) - (36y - 8.2)$

30. $(8.6x + 4) - (9.7x - 93)$

31. $(18t^2 - 4t + 2) - (-t^2 + 7t - 1)$

32. $(35x^2 + x - 5) - (17x^2 - x + 5)$

33. $(b^3 - 2b^2 + 10b + 11) + (b^2 - 3b - 12)$

34. $(-2z^3 + 5z^2 - 13z + 6) + (3z^2 - 7z - 6)$

35. Add $(6x^2 - 7)$ and $(-11x^2 - 11x + 20)$.

36. Add $(-2x^2 + 3x)$ and $(9x^2 - x + 14)$.

37. Subtract $\left(3z - \dfrac{3}{7} \right)$ from $\left(3z + \dfrac{6}{7} \right)$.

38. Subtract $\left(8y^2 - \dfrac{7}{10}y \right)$ from $\left(-5y^2 + \dfrac{3}{10}y \right)$.

Objective **C** *Find the value of each polynomial when $x = 2$. See Examples 10 and 11.*

39. $-3x + 7$

40. $-5x - 7$

41. $x^2 - 6x + 3$

42. $5x^2 + 4x - 100$

43. $\dfrac{3x^2}{2} - 14$

44. $\dfrac{7x^3}{14} - x + 5$

Find the value of each polynomial when $x = 5$. See Examples 10 and 11.

45. $2x + 10$

46. $-5x - 6$

47. x^2

48. x^3

49. $2x^2 + 4x - 20$

50. $4x^2 - 5x + 10$

Solve. See Example 11.

The distance in feet traveled by a free-falling object in t seconds is given by the polynomial

$16t^2$

Use this polynomial for Exercises 51 and 52.

51. Find the distance traveled by an object that falls for 6 seconds.

52. It takes 8 seconds for a hard hat to fall from the top of a building. How high is the building?

Office Supplies, Inc. manufactures office products. They determine that the total cost for manufacturing x file cabinets is given by the polynomial

$3000 + 20x$

Use this polynomial for Exercises 53 and 54.

53. Find the total cost to manufacture 10 file cabinets.

54. Find the total cost to manufacture 100 file cabinets.

An object is dropped from the deck of the Royal Gorge Bridge, which stretches across Royal Gorge at a height of 1053 feet above the Arkansas River. The height of the object above the river after t seconds is given by the polynomial

$$1053 - 16t^2$$

Use this polynomial for Exercises 55 and 56. (*Source:* Royal Gorge Bridge Co.)

55. How far above the river is an object that has been falling for 3 seconds?

56. How far above the river is an object that has been falling for 8 seconds?

Concept Extensions

Find the perimeter of each figure.

△ **57.**

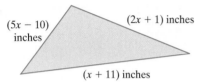

$(5x - 10)$ inches

$(2x + 1)$ inches

$(x + 11)$ inches

△ **58.**

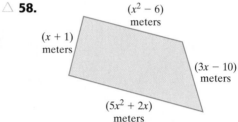

$(x^2 - 6)$ meters

$(x + 1)$ meters

$(3x - 10)$ meters

$(5x^2 + 2x)$ meters

Given the lengths in the figure below, we find the unknown length by subtracting. Use the information to find the unknown lengths in Exercises 59 and 60.

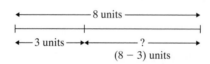

8 units

3 units

?

$(8 - 3)$ units

59.

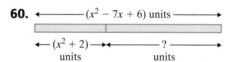

$(7x - 10)$ units

$(3x + 5)$ units

? units

60.

$(x^2 - 7x + 6)$ units

$(x^2 + 2)$ units

? units

Fill in the blanks.

61. $(3x^2 + \underline{\quad} x - \underline{\quad}) + (\underline{\quad} x^2 - 6x + 2) = 5x^2 + 14x - 4$

62. $(\underline{\quad} y^2 + 4y - 3) + (8y^2 - \underline{\quad} y + \underline{\quad}) = 9y^2 + 2y + 7$

63. Find the value of $7a^4 - 6a^2 + 2a - 1$ when $a = 1.2$.

64. Find the value of $3b^3 + 4b^2 - 100$ when $b = -2.5$.

65. For Exercises 55 and 56, the polynomial $1053 - 16t^2$ was used to give the height of an object above the river after t seconds. Find the height when $t = 8$ seconds and $t = 9$ seconds. Explain what happened and why.

C.2 MULTIPLICATION PROPERTIES OF EXPONENTS

Objectives

A Use the Product Rule for Exponents.

B Use the Power Rule for Exponents.

C Use the Power of a Product Rule for Exponents.

Objective **A** Using the Product Rule

Recall from Section 1.8 that an exponent has the same meaning whether the base is a number or a variable. For example,

$$5^3 = \underbrace{5 \cdot 5 \cdot 5}_{\text{3 factors of 5}} \quad \text{and} \quad x^3 = \underbrace{x \cdot x \cdot x}_{\text{3 factors of } x}$$

We can use this definition of an exponent to discover properties that will help us to simplify products and powers of exponential expressions.

For example, let's use the definition of an exponent to find the product of x^3 and x^4.

$$x^3 \cdot x^4 = (x \cdot x \cdot x)(x \cdot x \cdot x \cdot x)$$
$$= \underbrace{x \cdot x \cdot x \cdot x \cdot x \cdot x \cdot x}_{\text{7 factors of } x}$$
$$= x^7$$

Notice that the result is the same if we add the exponents.

$$x^3 \cdot x^4 = x^{3+4} = x^7$$

This suggests the following product rule or property for exponents.

Product Property for Exponents

If m and n are positive integers and a is a real number, then

$$a^m \cdot a^n = a^{m+n}$$

In other words, to multiply two exponential expressions with the same base, keep the base and add the exponents.

EXAMPLE 1 Multiply: $y^7 \cdot y^2$

Solution:

$$y^7 \cdot y^2 = y^{7+2} \quad \text{Use the product property for exponents.}$$
$$= y^9 \quad \text{Simplify.}$$

☐ **Work Practice Problem 1**

EXAMPLE 2 Multiply: $3x^5 \cdot 6x^3$

Solution:

$$3x^5 \cdot 6x^3 = (3 \cdot 6)(x^5 \cdot x^3) \quad \text{Apply the commutative and associative properties.}$$
$$= 18x^{5+3} \quad \text{Use the product property for exponents.}$$
$$= 18x^8 \quad \text{Simplify.}$$

☐ **Work Practice Problem 2**

PRACTICE PROBLEM 1

Multiply: $z^4 \cdot z^8$

PRACTICE PROBLEM 2

Multiply: $7y^5 \cdot 4y^9$

Answers

1. z^{12}, **2.** $28y^{14}$

PRACTICE PROBLEM 3

Multiply: $(-7r^6s^2)(-3r^2s^5)$

EXAMPLE 3 Multiply: $(-2a^4b^{10})(9a^5b^3)$

Solution: Use properties of multiplication to group numbers and like variables together.

$$(-2a^4b^{10})(9a^5b^3) = (-2 \cdot 9)(a^4 \cdot a^5)(b^{10} \cdot b^3)$$
$$= -18a^{4+5}b^{10+3}$$
$$= -18a^9b^{13}$$

🖥 **Work Practice Problem 3**

PRACTICE PROBLEM 4

Multiply: $9y^4 \cdot 3y^2 \cdot y$. (Recall that $y = y^1$.)

EXAMPLE 4 Multiply: $2x^3 \cdot 3x \cdot 5x^6$

Solution: First notice the factor $3x$. Since there is one factor of x in $3x$, it can also be written as $3x^1$.

$$2x^3 \cdot 3x^1 \cdot 5x^6 = (2 \cdot 3 \cdot 5)(x^3 \cdot x^1 \cdot x^6)$$
$$= 30x^{10}$$

🖥 **Work Practice Problem 4**

> **Helpful Hint** Don't forget that if an exponent is not written, it is assumed to be 1.

> **Helpful Hint** These examples will remind you of the difference between adding and multiplying terms.
>
> **Addition**
>
> $5x^3 + 3x^3 = (5 + 3)x^3 = 8x^3$
>
> $7x + 4x^2 = 7x + 4x^2$
>
> **Multiplication**
>
> $(5x^3)(3x^3) = 5 \cdot 3 \cdot x^3 \cdot x^3 = 15x^{3+3} = 15x^6$
>
> $(7x)(4x^2) = 7 \cdot 4 \cdot x \cdot x^2 = 28x^{1+2} = 28x^3$

Objective B Using the Power Rule

Next suppose that we want to simplify an exponential expression raised to a power. To see how we simplify $(x^2)^3$, we again use the definition of an exponent.

$$(x^2)^3 = \underbrace{(x^2) \cdot (x^2) \cdot (x^2)}_{3 \text{ factors for } x^2}$$ Apply the definition of an exponent.

$$= x^{2+2+2}$$ Use the product property for exponents.

$$= x^6$$ Simplify.

Notice the result is exactly the same if we multiply the exponents.

$$(x^2)^3 = x^{2 \cdot 3} = x^6$$

This suggests the following power rule or property for exponents.

Power Property for Exponents

If m and n are positive integers and a is a real number, then

$$(a^m)^n = a^{m \cdot n}$$

Answers
3. $21r^8s^7$, **4.** $27y^7$

In other words, to raise a power to a power, keep the base and multiply the exponents.

> **Helpful Hint**
>
> Take a moment to make sure that you understand when to apply the product rule and when to apply the power rule.
>
> | Product Property → Add Exponents | Power Property → Multiply Exponents |
> |---|---|
> | $x^5 \cdot x^7 = x^{5+7} = x^{12}$ | $(x^5)^7 = x^{5 \cdot 7} = x^{35}$ |
> | $y^6 \cdot y^2 = y^{6+2} = y^8$ | $(y^6)^2 = y^{6 \cdot 2} = y^{12}$ |

EXAMPLE 5 Simplify: $(y^8)^2$

Solution:

$$(y^8)^2 = y^{8 \cdot 2} \quad \text{Use the power property.}$$
$$= y^{16}$$

Work Practice Problem 5

PRACTICE PROBLEM 5
Simplify: $(z^3)^{10}$

EXAMPLE 6 Simplify: $(a^3)^4 \cdot (a^2)^9$

Solution:

$$(a^3)^4 \cdot (a^2)^9 = a^{12} \cdot a^{18} \quad \text{Use the power property.}$$
$$= a^{12+18} \quad \text{Use the product property.}$$
$$= a^{30} \quad \text{Simplify.}$$

Work Practice Problem 6

PRACTICE PROBLEM 6
Simplify: $(z^4)^5 \cdot (z^3)^7$

Objective C Using the Power of a Product Rule

Next, let's simplify the power of a product.

$$(xy)^3 = xy \cdot xy \cdot xy \qquad \text{Apply the definition of an exponent.}$$
$$= (x \cdot x \cdot x)(y \cdot y \cdot y) \qquad \text{Group like bases.}$$
$$= x^3 y^3 \qquad \text{Simplify.}$$

Notice that the power of a product can be written as the product of powers. This leads to the following power of a product rule or property.

Power of a Product Property for Exponents

If n is a positive integer and a and b are real numbers, then

$$(ab)^n = a^n b^n$$

In other words, to raise a product to a power, raise each factor to the power.

Answers
5. z^{30}, **6.** z^{41}

✔**Concept Check** Which property is needed to simplify $(x^6)^3$? Explain.
a. Product Property for Exponents
b. Power Property for Exponents
c. Power of a Product Property for Exponents

PRACTICE PROBLEM 7

Simplify: $(3b)^4$

EXAMPLE 7 Simplify: $(5t)^3$

Solution:

$$(5t)^3 = 5^3 t^3 \qquad \text{Apply the power of a product property.}$$
$$= 125t^3 \qquad \text{Write } 5^3 \text{ as } 125.$$

▢ **Work Practice Problem 7**

PRACTICE PROBLEM 8

Simplify: $(4x^2 y^6)^3$

EXAMPLE 8 Simplify: $(2a^5 b^3)^3$

Solution:

$$(2a^5 b^3)^3 = 2^3 (a^5)^3 (b^3)^3 \qquad \text{Apply the power of a product property.}$$
$$= 8a^{15} b^9 \qquad \text{Apply the power property.}$$

▢ **Work Practice Problem 8**

PRACTICE PROBLEM 9

Simplify: $(2x^2 y^4)^4 (3x^6 y^9)^2$

EXAMPLE 9 Simplify: $(3y^4 z^2)^4 (2y^3 z^5)^5$

Solution:

$$(3y^4 z^2)^4 (2y^3 z^5)^5 = 3^4 (y^4)^4 (z^2)^4 \cdot 2^5 (y^3)^5 (z^5)^5 \qquad \text{Apply the power of a product property.}$$
$$= 81y^{16} z^8 \cdot 32 y^{15} z^{25} \qquad \text{Apply the power property.}$$
$$= (81 \cdot 32)(y^{16} \cdot y^{15})(z^8 \cdot z^{25}) \qquad \text{Group like bases.}$$
$$= 2592 y^{31} z^{33} \qquad \text{Apply the product property.}$$

▢ **Work Practice Problem 9**

Answers
7. $81b^4$, **8.** $64x^6 y^{18}$, **9.** $144x^{20} y^{34}$

✔ **Concept Check Answer** b

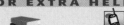

Objective A *Multiply. See Examples 1 through 4.*

1. $x^5 \cdot x^9$

2. $y^4 \cdot y^7$

3. $a^6 \cdot a$

4. $b \cdot b^8$

5. $3z^3 \cdot 5z^2$

6. $8r^2 \cdot 2r^{15}$

7. $-4x \cdot 10x$

8. $-9y \cdot 3y$

9. $(-5x^2y^3)(-5x^4y)$

10. $(-2xy^4)(-6x^3y^7)$

11. $(7ab)(4a^4b^5)$

12. $(3a^3b^6)(12a^2b^9)$

13. $2x \cdot 3x \cdot 7x$

14. $4y \cdot 3y \cdot 5y$

15. $a \cdot 4a^{11} \cdot 3a^5$

16. $b \cdot 7b^{10} \cdot 5b^8$

Objectives B C **Mixed Practice** *Simplify. See Examples 5 through 9.*

17. $(x^5)^3$

18. $(y^4)^7$

19. $(z^2)^{10}$

20. $(a^6)^9$

21. $(b^7)^6(b^2)^{10}$

22. $(x^2)^9 \cdot (x^5)^3$

23. $(3a)^4$

24. $(2y)^5$

25. $(a^{11}b^8)^3$

26. $(x^7y^4)^8$

27. $(11x^3y^6)^2$

28. $(9a^4b^3)^2$

29. $(-3y)(2y^7)^3$

30. $(-2x)(5x^2)^4$

31. $(4xy)^3(2x^3y^5)^2$

32. $(2xy)^4(3x^4y^3)^3$

Concept Extensions

Find the area of each figure.

△ **33.**

square $4x^6$ inches

△ **34.**

$9y^2$ centimeters

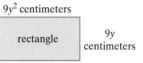

rectangle $9y$ centimeters

△ **35.**

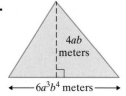

$4ab$ meters

$6a^3b^4$ meters

△ **36.**

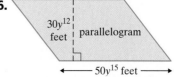

$30y^{12}$ feet   parallelogram

$50y^{15}$ feet

(*Hint:* Area = base · height)

Multiply and simplify.

37. $(14a^7b^6)^3(9a^6b^3)^4$

38. $(5x^{14}y^6)^7(3x^{20}y^{19})^5$

39. $(8.1x^{10})^5$

40. $(4.6a^{14})^4$

41. In your own words, explain why $x^2 \cdot x^3 = x^5$ and $(x^2)^3 = x^6$.

42. $(x^{90}y^{72})^3$

43. $(a^{20}b^{10}c^5)^5(a^9b^{12})^3$

C.3 MULTIPLYING POLYNOMIALS

Objectives

A Multiply a Monomial and any Polynomial.

B Multiply Two Binomials.

C Square a Binomial.

D Use the FOIL Order to Multiply Binomials.

E Multiply any Two Polynomials.

Objective **A** Multiplying a Monomial and a Polynomial

Recall that a polynomial that consists of one term is called a **monomial.** For example, $5x$ is a monomial. To multiply a monomial and any polynomial, we use the distributive property

$$a(b + c) = a \cdot b + a \cdot c$$

and apply properties of exponents.

EXAMPLE 1 Multiply: $5x(3x^2 + 2)$

Solution:

$$5x(3x^2 + 2) = 5x \cdot 3x^2 + 5x \cdot 2 \qquad \text{Apply the distributive property.}$$
$$= 15x^3 + 10x$$

■ **Work Practice Problem 1**

PRACTICE PROBLEM 1

Multiply: $3y(7y^2 + 5)$

EXAMPLE 2 Multiply: $2z(4z^2 + 6z - 9)$

Solution:

$$2z(4z^2 + 6z - 9) = 2z \cdot 4z^2 + 2z \cdot 6z + 2z(-9)$$
$$= 8z^3 + 12z^2 - 18z$$

■ **Work Practice Problem 2**

PRACTICE PROBLEM 2

Multiply: $5r(8r^2 - r + 11)$

To visualize multiplication by a monomial, let's look at two ways we can represent the area of the same rectangle.

The width of the rectangle is x and its length is $x + 3$. One way to calculate the area of the rectangle is

$$
\text{area} = \text{width} \cdot \text{length}
$$
$$
= x(x + 3)
$$

Another way to calculate the area of the rectangle is to find the sum of the areas of the smaller figures.

$$\text{area} = x^2 + 3x$$

Since the areas must be equal, we have that

$$x(x + 3) = x^2 + 3x \qquad \text{As expected by the distributive property}$$

Answers

1. $21y^3 + 15y$, **2.** $40r^3 - 5r^2 + 55r$

Objective B Multiplying Binomials

Recall from Appendix C.1 that a polynomial that consists of exactly two terms is called a **binomial.** To multiply two binomials, we use a version of the distributive property:

$$(b + c)a = b \cdot a + c \cdot a$$

EXAMPLE 3 Multiply: $(x + 2)(x + 3)$

Solution:

$$
\begin{aligned}
(x + 2)(x + 3) &= x(x + 3) + 2(x + 3) && \text{Apply the distributive property.} \\
&= x \cdot x + x \cdot 3 + 2 \cdot x + 2 \cdot 3 && \text{Apply the distributive property.} \\
&= x^2 + 3x + 2x + 6 && \text{Multiply.} \\
&= x^2 + 5x + 6 && \text{Combine like terms.}
\end{aligned}
$$

■ **Work Practice Problem 3**

EXAMPLE 4 Multiply: $(4y + 9)(3y - 2)$

Solution:

$$
\begin{aligned}
(4y + 9)(3y - 2) &= 4y(3y - 2) + 9(3y - 2) && \text{Apply the distributive property.} \\
&= 4y \cdot 3y + 4y(-2) + 9 \cdot 3y + 9(-2) && \text{Apply the distributive property.} \\
&= 12y^2 - 8y + 27y - 18 && \text{Multiply.} \\
&= 12y^2 + 19y - 18 && \text{Combine like terms}
\end{aligned}
$$

■ **Work Practice Problem 4**

Objective C Squaring a Binomial

Raising a binomial to the power of 2 is also called squaring a binomial. To square a binomial, we use the definition of an exponent, and then multiply.

EXAMPLE 5 Multiply: $(2x + 1)^2$

Solution:

$$
\begin{aligned}
(2x + 1)^2 &= (2x + 1)(2x + 1) && \text{Apply the definition of an exponent.} \\
&= 2x(2x + 1) + 1(2x + 1) && \text{Apply the distributive property.} \\
&= 2x \cdot 2x + 2x \cdot 1 + 1 \cdot 2x + 1 \cdot 1 && \text{Apply the distributive property.} \\
&= 4x^2 + 2x + 2x + 1 && \text{Multiply.} \\
&= 4x^2 + 4x + 1 && \text{Combine like terms.}
\end{aligned}
$$

■ **Work Practice Problem 5**

Objective D Using the FOIL Order to Multiply Binomials

Recall from Example 3 that

$$
\begin{aligned}
(x + 2)(x + 3) &= x \cdot x + x \cdot 3 + 2 \cdot x + 2 \cdot 3 \\
&= x^2 + 5x + 6
\end{aligned}
$$

One way to remember these products $x \cdot x$, $x \cdot 3$, $2 \cdot x$, and $2 \cdot 3$ is to use a special order for multiplying binomials, called the FOIL order. Of course, the product is the same no matter what order or method you choose to use.

FOIL stands for the products of the First terms, Outer terms, Inner terms, then Last terms. For example,

$$(x + 2)(x + 3) = x \cdot x + x \cdot 3 + 2 \cdot x + 2 \cdot 3 = x^2 + 3x + 2x + 6$$
$$= x^2 + 5x + 6$$

> **Helpful Hint**
> The product is the same no matter what order or method you choose to use.

EXAMPLES   Use the FOIL order to multiply.

6. $(3x - 6)(2x + 1)$
$$= 3x \cdot 2x + 3x \cdot 1 + (-6)(2x) + (-6)(1)$$
$$= 6x^2 + 3x - 12x - 6 \quad \text{Multiply.}$$
$$= 6x^2 - 9x - 6 \quad \text{Combine like terms.}$$

7. $(3x - 5)^2 = (3x - 5)(3x - 5)$
$$= 3x \cdot 3x + 3x(-5) + (-5)(3x) + (-5)(-5)$$
$$= 9x^2 - 15x - 15x + 25 \quad \text{Multiply.}$$
$$= 9x^2 - 30x + 25 \quad \text{Combine like terms.}$$

Work Practice Problems 6–7

> **Helpful Hint**
> Remember that the FOIL order can only be used to multiply **two binomials.**

Objective E Multiplying Polynomials

Recall from Appendix C.1 that a polynomial that consists of exactly three terms is called a **trinomial.** Next, we multiply a binomial by a trinomial.

EXAMPLE 8   Multiply: $(3a + 2)(a^2 - 6a + 3)$

Solution: Use the distributive property to multiply $3a$ by the trinomial $(a^2 - 6a + 3)$ and then 2 by the trinomial.

$(3a + 2)(a^2 - 6a + 3) = 3a(a^2 - 6a + 3) + 2(a^2 - 6a + 3)$ Apply the distributive property.

$= 3a \cdot a^2 + 3a(-6a) + 3a \cdot 3 +$
$\qquad 2 \cdot a^2 + 2(-6a) + 2 \cdot 3$ Apply the distributive property.

$= 3a^3 - 18a^2 + 9a + 2a^2 - 12a + 6$ Multiply.

$= 3a^3 - 16a^2 - 3a + 6$ Combine like terms.

Work Practice Problem 8

PRACTICE PROBLEMS 6–7

Use the FOIL order to multiply.
6. $(10x - 7)(x + 3)$
7. $(3x + 2)^2$

PRACTICE PROBLEM 8

Multiply:
$(2x + 5)(x^2 + 4x - 1)$

Answers
6. $10x^2 + 23x - 21$,
7. $9x^2 + 12x + 4$,
8. $2x^3 + 13x^2 + 18x - 5$

In general, we have the following.

To Multiply Two Polynomials

Multiply each term of the first polynomial by each term of the second polynomial, and then combine like terms.

A convenient method of multiplying polynomials is to use a vertical format similar to multiplying real numbers.

✔ **Concept Check** True or false? When a trinomial is multiplied by a trinomial, the result will have at most nine terms. Explain.

PRACTICE PROBLEM 9

EXAMPLE 9 Find the product of $(a^2 - 6a + 3)$ and $(3a + 2)$ vertically.

Multiply $(x^2 + 4x - 1)$ and $(2x + 5)$ vertically.

Solution:

$$
\begin{array}{r}
a^2 - 6a + 3 \\
\times \qquad 3a + 2 \\
\hline
2a^2 - 12a + 6 \\
3a^3 - 18a^2 + 9a \\
\hline
3a^3 - 16a^2 - 3a + 6
\end{array}
$$

Multiply $a^2 - 6a + 3$ by 2.

Multiply $a^2 - 6a + 3$ by $3a$. Line up like terms.

Combine like terms

Notice that this example is the same as Example 8 and of course the products are the same.

■ **Work Practice Problem 9**

Objective A *Multiply. See Examples 1 and 2.*

1. $3x(9x^2 - 3)$

2. $4y(10y^3 + 2y)$

3. $-5a(4a^2 - 6a + 1)$

4. $-2b(3b^2 - 2b + 5)$

5. $7x^2(6x^2 - 5x + 7)$

6. $6z^2(-3z^2 - z + 4)$

Objectives B C D Mixed Practice *Multiply. See Examples 3 through 7.*

7. $(x + 3)(x + 10)$

8. $(y + 5)(y + 9)$

9. $(2x - 6)(x + 4)$

10. $(7z + 1)(z - 6)$

11. $(6a + 4)^2$

12. $(8b - 3)^2$

Objective E *Multiply. See Examples 8 and 9.*

13. $(a + 6)(a^2 - 6a + 3)$

14. $(y + 4)(y^2 + 8y - 2)$

15. $(4x - 5)(2x^2 + 3x - 10)$

16. $(9z - 2)(2z^2 + z + 1)$

17. $(x^3 + 2x + x^2)(3x + 1 + x^2)$

18. $(y^2 - 2y + 5)(y^3 + 2 + y)$

Objectives A B C D E Mixed Practice *Multiply.*

19. $10r(-3r + 2)$

20. $5x(4x^2 + 5)$

21. $-2y^2(3y + y^2 - 6)$

22. $3z^3(4z^4 - 2z + z^3)$

23. $(x + 2)(x + 12)$

24. $(y + 7)(y - 7)$

25. $(2a + 3)(2a - 3)$

26. $(6s + 1)(3s - 1)$

27. $(x + 5)^2$

28. $(x + 3)^2$

29. $\left(b + \dfrac{3}{5}\right)\left(b + \dfrac{4}{5}\right)$

30. $\left(a - \dfrac{7}{10}\right)\left(a + \dfrac{3}{10}\right)$

31. $(6x + 1)(x^2 + 4x + 1)$

32. $(9y - 1)(y^2 + 3y - 5)$

33. $(7x + 5)^2$

34. $(5x + 9)^2$

35. $(2x - 1)^2$

36. $(4a - 3)^2$

37. $(2x^2 - 3)(4x^3 + 2x - 3)$

38. $(3y^2 + 2)(5y^2 - y + 2)$

39. $(x^3 + x^2 + x)(x^2 + x + 1)$

40. $(a^4 + a^2 + 1)(a^4 + a^2 - 1)$

41. $(2z^2 - z + 1)(5z^2 + z - 2)$

42. $(2b^2 - 4b + 3)(b^2 - b + 2)$

Concept Extensions

Find the area of each figure.

△ **43.**

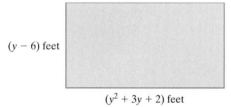

$(y - 6)$ feet

$(y^2 + 3y + 2)$ feet

△ **44.**

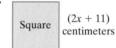

Square | $(2x + 11)$ centimeters

Find the area of the shaded figure. To do so, subtract the area of the smaller square from the area of the larger geometric figure.

△ **45.**

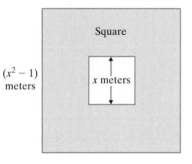

Square

$(x^2 - 1)$ meters

x meters

△ **46.**

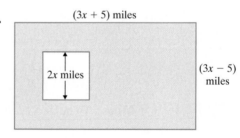

$(3x + 5)$ miles

$2x$ miles

$(3x - 5)$ miles

47. Suppose that a classmate asked you why $(2x + 1)^2$ is not $4x^2 + 1$. Write down your response to this classmate.

D Inductive and Deductive Reasoning

Logic and logical reasoning have applications in many fields, including science, law, psychology, and mathematics. For example, computers must have logic built into their circuits in order to process information correctly. We begin our study of logic by examining inductive reasoning.

Objective A Using Inductive Reasoning

Inductive Reasoning

This is the process of forming a general conclusion based on observing a number of specific examples or outcomes.

$$\text{Specific Observations} \xrightarrow{\text{to a}} \text{general conclusion}$$

EXAMPLE 1 Find the next number in the sequence, or listing of numbers.

1, 5, 25, 125

Solution: Each number after the first is obtained by multiplying the previous number by 5. If we assume that this pattern continues, the next number is $125 \times 5 = 625$.

Work Practice Problem 1

PRACTICE PROBLEM 1

Find the next number in the sequence

2, 6, 18, 54

EXAMPLE 2 Find the next two numbers in the given sequence.

1, 1, 2, 3, 5, 8

Solution: Each number after the first two numbers is obtained by adding the two previous numbers in the list. Notice that $1 + 1 = 2, 1 + 2 = 3, 2 + 3 = 5$, and so on. If this pattern is to continue, the next number in the sequence is $5 + 8 = 13$, and the next number is $8 + 13 = 21$.

Work Practice Problem 2

PRACTICE PROBLEM 2

Find the next number in the sequence

2, 4, 6, 10, 16

The sequence described in Example 2 is called the *Fibonacci sequence*. There are many examples of this sequence found in nature. This sequence also has many applications including those in science, business, economics, operations research, archeology, fine arts, architecture, and poetry.

Answers
1. 162, **2.** 26

PRACTICE PROBLEM 3

Find the next letter in each sequence.

a. S, M, T, W, T

b. A, F, D, I, G

EXAMPLE 3 Find the next letter in each sequence.

a. J, F, M, A, M

b. A, E, D, H, G

Solution:

a. Each letter is the first letter of some of the months of the year, in order: January, February, March, April, May. The next month is June, so the letter is J.

b. Let's look for a pattern by corresponding each letter of the alphabet to a number, according to order.

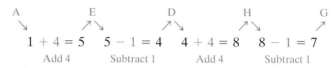

From this pattern, the next letter is

Work Practice Problem 3

EXAMPLE 4 Use inductive reasoning to find the next shape in the sequence.

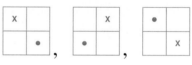

Solution: Notice that the "*x*" rotates clockwise in each square. Also, there is a dot always diagonally across from each *x*. Thus, we might reason that the next shape is the following.

Work Practice Problem 4

Next, let's study deductive reasoning. We begin with a definition.

PRACTICE PROBLEM 4

Use inductive reasoning to find the next possible shape in the sequence.

Objective **B** **Using Deductive Reasoning**

Deductive Reasoning

This is the process of forming a specific conclusion based on accepted assumptions.

$$\text{General Assumptions} \xrightarrow{\text{to a}} \text{specific conclusion}$$

In short, with inductive reasoning, we reason from specific examples observed to a general conclusion; with deductive reasoning, we reason logically from general statements or assumptions to a specific conclusion.

Diagrams, called *Venn diagrams,* can help us reason deductively. Let's discuss the diagram below that has to do with pet ownership.

Pet Ownership

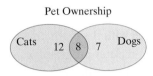

Since 8 people are in both regions, these 8 people have both cats and dogs as pets. See if you understand each answer below.

How many people have cats? $12 + 8 = 20$

How many people have cats and no dogs? 12

How many people have dogs? $8 + 7 = 15$

How many people have dogs and no cats? 7

EXAMPLE 5 The results of a survey of 50 people are as follows.

27 people like red apples.

25 people like green apples.

20 people like both red and green apples.

How many people like neither red nor green apples?

Solution: We draw a Venn diagram to organize the information in the survey. This survey concerns red apples and green apples which indicates that our diagram will consist of two circles, one representing people who like red apples and one representing people who like green apples. Since there are 20 people who like both red and green apples, we draw two overlapping circles and place 20 in the overlapping section.

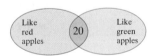

A total of 27 people liked red apples. This means that $27 - 20 = 7$ is the number of people who liked red apples only. Since a total of 25 people liked green apples, $25 - 20 = 5$ people liked green apples only.

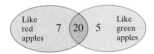

This means that $7 + 20 + 5 = 32$ people like red or green apples. Since 50 people were polled, $50 - 32 = 18$ people liked neither red nor green apples.

Work Practice Problem 5

Sometimes a grid may be useful in organizing information.

PRACTICE PROBLEM 5

The results of a survey of 30 people are as follows.

20 people like potato chips.

17 people like tortilla chips.

13 people like both potato and tortilla chips.

How many people like neither potato nor tortilla chips?

PRACTICE PROBLEM 6

Persons A, B, C, and D sit in the front row of their mathematics class. Use the statements below to determine their order.

1. Person D is sitting between persons A and B.
2. Person C is sitting next to person B only.
3. Person C is not on the far left.

EXAMPLE 6 Max, Jim, Michael, and Dong Ming have careers as an accountant, a mathematician, a computer programmer, and a manager, not necessarily in the given order. Use the statements below and determine which person is the mathematician.

1. Jim and Max went to lunch with the mathematician.
2. The accountant and the computer programmer taught Jim in college.
3. Max and Dong Ming went to Florida with the computer programmer.

Solution: Draw a grid to organize the information. Then record the information given in each statement. From statement 1, we know that both Jim and Max are not the mathematician. To indicate this on the grid, place X's in the appropriate places. (See below on the left.)

	math.	comp. prog.	acct.	manager
Jim	X			
Max	X			
Michael				
Dong Ming				

	math.	comp. prog.	acct.	manager
Jim	X	X	X	
Max	X			
Michael				
Dong Ming				

From statement 2, we know Jim is not the accountant and he is not the computer programmer, so place an X in the grid corresponding to Jim/accountant and an X in the grid corresponding to Jim/computer programmer. (See above on the right.)

At this point, notice that Jim must be the manager. Place a check mark in the grid corresponding to Jim/manager. Since Jim is the manager, no one else is and we can place X's in the rest of the manager column to indicate the no one else is a manager. (See below on the left.)

	math.	comp. prog.	acct.	manager
Jim	X	X	X	✓
Max	X			X
Michael			X	
Dong Ming				X

	math.	comp. prog.	acct.	manager
Jim	X	X	X	✓
Max	X	X		X
Michael				X
Dong Ming		X		X

From statement 3, we know Max and Dong Ming are not the computer programmer. Record this information in the grid. (See above on the right.) Notice that Max must be the accountant. Place a check mark in the grid under Max/accountant and mark the rest of that column with X's. (See below on the left.) **Now Dong Ming must be the mathematician** and Michael must be the computer programmer. (See below on the right.)

	math.	comp. prog.	acct.	manager
Jim	X	X	X	✓
Max	X	X	✓	X
Michael			X	X
Dong Ming		X	X	X

	math.	comp. prog.	acct.	manager
Jim	X	X	X	✓
Max	X	X	✓	X
Michael	X	✓	X	X
Dong Ming	✓	X	X	X

⬛ **Work Practice Problem 6**

Answer

6. A, D, B, C

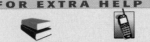

Determine whether each is an example of inductive or deductive reasoning.

1. My coat is red. My neighbor's coat is red. Therefore, all coats are red.

2. All typewriters type the letter b. I have a typewriter. Therefore, my typewriter will type the letter b.

3. Rabbits do not lay eggs. Therefore, my pet rabbit will not lay an egg.

4. The last two times Ken flew on a commercial jet, his luggage was lost. Ken reasons that the next time he flies on a commercial jet, his luggage will be also lost.

5. A scientist holds a piece of salt over a burning candle and notices that it burns with a yellow flame. She does this again with another piece of salt and notices that is also burns with a yellow flame. She therefore reasons that all salt burns with a yellow flame.

6. Sherlock Holmes knows that the murderer was either the butler, the maid, or the cook. The night of the murder, the cook catered a party in a nearby town and has plenty of witnesses who saw him. The butler was in the hospital with pneumonia. Therefore, Detective Holmes reasoned that the maid did it.

Use inductive reasoning to determine the next number or figure in each sequence.

7. 1, 3, 9, 27

8. 2, 4, 6, 8

9. A, Z, B, Y

10. A, C, E, G

11. 1, 4, 9, 16, 25

12. 2, 4, 8, 16

13. O, T, T, F, F, S, S

14. S, S, M, T, W, T

15. 9, 99, 999, 9999

16. 1, 10, 100, 1000

17. 2, 7, 4, 8, 6

18. 3, 1, 4, 2, 5

19. 9, 12, 20, 33, 51

20. 4, 13, 29, 52, 82

21. 1, 11, 38, 84, 151

22. 2, 12, 24, 41, 66

23.

24.

25.

26.

27.

28.

29.

30.

31.

32.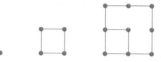

33.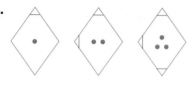

34.

35. Give an example occurring outside the classroom where you used inductive reasoning.

36. Give an example occurring outside the classroom where you used deductive reasoning.

Draw a Venn diagram illustrating each of the following statements. Draw a region representing birds and let a point represent Wendy.

37. Wendy is a bird.

38. Wendy is not a bird.

Draw a Venn diagram illustrating each of the following statements.

39. No bicycles are tricycles.

40. All whales are mammals.

41. Some roosters crow.

42. No trees have wheels.

43. All politicians make promises.

44. Some dryers are heated by electricity.

Use diagrams and deductive reasoning to solve each problem.

45. Four men in a wheelchair race finished 1st, 2nd, 3rd, and 4th.

Mark beat Bob.
Joey finished between Mark and Bob.
Sal beat Mark.

Who finished 3rd in the race?

46. Four women in a marathon finished 1st, 2nd, 3rd, and 4th.

Wynonna beat Mary.
Sally beat Wynonna.
June did not beat Mary.

Who finished 1st in the race?

47. 75 people in a health club were surveyed and the following information was gathered.

55 people drink water after exercising.
40 people drink Gatorade after exercising.
35 people drink water and Gatorade after exercising.

How many people drink neither water nor Gatorade after exercising?

48. In a poll of 200 people, the following information was gathered.

80 people listen to country music.
100 people listen to rock-n-roll music.
50 people listen to both country and rock-n-roll music.

How many people listen to country music only?

49. Aaron, Marty, Donna, and Maria have careers as a civil engineer, an electrical engineer, a mechanical engineer, and a nautical engineer, not necessarily in the given order. Given the information below, determine who is the civil engineer.

a. Aaron and Donna wrote a research paper with the electrical engineer.
b. Marty and Maria carpool with the civil engineer.
c. Aaron works on the same floor as the civil engineer and the nautical engineer.

50. Celeste, Bryan, Clay, and Eric are majoring in business, elementary education, art, and computer science but not necessarily in that order. Given the information below, determine who is majoring in art.

a. Celeste, Bryan, and the elementary education major are in a class together.
b. Bryan and the art major had lunch with the business major.
c. Clay and the elementary education major are cousins.
d. Celeste and the art major carpool together.

51. John, Leon, Alberto, and Julio sit in a theater according to the following.

Alberto is on the far left.
If Leon is on the far right, then John is not sitting next to him.

If Leon is on the far right, who is sitting next to him on his left?

52. Ralph, Anoa, Tumulish, and Pier sit on a bench during graduation ceremonies according to the following.

Tumulish is sitting on the far left.
If Anoa is sitting on the far right, then Ralph is not sitting next to her.

If Anoa is indeed sitting on the far right, list their seating order starting with the person sitting on the far left.

53. 100 people were surveyed and the results are as follows.

65 people said they drink Coke.
40 people said they drink Pepsi.
10 people said they drink both Coke and Pepsi.

How many people drink neither Coke nor Pepsi?

54. A poll was taken in Gotham City one day about the type of transportation used to commute to work. One hundred fifty-five people were polled.

70 people ride the bus.
95 people ride the subway.
30 people ride both the bus and the subway.

How many people ride neither the bus nor the subway?

ANSWERS TO SELECTED EXERCISES

CHAPTER 1 The Whole Numbers

Exercise Set 1.2 1. tens **3.** thousands **5.** hundred-thousands **7.** millions **9.** five hundred forty-two
11. seven thousand, eight hundred ninety-six **13.** twenty-six thousand, nine hundred ninety **15.** one million, six hundred twenty thousand
17. fifty-three million, five hundred twenty thousand, one hundred seventy **19.** sixty-four thousand, four hundred eighty-two
21. one thousand, six hundred seventy-nine **23.** thirteen million, six hundred thousand **25.** twelve thousand, six hundred sixty-two
27. two hundred two thousand, seven hundred **29.** 6587 **31.** 29,900 **33.** 16,504,019 **35.** 3,000,014 **37.** 220 **39.** 440,276
41. 70,251,710 **43.** 1815 **45.** 755 **47.** $400 + 6$ **49.** $5000 + 200 + 90$ **51.** $60,000 + 2000 + 400 + 7$ **53.** $30,000 + 600 + 80$
55. $30,000,000 + 9,000,000 + 600,000 + 80,000$ **57.** 5532; five thousand, five hundred thirty-two **59.** $5000 + 400 + 90 + 2$
61. Mt. Washington **63.** Golden retriever **65.** Labrador retriever; one hundred forty-four thousand, nine hundred thirty-four
67. 25 pounds **69.** 7632 **71.** no; one hundred five **73.** answers may vary **75.** Canton

Calculator Explorations 1. 134 **3.** 340 **5.** 2834

Mental Math 1. 16 **3.** 9000 **5.** 1620

Exercise Set 1.3 1. 36 **3.** 292 **5.** 49 **7.** 5399 **9.** 117 **11.** 512 **13.** 209,078 **15.** 25 **17.** 62 **19.** 212 **21.** 94
23. 910 **25.** 8273 **27.** 11,926 **29.** 1884 **31.** 16,717 **33.** 1110 **35.** 8999 **37.** 35,901 **39.** 632,389 **41.** 42 in. **43.** 25 ft
45. 24 in. **47.** 8 yd **49.** 29 in. **51.** 2093 **53.** 266 **55.** 544 **57.** 3452 **59.** 6684 ft **61.** 340 ft **63.** 291,147 motorcycles
65. 2425 ft **67.** 13,255 mi **69.** 124 ft **71.** 767,312 **73.** 8867 **75.** California **77.** 366 stores **79.** Florida and Georgia
81. answers may vary **83.** answers may vary **85.** 40 ft **87.** 1,044,473,765 **89.** correct **91.** incorrect; 933

Calculator Explorations 1. 770 **3.** 109 **5.** 8978

Mental Math 1. 7 **3.** 5 **5.** 0 **7.** 400 **9.** 500

Exercise Set 1.4 1. 44 **3.** 265 **5.** 135 **7.** 2254 **9.** 5545 **11.** 600 **13.** 25 **15.** 45 **17.** 146 **19.** 288 **21.** 168
23. 106 **25.** 447 **27.** 5723 **29.** 504 **31.** 89 **33.** 79 **35.** 39,914 **37.** 32,711 **39.** 5041 **41.** 31,213 **43.** 4 **45.** 20
47. 7 **49.** 72 **51.** 88 **53.** 264 pages **55.** 4 million sq km **57.** 6065 ft **59.** 23 points **61.** \$409 **63.** 358 mi **65.** \$389
67. 3,044,452 people **69.** 19,036 cocker spaniels **71.** 5920 sq ft **73.** Hartsfield Atlanta International **75.** 32 million
77. General Motors Corp., Time Warner, Procter & Gamble Co. **79.** \$1112 million or \$1,112,000,000 **81.** 1034 **83.** 9 **85.** 8518
87. 22,876 **89.** minuend: 48; subtrahend: 1 **91.** minuend: 70; subtrahend: 7 **93.** Jo; by 271 votes **95.** incorrect; 685 **97.** correct
99. $5269 - 2385 = 2884$ **101.** answers may vary **103.** no; 1089 more pages

Exercise Set 1.5 1. 630 **3.** 640 **5.** 1800 **7.** 400 **9.** 51,000 **11.** 43,000 **13.** 248,700 **15.** 36,000 **17.** 100,000
19. 60,000,000 **21.** 5280; 5300; 5000 **23.** 9440; 9400; 9000 **25.** 14,880; 14,900; 15,000 **27.** 380,000 Personnel **29.** 10,800 days
31. \$70,000,000,000 **33.** \$2,500,000 **35.** 159,000,000 users; 7,000,000 users **37.** 130 **39.** 380 **41.** 5500 **43.** 300 **45.** 8500
47. correct **49.** incorrect **51.** correct **53.** \$3100 **55.** 80 mi **57.** 6000 ft **59.** 1,400,000 people **61.** 14,000,000 votes
63. 52,000 children **65.** \$3,430,000,000; \$3,400,000,000; \$3,000,000,000 **67.** \$2,234,000,000; \$2,200,000,000; \$2,000,000,000
69. 4618, for example **71. a.** 8550 **b.** 8649 **73.** answers may vary **75.** 140 m

Calculator Explorations 1. 3456 **3.** 15,322 **5.** 272,291

Mental Math 1. 24 **3.** 0 **5.** 0 **7.** 87

Exercise Set 1.6 1. $4 \cdot 3 + 4 \cdot 9$ **3.** $2 \cdot 4 + 2 \cdot 6$ **5.** $10 \cdot 11 + 10 \cdot 7$ **7.** 252 **9.** 1872 **11.** 1662 **13.** 5310 **15.** 1372
17. 10,857 **19.** 11,326 **21.** 24,800 **23.** 0 **25.** 5900 **27.** 59,232 **29.** 142,506 **31.** 1,821,204 **33.** 3,949,935 **35.** 64,790
37. 800 **39.** 11,000 **41.** 74,060 **43.** 24,000 **45.** 45,000 **47.** 3,280,000 **49.** 240,000 **51.** 300,000 **53.** c **55.** c
57. 63 sq m **59.** 390 sq ft **61.** 770 **63.** 5400 **65.** 4480 **67.** 375 cal **69.** \$1890 **71. a.** 96 cans **b.** 192 cans
73. 9900 sq ft **75.** 56,000 sq ft **77.** 5828 pixels **79.** 1500 characters **81.** 1280 cal **83.** 71,343 mi
85. \$10, \$50; \$10, \$100; \$12, \$24; \$12, \$24; \$228 **87.** 21,700,000 qt **89.** 134 **91.** 1008 **93.** 24 **95.** 12
97. $5 \cdot 3$ or $3 \cdot 5$ **99. a.** $7 + 7 + 7 + 7$ or $4 + 4 + 4 + 4 + 4 + 4 + 4$ **b.** answers may vary

101.
$$
\begin{array}{r}
203 \\
\times\ \ 14 \\
\hline
812 \\
2030 \\
\hline
2842
\end{array}
$$
103. 2; 9 **105.** answers may vary **107.** 506 windows

Calculator Explorations 1. 53 **3.** 62 **5.** 261 **7.** 0

Mental Math 1. 5 **3.** 9 **5.** 0 **7.** 9 **9.** 1 **11.** 5 **13.** undefined **15.** 7 **17.** 0 **19.** 8

Exercise Set 1.7 1. 26 **3.** 37 **5.** 338 **7.** undefined **9.** 8 **11.** 25 **13.** 65 R 4 **15.** 225 R 4 **17.** 37 R 1 **19.** 265 R 5
21. 49 **23.** 13 **25.** 97 R 40 **27.** 206 R 10 **29.** 506 **31.** 202 R 7 **33.** 45 **35.** 98 R 100 **37.** 202 R 15 **39.** 579 R 72
41. 19 **43.** 513 R 1 **45.** 2082 R 26 **47.** 5030 **49.** 21 R 1 **51.** 2 R 30 **53.** 20 R 2 **55.** 58 students **57.** \$252,000

59. 415 bushels   **61.** 105 lane dividers   **63.** yes, she needs 176 ft; she has 9 ft left over   **65.** 27 touchdowns   **67.** 1760 yd   **69.** 26
71. 498   **73.** 79   **75.** 16°   **77.** 8862   **79.** 29,210   **81.** 589   **83.** undefined   **85.** 7 R 15   **87.** d   **89.** a   **91.** $3,376,500,000
93. increase; answers may vary   **95.** no; answers may vary   **97.** answers may vary

The Bigger Picture   1. 118   **2.** 28   **3.** 3285   **4.** 89 R 11   **5.** 0   **6.** 0   **7.** 19   **8.** undefined   **9.** 64   **10.** 1844

Integrated Review   1. 148   **2.** 6555   **3.** 1620   **4.** 562   **5.** 79   **6.** undefined   **7.** 9   **8.** 1   **9.** 0   **10.** 0   **11.** 0   **12.** 3
13. 2433   **14.** 9826   **15.** 213 R 3   **16.** 79,317   **17.** 27   **18.** 9   **19.** 138   **20.** 276   **21.** 1099 R 2   **22.** 111 R 1   **23.** 663 R 6
24. 1076 R 60   **25.** 1024   **26.** 9899   **27.** 30,603   **28.** 47,500   **29.** 65   **30.** 456   **31.** 7 R 1   **32.** 49   **33.** 86   **34.** 22
35. 8630; 8600; 9000   **36.** 1550; 1600; 2000   **37.** 10,900; 10,909; 11,000   **38.** 432,200; 432,200; 432,000   **39.** perimeter: 20 ft; area: 25 sq ft
40. perimeter: 42 in.; area: 98 sq in.   **41.** 26 mi   **42.** 26 m   **43.** 24   **44.** 124   **45.** Lake Pontchartrain bridge; 2175 ft   **46.** $5904

Exercise Set 1.8   1. 49   **3.** 237   **5.** 42   **7.** 600   **9. a.** 400 ft   **b.** 9600 sq ft   **11.** $15,500   **13.** 168 hr   **15.** 5758   **17.** 129 yr
19. 312 billion bricks   **21.** 719 towns   **23.** $21   **25.** 55 cal   **27.** 24   **29.** $33,506,850   **31.** 38,034,000 students   **33.** 3987 mi
35. 13 paychecks   **37.** $239   **39.** $1045   **41.** b will be cheaper by $3   **43.** IBM Corporation   **45.** 2113 patents   **47.** 99 patents
49. 2433   **51.** $14,754   **53.** 16,800 mg   **55. a.** 3750 sq ft   **b.** 375 sq ft   **c.** 3375 sq ft
57. $240   **59.** answers may vary

Calculator Explorations   1. 729   **3.** 1024   **5.** 2048   **7.** 2526   **9.** 4295   **11.** 8

Exercise Set 1.9   1. 3^4 **3.** 7^8 **5.** 12^3 **7.** $6^2 \cdot 5^3$ **9.** $9^3 \cdot 8$ **11.** $3 \cdot 2^5$ **13.** $3 \cdot 2^2 \cdot 5^3$ **15.** 49   **17.** 125   **19.** 64   **21.** 1
23. 7   **25.** 243   **27.** 256   **29.** 64   **31.** 81   **33.** 729   **35.** 100   **37.** 20   **39.** 729   **41.** 48   **43.** 54   **45.** 3   **47.** 8
49. 12   **51.** 4   **53.** 21   **55.** 11   **57.** 4   **59.** 17   **61.** 46   **63.** 10   **65.** 126   **67.** 105   **69.** 2   **71.** 35   **73.** 4
75. undefined   **77.** 30   **79.** 52   **81.** 44   **83.** 12   **85.** 21   **87.** 24   **89.** 28   **91.** 3   **93.** 25   **95.** 23   **97.** 13
99. 400 sq mi   **101.** 64 sq cm   **103.** false   **105.** false   **107.** $(2 + 3) \cdot 6 - 2$ **109.** $24 \div (3 \cdot 2) + 2 \cdot 5$ **111.** 1260 ft
113. 6,384,814   **115.** answers may vary; $(20 - 10) \cdot 5 \div 25 + 3$

The Bigger Picture   1. 64   **2.** 48   **3.** 9   **4.** 15   **5.** 22   **6.** 50   **7.** 688   **8.** 2160   **9.** 10 R 46   **10.** 27

Chapter 1 Vocabulary Check   1. whole numbers   **2.** perimeter   **3.** place value   **4.** exponent   **5.** area   **6.** square root
7. digits   **8.** sum   **9.** divisor   **10.** dividend   **11.** quotient   **12.** factor   **13.** product   **14.** minuend   **15.** subtrahend
16. difference   **17.** addend

Chapter 1 Review   1. hundreds   **2.** ten-millions   **3.** five thousand, four hundred eighty
4. forty-six million, two hundred thousand, one hundred twenty   **5.** $6000 + 200 + 70 + 9$
6. $400,000,000 + 3,000,000 + 200,000 + 20,000 + 5000$ **7.** 59,800   **8.** 6,304,000,000   **9.** 1,630,553   **10.** 2,968,528
11. San Antonio, TX   **12.** New York, NY   **13.** 63   **14.** 67   **15.** 48   **16.** 77   **17.** 956   **18.** 840   **19.** 7950   **20.** 7250
21. 4211   **22.** 1967   **23.** 1326   **24.** 886   **25.** 27,346   **26.** 39,300   **27.** 8032 mi   **28.** $197,699   **29.** 276 ft   **30.** 66 km
31. 14   **32.** 34   **33.** 65   **34.** 304   **35.** 3914   **36.** 7908   **37.** 17,897   **38.** 34,658   **39.** 531,341   **40.** 76,704   **41.** 397 pages
42. $25,626   **43.** May   **44.** August   **45.** $110   **46.** $240   **47.** 90   **48.** 50   **49.** 470   **50.** 500   **51.** 4800   **52.** 58,000
53. 50,000,000   **54.** 800,000   **55.** 73,000,000   **56.** 571,000   **57.** 7400   **58.** 4100   **59.** 2500 mi   **60.** 2,500,000   **61.** 1911
62. 1396   **63.** 1410   **64.** 2898   **65.** 800   **66.** 900   **67.** 3696   **68.** 1694   **69.** 0   **70.** 0   **71.** 16,994   **72.** 8954
73. 113,634   **74.** 44,763   **75.** 411,426   **76.** 636,314   **77.** 375,000   **78.** 108,000   **79.** 12,000   **80.** 35,000   **81.** 5,100,000
82. 7,600,000   **83.** 1150   **84.** 4920   **85.** 108   **86.** 112   **87.** 24 g   **88.** $4,897,341   **89.** 60 sq mi   **90.** 500 sq cm   **91.** 3
92. 4   **93.** 6   **94.** 7   **95.** 5 R 2   **96.** 4 R 2   **97.** undefined   **98.** 0   **99.** 1   **100.** 10   **101.** undefined   **102.** 0
103. 33 R 2   **104.** 19 R 7   **105.** 24 R 2   **106.** 35 R 15   **107.** 506 R 10   **108.** 907 R 40   **109.** 2793 R 140   **110.** 2012 R 60
111. 18 R 2   **112.** 21 R 2   **113.** 458 ft   **114.** 13 mi   **115.** 51   **116.** 59   **117.** 27 boxes   **118.** $192   **119.** 7 billion   **120.** 75¢
121. $898   **122.** 23,150 sq ft   **123.** 49   **124.** 125   **125.** 45   **126.** 400   **127.** 13   **128.** 10   **129.** 15   **130.** 7   **131.** 12
132. 9   **133.** 42   **134.** 33   **135.** 9   **136.** 2   **137.** 1   **138.** 0   **139.** 6   **140.** 29   **141.** 40   **142.** 72   **143.** 5
144. 7   **145.** 49 sq m   **146.** 9 sq in.   **147.** 307   **148.** 682   **149.** 2169   **150.** 2516   **151.** 901   **152.** 1411   **153.** 458 R 8
154. 237 R 1   **155.** 70,848   **156.** 95,832   **157.** 1644   **158.** 8481   **159.** 740   **160.** 258,000   **161.** 2000   **162.** 40,000
163. thirty-six thousand, nine hundred eleven   **164.** one hundred fifty-four thousand, eight hundred sixty-three   **165.** 70,943   **166.** 43,401
167. 64   **168.** 125   **169.** 12   **170.** 10   **171.** 12   **172.** 1   **173.** 2   **174.** 6   **175.** 4   **176.** 24   **177.** 24   **178.** 14
179. $59,452,000   **180.** $582,140,000   **181.** 53 full boxes with 18 left over   **182.** $86

Chapter 1 Test   1. eighty-two thousand, four hundred twenty-six   **2.** 402,550   **3.** 141   **4.** 113   **5.** 14,880   **6.** 766 R 42   **7.** 200
8. 10   **9.** 0   **10.** undefined   **11.** 33   **12.** 21   **13.** 8   **14.** 36   **15.** 5,698,000   **16.** 11,200,000   **17.** 52,000   **18.** 13,700
19. 1600   **20.** 92   **21.** 122   **22.** 1605   **23.** 7 R 2   **24.** $17   **25.** $126   **26.** 360 cal   **27.** $5755   **28.** 20 cm; 25 sq cm
29. 60 yd; 200 sq yd

CHAPTER 2   Integers and Introduction to Variables

Exercise Set 2.1   1. 9   **3.** 26   **5.** 6   **7.** 3   **9.** 117   **11.** 94   **13.** 5   **15.** 626   **17.** 20   **19.** 4   **21.** 4   **23.** 0   **25.** 33

27. 121   **29.** 121   **31.** 100   **33.** 60   **35.** 4   **37.** 16, 64, 144, 256   **39.** $x + 5$ **41.** $x + 8$ **43.** $20 - x$ **45.** $512x$ **47.** $\dfrac{x}{2}$

49. $5x + (17 + x)$ **51.** $5x$ **53.** $11 - x$ **55.** $x - 5$ **57.** $6 \div x$ or $\dfrac{6}{x}$ **59.** $50 - 8x$ **61.** incorrect   **63.** correct   **65.** 274,657

67. 777   **69.** $5x$ **71.** As t gets larger, $16t^2$ gets larger.

Exercise Set 2.2   1. −1445   **3.** +14,433   **5.** +118   **7.** −11,730   **9.** −339 million   **11.** −135; −157; Sara   **13.** −45

15.   **17.**   **19.**   **21.**

23. < **25.** < **27.** > **29.** < **31.** 5 **33.** 8 **35.** 0 **37.** 5 **39.** −5 **41.** 4 **43.** −23 **45.** 10 **47.** 7
49. −20 **51.** −3 **53.** 8 **55.** 14 **57.** 29 **59.** 8 **61.** −3 **63.** 23 **65.** −4 **67.** > **69.** < **71.** = **73.** <
75. > **77.** < **79.** > **81.** < **83.** 25, −25 **85.** 84, −84 **87.** Lake Maracaibo **89.** Lake Eyre **91.** Earth **93.** Saturn
95. 13 **97.** 35 **99.** 360 **101.** $-|-8|, -|3|, 2^2, -(-5)$ **103.** $-|-6|, -|1|, -|1|, -(-6)$ **105.** $-10, -|-9|, -(-2), |-12|, 5^2$ **107.** d
109. 5 **111.** false **113.** true **115.** false **117.** answers may vary **119.** no; answers may vary

Calculator Explorations **1.** −159 **3.** 44 **5.** −894, 855

Mental Math **1.** 5 **3.** −35 **5.** 0 **7.** 0

Exercise Set 2.3 **1.**

3.

5.

7. 35 **9.** −8 **11.** 0 **13.** 4 **15.** 2 **17.** −2 **19.** −9 **21.** −24 **23.** −57 **25.** −223 **27.** 0 **29.** 7 **31.** −3
33. −9 **35.** 30 **37.** 20 **39.** 51 **41.** −33 **43.** −20 **45.** −125 **47.** −7 **49.** −246 **51.** 16 **53.** 13 **55.** −33
57. −21 **59.** 21 **61.** −45 **63.** 9 **65.** 0 **67.** 0 **69.** −103 **71.** 1 **73.** −70 **75.** −27 **77.** 17 **79.** −10
81. $0 + (-165) + (-16) = -181$; 181 ft. below the surface **83.** Team 1:7; Team 2:6; winning team: Team 1 **85.** \$786,000,000
87. \$761,000,000 **89.** 2°C **91.** −\$12,198 **93.** −40°F **95.** −7679 m **97.** 44 **99.** 141 **101.** answers may vary **103.** −3
105. 10 **107.** true **109.** false **111.** answers may vary

Mental Math **1.** 0 **2.** 0

Exercise Set 2.4 **1.** 0 **3.** 5 **5.** −5 **7.** 14 **9.** 3 **11.** −18 **13.** −14 **15.** −33 **17.** 402 **19.** −14 **21.** −4 **23.** −7
25. −38 **27.** −17 **29.** 13 **31.** −38 **33.** −11 **35.** −127 **37.** −11 **39.** 2 **41.** 0 **43.** −1 **45.** −27 **47.** 40 **49.** −22
51. −8 **53.** 14 **55.** −8 **57.** 36 **59.** 0 **61.** 19 **63.** 428 degrees **65.** 39 degrees **67.** 265° F **69.** −\$16 **71.** −12°C
73. 154 ft **75.** 69 ft **77.** 652 ft **79.** 144 ft **81.** −\$532 billion **83.** 0 **85.** 8 **87.** 1058 **89.** answers may vary **91.** 16
93. −20 **95.** −4 **97.** 0 **99.** −12 **101.** false **103.** answers may vary

Integrated Review **1.** +29,028 **2.** −35,840 **3.** −7 **4.** **5.** > **6.** < **7.** < **8.** > **9.** 1 **10.** −4
11. 8 **12.** 5 **13.** −6 **14.** 3 **15.** −89 **16.** 0 **17.** 5 **18.** −20 **19.** −10 **20.** −2 **21.** 52 **22.** −3 **23.** 84 **24.** 6
25. 1 **26.** −19 **27.** 12 **28.** −4 **29.** −44 **30.** b, c, d **31.** a, b, c, d **32.** 10 **33.** −12 **34.** 12 **35.** 10 **36.** 56 **37.** −34

Exercise Set 2.5 **1.** 6 **3.** −36 **5.** −64 **7.** 0 **9.** −48 **11.** −8 **13.** 80 **15.** 0 **17.** −15 **19.** −4 **21.** −27 **23.** −25
25. −8 **27.** −4 **29.** −5 **31.** 8 **33.** 0 **35.** undefined **37.** −13 **39.** 0 **41.** −12 **43.** −54 **45.** 42 **47.** −24 **49.** 16
51. −2 **53.** −7 **55.** −4 **57.** 48 **59.** −1080 **61.** 0 **63.** −5 **65.** −6 **67.** 3 **69.** −1 **71.** −243 **73.** 180 **75.** 1
77. −20 **79.** −966 **81.** −2050 **83.** −28 **85.** −6 **87.** 25 **89.** −1 **91.** undefined **93.** 6 **95.** 8;2 **97.** 0;0
99. −3 **101.** 306 **103.** $(-4)(3) = -12$; a loss of 12 yd **105.** $(-20)(5) = -100$; a depth of 100 ft **107.** −\$2584 million
109. a. 194 condors **b.** 11 condors per year **111.** −210°C **113.** −189°C **115.** 225 **117.** 109 **119.** 8 **121.** −29 **123.** −19
125. −8 **127.** false **129.** true **131.** negative **133.** $(-5)^{17}, (-2)^{17}, (-2)^{12}, (-5)^{12}$ **135.** answers may vary

The Bigger Picture **1.** 5 **2.** 55 **3.** −6 **4.** −12 **5.** −12 **6.** 81 **7.** −81 **8.** −34 **9.** 10 **10.** −30 **11.** 30
12. −11 **13.** −30 **14.** −80 **15.** 15 **16.** 45

Calculator Explorations **1.** 48 **3.** −258

Mental Math **1.** base: 3; exponent: 2 **3.** base: 2; exponent: 3 **5.** base: −7; exponent: 5 **7.** base: 5; exponent: 7

Exercise Set 2.6 **1.** −64 **3.** −64 **5.** 24 **7.** 3 **9.** −7 **11.** −14 **13.** −43 **15.** −8 **17.** −13 **19.** −1 **21.** 4 **23.** −3
25. −55 **27.** 8 **29.** 16 **31.** 13 **33.** −65 **35.** 64 **37.** 452 **39.** 129 **41.** 3 **43.** −4 **45.** 4 **47.** 16 **49.** −27
51. 34 **53.** 65 **55.** −59 **57.** −7 **59.** −61 **61.** −11 **63.** 36 **65.** −117 **67.** 30 **69.** −3 **71.** −59 **73.** 1
75. −12 **77.** 0 **79.** −20 **81.** 9 **83.** −16 **85.** 1 **87.** −50 **89.** 4050 **91.** 45 **93.** 32 in. **95.** 30 ft **97.** −2
99. −5°F **101.** $2 \cdot (7 - 5) \cdot 3$ **103.** $-6 \cdot (10 - 4)$ **105.** answers may vary **107.** answers may vary **109.** 20,736 **111.** 9

Chapter 2 Vocabulary Check **1.** opposites **2.** signed **3.** absolute value **4.** integers **5.** variable **6.** negative **7.** positive

Chapter 2 Review **1.** 5 **2.** 17 **3.** undefined **4.** 0 **5.** 121 **6.** 2 **7.** 4 **8.** 20 **9.** $x - 5$ **10.** $x + 7$ **11.** $10 \div x$
12. $5x$ **13.** −1435 **14.** +7562 **15.** **16.**
17. 12 **18.** 0 **19.** −6 **20.** 9 **21.** −9 **22.** 2 **23.** > **24.** < **25.** > **26.** > **27.** 12 **28.** −3 **29.** false
30. true **31.** true **32.** true **33.** 2 **34.** 14 **35.** 4 **36.** 17 **37.** −23 **38.** −22 **39.** −21 **40.** −70 **41.** 0 **42.** 0
43. −151 **44.** −606 **45.** −20°C **46.** −150 ft **47.** −9 **48.** +1 or 1 **49.** 99°F **50.** 112°F **51.** 8 **52.** −16 **53.** −11
54. −27 **55.** 20 **56.** 8 **57.** 0 **58.** −32 **59.** 0 **60.** −7 **61.** −10 **62.** −9 **63.** −25 **64.** 692 ft **65.** −3°F
66. −4°F **67.** true **68.** false **69.** true **70.** true **71.** 21 **72.** −18 **73.** −64 **74.** 60 **75.** 25 **76.** −1 **77.** 0
78. 24 **79.** −5 **80.** 3 **81.** 0 **82.** undefined **83.** −20 **84.** −9 **85.** 38 **86.** −5 **87.** $(-5)(2) = -10$
88. $(-50)(4) = -200$ **89.** −18°F **90.** −3°F **91.** 28°F **92.** −26°F **93.** 49 **94.** −49 **95.** −32 **96.** −32 **97.** 0
98. −8 **99.** −16 **100.** 35 **101.** −28 **102.** −44 **103.** 3 **104.** −1 **105.** 7 **106.** −17 **107.** 39 **108.** −26 **109.** 7
110. −80 **111.** −2 **112.** −12 **113.** −3 **114.** −35 **115.** −5 **116.** 5 **117.** −1 **118.** −7 **119.** 4 **120.** −4 **121.** 3
122. 108 **123.** 16 **124.** −16 **125.** −15 **126.** −19 **127.** 48 **128.** −21 **129.** 21 **130.** −5 **131.** −\$9 **132.** 6°C
133. 13,118 ft **134.** −27°C **135.** 2 **136.** 4 **137.** 3 **138.** 37 **139.** −5 **140.** −25 **141.** −20 **142.** 17

Chapter 2 Test **1.** 3 **2.** −6 **3.** −100 **4.** 4 **5.** −30 **6.** 12 **7.** 65 **8.** 5 **9.** 12 **10.** −6 **11.** 50 **12.** −2
13. −11 **14.** −46 **15.** −117 **16.** 3456 **17.** 28 **18.** −213 **19.** −1 **20.** −2 **21.** 2 **22.** −5 **23.** −32 **24.** −12

25. -3 **26.** 5 **27.** -1 **28.** -54 **29.** 1 **30.** -17 **31.** 88 ft below sea level **32.** 45 **33.** 31,642 **34.** 3820 ft below sea level **35.** -4 **36. a.** $17x$ **b.** $20 - 2x$

Cumulative Review **1.** ten-thousands; Sec. 1.2, Ex. 1 **2.** hundreds; Sec. 1.2 **3.** tens; Sec. 1.2, Ex. 2 **4.** thousands; Sec. 1.2 **5.** millions; Sec. 1.2, Ex. 3 **6.** hundred-thousands; Sec. 1.2 **7. a.** $<$ **b.** $>$ **c.** $>$; Sec. 2.2, Ex. 3 **8. a.** $>$ **b.** $<$ **c.** $>$; Sec. 2.2 **9.** 39; Sec. 1.3, Ex. 3 **10.** 39; Sec. 1.3 **11.** 7321; Sec. 1.4, Ex. 2 **12.** 3013; Sec. 1.4 **13.** 2440 km; Sec. 1.4, Ex. 5 **14.** \$525; Sec. 1.4 **15.** 570; Sec. 1.5, Ex. 1 **16.** 600; Sec. 1.5 **17.** 1800; Sec. 1.5, Ex. 5 **18.** 5000; Sec. 1.5 **19. a.** $3 \cdot 4 + 3 \cdot 5$ **b.** $10 \cdot 6 + 10 \cdot 8$ **c.** $2 \cdot 7 + 2 \cdot 3$; Sec. 1.6, Ex. 2 **20. a.** $5 \cdot 2 + 5 \cdot 12$ **b.** $9 \cdot 3 + 9 \cdot 6$ **b.** $4 \cdot 8 + 4 \cdot 1$; Sec. 1.6 **21.** 78,875; Sec. 1.6, Ex. 5 **22.** 31,096; Sec. 1.6 **23. a.** 6 **b.** 9 **c.** 6; Sec. 1.7, Ex. 1 **24. a.** 7 **b.** 8 **c.** 12; Sec. 1.7 **25.** 741; Sec. 1.7, Ex. 4 **26.** 456; Sec. 1.7 **27.** 7 boxes; Sec. 1.7, Ex. 11 **28.** \$9; Sec. 1.7 **29.** 64; Sec. 1.9, Ex. 5 **30.** 125; Sec. 1.9 **31.** 7; Sec. 1.9, Ex. 6 **32.** 4; Sec. 1.9 **33.** 180; Sec. 1.9, Ex. 8 **34.** 56; Sec. 1.9 **35.** 2; Sec. 1.9, Ex. 13 **36.** 5; Sec. 1.9 **37.** 15; Sec. 2.1, Ex. 1 **38.** 14; Sec. 2.1 **39. a.** 2 **b.** 5 **c.** 0; Sec. 2.2, Ex. 4 **40. a.** 4 **b.** 7; Sec. 2.2 **41.** 3; Sec. 2.3, Ex. 7 **42.** 5; Sec. 2.3 **43.** 14; Sec. 2.4, Ex. 12 **44.** 5; Sec. 2.4 **45.** -21; Sec. 2.5, Ex. 1 **46.** -10; Sec. 2.5 **47.** 0; Sec. 2.5, Ex. 3 **48.** -54; Sec. 2.5 **49.** -16; Sec. 2.6, Ex. 8 **50.** -27; Sec. 2.6

CHAPTER 3 Fractions

Mental Math **1.** numerator: 1; denominator: 2; proper **3.** numerator: 10; denominator: 3; improper **5.** numerator: 15; denominator: 15; improper

Exercise Set 3.1. **1.** $\frac{1}{3}$ **3. a.** $\frac{11}{4}$ **b.** $2\frac{3}{4}$ **5. a.** $\frac{23}{6}$ **b.** $3\frac{5}{6}$ **7.** $\frac{7}{12}$ **9.** $\frac{3}{7}$ **11.** $\frac{4}{9}$ **13. a.** $\frac{4}{3}$ **b.** $1\frac{1}{3}$ **15. a.** $\frac{11}{2}$ **b.** $5\frac{1}{2}$

17. $\frac{1}{6}$ **19.** $\frac{5}{8}$ **21.** **23.** 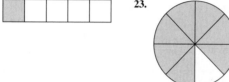 **25.** **27.**

29. $\frac{42}{131}$ **31. a.** 89 **b.** $\frac{89}{131}$ **33.** $\frac{8}{43}$ **35.** $\frac{27}{70}$ of the hard drive **37.** $\frac{11}{31}$ of the month **39.** $\frac{10}{31}$ of the class

41. a. $\frac{33}{50}$ of the states **b.** 17 states **c.** $\frac{17}{50}$ of the states **43. a.** $\frac{21}{50}$ **b.** 29 **c.** $\frac{29}{50}$ **45.** 1 **47.** -5 **49.** 0 **51.** 1

53. undefined **55.** 3 **57.** 9 **59.** 125 **61.** 7^5 **63.** $2^3 \cdot 3$ **65.** $\frac{-11}{2}$ and $\frac{11}{-2}$ **67.** $\frac{-45}{57}$ and $-\frac{45}{57}$ **69.** $\frac{2}{3}$

71. **73.** $\frac{6253}{8851}$ of the restaurants **75.** $\frac{1651}{2285}$ of the affiliates

Calculator Explorations **1.** $\frac{4}{7}$ **3.** $\frac{20}{27}$ **5.** $\frac{15}{8}$ **7.** $\frac{9}{2}$

Mental Math **1.** Yes, Yes, Yes **3.** $2 \cdot 5$ **5.** $3 \cdot 7$ **7.** 3^2

Exercise Set 3.2 **1.** $2^2 \cdot 5$ **3.** $2^4 \cdot 3$ **5.** $3^2 \cdot 5$ **7.** $2 \cdot 3^4$ **9.** $2 \cdot 5 \cdot 11$ **11.** $5 \cdot 17$ **13.** $2^4 \cdot 3 \cdot 5$ **15.** $2^2 \cdot 3^2 \cdot 23$ **17.** $\frac{1}{4}$ **19.** $\frac{2}{21}$

21. $\frac{7}{8}$ **23.** $\frac{2}{3}$ **25.** $\frac{7}{10}$ **27.** $-\frac{7}{9}$ **29.** $\frac{3}{5}$ **31.** $\frac{27}{64}$ **33.** $\frac{5}{8}$ **35.** $-\frac{5}{8}$ **37.** $\frac{3}{2}$ **39.** $\frac{3}{4}$ **41.** $\frac{5}{14}$ **43.** $\frac{3}{14}$ **45.** $-\frac{11}{17}$

47. $\frac{7}{8}$ **49.** 14 **51.** equivalent **53.** not equivalent **55.** equivalent **57.** equivalent **59.** not equivalent **61.** not equivalent

63. $\frac{1}{4}$ of a shift **65.** $\frac{1}{2}$ mi **67. a.** $\frac{3}{10}$ **b.** 35 states **c.** $\frac{7}{10}$ **69.** $\frac{5}{12}$ of the wall **71. a.** 22. **b.** $\frac{11}{25}$ **73.** 364 **75.** 2322 **77.** 2520

79. answers may vary **81.** $\frac{3}{5}$ **83.** $\frac{9}{25}$ **85.** $\frac{1}{25}$ **87.** $2^2 \cdot 3^5 \cdot 5 \cdot 7$ **89.** answers may vary **91.** no; answers may vary **93.** $\frac{2}{25}$

95. answers may vary **97.** 2235, 105, 900, 1470 **99.** 15; answers may vary

Mental Math **1.** $\frac{2}{15}$ **3.** $\frac{6}{35}$ **5.** $\frac{9}{8}$

Exercise Set 3.3 **1.** $\frac{7}{12}$ **3.** $-\frac{5}{28}$ **5.** $\frac{1}{15}$ **7.** $\frac{6}{35}$ **9.** $\frac{5}{28}$ **11.** $\frac{1}{70}$ **13.** 0 **15.** $\frac{18}{55}$ **17.** $\frac{1}{56}$ **19.** $\frac{1}{125}$ **21.** $\frac{4}{9}$ **23.** $-\frac{4}{27}$

25. $\frac{4}{5}$ **27.** $-\frac{1}{6}$ **29.** $-\frac{16}{9}$ **31.** $-\frac{1}{6}$ **33.** $\frac{1}{100}$ **35.** $\frac{35}{36}$ **37.** $\frac{8}{45}$ **39.** undefined **41.** 0 **43.** $\frac{10}{27}$ **45.** $-\frac{1}{4}$ **47.** $\frac{3}{4}$

49. $\frac{9}{16}$ **51.** $\frac{77}{2}$ **53.** $\frac{8}{3}$ **55.** $\frac{2}{5}$ **57. a.** $\frac{1}{3}$ **b.** $\frac{12}{25}$ **59. a.** $-\frac{36}{55}$ **b.** $-\frac{44}{45}$ **61.** 50 **63.** 20 **65.** $\frac{3}{2}$ in. **67.** 868 mi

69. $\frac{3}{16}$ in. **71.** 600 cal **73.** \$1838 **75.** $\frac{1}{14}$ sq ft **77.** 3840 mi **79.** 2400 mi **81.** 201 **83.** 196 **85.** answers may vary

87. 5 **89.** 640 aircraft **91.** 37 **93.** 1280 news/talk stations

The Bigger Picture **1.** $\frac{16}{27}$ **2.** $\frac{3}{4}$ **3.** $\frac{4}{3}$ or $1\frac{1}{3}$ **4.** $\frac{12}{5}$ or $2\frac{2}{5}$ **5.** 8 **6.** 72 **7.** $\frac{1}{24}$ **8.** 40 **9.** 35 **10.** 24

Mental Math 1. unlike 3. like 5. like 7. unlike

Exercise Set 3.4 1. $\frac{3}{7}$ 3. $\frac{1}{5}$ 5. $\frac{2}{3}$ 7. $-\frac{1}{4}$ 9. $-\frac{1}{2}$ 11. $\frac{13}{11}$ 13. $\frac{7}{13}$ 15. $-\frac{1}{9}$ 17. $\frac{6}{11}$ 19. $\frac{3}{5}$ 21. 1 23. $\frac{3}{4}$

25. $\frac{-10}{3}$ 27. $\frac{4}{5}$ 29. $-\frac{19}{33}$ 31. $\frac{13}{21}$ 33. $\frac{9}{10}$ 35. $\frac{-13}{14}$ 37. $-\frac{3}{4}$ 39. 1 in. 41. 2 m 43. $\frac{3}{2}$ or $1\frac{1}{2}$ hr 45. $\frac{7}{25}$ 47. $\frac{1}{50}$

49. $\frac{7}{10}$ mi 51. $\frac{3}{4}$ 53. $\frac{21}{50}$ 55. 45 57. 72 59. 24 61. 42 63. 150 65. 900 67. 1800 69. 20 71. 15

73. 36 75. 90 77. 56 79. $2 \cdot 5$ 81. 2^3 83. $\frac{5}{8}$ 85. $\frac{8}{11}$ 87. $\frac{2}{7} + \frac{9}{7} = \frac{11}{7}$ 89. answers may vary 91. 1; answers may vary

93. 814 95. answers may vary 97. a, b, and d

Integrated Review 1. $\frac{3}{6}$ 2. $\frac{7}{4}$ or $1\frac{3}{4}$ 3. $\frac{73}{85}$ 4. 5. -1 6. 17

7. 0 8. undefined 9. $5 \cdot 13$ 10. $2 \cdot 5 \cdot 7$ 11. $3^2 \cdot 5 \cdot 7$ 12. $3^2 \cdot 7^2$ 13. $\frac{1}{7}$ 14. $\frac{6}{5}$ 15. $-\frac{14}{15}$ 16. $-\frac{9}{10}$ 17. $\frac{2}{5}$ 18. $\frac{3}{8}$

19. $\frac{11}{14}$ 20. $\frac{7}{11}$ 21. not equivalent 22. equivalent 23. a. $\frac{1}{25}$ b. 48 c. $\frac{24}{25}$ 24. a. $\frac{55}{92}$ b. 185 c. $\frac{37}{92}$ 25. 30 26. 14

27. 90 28. $\frac{28}{36}$ 29. $\frac{55}{75}$ 30. $\frac{40}{48}$ 31. $\frac{6}{5}$ 32. $\frac{3}{5}$ 33. $\frac{3}{5}$ 34. $\frac{27}{20}$ 35. $\frac{9}{35}$ 36. $\frac{12}{35}$ 37. $\frac{98}{5}$ 38. $\frac{9}{250}$ 39. $-\frac{28}{45}$

40. $\frac{10}{11}$ 41. $-\frac{2}{3}$ 42. $-\frac{2}{45}$ 43. 24 lots 44. $\frac{3}{4}$ ft

Calculator Explorations 1. $\frac{37}{80}$ 3. $\frac{95}{72}$ 5. $\frac{394}{323}$

Mental Math 1. 6 3. 12 5. 56 7. 12

Exercise Set 3.5 1. $\frac{5}{6}$ 3. $\frac{1}{6}$ 5. $\frac{-4}{33}$ 7. $-\frac{3}{14}$ 9. $\frac{3}{5}$ 11. $\frac{19}{12}$ 13. $\frac{11}{36}$ 15. $\frac{12}{7}$ 17. $\frac{89}{99}$ 19. $\frac{1}{2}$ 21. $\frac{13}{27}$ 23. $-\frac{8}{33}$

25. $\frac{3}{14}$ 27. $\frac{1}{35}$ 29. $-\frac{11}{36}$ 31. $\frac{1}{20}$ 33. $\frac{33}{56}$ 35. $\frac{17}{16}$ 37. $\frac{8}{9}$ 39. $-\frac{11}{30}$ 41. $-\frac{53}{42}$ 43. $\frac{11}{18}$ 45. $\frac{98}{143}$ 47. $-\frac{11}{60}$

49. $\frac{19}{20}$ 51. $\frac{56}{45}$ 53. $-\frac{5}{24}$ 55. $-\frac{9}{1000}$ 57. $<$ 59. $>$ 61. $>$ 63. $\frac{13}{12}$ 65. $\frac{1}{4}$ 67. $\frac{11}{6}$ 69. $\frac{34}{15}$ or $2\frac{4}{15}$ cm

71. $\frac{17}{10}$ or $1\frac{7}{10}$ m 73. $\frac{61}{264}$ mi 75. $\frac{47}{32}$ in. 77. $\frac{49}{100}$ of the students 79. $\frac{77}{100}$ of Americans 81. $\frac{19}{25}$ 83. 20 85. -6

87. $\frac{3}{5} + \frac{4}{5} = \frac{7}{5}$ 89. $\frac{223}{540}$ 91. $\frac{49}{44}$ 93. answers may vary

Exercise Set 3.6 1. $\frac{1}{6}$ 3. $\frac{3}{7}$ 5. $\frac{1}{6}$ 7. $\frac{23}{22}$ 9. $\frac{2}{13}$ 11. $\frac{17}{60}$ 13. $\frac{5}{8}$ 15. $\frac{35}{9}$ 17. $-\frac{17}{45}$ 19. $\frac{11}{8}$ 21. $\frac{29}{10}$ 23. $\frac{27}{32}$

25. $\frac{1}{81}$ 27. $\frac{9}{64}$ 29. $\frac{7}{6}$ 31. $-\frac{2}{5}$ 33. $-\frac{2}{9}$ 35. $\frac{5}{2}$ 37. $\frac{7}{2}$ 39. $\frac{4}{9}$ 41. $-\frac{13}{2}$ 43. $\frac{9}{25}$ 45. $-\frac{5}{32}$ 47. 1 49. $\frac{1}{10}$

51. $\frac{7}{3}$ 53. $\frac{18}{5}$ 55. $\frac{53}{8}$ 57. $\frac{41}{15}$ 59. $\frac{83}{7}$ 61. $\frac{84}{13}$ 63. $\frac{187}{20}$ 65. $\frac{500}{3}$ 67. $3\frac{2}{5}$ 69. $4\frac{5}{8}$ 71. $3\frac{2}{15}$ 73. 15 75. $1\frac{7}{175}$

77. $6\frac{65}{112}$ 79. $\frac{7}{2}$ 81. $\frac{49}{6}$ 83. answers may vary 85. $\frac{5}{8}$ 87. $\frac{11}{56}$ 89. halfway between a and b 91. false 93. false

95. true 97. no; answers may vary 99. addition, multiplication, subtraction, division 101. subtraction, multiplication, division, addition

Calculator Explorations 1. $\frac{280}{11}$ 3. $\frac{3776}{35}$ 5. $26\frac{1}{14}$ 7. $92\frac{3}{10}$

Mental Math 1. a 3. b

Exercise Set 3.7 1. 3. 5. $\frac{8}{21}$ 7. $4\frac{2}{3}$ 9. Exact: $\frac{77}{10}$ or $7\frac{7}{10}$ Estimate: 8

11. Exact: $\frac{836}{35}$ or $23\frac{31}{35}$ Estimate: 24 13. $\frac{25}{2}$ or $12\frac{1}{2}$ 15. $5\frac{1}{2}$ 17. $18\frac{2}{3}$ 19. Exact: $6\frac{4}{5}$ Estimate: 7 21. Exact: $13\frac{11}{14}$ Estimate: 14 23. Exact: $17\frac{7}{25}$ Estimate: 17 25. $47\frac{53}{84}$

27. $25\frac{5}{14}$ 29. $13\frac{13}{24}$ 31. Exact: $2\frac{3}{5}$ Estimate: 3 33. Exact: $7\frac{5}{14}$ Estimate: 7 35. Exact: $\frac{24}{25}$ Estimate: 1 37. $3\frac{5}{9}$ 39. $15\frac{3}{4}$ 41. 4 43. $5\frac{11}{14}$ 45. $6\frac{2}{9}$

47. $\frac{25}{33}$ 49. $35\frac{13}{18}$ 51. $2\frac{1}{2}$ 53. $72\frac{19}{30}$ 55. $\frac{11}{14}$ 57. $\frac{5}{6}$ Tbsp 59. $\frac{39}{2}$ or $19\frac{1}{2}$ in. 61. $3\frac{367}{625}$ sq in. 63. $\frac{1}{16}$ in.

65. no; she will be $\frac{1}{12}$ ft short   **67.** $7\frac{13}{20}$ in.   **69.** $3\frac{3}{16}$ mi   **71.** $4\frac{2}{3}$ m   **73.** $92\frac{99}{100}$ m   **75.** $9\frac{7}{12}$ min   **77.** $1\frac{4}{5}$ min

79. $21\frac{5}{24}$ m   **81.** $-10\frac{3}{25}$ **83.** $-24\frac{7}{8}$ **85.** $-13\frac{59}{60}$ **87.** $-\frac{1}{2}$ **89.** $-1\frac{23}{24}$ **91.** $\frac{73}{1000}$ **93.** 4   **95.** 167   **97.** a, b, c

99. incorrect; to divide mixed numbers, first write each mixed number as an improper fraction.   **101.** c   **103.** d   **105.** answers may vary

107. incorrect; $3\frac{2}{3} \cdot 1\frac{1}{7} = \frac{11}{3} \cdot \frac{8}{7} = \frac{88}{21}$ or $4\frac{4}{21}$ **109.** answers may vary

The Bigger Picture   **1.** $\frac{5}{17}$ **2.** $\frac{4}{5}$ **3.** $\frac{29}{30}$ **4.** $\frac{1}{24}$ **5.** $1\frac{33}{40}$ **6.** $\frac{27}{64}$ **7.** $12\frac{3}{7}$ **8.** $9\frac{13}{24}$ **9.** $\frac{16}{33}$ **10.** $\frac{34}{27}$ or $1\frac{7}{27}$

Chapter 3 Vocabulary Check   **1.** reciprocals   **2.** composite number   **3.** equivalent   **4.** improper fraction   **5.** prime number
6. simplest form   **7.** proper fraction   **8.** mixed number   **9.** numerator, denominator   **10.** prime factorization   **11.** undefined
12. 0   **13.** like   **14.** least common denominator

Chapter 3 Review   **1.** proper   **2.** improper   **3.** proper   **4.** mixed number   **5.** $\frac{2}{6}$ **6.** $\frac{4}{7}$ **7.** $\frac{7}{3}$ or $2\frac{1}{3}$ **8.** $\frac{13}{4}$ or $3\frac{1}{4}$ **9.** $\frac{11}{12}$

10. a. 108   **b.** $\frac{108}{131}$ **11.** 1   **12.** -1 **13.** -1 **14.** 1   **15.** 0   **16.** undefined   **17.** undefined   **18.** -15 **19.** $2^2 \cdot 17$

20. $2 \cdot 3^2 \cdot 5$ **21.** $5 \cdot 157$ **22.** $3 \cdot 5 \cdot 17$ **23.** $\frac{3}{7}$ **24.** $\frac{5}{9}$ **25.** $-\frac{1}{3}$ **26.** $-\frac{1}{2}$ **27.** $\frac{29}{32}$ **28.** $\frac{18}{23}$ **29.** 8   **30.** 6

31. $\frac{2}{3}$ ft   **32.** $\frac{3}{5}$ of the cars   **33.** no   **34.** yes   **35.** $-\frac{3}{10}$ **36.** $\frac{5}{14}$ **37.** 9   **38.** $\frac{5}{3}$ **39.** $-\frac{1}{27}$ **40.** $\frac{25}{144}$ **41.** $\frac{2}{15}$

42. $-\frac{63}{10}$ **43.** $\frac{1}{7}$ **44.** $\frac{23}{14}$ **45.** -2 **46.** $\frac{15}{4}$ **47.** $-\frac{5}{6}$ **48.** $\frac{27}{2}$ **49.** $\frac{12}{7}$ **50.** $\frac{-15}{2}$ **51.** $\frac{77}{48}$ sq ft   **52.** $\frac{4}{9}$ sq m   **53.** $\frac{3}{25}$

54. $-\frac{2}{3}$ **55.** $\frac{1}{7}$ **56.** $\frac{3}{-10}$ **57.** $\frac{3}{4}$ of his homework   **58.** $\frac{3}{2}$ mi   **59.** 55   **60.** 120   **61.** 252   **62.** 72   **63.** $\frac{56}{64}$ **64.** $\frac{20}{26}$

65. $\frac{16}{60}$ **66.** $\frac{25}{60}$ **67.** $\frac{11}{18}$ **68.** $\frac{7}{15}$ **69.** $\frac{7}{26}$ **70.** $-\frac{17}{36}$ **71.** $\frac{41}{42}$ **72.** $\frac{43}{-72}$ **73.** $\frac{13}{45}$ **74.** $\frac{5}{18}$ **75.** $\frac{19}{9}$ m   **76.** $\frac{3}{2}$ ft

77. $\frac{1}{4}$ yd   **78.** $\frac{7}{10}$ has been cleaned   **79.** $<$ **80.** $>$ **81.** $>$ **82.** $<$ **83.** $\frac{4}{7}$ **84.** $\frac{22}{7}$ **85.** $\frac{4}{9}$ **86.** $-\frac{3}{10}$ **87.** $3\frac{3}{4}$

88. 3   **89.** 1   **90.** $31\frac{1}{4}$ **91.** $\frac{11}{5}$ **92.** $\frac{35}{9}$ **93.** $\frac{8}{13}$ **94.** $-\frac{1}{27}$ **95.** $\frac{29}{110}$ **96.** $-\frac{1}{7}$ **97.** $45\frac{16}{21}$ **98.** $20\frac{7}{24}$ **99.** $5\frac{16}{35}$

100. $3\frac{4}{55}$ **101.** Exact: $\frac{26}{5}$ or $5\frac{1}{5}$ **102.** Exact: $\frac{60}{11}$ or $5\frac{5}{11}$ **103.** $\frac{21}{4}$ or $5\frac{1}{4}$ **104.** $\frac{121}{46}$ or $2\frac{29}{46}$ **105.** 22 mi   **106.** $\frac{21}{20}$ or $1\frac{1}{20}$ mi
Estimate: 6   Estimate: 8

107. $\frac{110}{3}$ or $36\frac{2}{3}$ g   **108.** $\frac{135}{4}$ or $33\frac{3}{4}$ in.   **109.** each measurement is $4\frac{1}{4}$ in.   **110.** $\frac{7}{10}$ yd   **111.** $-27\frac{5}{14}$ **112.** $1\frac{5}{27}$ **113.** $-3\frac{15}{16}$

114. $-\frac{33}{40}$ **115.** $\frac{7}{12}$ **116.** $\frac{1}{4}$ **117.** 9   **118.** $\frac{27}{2}$ or $13\frac{1}{2}$ **119.** $\frac{1}{6}$ **120.** $\frac{1}{5}$ **121.** $\frac{11}{12}$ **122.** $\frac{27}{55}$ **123.** Exact: 10
Estimate: 8

124. Exact: $\frac{51}{4}$ or $12\frac{3}{4}$ **125.** $\frac{7}{3}$ or $2\frac{1}{3}$ **126.** $\frac{32}{5}$ or $6\frac{2}{5}$ **127.** $13\frac{5}{12}$ **128.** $12\frac{3}{8}$ **129.** $3\frac{16}{35}$ **130.** $8\frac{1}{21}$ **131.** $\frac{11}{25}$ **132.** $\frac{1}{144}$
Estimate: 12

133. $-\frac{1}{12}$ **134.** $6\frac{7}{20}$ lb   **135.** $44\frac{1}{2}$ yd   **136.** $\frac{81}{2}$ or $40\frac{1}{2}$ sq ft   **137.** $\frac{47}{61}$ in.

Chapter 3 Test   **1.** $\frac{7}{16}$ **2.** $\frac{23}{3}$ **3.** $18\frac{3}{4}$ **4.** $\frac{4}{35}$ **5.** $-\frac{3}{5}$ **6.** not equivalent   **7.** equivalent   **8.** $2^2 \cdot 3 \cdot 7$ **9.** $3^2 \cdot 5 \cdot 11$

10. 72   **11.** $\frac{8}{9}$ **12.** $-\frac{2}{3}$ **13.** $\frac{4}{3}$ or $1\frac{1}{3}$ **14.** $-\frac{4}{3}$ **15.** $\frac{8}{21}$ **16.** $\frac{13}{24}$ **17.** $\frac{16}{45}$ **18.** 16   **19.** $\frac{1}{7}$ **20.** $\frac{7}{50}$ **21.** $\frac{4}{11}$

22. 9   **23.** $\frac{3}{4}$ **24.** $14\frac{1}{40}$ **25.** $16\frac{8}{11}$ **26.** $\frac{64}{3}$ or $21\frac{1}{3}$ **27.** $\frac{45}{2}$ or $22\frac{1}{2}$ **28.** $-\frac{5}{3}$ or $-1\frac{2}{3}$ **29.** $\frac{9}{16}$ **30.** $\frac{3}{8}$ **31.** $\frac{11}{12}$

32. $\frac{76}{21}$ **33.** $\frac{5}{2}$ or $2\frac{1}{2}$ **34.** $3\frac{3}{4}$ ft   **35.** $\frac{23}{50}$ **36.** $\frac{13}{50}$ **37.** \$2820   **38.** perimeter: $3\frac{1}{3}$ ft; area: $\frac{2}{3}$ sq ft   **39.** 24 mi

Cumulative Review   **1.** one hundred twenty-six; Sec. 1.2, Ex. 5   **2.** one hundred fifteen; Sec. 1.2
3. twenty-seven thousand thirty-four; Sec. 1.2, Ex. 6   **4.** six thousand five hundred seventy-three; Sec. 1.2   **5.** 159; Sec. 1.3, Ex. 1
6. 631; Sec. 1.3   **7.** 514; Sec. 1.4, Ex. 3   **8.** 933; Sec. 1.4   **9.** 278,000; Sec. 1.5, Ex. 2   **10.** 1440; Sec. 1.5
11. 57,600 megabytes; Sec. 1.6, Ex. 11   **12.** 1305 mi; Sec. 1.6   **13.** 7089 R 5; Sec. 1.7, Ex. 7.   **14.** 379 R 10; Sec. 1.7   **15.** 4^3; Sec. 1.9, Ex. 1
16. 7^2; Sec. 1.9   **17.** $6^3 \cdot 8^5$; Sec. 1.9, Ex. 4   **18.** $9^4 \cdot 5^2$; Sec. 1.9   **19.** 8; Sec. 2.1, Ex. 2   **20.** 52; Sec. 2.1   **21.** -150; Sec. 2.2, Ex. 1
22. -21; Sec. 2.2   **23.** -4; Sec. 2.3, Ex. 3   **24.** 5; Sec. 2.3   **25.** 3; Sec. 2.4, Ex. 9   **26.** 10; Sec. 2.4   **27.** 25; Sec. 2.5, Ex. 8
28. -16; Sec. 2.5   **29.** -16; Sec. 2.6, Ex. 5   **30.** 25; Sec. 2.6   **31.** $3 \cdot 3 \cdot 5$ or $3^2 \cdot 5$; Sec. 3.2, Ex. 1   **32.** $2 \cdot 2 \cdot 23$ or $2^2 \cdot 23$; Sec. 3.2

33. $\frac{10}{33}$; Sec. 3.3, Ex. 1   **34.** $\frac{2}{35}$; Sec. 3.3   **35.** $\frac{1}{8}$; Sec. 3.3, Ex. 2   **36.** $\frac{3}{25}$; Sec. 3.3   **37.** $\frac{2}{5}$; Sec. 3.1, Ex. 3   **38.** $2^2 \cdot 3 \cdot 13$; Sec. 3.2

39. a. $\frac{38}{9}$ **b.** $\frac{19}{11}$; Sec. 3.6, Ex. 8   **40.** $\frac{39}{5}$; Sec. 3.6   **41.** $\frac{7}{11}$; Sec. 3.2, Ex. 5   **42.** $\frac{2}{3}$; Sec. 3.2   **43.** $\frac{35}{12}$ or $2\frac{11}{12}$; Sec. 3.7, Ex. 2

44. $\frac{8}{3}$; Sec. 3.7   **45.** $\frac{5}{12}$; Sec. 3.3, Ex. 10   **46.** $\frac{11}{56}$; Sec. 3.7

CHAPTER 4   Decimals

Mental Math   1. tens   **3.** tenths

Exercise Set 4.1   1. six and fifty-two hundredths   **3.** sixteen and twenty-three hundredths   **5.** negative two hundred five thousandths
7. one hundred sixty-seven and nine thousandths   **9.** two hundred and five thousandths   **11.** one hundred five and six tenths
13. thirty-one and four hundredths   **15.** R. W. Financial; 321.42; Three hundred twenty-one and 42/100

17. Bell South; 59.68; Fifty-nine and 68/100   **19.** 6.5   **21.** 9.08   **23.** -705.625 **25.** 0.0064   **27.** $\frac{3}{10}$ **29.** $\frac{27}{100}$ **31.** $\frac{4}{5}$

33. $-5\frac{47}{100}$ **35.** $\frac{6}{125}$ **37.** $7\frac{1}{125}$ **39.** $15\frac{401}{500}$ **41.** $\frac{601}{2000}$ **43.** 0.8; $\frac{8}{10}$ or $\frac{4}{5}$ **45.** seventy-seven thousandths; $\frac{77}{1000}$ **47.** <
49. <   **51.** <   **53.** =   **55.** <   **57.** >   **59.** <   **61.** >   **63.** 0.6   **65.** 0.23   **67.** 0.594   **69.** 98,210   **71.** -17.67
73. -0.5 **75.** \$27   **77.** \$0.20   **79.** 2.2 cm   **81.** 2.41 hr   **83.** \$48   **85.** 24.623 hr   **87.** 5766   **89.** 35   **91.** b   **93.** a
95. answers may vary   **97.** 7.12   **99.** $\frac{26,849,576}{100,000,000,000}$ **101.** answers may vary   **103.** answers may vary   **105.** 0.0612; 0.0586

Calculator Explorations   1. 328.742   **3.** 5.2414   **5.** 865.392

Mental Math   1. 0.5   **3.** 1.26   **5.** 8.9   **7.** 0.6

Exercise Set 4.2   1. 3.5   **3.** 6.83   **5.** 27.0578   **7.** 56.432   **9.** -8.57 **11.** 11.16   **13.** Exact: 465.56; Estimate: $\begin{array}{r} 230 \\ +\,230 \\ \hline 460 \end{array}$

15. Exact: 115.123; Estimate: $\begin{array}{r} 100 \\ 6 \\ +\;\;9 \\ \hline 115 \end{array}$ **17.** 56.432   **19.** 6.5   **21.** 15.3   **23.** 598.23   **25.** Exact: 1.83; Estimate: $6 - 4 = 2$

27. 861.6   **29.** Exact: 876.6; Estimate: $\begin{array}{r} 1000 \\ -\,100 \\ \hline 900 \end{array}$ **31.** 194.4   **33.** -6.32 **35.** -6.4 **37.** 3.1   **39.** 2.9988   **41.** 16.3

43. 3.1   **45.** -5.62 **47.** 776.89   **49.** -549.8 **51.** 861.6   **53.** 115.123   **55.** 0.088   **57.** -180.44 **59.** -1.1 **61.** 3.81
63. 3.39   **65.** 1.61   **67.** \$454.71   **69.** \$0.14   **71.** 28.56 m   **73.** 11.2 in.   **75.** \$7.52   **77.** 285.8 mph
79. \$3.4 billion   **81.** 240.8 in.   **83.** 67.44 ft   **85.** 715.05 hr   **87.** Switzerland   **89.** 8.1 lb

91.

Country	Pounds of Chocolate per Person
Switzerland	22.0
Norway	16.0
Germany	15.8
United Kingdom	14.5
Belgium	13.9

93. 138   **95.** $\frac{1}{125}$ **97.** 6.08 in.   **99.** \$1.20
101. 1 nickel, 1 dime, and 2 pennies; 3 nickels and 2 pennies; 1 dime and 7 pennies
103. answers may vary   **105.** 0.777 mi

Mental Math   1. 4   **3.** 4   **5.** 5

Exercise Set 4.3   1. 1.3   **3.** 0.6   **5.** -17.595 **7.** 39.273   **9.** Exact: 22.26; Estimate: $5 \times 4 = 20$ **11.** 0.4032

13. Exact: 8.23854; Estimate: $\begin{array}{r} 1 \\ \times\;8 \\ \hline 8 \end{array}$ **15.** 11.2746   **17.** 65   **19.** 0.65   **21.** -7093 **23.** 709.3   **25.** 0.0983   **27.** 0.03762

29. 0.0492   **31.** 14,790   **33.** 1.29   **35.** -9.3762 **37.** 0.5623   **39.** 43.274   **41.** 5,500,000,000   **43.** 49,800,000   **45.** 353,000
47. -0.6 **49.** 17.3   **51.** $8\pi \approx 25.12$ m   **53.** $10\pi \approx 31.4$ cm   **55.** $18.2\pi \approx 57.148$ yd   **57.** 24.8 g   **59.** \$4550   **61.** 250π ft ≈ 785 ft
63. 135π m ≈ 423.9 m   **65.** 64.9605 in.   **67.** \$555.20   **69. a.** 62.8 m and 125.6 m **b.** yes   **71.** 7.2 sq in.   **73.** 8   **75.** -9 **77.** 3.64
79. 3.56   **81.** -0.1105 **83.** 3,831,600 mi   **85.** answers may vary   **87.** answers may vary

Calculator Explorations   1. not reasonable   **3.** reasonable

Mental Math   **1.** 5.9   **3.** 0   **5.** 1   **7.** undefined

Exercise Set 4.4   **1.** 4.6   **3.** 0.094   **5.** 300   **7.** 5.8   **9.** Exact: 6.6; Estimate: $6\overline{)36}^{\,6}$ **11.** 0.413   **13.** -300 **15.** 7   **17.** 4.8
19. 2100   **21.** 5.8   **23.** 6.6   **25.** Exact: 9.8; Estimate: $7\overline{)70}^{\,10}$ **27.** 9.6   **29.** 45   **31.** 54.592   **33.** 0.0055   **35.** 179   **37.** 23.87
39. 113.1   **41.** 0.54982   **43.** 2.687   **45.** -0.0129 **47.** 12.6   **49.** 1.31   **51.** 0.045625   **53.** 0.413   **55.** -7 **57.** -4.8
59. 2100   **61.** 30   **63.** 7000   **65.** -0.69 **67.** 0.024   **69.** 65   **71.** -5.65 **73.** -7.0625 **75.** 24 mo   **77.** $3641.30
79. 5.1 m   **81.** 11.4 boxes   **83.** 24 tsp   **85.** 8 days   **87.** 20.45 points   **89.** $\frac{9}{10}$ **91.** $\frac{1}{20}$ **93.** 4.26   **95.** 1.578   **97.** -26.66
99. 904.29   **101.** c   **103.** b   **105.** 85.5   **107.** 14.345 million, or 14,345,000 CDs   **109.** 45.2 cm   **111.** answers may vary
113. 65.2–82.6 knots

The Bigger Picture   **1.** 22.172   **2.** 3.951   **3.** 9133.2   **4.** -6.8 **5.** 1.404   **6.** 8.66   **7.** 0.051   **8.** 2.14   **9.** $\frac{2}{15}$ **10.** $-\frac{16}{75}$

Integrated Review   **1.** 2.57   **2.** 4.05   **3.** 8.9   **4.** 3.5   **5.** 0.16   **6.** 0.24   **7.** 0.27   **8.** 0.52   **9.** -4.8 **10.** 6.09   **11.** 75.56
12. 289.12   **13.** -24.974 **14.** -43.875 **15.** -8.6 **16.** 5.4   **17.** -280 **18.** 1600   **19.** 224.938   **20.** 145.079   **21.** 0.56
22. -0.63 **23.** 27.6092   **24.** 145.6312   **25.** 5.4   **26.** -17.74 **27.** -414.44 **28.** -1295.03 **29.** -34 **30.** -28 **31.** 116.81
32. 18.79   **33.** 156.2   **34.** 1.562   **35.** 25.62   **36.** 5.62   **37.** yes; answers may vary   **38.** 200 mi

Exercise Set 4.5   **1.** 0.2   **3.** 0.68   **5.** 0.75   **7.** -0.08 **9.** 1.2   **11.** $0.91\overline{6}$ **13.** 0.425   **15.** 0.45   **17.** $-0.\overline{3}$ **19.** 0.4375
21. $0.\overline{63}$ **23.** 5.85   **25.** 0.624   **27.** -0.33 **29.** 0.44   **31.** 0.6   **33.** 0.68   **35.** 0.62   **37.** 0.71   **39.** <   **41.** =   **43.** <
45. <   **47.** <   **49.** >   **51.** <   **53.** <   **55.** 0.32, 0.34, 0.35   **57.** 0.49, 0.491, 0.498   **59.** 5.23, $\frac{42}{8}$, 5.34   **61.** $\frac{17}{8}$, 2.37, $\frac{12}{5}$
63. 0.06   **65.** -3 **67.** 5.29   **69.** 7.6   **71.** 0.2025   **73.** -1.29 **75.** -15.4 **77.** -3.7 **79.** 25.65 sq in.   **81.** 0.248 sq yd
83. 5.76   **85.** 5.7   **87.** 3.6   **89.** 72   **91.** $\frac{5}{2}$ **93.** = 1   **95.** > 1   **97.** < 1   **99.** 0.192   **101.** 6000 stations
103. answers may vary   **105.** answers may vary

Calculator Explorations   **1.** 32   **3.** 3.873   **5.** 9.849

Exercise Set 4.6   **1.** 2   **3.** 8   **5.** $\frac{1}{9}$ **7.** $\frac{4}{8} = \frac{1}{2}$ **9.** 1.732   **11.** 3.873   **13.** 6.856   **15.** 5.099   **17.** 16   **19.** 3.742   **21.** $\frac{7}{12}$
23. 8.426   **25.** 13 in.   **27.** 6.633 cm   **29.** 52.802 m   **31.** 117 mm   **33.** 5   **35.** 12   **37.** 17.205   **39.** 44.822   **41.** 42.426
43. 1.732   **45.** 8.5   **47.** 141.42 yd   **49.** 25.0 ft   **51.** 340 ft   **53.** $\frac{5}{6}$ **55.** $\frac{2}{5}$ **57.** $\frac{5}{12}$ **59.** 6, 7   **61.** 10, 11
63. answers may vary   **65.** no

Chapter 4 Vocabulary Check   **1.** decimal   **2.** numerator; denominator   **3.** vertically   **4.** and   **5.** sum   **6.** square root
7. right triangle; hypotenuse; legs

Chapter 4 Review   **1.** tenths   **2.** hundred-thousandths   **3.** negative twenty-three and forty-five hundredths   **4.** three hundred forty-five
hundred-thousandths   **5.** one hundred nine and twenty-three hundredths   **6.** two hundred and thirty-two millionths   **7.** 2.15
8. -503.102 **9.** 16,025.0014   **10.** $\frac{4}{25}$ **11.** $-12\frac{23}{1000}$ **12.** $1\frac{9}{2000}$ **13.** $\frac{231}{100,000}$ **14.** $25\frac{1}{4}$ **15.** >   **16.** =
17. <   **18.** >   **19.** 0.6   **20.** 0.94   **21.** -42.90 **22.** 16.349   **23.** 13,500 people   **24.** $10\frac{3}{4}$ tsp   **25.** 9.5   **26.** 5.1
27. -7.28 **28.** -12.04 **29.** 320.312   **30.** 148.74236   **31.** 1.7   **32.** 2.49   **33.** -1324.5 **34.** -10.136 **35.** 65.02   **36.** 199.99802
37. 52.6 mi   **38.** -5.7 **39.** 22.2 in.   **40.** 38.9 ft   **41.** 72   **42.** 9345   **43.** -78.246 **44.** 73,246.446   **45.** 14π m ≈ 43.96 m
46. 63.8 mi   **47.** 887,000,000   **48.** 600,000   **49.** 0.0877   **50.** 15.825   **51.** 70   **52.** -0.21 **53.** 8.059   **54.** 30.4   **55.** 0.0267
56. -9.3 **57.** 7.3 m   **58.** 45 mo   **59.** 0.8   **60.** -0.923 **61.** $2.\overline{3}$ or 2.333   **62.** $0.21\overline{6}$ or 0.217   **63.** =   **64.** <   **65.** <
66. <   **67.** 0.837, 0.839, $\frac{17}{20}$ **68.** 0.42, $\frac{3}{7}$, 0.43   **69.** $\frac{19}{12}$, 1.63, $\frac{18}{11}$ **70.** -11.94 **71.** 3.89   **72.** -129 **73.** 0.81   **74.** 55   **75.** 7.26
76. 6.9 sq ft   **77.** 5.46 sq in.   **78.** 8   **79.** 12   **80.** $\frac{2}{5}$ **81.** $\frac{1}{10}$ **82.** 13   **83.** 29   **84.** 10.7   **85.** 93   **86.** 127.3 ft   **87.** 88.2 ft
88. two hundred and thirty-two ten-thousandths   **89.** $-16,025.014$ **90.** $\frac{231}{100,000}$ **91.** 0.75, $\frac{6}{7}$, $\frac{8}{9}$ **92.** -0.07 **93.** 0.1125   **94.** 51.057
95. >   **96.** <   **97.** <   **98.** 42.90   **99.** 16.349   **100.** $123.00   **101.** $3646.00   **102.** -1.7 **103.** 2.49   **104.** 320.312
105. -148.74236 **106.** 8.128   **107.** -7.245 **108.** 4900   **109.** 23.904   **110.** 9600 sq ft   **111.** no   **112.** 0.1024   **113.** 3.6
114. 1   **115.** 6   **116.** $\frac{4}{9}$ **117.** 86.6   **118.** 20.8   **119.** 48.1   **120.** 19.7

Chapter 4 Test   **1.** forty-five and ninety-two thousandths   **2.** 3000.059   **3.** 17.595   **4.** -51.20 **5.** -20.42 **6.** 40.902   **7.** 0.037
8. 34.9   **9.** 0.862   **10.** <   **11.** <   **12.** $\frac{69}{200}$ **13.** $-24\frac{73}{100}$ **14.** -0.5 **15.** 0.941   **16.** 1.93   **17.** -6.2 **18.** 11.4   **19.** 7
20. 12.530   **21.** $\frac{4}{5}$ **22.** 5.66 cm   **23.** 2.31 sq mi   **24.** 18π mi, 56.52 mi   **25. a.** 9904 sq ft   **b.** 198.08 oz   **26.** 54 mi
27. 4,583,000,000

Cumulative Review **1.** eighty-five; Sec. 1.2, Ex. 4 **2.** one hundred seven; Sec. 1.2 **3.** one hundred twenty-six; Sec. 1.2, Ex. 5
4. five thousand, twenty-six; Sec. 1.2 **5.** 159; Sec. 1.3, Ex. 1 **6.** 19 in.; Sec. 1.3 **7.** 514; Sec. 1.4, Ex. 3 **8.** 121 R 1; Sec. 1.7
9. 278,000; Sec. 1.5, Ex. 2 **10.** 1, 2, 3, 5, 6, 10, 15, 30; Sec. 1.5 **11.** 20,296; Sec. 1.6, Ex. 4 **12.** 0; Sec. 1.6
13. a. 8 **b.** 11 **c.** 1 **d.** 1 **e.** 10 **f.** 1; Sec. 1.7, Ex. 2 **14.** 25; Sec. 1.7 **15.** 1038 mi; Sec. 1.8, Ex. 1 **16.** 11; Sec. 1.9
17. 64; Sec. 1.9, Ex. 5 **18.** 125; Sec. 1.9 **19.** 32; Sec. 1.9, Ex. 7 **20.** 1000; Sec. 1.9 **21.** 2; Sec. 2.1, Ex. 3 **22.** 6; Sec. 2.1
23. a. -11 **b.** 2 **c.** 0; Sec. 2.2, Ex. 5 **24. a.** 7 **b.** -4 **c.** 1; Sec. 2.2 **25.** -23; Sec. 2.3, Ex. 4 **26.** -22; Sec. 2.3
27. 180; Sec. 1.9, Ex. 8 **28.** 32; Sec. 1.9 **29.** -49; Sec. 2.5, Ex. 9 **30.** -32; Sec. 2.5 **31.** 25; Sec. 2.5, Ex. 8 **32.** -9; Sec. 2.5

33. $\frac{4}{3}$ or $1\frac{1}{3}$; Sec. 3.1, Ex. 11 **34.** $\frac{11}{4}$ or $2\frac{3}{4}$; Sec. 3.1 **35.** $\frac{5}{2}$ or $2\frac{1}{2}$; Sec. 3.1, Ex. 12 **36.** $\frac{14}{3}$ or $4\frac{2}{3}$; Sec. 3.1 **37.** $2^2 \cdot 3^2 \cdot 7$; Sec. 3.2, Ex. 3

38. 62; Sec. 1.4 **39.** $-\frac{36}{13}$; Sec. 3.2, Ex. 8 **40.** $\frac{79}{8}$; Sec. 3.6 **41.** equivalent; Sec. 3.2, Ex. 10 **42.** >; Sec. 3.5

43. $\frac{10}{33}$; Sec. 3.3, Ex. 1 **44.** $\frac{3}{2}$ or $1\frac{1}{2}$; Sec. 3.7 **45.** $\frac{1}{8}$; Sec. 3.3, Ex. 2 **46.** 37; Sec. 3.7 **47.** 829.6561; Sec. 4.2, Ex. 2

48. 230.8628; Sec. 4.2 **49.** 18.408; Sec. 4.3, Ex. 1 **50.** 28.251; Sec. 4.3

CHAPTER 5   Ratio, Proportion, and Measurement

Exercise Set 5.1 **1.** $\frac{2}{3}$ **3.** $\frac{77}{100}$ **5.** $\frac{463}{821}$ **7.** $\frac{3}{4}$ **9.** $\frac{8}{25}$ **11.** $\frac{12}{7}$ **13.** $\frac{2}{7}$ **15.** $\frac{4}{1}$ **17.** $\frac{47}{25}$ **19.** $\frac{17}{40}$ **21.** $\frac{5}{4}$ **23.** $\frac{15}{1}$

25. $\frac{1}{49}$ **27.** $\frac{1 \text{ shrub}}{3 \text{ ft}}$ **29.** $\frac{3 \text{ returns}}{20 \text{ sales}}$ **31.** $\frac{2 \text{ phone lines}}{9 \text{ employees}}$ **33.** $\frac{9 \text{ gal}}{2 \text{ acres}}$ **35.** 110 cal/oz **37.** 90 wingbeats/sec

39. \$50,000/yr **41.** 7600 sq mi/county **43.** 300 good/defective **45.** \$46,600/house **47. a.** 31.25 computer boards/hr
b. 33.5 computer boards/hr **c.** Lamont **49. a.** ≈ 27.6 miles/gal **b.** ≈ 29.2 miles/gal **c.** the truck
51. 8 oz: \$0.149 per oz; 12 oz: \$0.133 per oz; 12 oz **53.** 16 oz: \$0.106 per oz; 6 oz: \$0.115 per oz; 16 oz
55. 12 oz: \$0.191 per oz; 8 oz: \$0.186 per oz; 8 oz **57.** 100: \$0.006 per napkin; 180: \$0.005 per napkin; 180 napkins
59. 2.3 **61.** 0.15 **63.** no; answers may vary **65.** no; $\frac{2}{5}$ **67.** yes, the machine should be repaired
69. miles driven: 257, 352, 347; miles per gallon: 19.2, 22.3, 21.6 **71.** 544 students/school **73.** answers may vary **75.** no; answers may vary

77. a. $\frac{19}{50}$ **b.** $\frac{19}{31}$ **c.** no; answers may vary

Mental Math **1.** true **3.** false **5.** true

Exercise Set 5.2 **1.** $\frac{10 \text{ diamonds}}{6 \text{ opals}} = \frac{5 \text{ diamonds}}{3 \text{ opals}}$ **3.** $\frac{3 \text{ printers}}{12 \text{ computers}} = \frac{1 \text{ printer}}{4 \text{ computers}}$ **5.** $\frac{6 \text{ eagles}}{58 \text{ sparrows}} = \frac{3 \text{ eagles}}{29 \text{ sparrows}}$

7. $\frac{2\frac{1}{4} \text{ cups flour}}{24 \text{ cookies}} = \frac{6\frac{3}{4} \text{ cups flour}}{72 \text{ cookies}}$ **9.** $\frac{22 \text{ vanilla wafers}}{1 \text{ cup cookie crumbs}} = \frac{55 \text{ vanilla wafers}}{2.5 \text{ cups cookie crumbs}}$ **11.** true **13.** false **15.** true **17.** true

19. false **21.** false **23.** true **25.** false **27.** true **29.** $\frac{8}{12} = \frac{4}{6}$; true **31.** $\frac{5}{2} = \frac{13}{5}$; false **33.** $\frac{1.8}{2} = \frac{4.5}{5}$; true

35. $\frac{\frac{2}{3}}{\frac{1}{5}} = \frac{\frac{2}{5}}{\frac{1}{9}}$; false **37.** 3 **39.** -9 **41.** 4 **43.** 3.2 **45.** 38.4 **47.** 25 **49.** 0.0025 **51.** 1 **53.** $\frac{9}{20}$ **55.** 12 **57.** $\frac{3}{4}$

59. $\frac{35}{18}$ **61.** < **63.** > **65.** < **67.** $\frac{9}{3} = \frac{15}{5}; \frac{5}{15} = \frac{3}{9}; \frac{15}{9} = \frac{5}{3}$ **69.** $\frac{6}{1} = \frac{18}{3}; \frac{3}{18} = \frac{1}{6}; \frac{18}{6} = \frac{3}{1}$ **71.** $\frac{d}{b} = \frac{c}{a}; \frac{a}{c} = \frac{b}{d}; \frac{b}{a} = \frac{d}{c}$
73. answers may vary **75.** 0 **77.** 1400 **79.** 252.5

The Bigger Picture **1.** $\frac{1}{4}$ **2.** $\frac{7}{200}$ **3.** $\frac{7}{2}$ or $3\frac{1}{2}$ **4.** $\frac{9}{20}$ **5.** 7.62 **6.** 0.152 **7.** 8 **8.** $\frac{5}{2}$ or $2\frac{1}{2}$ **9.** 0.004 **10.** $\frac{35}{12}$ or $2\frac{11}{12}$

Exercise Set 5.3 **1.** 12 passes **3.** 165 min **5.** 630 applications **7.** 23 ft **9.** 270 sq ft **11.** 56 mi **13.** 450 km **15.** 24 oz
17. 16 bags **19.** \$162,000 **21.** 15 hits **23.** 27 people **25.** 86 wk **27.** 6 people **29.** 112 ft; 11-in. difference **31.** 102.9 mg
33. 1248 feet; coincidentally, this is the actual height of the Empire State Building **35.** 434 emergency room visits **37.** 427.5 cal

39. $2\frac{2}{3}$ lb **41.** 2.4 c **43. a.** 0.1 gal **b.** 13 fl oz **45. a.** 2062.5 mg **b.** no **47.** $3 \cdot 5$ **49.** $2^2 \cdot 5$ **51.** $2^3 \cdot 5^2$ **53.** 2^5

55. 0.8 ml **57.** 1.25 ml **59.** $11 \approx 12$ or 1 dozen; $1.5 \times 8 = 12$; 12 cups of milk **61.** $4\frac{2}{3}$ ft **63.** answers may vary

Integrated Review **1.** $\frac{9}{10}$ **2.** $\frac{9}{25}$ **3.** $\frac{43}{50}$ **4.** $\frac{8}{23}$ **5.** $\frac{173}{139}$ **6.** $\frac{6}{7}$ **7.** $\frac{7}{26}$ **8.** $\frac{20}{33}$ **9.** $\frac{2}{3}$ **10.** $\frac{1}{8}$ **11. a.** 10 **b.** $\frac{1}{2}$ **12.** $\frac{2}{3}$

13. $\frac{1 \text{ office}}{4 \text{ graduate assistants}}$ **14.** $\frac{2 \text{ lights}}{5 \text{ ft}}$ **15.** $\frac{16 \text{ computers}}{25 \text{ households}}$ **16.** $\frac{9 \text{ students}}{2 \text{ computers}}$ **17.** 55 mi/hr **18.** 140 ft/sec

19. 6 books/student **20.** 154 lb/adult **21.** 3 packs: \$0.80 per pack; 8 packs: \$0.75 per pack; 8 packs
22. 4: \$0.92 per battery; 10: \$0.99 per battery; 4 batteries **23.** no **24.** yes **25.** 24 **26.** 32.5 **27.** $2.\overline{72}$ or $2\frac{8}{11}$ **28.** 18

Mental Math **1.** 1 ft **3.** 2 ft **5.** 1 yd **7.** no **9.** yes **11.** no

Exercise Set 5.4 **1.** 5 ft **3.** 36 ft **5.** 8 mi **7.** $8\frac{1}{2}$ ft **9.** $3\frac{1}{3}$ yd **11.** 33,792 ft **13.** 4.5 yd **15.** 0.25 ft **17.** 13 yd 1 ft **19.** 3 ft 5 in. **21.** 1 mi 4720 ft **23.** 62 in. **25.** 23 ft **27.** 84 in. **29.** 12 ft 3 in. **31.** 22 yd 1 ft **33.** 8 ft 5 in. **35.** 5 ft 6 in. **37.** 3 ft 4 in. **39.** 50 yd 2 ft **41.** 4000 cm **43.** 4.0 cm **45.** 0.3 km **47.** 1.4 m **49.** 15 m **51.** 42,000 cm **53.** 7000 m **55.** 83 mm **57.** 0.201 dm **59.** 40 mm **61.** 8.94 m **63.** 2.94 m or 2940 mm **65.** 1.29 cm or 12.9 mm **67.** 12.640 km or 12,640 m **69.** 54.9 m **71.** 1.55 km **73.** $348\frac{2}{3}$ yd; 12,552 in. **75.** $11\frac{2}{3}$ yd; 420 in. **77.** 5000 mm; 0.005 km; 500 cm **79.** 0.065 m; 65 mm; 0.000065 km **81.** 342,000 m; 342,000,000 mm; 34,200,000 cm **83.** 10 ft 6 in. **85.** 13 ft 11 in. **87.** 9.12 m **89.** 26.7 mm **91.** 15 ft 9 in. **93.** 3.35 m **95.** $105\frac{1}{3}$ yd **97.** $\frac{21}{100}$ **99.** 0.13 **101.** 0.25 **103.** Estimate: 13 yd **105.** answers may vary: for example, $1\frac{1}{3}$ yd or 48 in. **107.** answers may vary

Mental Math **1.** 1 lb **3.** 2000 lb **5.** 16 oz **7.** 1 ton **9.** no **11.** yes **13.** no

Exercise Set 5.5 **1.** 32 oz **3.** 10,000 lb **5.** 6 tons **7.** $3\frac{3}{4}$ lb **9.** $1\frac{3}{4}$ tons **11.** 260 oz **13.** 9800 lb **15.** 76 oz **17.** 1.5 tons **19.** $\frac{1}{20}$ lb **21.** 92 oz **23.** 161 oz **25.** 5 lb 9 oz **27.** 53 lb 10 oz **29.** 9 tons 390 lb **31.** 3 tons 175 lb **33.** 8 lb 11 oz **35.** 31 lb 2 oz **37.** 1 ton 700 lb **39.** 0.5 kg **41.** 4000 mg **43.** 25,000 g **45.** 0.048 g **47.** 0.0063 kg **49.** 15,140 mg **51.** 4010 g **53.** 350,000 cg **55.** 13.5 mg **57.** 5.815 g or 5815 mg **59.** 1850 mg or 1.850 g **61.** 1360 g or 1.360 kg **63.** 13.52 kg **65.** 2.125 kg **67.** 200,000 lb; 3,200,000 oz **69.** $\frac{269}{400}$ or 0.6725 ton; 21,520 oz **71.** 0.5 g; 0.0005 kg; 50 cg **73.** 21,000 g; 21,000,000 mg; 2,100,000 cg **75.** 8.064 kg **77.** 30 mg **79.** 5 lb 8 oz **81.** 35 lb 14 oz **83.** 250 mg **85.** 144 mg **87.** 6.12 kg **89.** 130 lb **91.** 211 lb **93.** 0.16 **95.** 0.875 **97.** answers may vary **99.** true **101.** answers may vary

Mental Math **1.** 1 pt **3.** 1 gal **5.** 1 qt **7.** 1 c **9.** 2 c **11.** 4 qt **13.** no **15.** no

Exercise Set 5.6 **1.** 4 c **3.** 16 pt **5.** $2\frac{1}{2}$ gal **7.** 5 pt **9.** 8 c **11.** $3\frac{3}{4}$ qt **13.** 768 fl oz **15.** 9 c **17.** 23 qt **19.** $\frac{1}{4}$ pt **21.** 14 gal 2 qt **23.** 4 gal 3 qt 1 pt **25.** 22 pt **27.** 10 gal 1 qt **29.** 4 c 4 fl oz **31.** 1 gal 1 qt **33.** 2 gal 3 qt 1 pt **35.** 2 qt 1 c **37.** 17 gal **39.** 4 gal 3 qt **41.** 5000 ml **43.** 4.5 L **45.** 320 cl **47.** 0.41 kl **49.** 0.064 L **51.** 160 L **53.** 3600 ml **55.** 0.00016 kl **57.** 22.5 L **59.** 4.5 L or 4500 ml **61.** 8410 ml or 8.41 L **63.** 10,600 ml or 10.6 L **65.** 3840 ml **67.** 162.4 L **69.** 336 c; 84 qt; 168 pt **71.** $\frac{1}{4}$ gal; 1 qt; 2 pt **73.** 1.59 L **75.** 18.954 L **77.** yes **79.** $0.316 **81.** $\frac{4}{5}$ **83.** $\frac{3}{5}$ **85.** $\frac{9}{10}$ **87.** answers may vary **89.** answers may vary **91.** answers may vary **93.** 1.5 cc **95.** 2.7 cc **97.** 54 u or 0.54 cc **99.** 86 u or 0.86 cc

Exercise Set 5.7 **1.** 19.55 fl oz **3.** 218.44 cm **5.** 40 oz **7.** 57.66 mi **9.** 3.77 gal **11.** 13.5 kg **13.** 1.5 m; $1\frac{2}{3}$ yd; 150 cm; 60 in. **15.** 54.9 m; 5486.4 cm; 180 ft; 2160 in. **17.** 3.94 in. **19.** 112.7 kph **21.** 0.008 oz **23.** yes **25.** 380 ml **27.** 90 mm **29.** 112.5 g **31.** 104 mph **33.** 26.24 ft **35.** 3 mi **37.** 8 fl oz **39.** a **41.** b **43.** c **45.** d **47.** d **49.** 29 **51.** 9 **53.** 5 **55.** 36 **57.** 2.13 sq m **59.** 1.19 sq m **61.** 1.69 sq m **63.** 21.3 mg–25.56 mg **65.** 800 sq m or 8606.72 sq ft

Vocabulary Check **1.** ratio **2.** proportion **3.** unit rate **4.** unit price **5.** rate **6.** cross products **7.** equal **8.** not equal **9.** weight **10.** mass **11.** meter **12.** unit fractions **13.** liter **14.** calorie

Chapter 5 Review **1.** $\frac{23}{37}$ **2.** $\frac{11}{13}$ **3.** $\frac{17}{35}$ **4.** $\frac{18}{35}$ **5. a.** 6 **b.** $\frac{3}{10}$ **6. a.** 3 **b.** $\frac{3}{20}$ **7.** $\frac{1 \text{ stillborn birth}}{125 \text{ live births}}$ **8.** $\frac{3 \text{ professors}}{10 \text{ assistants}}$

9. $1.74/diskette **10.** $1\frac{1}{3}$ gal/acre **11.** $46.80/course **12.** 13 bushels/tree **13.** 8 oz: $0.124 per oz; 12 oz: $0.141 per oz; 8-oz size **14.** 18 oz: $0.083; 28 oz: $0.085; 18-oz size

15. $\frac{16 \text{ sandwiches}}{8 \text{ players}} = \frac{2 \text{ sandwiches}}{1 \text{ player}}$ **16.** $\frac{12 \text{ tires}}{3 \text{ cars}} = \frac{4 \text{ tires}}{1 \text{ car}}$ **17.** no **18.** yes **19.** 5 **20.** 15 **21.** 32 **22.** 5.625 **23.** 60 **24.** $7\frac{1}{5}$ **25.** 0.94 **26.** $1\frac{1}{8}$ **27.** 14 **28.** 35 **29.** 8 bags **30.** 16 bags **31.** $40\frac{1}{2}$ ft **32.** $8\frac{1}{4}$ in. **33.** 9 ft **34.** 18 in. **35.** 17 yd 1 ft **36.** 3 ft 10 in. **37.** 4200 cm **38.** 0.00231 km **39.** 21 yd 1 ft **40.** 7 ft 5 in. **41.** 9.5 cm or 95 mm **42.** 2.45 km **43.** 126 ft 8 in. **44.** 0.24 sq m **45.** 4.125 lb **46.** 4600 lb **47.** 3 lb 4 oz **48.** 5 tons 300 lb **49.** 0.027 g **50.** 40,000 g **51.** 3 lb 9 oz **52.** 33 lb 8 oz **53.** 4 lb 4 oz **54.** 1.1625 kg **55.** 7 pt **56.** 72 c **57.** 4 qt 1 pt **58.** 3 gal 3 qt **59.** 3800 ml **60.** 0.042 dl **61.** 1 gal 1 qt **62.** 736 ml or 0.736 L **63.** 10.88 L **64.** yes **65.** 22.96 ft **66.** 10.55 m **67.** 4.55 gal **68.** 8.27 qt **69.** 425.25 g **70.** 10.35 kg **71.** 109 yd **72.** 180.4 lb **73.** 3.18 qt **74.** 2.36 in. **75.** $\frac{3}{5}$ **76.** $\frac{1}{8}$ **77.** $\frac{1 \text{ teacher}}{9 \text{ students}}$ **78.** $\frac{1 \text{ nurse}}{4 \text{ patients}}$ **79.** 34 mi/hr **80.** 2 gal/cow **81.** 4 oz: $1.235; 8 oz: $1.248; 4-oz size **82.** 12 oz: $0.054; 64 oz: $0.047; 64-oz size **83.** $\frac{2 \text{ cups cookie dough}}{30 \text{ cookies}} = \frac{4 \text{ cups cookie dough}}{60 \text{ cookies}}$ **84.** $\frac{5 \text{ nickels}}{3 \text{ dollars}} = \frac{20 \text{ nickels}}{12 \text{ dollars}}$ **85.** 1.6 **86.** 25 **87.** 13,200 ft **88.** 10.75 ft **89.** 4 tons 200 lb **90.** 500 cm **91.** 1.4 g **92.** 0.000286 km **93.** 9117 m or 9.117 km **94.** 8 gal 2 qt

Chapter 5 Test **1.** $\frac{15}{2}$ **2.** $\frac{13 \text{ in.}}{10 \text{ days}}$ **3.** $\frac{43}{50}$ **4.** $\frac{47}{78}$ **5.** $\frac{138}{77}$ **6.** 81.25 km/hr **7.** 28 students/teacher **8.** 9 in./sec **9.** 8-oz size **10.** true **11.** 5 **12.** $4\frac{4}{11}$ **13.** -8 **14.** $\frac{7}{8}$ **15.** $49\frac{1}{2}$ ft **16.** $3\frac{3}{4}$ hr **17.** $53\frac{1}{3}$ g **18.** 23 ft 4 in. **19.** 10 qt

20. 1.875 lb   **21.** 0.04 g   **22.** 36 mm   **23.** 830 ml   **24.** 3 lb 13 oz   **25.** 2 gal 3 qt   **26.** 2.256 km or 2256 m   **27.** 5.6 m
28. 4 gal 3 qt   **29.** 91.4 m   **30.** 16 ft 6 in.   **31.** 493 ft 6 in.   **32.** 150.368 m   **33.** 3.1 mi

Cumulative Review   1. a. 3   **b.** 5   **c.** 0   **d.** 7; Sec. 1.4, Ex. 1   **2. a.** 0   **b.** 20   **c.** 0   **d.** 20 ; Sec. 1.6
3. 249,000; Sec. 1.5, Ex. 3   **4.** 249,000; Sec. 1.5   **5. a.** 200   **b.** 1230; Sec. 1.6, Ex. 3   **6.** 373 R 24; Sec. 1.7   **7.** $6171; Sec. 1.8, Ex. 3

8. 16,591 feet; Sec. 1.8   **9.** $2^4 \cdot 5$; Sec. 3.2, Ex. 2   **10.** 8; Sec. 1.9   **11.** $\frac{3}{5}$; Sec. 3.2, Ex. 4   **12.** 243; Sec. 1.9   **13.** $-\frac{1}{8}$; Sec. 3.3, Ex. 5

14. $\frac{123}{8}$ or $15\frac{3}{8}$; Sec. 3.7   **15.** $\frac{2}{5}$; Sec. 3.3, Ex. 6   **16.** $\frac{5}{54}$; Sec. 3.3   **17.** $\frac{5}{7}$; Sec. 3.4, Ex. 1   **18.** $\frac{19}{30}$; Sec. 3.4   **19.** 2; Sec. 3.4, Ex. 3

20. $\frac{4}{5}$; Sec. 3.4   **21.** 14; Sec. 3.4, Ex. 11   **22.** $\frac{49}{50}$; Sec. 3.5   **23.** $\frac{7}{14}$; Sec. 3.4, Ex. 16   **24.** yes; Sec. 3.2   **25.** $-\frac{8}{33}$; Sec. 3.5, Ex. 5

26. $7\frac{47}{72}$; Sec. 3.7   **27.** $\frac{1}{6}$ hr; Sec. 3.5, Ex. 11   **28.** 27; Sec. 1.9   **29.** $7\frac{17}{24}$; Sec. 3.7, Ex. 9   **30.** $\frac{16}{27}$; Sec. 3.6

31. <; Sec. 3.5, Ex. 7   **32.** 14,000,000; Sec. 1.6   **33.** negative five and eighty-two hundredths; Sec. 4.1, Ex. 1b   **34.** 0.075; Sec. 4.1
35. 736.2; Sec. 4.1, Ex. 15   **36.** 736.236; Sec. 4.1   **37.** 25.454; Sec. 4.2, Ex. 1   **38.** 681.24; Sec. 4.2   **39.** 0.8496; Sec. 4.3, Ex. 2
40. 0.375; Sec. 4.5   **41.** −0.052; Sec. 4.4, Ex. 3   **42.** $\frac{79}{10}$; Sec. 4.5   **43.** −3.7; Sec. 4.5, Ex. 12   **44.** 3; Sec. 5.2

45. $\frac{4}{9}, \frac{9}{20}$, 0.456; Sec. 4.5, Ex. 10   **46.** 140 m/sec; Sec. 5.1   **47.** $\frac{3}{2}$; Sec. 5.1, Ex. 2   **48.** $\frac{1}{3}$; Sec. 5.1   **49.** $\frac{26}{31}$; Sec. 5.1, Ex. 3   **50.** $\frac{1}{10}$; Sec. 5.1

CHAPTER 6   Percent

Mental Math   1. 13%   **3.** 87%   **5.** 1%

Exercise Set 6.1   1. 81%   **3.** 9%   **5.** chocolate chip; 52%   **7.** 0.48   **9.** 0.06   **11.** 1.00 or 1   **13.** 0.613   **15.** 0.028   **17.** 0.006

19. 3.00 or 3   **21.** 0.3258   **23.** $\frac{3}{25}$ **25.** $\frac{1}{25}$ **27.** $\frac{9}{200}$ **29.** $\frac{7}{4}$ or $1\frac{3}{4}$ **31.** $\frac{1}{16}$ **33.** $\frac{31}{300}$ **35.** $\frac{179}{800}$ **37.** 0.3%   **39.** 22%

41. 530%   **43.** 5.6%   **45.** 33.28%   **47.** 300%   **49.** 70%   **51.** 70%   **53.** 40%   **55.** 34%   **57.** $37\frac{1}{2}$%   **59.** $77\frac{7}{9}$%

61. 250%   **63.** 190%   **65.** 63.64%   **67.** 26.67%   **69.** 0.35, $\frac{7}{20}$; 20%, 0.2; 50%, $\frac{1}{2}$; 0.7, $\frac{7}{10}$; 37.5%, 0.375

71. 0.4, $\frac{2}{5}$; $23\frac{1}{2}$%, $\frac{47}{200}$; 80%, 0.8; $0.333\overline{3}$, $\frac{1}{3}$; 87.5%, 0.875; 0.075, $\frac{3}{40}$ **73.** 2, 2; 280%, $2\frac{4}{5}$; 7.05, $7\frac{1}{20}$; 454%, 4.54   **75.** 0.148; $\frac{37}{250}$

77. 0.23; $\frac{23}{100}$ **79.** 0.004; $\frac{1}{250}$ **81.** 0.12; $\frac{3}{25}$ **83.** $n = 15$ **85.** $n = 12$ **87. a.** 52.9%   **b.** 52.86%   **89.** b, d   **91.** 4%   **93.** 75%

95. greater   **97.** 0.266; 26.6%   **99.** network systems and data communication analyst   **101.** 0.49   **103.** answers may vary

Mental Math   1. percent: 42%; base: 50; amount: 21   **3.** percent: 125%; base: 86; amount: 107.5

Exercise Set 6.2   1. $15\% \cdot 72 = n$ **3.** $30\% \cdot n = 80$ **5.** $1.9 = 40\% \cdot n$ **7.** $n \cdot 90 = 20$ **9.** $n = 9\% \cdot 43$ **11.** 3.5   **13.** 7.28
15. 600   **17.** 10   **19.** 110%   **21.** 32%   **23.** 1   **25.** 45   **27.** 500   **29.** 400%   **31.** 25.2   **33.** 45%   **35.** 35
37. 0.624   **39.** 0.5%   **41.** 145   **43.** 63%   **45.** $n = 30$ **47.** $n = 3\frac{7}{11}$ **49.** $\frac{17}{12} = \frac{n}{20}$ **51.** $\frac{8}{9} = \frac{14}{n}$ **53.** c   **55.** b
57. Some number equals thirty-three and one-third percent of twenty-four.   **59.** a   **61.** c   **63.** a   **65.** a   **67.** answers may vary
69. 686.625   **71.** 12,285

The Bigger Picture   1. $\frac{19}{45}$ **2.** 63   **3.** −0.021   **4.** 8   **5.** 48   **6.** 1.6   **7.** 250%   **8.** 45.6 or $45\frac{3}{5}$ **9.** 28%   **10.** 180

Mental Math   1. amount: 12.6; base: 42; percent: 30   **3.** amount: 102; base: 510; percent: 20

Exercise Set 6.3   1. $\frac{a}{65} = \frac{32}{100}$ **3.** $\frac{a}{130} = \frac{19}{100}$ **5.** $\frac{2.3}{b} = \frac{58}{100}$ **7.** $\frac{75}{b} = \frac{40}{100}$ **9.** $\frac{70}{200} = \frac{p}{100}$ **11.** 5.5   **13.** 18.9   **15.** 400
17. 10   **19.** 125%   **21.** 28%   **23.** 29   **25.** 1.92   **27.** 1000   **29.** 210%   **31.** 55.18   **33.** 45%   **35.** 85   **37.** 0.864
39. 0.6%   **41.** 140   **43.** 113%   **45.** $-\frac{7}{8}$ **47.** $3\frac{2}{15}$ **49.** 0.7   **51.** 2.19   **53.** answers may vary   **55.** yes
57. answers may vary   **59.** 12,011.2   **61.** 7270.6

The Bigger Picture 1. $\frac{19}{45}$ **2.** 63   **3.** −0.021   **4.** 8   **5.** 48   **6.** 1.6   **7.** 250%   **8.** $45\frac{3}{5}$ or 45.6   **9.** 28%   **10.** 180

Integrated Review 1. 12%   **2.** 68%   **3.** 12.5%   **4.** 250%   **5.** 520%   **6.** 800%   **7.** 6%   **8.** 44%   **9.** 750%   **10.** 325%
11. 3%   **12.** 5%   **13.** 0.65   **14.** 0.31   **15.** 0.08   **16.** 0.07   **17.** 1.42   **18.** 4   **19.** 0.029   **20.** 0.066   **21.** 0.03; $\frac{3}{100}$

22. 0.05; $\frac{1}{20}$ **23.** 0.0525; $\frac{21}{400}$ **24.** 0.1275; $\frac{51}{400}$ **25.** 0.38; $\frac{19}{50}$ **26.** 0.45; $\frac{9}{20}$ **27.** 0.123; $\frac{37}{300}$ **28.** 0.167; $\frac{1}{6}$ **29.** 8.4   **30.** 100
31. 250   **32.** 120%   **33.** 28%   **34.** 76   **35.** 11   **36.** 130%   **37.** 86%   **38.** 37.8   **39.** 150   **40.** 62

Exercise Set 6.4   1. 1600 bolts   **3.** $662.40   **5.** 15%   **7.** 295 components   **9.** 13.6%   **11.** 100, 102 dental hygienists   **13.** 50%
15. 29.2%   **17.** 496 chairs; 5704 chairs   **19.** $136   **21.** $867.87; $20,153.87   **23.** 93,870 physician assistants   **25.** 28 million; 63 million

27. 10; 25%   **29.** 102; 120%   **31.** 2; 25%   **33.** 120; 75%   **35.** 44%   **37.** 21.5%   **39.** 1.3%   **41.** 153.4%   **43.** 893.8%
45. 81.3%   **47.** 300%   **49.** 21.6%   **51.** 4.56   **53.** 11.18   **55.** 58.54   **57.** The increased number is double the original number.
59. a. percent increase $= \dfrac{30}{150} = 20\%$ **b.** percent decrease $= \dfrac{30}{180} = 16\dfrac{2}{3}\%$ **c.** False; the percents are different.

Exercise Set 6.5   1. $7.50   **3.** $858.93   **5.** 9.5%   **7. a.** $120   **b.** $130.20   **9.** $1917   **11.** $11,500   **13.** 6%   **15.** $112.35
17. $49,474.24   **19.** 14%   **21.** $1888.50   **23.** $85,500   **25.** $6.80; $61.20   **27.** $48.25; $48.25   **29.** $75.25; $139.75
31. $3255; $18,445   **33.** $45; $255   **35.** $52.74; $638.74   **37.** $4.51; $86.51   **39.** $7074   **41.** 8%   **43.** 1200   **45.** 132   **47.** 16
49. d   **51.** $4.00; $6.00; $8.00   **53.** $7.20; $10.80; $14.40   **55.** A discount of 60% is better; answers may vary   **57.** $26,838.45

Calculator Explorations   1. 1.56051   **3.** 8.06231   **5.** $634.49

Exercise Set 6.6   1. $32   **3.** $73.60   **5.** $750   **7.** $33.75   **9.** $700   **11.** $78,125   **13.** $5562.50   **15.** $12,580   **17.** $46,815.40
19. $2327.15   **21.** $58,163.60   **23.** $240.75   **25.** $938.66   **27.** $971.90   **29.** 32 yd   **31.** 35 m   **33.** answers may vary
35. answers may vary

Chapter 6 Vocabulary Check   1. of   **2.** is   **3.** percent   **4.** compound interest   **5.** $\dfrac{\text{amount}}{\text{base}}$ **6.** 100%   **7.** 0.01   **8.** $\dfrac{1}{100}$

Chapter 6 Review   1. 37%   **2.** 77%   **3.** 0.83   **4.** 0.75   **5.** 0.735   **6.** 0.015   **7.** 1.25   **8.** 1.45   **9.** 0.005   **10.** 0.007
11. 2.00 or 2   **12.** 4.00 or 4   **13.** 0.2625   **14.** 0.8534   **15.** 260%   **16.** 5.5%   **17.** 35%   **18.** 102%   **19.** 72.5%   **20.** 25.2%
21. 7.6%   **22.** 8.5%   **23.** 71%   **24.** 65%   **25.** 400%   **26.** 900%   **27.** $\dfrac{1}{100}$ **28.** $\dfrac{1}{10}$ **29.** $\dfrac{1}{4}$ **30.** $\dfrac{17}{200}$ **31.** $\dfrac{51}{500}$ **32.** $\dfrac{1}{6}$
33. $\dfrac{1}{3}$ **34.** $1\dfrac{1}{10}$ **35.** 20%   **36.** 70%   **37.** $83\dfrac{1}{3}\%$ **38.** $166\dfrac{2}{3}\%$ **39.** 125%   **40.** 60%   **41.** 6.25%   **42.** 62.5%
43. 100,000   **44.** 8000   **45.** 23%   **46.** 114.5   **47.** 3000   **48.** 150%   **49.** 418   **50.** 300   **51.** 64.8   **52.** 180%   **53.** 110%
54. 165   **55.** 66%   **56.** 16%   **57.** 20.9%   **58.** 106.25%   **59.** $206,400   **60.** $13.23   **61.** $263.75   **62.** $1.15   **63.** $5000
64. $300.38   **65.** discount: $900; sale price: $2100   **66.** discount: $9; sale price: $81   **67.** $160   **68.** $325   **69.** $30,104.64
70. $17,506.56   **71.** $80.61   **72.** $32,830.10   **73.** 0.038   **74.** 0.245   **75.** 0.009   **76.** 54%   **77.** 9520%   **78.** 30%
79. $\dfrac{47}{100}$ **80.** $\dfrac{8}{125}$ **81.** $\dfrac{7}{125}$ **82.** $37\dfrac{1}{2}$ **83.** $15\dfrac{5}{13}\%$ **84.** 120%   **85.** 268.75   **86.** 110%   **87.** 708.48   **88.** 134%   **89.** 300%
90. 38.4   **91.** 560   **92.** 325%   **93.** 26%   **94.** $6786.50   **95.** $617.70   **96.** $3.45   **97.** 12.5%   **98.** $1491   **99.** $11,687.50

Chapter 6 Test   1. 0.85   **2.** 5   **3.** 0.008   **4.** 5.6%   **5.** 610%   **6.** 39%   **7.** $\dfrac{6}{5}$ **8.** $\dfrac{77}{200}$ **9.** $\dfrac{1}{500}$ **10.** 55%   **11.** 37.5%
12. $155\dfrac{5}{9}\%$ **13.** 33.6   **14.** 1250   **15.** 75%   **16.** 38.4 lb   **17.** $56,750   **18.** $358.43   **19.** 5%   **20.** discount: $18; sale price: $102
21. $395   **22.** 1%   **23.** $647.50   **24.** $2005.64   **25.** $427

Cumulative Review   1. 206 cases; 12 cans; yes; Sec. 1.8, Ex. 2   **2.** 31,084; Sec. 1.6   **3. a.** $4\dfrac{2}{7}$ **b.** $1\dfrac{1}{15}$ **c.** 14; Sec. 3.6, Ex. 9
4. a. $\dfrac{19}{7}$ **b.** $\dfrac{101}{10}$ **c.** $\dfrac{43}{8}$; Sec. 3.6   **5.** $-\dfrac{10}{27}$; Sec. 3.2, Ex. 6   **6.** 44; Sec. 1.7   **7.** $\dfrac{23}{56}$; Sec. 3.3, Ex. 4   **8.** 76,500; Sec. 1.5
9. $\dfrac{4}{5}$; Sec. 3.3, Ex. 11   **10.** $\dfrac{15}{4}$ or $3\dfrac{3}{4}$; Sec. 3.1   **11.** $\dfrac{4}{5}$ in.; Sec. 3.4, Ex. 9   **12.** 50; Sec. 1.9   **13.** 60; Sec. 3.4, Ex. 12   **14.** $\dfrac{1}{3}$; Sec. 3.4
15. $\dfrac{2}{3}$; Sec. 3.5, Ex. 1   **16.** 340; Sec. 3.3   **17.** $3\dfrac{5}{14}$; Sec. 3.7, Ex. 13   **18.** 33; Sec. 1.9   **19.** $\dfrac{3}{20}$; Sec. 3.7, Ex. 6   **20.** $33\dfrac{27}{40}$; Sec. 3.7
21. $\dfrac{1}{16}$; Sec. 3.3, Ex. 8b   **22.** $6\dfrac{3}{8}$; Sec. 3.7   **23.** -0.625; Sec. 4.5, Ex. 2   **24.** 0.09; Sec. 4.5   **25.** 3.14; Sec. 4.5, Ex. 4   **26.** 0.0048; Sec. 4.5
27. $2.18; Sec. 4.1, Ex. 17   **28.** 27.94; Sec. 4.2   **29.** 829.6561; Sec. 4.2, Ex. 2   **30.** 1248.3; Sec. 4.3   **31.** 18.408; Sec. 4.3, Ex. 1
32. 76,300; Sec. 4.3   **33.** 0.7861; Sec. 4.4, Ex. 8   **34.** 1.276; Sec. 4.4   **35.** 0.012; Sec. 4.4, Ex. 9   **36.** 50.65; Sec. 4.4
37. 7.236; Sec. 4.5, Ex. 11   **38.** 0.191; Sec. 4.5   **39.** 0.25; Sec. 4.5, Ex. 1   **40.** $0.\overline{5} \approx 0.556$; Sec. 4.5
41. no; Sec. 5.2, Ex. 3   **42.** 0.052 per tortilla; 0.058 per tortilla; 18 tortilla pkg is better buy; Sec. 5.1   **43.** $17\dfrac{1}{2}$ mi; Sec. 5.3, Ex. 1   **44. a.** 0.07   **b.** 2   **c.** 0.005; Sec. 6.1
45. $n = 25\% \cdot 0.008$; Sec. 6.2, Ex. 3   **46.** 37.5% or $37\dfrac{1}{2}\%$; Sec. 6.1

CHAPTER 7 Statistics and Probability

Exercise Set 7.1   1. 2004   **3.** 4000 cars   **5.** 10,500 cars   **7. a.** 2000, 2001, 2005   **b.** 250 fewer cars in 2000, 750 fewer cars in 2001,
500 fewer cars in 2005   **9.** 1999, 2002   **11.** 22.5 oz   **13.** 1998, 2001, 2004   **15.** 3 oz/wk   **17.** $5\dfrac{2}{3}$ symbols   **19.** April
21. 19 deaths   **23.** February, March, April, May, June   **25.** 18.5 million or 18,500,000   **27.** Tokyo: 34 million or 34,000,000
29. New York: 21.7 million or 21,700,000   **31.** 14 million or 14,000,000   **33.** 15 adults   **35.** 61 adults   **37.** 24 adults
39. 12 adults   **41.** $\dfrac{9}{100}$ **43.** 45–54   **45.** 21 million householders   **47.** 44 million householders

49. answers may vary   **51.** |; 1   **53.** ⊦⊦⊦ |||; 8   **55.** ⊦⊦⊦ |; 6   **57.** ⊦⊦⊦ |; 6   **59.** ||; 2   **61.**

63. 2.7 goals   **65.** 1982   **67.** decrease   **69.** 1990   **71.** 3.6   **73.** 6.2
75. 25%   **77.** 34%   **79.** 83°F   **81.** Sunday; 68°F   **83.** Tuesday: 13°F
85. answers may vary

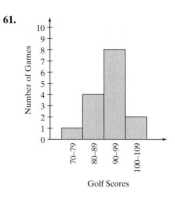

Golf Scores

Exercise Set 7.2   **1.** parent or guardian's home   **3.** $\frac{9}{35}$ **5.** $\frac{9}{16}$ **7.** Asia   **9.** 37%   **11.** 17,100,000 sq mi   **13.** 2,850,000 sq mi

15. 55%   **17.** nonfiction   **19.** 31,400 books   **21.** 27,632 books   **23.** 25,120 books   **25.**   **27.** $2^2 \times 5$

29. $2^3 \times 5$ **31.** 5×17 **33.** answers may vary   **35.** 129,600,002 sq km

37. 55,542,858 sq km   **39.** true

Integrated Review   **1.** 69 lb   **2.** 78 lb   **3.** 12 lb   **4.** 2001 and 2002   **5.** Oroville Dam; 755 ft   **6.** New Bullards Bar Dam; 635 ft
7. 15 ft   **8.** 4 dams   **9.** Thursday and Saturday; 100°F   **10.** Monday; 82°F   **11.** Sunday, Monday, and Tuesday
12. Wednesday, Thursday, Friday, and Saturday   **13.** 70 qt containers   **14.** 52 qt containers   **15.** 2 qt containers   **16.** 6 qt containers
17. ||; 2   **18.** |; 1   **19.** |||; 3   **20.** ⊦⊦⊦ |; 6   **21.** ⊦⊦⊦; 5   **22.**

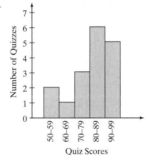

Quiz Scores

Mental Math   **1.** 4   **3.** 3

Exercise Set 7.3   **1.** mean: 29; median: 28; no mode   **3.** mean: 8.1; median: 8.2; mode: 8.2   **5.** mean: 0.6; median: 0.6; mode: 0.2 and 0.6
7. mean: 370.9; median: 313.5; no mode   **9.** 1416 ft   **11.** 1332 ft   **13.** answers may vary   **15.** 2.79   **17.** 3.46   **19.** 6.8   **21.** 6.9

23. 85.5   **25.** 73   **27.** 70 and 71   **29.** 9 rates   **31.** $\frac{1}{3}$ **33.** $\frac{3}{5}$ **35.** $\frac{11}{15}$ **37.** 35, 35, 37, 43

Mental Math   **1.** $\frac{1}{2}$ **3.** $\frac{1}{2}$

Exercise Set 7.4 **1.**

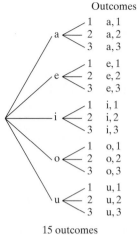

15 outcomes

3.

Outcomes

Red — Red
Blue — Blue
Yellow — Yellow

3 outcomes

5.

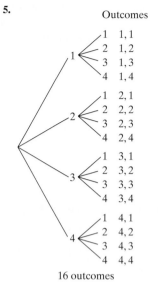

16 outcomes

7.

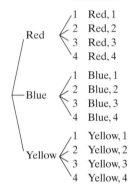

12 outcomes

9.

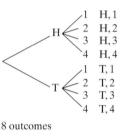

8 outcomes

11. $\frac{1}{6}$ **13.** $\frac{1}{3}$ **15.** $\frac{1}{2}$ **17.** $\frac{5}{6}$ **19.** $\frac{1}{3}$ **21.** 1 **23.** $\frac{2}{3}$

25. $\frac{1}{7}$ **27.** $\frac{2}{7}$ **29.** $\frac{2}{7}$ **31.** $\frac{19}{100}$ **33.** $\frac{1}{20}$ **35.** $\frac{5}{6}$ **37.** $\frac{1}{6}$

39. $\frac{20}{3}$ or $6\frac{2}{3}$ **41.** $\frac{1}{52}$ **43.** $\frac{1}{13}$ **45.** $\frac{1}{4}$ **47.** $\frac{1}{2}$ **49.** $\frac{1}{12}$

51. 0 **53.** answers may vary

Chapter 7 Vocabulary Check **1.** bar **2.** mean **3.** outcomes **4.** pictograph **5.** mode **6.** line **7.** median **8.** tree diagram
9. experiment **10.** circle **11.** probability **12.** histogram; class interval; class frequency

Chapter 7 Review **1.** 475,000 **2.** 175,000 **3.** 650,000 **4.** 375,000 **5.** Midwest, South, and West **6.** Northeast **7.** 7.5%
8. 2003 **9.** 1980, 1990, 2000, 2003 **10.** answers may vary **11.** $2,100,000 **12.** $1,200,000
13. 1991 and 1992, 2000 and 2001, 2001 and 2002 **14.** 1999 and 2000 **15.** 1990, 1991, 1992, 1993, 1994 **16.** 4 employees **17.** 1 employee
18. 9 employees **19.** 18 employees **20.** ⊞⊞; 5 **21.** |||; 3 **22.** ||||; 4 **23.** **24.** mortgage payment

25. utilities **26.** $1225 **27.** $700 **28.** $\frac{39}{160}$ **29.** $\frac{7}{40}$ **30.** $\frac{5}{7}$

31. 20 states **32.** 11 states **33.** 1 state **34.** 29 states

35. mean: 17.8; median: 14; no mode **36.** mean: 58.1; median: 60; mode: 45 and 86

37. mean: 24,500; median: 20,000; mode: 20,000

38. mean: 447.3; median: 420; mode: 400

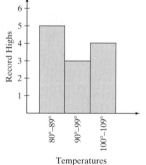

Temperatures

39. 3.25   **40.** 2.57   **41.**

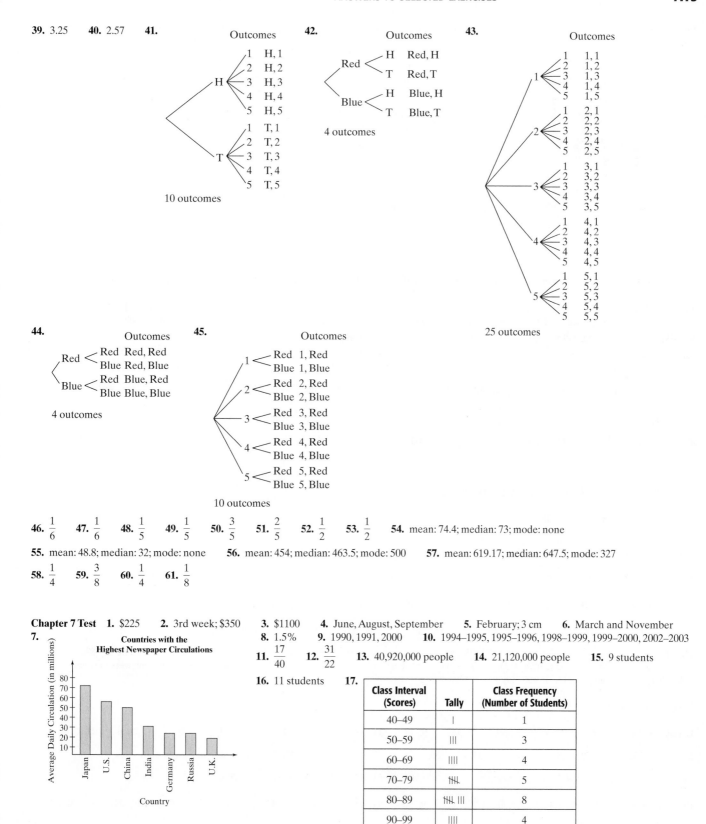

42.

Outcomes

Red ⟨ H   Red, H
        T   Red, T

Blue ⟨ H   Blue, H
        T   Blue, T

4 outcomes

43.

Outcomes

25 outcomes

44.

Outcomes

Red ⟨ Red   Red, Red
       Blue Red, Blue
Blue ⟨ Red   Blue, Red
       Blue Blue, Blue

4 outcomes

45.

Outcomes

1 ⟨ Red 1, Red
    Blue 1, Blue
2 ⟨ Red 2, Red
    Blue 2, Blue
3 ⟨ Red 3, Red
    Blue 3, Blue
4 ⟨ Red 4, Red
    Blue 4, Blue
5 ⟨ Red 5, Red
    Blue 5, Blue

10 outcomes

46. $\frac{1}{6}$ **47.** $\frac{1}{6}$ **48.** $\frac{1}{5}$ **49.** $\frac{1}{5}$ **50.** $\frac{3}{5}$ **51.** $\frac{2}{5}$ **52.** $\frac{1}{2}$ **53.** $\frac{1}{2}$ **54.** mean: 74.4; median: 73; mode: none

55. mean: 48.8; median: 32; mode: none   **56.** mean: 454; median: 463.5; mode: 500   **57.** mean: 619.17; median: 647.5; mode: 327

58. $\frac{1}{4}$ **59.** $\frac{3}{8}$ **60.** $\frac{1}{4}$ **61.** $\frac{1}{8}$

Chapter 7 Test   **1.** $225   **2.** 3rd week; $350   **3.** $1100   **4.** June, August, September   **5.** February; 3 cm   **6.** March and November
7.

Countries with the Highest Newspaper Circulations

8. 1.5%   **9.** 1990, 1991, 2000   **10.** 1994–1995, 1995–1996, 1998–1999, 1999–2000, 2002–2003
11. $\frac{17}{40}$ **12.** $\frac{31}{22}$ **13.** 40,920,000 people   **14.** 21,120,000 people   **15.** 9 students
16. 11 students   **17.**

Class Interval (Scores)	Tally	Class Frequency (Number of Students)
40–49	I	1
50–59	III	3
60–69	IIII	4
70–79	TℋL	5
80–89	TℋL III	8
90–99	IIII	4

18.

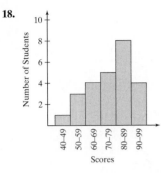

19. mean: 38.4; median: 42; no mode   **20.** mean: 12.625; median: 12.5; mode: 12 and 16

21. 3.07   **22.**

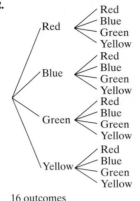

16 outcomes

23.

H
  H
  T
T
  H
  T

4 outcomes

24. $\dfrac{1}{10}$ **25.** $\dfrac{1}{5}$

Cumulative Review   **1.** one hundred six million, fifty-two thousand, four hundred forty-seven; Sec. 1.2, Ex. 7   **2.** two hundred seventy-six thousand, four; Sec. 1.2   **3.** 13 in.; Sec. 1.3, Ex. 5   **4.** 18 in.; Sec. 1.3   **5.** 726; Sec. 1.4, Ex. 4   **6.** 9585; Sec. 1.4   **7.** 249,000; Sec. 1.5, Ex. 3   **8.** 844,000; Sec. 1.5   **9.** 200; Sec. 1.6, Ex. 3a   **10.** 29,230; Sec. 1.6   **11.** 208; Sec. 1.7, Ex. 5   **12.** 86; Sec. 1.7   **13.** 7; Sec. 1.9, Ex. 12   **14.** 35; Sec. 1.9   **15.** 26; Sec. 2.1, Ex. 4   **16.** 10; Sec. 2.1   **17. a.** <   **b.** >   **c.** >; Sec. 2.2, Ex. 3   **18. a.** <   **b.** >; Sec. 2.2   **19.** 3; Sec. 2.3, Ex. 1   **20.** −7; Sec. 2.3   **21.** −6; Sec. 2.3, Ex. 5   **22.** −4; Sec. 2.3   **23.** 8; Sec. 2.3, Ex. 6   **24.** 17; Sec. 2.3   **25.** −14; Sec. 2.4, Ex. 2   **26.** −5; Sec. 2.4   **27.** 11; Sec. 2.4, Ex. 3   **28.** 29; Sec. 2.4   **29.** −4; Sec. 2.4, Ex. 4   **30.** −3; Sec. 2.4   **31.** −2; Sec. 2.5, Ex. 10   **32.** 6; Sec. 2.5   **33.** 5; Sec. 2.5, Ex. 11   **34.** −13; Sec. 2.5   **35.** −16; Sec. 2.5, Ex. 12   **36.** −10; Sec. 2.5   **37.** $8\dfrac{3}{10}$; Sec. 3.7, Ex. 11   **38.** $\dfrac{34}{3}$ or $11\dfrac{1}{3}$; Sec. 3.7   **39.** $\dfrac{\$180}{1 \text{ week}}$; Sec. 5.1, Ex. 7   **40.** $\dfrac{68 \text{ mi}}{1 \text{ hr}}$ or 68 mi/hr; Sec. 5.1   **41.** $2\dfrac{1}{3}$ yd; Sec. 5.4, Ex. 2   **42.** 5000 pounds; Sec. 5.5   **43.** 0.0235g; Sec. 5.5, Ex. 7   **44.** 1060 mm; Sec. 5.4   **45.** $\dfrac{1}{6}$; Sec. 4.6, Ex. 2   **46.** $\dfrac{1}{5}$; Sec. 4.6   **47.** 14, 77; Sec. 7.3, Ex. 5   **48.** 56; Sec. 7.3   **49.** $\dfrac{1}{4}$; Sec. 7.4, Ex. 3   **50.** $\dfrac{3}{5}$; Sec. 7.4

CHAPTER 8   Introduction to Algebra

Mental Math   **1.** unlike   **3.** like   **5.** unlike   **7.** like

Exercise Set 8.1   **1.** −3   **3.** −2   **5.** 4   **7.** −3   **9.** −10   **11.** 133   **13.** −15   **15.** −4   **17.** $-\dfrac{4}{3}$ or $-1\dfrac{1}{3}$ **19.** −12   **21.** $\dfrac{3}{2}$ or $1\dfrac{1}{2}$ **23.** −10.6   **25.** $8x$ **27.** $-4n$ **29.** $-2c$ **31.** $-4x$ **33.** $13a - 8$ **35.** $-0.9x + 11.2$ **37.** $2x - 7$ **39.** $-5x + 4y - 5$ **41.** $\dfrac{1}{2} - \dfrac{53}{60}x$ **43.** $-4.8m - 4.1$ **45.** $30x$ **47.** $-22y$ **49.** $-4.2a$ **51.** $-4a$ **53.** $2y + 4$ **55.** $15a - 40$ **57.** $-12x - 28$ **59.** $6x - 0.12$ **61.** $-4x - \dfrac{3}{2}$ **63.** $2x - 9$ **65.** $27n - 20$ **67.** $7w + 15$ **69.** $-11x + 8$ **71.** 2000 sq ft   **73.** 64 ft   **75.** \$360   **77.** $16y^2$ sq cm   **79.** 78.5 sq ft   **81.** $(3x + 6)$ ft   **83.** 23°F   **85.** 288 cu in.   **87.** $91.2x$ cu in.   **89.** −3   **91.** 8   **93.** 0   **95.** incorrect; $5(3x - 2) = 15x - 10$ **97.** correct   **99.** distributive   **101.** associative   **103.** answers may vary   **105.** $(20x + 16)$ sq mi   **107.** 45,996.2 sq in.   **109.** $4824q + 12,274$

Mental Math   **1.** 2   **3.** −1

Exercise Set 8.2   **1.** yes   **3.** no   **5.** yes   **7.** yes   **9.** 18   **11.** −8   **13.** 9   **15.** −16   **17.** 3   **19.** $\dfrac{1}{8}$ **21.** 6   **23.** 8   **25.** 5.3   **27.** −1   **29.** −20.1   **31.** 2   **33.** 0   **35.** −28   **37.** 1   **39.** 1   **41.** 1   **43.** subtract $\dfrac{2}{3}$ from both sides   **45.** add $\dfrac{4}{5}$ to both sides   **47.** answers may vary   **49.** 162,964   **51.** 1949 yd   **53.** \$23,842,000,000

Exercise Set 8.3   **1.** 4   **3.** −4   **5.** −30   **7.** −17   **9.** 50   **11.** 25   **13.** −30   **15.** $\dfrac{1}{3}$ **17.** $-\dfrac{2}{3}$ **19.** −4   **21.** 8   **23.** 1.3   **25.** 2   **27.** 0   **29.** −0.05   **31.** $-\dfrac{15}{64}$ **33.** $\dfrac{2}{3}$ **35.** 6   **37.** 0   **39.** −2   **41.** −8   **43.** 1   **45.** 72   **47.** 25   **49.** 1   **51.** −10   **53.** addition   **55.** division   **57.** answers may vary   **59.** −3648   **61.** 6.5 hr   **63.** 58.8 mph

Integrated Review   **1.** 4   **2.** −6   **3.** 1   **4.** −4   **5.** $8x$ **6.** $-4y$ **7.** $-2a - 2$ **8.** $-2x + 3y - 7$ **9.** $-20x$ **10.** $5y + 10$ **11.** $3x + 12$ **12.** $11x + 16$ **13.** $(12x - 6)$ sq m   **14.** $25y^2$ sq in.   **15.** 13   **16.** −9   **17.** $\dfrac{7}{10}$ **18.** 0   **19.** −4   **20.** 25   **21.** −1   **22.** −3   **23.** 6   **24.** 8   **25.** $-\dfrac{9}{11}$ **26.** 5

Calculator Explorations   1. yes   **3.** no   **5.** yes

Exercise Set 8.4   1. 3   **3.** 1.9   **5.** −4   **7.** 100   **9.** −3.9   **11.** −4   **13.** −12   **15.** −3   **17.** −1   **19.** −45   **21.** 5
23. −5   **25.** 8   **27.** 0   **29.** −22   **31.** 6   **33.** 5   **35.** −3   **37.** 5   **39.** 2   **41.** −4   **43.** −1   **45.** 4   **47.** −2

49. 3   **51.** −1   **53.** 8   **55.** 4   **57.** 3   **59.** 64   **61.** $\frac{1}{9}$ **63.** $\frac{3}{2}$ **65.** −54   **67.** 2   **69.** $\frac{9}{5}$ **71.** $-42 + 16 = -26$

73. $-5(-29) = 145$ **75.** $3(-14 - 2) = -48$ **77.** $\frac{100}{2(50)} = 1$ **79.** 97 million returns   **81.** 20 million returns   **83.** b   **85.** a
87. $6x - 10 = 5x - 7$ **89.** 136.04°F   **91.** −81.4°F
$\ \ 6x = 5x + 3$
$\ \ \ \ x = 3$

The Bigger Picture   1. −5   **2.** 11   **3.** −35   **4.** 103   **5.** 75   **6.** −11   **7.** 11.4   **8.** 150%   **9.** −6   **10.** 2.7

Exercise Set 8.5   1. $-5 + x = -7$ **3.** $3x = 27$ **5.** $-20 - x = 104$ **7.** $2x = 108$ **9.** $5(-3 + x) = -20$ **11.** $9 + 3x = 33$; 8
13. $3 + 4 + x = 16$; 9   **15.** $x - 3 = \frac{10}{5}$; 5   **17.** $30 - x = 3(x + 6)$; 3   **19.** $5x - 40 = x + 8$; 12   **21.** $3(x - 5) = \frac{108}{12}$; 8
23. $4x = 30 - 2x$; 5   **25.** Bush: 286 votes; Kerry: 252 votes   **27.** bamboo: 36 inches; kelp: 18 inches   **29.** India: 8407; US: 5758
31. Gamecube: $150; games: $450   **33.** Michigan Stadium: 107,501; Neyland Stadium: 102,854   **35.** California: 309 thousand; Washington:
103 thousand   **37.** crow: 9 oz; finch: 4 oz   **39.** 2010: 275,215; 2020: 808,416   **41.** $225   **43.** 70 points   **45.** 590   **47.** 1000   **49.** 3000
51. answers may vary   **53.** $8250   **55.** $5

Chapter 8 Vocabulary Check   1. simplified; combined   **2.** like   **3.** variable   **4.** algebraic expression   **5.** terms
6. numerical coefficient   **7.** evaluating the expression

Chapter 8 Review   1. 1   **2.** −11   **3.** undefined   **4.** 0   **5.** 11.3   **6.** $\frac{55}{6}$ or $9\frac{1}{6}$ **7.** 8 cu ft   **8.** 64 cu ft   **9.** $1800   **10.** $300

11. $-15x$ **12.** $-\frac{7}{30}x$ **13.** $-6y - 10$ **14.** $-6a - 7$ **15.** $-8y + 2$ **16.** $4.6x - 11.9$ **17.** $-8y$ **18.** $15y - 24$ **19.** $11x - 12$

20. $4x - 7$ **21.** $-5a + 4$ **22.** $12y - 9$ **23.** $(6x - 3)$ sq yd   **24.** $25y^2$ sq m   **25.** yes   **26.** no   **27.** −2   **28.** 7   **29.** $-\frac{1}{2}$

30. $-\frac{6}{11}$ **31.** −6   **32.** −20   **33.** 1.3   **34.** 2.4   **35.** 7   **36.** −9   **37.** 1   **38.** −5   **39.** $-\frac{4}{5}$ **40.** −24   **41.** −120

42. 13   **43.** 4   **44.** 3   **45.** 5   **46.** 12   **47.** 63   **48.** 33   **49.** −2.25   **50.** 1.3   **51.** 2   **52.** 6   **53.** 11   **54.** −5   **55.** 6

56. 8   **57.** $20 - (-8) = 28$ **58.** $5(-2 + 6) = -20$ **59.** $\frac{-75}{5 + 20} = -3$ **60.** $-2 - 19 = -21$ **61.** $x + 8 = 40$ **62.** $2x - 12 = 10$

63. 5   **64.** −16   **65.** incumbent: 14,752 votes; challenger: 3546 votes   **66.** 42 CDs   **67.** 29   **68.** $-\frac{1}{4}$ **69.** $-11x$ **70.** $-35x$
71. $22x - 19$ **72.** $-9x - 32$ **73.** no   **74.** yes   **75.** −1   **76.** −25   **77.** 13   **78.** −6   **79.** 17   **80.** 7   **81.** −22

82. −6   **83.** $-\frac{3}{4}$ **84.** −4   **85.** 2   **86.** $-\frac{8}{3}$ **87.** 12   **88.** −8   **89.** 0   **90.** 0   **91.** 5   **92.** 1

Chapter 8 Test   1. −1   **2.** $-5x + 5$ **3.** $-6y - 14$ **4.** $14z - 8$ **5.** $4(3x - 1) = (12x - 4)$ sq m   **6.** 7   **7.** $-\frac{1}{2}$ **8.** −12

9. 40   **10.** 24   **11.** 3   **12.** −2   **13.** −2   **14.** 4.5   **15.** 0   **16.** −2   **17.** $\frac{22}{3}$ **18.** 4   **19.** 0   **20.** 6000 sq ft   **21.** 30 sq ft

22. −2   **23.** 34 points   **24.** 244 women

Cumulative Review   1. ten-thousands; Sec. 1.2, Ex. 1   **2.** two thousand thirty-six; Sec. 1.2   **3.** 184,046; Sec. 1.3, Ex. 2   **4.** 39; Sec. 1.7

5. 13 in.; Sec. 1.3, Ex. 5   **6.** 17; Sec. 1.4   **7.** $96,361; Sec. 1.3, Ex. 7   **8.** 5; Sec. 1.9   **9.** 7321; Sec. 1.4, Ex. 2   **10.** 64; Sec. 1.9

11. a. R   **b.** 44; Sec. 1.3, Ex. 8   **12.** $-\frac{1}{8}$; Sec. 3.3   **13.** 4; Sec. 2.2, Ex. 6a   **14.** −20; Sec. 2.2   **15.** −5; Sec. 2.2, Ex. 6b   **16.** 0; Sec. 2.2

17. −23; Sec. 2.3, Ex. 4   **18.** −3.6; Sec. 4.2   **19.** −10; Sec. 2.3, Ex. 14   **20.** $\frac{1}{10}$; Sec. 3.5   **21.** −7; Sec. 2.4, Ex. 6   **22.** 5.8; Sec. 4.2

23. 1; Sec. 2.4, Ex. 7   **24.** $-\frac{31}{120}$; Sec. 3.5   **25.** 10; Sec. 2.5, Ex. 2   **26.** −9.6; Sec. 4.3   **27.** 24; Sec. 2.5, Ex. 7   **28.** −4; Sec. 3.7

29. 3; Sec. 2.6, Ex. 6   **30.** 9.7; Sec. 8.2   **31.** 0.8496; Sec. 4.3, Ex. 2   **32.** 53.1; Sec. 4.3   **33. a.** $\frac{5}{7}$ **b.** $\frac{7}{24}$; Sec. 5.1, Ex. 6   **34.** $\frac{23}{36}$; Sec. 3.5

35. 5 (Sec. 6.2, Ex. 9)   **36.** $\frac{7}{12}$; Sec. 3.3   **37.** 75% (Sec. 6.2, Ex. 11)   **38.** $\frac{18}{23}$; Sec. 3.7   **39.** 48 oz; Sec. 5.5, Ex. 2   **40.** 24,000; Sec. 1.5

41. 11.3L or 11,300 mL; Sec. 5.6, Ex. 7   **42.** 0.024; Sec. 4.1   **43.** yes; Sec. 5.2, Ex. 4   **44.** yes; Sec. 5.2   **45.** 22.4 cc; Sec. 5.3, Ex. 2

46. 262.5 mi; Sec. 5.3   **47.** 0.046; Sec. 6.1, Ex. 4   **48.** 4.52; Sec. 6.1   **49.** $\frac{1}{3}$; Sec. 6.1, Ex. 11   **50.** $\frac{27}{100}$; Sec. 6.1

51. $5 = n \cdot 20$; Sec. 6.2, Ex. 1   **52.** $\frac{5}{20} = \frac{p}{100}$; Sec. 6.3   **53.** sales tax: $6.41; total price: $91.91; Sec. 6.5, Ex. 1   **54.** $1610; Sec. 6.5
55. a. 15 reptile species   **b.** birds; Sec. 7.1, Ex. 2   **56.** mean: 8; median: 9; mode: 11; Sec. 7.3

CHAPTER 9   Geometry

Exercise Set 9.1   1. line; line YZ or $\overleftrightarrow{YZ}$ **3.** line segment; line segment LM or $\overline{LM}$ **5.** line segment; line segment PQ or $\overline{PQ}$
7. ray; ray UW or $\overrightarrow{UW}$ **9.** 90°   **11.** 0°; 90°   **13.** straight   **15.** right   **17.** obtuse   **19.** right   **21.** 73°   **23.** 163°   **25.** 32°
27. 75°   **29.** $\angle MNP$ and $\angle RNO$; $\angle PNQ$ and $\angle QNR$ **31.** $\angle SPT$ and $\angle TPQ$; $\angle SPR$ and $\angle RPQ$; $\angle SPT$ and $\angle SPR$; $\angle TPQ$ and $\angle QPR$
33. 32°   **35.** 132°   **37.** $m\angle x = 35°$; $m\angle y = 145°$; $m\angle z = 145°$ **39.** $m\angle x = 77°$; $m\angle y = 103°$; $m\angle z = 77°$
41. $m\angle x = 100°$; $m\angle y = 80°$; $m\angle z = 100°$ **43.** $m\angle x = 134°$; $m\angle y = 46°$; $m\angle z = 134°$ **45.** $\angle ABC$ or $\angle CBA$ **47.** $\angle DBE$ or $\angle EBD$
49. 15°   **51.** 50°   **53.** 65°   **55.** 95°   **57.** $\frac{9}{8}$ or $1\frac{1}{8}$ **59.** $\frac{7}{32}$ **61.** $\frac{5}{6}$ **63.** $\frac{4}{3}$ or $1\frac{1}{3}$ **65.** 54.8°   **67.** false   **69.** true
71. $m\angle a = 60°$; $m\angle b = 50°$; $m\angle c = 110°$; $m\angle d = 70°$; $m\angle e = 120°$ **73.** 45°, 45°

Exercise Set 9.2   1. pentagon   **3.** hexagon   **5.** quadrilateral   **7.** pentagon   **9.** equilateral   **11.** scalene; right   **13.** isosceles
15. 25°   **17.** 13°   **19.** 40°   **21.** diameter   **23.** rectangle   **25.** parallelogram   **27.** hypotenuse   **29.** 14 m   **31.** 14.5 cm
33. 40.6 cm   **35.** 36 in.   **37.** cylinder   **39.** rectangular solid   **41.** cone   **43.** cube   **45.** rectangular solid   **47.** sphere
49. pyramid   **51.** 14.8 in.   **53.** 13 mi   **55.** 72,368 mi   **57.** 108   **59.** 12.56   **61.** true   **63.** true   **65.** false
67. yes; answers may vary   **69.** answers may vary

Exercise Set 9.3   1. 64 ft   **3.** 120 cm   **5.** 21 in.   **7.** 48 ft   **9.** 12 in.   **11.** 105 cm   **13.** 21 ft   **15.** 60 ft   **17.** 346 yd   **19.** 22 ft
21. $66   **23.** 36 in.   **25.** 28 in.   **27.** $24.08   **29.** 96 m   **31.** 66 ft   **33.** 128 mi   **35.** 17π cm; 53.38 cm   **37.** 16π mi; 50.24 mi
39. 26π m; 81.64 m   **41.** $31\frac{3}{7}$ ft ≈ 31.43 ft   **43.** 12,560 ft   **45.** 30.7 mi   **47.** 14π ≈ 43.96 cm   **49.** 40 mm   **51.** 84 ft   **53.** 23
55. 1   **57.** 10   **59.** 216   **61.** perimeter   **63.** area   **65.** area   **67.** perimeter   **69. a.** width: 30 yd; length: 40 yd
b. 140 yd   **71.** b   **73. a.** 62.8 m; 125.6 m   **b.** yes   **75.** $44 + 10\pi$ ≈ 75.4 m   **77.** 6 ft   **79.** 27.4 m

Exercise Set 9.4   1. 7 sq m   **3.** $9\frac{3}{4}$ sq yd   **5.** 15 sq yd   **7.** 2.25π sq in. ≈ 7.065 sq in.   **9.** 17.64 sq ft   **11.** 28 sq m   **13.** 22 sq yd
15. $36\frac{3}{4}$ sq ft   **17.** $22\frac{1}{2}$ sq in.   **19.** 25 sq cm   **21.** 86 sq mi   **23.** 24 sq cm   **25.** 36π sq in. ≈ $113\frac{1}{7}$ sq in.   **27.** 168 sq ft
29. 113,625 sq ft   **31.** 4π ≈ 12.56 sq ft   **33.** 128 sq in.; $\frac{8}{9}$ sq ft   **35.** 510 sq in.   **37.** 168 sq ft   **39.** 9200 sq ft   **41.** 381 sq ft
43. 14π in. ≈ 43.96 in.   **45.** 25 ft   **47.** $12\frac{3}{4}$ ft   **49.** 12-in. pizza   **51.** $1\frac{1}{3}$ sq ft; 192 sq in.   **53.** 7.74 sq in.   **55.** 1296π ≈ 4069.44 sq in.
57. 298.5 sq m   **59.** no; answers may vary

Exercise Set 9.5   1. $V = 72$ cu in.; $SA = 108$ sq in.   **3.** $V = 512$ cu cm; $SA = 384$ sq cm   **5.** $V = 4\pi$ cu yd ≈ $12\frac{4}{7}$ cu yd;
$SA = (2\sqrt{13}\pi + 4\pi)$ sq yd ≈ 35.20 sq yd   **7.** $V = \frac{500}{3}\pi$ cu in. ≈ $523\frac{17}{21}$ cu in.; $SA = 100\pi$ sq in. ≈ $314\frac{2}{7}$ sq in.
9. $V = 9\pi$ cu in. ≈ $28\frac{2}{7}$ cu in.   **11.** $V = 75$ cu cm   **13.** $2\frac{10}{27}$ cu in.   **15.** $V = 8.4$ cu ft; $SA = 26$ sq ft   **17.** $10\frac{5}{6}$ cu in.
19. 960 cu cm   **21.** $V = \frac{1372}{3}\pi$ cu in. or $457\frac{1}{3}\pi$ cu in.; $SA = 196\pi$ sq in.   **23.** $7\frac{1}{2}$ cu ft   **25.** $12\frac{4}{7}$ cu cm
27. 36π cu in. ≈ 113.04 cu in.   **29.** 25   **31.** 9   **33.** 5   **35.** 20   **37. a.** width: 40 yd; length: 60 yd   **b.** 2400 sq yd   **39.** 2,583,283 cu m
41. 2,583,669 cu m   **43.** 26,696.5 cu ft   **45.** answers may vary

Integrated Review   1. 153°; 63°   **2.** $m\angle x = 75°$; $m\angle y = 105°$; $m\angle z = 75°$ **3.** $m\angle x = 128°$; $m\angle y = 52°$; $m\angle z = 128°$ **4.** $m\angle x = 52°$
5. 4.6 in.   **6.** $4\frac{1}{4}$ in.   **7.** 20 m; 25 sq m   **8.** 12 ft; 6 sq ft   **9.** 10π cm ≈ 31.4 cm; 25π sq cm ≈ 78.5 sq cm   **10.** 32 mi; 44 sq mi
11. 54 cm; 143 sq cm   **12.** 62 ft; 238 sq ft   **13.** $V = 64$ cu in.; $SA = 96$ sq in.   **14.** $V = 30.6$ cu ft; $SA = 63$ sq ft   **15.** $V = 400$ cu cm
16. $V = 4\frac{1}{2}\pi$ cu mi ≈ $14\frac{1}{7}$ cu mi

Mental Math   1. $\angle A$ and $\angle D$, $\angle B$ and $\angle E$, $\angle C$ and $\angle F$, $\frac{a}{d} = \frac{b}{e} = \frac{c}{f}$

Exercise Set 9.6   1. congruent   **3.** not congruent   **5.** congruent   **7.** congruent   **9.** $\frac{2}{1}$ **11.** $\frac{3}{2}$ **13.** 4.5   **15.** 6   **17.** 5
19. 13.5   **21.** 17.5   **23.** 8   **25.** 21.25   **27.** 10   **29.** 500 ft   **31.** 60 ft   **33.** 14.4 ft   **35.** 200 ft, 300 ft, 425 ft   **37.** 17.5   **39.** 81
41. $3\frac{8}{9}$ in.; no   **43.** 32.7

Chapter 9 Vocabulary Check   1. right triangle; hypotenuse; legs   **2.** line segment   **3.** complementary   **4.** line   **5.** perimeter
6. angle; vertex   **7.** congruent   **8.** area   **9.** ray   **10.** similar   **11.** transversal   **12.** straight   **13.** volume   **14.** vertical
15. adjacent   **16.** obtuse   **17.** right   **18.** acute   **19.** supplementary

Chapter 9 Review   1. right   **2.** straight   **3.** acute   **4.** obtuse   **5.** 65°   **6.** 75°   **7.** 58°   **8.** 98°   **9.** 90°   **10.** 25°
11. $\angle a$ and $\angle b$; $\angle b$ and $\angle c$; $\angle c$ and $\angle d$; $\angle d$ and $\angle a$ **12.** $\angle x$ and $\angle w$; $\angle y$ and $\angle z$ **13.** $m\angle x = 100°$; $m\angle y = 80°$; $m\angle z = 80°$
14. $m\angle x = 155°$; $m\angle y = 155°$; $m\angle z = 25°$ **15.** $m\angle x = 53°$; $m\angle y = 53°$; $m\angle z = 127°$ **16.** $m\angle x = 42°$; $m\angle y = 42°$; $m\angle z = 138°$
17. 103°   **18.** 60°   **19.** 60°   **20.** 65°   **21.** $4\frac{2}{10}$ m or $4\frac{1}{5}$ m   **22.** 7 ft   **23.** 9.5 m   **24.** $15\frac{1}{5}$ cm   **25.** cube   **26.** cylinder

27. pyramid   **28.** rectangular solid   **29.** 18 in.   **30.** 2.35 m   **31.** pentagon   **32.** hexagon   **33.** equilateral   **34.** isosceles, right
35. 89 m   **36.** 30.6 cm   **37.** 36 m   **38.** 90 ft   **39.** 32 ft   **40.** 440 ft   **41.** 5.338 in.   **42.** 31.4 yd   **43.** 240 sq ft   **44.** 140 sq m
45. 600 sq cm   **46.** 189 sq yd   **47.** 49π sq ft $\approx$ 153.86 sq ft   **48.** 82.81 sq m   **49.** 119 sq in.   **50.** 1248 sq cm   **51.** 144 sq m

52. 432 sq ft   **53.** 130 sq ft   **54.** $V = 15\frac{5}{8}$ cu in.; $SA = 37\frac{1}{2}$ sq in.   **55.** $V = 84$ cu ft; $SA = 136$ sq ft

56. $V = 20,000\pi$ cu cm $\approx$ 62,800 cu cm   **57.** $V = \frac{1}{6}\pi$ cu km $\approx \frac{11}{21}$ cu km   **58.** $2\frac{2}{3}$ cu ft   **59.** 307.72 cu in.   **60.** $7\frac{1}{2}$ cu ft

61. 0.5π cu ft or $\frac{1}{2}\pi$ cu ft   **62.** $37\frac{1}{2}$ **63.** $13\frac{1}{3}$ **64.** 17.4   **65.** approximately 33 ft   **66.** $x = \frac{5}{6}$ in.; $y = 2\frac{1}{6}$ in.
67. 108°   **68.** 89°   **69.** 82°   **70.** 78°   **71.** 95°   **72.** 57°   **73.** 13 m   **74.** 12.6 cm   **75.** 22 dm   **76.** 27.3 in.   **77.** 194 ft
78. 1624 sq m   **79.** 9π sq m $\approx$ 28.26 sq m   **80.** $346\frac{1}{2}$ cu in.   **81.** $V = 140$ cubic in.; $SA = 166$ sq in.   **82.** 1260 cu ft   **83.** 28.728 cu ft

84. 12   **85.** $6\frac{1}{2}$

Chapter 9 Test **1.** 12°   **2.** 56°   **3.** 57°   **4.** $m\angle x = 118°$; $m\angle y = 62°$; $m\angle z = 118°$ **5.** $m\angle x = 73°$; $m\angle y = 73°$; $m\angle z = 73°$
6. 6.2 m   **7.** $10\frac{1}{4}$ in.   **8.** 26°   **9.** circumference $= 18\pi \approx 56.52$ in.; area $= 81\pi \approx 254.34$ sq in.

10. perimeter = 24.6 yd; area = 37.1 sq yd   **11.** perimeter = 68 in.; area = 185 sq in.   **12.** $V = 62\frac{6}{7}$ cu in.   **13.** $V = 30$ cu ft; $SA = 62$ sq ft

14. 16 in.   **15.** 18 cu ft   **16.** 62 ft; $115.94   **17.** 198.08 oz   **18.** 7.5   **19.** approximately 69 ft

Cumulative Review **1.** negative five and eighty-two hundredths; Sec. 4.1, Ex. 1b   **2.** $\frac{53}{66}$; Sec. 3.5   **3.** 736.2; Sec. 4.1, Ex. 15   **4.** 700; Sec. 4.1

5. 47.06; Sec. 4.2, Ex. 3   **6.** $-\frac{20}{11}$ or $-1\frac{9}{11}$; Sec. 3.7   **7.** 76.8; Sec. 4.3, Ex. 5   **8.** $\frac{7}{66}$; Sec. 3.3   **9.** $-76,300$; Sec. 4.3, Ex. 7

10. $\frac{23}{2}$ or $11\frac{1}{2}$; Sec. 3.7   **11.** 38.6; Sec. 4.4, Ex. 1   **12.** 0.567; Sec. 4.4   **13.** -3.7; Sec. 4.5, Ex. 12   **14.** $\frac{3}{5}$ or 0.6; Sec. 4.5

15. $>$; Sec. 4.5, Ex. 8   **16.** $<$; Sec. 4.5   **17.** $\frac{26}{31}$; Sec. 5.1, Ex. 3   **18.** $\frac{16}{45}$; Sec. 3.5   **19.** yes; Sec. 5.2, Ex. 2   **20.** $\frac{35}{2}$ or $17\frac{1}{2}$; Sec. 5.2

21. 17%; Sec. 6.1, Ex. 1   **22.** 10; Sec. 8.3   **23.** $\frac{19}{1000}$; Sec. 6.1, Ex. 9   **24.** $\frac{13}{50}$; Sec. 6.1   **25.** $\frac{5}{4}$ or $1\frac{1}{4}$; Sec. 6.1, Ex. 10   **26.** $5\frac{3}{5}$; Sec. 6.1
27. 255; Sec. 6.2, Ex. 8   **28.** 15%; Sec. 6.2 or 6.3   **29.** 52; Sec. 6.3, Ex. 9   **30.** 9; Sec. 1.9   **31.** 775 freshmen; Sec. 6.4, Ex. 2
32. $2.25/sq ft; Sec. 5.1   **33.** $1710; Sec. 6.5, Ex. 3   **34.** 35 exercises; Sec. 5.3   **35.** 96 in.; Sec. 5.4, Ex. 1   **36.** 2 yd 2 ft 4 in.; Sec. 5.4
37. 3200 g; Sec. 5.5, Ex. 6   **38.** 0.07 m; Sec. 5.4   **39.** 3 gal 3 qt; Sec. 5.6, Ex. 3   **40.** 70,052; Sec. 1.2   **41.** 50°; Sec. 9.2, Ex. 1

42. 33 m; Sec. 9.3   **43.** 28 in.; Sec. 9.3, Ex. 1   **44.** -4; Sec. 8.4   **45.** $\frac{2}{5}$; Sec. 4.6, Ex. 3   **46.** $\frac{3}{4}$; Sec. 4.6

APPENDIX A   Tables

A1: One Hundred Addition Facts **1.** 5   **3.** 5   **5.** 12   **7.** 8   **9.** 14   **11.** 12   **13.** 10   **15.** 9   **17.** 11   **19.** 18   **21.** 10
23. 10   **25.** 17   **27.** 13   **29.** 12   **31.** 16   **33.** 7   **35.** 4   **37.** 8   **39.** 8   **41.** 6   **43.** 16   **45.** 9   **47.** 12   **49.** 7
51. 2   **53.** 11   **55.** 8   **57.** 5   **59.** 14   **61.** 13   **63.** 7   **65.** 7   **67.** 13   **69.** 5   **71.** 4   **73.** 16   **75.** 14   **77.** 1
79. 4   **81.** 10   **83.** 8   **85.** 5   **87.** 10   **89.** 11   **91.** 12   **93.** 9   **95.** 9   **97.** 14   **99.** 9

A2: One Hundred Multiplication Facts **1.** 1   **3.** 56   **5.** 32   **7.** 28   **9.** 4   **11.** 63   **13.** 6   **15.** 30   **17.** 24   **19.** 18   **21.** 40
23. 32   **25.** 54   **27.** 56   **29.** 54   **31.** 2   **33.** 36   **35.** 12   **37.** 36   **39.** 12   **41.** 48   **43.** 8   **45.** 0   **47.** 27   **49.** 15
51. 45   **53.** 0   **55.** 81   **57.** 0   **59.** 0   **61.** 18   **63.** 3   **65.** 36   **67.** 63   **69.** 35   **71.** 42   **73.** 40   **75.** 0   **77.** 9
79. 15   **81.** 5   **83.** 0   **85.** 21   **87.** 0   **89.** 16   **91.** 0   **93.** 4   **95.** 6   **97.** 18   **99.** 0

APPENDIX C   Exponents and Polynomials

Exercise Set Appendix C.1 **1.** $-5x - 24$ **3.** $-9z^2 - 2z + 6$ **5.** $9y^2 + 25y - 40$ **7.** $-4.3a^4 - 2a^2 + 9$ **9.** $4a - 8$ **11.** $-2x^2 + 4x + 1$
13. $-20y^3 + 12y^2 - 4$ **15.** $-x + 16$ **17.** $8y^2 - 10y - 8$ **19.** $5x - 12$ **21.** $y - 4$ **23.** $4x^2 + x - 16$ **25.** $9x - 4.1$

27. $15a - 7$ **29.** $-15y + 3.6$ **31.** $19t^2 - 11t + 3$ **33.** $b^3 - b^2 + 7b - 1$ **35.** $-5x^2 - 11x + 13$ **37.** $\frac{9}{7}$ **39.** 1   **41.** -5

43. -8 **45.** 20   **47.** 25   **49.** 50   **51.** 576 ft   **53.** $3200   **55.** 909 ft   **57.** $(8x + 2)$ in.   **59.** $(4x - 15)$ units   **61.** 20; 6; 2

63. 7.2752   **65.** 29 ft; -243 ft; answers may vary

Exercise Set Appendix C.2 **1.** x^{14} **3.** a^7 **5.** $15z^5$ **7.** $-40x^2$ **9.** $25x^6y^4$ **11.** $28a^5b^6$ **13.** $42x^3$ **15.** $12a^{17}$ **17.** x^{15} **19.** z^{20}
21. b^{62} **23.** $81a^4$ **25.** $a^{33}b^{24}$ **27.** $121x^6y^{12}$ **29.** $-24y^{22}$ **31.** $256x^9y^{13}$ **33.** $16x^{12}$ sq in.   **35.** $12a^4b^5$ sq m   **37.** $18,003,384a^{45}b^{30}$
39. $34,867.84401x^{50}$ **41.** answers may vary   **43.** $a^{127}b^{86}c^{25}$

Exercise Set Appendix C.3 **1.** $27x^3 - 9x$ **3.** $-20a^3 + 30a^2 - 5a$ **5.** $42x^4 - 35x^3 + 49x^2$ **7.** $x^2 + 13x + 30$ **9.** $2x^2 + 2x - 24$
11. $36a^2 + 48a + 16$ **13.** $a^3 - 33a + 18$ **15.** $8x^3 + 2x^2 - 55x + 50$ **17.** $x^5 + 4x^4 + 6x^3 + 7x^2 + 2x$ **19.** $-30r^2 + 20r$

21. $-6y^3 - 2y^4 + 12y^2$ **23.** $x^2 + 14x + 24$ **25.** $4a^2 - 9$ **27.** $x^2 + 10x + 25$ **29.** $b^2 + \frac{7}{5}b + \frac{12}{25}$ **31.** $6x^3 + 25x^2 + 10x + 1$
33. $49x^2 + 70x + 25$ **35.** $4x^2 - 4x + 1$ **37.** $8x^5 - 8x^3 - 6x^2 - 6x + 9$ **39.** $x^5 + 2x^4 + 3x^3 + 2x^2 + x$ **41.** $10z^4 - 3z^3 + 3z - 2$
43. $(y^3 - 3y^2 - 16y - 12)$ sq ft   **45.** $(x^4 - 3x^2 + 1)$ sq m   **47.** answers may vary

APPENDIX D   Inductive and Deductive Reasoning

Exercise Set Appendix D   **1.** inductive   **3.** deductive   **5.** inductive   **7.** 81   **9.** C   **11.** 36   **13.** E   **15.** 99999   **17.** 9   **19.** 74

21. 241   **23.**   **25.**   **27.**   **29.**   **31.**   **33.**

35. answers may vary   **37.**   **39.**   **41.**   **43.**

45. Joey   **47.** 15 people   **49.** Donna   **51.** Julio   **53.** 5 people

SOLUTIONS TO SELECTED EXERCISES

CHAPTER 1

Exercise Set 1.2

1. The place value of the 5 in 352 is tens.

5. The place value of the 5 in 62,500,000 is hundred-thousands.

9. 542 is written as five hundred forty-two.

13. 26,990 is written as twenty-six thousand, nine hundred ninety.

17. 53,520,170 is written as fifty-three million, five hundred twenty thousand, one hundred seventy.

21. 1679 is written as one thousand, six hundred seventy-nine.

25. 12,662 is written as twelve thousand, six hundred sixty-two.

29. Six thousand, five hundred eighty-seven in standard form is 6587.

33. Sixteen million, five hundred four thousand, nineteen in standard form is 16,504,019.

37. Two hundred twenty in standard form is 220.

41. Seventy million, two hundred fifty-one thousand, seven hundred ten in standard form is 70,251,710.

45. Seven hundred fifty-five in standard form is 755.

49. $5290 = 5000 + 200 + 90$

53. $30,680 = 30,000 + 600 + 80$

57. 5532 is written as five thousand, five hundred thirty-two.

61. The tallest mountain in New England is Mt. Washington.

65. The Labrador retriever breed has the most American Kennel Club registrations. 144,934 is written as one hundred forty-four thousand, nine hundred thirty-four.

69. The largest number results when the largest digit available is used for each place value when reading from left to right. Thus, the largest number possible is 7632.

73. answers may vary

Exercise Set 1.3

1.
$$\begin{array}{r} 14 \\ + 22 \\ \hline 36 \end{array}$$

5.
$$\begin{array}{r} 12 \\ 13 \\ + 24 \\ \hline 49 \end{array}$$

9.
$$\begin{array}{r} 53 \\ + 64 \\ \hline 117 \end{array}$$

13.
$$\begin{array}{r} \overset{1\ \ 1\ 1}{22{,}781} \\ + 186{,}297 \\ \hline 209{,}078 \end{array}$$

17.
$$\begin{array}{r} \overset{2}{6} \\ 21 \\ 14 \\ 9 \\ + 12 \\ \hline 62 \end{array}$$

21.
$$\begin{array}{r} \overset{1}{62} \\ 18 \\ + 14 \\ \hline 94 \end{array}$$

25.
$$\begin{array}{r} \overset{1\,1\,1}{7542} \\ 49 \\ + 682 \\ \hline 8273 \end{array}$$

29.
$$\begin{array}{r} \overset{1\ \,2}{627} \\ 628 \\ + 629 \\ \hline 1884 \end{array}$$

33.
$$\begin{array}{r} \overset{1\,1}{507} \\ 593 \\ + 10 \\ \hline 1110 \end{array}$$

37.
$$\begin{array}{r} \overset{1\,1\ \,2\,2}{49} \\ 628 \\ 5\,762 \\ + 29{,}462 \\ \hline 35{,}901 \end{array}$$

41.
$$\begin{array}{r} \overset{2}{9} \\ 12 \\ 9 \\ + 12 \\ \hline 42 \end{array}$$
The perimeter is 42 inches.

45. Opposite sides of a rectangle have the same length.
$$\begin{array}{r} \overset{2}{4} \\ 8 \\ 4 \\ + 8 \\ \hline 24 \end{array}$$
The perimeter is 24 inches.

49. $8 + 3 + 5 + 7 + 5 + 1 = 8 + 1 + 3 + 7 + 5 + 5$
$$= 9 + 10 + 10$$
$$= 29$$
The perimeter is 29 inches.

53.
$$\begin{array}{r} \overset{1\,3}{76} \\ 39 \\ 8 \\ 17 \\ + 126 \\ \hline 266 \end{array}$$

57.
$$\begin{array}{r} \overset{1\,2\,1}{2686} \\ 686 \\ + 80 \\ \hline 3452 \end{array}$$

61.
$$\overset{21}{78}$$
90
102
+ 70
340

He needs 340 feet of wiring.

65.
$$\overset{1\,1}{1430}$$
675
+ 320
2425

The total height of Yosemite Falls is 2425 feet.

69. The sides of a square are all the same length.
$$\overset{1}{31}$$
31
31
+ 31
124

The perimeter of the board is 124 feet.

73. To find the number of Blockbusters worldwide, we add.
$$\overset{1}{5670}$$
+ 3197
8867

There are 8867 Blockbuster stores worldwide.

77. The states with the most Target stores are California, Texas, and Florida.
$$\overset{1\,1}{184}$$
104
+ 78
366

There are 366 Target stores in these states.

81. answers may vary

85.
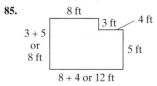

Perimeter = (8 + 12 + 5 + 4 + 3 + 8) ft
          = 40 ft

89.
$$\overset{12\,1}{773}$$
659
+ 481
1913

The given answer is correct.

Exercise Set 1.4

1.
67
− 23
44

Check:
44
+ 23
67

5.
167
− 32
135

Check:
135
+ 32
167

9.
6998
− 1453
5545

Check:
5545
+ 1453
6998

13.
62
− 37
25

Check:
$$\overset{1}{25}$$
+ 37
62

17.
938
− 792
146

Check:
$$\overset{1}{146}$$
+ 792
938

21.
600
− 432
168

Check:
$$\overset{1\,1}{168}$$
+ 432
600

25.
923
− 476
447

Check:
$$\overset{1\,1}{447}$$
+ 476
923

29.
533
− 29
504

Check:
$$\overset{1}{504}$$
+ 29
533

33.
1983
− 1904
79

Check:
$$\overset{1}{79}$$
+ 1904
1983

37.
50,000
− 17,289
32,711

Check:
$$\overset{1\,1\ \ 1\,1}{32,711}$$
+ 17,289
50,000

41.   51,111
         − 19,898
         ─────────
          31,213

Check:
         11 11
         31,213
        + 19,898
         ─────────
          51,111

45.   41
         − 21
         ────
          20

The difference of 41 and 21 is 20.

49.   108
         − 36
         ────
          72

108 less 36 is 72.

53.   503
         − 239
         ─────
          264

Dyllis has 264 more pages to read.

57.   20,320
         − 14,255
         ─────────
           6 065

The peak of Mt. McKinley is 6065 feet higher than the peak of Long's Peak.

61.   538
         − 129
         ─────
          409

There will be $409 left in his account.

65.   914
         − 525
         ─────
          389

She will have $389 left in her savings account after buying the VCR.

69.   29,393
         − 10,357
         ─────────
          19,036

There were 19,036 cocker spaniels registered with the AKC in 2003.

73. The tallest bar corresponds to Hartsfield Atlanta International, so that is the busiest airport.

77. The companies that spent more than $3000 million on advertising in 2003 were General Motors Corp., Time Warner, and Procter & Gamble Co.

81.   11
          986
         + 48
         ─────
         1034

85.   9000
         − 482
         ─────
          8518

89. In   48
            − 1 , 48 is the minuend and 1 is the subtrahend.

93. Votes for Jo:
         1 2 1
          276
          362
          201
        + 179
         ──────
         1018

Votes for Trudy:
         1 1
         295
         122
         312
        + 18
         ─────
          747

Since Jo received more votes, she won the election.

         1018
        − 747
         ──────
          271

Jo won the election by 271 votes.

97.   11
          141
         + 888
         ──────
         1029

The given answer is correct.

101. answers may vary

Exercise Set 1.5

1. To round 632 to the nearest ten, observe that the digit in the ones place is 2. Since this digit is less than 5, we do not add 1 to the digit in the tens place. The number 632 rounded to the nearest ten is 630.

5. To round 1792 to the nearest hundred, observe that the digit in the tens place is 9. Since this digit is at least 5, we need to add 1 to the digit in the hundreds place. The number 1792 rounded to the nearest hundred is 1800.

9. To round 51,096 to the nearest thousand, observe that the digit in the hundreds place is 0. Since this digit is less than 5, we do not add 1 to the digit in the thousands place. The number 51,096 rounded to the nearest thousand is 51,000.

13. To round 248,695 to the nearest hundred, observe that the digit in the tens place is 9. Since this digit is at least 5, we need to add 1 to the digit in the hundreds place. The number 248,695 rounded to the nearest hundred is 248,700.

17. To round 99,995 to the nearest ten, observe that the digit in the ones place is 5. Since this digit is at least 5, we need to add 1 to the digit in the hundreds place. The number 99,995 rounded to the nearest ten is 100,000.

		Tens	Hundreds	Thousands
21.	5281	5280	5300	5000
25.	14,876	14,880	14,900	15,000

29. To round 10,759 to the nearest hundred, observe that the digit in the tens place is 5. Since this digit is at least 5, we need to add 1 to the digit in the hundreds place. The number 10,759 rounded to the nearest hundred is 10,800.

33. To round 2,486,609 to the nearest hundred-thousand, observe that the digit in the ten-thousands place is 8. Since this digit is at least 5, we need to add 1 to the digit in the hundred-thousands place. The number 2,486,609 rounded to the nearest hundred-thousand is 2,500,000.

37.   29 rounds to   30
          35 rounds to   40
          42 rounds to   40
        + 16 rounds to + 20
                          ─────
                           130

The estimated sum is 130.

41.
$$
\begin{array}{l}
1812 \text{ rounds to} \quad 1800 \\
1776 \text{ rounds to} \quad 1800 \\
\underline{+\ 1945} \text{ rounds to} \ \underline{+\ 1900} \\
\phantom{+\ 1945 \text{ rounds to} +\ } 5500
\end{array}
$$
The estimated sum is 5500.

45.
$$
\begin{array}{l}
2995 \text{ rounds to} \quad 3000 \\
1649 \text{ rounds to} \quad 1600 \\
\underline{+\ 3940} \text{ rounds to} \ \underline{+\ 3900} \\
\phantom{+\ 3940 \text{ rounds to} +\ } 8500
\end{array}
$$
The estimated sum is 8500.

49. $432 + 679 + 198$ is approximately
$400 + 700 + 200 = 1300$.
The answer of 1139 is incorrect.

53.
$$
\begin{array}{l}
799 \text{ rounds to} \quad 800 \\
1299 \text{ rounds to} \quad 1300 \\
\underline{+\ 999} \text{ rounds to} \ \underline{+\ 1000} \\
\phantom{+\ 999 \text{ rounds to} +\ } 3100
\end{array}
$$
The total cost is approximately $3100.

57.
$$
\begin{array}{l}
20{,}320 \text{ rounds to} \quad 20{,}000 \\
\underline{-\ 14{,}410} \text{ rounds to} \ \underline{-\ 14{,}000} \\
\phantom{-\ 14{,}410 \text{ rounds to} -\ } 6\,000
\end{array}
$$
The difference in elevation is approximately 6000 feet.

61.
$$
\begin{array}{l}
41{,}126{,}233 \text{ rounds to} \quad 41{,}000{,}000 \\
\underline{-\ 27{,}174{,}898} \text{ rounds to} \ \underline{-\ 27{,}000{,}000} \\
\phantom{-\ 27{,}174{,}898 \text{ rounds to} } 14{,}000{,}000
\end{array}
$$
Lyndon Johnson won the election by approximately 14,000,000 votes.

65. 3430 million dollars $= 3430 \times \$1{,}000{,}000 = \$3{,}430{,}000{,}000$;
rounded to the nearest hundred-million is $3,400,000,000; rounded to the nearest billion is $3,000,000,000.

69. Any number between 4550 and 4649, when rounded to the nearest hundred, will round to 4600. 4618 is one example.

73. answers may vary

Exercise Set 1.6

1. $4(3 + 9) = 4 \cdot 3 + 4 \cdot 9$

5. $10(11 + 7) = 10 \cdot 11 + 10 \cdot 7$

9.
$$
\begin{array}{r}
624 \\
\times \quad 3 \\
\hline
1872
\end{array}
$$

13.
$$
\begin{array}{r}
1062 \\
\times \quad 5 \\
\hline
5310
\end{array}
$$

17.
$$
\begin{array}{r}
231 \\
\times \quad 47 \\
\hline
1\,617 \\
9\,240 \\
\hline
10{,}857
\end{array}
$$

21.
$$
\begin{array}{r}
620 \\
\times \quad 40 \\
\hline
0 \\
24\,800 \\
\hline
24{,}800
\end{array}
$$

25. $(590)(1)(10) = 5900$

29.
$$
\begin{array}{r}
609 \\
\times \quad 234 \\
\hline
2\,436 \\
18\,270 \\
121\,800 \\
\hline
142{,}506
\end{array}
$$

33.
$$
\begin{array}{r}
1941 \\
\times \quad 2035 \\
\hline
9\,705 \\
58\,230 \\
3\,882\,000 \\
\hline
3{,}949{,}935
\end{array}
$$

37. $8 \times 100 = 800$

41. $7406 \cdot 10 = 74{,}060$

45. $50 \cdot 900 = 45{,}000$

49.
$$
\begin{array}{l}
576 \text{ rounds to} \quad 600 \\
\underline{\times\ 354} \text{ rounds to} \ \underline{\times\ 400} \\
\phantom{\times\ 354 \text{ rounds to} \times} 240{,}000
\end{array}
$$
576×354 is approximately 240,000.

53. The best estimate is c, 1600, since 38×42 is approximately 40×40.

57. Area $= $ length $\cdot$ width
$\phantom{\text{Area}} = (9 \text{ meters})(7 \text{ meters})$
$\phantom{\text{Area}} = 63 \text{ square meters}$
The area is 63 square meters.

61. $70 \times 11 = 770$

65. $2 \times 2240 = 4480$

69.
$$
\begin{array}{r}
54 \\
\times \quad 35 \\
\hline
270 \\
1620 \\
\hline
1890
\end{array}
$$
The total cost of the books for the class is $1890.

73. $90 \times 110 = 9900$
The area is 9900 square feet.

77.
$$
\begin{array}{r}
62 \\
\times \quad 94 \\
\hline
248 \\
5580 \\
\hline
5828
\end{array}
$$
There are 5828 pixels on the screen.

81.
$$
\begin{array}{r}
160 \\
\times \quad 8 \\
\hline
1280
\end{array}
$$
There are 1280 calories in 8 ounces of the peanuts.

85.

T-Shirt Size	Number of Shirts Ordered	Cost per Shirt	Cost per Size Ordered
S	3	$10	$30
M	5	$10	$50
L	10	$10	$100
XL	2	$12	$24
XXL	2	$12	$24
		Total Cost:	$228

89.
$$
\begin{array}{r}
\overset{1}{1}26 \\
+ \quad 8 \\
\hline
134
\end{array}
$$

93.
$$
\begin{array}{r}
\overset{1}{1}8 \\
+ \quad 6 \\
\hline
24
\end{array}
$$

97. $3 + 3 + 3 + 3 + 3 = 5 \cdot 3$ or $3 \cdot 5$

101.
$$
\begin{array}{r}
203 \\
\times\ 14 \\
\hline
812 \\
2030 \\
\hline
2842
\end{array}
$$

105. answers may vary

Exercise Set 1.7

1.
$$
\begin{array}{r}
26 \\
3\overline{)\ 78} \\
-6 \\
\hline
18 \\
-18 \\
\hline
0
\end{array}
$$
Check: $26 \cdot 3 = 78$

5.
$$
\begin{array}{r}
338 \\
3\overline{)1014} \\
-9 \\
\hline
11 \\
-9 \\
\hline
24 \\
-24 \\
\hline
0
\end{array}
$$
Check: $338 \cdot 3 = 1014$

9.
$$
\begin{array}{r}
8 \\
6\overline{)\ 48} \\
-48 \\
\hline
0
\end{array}
$$
Check: $8 \cdot 6 = 48$

13.
$$
\begin{array}{r}
65\ \text{R }4 \\
9\overline{)\ 589} \\
-54 \\
\hline
49 \\
-45 \\
\hline
4
\end{array}
$$
Check: $65 \cdot 9 + 4 = 585 + 4 = 589$

17.
$$
\begin{array}{r}
37\ \text{R }1 \\
5\overline{)\ 186} \\
-15 \\
\hline
36 \\
-35 \\
\hline
1
\end{array}
$$
Check: $37 \cdot 5 + 1 = 185 + 1 = 186$

21.
$$
\begin{array}{r}
49 \\
23\overline{)1127} \\
-92 \\
\hline
207 \\
-207 \\
\hline
0
\end{array}
$$
Check: $49 \cdot 23 = 1127$

25.
$$
\begin{array}{r}
97\ \text{R }40 \\
97\overline{)\ 9449} \\
-873 \\
\hline
719 \\
-679 \\
\hline
40
\end{array}
$$
Check: $97 \cdot 97 + 40 = 9409 + 40 = 9449$

29.
$$
\begin{array}{r}
506 \\
13\overline{)\ 6578} \\
-65 \\
\hline
07 \\
-0 \\
\hline
78 \\
-78 \\
\hline
0
\end{array}
$$
Check: $506 \cdot 13 = 6578$

33.
$$
\begin{array}{r}
45 \\
236\overline{)10620} \\
-944 \\
\hline
1180 \\
-1180 \\
\hline
0
\end{array}
$$
Check: $45 \cdot 236 = 10,620$

37.
$$
\begin{array}{r}
202\ \text{R }15 \\
102\overline{)\ 20619} \\
-204 \\
\hline
21 \\
-0 \\
\hline
219 \\
-204 \\
\hline
15
\end{array}
$$
Check: $202 \cdot 102 + 15 = 20,604 + 15 = 20,619$

41.
$$
\begin{array}{r}
19 \\
7\overline{)133} \\
-7 \\
\hline
63 \\
-63 \\
\hline
0
\end{array}
$$

45.
$$
\begin{array}{r}
2082\ \text{R }26 \\
30\overline{)\ 62486} \\
-60 \\
\hline
24 \\
-0 \\
\hline
248 \\
-240 \\
\hline
86 \\
-60 \\
\hline
26
\end{array}
$$

49.
$$
\begin{array}{r}
21\ \text{R }1 \\
4\overline{)\ 85} \\
-8 \\
\hline
05 \\
-4 \\
\hline
1
\end{array}
$$
The quotient of 85 and 4 is 21 R 1.

53.
$$
\begin{array}{r}
20\ \text{R }2 \\
3\overline{)\ 62} \\
-6 \\
\hline
02 \\
-0 \\
\hline
2
\end{array}
$$
The quotient of 62 and 3 is 20 R 2.

57.
$$
\begin{array}{r}
252000 \\
21\overline{)\,5292000} \\
-42 \\
\hline
109 \\
-105 \\
\hline
42 \\
42 \\
\hline
0
\end{array}
$$

Each person won $252,000.

61. A white stripe and the space after it (one lane divider) takes up 50 feet.
$$
\begin{array}{r}
105 \\
50\overline{)\,5280} \\
-50 \\
\hline
28 \\
-0 \\
\hline
280 \\
250 \\
\hline
30
\end{array}
$$

There are 105 whole lane dividers in 1 mile.

65.
$$
\begin{array}{r}
27 \\
6\overline{)\,162} \\
-12 \\
\hline
42 \\
-42 \\
\hline
0
\end{array}
$$

Priest Holmes scored 27 touchdowns in the 2003 season.

69. There are six numbers,
$$
\begin{array}{r}
\overset{2}{1}4 \\
22 \\
45 \\
18 \\
30 \\
+\,27 \\
\hline
156
\end{array}
\qquad
\begin{array}{r}
26 \\
6\overline{)\,156} \\
-12 \\
\hline
36 \\
-36 \\
\hline
0
\end{array}
$$

The average is 26.

73. There are five numbers.
$$
\begin{array}{r}
\overset{2}{8}6 \\
79 \\
81 \\
69 \\
+\,80 \\
\hline
395
\end{array}
\qquad
\begin{array}{r}
79 \\
5\overline{)\,395} \\
-35 \\
\hline
45 \\
-45 \\
\hline
0
\end{array}
$$

The average is 79.

77.
$$
\begin{array}{r}
\overset{1\,2}{7}8 \\
236 \\
42 \\
+\,8506 \\
\hline
8862
\end{array}
$$

81.
$$
\begin{array}{r}
635 \\
-\,46 \\
\hline
589
\end{array}
$$

85.
$$
\begin{array}{r}
7\ R\ 15 \\
28\overline{)\,211} \\
-196 \\
\hline
15
\end{array}
$$

89. 100 divided by 10 is written as 100 ÷ 10, a.

93. The average will increase; answers may vary.

97. answers may vary

Exercise Set 1.8

1.

41	increased by	8	is	some number
↓	↓	↓	↓	↓
41	+	8	=	some number

$$
\begin{array}{r}
41 \\
+\,8 \\
\hline
49
\end{array}
$$

5.

The total of	35	and	7	is	some number
	↓	↓	↓	↓	↓
	35	+	7	=	some number

$$
\begin{array}{r}
35 \\
+\,7 \\
\hline
42
\end{array}
$$

9. a.

Perimeter	is	two	times	length	plus	two	times	width
↓	↓	↓	↓	↓	↓	↓	↓	↓
Perimeter	=	2	·	120	+	2	·	80

$$= 2 \cdot 120 + 2 \cdot 80$$
$$= 240 + 160$$
$$= 400$$

The perimeter is 400 feet.

b.

Area	is	length	times	width
↓	↓	↓	↓	↓
Area	=	120	×	80

$$
\begin{array}{r}
120 \\
\times\ 80 \\
\hline
9600
\end{array}
$$

The area is 9600 square feet.

13.

Hours per week	is	hours per day	times	days per week
↓	↓	↓	↓	↓
Hours per week	=	24	×	7

$$
\begin{array}{r}
24 \\
\times\ 7 \\
\hline
168
\end{array}
$$

There are 168 hours in a week.

17.

Difference in years	is	Governors Island National Monument	minus	Yellowstone National Park
↓	↓	↓	↓	↓
Difference	=	2001	−	1872

$$
\begin{array}{r}
2001 \\
-\,1872 \\
\hline
129
\end{array}
$$

Yellowstone is 129 years older than Governors Island.

21.

Total	is	number of Fairview	plus	number of Midway	plus	number of Riverside
↓	↓	↓	↓	↓	↓	↓
Total	=	287	+	252	+	180

$$= 287 + 252 + 180 = 719$$

There are a total of 719 towns named Fairview, Midway, or Riverside.

25.

Calories in 1 ounce	is	calories	per	ounces
↓	↓	↓	↓	↓
Calories in 1 ounce	=	165	÷	3

$$
\begin{array}{r}
55 \\
3)\overline{165} \\
-15 \\
\hline
15 \\
-15 \\
\hline
0
\end{array}
$$

There are 55 calories in 1 ounce of canned tuna.

29.

Average	is	total sales	divided by	number of stores
↓	↓	↓	↓	↓
Average	=	2,446,000,050	÷	73

$$
\begin{array}{r}
33506850 \\
73)\overline{2446000050} \\
-219 \\
\hline
256 \\
-219 \\
\hline
370 \\
-365 \\
\hline
500 \\
-438 \\
\hline
620 \\
-584 \\
\hline
365 \\
-365 \\
\hline
00
\end{array}
$$

The average sales by each store is $33,506,850.

33.

Northern length	is	Southern length	plus	2054
↓	↓	↓	↓	↓
Length	=	1933	+	2054
			= 1933 + 2054 = 3987	

The northern boundary of the conterminous United States is 3987 miles long.

37.

Total cost	is	number of sweaters	times	cost of sweater	plus	number of shirts	times	cost of shirt
↓	↓	↓	↓	↓	↓	↓	↓	↓
Total	=	3	·	38	+	5	·	25

$= 3 \cdot 38 + 5 \cdot 25 = 114 + 125 = 239$

The total cost is $239.

41. Option a: a hamburger, onion rings, a candy bar, and a soda cost $4 + $3 + $2 + $1 = $10.

Option b: a hot dog, an apple, french fries, and a soda cost $3 + $1 + $2 + $1 = $7

Thus option b is cheaper by $10 − $7 or $3.

45. The most patents received was 3415, the fewest received was 1302.

$$
\begin{array}{r}
3415 \\
-1302 \\
\hline
2113
\end{array}
$$

The company with the most patents received 2113 more than the company with the fewest patents.

49. The three largest numbers of patents received are 3415, 1992, and 1893.

$(3415 + 1992 + 1893) \div 3 = 7300 \div 3 = 2433$ R 1. The whole number average is 2433 patents.

53. There are 7 days in a week.

$7 \cdot 2400 = 16{,}800$

No more than 16,800 milligrams of sodium should be consumed in one week.

57. 48,551,700,000 rounded to the nearest hundred-million is 48,600,000,000.

$48{,}600{,}000{,}000 \div 202{,}500{,}000 = 240$

The average value of each money order was $240.

Exercise Set 1.9

1. $3 \cdot 3 \cdot 3 \cdot 3 = 3^4$

5. $12 \cdot 12 \cdot 12 = 12^3$

9. $9 \cdot 9 \cdot 9 \cdot 8 = 9^3 \cdot 8$

13. $3 \cdot 2 \cdot 2 \cdot 5 \cdot 5 \cdot 5 = 3 \cdot 2^2 \cdot 5^3$

17. $5^3 = 5 \cdot 5 \cdot 5 = 125$

21. $1^{10} = 1 \cdot 1 \cdot 1 \cdot 1 \cdot 1 \cdot 1 \cdot 1 \cdot 1 \cdot 1 \cdot 1 = 1$

25. $3^5 = 3 \cdot 3 \cdot 3 \cdot 3 \cdot 3 = 243$

29. $4^3 = 4 \cdot 4 \cdot 4 = 64$

33. $9^3 = 9 \cdot 9 \cdot 9 = 729$

37. $20^1 = 20$

41. $3 \cdot 2^4 = 3 \cdot 2 \cdot 2 \cdot 2 \cdot 2 = 48$

45. $\sqrt{9} = 3$ since $3 \cdot 3 = 9$.

49. $\sqrt{144} = 12$ since $12 \cdot 12 = 144$.

53. $15 + 3 \cdot 2 = 15 + 6 = 21$

57. $28 \div 4 - 3 = 7 - 3 = 4$

61. $6 \cdot 5 + 8 \cdot 2 = 30 + 8 \cdot 2 = 30 + 16 = 46$

65.
$$
\begin{aligned}
(3 + 5^2) \div 2 \cdot 3^2 &= (3 + 25) \div 2 \cdot 3^2 \\
&= 28 \div 2 \cdot 3^2 \\
&= 28 \div 2 \cdot 9 \\
&= 14 \cdot 9 \\
&= 126
\end{aligned}
$$

69. $\dfrac{18 + 6}{2^4 - 2^2} = \dfrac{24}{16 - 4} = \dfrac{24}{12} = 2$

73. $\dfrac{7(9 - 6) + 3}{3^2 - 3} = \dfrac{7(3) + 3}{9 - 3} = \dfrac{21 + 3}{6} = \dfrac{24}{6} = 4$

77.
$$
\begin{aligned}
2^3 \cdot 4 - (10 \div 5) &= 2^3 \cdot 4 - 2 \\
&= 8 \cdot 4 - 2 \\
&= 32 - 2 \\
&= 30
\end{aligned}
$$

81.
$$
\begin{aligned}
(7 \cdot 5) + [9 \div (3 \div 3)] &= (7 \cdot 5) + [9 \div 1] \\
&= 35 + [9 \div 1] \\
&= 35 + 9 \\
&= 44
\end{aligned}
$$

85.
$$
\begin{aligned}
\frac{9^2 + 2^2 - 1^2}{8 \div 2 \cdot 3 \cdot 1 \div 3} &= \frac{81 + 4 - 1}{4 \cdot 3 \cdot 1 \div 3} \\
&= \frac{85 - 1}{12 \cdot 1 \div 3} \\
&= \frac{84}{12 \div 3} \\
&= \frac{84}{4} \\
&= 21
\end{aligned}
$$

89.
$$
\begin{aligned}
4 \cdot \sqrt{49} - 0 \div \sqrt{100} &= 4 \cdot 7 - 0 \div 10 \\
&= 28 - 0 \div 10 \\
&= 28 - 0 \\
&= 28
\end{aligned}
$$

93.
$$
\begin{aligned}
\sqrt{81} \div \sqrt{9} + 4^2 \cdot 2 - 10 &= 9 \div 3 + 16 \cdot 2 - 10 \\
&= 3 + 16 \cdot 2 - 10 \\
&= 3 + 32 - 10 \\
&= 35 - 10 \\
&= 25
\end{aligned}
$$

97.
$$
\begin{aligned}
7^2 - \{18 - [40 \div (4 \cdot 2) + \sqrt{4}] + 5^2\} \\
= 7^2 - \{18 - [40 \div 8 + \sqrt{4}] + 5^2\} \\
= 7^2 - \{18 - [40 \div 8 + 2] + 5^2\} \\
= 7^2 - \{18 - [5 + 2] + 5^2\} \\
= 7^2 - \{18 - 7 + 5^2\} \\
= 7^2 - \{18 - 7 + 25\} \\
= 7^2 - \{11 + 25\} \\
= 7^2 - 36 \\
= 49 - 36 \\
= 13
\end{aligned}
$$

101. $\text{Area} = (\text{side})^2$
$$= (8 \text{ centimeters})^2$$
$$= 64 \text{ square centimeters}$$

105. False; 2^5 is $2 \cdot 2 \cdot 2 \cdot 2 \cdot 2 = 32$ while $5 \cdot 5 = 25$.

109. $24 \div (3 \cdot 2) + 2 \cdot 5 = 24 \div 6 + 2 \cdot 5$
$$= 4 + 2 \cdot 5$$
$$= 4 + 10$$
$$= 14$$

113. $(7 + 2^4)^5 - (3^5 - 2^4)^2 = (7 + 16)^5 - (243 - 16)^2$
$$= 23^5 - 227^2$$
$$= 6{,}436{,}343 - 51{,}529$$
$$= 6{,}384{,}814$$

Chapter 1 Test

1. 82,426 is written as eighty-two thousand, four hundred twenty-six.

5.
$$\begin{array}{r} 496 \\ \times \quad 30 \\ \hline 0 \\ 14\,880 \\ \hline 14{,}880 \end{array}$$

9. $0 \div 49 = 0$

13.
$$\frac{64 \div 8 \cdot 2}{\left(\sqrt{9} - \sqrt{4}\right)^2 + 1} = \frac{8 \cdot 2}{(3 - 2)^2 + 1}$$
$$= \frac{16}{1^2 + 1}$$
$$= \frac{16}{1 + 1}$$
$$= \frac{16}{2}$$
$$= 8$$

17. To round 52,369 to the nearest thousand, observe that the digit in the hundreds place is 3. Since this digit is less than 5, we do not add 1 to the digit in the thousands place. The number 52,369 rounded to the nearest thousand is 52,000.

21.
$$\begin{array}{r} \overset{1}{15} \\ + \ 107 \\ \hline 122 \end{array}$$

The sum of 15 and 107 is 122.

25.
$$\begin{array}{r} 725 \\ - \ 599 \\ \hline 126 \end{array}$$

The more expensive refrigerator costs $126 more than the less expensive one.

29. $\text{Perimeter} = 2(\text{length}) + 2(\text{width})$
$$= 2(20 \text{ yards}) + 2(10 \text{ yards})$$
$$= 40 \text{ yards} + 20 \text{ yards}$$
$$= 60 \text{ yards}$$

The perimeter is 60 yards.

$\text{Area} = (\text{length}) \cdot (\text{width})$
$$= (20 \text{ yards}) \cdot (10 \text{ yards})$$
$$= 200 \text{ square yards}$$

The area is 200 square yards.

CHAPTER 2

Exercise Set 2.1

1. $3 + 2z = 3 + 2(3)$
$$= 3 + 6$$
$$= 9$$

5. $z - x + y = 3 - 2 + 5$
$$= 6$$

9. $y^3 - 4x = 5^3 - 4(2)$
$$= 125 - 4(2)$$
$$= 125 - 8$$
$$= 117$$

13. $8 - (y - x) = 8 - (5 - 2)$
$$= 8 - 3$$
$$= 5$$

17. $\dfrac{6xy}{z} = \dfrac{6 \cdot 2 \cdot 5}{3}$
$$= \frac{60}{3}$$
$$= 20$$

21. $\dfrac{x + 2y}{z} = \dfrac{2 + 2 \cdot 5}{3}$
$$= \frac{2 + 10}{3}$$
$$= \frac{12}{3}$$
$$= 4$$

25. $2y^2 - 4y + 3 = 2 \cdot 5^2 - 4 \cdot 5 + 3$
$$= 2 \cdot 25 - 4 \cdot 5 + 3$$
$$= 50 - 20 + 3$$
$$= 33$$

29. $(xy + 1)^2 = (2 \cdot 5 + 1)^2$
$$= (10 + 1)^2$$
$$= (11)^2$$
$$= 121$$

33. $xy(5 + z - x) = 2 \cdot 5(5 + 3 - 2)$
$$= 2 \cdot 5(8 - 2)$$
$$= 2 \cdot 5(6)$$
$$= 10(6)$$
$$= 60$$

37.

t	1	2	3	4
$16t^2$	$16(1)^2$	$16(2)^2$	$16(3)^2$	$16(4)^2$
	$16 \cdot 1$	$16 \cdot 4$	$16 \cdot 9$	$16 \cdot 16$
	16	64	144	256

41. $x + 8$

45. $512x$

49. $5x + (17 + x)$

53. $11 - x$

57. $6 \div x$ or $\dfrac{6}{x}$

61. incorrect;
$$2y + 3z = 2(0) + 3(7)$$
$$= 0 + 21$$
$$= 21$$

65. $x^4 - y^2 = (23)^4 - (72)^2$
$$= 279{,}841 - 5184$$
$$= 274{,}657$$

69. Compare expressions:
$$\frac{x}{3} = \left(\frac{1}{3}\right)x$$
$$\left(\frac{1}{3}\right)x < 2x < 5x$$

$5x$ is the largest.

Exercise Set 2.2

1. If 0 represents ground level, then 1445 feet underground is -1445.

5. If 0 represents zero degrees Fahrenheit, then 118 degrees above zero is $+118$.

9. -339 million

13. If 0 represents 0 percent a loss of 45 percent is -45.

17. ◄—●++|++|●++|●++|●++|●+|+—►
$-7\ -6\ -5\ -4\ -3\ -2\ -1\quad 0\quad 1$

21. ◄—●++|++●|++|++|++●|++|●+|+—►
$-7\ -6\ -5\ -4\ -3\ -2\ -1\quad 0\quad 1$

25. $-7 < -5$

29. $-26 < 26$

33. $|-8| = 8$, because -8 is 8 units from 0.

37. $|-5| = 5$, because -5 is 5 units from 0.

41. The opposite of -4 is $-(-4) = 4$.

45. The opposite of -10 is $-(-10) = 10$.

49. $-|20| = -20$
The opposite of the absolute value of 20 is the opposite of 20.

53. $-(-8) = 8$
The opposite of negative 8 is 8.

57. $-(-29) = 29$
The opposite of negative 29 is 29.

61. $-|-3| = -3$

65. $-|4| = -4$

69. $|-9| ? |-14|$
$9 ? 14$
$9 < 14$

73. $-|-10| ? -(-10)$
$-10 ? 10$
$-10 < 10$

77. $|0| ? |-9|$
$0 ? 9$
$0 < 9$

81. $-(-12) ? -(-18)$
$12 < 18$

85. If -84 is the opposite of a number, then the original number is $-(-84) = 84$. The absolute value of 84 is $|84| = 84$.

89. The lake with the second lowest elevation is the lake that corresponds to the second smallest number labeled on each bar. That number is -52, which corresponds to Lake Eyre. The surface of Lake Eyre is 52 feet below sea level.

93. The planet with an average temperature closest to $-200°F$ is the planet whose temperature is $-218°F$. Graph these temperatures on a number line and you will see this. The planet is Saturn.

97. $15 + 20 = 35$

101. $2^2 = 4$, $-|3| = -3$, $-(-5) = 5$, and $-|8| = -8$, so the integers in order from least to greatest are $-|8|$, $-|3|$, 2^2, $-(-5)$.

105. $-(-2) = 2$, $5^2 = 25$, $-10 = -10$, $-|-9| = -9$, $|-12| = 12$, so the integers in order from least to greatest are -10, $-|-9|$, $-(-2)$, $|-12|$, 5^2.

109. $-(-|-5|) = -(-5) = 5$

113. True; consider the values on a number line.

117. Answers may vary.

Exercise Set 2.3

1. $-1 + (-6) = -7$

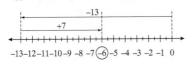

5. $-13 + 7 = -6$

9. $|-6| + |-2| = 8$
Common sign is negative, so answer is -8.

13. $|6| - |-2| = 4$
$6 > 2$ so answer is $+4$.

17. $|-5| - |3| = 2$
$5 > 3$ so answer is -2.

21. $|-12| + |-12| = 24$
Common sign is negative, so answer is -24.

25. $|-123| + |-100| = 223$
Common sign is negative, so answer is -223.

29. $|12| - |-5| = 7$
$12 > 5$, so answer is $+7$.

33. $|-12| - |3| = 9$
$12 > 3$, so answer is -9.

37. $|57| - |-37| = 20$
$57 > 37$, so answer is $+20$.

41. $|-67| - |34| = 33$
$67 > 34$, so answer is -33.

45. $|-82| + |-43| = 125$
Common sign is negative, so -125.

49. $-52 + (-77) + (-117)$
$= -129 + (-117)$ add from left to right
$= -246$ add from left to right

53. $(-10) + 14 + 25 + (-16)$
$= 4 + 25 + (-16)$ add from left to right
$= 29 + (-16)$ add from left to right
$= 13$ add from left to right

57. $-26 + 5 = -21$

61. $-14 + (-31) = -45$

65. $-87 + 87 = 0$

69. $0 + (-103) = -103$

73. $x + y$
$= (-20) + (-50)$ substitute values
$= -70$ add from left to right

77. $-8 + 25 = 17$

81. $0 + (-165) + (-16) = -165 + (-16) = -181$
The diver is 181 feet below the surface.

85. The height of the bar for 2000 is marked as 786, so the net income for Apple, Inc. in 2000 was $786,000,000.

89. $-10 + 12 = 2$
The temperature at 11 p.m. was $2°C$.

93. $-66 + 26 = -40$
Kansas's record low temperature is $-40°F$.

97. $44 - 0 = 44$

101. answers may vary

105. Since the signs are different, the absolute values should be subtracted, rather than added.
$-4 + 14 = 10$

109. False; since a positive number and a negative number have different signs, the sign of the sum will be the sign of the number with the larger absolute value. This could be the positive number or the negative number.

Exercise Set 2.4

1. $-5 - (-5) = -5 + 5 = 0$

5. $3 - 8 = 3 + (-8) = -5$

9. $-5 - (-8) = -5 + 8 = 3$

13. $2 - 16 = 2 + (-16) = -14$

17. $362 - (-40) = 362 + 40 = 402$

21. $-7 - (-3) = -7 + 3 = -4$

25. $-20 - 18 = -20 + (-18) = -38$

29. $2 - (-11) = 2 + 11 = 13$

33. $9 - 20 = 9 + (-20) = -11$

37. $48 - 59 = 48 + (-59) = -11$

41. $12 - 5 - 7 = 12 + (-5) + (-7)$
$= 7 + (-7)$
$= 0$

45. $-10 + (-5) - 12 = -10 + (-5) + (-12)$
$= -15 + (-12)$
$= -27$

49. $-(-6) - 12 + (-16) = 6 + (-12) + (-16)$
$= -6 + (-16)$
$= -22$

53. $-3 + 4 - (-23) - 10 = -3 + 4 + 23 + (-10)$
$= 1 + 23 + (-10)$
$= 24 + (-10)$
$= 14$

57. $x - y = 6 - (-30)$ show substitution exactly
$= 6 + (30)$ change subtraction to addition
$= 36$

61. $x - y = 1 - (-18)$ show substitution exactly
$= 1 + (18)$ change subtraction to addition
$= 19$

65. The two planets with the lowest temperature correspond to the two longest bars on the graph below the horizontal line representing 0°F. Neptune's average temperature is −330°F and Pluto's average temperature is −369°F.
$-330 - (-369) = -330 + 369$
$= 39$
The difference in average temperature is 39°F.

69. Subtract check amounts from the checking account, and add the deposit.

$125 - 117 + 45 - 69$
$= 125 + (-117) + 45 + (-69)$
$= 8 + 45 + (-69)$
$= 53 + (-69)$
$= -16$
Aaron has overdrawn his checking account by $16.

73. $-282 - (-436) = -282 + 436$
$= 154$
The difference in elevation is 154 feet.

77. $600 - (-52) = 600 + 52 = 652$ feet

81. $725 - 1257 = 725 + (-1257) = -532$
The U.S. trade balance in 2003 was −$532 billion.

85. $1 \cdot 8 = 8$

89. answers may vary

93. $10 - 30 = 10 + (-30) = -20$

97. $|-6| - |6| = 6 - 6 = 0$

101. False.$|-8 - 3| = |-8 + (-3)| = |-11| = 11$

Exercise Set 2.5

1. $-2(-3) = 6$

5. $8(-8) = -64$

9. $6(-4)(2) = -24(2) = -48$

13. $-4(4)(-5) = -16(-5) = 80$

17. $-5(3)(-1)(-1) = -15(-1)(-1)$
$= 15(-1)$
$= -15$

21. $(-3)^3 = (-3)(-3)(-3) = 9(-3) = -27$

25. $(-2)^3 = (-2)(-2)(-2) = 4(-2) = -8$

29. $\dfrac{-30}{6} = -5$

33. $\dfrac{0}{14} = 0$

37. $\dfrac{39}{-3} = -13$

41. $-4(3) = -12$

45. $-7(-6) = 42$

49. $(-4)^2 = (-4)(-4) = 16$

53. $-\dfrac{56}{8} = -7$

57. $4(-4)(-3) = -16(-3) = 48$

61. $3 \cdot (-2) \cdot 0 = (-6) \cdot 0 = 0$

65. $240 \div (-40) = -6$

69. $-1^4 = -(1 \cdot 1 \cdot 1 \cdot 1) = -1$

73. $-2(3)(5)(-6) = (-6)(5)(-6)$
$= (-30)(-6)$
$= 180$

77. $-2(-2)(-5) = 4(-5) = -20$

81.
$$
\begin{array}{r}
25 \\
\times\ 82 \\
\hline
50 \\
2000 \\
\hline
2050 \\
\end{array}
$$
$25 \cdot (-82) = -2050$

85. $a \cdot b = (3) \cdot (-2) = -6$

89. $\dfrac{x}{y} = \dfrac{5}{-5}$ show substitution exactly
$= -1$

93. $\dfrac{x}{y} = \dfrac{-36}{-6}$ show substitution exactly
$= 6$

97. $x \cdot y = (0)(-6)$ show substitution exactly
$= 0$ multiplication property of zero
$\dfrac{x}{y} = \dfrac{0}{-6}$ show substitution exactly
$= 0$ zero division property

101. $(-51)(-6) = 306$

105. $(-20)(5) = -100$
He is at a depth of 100 feet.

109. **a.** $221 - 27 = 194$
There were 194 more condors in 2004 than in 1987.

b. $\dfrac{194}{17} \approx 11.41$, rounded to nearest whole : 11
Over the seventeen years from 1987 to 2004 the average change in the number of condors per year was 11 condors per year.

113. $-3(63) = -189$; so the melting point of argon is −189°C

117. $90 + 12^2 - 5^3 = 90 + 144 - 125 = 234 - 125 = 109$

121. $-87 \div 3 = -29$

125. $-4 - 15 - (-11) = -4 + (-15) + 11 = -19 + 11 = -8$

129. true

133. $(-5)^{17}$ and $(-2)^{17}$ are both negative numbers, since a negative number raised to an odd exponent gives you a negative number. And, since $-5 < -2$, then $(-5)^{17} < (-2)^{17}$. Similarly, $(-5)^{12}$ and $(-2)^{12}$ are both positive numbers, since a negative number raised to an even exponent gives you a positive number. And since $|-2| < |-5|$, $(-2)^{12} < (-5)^{12}$. So the correct order from least to greatest is $(-5)^{17}, (-2)^{17}, (-2)^{12}, (-5)^{12}$.

Exercise Set 2.6

1. $(-4)^3 = (-4)(-4)(-4)$
$= 16(-4)$
$= -64$

5. $6 \cdot 2^2$
$= 6 \cdot 4$ exponents first
$= 24$

9. $9 - 12 - 4$
$= 9 + (-12) + (-4)$ change to addition
$= -3 + (-4)$
$= -7$

13. $5(-9) + 2$
$= -45 + 2$ multiply before adding
$= -43$

17. $6 + 7 \cdot 3 - 40$
$= 6 + 21 - 40$ multiply before adding
$= 6 + 21 + (-40)$ change to addition
$= 27 + (-40)$
$= -13$

21.　$\dfrac{24}{10 + (-4)}$

$= \dfrac{24}{6}$　　　simplify the bottom of the fraction bar first

$= 4$

25.　$(-19) - 12(3)$

$= (-19) - 36$　　multiply before adding

$= (-19) + (-36)$　　change to addition

$= -55$

29.　$\left[8 + (-4)\right]^2$

$= (4)^2$　　　grouping symbols first

$= 16$

33.　$16 - (-3)^4$

$= 16 - 81$　　exponents first

$= 16 + (-81)$　　change to addition

$= -65$

37.　$7 \cdot 8^2 + 4$

$= 7 \cdot 64 + 4$　　exponents first

$= 448 + 4$　　multiply before adding

$= 452$

41.　$|3 - 12| \div 3$

$= |-9| \div 3$　　grouping symbols first

$= 9 \div 3$

$= 3$

45.　$(5 - 9)^2 \div (4 - 2)^2$

$= (-4)^2 \div (2)^2$　　grouping symbols first

$= 16 \div 4$　　exponents next

$= 4$

49.　$(-12 - 20) \div 16 - 25$

$= (-32) \div 16 - 25$　　grouping symbols first

$= -2 - 25$　　divide before subtracting

$= -27$

53.　$(2 - 7) \cdot (6 - 19)$

$= (-5) \cdot (-13)$　　grouping symbols first

$= 65$

57.　$(-36 \div 6) - (4 \div 4)$

$= -6 - 1$　　divide before subtracting

$= -7$

61.　$(-5)^2 - 6^2$

$= 25 - 36$　　exponents first (watch the signs)

$= -11$

65.　$2(8 - 10)^2 - 5(1 - 6)^2$

$= 2(-2)^2 - 5(-5)^2$

$= 2(-2)(-2) - 5(-5)(-5)$

$= 2(-2)(-2) + (-5)(-5)(-5)$

$= (-4)(-2) + (25)(-5)$

$= 8 + (-125)$

$= -117$

69.　$\dfrac{(-7)(-3) - (4)(3)}{3[7 \div (3 - 10)]} = \dfrac{(-7)(-3) - (4)(3)}{3[7 \div (3 + (-10))]}$

$= \dfrac{21 + (-12)}{3[7 \div (-7)]}$

$= \dfrac{9}{3(-1)}$

$= \dfrac{9}{-3}$

$= -3$

73.　$x + y + z$

$= -2 + 4 + (-1)$　　show substitution exactly

$= 2 + (-1)$

$= 1$

77.　$x^2 - y$

$= (-2)^2 - 4$　　show substitution exactly

$= (-2)(-2) - 4$

$= 4 - 4$

$= 0$

81.　$x^2 = (-3)^2$　　show substitution exactly

$= (-3)(-3)$

$= 9$

85.　$10 - x^2 = 10 - (-3)^2$　　show substitution exactly

$= 10 - (-3)(-3)$　　multiplication first

$= 10 - 9$

$= 1$

89.　$45 \cdot 90 = 4050$

$$
\begin{array}{r}
45 \\
\times 90 \\
\hline
00 \\
4050 \\
\hline
4050
\end{array}
$$

93.　Perimeter $= 8 + 8 + 8 + 8$

$= 32$ in.

97.　Average $= \dfrac{-10 + 8 + (-4) + 2 + 7 + (-5) + (-12)}{7}$

$= \dfrac{-14}{7} = -2$

101.　$2 \cdot (7 - 5) \cdot 3$

$= 2 \cdot 2 \cdot 3 = 12$

105.　Parentheses are not necessary here because in the order of operations, we always multiply before we add

$3 + (4 \cdot 5) = 3 + 4 \cdot 5 = 23$

109.　$(-12)^4$

$= (-12)(-12)(-12)(-12)$

$= (144)(144) = 20{,}736$

Chapter 2 Test

1.　$-5 + 8 = 3$

5.　$(-18) + (-12) = -30$

9.　$|-25| + (-13) = 25 + (-13) = 12$

13.　$(-8) + 9 \div (-3) = -8 + (-3) = -11$

17.　$-(-7)^2 \div 7 \cdot (-4) = -49 \div 7 \cdot (-4)$

$= -7 \cdot (-4)$

$= 28$

21.　$\dfrac{(-3)(-2) + 12}{-1(-4 - 5)} = \dfrac{6 + 12}{-1(-9)} = \dfrac{18}{9} = 2$

25.　$3x + y = 3(0) + (-3)$　　substitute exactly

$= 0 + (-3)$

$= -3$

29.　$10 - y^2 = 10 - (-3)^2$　　substitute exactly

$= 10 - (-3)(-3)$

$= 10 - 9$

$= 1$

33.　$6288 - (-25{,}354) = 6288 + 25{,}354 = 31{,}642$

The difference in elevation is 31,642 feet. As an integer, the answer is 31,642.

CHAPTER 3

Exercise Set 3.1

1. 1 out of 3 equal parts is shaded: $\dfrac{1}{3}$

5. Each part is $\dfrac{1}{6}$ of a whole and there are 23 parts shaded, or 3 wholes and 5 more parts.

   a. $\dfrac{23}{6}$ **b.** $3\dfrac{5}{6}$

9. 3 out of 7 equal parts are shaded: $\dfrac{3}{7}$

13. Each part is $\dfrac{1}{3}$ of a whole and there are 4 parts shaded, or 1 whole and 1 more part.

   a. $\dfrac{4}{3}$ **b.** $1\dfrac{1}{3}$

17. 1 out of 6 equal parts is shaded: $\dfrac{1}{6}$

21.

25.

29. freshmen $\rightarrow \dfrac{42}{}$
students $\rightarrow \dfrac{}{131}$

$\dfrac{42}{131}$ of the students are freshmen.

33. born in Virginia $\rightarrow \dfrac{8}{}$
U.S. presidents $\rightarrow \dfrac{}{43}$

$\dfrac{8}{43}$ of U.S. presidents were born in Virginia.

37. 11 of the 31 days of March is $\dfrac{11}{31}$ of the month.

41. There are 50 states total. 33 states contain federal Indian reservations.

   a. $\dfrac{33}{50}$ of the states contain Indian reservations.

   b. $50 - 33 = 17$

     17 states do not contain Indian reservations.

   c. $\dfrac{17}{50}$ of the states do not contain Indian reservations.

45. $\dfrac{12}{12} = 12 \div 12 = 1$

49. $\dfrac{0}{-2} = 0 \div -2 = 0$

53. $\dfrac{-9}{0} = -9 \div 0 =$ undefined

57. $3^2 = 3 \cdot 3 = 9$

61. $7 \cdot 7 \cdot 7 \cdot 7 \cdot 7 = 7^5$

65. $-\dfrac{11}{2} = \boxed{\dfrac{-11}{2}} = \boxed{\dfrac{11}{-2}}$

69.
$\frac{1}{2}$

$\frac{2}{3}$

Since $\dfrac{2}{3}$ has the larger shaded area, $\dfrac{2}{3}$ is the larger fraction.

73. $6253 + 2348 + 14 + 26 + 210 = 8851$

There are a total of 8851 restaurants, of which 6253 are named "Wendy's." $\dfrac{6253}{8851}$ of the restaurants are named "Wendy's."

Exercise Set 3.2

1. $20 = 2 \cdot 10$
$\downarrow\ \downarrow\downarrow$
$2 \cdot 2 \cdot 5 = 2^2 \cdot 5$

5. $45 = 9 \cdot 5$
$\downarrow\downarrow\ \downarrow$
$3 \cdot 3 \cdot 5 = 3^2 \cdot 5$

9. $110 = 2 \cdot 55$
$\downarrow\ \downarrow\downarrow$
$2 \cdot 5 \cdot 11 = 2 \cdot 5 \cdot 11$

13. $240 = 2 \cdot 120$
$\downarrow\ \downarrow\ \searrow$
$2 \cdot 2 \cdot 60$
$\downarrow\ \downarrow\ \downarrow\ \searrow$
$2 \cdot 2 \cdot 2 \cdot 30$
$\downarrow\ \downarrow\ \downarrow\ \downarrow\ \searrow$
$2 \cdot 2 \cdot 2 \cdot 2 \cdot 15$
$\downarrow\ \downarrow\ \downarrow\ \downarrow\ \downarrow\searrow$
$2 \cdot 2 \cdot 2 \cdot 2 \cdot 3 \cdot 5 = 2^4 \cdot 3 \cdot 5$

17. $\dfrac{3}{12} = \dfrac{3 \cdot 1}{3 \cdot 4} = \dfrac{1}{4}$

21. $\dfrac{14}{16} = \dfrac{2 \cdot 7}{2 \cdot 8} = \dfrac{7}{8}$

25. $\dfrac{35}{50} = \dfrac{5 \cdot 7}{5 \cdot 10} = \dfrac{7}{10}$

29. $\dfrac{24}{40} = \dfrac{8 \cdot 3}{8 \cdot 5} = \dfrac{3}{5}$

33. $\dfrac{25}{40} = \dfrac{5 \cdot 5}{5 \cdot 8} = \dfrac{5}{8}$

37. $\dfrac{36}{24} = \dfrac{12 \cdot 3}{12 \cdot 2} = \dfrac{3}{2}$

41. $\dfrac{70}{196} = \dfrac{14 \cdot 5}{14 \cdot 14} = \dfrac{5}{14}$

45. $-\dfrac{55}{85} = -\dfrac{5 \cdot 11}{5 \cdot 17} = -\dfrac{11}{17}$

49. $\dfrac{224}{16} = \dfrac{16 \cdot 14}{16 \cdot 1} = \dfrac{14}{1} = 14$

53. Not equivalent, since the cross products are not equal: $7 \cdot 8 = 56$ and $5 \cdot 11 = 55$

57. Equivalent, since the cross products are equal: $3 \cdot 18 = 54$ and $9 \cdot 6 = 54$

61. Not equivalent, since the cross products are not equal: $8 \cdot 24 = 192$ and $12 \cdot 18 = 216$

65. $\dfrac{2640 \text{ feet}}{5280 \text{ feet}} = \dfrac{2640 \cdot 1}{2640 \cdot 2} = \dfrac{1}{2}$

2640 feet represents $\dfrac{1}{2}$ of a mile.

69. $\dfrac{10 \text{ inches}}{24 \text{ inches}} = \dfrac{2 \cdot 5}{2 \cdot 12} = \dfrac{5}{12}$

$\dfrac{5}{12}$ of the wall is concrete.

73.
$$\begin{array}{r} 91 \\ \times\ 4 \\ \hline 364 \end{array}$$

77.
$$\begin{array}{r} 72 \\ \times\ 35 \\ \hline 360 \\ 2160 \\ \hline 2520 \end{array}$$

81. $\dfrac{3975}{6625} = \dfrac{3 \cdot 1325}{5 \cdot 1325} = \dfrac{3}{5}$

85. $3 + 1 = 4$ blood donors having an AB blood type.
$\dfrac{4 \text{ donors}}{100 \text{ donors}} = \dfrac{4 \cdot 1}{4 \cdot 25} = \dfrac{1}{25}$

$\dfrac{1}{25}$ of blood donors have an AB blood type.

89. answers may vary

93. $\dfrac{2}{25}$

97. 2235, 105, 900, 1470 are divisible by 5 because each number ends with a 0 or 5. These numbers are also divisible by 3 because the sum of the digits for each number is divisible by 3.

Exercise Set 3.3

1. $\dfrac{7}{8} \cdot \dfrac{2}{3} = \dfrac{7 \cdot 2}{8 \cdot 3} = \dfrac{7 \cdot 2}{2 \cdot 2 \cdot 2 \cdot 3} = \dfrac{7}{2 \cdot 2 \cdot 3} = \dfrac{7}{12}$

5. $-\dfrac{1}{2} \cdot -\dfrac{2}{15} = \dfrac{1 \cdot 2}{2 \cdot 15} = \dfrac{1}{15}$

9. $\dfrac{2}{7} \cdot \dfrac{5}{8} = \dfrac{2 \cdot 5}{7 \cdot 2 \cdot 2 \cdot 2} = \dfrac{5}{7 \cdot 2 \cdot 2} = \dfrac{5}{28}$

13. $0 \cdot \dfrac{8}{9} = 0$

17. $\dfrac{11}{20} \cdot \dfrac{1}{7} \cdot \dfrac{5}{22} = \dfrac{11 \cdot 1 \cdot 5}{20 \cdot 7 \cdot 22} = \dfrac{11 \cdot 1 \cdot 5}{5 \cdot 2 \cdot 2 \cdot 7 \cdot 11 \cdot 2} = \dfrac{1}{2 \cdot 2 \cdot 7 \cdot 2} = \dfrac{1}{56}$

21. $\left(-\dfrac{2}{3}\right)^2 = -\dfrac{2}{3} \cdot -\dfrac{2}{3} = \dfrac{2 \cdot 2}{3 \cdot 3} = \dfrac{4}{9}$

25. $\dfrac{2}{3} \div \dfrac{5}{6} = \dfrac{2}{3} \cdot \dfrac{6}{5} = \dfrac{2 \cdot 6}{3 \cdot 5} = \dfrac{2 \cdot 2 \cdot 3}{3 \cdot 5} = \dfrac{2 \cdot 2}{5} = \dfrac{4}{5}$

29. $\dfrac{8}{9} \div -\dfrac{1}{2} = \dfrac{8}{9} \cdot -\dfrac{2}{1} = -\dfrac{8 \cdot 2}{9 \cdot 1} = -\dfrac{16}{9}$

33. $\dfrac{1}{10} \div \dfrac{10}{1} = \dfrac{1}{10} \cdot \dfrac{1}{10} = \dfrac{1 \cdot 1}{10 \cdot 10} = \dfrac{1}{100}$

37. $\dfrac{3}{25} \div \dfrac{27}{40} = \dfrac{3}{25} \cdot \dfrac{40}{27} = \dfrac{3 \cdot 5 \cdot 2 \cdot 2 \cdot 2}{5 \cdot 5 \cdot 3 \cdot 3 \cdot 3} = \dfrac{2 \cdot 2 \cdot 2}{5 \cdot 3 \cdot 3} = \dfrac{8}{45}$

41. $0 \div \dfrac{7}{8} = 0 \cdot \dfrac{8}{7} = 0$

45. $-\dfrac{5}{28} \cdot \dfrac{35}{25} = -\dfrac{5 \cdot 35}{28 \cdot 25} = -\dfrac{5 \cdot 5 \cdot 7}{2 \cdot 2 \cdot 7 \cdot 5 \cdot 5} = -\dfrac{1}{2 \cdot 2} = -\dfrac{1}{4}$

49. $\left(-\dfrac{3}{4}\right)^2 = -\dfrac{3}{4} \cdot -\dfrac{3}{4} = \dfrac{3 \cdot 3}{4 \cdot 4} = \dfrac{3 \cdot 3}{2 \cdot 2 \cdot 2 \cdot 2} = \dfrac{9}{16}$

53. $\dfrac{4}{8} \div \dfrac{3}{16} = \dfrac{4}{8} \cdot \dfrac{16}{3} = \dfrac{4 \cdot 16}{8 \cdot 3} = \dfrac{2 \cdot 2 \cdot 2 \cdot 2 \cdot 2 \cdot 2}{2 \cdot 2 \cdot 2 \cdot 3} = \dfrac{2 \cdot 2 \cdot 2}{3} = \dfrac{8}{3}$

57. a. $xy = \dfrac{2}{5} \cdot \dfrac{5}{6} = \dfrac{2 \cdot 5}{5 \cdot 6} = \dfrac{2 \cdot 5}{5 \cdot 2 \cdot 3} = \dfrac{1}{3}$

   b. $x \div y = \dfrac{2}{5} \div \dfrac{5}{6} = \dfrac{2}{5} \cdot \dfrac{6}{5} = \dfrac{2 \cdot 2 \cdot 3}{5 \cdot 5} = \dfrac{12}{25}$

61. $\dfrac{1}{4}$ of $200 = \dfrac{1}{4} \cdot 200 = \dfrac{1}{4} \cdot \dfrac{200}{1} = \dfrac{1 \cdot 200}{4 \cdot 1} = \dfrac{1 \cdot 2 \cdot 2 \cdot 2 \cdot 5 \cdot 5}{2 \cdot 2 \cdot 1}$
$= 2 \cdot 5 \cdot 5 = 50$

65. $\dfrac{3}{16} \cdot 8 = \dfrac{3}{16} \cdot \dfrac{8}{1} = \dfrac{3 \cdot 8}{16 \cdot 1} = \dfrac{3 \cdot 8}{2 \cdot 8 \cdot 1} = \dfrac{3}{2 \cdot 1} = \dfrac{3}{2}$ in.

The screw is $\dfrac{3}{2}$ in. deep after 8 turns.

69. $\dfrac{1}{2}$ of $\dfrac{3}{8} = \dfrac{1}{2} \cdot \dfrac{3}{8} = \dfrac{1 \cdot 3}{2 \cdot 8} = \dfrac{3}{16}$ in.

The radius of the circle is $\dfrac{3}{16}$ in.

73. $\dfrac{2}{3}$ of $2757 = \dfrac{2}{3} \cdot 2757 = \dfrac{2}{3} \cdot \dfrac{2757}{1} = \dfrac{2 \cdot 3 \cdot 919}{3 \cdot 1} = \dfrac{2 \cdot 919}{1} = 1838$

The sale price of the cruise is \$1838.

77. $\dfrac{8}{25} \cdot 12{,}000 = \dfrac{8}{25} \cdot \dfrac{12000}{1} = \dfrac{8 \cdot 25 \cdot 480}{25 \cdot 1} = \dfrac{8 \cdot 480}{1} = 3840$

The family drove 3840 miles for work.

81. $\begin{aligned} 27 \\ 76 \\ + \ 98 \\ \hline 201 \end{aligned}$

85. answers may vary

89. $258 \div \dfrac{129}{320} = \dfrac{258}{1} \cdot \dfrac{320}{129} = \dfrac{258 \cdot 320}{1 \cdot 129} = \dfrac{2 \cdot 129 \cdot 320}{1 \cdot 129}$
$= \dfrac{2 \cdot 320}{1} = 640$

640 aircraft make up the entire air fleet.

93. $\dfrac{32}{265}$ of $10{,}600 = \dfrac{32}{265} \cdot 10600 = \dfrac{32}{265} \cdot \dfrac{10600}{1} = \dfrac{32 \cdot 10600}{265 \cdot 1}$
$= \dfrac{32 \cdot 265 \cdot 40}{265 \cdot 1} = \dfrac{32 \cdot 40}{1} = 1280$

There were 1280 news/talk stations in 2004.

Exercise Set 3.4

1. $\dfrac{1}{7} + \dfrac{2}{7} = \dfrac{1 + 2}{7} = \dfrac{3}{7}$

5. $\dfrac{2}{9} + \dfrac{4}{9} = \dfrac{2 + 4}{9} = \dfrac{6}{9} = \dfrac{3 \cdot 2}{3 \cdot 3} = \dfrac{2}{3}$

9. $-\dfrac{3}{14} + \left(-\dfrac{4}{14}\right) = \dfrac{-3 + (-4)}{14} = \dfrac{-7}{14} = -\dfrac{7}{14} = -\dfrac{7 \cdot 1}{7 \cdot 2} = -\dfrac{1}{2}$

13. $\dfrac{4}{13} + \dfrac{2}{13} + \dfrac{1}{13} = \dfrac{4 + 2 + 1}{13} = \dfrac{7}{13}$

17. $\dfrac{10}{11} - \dfrac{4}{11} = \dfrac{10 - 4}{11} = \dfrac{6}{11}$

21. $\dfrac{7}{4} - \dfrac{3}{4} = \dfrac{7 - 3}{4} = \dfrac{4}{4} = 1$

25. $-\dfrac{25}{12} - \dfrac{15}{12} = \dfrac{-25 - 15}{12} = \dfrac{-40}{12} = -\dfrac{40}{12} = -\dfrac{4 \cdot 10}{4 \cdot 3} = -\dfrac{10}{3}$

29. $-\dfrac{27}{33} - \left(-\dfrac{8}{33}\right) = -\dfrac{27}{33} + \dfrac{8}{33} = \dfrac{-27 + 8}{33} = \dfrac{-19}{33} = -\dfrac{19}{33}$

33. $\dfrac{99}{100} - \dfrac{9}{100} = \dfrac{99 - 9}{100} = \dfrac{90}{100} = \dfrac{10 \cdot 9}{10 \cdot 10} = \dfrac{9}{10}$

37. $-\dfrac{3}{16} + \left(-\dfrac{7}{16}\right) + \left(-\dfrac{2}{16}\right) = \dfrac{-3 + (-7) + (-2)}{16}$
$= \dfrac{-12}{16} = -\dfrac{12}{16} = -\dfrac{4 \cdot 3}{4 \cdot 4} = -\dfrac{3}{4}$

41. The perimeter is the distance around. Opposite sides of a rectangle have equal length.

Perimeter $= \dfrac{7}{12} + \dfrac{5}{12} + \dfrac{7}{12} + \dfrac{5}{12} = \dfrac{7 + 5 + 7 + 5}{12} = \dfrac{24}{12}$
$= \dfrac{12 \cdot 2}{12 \cdot 1} = \dfrac{2}{1} = 2$

The perimeter is 2 meters.

45. North America takes up $\dfrac{16}{100}$ of the world's land area, while South America takes up $\dfrac{12}{100}$ of the land area.

$\dfrac{16}{100} + \dfrac{12}{100} = \dfrac{16 + 12}{100} = \dfrac{28}{100} = \dfrac{4 \cdot 7}{4 \cdot 25} = \dfrac{7}{25}$

$\dfrac{7}{25}$ of the world's land area is within North America and South America.

49. To find the remaining amount of track to be inspected, subtract the $\dfrac{5}{20}$ mile that has already been inspected from the $\dfrac{19}{20}$ mile total that must be inspected.

$\dfrac{19}{20} - \dfrac{5}{20} = \dfrac{19 - 5}{20} = \dfrac{14}{20} = \dfrac{2 \cdot 7}{2 \cdot 10} = \dfrac{7}{10}$

$\dfrac{7}{10}$ of a mile of track remains to be inspected.

53. To find the fraction of states that had maximum speed limits less than 70 mph, subtract the fraction that had speed limits of 70 mph $\left(\dfrac{16}{50}\right)$ from the fraction that had speed limits up to and including 70 mph $\left(\dfrac{37}{50}\right)$.

$$\frac{37}{50} - \frac{16}{50} = \frac{37 - 16}{50} = \frac{21}{50}$$

$\dfrac{21}{50}$ of the states had maximum speed limits less than 70 mph.

57. Multiples of 24: 24, 48, $\boxed{72}$, 96

Multiples of 36: 36, $\boxed{72}$, 108

LCM: 72

61. $6 = \boxed{2} \cdot \boxed{3}$

$7 = \boxed{7}$

LCM: $2 \cdot 3 \cdot 7 = 42$

65. $30 = 2 \cdot 3 \cdot 5$

$36 = \boxed{2 \cdot 2} \cdot \boxed{3 \cdot 3}$

$50 = 2 \cdot \boxed{5 \cdot 5}$

LCM: $2 \cdot 2 \cdot 3 \cdot 3 \cdot 5 \cdot 5$
$= 900$

69. $\dfrac{4}{7} = \dfrac{4 \cdot 5}{7 \cdot 5} = \dfrac{20}{35}$

73. $\dfrac{4}{9} = \dfrac{4 \cdot 9}{9 \cdot 9} = \dfrac{36}{81}$

77. $\dfrac{14}{17} = \dfrac{14 \cdot 4}{17 \cdot 4} = \dfrac{56}{68}$

81. $8 = 2 \cdot 4$

$\downarrow \ \downarrow \searrow$

$2 \cdot 2 \cdot 2 = 2^3$

85. $\dfrac{4}{11} + \dfrac{5}{11} - \dfrac{3}{11} + \dfrac{2}{11} = \dfrac{4 + 5 - 3 + 2}{11} = \dfrac{8}{11}$

89. answers may vary

93. $\dfrac{37}{165} = \dfrac{37 \cdot 22}{165 \cdot 22} = \dfrac{814}{3630}$

97. **a.** $\dfrac{10}{15} = \dfrac{5 \cdot 2}{5 \cdot 3} = \dfrac{2}{3}$

b. $\dfrac{40}{60} = \dfrac{20 \cdot 2}{20 \cdot 3} = \dfrac{2}{3}$

c. $\dfrac{16}{20} = \dfrac{4 \cdot 4}{4 \cdot 5} = \dfrac{4}{5}$

d. $\dfrac{200}{300} = \dfrac{100 \cdot 2}{100 \cdot 3} = \dfrac{2}{3}$

a, b, and d are equivalent to $\dfrac{2}{3}$

Exercise Set 3.5

1. The LCD of 3 and 6 is 6.

$$\frac{2}{3} + \frac{1}{6} = \frac{2 \cdot 2}{3 \cdot 2} + \frac{1}{6} = \frac{4}{6} + \frac{1}{6} = \frac{5}{6}$$

5. The LCD of 11 and 33 is 33.

$$-\frac{2}{11} + \frac{2}{33} = -\frac{2 \cdot 3}{11 \cdot 3} + \frac{2}{33} = -\frac{6}{33} + \frac{2}{33} = \frac{-6 + 2}{33} = \frac{-4}{33} = -\frac{4}{33}$$

9. The LCD of 35 and 7 is 35.

$$\frac{11}{35} + \frac{2}{7} = \frac{11}{35} + \frac{2 \cdot 5}{7 \cdot 5} = \frac{11}{35} + \frac{10}{35} = \frac{11 + 10}{35} = \frac{21}{35} = \frac{7 \cdot 3}{7 \cdot 5} = \frac{3}{5}$$

13. The LCD of 12 and 9 is 36.

$$\frac{5}{12} - \frac{1}{9} = \frac{5 \cdot 3}{12 \cdot 3} - \frac{1 \cdot 4}{9 \cdot 4} = \frac{15}{36} - \frac{4}{36} = \frac{15 - 4}{36} = \frac{11}{36}$$

17. The LCD of 11 and 9 is 99.

$$\frac{5}{11} + \frac{4}{9} = \frac{5 \cdot 9}{11 \cdot 9} + \frac{4 \cdot 11}{9 \cdot 11} = \frac{45}{99} + \frac{44}{99} = \frac{45 + 44}{99} = \frac{89}{99}$$

21. The LCD of 3, 9, and 27 is 27.

$$\frac{1}{3} + \frac{1}{9} + \frac{1}{27} = \frac{1 \cdot 9}{3 \cdot 9} + \frac{1 \cdot 3}{9 \cdot 3} + \frac{1}{27} = \frac{9}{27} + \frac{3}{27} + \frac{1}{27}$$

$$= \frac{9 + 3 + 1}{27} = \frac{13}{27}$$

25. The LCD of 14 and 7 is 14.

$$\frac{9}{14} - \frac{3}{7} = \frac{9}{14} - \frac{3 \cdot 2}{7 \cdot 2} = \frac{9}{14} - \frac{6}{14} = \frac{9 - 6}{14} = \frac{3}{14}$$

29. The LCD of 9 and 12 is 36.

$$\frac{1}{9} - \frac{5}{12} = \frac{1 \cdot 4}{9 \cdot 4} - \frac{5 \cdot 3}{12 \cdot 3} = \frac{4}{36} - \frac{15}{36} = \frac{4 - 15}{36} = \frac{-11}{36} = -\frac{11}{36}$$

33. The LCD of 7 and 8 is 56.

$$\frac{5}{7} - \frac{1}{8} = \frac{5 \cdot 8}{7 \cdot 8} - \frac{1 \cdot 7}{8 \cdot 7} = \frac{40}{56} - \frac{7}{56} = \frac{40 - 7}{56} = \frac{33}{56}$$

37. $\dfrac{5}{9} + \dfrac{3}{9} = \dfrac{5 + 3}{9} = \dfrac{8}{9}$

41. The LCD of 6 and 7 is 42.

$$-\frac{5}{6} - \frac{3}{7} = -\frac{5 \cdot 7}{6 \cdot 7} - \frac{3 \cdot 6}{7 \cdot 6} = -\frac{35}{42} - \frac{18}{42} = \frac{-35 - 18}{42} = \frac{-53}{42} = -\frac{53}{42}$$

45. The LCD of 11 and 13 is 143.

$$\frac{5}{11} + \frac{3}{13} = \frac{5 \cdot 13}{11 \cdot 13} + \frac{3 \cdot 11}{13 \cdot 11} = \frac{65}{143} + \frac{33}{143} = \frac{65 + 33}{143} = \frac{98}{143}$$

49. The LCD of 5, 4, and 2 is 20.

$$\frac{6}{5} - \frac{3}{4} + \frac{1}{2} = \frac{6 \cdot 4}{5 \cdot 4} - \frac{3 \cdot 5}{4 \cdot 5} + \frac{1 \cdot 10}{2 \cdot 10} = \frac{24}{20} - \frac{15}{20} + \frac{10}{20}$$

$$= \frac{24 - 15 + 10}{20} = \frac{19}{20}$$

53. The LCD of 12, 24, and 6 is 24.

$$-\frac{9}{12} + \frac{17}{24} - \frac{1}{6} = -\frac{9 \cdot 2}{12 \cdot 2} + \frac{17}{24} - \frac{1 \cdot 4}{6 \cdot 4} = -\frac{18}{24} + \frac{17}{24} - \frac{4}{24}$$

$$= \frac{-18 + 17 - 4}{24} = \frac{-5}{24} = -\frac{5}{24}$$

57. The LCD of these fractions is 70. Let's write each fraction as an equivalent fraction with a denominator of 70.

$$\frac{2}{7} = \frac{2 \cdot 10}{7 \cdot 10} = \frac{20}{70} \quad \text{and} \quad \frac{3}{10} = \frac{3 \cdot 7}{10 \cdot 7} = \frac{21}{70}$$

Since $20 < 21$, then $\dfrac{20}{70} < \dfrac{21}{70}$ or $\dfrac{2}{7} < \dfrac{3}{10}$

61. The LCD of these fractions is 28. Let's write each fraction as an equivalent fraction with a denominator of 28.

$$-\frac{3}{4} = -\frac{3 \cdot 7}{4 \cdot 7} = -\frac{21}{28} \quad \text{and} \quad -\frac{11}{14} = -\frac{11 \cdot 2}{14 \cdot 2} = -\frac{22}{28}$$

Since $-21 > -22$, then $-\dfrac{21}{28} > -\dfrac{22}{28}$ or $-\dfrac{3}{4} > -\dfrac{11}{14}$

65. $xy = \dfrac{1}{3} \cdot \dfrac{3}{4} = \dfrac{1 \cdot 3}{3 \cdot 4} = \dfrac{1}{4}$

69. Perimeter

$$= \frac{1}{3} + \frac{4}{5} + \frac{1}{3} + \frac{4}{5} = \frac{2}{3} + \frac{8}{5} = \frac{2 \cdot 5}{3 \cdot 5} + \frac{8 \cdot 3}{5 \cdot 3}$$

$$= \frac{10}{15} + \frac{24}{15} = \frac{10 + 24}{15} = \frac{34}{15} \text{ or } 2\frac{4}{15} \text{ cm}$$

73. Subtract the distance domestic European honeybees will chase a person from the distance killer bees will chase a person. The LCD of 4 and 264 is 264.

$$\frac{1}{4} - \frac{5}{264} = \frac{1 \cdot 66}{4 \cdot 66} - \frac{5}{264} = \frac{66}{264} - \frac{5}{264} = \frac{61}{264}.$$

Killer bees will chase a person $\frac{61}{264}$ mile farther.

77. Subtract the fraction of students who name art as their favorite subject from the fraction that name math, science, or art as their favorite subject. The LCD of 20 and 25 is 100.

$$\frac{13}{20} - \frac{4}{25} = \frac{13}{20} \cdot \frac{5}{5} - \frac{4}{25} \cdot \frac{4}{4} = \frac{65}{100} - \frac{16}{100} = \frac{49}{100}$$

$\frac{49}{100}$ of American students age 10 to 17 name math or science as their favorite subject.

81. The Pacific Ocean takes up $\frac{1}{2}$ of the world's water area, while the Atlantic Ocean takes up $\frac{13}{50}$ of the water area. The LCD of 2 and 50 is 50.

$$\frac{1}{2} + \frac{13}{50} = \frac{1}{2} \cdot \frac{25}{25} + \frac{13}{50} = \frac{25}{50} + \frac{13}{50} = \frac{25 + 13}{50} = \frac{38}{50} = \frac{2 \cdot 19}{2 \cdot 25} = \frac{19}{25}$$

$\frac{19}{25}$ of the world's water area is within the Pacific Ocean and the Atlantic Ocean.

85. $(8 - 6) \cdot (4 - 7) = (2) \cdot (-3) = -6$

89. The LCD of 3, 4, and 540 is 540.

$$\frac{2}{3} - \frac{1}{4} - \frac{2}{540} = \frac{2}{3} \cdot \frac{180}{180} - \frac{1}{4} \cdot \frac{135}{135} - \frac{2}{540} = \frac{360}{540} - \frac{135}{540} - \frac{2}{540}$$

$$= \frac{360 - 135 - 2}{540} = \frac{223}{540}$$

93. answers may vary

Exercise Set 3.6

1. $\dfrac{\frac{1}{8}}{\frac{3}{4}} = \frac{1}{8} \div \frac{3}{4} = \frac{1}{8} \cdot \frac{4}{3} = \frac{1 \cdot 4}{8 \cdot 3} = \frac{1 \cdot 4}{2 \cdot 4 \cdot 3} = \frac{1}{6}$

5. $\dfrac{\frac{2}{27}}{\frac{4}{9}} = \frac{2}{27} \div \frac{4}{9} = \frac{2}{27} \cdot \frac{9}{4} = \frac{2 \cdot 9}{27 \cdot 4} = \frac{2 \cdot 3 \cdot 3}{3 \cdot 3 \cdot 3 \cdot 2 \cdot 2} = \frac{1}{3 \cdot 2} = \frac{1}{6}$

9. $\dfrac{\frac{3}{4}}{5 - \frac{1}{8}} = \dfrac{8 \cdot \left(\frac{3}{4}\right)}{8 \cdot \left(\frac{5}{1} - \frac{1}{8}\right)} = \dfrac{6}{8 \cdot \left(\frac{5}{1}\right) - 8 \cdot \left(\frac{1}{8}\right)}$

$$= \frac{6}{40 - 1} = \frac{6}{39} = \frac{3 \cdot 2}{3 \cdot 13} = \frac{2}{13}$$

13. $\frac{5}{6} \div \frac{1}{3} \cdot \frac{1}{4} = \frac{5}{6} \cdot \frac{3}{1} \cdot \frac{1}{4} = \frac{5 \cdot 3 \cdot 1}{2 \cdot 3 \cdot 1 \cdot 2 \cdot 2} = \frac{5}{2 \cdot 2 \cdot 2} = \frac{5}{8}$

17. $\left(\frac{2}{9} + \frac{4}{9}\right)\left(\frac{1}{3} - \frac{9}{10}\right)$

$$= \left(\frac{2 + 4}{9}\right)\left(\frac{1}{3} \cdot \frac{10}{10} - \frac{9}{10} \cdot \frac{3}{3}\right) = \left(\frac{6}{9}\right)\left(\frac{10}{30} - \frac{27}{30}\right) = \left(\frac{6}{9}\right)\left(\frac{-17}{30}\right)$$

$$= -\frac{6 \cdot 17}{9 \cdot 30} = -\frac{3 \cdot 2 \cdot 17}{3 \cdot 3 \cdot 5 \cdot 2 \cdot 3} = -\frac{17}{3 \cdot 3 \cdot 5} = -\frac{17}{45}$$

21. $2 \cdot \left(\frac{1}{4} + \frac{1}{5}\right) + 2 = 2 \cdot \left(\frac{1}{4} \cdot \frac{5}{5} + \frac{1}{5} \cdot \frac{4}{4}\right) + 2 = 2 \cdot \left(\frac{5}{20} + \frac{4}{20}\right) + 2$

$$= 2 \cdot \left(\frac{5 + 4}{20}\right) + 2 = 2 \cdot \frac{9}{20} + 2 = \frac{2}{1} \cdot \frac{9}{20} + 2 = \frac{2 \cdot 9}{1 \cdot 2 \cdot 10} + 2$$

$$= \frac{9}{10} + \frac{2}{1} \cdot \frac{10}{10} = \frac{9}{10} + \frac{20}{10} = \frac{9 + 20}{10} = \frac{29}{10}$$

25. $\left(\frac{2}{3} - \frac{5}{9}\right)^2 = \left(\frac{2}{3} \cdot \frac{3}{3} - \frac{5}{9}\right)^2 = \left(\frac{6}{9} - \frac{5}{9}\right)^2 = \left(\frac{6 - 5}{9}\right)^2 = \left(\frac{1}{9}\right)^2$

$$= \frac{1}{9} \cdot \frac{1}{9} = \frac{1 \cdot 1}{9 \cdot 9} = \frac{1}{81}$$

29. $5y - z = 5\left(\frac{2}{5}\right) - \frac{5}{6} = 2 - \frac{5}{6} = \frac{2}{1} \cdot \frac{6}{6} - \frac{5}{6} = \frac{12}{6} - \frac{5}{6} = \frac{7}{6}$

33. $x^2 - yz = \left(-\frac{1}{3}\right)^2 - \left(\frac{2}{5}\right)\left(\frac{5}{6}\right) = \left(-\frac{1}{3}\right)\left(-\frac{1}{3}\right) - \frac{2 \cdot 5}{5 \cdot 2 \cdot 3} = \frac{1}{9} - \frac{1}{3}$

$$= \frac{1}{9} - \frac{1}{3} \cdot \frac{3}{3} = \frac{1}{9} - \frac{3}{9} = \frac{1 - 3}{9} = \frac{-2}{9} = -\frac{2}{9}$$

37. $\left(\frac{3}{2}\right)^3 + \left(\frac{1}{2}\right)^3 = \frac{27}{8} + \frac{1}{8} = \frac{28}{8} = \frac{4 \cdot 7}{4 \cdot 2} = \frac{7}{2}$

41. $\dfrac{2 + \frac{1}{6}}{1 - \frac{4}{3}} = \dfrac{6\left(2 + \frac{1}{6}\right)}{6\left(1 - \frac{4}{3}\right)} = \dfrac{6 \cdot 2 + 6 \cdot \frac{1}{6}}{6 \cdot 1 - 6 \cdot \frac{4}{3}} = \frac{12 + 1}{6 - 8} = \frac{13}{-2} = -\frac{13}{2}$

45. $\left(\frac{3}{4} - 1\right)\left(\frac{1}{8} + \frac{1}{2}\right) = \left(\frac{3}{4} - \frac{4}{4}\right)\left(\frac{1}{8} + \frac{4}{8}\right) = \left(-\frac{1}{4}\right)\left(\frac{5}{8}\right)$

$$= -\frac{1 \cdot 5}{4 \cdot 8} = -\frac{5}{32}$$

49. $\dfrac{\frac{1}{2} - \frac{3}{8}}{\frac{3}{4} + \frac{1}{2}} = \dfrac{8\left(\frac{1}{2} - \frac{3}{8}\right)}{8\left(\frac{3}{4} + \frac{1}{2}\right)} = \dfrac{8 \cdot \frac{1}{2} - 8 \cdot \frac{3}{8}}{8 \cdot \frac{3}{4} + 8 \cdot \frac{1}{2}} = \frac{4 - 3}{6 + 4} = \frac{1}{10}$

53. $3\frac{3}{5} = \frac{5 \cdot 3 + 3}{5} = \frac{18}{5}$

57. $2\frac{11}{15} = \frac{15 \cdot 2 + 11}{15} = \frac{41}{15}$

61. $6\frac{6}{13} = \frac{13 \cdot 6 + 6}{13} = \frac{84}{13}$

65. $166\frac{2}{3} = \frac{3 \cdot 166 + 2}{3} = \frac{500}{3}$

69.
```
     4R5
  8)37
    -32
      5
```
$\dfrac{37}{8} = 4\frac{5}{8}$

73.
```
      15
 15)225
    -15
     75
    -75
      0
```
$\dfrac{225}{15} = 15$

77.
```
       6R65
 112)737
    -672
      65
```
$\dfrac{737}{112} = 6\frac{65}{112}$

81. $9 - \dfrac{5}{6}$

$= \dfrac{9}{1} \cdot \dfrac{6}{6} - \dfrac{5}{6}$

$= \dfrac{54}{6} - \dfrac{5}{6}$

$= \dfrac{49}{6}$

85. $\dfrac{\dfrac{1}{2}+\dfrac{3}{4}}{2}=\dfrac{4\left(\dfrac{1}{2}+\dfrac{3}{4}\right)}{4(2)}=\dfrac{4\cdot\dfrac{1}{2}+4\cdot\dfrac{3}{4}}{4\cdot2}=\dfrac{2+3}{8}=\dfrac{5}{8}$

89. The average of a and b should be halfway between a and b.

93. False, if the absolute value of the negative fraction is greater than the absolute value of the positive fraction

97. No; answers may vary

101. Subtraction, multiplication, division, addition

Exercise Set 3.7

1.

5. $2\dfrac{2}{3}\cdot\dfrac{1}{7}=\dfrac{8}{3}\cdot\dfrac{1}{7}=\dfrac{8}{21}$

9. Exact: $2\dfrac{1}{5}\cdot3\dfrac{1}{2}=\dfrac{11}{5}\cdot\dfrac{7}{2}=\dfrac{77}{10}$ or $7\dfrac{7}{10}$

Estimate: $2\dfrac{1}{5}$ rounds to 2, $3\dfrac{1}{2}$ rounds to 4.

$2\cdot4=8$ so the answer is reasonable.

13. $5\cdot2\dfrac{1}{2}=\dfrac{5}{1}\cdot\dfrac{5}{2}=\dfrac{25}{2}$ or $12\dfrac{1}{2}$

17. $2\dfrac{2}{3}\div\dfrac{1}{7}=\dfrac{8}{3}\cdot\dfrac{7}{1}=\dfrac{56}{3}$ or $18\dfrac{2}{3}$

21. Exact: $10\dfrac{3}{14}+3\dfrac{4}{7}=10\dfrac{3}{14}+3\dfrac{8}{14}=13\dfrac{11}{14}$

Estimate: $10\dfrac{3}{14}$ rounds to 10, $3\dfrac{4}{7}$ rounds to 4.

$10+4=14$ so the answer is reasonable.

25.

$\begin{array}{c}12\dfrac{3}{14}\\10\\+\,25\dfrac{5}{12}\\\hline\end{array}\qquad\begin{array}{c}12\dfrac{18}{84}\\10\\+\,25\dfrac{35}{84}\\\hline47\dfrac{53}{84}\end{array}$

29.

$\begin{array}{c}3\dfrac{5}{8}\\2\dfrac{1}{6}\\+\,7\dfrac{3}{4}\\\hline\end{array}\qquad\begin{array}{c}3\dfrac{15}{24}\\2\dfrac{4}{24}\\+\,7\dfrac{18}{24}\\\hline12\dfrac{37}{24}=12+1\dfrac{13}{24}=13\dfrac{13}{24}\end{array}$

33.

$\begin{array}{c}10\dfrac{13}{14}\\-\,3\dfrac{4}{7}\\\hline\end{array}\qquad\begin{array}{c}10\dfrac{13}{14}\\-\,3\dfrac{8}{14}\\\hline7\dfrac{5}{14}\end{array}$

Exact:

Estimate: $10\dfrac{13}{14}$ rounds to 11, $3\dfrac{4}{7}$ rounds to 4.

$11-4=7$ so the answer is reasonable.

37.

$\begin{array}{c}6\\-\,2\dfrac{4}{9}\\\hline\end{array}\qquad\begin{array}{c}5\dfrac{9}{9}\\-\,2\dfrac{4}{9}\\\hline3\dfrac{5}{9}\end{array}$

41. $\begin{array}{c}2\dfrac{3}{4}\\+\,1\dfrac{1}{4}\\\hline3\dfrac{4}{4}=3+1=4\end{array}$

45. $3\dfrac{1}{9}\cdot2$

$=\dfrac{28}{9}\cdot\dfrac{2}{1}=\dfrac{56}{9}=6\dfrac{2}{9}$

49. $22\dfrac{4}{9}+13\dfrac{5}{18}=22\dfrac{8}{18}+13\dfrac{5}{18}=35\dfrac{13}{18}$

53.

$\begin{array}{c}15\dfrac{1}{5}\\20\dfrac{3}{10}\\+\,37\dfrac{2}{15}\\\hline\end{array}\qquad\begin{array}{c}15\dfrac{6}{30}\\20\dfrac{9}{30}\\+\,37\dfrac{4}{30}\\\hline72\dfrac{19}{30}\end{array}$

57. $3\dfrac{1}{3}\div4$

$=\dfrac{10}{3}\cdot\dfrac{1}{4}=\dfrac{10}{12}=\dfrac{2\cdot5}{2\cdot6}=\dfrac{5}{6}$

$\dfrac{5}{6}$ Tbsp should be taken in each dose.

61. $2\dfrac{9}{25}\cdot1\dfrac{13}{25}$

$=\dfrac{59}{25}\cdot\dfrac{38}{25}=\dfrac{2242}{625}=3\dfrac{367}{625}$

The area of the face of this camera is $3\dfrac{367}{625}$ sq. in.

65. $15\dfrac{2}{3}-3\dfrac{1}{4}-2\dfrac{1}{2}$

$=15\dfrac{8}{12}-3\dfrac{3}{12}-2\dfrac{6}{12}$

$=14\dfrac{20}{12}-3\dfrac{3}{12}-2\dfrac{6}{12}$

$=9\dfrac{11}{12}$

The remaining piece will not do because it is $9\dfrac{11}{12}$ ft, and it needs to be 10 ft. Since $10-9\dfrac{11}{12}=9\dfrac{12}{12}-9\dfrac{11}{12}=\dfrac{1}{12}$, the piece is short by $\dfrac{1}{12}$ of a foot.

69. $12\dfrac{3}{4}\div4=\dfrac{51}{4}\div\dfrac{4}{1}=\dfrac{51}{4}\cdot\dfrac{1}{4}=\dfrac{51}{16}=3\dfrac{3}{16}$ miles per day

73. Add the height of the pedestal to the height of the copper figure.

$46\dfrac{1}{20}+46\dfrac{47}{50}=46\dfrac{5}{100}+46\dfrac{94}{100}=92\dfrac{99}{100}$

The overall height of the Statue of Liberty from the base of the pedestal to the tip of the torch is $92\dfrac{99}{100}$ meters.

77. Subtract the length of the August 21, 2017, eclipse from the April 8, 2024, eclipse.

$$4\frac{7}{15} \qquad 4\frac{7}{15} \qquad 3\frac{22}{15}$$
$$\underline{-2\frac{2}{3}} \qquad \underline{-2\frac{10}{15}} \qquad \underline{-2\frac{10}{15}}$$
$$\qquad\qquad\qquad\qquad\qquad 1\frac{12}{15} = 1\frac{4}{5}$$

The April 8, 2024, eclipse will be $1\frac{4}{5}$ minutes longer than the August 21, 2017, eclipse.

81. $-4\frac{2}{5} \cdot 2\frac{3}{10} = -\frac{22}{5} \cdot \frac{23}{10} = -\frac{2 \cdot 11 \cdot 23}{5 \cdot 2 \cdot 5} = -\frac{253}{25} = -10\frac{3}{25}$

85. $-31\frac{2}{15} + 17\frac{3}{20} = -31\frac{8}{60} + 17\frac{9}{60} = -30\frac{68}{60} + 17\frac{9}{60} = -13\frac{59}{60}$

89. $11\frac{7}{8} - 13\frac{5}{6} = 11\frac{21}{24} - 13\frac{20}{24} = -\left(13\frac{20}{24} - 11\frac{21}{24}\right)$
$$= -\left(12\frac{44}{24} - 11\frac{21}{24}\right) = -1\frac{23}{24}$$

93. $20 \div 10 \cdot 2 = 2 \cdot 2 = 4$

97. a. $9\frac{5}{5} = 9 + 1 = 10$

b. $9\frac{100}{100} = 9 + 1 = 10$

c. $6\frac{44}{11} = 6 + 4 = 10$

d. $8\frac{13}{13} = 8 + 1 = 9$

a, b, and c are equivalent to 10.

101. $20\frac{1}{4}$ rounds to 20, and $\frac{5}{6}$ rounds to 1;

since $20 \div 1 = 20$, the best estimate is c.

105. answers may vary

109. answers may vary

Chapter 3 Test

1. 7 out of 16 equal parts are shaded: $\frac{7}{16}$

5. $-\frac{42}{70} = -\frac{2 \cdot 3 \cdot 7}{2 \cdot 5 \cdot 7} = -\frac{3}{5}$

9. $495 = 5 \cdot 99$
$$\quad\;\; \downarrow \;\; \downarrow\searrow$$
$$\quad 5 \cdot 9 \cdot 11$$
$$\quad \downarrow \;\; \downarrow\searrow \;\;\searrow$$
$$5 \cdot 3 \cdot 3 \cdot 11 = 3^2 \cdot 5 \cdot 11$$

13. $\frac{4}{4} \div \frac{3}{4} = \frac{4}{4} \cdot \frac{4}{3} = \frac{4 \cdot 4}{4 \cdot 3} = \frac{4}{3}$ or $1\frac{1}{3}$

17. $\frac{-2}{3} \cdot -\frac{8}{15} = \frac{2}{3} \cdot \frac{8}{15} = \frac{16}{45}$

21. $\frac{3}{8} \cdot \frac{16}{6} \cdot \frac{4}{11} = \frac{3 \cdot 2 \cdot 2 \cdot 2 \cdot 2 \cdot 2}{2 \cdot 2 \cdot 2 \cdot 2 \cdot 3 \cdot 11}$
$$= \frac{2 \cdot 2}{11} = \frac{4}{11}$$

25.
$$19 \qquad 18\frac{11}{11}$$
$$\underline{-2\frac{3}{11}} \qquad \underline{-2\frac{3}{11}}$$
$$\qquad\qquad 16\frac{8}{11}$$

29. $\frac{1}{2} \div \frac{2}{3} \cdot \frac{3}{4} = \frac{1}{2} \cdot \frac{3}{2} \cdot \frac{3}{4} = \frac{9}{16}$

33. $-5\left(-\frac{1}{2}\right) = -\frac{5}{1} \cdot -\frac{1}{2} = \frac{5}{2}$ or $2\frac{1}{2}$

37. $\frac{3}{50}$ of $47,000

$$= \frac{3}{50} \cdot \frac{47000}{1} = \frac{3 \cdot 50 \cdot 940}{50 \cdot 1} = \frac{2820}{1} = 2820$$

$2820 was spent on health care.

CHAPTER 4

Exercise Set 4.1

1. 6.52 in words is six and fifty-two hundredths.

5. −0.205 in words is negative two hundred five thousandths.

9. 200.005 in words is two hundred and five thousandths.

13. 31.04 in words is thirty one and four hundredths

17. The check should be paid to "Bell South," for the amount of "59.68," which is written in words as "Fifty-nine and $\frac{68}{100}$."

21. Nine and eight hundredths is 9.08.

25. Sixty-four ten-thousandths is 0.0064.

29. $0.27 = \frac{27}{100}$

33. $-5.47 = -5\frac{47}{100}$

37. $7.008 = 7\frac{8}{1000} = 7\frac{1}{125}$

41. $0.3005 = \frac{3005}{10,000} = \frac{601}{2000}$

45. In words, 0.077 is seventy-seven thousandths. As a fraction, $0.077 = \frac{77}{1000}$.

49.
$$0.57 \qquad 0.54$$
$$\;\uparrow \qquad\;\; \uparrow$$
$$\;7 > \quad 4$$
so $0.57 > 0.54$
Thus $-0.57 < -0.54$

53.
$$0.54900 \qquad 0.549$$
$$\quad\uparrow \qquad\qquad \uparrow$$
$$\quad 9 \quad = \qquad 9$$
so $0.54900 = 0.549$

57.
$$1.0621 \qquad 1.07$$
$$\quad\uparrow \qquad\qquad \uparrow$$
$$\quad 6 \quad < \qquad 7$$
so $1.0621 < 1.07$
Thus, $-1.0621 > -1.07$.

61.
$$0.023 \qquad 0.024$$
$$\quad\uparrow \qquad\quad \uparrow$$
$$\quad 3 \;<\; 4$$
so $0.023 < 0.024$
Thus, $-0.023 > -0.024$.

65. To round 0.234 to the nearest hundredth, observe that the digit in the thousandths place is 4. Since this digit is less than 5, we do not add 1 to the digit in the hundredths place. The number 0.234 rounded to the nearest hundredth is 0.23.

69. To round 98,207.23 to the nearest ten, observe that the digit in the ones place is 7. Since this digit is 5 or greater, add 1 to the digit in the tens place. The number 98,207.203 rounded to the nearest ten is 98,210.

73. To round −0.501 to the nearest tenth, observe that the digit in the hundredths place is 0. Since this digit is 5 or less, we do not add 1 to the digit in the tenths place. The number −0.501 rounded to the nearest tenth is −0.5.

77. To round 0.1992 to the nearest hundredth, observe that the digit in the thousandths place is 9. Since this digit is at least 5, we need to add 1 to the digit in the hundredths place. The number 0.1992 rounded to the nearest hundredth is 0.2. The amount is $0.20.

81. To round 2.4075 to the nearest hundredth, observe that the digit in the thousandths place is 7. Since this digit is at least 5, we need to add 1 to the digit in the hundredths place. The number 2.4075 rounded to the nearest hundredth is 2.41. The time is 2.41 hours.

85. To round 24.6229 to the nearest thousandth, observe that the digit in the ten-thousandths place is 9. Since this digit is at least 5, we need to add 1 to the digit in the thousandths place. 24.6229 rounded to the nearest thousandth is 24.623. The day length is 24.623 hours.

89.
$$\begin{array}{r} 82 \\ -47 \\ \hline 35 \end{array}$$

93. To round 2849.1738 to the nearest hundredth, observe that the digit in the thousandths place is 3. Since this digit is less than 5, we do not add 1 to the digit in the hundredths place. 2849.1738 rounded to the nearest hundredth is 2849.17, which is choice a.

97. $7\dfrac{12}{100} = 7.12$

101. answers may vary

105. 0.0612 rounded to the nearest hundredth is 0.06. 0.066 rounds to 0.07. 0.0586 rounds to 0.06. 0.0506 rounds to 0.05. Thus, 0.0612 and 0.0586 round to 0.06.

Exercise Set 4.2

1.
$$\begin{array}{r} 1.3 \\ +2.2 \\ \hline 3.5 \end{array}$$

5.
$$\begin{array}{r} 24.6000 \\ 2.3900 \\ +0.0678 \\ \hline 27.0578 \end{array}$$

9. −2.6 + (−5.97)
Add the absolute values.
$$\begin{array}{r} 2.60 \\ +5.97 \\ \hline 8.57 \end{array}$$
Attach the common sign.
−8.57

13. Exact:
$$\begin{array}{r} \overset{1\ \ 1}{234.89} \\ +230.67 \\ \hline 465.56 \end{array}$$
Estimate:
$$\begin{array}{r} 230 \\ +230 \\ \hline 460 \end{array}$$

17.
$$\begin{array}{r} \overset{1\ \ \ 1}{45.023} \\ 3.006 \\ +8.403 \\ \hline 56.432 \end{array}$$

21.
$$\begin{array}{r} 18.0 \\ -2.7 \\ \hline 15.3 \end{array}$$
Check:
$$\begin{array}{r} \overset{1}{15.3} \\ +2.7 \\ \hline 18.0 \end{array}$$

25. Exact:
$$\begin{array}{r} 5.90 \\ -4.07 \\ \hline 1.83 \end{array}$$
Estimate:
$$\begin{array}{r} 6 \\ -4 \\ \hline 2 \end{array}$$
Check:
$$\begin{array}{r} \overset{1}{1.83} \\ +4.07 \\ \hline 5.90 \end{array}$$

29. Exact:
$$\begin{array}{r} 1000.0 \\ -123.4 \\ \hline 876.6 \end{array}$$
Estimate:
$$\begin{array}{r} 1000 \\ -100 \\ \hline 900 \end{array}$$

33. −1.12 − 5.2 = −1.12 + (−5.2)
Add the absolute values.
$$\begin{array}{r} 1.12 \\ +5.20 \\ \hline 6.32 \end{array}$$
Attach the common sign.
−6.32

37. −2.6 − (−5.7) = −2.6 + 5.7
Subtract the absolute values.
$$\begin{array}{r} 5.7 \\ -2.6 \\ \hline 3.1 \end{array}$$
Attach the sign of the larger absolute value.
3.1

41.
$$\begin{array}{r} 23.0 \\ -6.7 \\ \hline 16.3 \end{array}$$
Check:
$$\begin{array}{r} \overset{11}{16.3} \\ +6.7 \\ \hline 23.0 \end{array}$$

45. − 6.06 + 0.44
Subtract the absolute values.
$$\begin{array}{r} 6.06 \\ -0.44 \\ \hline 5.62 \end{array}$$
Attach the sign of the larger absolute value.
−5.62

49. 50.2 − 600 = 50.2 + (−600)
Subtract the absolute values.
$$\begin{array}{r} 600.0 \\ -50.2 \\ \hline 549.8 \end{array}$$
Attach the sign of the larger absolute value.
−549.8

53.
$$\begin{array}{r} 100.009 \\ 6.080 \\ +9.034 \\ \hline 115.123 \end{array}$$

57. −102.4 − 78.04 = −102.4 + (−78.04)
Add the absolute values.
$$\begin{array}{r} 102.40 \\ +78.04 \\ \hline 180.44 \end{array}$$
Attach the common sign.
−180.44

61. $x + z = 3.6 + 0.21 = 3.81$

65. $y - x + z = 5 - 3.6 + 0.21$
$$\begin{aligned} &= 5.00 - 3.60 + 0.21 \\ &= 1.40 + 0.21 \\ &= 1.61 \end{aligned}$$

69. To see how much the price changed, we subtract.
$$\begin{array}{r} 2.879 \\ -2.739 \\ \hline 0.140 \end{array}$$
The price changed by $0.14.

73. Perimeter $= 3.6 + 2.0 + 3.6 + 2.0$
$$= 11.2 \text{ in.}$$

77. The phrase "How much faster" indicates that we should subtract the average wind speed from the record speed.
$$\begin{array}{r} 321.0 \\ -35.2 \\ \hline 285.8 \end{array}$$
The highest wind speed is 285.8 miles per hour faster than the average wind speed.

81. To see how much snow Blue Canyon receives, we add.

$$\begin{array}{r} \overset{1}{1}29.2 \\ + 111.6 \\ \hline 240.8 \end{array}$$

Blue Canyon receives 240.8 in. of snow on average per year.

85. The phrase "Find the total" indicates that we should add durations of the flights.

$$\begin{array}{r} \overset{212}{3}\overset{11}{3}0.583 \\ 94.567 \\ 147.000 \\ + 142.900 \\ \hline 715.050 \end{array}$$

James A. Lovell spent 715.05 hours in spaceflight.

89. The phrase "How much more" indicates that we should subtract the least amount from the greatest.

$$\begin{array}{r} 22.0 \\ - 13.9 \\ \hline 8.1 \end{array}$$

The greatest consumption is 8.1 pounds per year greater than the least.

93.
$$\begin{array}{r} 46 \\ \times\ 3 \\ \hline 138 \end{array}$$

97. The unknown length, plus the sum of 2.3 and 2.3, totals 10.68.

$$\begin{array}{r} 2.3 \\ + 2.3 \\ \hline 4.6 \end{array} \qquad \begin{array}{r} 10.68 \\ - 4.60 \\ \hline 6.08 \end{array}$$

The unknown length is 6.08 inches.

101. 1 nickel, 1 dime, and 2 pennies = 0.05 + 0.10 + 0.01 + 0.01 = \$0.17; also, 3 nickels and 2 pennies = 0.05 + 0.05 + 0.05 + 0.01 + 0.01 = \$0.17; also, 1 dime and 7 pennies = 0.10 + 0.01 + 0.01 + 0.01 + 0.01 + 0.01 + 0.01 + 0.01 = \$0.17

105.
$$\begin{array}{r} 256,436.012 \\ - 256,435.235 \\ \hline 0.777 \end{array}$$

The moon is 0.777 miles farther in the second measurement.

Exercise Set 4.3

1.
$$\begin{array}{r} 0.26 \\ \times\ 5 \\ \hline 1.30 \text{ or } 1.3 \end{array}$$

5. The product, $(-2.3)(7.65)$, is negative.

$$\begin{array}{r} 7.65 \quad \text{2 decimal places} \\ \times\ 2.3 \quad \text{1 decimal place} \\ \hline 2295 \\ 15300 \\ \hline -17.595 \quad \text{3 decimal places and include negative sign} \end{array}$$

9. Exact: $5.3 \times 4.2 = 22.26$
Estimate: $5 \times 4 = 20$

13. Exact:
$$\begin{array}{r} 1.0047 \\ \times\ 8.2 \\ \hline 8.23854 \end{array}$$
Estimate:
$$\begin{array}{r} 1 \\ \times 8 \\ \hline 8 \end{array}$$

17. $6.5 \times 10 = 65$

21. $(-7.093)(1000) = -7093$

25. $(-9.83)(-0.01) = 0.0983$

29.
$$\begin{array}{r} 0.123 \\ \times\ 0.4 \\ \hline 0.0492 \end{array}$$

33.
$$\begin{array}{r} 8.6 \\ \times\ 0.15 \\ \hline 430 \\ 860 \\ \hline 1.290 \text{ or } 1.29 \end{array}$$

37. $562.3 \times 0.001 = 0.5623$

41. 5.5 billion $= 5.5 \times 1$ billion
$= 5.5 \times 1,000,000,000$
$= 5,500,000,000$
The silos hold enough to make 5,500,000,000 bars.

45. 353 thousand $= 353 \times 1$ thousand
$= 353 \times 1000$
$= 353,000$
353,000 people visited the park each week.

49. $xz - y = 3(5.7) - (-0.2)$
$= 17.1 + 0.2$
$= 17.3$

53. Circumference $= \pi \cdot$ diameter
$C = \pi \cdot 10 = 10\pi$
$C \approx 10(3.14) = 31.4$
The circumference is 10π centimeters, which is approximately 31.4 centimeters.

57. Multiply the number of ounces by the number of grams of saturated fat in 1 ounce.

$$\begin{array}{r} 6.2 \\ \times\ 4 \\ \hline 24.8 \end{array}$$

There are 24.8 grams of saturated fat in a 4-ounce serving of cream cheese.

61. Circumference $= \pi \cdot$ diameter
$C = \pi \cdot 250 = 250\pi$

$$\begin{array}{r} 250 \\ \times\ 3.14 \\ \hline 1000 \\ 2500 \\ 75000 \\ \hline 785.00 \end{array}$$

The circumference is 250π feet, which is approximately 785 feet.

65. Multiply her height in meters by the number of inches in 1 meter.

$$\begin{array}{r} 39.37 \\ \times\ 1.65 \\ \hline 19685 \\ 236220 \\ 393700 \\ \hline 64.9605 \end{array}$$

She is approximately 64.9605 inches tall.

69. a. Circumference $= 2 \cdot \pi \cdot$ radius
Smaller circle:
$C = 2 \cdot \pi \cdot 10 = 20\pi$
$C \approx 20(3.14) = 62.8$
The circumference of the smaller circle is approximately 62.8 meters.
Larger circle:
$C = 2 \cdot \pi \cdot 20 = 40\pi$
$C \approx 40(3.14) = 125.6$
The circumference of the larger circle is approximately 125.6 meters.

b. Yes, the circumference gets doubled when the radius is doubled.

73.
$$\begin{array}{r} 8 \\ 365\overline{)\ 2920} \\ -2920 \\ \hline 0 \end{array}$$

77.
$$\begin{array}{r} 3.60 \\ + 0.04 \\ \hline 3.64 \end{array}$$

81. The product of a negative number and a positive number is a negative number.

$$
\begin{array}{r}
0.221 \\
\times \;\; 0.5 \\
\hline
0.1105
\end{array}
$$

The product is -0.1105

85. answers may vary

Exercise Set 4.4

1.
$$
\begin{array}{r}
4.6 \\
3\overline{)\;13.8} \\
-12 \\
\hline
18 \\
18 \\
\hline
0
\end{array}
$$

5. $0.06\overline{)18}$ becomes
$$
\begin{array}{r}
300 \\
6\overline{)\;1800} \\
-18 \\
\hline
000
\end{array}
$$

9. Exact: $5.5\overline{)36.3}$ becomes
$$
\begin{array}{r}
6.6 \\
55\overline{)\;363.0} \\
-330 \\
\hline
33\,0 \\
-33\,0 \\
\hline
0
\end{array}
$$

Estimate:
$$
\begin{array}{r}
6 \\
6\overline{)36}
\end{array}
$$

13. A negative number divided by a positive number is a negative number.

$0.06\overline{)18}$ becomes
$$
\begin{array}{r}
300 \\
6\overline{)1800}
\end{array}
$$

The quotient is -300.

17. $0.27\overline{)1.296}$ becomes
$$
\begin{array}{r}
4.8 \\
27\overline{)\;129.6} \\
-108 \\
\hline
21\,6 \\
-21\,6 \\
\hline
0
\end{array}
$$

21. $4.756 \div 0.82$

$0.82\overline{)4.756}$ Move the decimal points 2 places.
$$
\begin{array}{r}
5.8 \\
82.\overline{)475.6} \\
-410 \\
\hline
65\,6 \\
-65\,6 \\
\hline
0
\end{array}
$$

25. Exact: $7.2\overline{)70.56}$ becomes
$$
\begin{array}{r}
9.8 \\
72\overline{)\;705.6} \\
-648 \\
\hline
57\,6 \\
-57\,6 \\
\hline
0
\end{array}
$$

Estimate:
$$
\begin{array}{r}
10 \\
7\overline{)\;70}
\end{array}
$$

29. $0.027\overline{)1.215}$ becomes
$$
\begin{array}{r}
45 \\
27\overline{)\;1215} \\
-108 \\
\hline
135 \\
-135 \\
\hline
0
\end{array}
$$

$\dfrac{1.215}{0.027} = 45$

33. $3.78\overline{)0.02079}$ becomes
$$
\begin{array}{r}
0.0055 \\
378\overline{)\;2.0790} \\
-1\,890 \\
\hline
1890 \\
-1\,890 \\
\hline
0
\end{array}
$$

37. $0.023\overline{)0.549}$ becomes
$$
\begin{array}{r}
23.869 \approx 23.87 \\
23\overline{)\;549.000} \\
-46 \\
\hline
89 \\
-69 \\
\hline
20\,0 \\
-18\,4 \\
\hline
1\,60 \\
-1\,38 \\
\hline
220 \\
-207 \\
\hline
13
\end{array}
$$

41. $\dfrac{54.982}{100} = 0.54982$

45. $12.9 \div (-1000) = -0.0129$

49. $\dfrac{13.1}{10} = 1.31$

53. $1.239 \div 3$
$$
\begin{array}{r}
0.413 \\
3\overline{)1.239} \\
-12 \\
\hline
03 \\
-3 \\
\hline
09 \\
-9 \\
\hline
0
\end{array}
$$

57. $-1.296 \div 0.27$

$0.27\overline{)1.296}$ Move the decimal points 2 places.
$$
\begin{array}{r}
4.8 \\
27.\overline{)129.6} \\
-108 \\
\hline
21\,6 \\
-21\,6 \\
\hline
0
\end{array}
$$

The quotient is -4.8.

61. $-18 \div -0.6$

$0.6\overline{)18.0}$ Move the decimal points 1 place.
$$
\begin{array}{r}
30. \\
6.\overline{)180.} \\
-18 \\
\hline
00 \\
-0 \\
\hline
0
\end{array}
$$

65. $-1.104 \div 1.6$
$$
\begin{array}{r}
0.69 \\
16\overline{)11.04} \\
-96 \\
\hline
144 \\
-144 \\
\hline
0
\end{array}
$$

Thus $-1.104 \div 1.6 = -0.69$

69. $\dfrac{4.615}{0.071} = \dfrac{4615}{71}$

$$
\begin{array}{r}
65 \\
71\overline{)4615} \\
-426 \\
\hline
355 \\
-355 \\
\hline
0
\end{array}
$$

73. $x \div y$

$5.65 \div -0.8$

$0.8\overline{)5.65}$ Move the decimal points 1 place.

$$
\begin{array}{r}
7.0625 \\
8.)\overline{56.5000} \\
-56 \\
\hline
05 \\
-0 \\
\hline
50 \\
-48 \\
\hline
20 \\
-16 \\
\hline
40 \\
-40 \\
\hline
0
\end{array}
$$

The quotient is -7.0625.

77. There are 52 weeks in one year. Therefore, there are $40 \times 52 = 2080$ hours per year.

$$
\begin{array}{r}
3641.301 \approx 3641.30 \\
2080\overline{)7573907.000} \\
-6240 \\
\hline
13339 \\
-12480 \\
\hline
8590 \\
-8320 \\
\hline
2707 \\
-2080 \\
\hline
6270 \\
-6240 \\
\hline
300 \\
-0 \\
\hline
3000 \\
-2080 \\
\hline
920
\end{array}
$$

His hourly wage was $3641.30.

81. Divide the number of crayons by 64.

11.40 rounded to the nearest tenth is 11.4 boxes.

$$
\begin{array}{r}
64\overline{)730.00} \\
-64 \\
\hline
90 \\
-64 \\
\hline
260 \\
-256 \\
\hline
40
\end{array}
$$

85. From Exercise 83, we know that there are 24 teaspoons in 4 fluid ounces. Thus, there are 48 half teaspoons (0.5 tsp) or doses in 4 fluid ounces. To see how long the medicine will last, if a dose is taken every 4 hours, there are $24 \div 4 = 6$ doses taken per day. 48 (doses) ÷ 6 (per day) = 8 days. The medicine will last 8 days.

89. $0.9 = \dfrac{9}{10}$

93. $0.3\overline{)1.278}$ becomes

$$
\begin{array}{r}
4.26 \\
3\overline{)12.78} \\
-12 \\
\hline
07 \\
-6 \\
\hline
18 \\
-18 \\
\hline
0
\end{array}
$$

$1.278 \div 0.3 = 4.26$

97. A negative number times a positive number is a negative product.

$$
\begin{array}{r}
8.6 \\
\times\ 3.1 \\
\hline
86 \\
2580 \\
\hline
26.66
\end{array}
$$

The product is -26.66.

101. 8.62×41.7 is approximately $9 \times 40 = 360$, which is choice c.

105. Add the numbers, then divide by 4.

$$
\begin{array}{r}
\overset{2}{8}6 \\
78 \\
91 \\
+\ 87 \\
\hline
342
\end{array}
$$

$$
\begin{array}{r}
85.5 \\
4\overline{)342.0} \\
-32 \\
\hline
22 \\
-20 \\
\hline
2\,0 \\
2\,0 \\
\hline
0
\end{array}
$$

The average is 85.5.

109.

$$
\begin{array}{r}
45.2 \\
4\overline{)180.8} \\
-16 \\
\hline
20 \\
-20 \\
\hline
0\,8 \\
-8 \\
\hline
0
\end{array}
$$

Each side has length 45.2 centimeters.

113. $1.15\overline{)75}$ becomes

$$
\begin{array}{r}
65.21 \approx 65.2 \\
115\overline{)7500.00} \\
-690 \\
\hline
600 \\
-575 \\
\hline
25\,0 \\
-23\,0 \\
\hline
2\,00 \\
-1\,15 \\
\hline
85
\end{array}
$$

$1.15\overline{)95}$ becomes

$$
\begin{array}{r}
82.60 \approx 82.6 \\
115\overline{)9500.00} \\
-920 \\
\hline
300 \\
-230 \\
\hline
70\,0 \\
-69\,0 \\
\hline
1\,00 \\
-0 \\
\hline
1\,00
\end{array}
$$

The range of wind speeds is 65.2–82.6 knots.

Exercise Set 4.5

1. $5\overline{)1.0}$ $\dfrac{1}{5} = 0.2$
$$\begin{array}{r} 0.2 \\ \underline{-1\,0} \\ 0 \end{array}$$

5. $4\overline{)3.00}$ $\dfrac{3}{4} = 0.75$
$$\begin{array}{r} 0.75 \\ \underline{-2\,8} \\ 20 \\ \underline{-20} \\ 0 \end{array}$$

9. $5\overline{)6.0}$ $\dfrac{6}{5} = 1.2$
$$\begin{array}{r} 1.2 \\ \underline{-5} \\ 1\,0 \\ \underline{-1\,0} \\ 0 \end{array}$$

13. $40\overline{)17.000}$ $\dfrac{17}{40} = 0.425$
$$\begin{array}{r} 0.425 \\ \underline{-16\,0} \\ 1\,00 \\ \underline{-80} \\ 200 \\ \underline{200} \\ 0 \end{array}$$

17. $3\overline{)1.000}$ $-\dfrac{1}{3} = -0.\overline{3}$
$$\begin{array}{r} 0.333\ldots \\ \underline{-9} \\ 10 \\ \underline{-9} \\ 10 \\ \underline{9} \\ 1 \end{array}$$

21. $11\overline{)7.000000}$ $\dfrac{7}{11} = 0.\overline{63}$
$$\begin{array}{r} 0.636363\ldots \\ \underline{-6\,6} \\ 40 \\ \underline{-33} \\ 70 \\ \underline{-66} \\ 40 \\ \underline{-33} \\ 70 \\ \underline{-60} \\ 40 \\ \underline{-33} \\ 7 \end{array}$$

25. $125\overline{)78.000}$ $\dfrac{78}{125} = 0.624$
$$\begin{array}{r} 0.624 \\ \underline{-75\,0} \\ 3\,00 \\ \underline{-2\,50} \\ 500 \\ \underline{-500} \\ 0 \end{array}$$

29. $\dfrac{7}{16} = 0.4375 \approx 0.44$

33. $25\overline{)17.00}$ $\dfrac{17}{25} = 0.68$
$$\begin{array}{r} 0.68 \\ \underline{-15\,0} \\ 2\,00 \\ \underline{2\,00} \\ 0 \end{array}$$

37. $94\overline{)67.000}$ $\dfrac{67}{94} \approx 0.71$
$$\begin{array}{r} 0.712 \approx 0.71 \\ \underline{-65\,8} \\ 1\,20 \\ \underline{-94} \\ 260 \\ \underline{-188} \\ 72 \end{array}$$

41. $200\overline{)43.000}$
$$\begin{array}{r} 0.215 \\ \underline{-40\,0} \\ 3\,00 \\ \underline{-2\,00} \\ 1\,000 \\ \underline{-1\,000} \\ 0 \end{array}$$

$0.215 = \dfrac{43}{200}$

45. $6\overline{)5.000}$
$$\begin{array}{r} 0.833\ldots \\ \underline{-4\,8} \\ 20 \\ \underline{-18} \\ 20 \\ \underline{-18} \\ 2 \end{array}$$

$\dfrac{5}{6} = 0.8\overline{3}$ and $0.\overline{6} < 0.8\overline{3}$, or $0.\overline{6} < \dfrac{5}{6}$

49. $7\overline{)4.000}$
$$\begin{array}{r} 0.571 \\ \underline{-3\,5} \\ 50 \\ \underline{-49} \\ 10 \\ \underline{-7} \\ 3 \end{array}$$

$\dfrac{4}{7} \approx 0.57$ and $0.57 > 0.14$, so $\dfrac{4}{7} > 0.14$.

53. $64\overline{)456.000}$
$$\begin{array}{r} 7.125 \\ \underline{-448} \\ 8\,0 \\ \underline{-6\,4} \\ 1\,60 \\ \underline{-1\,28} \\ 320 \\ \underline{-320} \\ 0 \end{array}$$

$\dfrac{456}{64} = 7.125$ and $7.123 < 7.125$, so

$7.123 < \dfrac{456}{64}$

57. $0.49 = 0.490$
$0.49, 0.491, 0.498$

61. $\dfrac{12}{5} = 2.400$

$2.37 = 2.370$

$\dfrac{17}{8} = 2.125$

$\dfrac{17}{8}, 2.37, \dfrac{12}{5}$

65. $\dfrac{1 + 0.8}{-0.6} = \dfrac{1.8}{-0.6} = \dfrac{18}{-6} = -3$

69. $(3.1 + 0.7)(2.9 - 0.9) = (3.8)(2.0) = 7.6$

73. $\dfrac{7 + 0.74}{-6} = \dfrac{7.74}{-6} = -1.29$

77. $\dfrac{1}{4}(-9.6 - 5.2) = \dfrac{1}{4}(-14.8)$
$\phantom{\dfrac{1}{4}(-9.6 - 5.2)} = -3.7$

81. Area $= l \cdot w$
$ = (0.62)\left(\dfrac{2}{5}\right)$
$ = (0.62)(0.4)$
$ = 0.248$
The area is 0.248 sq yd.

85. $x - y$
$6 - (0.3)$
$= 5.7$

89. $6^2 \cdot 2 = 36 \cdot 2$
$ = 72$

93. $1.0 = 1$

97. $\dfrac{99}{100} = 0.99$

$0.99 < 1$

101. 2047 rounds to 2000
1282 rounds to 1300
  812 rounds to   800
  703 rounds to   700
  665 rounds to   700
  497 rounds to   500
$\overline{6000}$

The total number of stations is estimated to be 6000.

105. answers may vary

Exercise Set 4.6

1. $\sqrt{4} = 2$ because $2^2 = 4$.

5. $\sqrt{\dfrac{1}{81}} = \dfrac{1}{9}$ because $\dfrac{1}{9} \cdot \dfrac{1}{9} = \dfrac{1}{81}$.

9. $\sqrt{3} \approx 1.732$

13. $\sqrt{47} \approx 6.856$

17. $\sqrt{256} = 16$ because $16^2 = 256$.

21. $\sqrt{\dfrac{49}{144}} = \dfrac{7}{12}$ because $\dfrac{7}{12} \cdot \dfrac{7}{12} = \dfrac{49}{144}$.

25. hypotenuse $= \sqrt{(\text{leg})^2 + (\text{other leg})^2}$
$ = \sqrt{(5)^2 + (12)^2}$
$ = \sqrt{25 + 144}$
$ = \sqrt{169}$
$ = 13$
The hypotenuse is 13 inches.

29. hypotenuse $= \sqrt{(\text{leg})^2 + (\text{other leg})^2}$
$ = \sqrt{(22)^2 + (48)^2}$
$ = \sqrt{484 + 2304}$
$ = \sqrt{2788}$
$ \approx 52.802$
The hypotenuse is about 52.802 meters.

33.

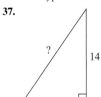

hypotenuse $= \sqrt{(\text{leg})^2 + (\text{other leg})^2}$
$ = \sqrt{(3)^2 + (4)^2}$
$ = \sqrt{9 + 16}$
$ = \sqrt{25}$
$ = 5$
The hypotenuse has length 5 units.

37.

hypotenuse $= \sqrt{(\text{leg})^2 + (\text{other leg})^2}$
$ = \sqrt{(10)^2 + (14)^2}$
$ = \sqrt{100 + 196}$
$ = \sqrt{296}$
$ \approx 17.205$
The hypotenuse is about 17.205 units.

41.

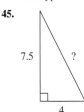

hypotenuse $= \sqrt{(\text{leg})^2 + (\text{other leg})^2}$
$ = \sqrt{(30)^2 + (30)^2}$
$ = \sqrt{900 + 900}$
$ = \sqrt{1800}$
$ \approx 42.426$
The hypotenuse is about 42.426 units.

45.

hypotenuse $= \sqrt{(\text{leg})^2 + (\text{other leg})^2}$
$ = \sqrt{(7.5)^2 + (4)^2}$
$ = \sqrt{56.25 + 16}$
$ = \sqrt{72.25}$
$ = 8.5$
The hypotenuse has length 8.5 units.

49. leg $= \sqrt{(\text{hypotenuse})^2 - (\text{other leg})^2}$

$= \sqrt{(32)^2 - (20)^2}$

$= \sqrt{1024 - 400}$

$= \sqrt{624}$

≈ 25.0

The tree is about 25 feet tall.

53. $\frac{10}{12} = \frac{5}{6}$

57. $\frac{30}{72} = \frac{5}{12}$

61. Since 101 is between $100 = 10 \cdot 10$ and $121 = 11 \cdot 11$, $\sqrt{101}$ is between 10 and 11; $\sqrt{101} \approx 10.05$.

65. $\sqrt{(20)^2 + (45)^2} = \sqrt{400 + 2025}$

$= \sqrt{2425}$

≈ 49.244

Since $\sqrt{(20)^2 + (45)^2} \neq 50$, the set does not form the sides of a right triangle.

Chapter 4 Test

1. 45.092 is forty-five and ninety-two thousandths.

5. $9.83 - 30.25 = 9.83 + (-30.25)$

Subtract the absolute values.

$\begin{array}{r} 30.25 \\ -\ 9.83 \\ \hline 20.42 \end{array}$

Attach the sign of the larger absolute value.

-20.42

9. 0.8623 rounded to the nearest thousandth is 0.862.

13. $-24.73 = -24\frac{73}{100}$

17. $\frac{0.23 + 1.63}{-0.3} = \frac{1.86}{-0.3} = -6.2$

21. $\sqrt{\frac{64}{100}} = \frac{8}{10} = \frac{4}{5}$ since $\left(\frac{8}{10}\right)^2 = \frac{64}{100}$.

25. a. $\begin{array}{r} 123.8 \\ \times\ \ \ 80 \\ \hline 9904.0 \end{array}$

The area of the lawn is 9904 square feet.

b. Multiply the number of square feet by the number of ounces per square foot.

$\begin{array}{r} 9904 \\ \times\ 0.02 \\ \hline 198.08 \end{array}$

198.08 ounces of insecticide are needed.

CHAPTER 5

Exercise Set 5.1

1. The ratio of 16 to 24 is $\frac{16}{24} = \frac{8 \cdot 2}{8 \cdot 3} = \frac{2}{3}$.

5. The ratio of 4.63 to 8.21 is $\frac{4.63}{8.21} = \frac{4.63 \cdot 100}{8.21 \cdot 100} = \frac{463}{821}$.

9. The ratio of \$32 to \$100 is $\frac{32}{100} = \frac{4 \cdot 8}{4 \cdot 25} = \frac{8}{25}$

13. The ratio of $3\frac{1}{2}$ to $12\frac{1}{4}$ is

$\frac{3\frac{1}{2}}{12\frac{1}{4}} = 3\frac{1}{2} \div 12\frac{1}{4}$

$= \frac{7}{2} \div \frac{49}{4}$

$= \frac{7}{2} \cdot \frac{4}{49}$

$= \frac{7 \cdot 2 \cdot 2}{2 \cdot 7 \cdot 7}$

$= \frac{2}{7}$

17. The ratio of length to width is $\frac{94 \text{ feet}}{50 \text{ feet}} = \frac{94}{50} = \frac{2 \cdot 47}{2 \cdot 25} = \frac{47}{25}$.

21. The ratio of women to men is $\frac{125 \text{ women}}{100 \text{ men}} = \frac{5 \cdot 5 \cdot 5}{2 \cdot 2 \cdot 5 \cdot 5}$

$= \frac{5}{2 \cdot 2} = \frac{5}{4}$

25. There is $50 - 49 = 1$ state without Target stores. The ratio of states without Target stores to states with Target stores is

$\frac{1 \text{ state}}{49 \text{ states}} = \frac{1}{49}$.

29. The rate of 15 returns for 100 sales is

$\frac{15 \text{ returns}}{100 \text{ sales}} = \frac{15}{100} = \frac{5 \cdot 3}{5 \cdot 20} = \frac{3}{20} = \frac{3 \text{ returns}}{20 \text{ sales}}$

33. The rate of 18 gallons for 4 acres is $\frac{18}{4} = \frac{2 \cdot 9}{2 \cdot 2} = \frac{9 \text{ gal}}{2 \text{ acres}}$

37. 1 minute = 60 seconds

$\begin{array}{r} 90 \\ 60{\overline{\smash{\big)}\,5400}} \\ \underline{-\ 540} \\ 00 \\ \underline{-\ 0} \\ 0 \end{array}$

$\frac{5400 \text{ wingbeats}}{1 \text{ minute}} = \frac{5400 \text{ wingbeats}}{60 \text{ seconds}}$

$= \frac{90 \text{ wingbeats}}{1 \text{ second}}$

$= 90 \text{ wingbeats/second}$

41. $\begin{array}{r} 7600 \\ 15{\overline{\smash{\big)}\,114000}} \\ \underline{-\ 105} \\ 90 \\ \underline{-\ 90} \\ 00 \\ \underline{-\ 0} \\ 00 \\ \underline{-\ 0} \\ 0 \end{array}$

$\frac{114,000 \text{ sq mi}}{15 \text{ counties}} = \frac{7600 \text{ sq mi}}{1 \text{ county}} = 7600 \text{ sq mi/county}$

45.
$$
\begin{array}{r}
46600 \\
25\overline{)1165000} \\
-100 \\
\hline
165 \\
-150 \\
\hline
150 \\
-150 \\
\hline
00 \\
-0 \\
\hline
00 \\
-0 \\
\hline
0
\end{array}
$$

$$\frac{\$1{,}165{,}000}{25 \text{ houses}} = \frac{\$46{,}600}{1 \text{ house}} = \$46{,}600/\text{house}$$

49. a. $14.5\overline{)400}$ becomes $145\overline{)4000.00}$
$$
\begin{array}{r}
27.58 \approx 27.6 \\
-290 \\
\hline
1100 \\
-1015 \\
\hline
85\,0 \\
-72\,5 \\
\hline
12\,50 \\
-11\,60 \\
\hline
90
\end{array}
$$

The unit rate for the car is approximately 27.6 miles/gallon.

b. $9.25\overline{)270}$ becomes $925\overline{)27000.00}$
$$
\begin{array}{r}
29.18 \approx 29.2 \\
-1850 \\
\hline
8500 \\
-8325 \\
\hline
175\,0 \\
-92\,5 \\
\hline
82\,50 \\
-74\,00 \\
\hline
8\,50
\end{array}
$$

The unit rate for the truck is approximately 29.2 miles/gallon.

c. Since the unit rate of the truck is larger, the truck gets better gas mileage.

53. $16\overline{)1.6900}$
$$
\begin{array}{r}
0.1056 \approx 0.106 \\
-16 \\
\hline
09 \\
-0 \\
\hline
90 \\
-80 \\
\hline
100 \\
-96 \\
\hline
4
\end{array}
$$

The 16-ounce size costs about $0.106 per ounce.

$$
\begin{array}{r}
0.115 \\
6\overline{)0.690} \\
-6 \\
\hline
09 \\
-6 \\
\hline
30 \\
-30 \\
\hline
0
\end{array}
$$

The 6-ounce size costs $0.115 per ounce.
The 16-ounce size is the better buy.

57. $100\overline{)0.5900}$
$$
\begin{array}{r}
0.0059 \approx 0.006 \\
-500 \\
\hline
900 \\
-900 \\
\hline
0
\end{array}
$$

The 100-count napkins cost about $0.006 per napkin.

$$
\begin{array}{r}
0.0051 \approx 0.005 \\
180\overline{)0.9300} \\
-900 \\
\hline
300 \\
-180 \\
\hline
120
\end{array}
$$

The 180-count napkins cost about $0.005 per napkin.
The 180-count package is the better buy.

61. $3.7\overline{)0.555} = 37\overline{)5.55}$
$$
\begin{array}{r}
0.15 \\
3\,7 \\
\hline
185 \\
185 \\
\hline
0
\end{array}
$$

65. $\dfrac{6 \text{ inches}}{15 \text{ inches}}$ is not in simplest form. $\dfrac{6}{15} = \dfrac{3 \cdot 2}{3 \cdot 5} = \dfrac{2}{5}$

69. Fill in the "Miles Driven" column by subtracting "Beginning Odometer Reading" from "Ending Odometer Reading." Fill in the "Miles per Gallon" column by dividing "Miles Driven" by "Gallons of Gas Used," and rounding to the nearest tenth.

Miles Driven	Miles per Gallon
257	19.2
352	22.3
347	21.6

73. answers may vary

77. a. $\dfrac{19 \text{ states}}{50 \text{ states}} = \dfrac{19}{50}$

b. $50 - 19 = 31$ states without mandatory helmet laws.

$\dfrac{19 \text{ with laws}}{31 \text{ without laws}} = \dfrac{19}{31}$

c. no; answers may vary

Exercise Set 5.2

1. $\dfrac{10 \text{ diamonds}}{6 \text{ opals}} = \dfrac{5 \text{ diamonds}}{3 \text{ opals}}$

5. $\dfrac{6 \text{ eagles}}{58 \text{ sparrows}} = \dfrac{3 \text{ eagles}}{29 \text{ sparrows}}$

9. $\dfrac{22 \text{ vanilla wafers}}{1 \text{ cup cookie crumbs}} = \dfrac{55 \text{ vanilla wafers}}{2.5 \text{ cups cookie crumbs}}$

13. $\dfrac{8}{6} \overset{?}{=} \dfrac{9}{7}$

$8 \cdot 7 \overset{?}{=} 9 \cdot 6$

$56 \neq 54$

false

17. $\dfrac{5}{8} \overset{?}{=} \dfrac{625}{1000}$

$5 \cdot 1000 \overset{?}{=} 8 \cdot 625$

$5000 = 5000$

true

21. $\dfrac{8}{10} \overset{?}{=} \dfrac{5.6}{0.7}$

$8(0.7) \overset{?}{=} 10(5.6)$

$5.6 \neq 56$

false

25. $\dfrac{2\frac{2}{5}}{\frac{2}{3}} \overset{?}{=} \dfrac{1\frac{1}{9}}{\frac{1}{4}}$

$2\dfrac{2}{5} \cdot \dfrac{1}{4} \overset{?}{=} 1\dfrac{1}{9} \cdot \dfrac{2}{3}$

$\dfrac{12}{5} \cdot \dfrac{1}{4} \overset{?}{=} \dfrac{10}{9} \cdot \dfrac{2}{3}$

$\dfrac{3}{5} \neq \dfrac{20}{27}$

false

29. $\dfrac{8}{12} \overset{?}{=} \dfrac{4}{6}$

$8 \cdot 6 \overset{?}{=} 12 \cdot 4$

$48 = 48$

true

33. $\dfrac{1.8}{2} \overset{?}{=} \dfrac{4.5}{5}$

$1.8(5) \overset{?}{=} 4.5(2)$

$9 = 9$

true

37. $\dfrac{n}{5} = \dfrac{6}{10}$

$10n = 6 \cdot 5$

$10n = 30$

$n = 3$

41. $\dfrac{n}{8} = \dfrac{50}{100}$

$100n = 8 \cdot 50$

$100n = 400$

$n = 4$

45. $\dfrac{24}{n} = \dfrac{60}{96}$

$24 \cdot 96 = 60n$

$2304 = 60n$

$38.4 = n$

49. $\dfrac{0.05}{12} = \dfrac{n}{0.6}$

$0.05(0.6) = 12n$

$0.03 = 12n$

$0.0025 = n$

53. $\dfrac{\frac{1}{3}}{\frac{3}{8}} = \dfrac{\frac{2}{5}}{n}$

$\dfrac{1}{3}n = \dfrac{3}{8} \cdot \dfrac{2}{5}$

$\dfrac{1}{3}n = \dfrac{3}{20}$

$n = \dfrac{3}{20} \div \dfrac{1}{3}$

$n = \dfrac{3}{20} \cdot \dfrac{3}{1}$

$n = \dfrac{9}{20}$

57. $\dfrac{n}{1\frac{1}{5}} = \dfrac{4\frac{1}{6}}{6\frac{2}{3}}$

$\left(6\dfrac{2}{3}\right)n = \left(1\dfrac{1}{5}\right)\left(4\dfrac{1}{6}\right)$

$\dfrac{20}{3}n = \dfrac{6}{5} \cdot \dfrac{25}{6}$

$\dfrac{20}{3}n = \dfrac{5}{1}$

$n = \dfrac{5}{1} \div \dfrac{20}{3}$

$n = \dfrac{5}{1} \cdot \dfrac{3}{20}$

$n = \dfrac{3}{4}$

61. 8.01   8.1

$\uparrow$ $\uparrow$

0 $<$ 1 so

$8.01 < 8.1$

65. $5\dfrac{1}{3} = \dfrac{16}{3}$

$6\dfrac{2}{3} = \dfrac{20}{3}$

$16 < 20$, so $5\dfrac{1}{3} < 6\dfrac{2}{3}$

69. $\dfrac{6}{18} = \dfrac{1}{3}$

$\dfrac{6}{1} = \dfrac{18}{3}$

$\dfrac{3}{18} = \dfrac{1}{6}$

$\dfrac{18}{6} = \dfrac{3}{1}$

73. answers may vary

77. $\dfrac{n}{1150} = \dfrac{588}{483}$

$483n = 1150 \cdot 588$

$483n = 676{,}200$

$n = 1400$

Exercise Set 5.3

1. Let n = number of passes completed.

completed $\rightarrow \dfrac{n}{27} = \dfrac{4}{9} \leftarrow$ completed

attempted $\rightarrow$ $\phantom{\dfrac{n}{27}}$ $\phantom{\dfrac{4}{9}}$ $\leftarrow$ attempted

$9n = 4 \cdot 27$

$9n = 108$

$n = 12$

12 passes were completed.

5. Let n = number of applications received.

applications $\rightarrow \dfrac{n}{180} = \dfrac{7}{2} \leftarrow$ applications

accepted $\rightarrow$ $\phantom{\dfrac{n}{180}}$ $\phantom{\dfrac{7}{2}}$ $\leftarrow$ accepted

$2n = 7 \cdot 180$

$2n = 1260$

$n = 630$

630 applications were received.

9. Let n = square feet of floor space needed.

floor space $\rightarrow \dfrac{n}{30} = \dfrac{9}{1} \leftarrow$ floor space

students $\rightarrow$ $\phantom{\dfrac{n}{30}}$ $\phantom{\dfrac{9}{1}}$ $\leftarrow$ students

$1 \cdot n = 9 \cdot 30$

$n = 270$

270 square feet of floor space are needed.

13. Let n = number of kilometers between Milan and Rome.

kilometers $\rightarrow \dfrac{n}{15} = \dfrac{30}{1} \leftarrow$ kilometers
cm on map $\rightarrow$ $\qquad \leftarrow$ cm on map
$$1 \cdot n = 15 \cdot 30$$
$$n = 450$$

Milan and Rome are 450 kilometers apart.

17. Let n = number of bags of fertilizer. The area of the lawn is $260 \cdot 180 = 46,800$ square feet.

bags $\rightarrow \dfrac{n}{46,800} = \dfrac{1}{3000} \leftarrow$ bags
square feet $\rightarrow$ $\qquad \leftarrow$ square feet
$$3000n = 1 \cdot 46,800$$
$$300n = 46,800$$
$$n = 15.6$$

Since only whole bags of fertilizer can be purchased, 16 bags should be purchased.

21. Let n = the number of hits the player is expected to get.

hits $\rightarrow \dfrac{n}{40} = \dfrac{3}{8} \leftarrow$ hits
times at bat $\rightarrow$ $\qquad \leftarrow$ times at bat
$$8n = 3 \cdot 40$$
$$8n = 120$$
$$n = 15$$

The Cubs player would be expected to get 15 hits.

25. Let n = the number of weeks the envelopes are expected to last.

weeks $\rightarrow \dfrac{n}{144} = \dfrac{3}{5} \leftarrow$ weeks
boxes $\rightarrow$ $\qquad \leftarrow$ boxes
$$5n = 3 \cdot 144$$
$$5n = 432$$
$$n = 86.4$$

A gross of boxes of envelopes would be expected to last 86 weeks.

29. Let n = estimated head-to-toe height of the Statue of Liberty.

height $\rightarrow \dfrac{n}{42} = \dfrac{5\frac{1}{3}}{2} \leftarrow$ height
arm length $\rightarrow$ $\qquad \leftarrow$ arm length
$$2n = 5\frac{1}{3} \cdot 42$$
$$2n = \frac{16}{3} \cdot 42$$
$$2n = 224$$
$$n = 112$$

The head-to-toe height of the Statue of Liberty is estimated to be 112 feet.

$$112 - 111\frac{1}{12} = \frac{11}{12}$$

The difference is $\frac{11}{12}$ foot, or 11 inches.

33. Let n = the estimated height of the Empire State Building.

height $\rightarrow \dfrac{n}{102} = \dfrac{881}{72} \leftarrow$ height
stories $\rightarrow$ $\qquad \leftarrow$ stories
$$72n = 102 \cdot 881$$
$$72n = 89,862$$
$$n \approx 1248$$

The height of the Empire State Building is approximately 1248 feet.

37. Let n = the number of calories in a nine-piece order.

calories $\rightarrow \dfrac{n}{9} = \dfrac{190}{4} \leftarrow$ calories
pieces $\rightarrow$ $\qquad \leftarrow$ pieces
$$4n = 9(190)$$
$$4n = 1710$$
$$n = 427.5$$

There are 427.5 calories in a 9-piece order.

41. Let n = the amount of rock salt to be used.

salt $\rightarrow \dfrac{n}{12} = \dfrac{1}{5} \leftarrow$ salt
ice $\rightarrow$ $\qquad \leftarrow$ ice
$$5n = 12 \cdot 1$$
$$5n = 12$$
$$n = 2.4$$

2.4 cups of rock salt should be used.

45. a. Let n = the number of milligrams in a daily dose.

milligrams $\rightarrow \dfrac{n}{275} = \dfrac{150}{20} \leftarrow$ milligrams
pounds $\rightarrow$ $\qquad \leftarrow$ pounds
$$20n = 275 \cdot 150$$
$$20n = 41,250$$
$$n = 2062.5$$

The man should receive 2062.5 milligrams daily.

b. One day is 24 hours, so the man receives 3 500-milligram doses, for a total of 1500 milligrams, daily. Since his daily dose should be 2062.5 milligrams, the dosage is not correct.

49.
$$\begin{array}{r} 5 \\ 2\overline{)10} \\ 2\overline{)20} \end{array}$$
$$20 = 2 \cdot 2 \cdot 5 = 2^2 \cdot 5$$

53.
$$\begin{array}{r} 2 \\ 2\overline{)\ 4} \\ 2\overline{)\ 8} \\ 2\overline{)16} \\ 2\overline{)32} \end{array}$$
$$32 = 2 \cdot 2 \cdot 2 \cdot 2 \cdot 2 = 2^5$$

57. Let n = the number of ml of medicine to be administered.

mg $\rightarrow \dfrac{10}{n} = \dfrac{8}{1} \leftarrow$ mg
ml $\rightarrow$ $\qquad \leftarrow$ ml
$$10 = 8n$$
$$\frac{1}{8} \cdot 10 = n$$
$$1.25 = n$$

1.25 ml of medicine should be administered.

61.
first weight $\rightarrow \dfrac{40}{n} = \dfrac{60}{7} \leftarrow$ second weight
second distance $\rightarrow$ $\qquad \leftarrow$ first distance
$$40 \cdot 7 = 60n$$
$$280 = 60n$$
$$\frac{1}{60} \cdot 280 = n$$
$$\frac{14}{3} = n$$

The distance should be $\frac{14}{3}$ or $4\frac{2}{3}$ feet.

Exercise Set 5.4

1. $60 \text{ in.} = \dfrac{60 \text{ in.}}{1} \cdot \dfrac{1 \text{ ft}}{12 \text{ in.}} = \dfrac{60}{12} \text{ ft} = 5 \text{ ft}$

5. $42,240 \text{ ft} = \dfrac{42,240 \text{ ft}}{1} \cdot \dfrac{1 \text{ mi}}{5280 \text{ ft}}$
$$= \dfrac{42,240}{5280} \text{ mi}$$
$$= 8 \text{ mi}$$

9. $10 \text{ ft} = \dfrac{10 \text{ ft}}{1} \cdot \dfrac{1 \text{ yd}}{3 \text{ ft}} = \dfrac{10}{3} \text{ yd} = 3\frac{1}{3} \text{ yd}$

13. $162 \text{ in.} = \dfrac{162 \text{ in.}}{1} \cdot \dfrac{1 \text{ ft}}{12 \text{ in.}} \cdot \dfrac{1 \text{ yd}}{3 \text{ ft}}$
$$= \dfrac{162}{36} \text{ yd}$$
$$= 4.5 \text{ yd}$$

17. $40 \text{ ft} = \dfrac{40 \text{ ft}}{1} \cdot \dfrac{1 \text{ yd}}{3 \text{ ft}} = \dfrac{40}{3} \text{ yd}$

$$\begin{array}{r} 13 \text{ yd } 1 \text{ ft} \\ 3\overline{)\ 40} \\ \underline{-3} \\ 10 \\ \underline{-9} \\ 1 \end{array}$$

21. $10{,}000 \text{ ft} = \dfrac{10{,}000 \text{ ft}}{1} \cdot \dfrac{1 \text{ mi}}{5280 \text{ ft}} = \dfrac{10{,}000}{5280} \text{ mi}$

$$5280\overline{)10{,}000}\;\;\; ^{1 \text{ mi } 4720 \text{ ft}}$$
$$\underline{-\;5\,280}$$
$$4\,720$$

25. $7 \text{ yd } 2 \text{ ft} = \dfrac{7 \text{ yd}}{1} \cdot \dfrac{3 \text{ ft}}{1 \text{ yd}} + 2 \text{ ft}$

$\phantom{7 \text{ yd } 2 \text{ ft}} = 21 \text{ ft} + 2 \text{ ft}$

$\phantom{7 \text{ yd } 2 \text{ ft}} = 23 \text{ ft}$

29. $5 \text{ ft } 8 \text{ in.} + 6 \text{ ft } 7 \text{ in.} = 11 \text{ ft } 15 \text{ in.}$

$\phantom{5 \text{ ft } 8 \text{ in.} + 6 \text{ ft } 7 \text{ in.}} = 11 \text{ ft} + 1 \text{ ft } 3 \text{ in.}$

$\phantom{5 \text{ ft } 8 \text{ in.} + 6 \text{ ft } 7 \text{ in.}} = 12 \text{ ft } 3 \text{ in.}$

33. $24 \text{ ft } 8 \text{ in.}$
$\underline{-\;16 \text{ ft } 3 \text{ in.}}$
  $8 \text{ ft } 5 \text{ in.}$

37. $6 \text{ ft } 8 \text{ in.} \div 2 = 3 \text{ ft } 4 \text{ in.}$

41. $40 \text{ m} = \dfrac{40 \text{ m}}{1} \cdot \dfrac{100 \text{ cm}}{1 \text{ m}} = 4000 \text{ cm}$

45. $300 \text{ m} = \dfrac{300 \text{ m}}{1} \cdot \dfrac{1 \text{ km}}{1000 \text{ m}} = \dfrac{300}{1000} \text{ km} = 0.3 \text{ km}$

49. $1500 \text{ cm} = \dfrac{1500 \text{ cm}}{1} \cdot \dfrac{1 \text{ m}}{100 \text{ cm}} = \dfrac{1500}{100} \text{ m} = 15 \text{ m}$

53. $7 \text{ km} = \dfrac{7 \text{ km}}{1} \cdot \dfrac{1000 \text{ m}}{1 \text{ km}} = 7000 \text{ m}$

57. $20.1 \text{ mm} = \dfrac{20.1 \text{ mm}}{1} \cdot \dfrac{1 \text{ dm}}{100 \text{ mm}}$

$\phantom{20.1 \text{ mm}} = \dfrac{20.1}{100} \text{ dm}$

$\phantom{20.1 \text{ mm}} = 0.201 \text{ dm}$

61. 8.6 m
$\underline{+\;0.34 \text{ m}}$
  8.94 m

65. 24.8 mm $\quad$ 24.8 mm $\qquad$ 2.48 cm
$\underline{-\;1.19 \text{ cm}}$ $\;\;$ $\underline{-\;11.9 \text{ mm}}$ or $\underline{-\;1.19 \text{ cm}}$
 12.9 mm $\qquad$ 1.29 cm

69. $18.3 \text{ m} \times 3 = 54.9 \text{ m}$

73.

	Yards	Feet	Inches
Chrysler Building in New York City	$348\frac{2}{3}$	1046	12,552

	meters	millimeters	kilometers	centimeters
77. Length of elephant	5	5000	0.005	500
81. Distance from London to Paris	342,000	342,000,000	342	34,200,000

85. $16 \text{ ft } 5 \text{ in.}$ $\quad$ $15 \text{ ft } 17 \text{ in.}$
$\underline{-\;2 \text{ ft } 6 \text{ in.}}$ $\;\;$ $\underline{-\;2 \text{ ft }\;\; 6 \text{ in.}}$
 $13 \text{ ft } 11 \text{ in.}$

A hand of the Statue of Liberty is 13 ft 11 in. longer than the width of an eye.

89. 80 mm $\quad$ 80.0 mm
$\underline{-\;5.33 \text{ cm}}$ $\;\;$ $\underline{-\;53.3 \text{ mm}}$
 26.7 mm

The ice must be 26.7 mm thicker before skating is allowed.

93.
$$20\overline{)67.00}\;\;\; ^{3.35}$$
$$\underline{-\;60}$$
$$\;\;7\,0$$
$$\underline{-\;6\,0}$$
$$\;\;\;1\,00$$
$$\underline{-\;1\,00}$$
$$\;\;\;\;\;\;0$$

Each piece will be 3.35 meters long.

97. $0.21 = \dfrac{21}{100}$

101. $\dfrac{1}{4} = \dfrac{1}{4} \cdot \dfrac{25}{25}$

$\phantom{\dfrac{1}{4}} = \dfrac{25}{100}$

$\phantom{\dfrac{1}{4}} = 0.25$

105. answers may vary. For example, $1\frac{1}{3}$ yd or 48 in.

Exercise Set 5.5

1. $2 \text{ lb} = \dfrac{2 \text{ lb}}{1} \cdot \dfrac{16 \text{ oz}}{1 \text{ lb}} = 2 \cdot 16 \text{ oz} = 32 \text{ oz}$

5. $12{,}000 \text{ lb} = \dfrac{12{,}000 \text{ lb}}{1} \cdot \dfrac{1 \text{ ton}}{2000 \text{ lb}}$

$\phantom{12{,}000 \text{ lb}} = \dfrac{12{,}000}{2000} \text{ tons}$

$\phantom{12{,}000 \text{ lb}} = 6 \text{ tons}$

9. $3500 \text{ lb} = \dfrac{3500 \text{ lb}}{1} \cdot \dfrac{1 \text{ ton}}{2000 \text{ lb}}$

$\phantom{3500 \text{ lb}} = \dfrac{3500}{2000} \text{ tons}$

$\phantom{3500 \text{ lb}} = \dfrac{7}{4} \text{ tons}$

$\phantom{3500 \text{ lb}} = 1\dfrac{3}{4} \text{ tons}$

13. $4.9 \text{ tons} = \dfrac{4.9 \text{ tons}}{1} \cdot \dfrac{2000 \text{ lb}}{1 \text{ ton}}$

$\phantom{4.9 \text{ tons}} = 4.9 \cdot 2000 \text{ lb}$

$\phantom{4.9 \text{ tons}} = 9800 \text{ lb}$

17. $2950 \text{ lb} = \dfrac{2950 \text{ lb}}{1} \cdot \dfrac{1 \text{ ton}}{2000 \text{ lb}}$

$\phantom{2950 \text{ lb}} = \dfrac{2950}{2000} \text{ tons}$

$\phantom{2950 \text{ lb}} = \dfrac{59}{40} \text{ tons}$

$\phantom{2950 \text{ lb}} \approx 1.5 \text{ tons}$

21. $5\dfrac{3}{4} \text{ lb} = \dfrac{23}{4} \text{ lb} = \dfrac{\frac{23}{4} \text{ lb}}{1} \cdot \dfrac{16 \text{ oz}}{1 \text{ lb}}$

$\phantom{5\dfrac{3}{4} \text{ lb}} = \dfrac{23}{4} \cdot 16 \text{ oz} = 23 \cdot 4 \text{ oz} = 92 \text{ oz}$

25. $89 \text{ oz} = \dfrac{89 \text{ oz}}{1} \cdot \dfrac{1 \text{ lb}}{16 \text{ oz}} = \dfrac{89}{16} \text{ lb}$

$$16\overline{)89}\;\;\; ^{5 \text{ lb } 9 \text{ oz}}$$
$$\underline{-\;80}$$
$$\;\;\;9$$

$89 \text{ oz} = 5 \text{ lb } 9 \text{ oz}$

29. $6 \text{ tons } 1540 \text{ lb} + 2 \text{ tons } 850 \text{ lb}$

$ = 8 \text{ tons } 2390 \text{ lb}$

$ = 8 \text{ tons} + 1 \text{ ton } 390 \text{ lb}$

$ = 9 \text{ tons } 390 \text{ lb}$

33.
$$\begin{array}{r} 12\text{ lb }4\text{ oz} \\ -\ 3\text{ lb }9\text{ oz} \\ \hline \end{array} \qquad \begin{array}{r} 11\text{ lb }20\text{ oz} \\ -\ 3\text{ lb }\ 9\text{ oz} \\ \hline 8\text{ lb }11\text{ oz} \end{array}$$

37. 6 tons 1500 lb $\div 5 = \dfrac{6}{5}$ tons 300 lb

$$= 1\frac{1}{5}\text{ tons }300\text{ lb}$$

$$= 1\text{ ton} + \frac{2000\text{ lb}}{5} + 300\text{ lb}$$

$$= 1\text{ ton} + 400\text{ lb} + 300\text{ lb}$$

$$= 1\text{ ton }700\text{ lb}$$

41. $4\text{ g} = \dfrac{4\text{ g}}{1} \cdot \dfrac{1000\text{ mg}}{1\text{ g}} = 4 \cdot 1000\text{ mg} = 4000\text{ mg}$

45. $48\text{ mg} = \dfrac{48\text{ mg}}{1} \cdot \dfrac{1\text{ g}}{1000\text{ mg}} = \dfrac{48}{1000}\text{ g} = 0.048\text{ g}$

49. $15.14\text{ g} = \dfrac{15.14\text{ g}}{1} \cdot \dfrac{1000\text{ mg}}{1\text{ g}}$

$$= 15.14 \cdot 1000\text{ mg}$$

$$= 15,140\text{ mg}$$

53. $35\text{ hg} = \dfrac{35\text{ hg}}{1} \cdot \dfrac{10,000\text{ cg}}{1\text{ hg}}$

$$= 35 \cdot 10,000\text{ cg}$$

$$= 350,000\text{ cg}$$

57. $205\text{ mg} + 5.61\text{ g} = 0.205\text{ g} + 5.61\text{ g} = 5.815\text{ g}$
or
$205\text{ mg} + 5.61\text{ g} = 205\text{ mg} + 5610\text{ mg}$
$$= 5815\text{ mg}$$

61. $1.61\text{ kg} - 250\text{ g} = 1.61\text{ kg} - 0.250\text{ kg} = 1.36\text{ kg}$
or
$1.61\text{ kg} - 250\text{ g} = 1610\text{ g} - 250\text{ g} = 1360\text{ g}$

65. $17\text{ kg} \div 8 = \dfrac{17}{8}\text{ kg}$

$$\begin{array}{r} 2.125 \\ 8\overline{)\ 17.000} \\ -16 \\ \hline 1\ 0 \\ -\ 8 \\ \hline 20 \\ -16 \\ \hline 40 \\ -40 \\ \hline 0 \end{array}$$

$17\text{ kg} \div 8 = 2.125\text{ kg}$

69.

Object	Tons	Pounds	Ounces
A 12-inch cube of osmium	$\dfrac{269}{400}$ or 0.6725	1345	$21,520$

73.

Object	Grams	Kilograms	Milligrams	Centigrams
A six-year-old boy	$21,000$	21	$21,000,000$	$2,100,000$

77. $0.09\text{ g} = \dfrac{0.09\text{ g}}{1} \cdot \dfrac{1000\text{ mg}}{1\text{ g}} = 0.09 \cdot 1000\text{ mg} = 90\text{ mg}$

$90\text{ mg} - 60\text{ mg} = 30\text{ mg}$
The extra-strength tablet contains 30 mg more medication.

81.
$$\begin{array}{r} 64\text{ lb }\ 8\text{ oz} \\ -28\text{ lb }10\text{ oz} \\ \hline \end{array} \qquad \begin{array}{r} 63\text{ lb }24\text{ oz} \\ -28\text{ lb }10\text{ oz} \\ \hline 35\text{ lb }14\text{ oz} \end{array}$$
Carla's zucchini was 35 lb 14 oz lighter than the record weight.

85. $3 \times 16 = 48$
3 cartons contain 48 boxes of fruit.
$3\text{ mg} \times 48 = 144\text{ mg}$
3 cartons contain 144 mg of preservatives.

89. $3\text{ lb }4\text{ oz} \times 10 = 30\text{ lb }40\text{ oz}$
$$= 30\text{ lb} + 2\text{ lb }8\text{ oz}$$
$$= 32\text{ lb }8\text{ oz}$$
Each box weighs 32 lb 8 oz.
$32\text{ lb }8\text{ oz} \times 4 = 128\text{ lb }32\text{ oz}$
$$= 128\text{ lb} + 2\text{ lb}$$
$$= 130\text{ lb}$$
4 boxes of meat weigh 130 lb.

93. $\dfrac{4}{25} = \dfrac{4}{25} \cdot \dfrac{4}{4} = \dfrac{16}{100} = 0.16$

97. answers may vary

101. answers may vary

Exercise Set 5.6

1. $32\text{ fl oz} = \dfrac{32\text{ fl oz}}{1} \cdot \dfrac{1\text{ c}}{8\text{ fl oz}} = \dfrac{32}{8}\text{ c} = 4\text{ c}$

5. $10\text{ qt} = \dfrac{10\text{ qt}}{1} \cdot \dfrac{1\text{ gal}}{4\text{ qt}} = \dfrac{10}{4}\text{ gal} = 2\dfrac{1}{2}\text{ gal}$

9. $2\text{ qt} = \dfrac{2\text{ qt}}{1} \cdot \dfrac{2\text{ pt}}{1\text{ qt}} \cdot \dfrac{2\text{ c}}{1\text{ pt}} = 2 \cdot 2 \cdot 2\text{ c} = 8\text{ c}$

13. $6\text{ gal} = \dfrac{6\text{ gal}}{1} \cdot \dfrac{4\text{ qt}}{1\text{ gal}} \cdot \dfrac{2\text{ pt}}{1\text{ qt}} \cdot \dfrac{2\text{ c}}{1\text{ pt}} \cdot \dfrac{8\text{ fl oz}}{1\text{ c}}$

$$= 6 \cdot 4 \cdot 2 \cdot 2 \cdot 8\text{ fl oz}$$

$$= 768\text{ fl oz}$$

17. $5\text{ gal }3\text{ qt} = \dfrac{5\text{ gal}}{1} \cdot \dfrac{4\text{ qt}}{1\text{ gal}} + 3\text{ qt}$

$$= 5 \cdot 4\text{ qt} + 3\text{ qt}$$

$$= 20\text{ qt} + 3\text{ qt}$$

$$= 23\text{ qt}$$

21. $58\text{ qt} = 56\text{ qt} + 2\text{ qt}$

$$= \dfrac{56\text{ qt}}{1} \cdot \dfrac{1\text{ gal}}{4\text{ qt}} + 2\text{ qt}$$

$$= \dfrac{56}{4}\text{ gal} + 2\text{ qt}$$

$$= 14\text{ gal }2\text{ qt}$$

25. $2\dfrac{3}{4}\text{ gal} = \dfrac{11}{4}\text{ gal}$

$$= \dfrac{\frac{11}{4}\text{ gal}}{1} \cdot \dfrac{4\text{ qt}}{1\text{ gal}} \cdot \dfrac{2\text{ pt}}{1\text{ qt}}$$

$$= \dfrac{11}{4} \cdot 4 \cdot 2\text{ pt}$$

$$= 22\text{ pt}$$

29. $1\text{ c }5\text{ fl oz} + 2\text{ c }7\text{ fl oz} = 3\text{ c }12\text{ fl oz}$
$$= 3\text{ c} + 1\text{ c }4\text{ fl oz}$$
$$= 4\text{ c }4\text{ fl oz}$$

33.
$$\begin{array}{r} 3\text{ gal }1\text{ qt} \\ -\ 1\text{ qt }1\text{ pt} \\ \hline \end{array} \qquad \begin{array}{r} 2\text{ gal }5\text{ qt} \\ -\ 1\text{ qt }1\text{ pt} \\ \hline \end{array} \qquad \begin{array}{r} 2\text{ gal }4\text{ qt }2\text{ pt} \\ -\ 1\text{ qt }1\text{ pt} \\ \hline 2\text{ gal }3\text{ qt }1\text{ pt} \end{array}$$

37. $8\text{ gal }2\text{ qt} \times 2 = 16\text{ gal }4\text{ qt}$
$$= 16\text{ gal} + 1\text{ gal}$$
$$= 17\text{ gal}$$

41. $5\text{ L} = \dfrac{5\text{ L}}{1} \cdot \dfrac{1000\text{ ml}}{1\text{ L}} = 5000\text{ ml}$

45. $3.2\text{ L} = \dfrac{3.2\text{ L}}{1} \cdot \dfrac{100\text{ cl}}{1\text{ L}} = 320\text{ cl}$

49. $64 \text{ ml} = \dfrac{64 \text{ ml}}{1} \cdot \dfrac{1 \text{ L}}{1000 \text{ ml}} = \dfrac{64}{1000} \text{ L} = 0.064 \text{ L}$

53. $3.6 \text{ L} = \dfrac{3.6 \text{ L}}{1} \cdot \dfrac{1000 \text{ ml}}{1 \text{ L}} = 3600 \text{ ml}$

57. $2.9 \text{ L} + 19.6 \text{ L} = 22.5 \text{ L}$

61.
$$\begin{array}{r} 8.6 \text{ L} \\ - \ 190 \text{ ml} \\ \hline \end{array} \quad \begin{array}{r} 8600 \text{ ml} \\ - \ 190 \text{ ml} \\ \hline 8410 \text{ ml} \end{array} \quad \text{or} \quad \begin{array}{r} 8.60 \text{ L} \\ - \ 0.19 \text{ L} \\ \hline 8.41 \text{ L} \end{array}$$

65. $480 \text{ ml} \times 8 = 3840 \text{ ml}$

69.

Capacity	Cups	Gallons	Quarts	Pints
An average-size bath of water	336	21	84	168

73.
$$\begin{array}{r} 2 \text{ L} \\ - \ 410 \text{ ml} \\ \hline \end{array} \quad \begin{array}{r} 2.000 \text{ L} \\ - \ 0.410 \text{ L} \\ \hline 1.590 \text{ L} \end{array}$$
There is 1.59 L left in the bottle.

77. $5 \text{ pt } 1 \text{ c} + 2 \text{ pt } 1 \text{ c} = 7 \text{ pt } 2 \text{ c}$
$= 7 \text{ pt} + 1 \text{ pt}$
$= 8 \text{ pt}$
$= \dfrac{8 \text{ pt}}{1} \cdot \dfrac{1 \text{ qt}}{2 \text{ pt}}$
$= \dfrac{8}{2} \text{ qt}$
$= \dfrac{4 \text{ qt}}{1} \cdot \dfrac{1 \text{ gal}}{4 \text{ qt}}$
$= \dfrac{4}{4} \text{ gal}$
$= 1 \text{ gal}$
Yes, the liquid can be poured into the container without causing it to overflow.

81. $\dfrac{20}{25} = \dfrac{4 \cdot 5}{5 \cdot 5} = \dfrac{4}{5}$

85. $\dfrac{72}{80} = \dfrac{8 \cdot 9}{8 \cdot 10} = \dfrac{9}{10}$

89. answers may vary

93. B indicates 1.5 cc.

97. B indicates 54 u or 0.54 cc.

Exercise Set 5.7

1. $578 \text{ ml} \approx \dfrac{578 \text{ ml}}{1} \cdot \dfrac{1 \text{ fl oz}}{29.57 \text{ ml}} \approx 19.55 \text{ fl oz}$

5. $1000 \text{ g} \approx \dfrac{1000 \text{ g}}{1} \cdot \dfrac{0.04 \text{ oz}}{1 \text{ g}} \approx 40 \text{ oz}$

9. $14.5 \text{ L} \approx \dfrac{14.5 \text{ L}}{1} \cdot \dfrac{0.26 \text{ gal}}{1 \text{ L}} \approx 3.77 \text{ gal}$

13.

	Meters	Yards	Centimeters	Feet	Inches
The height of a woman	1.5	$1\frac{2}{3}$	150	5	60

17. $10 \text{ cm} = \dfrac{10 \text{ cm}}{1} \cdot \dfrac{1 \text{ in.}}{2.54 \text{ cm}} \approx 3.94 \text{ in.}$
The balance beam is approximately 3.94 inches wide.

21. $200 \text{ mg} = 0.2 \text{ g} \approx \dfrac{0.2 \text{ g}}{1} \cdot \dfrac{0.04 \text{ oz}}{1 \text{ g}} \approx 0.008 \text{ oz}$

25. $12 \text{ fl oz} \approx \dfrac{12 \text{ fl oz}}{1} \cdot \dfrac{29.57 \text{ ml}}{1 \text{ fl oz}} \approx 355 \text{ ml}$
The 380-ml size is larger.

29. $1.5 \text{ lb} - 1.25 \text{ lb} = 0.25 \text{ lb}$
$0.25 \text{ lb} \approx \dfrac{0.25 \text{ lb}}{1} \cdot \dfrac{0.45 \text{ kg}}{1 \text{ lb}} \cdot \dfrac{1000 \text{ g}}{1 \text{ kg}} \approx 112.5 \text{ g}$
The difference is approximately 112.5 g.

33. $8 \text{ m} \approx \dfrac{8 \text{ m}}{1} \cdot \dfrac{3.28 \text{ ft}}{1 \text{ m}} \approx 26.24 \text{ ft}$
The base diameter is approximately 26.24 ft.

37. One dose every 4 hours results in $\dfrac{24}{4} = 6$ doses per day and
$6 \times 7 = 42$ doses per week.
$5 \text{ ml} \times 42 = 210 \text{ ml}$
$210 \text{ ml} \approx \dfrac{210 \text{ ml}}{1} \cdot \dfrac{1 \text{ fl oz}}{29.57 \text{ ml}} \approx 7.1 \text{ fl oz}$
8 fluid ounces of medicine should be purchased.

41. A liter has greater capacity than a quart; b.

45. An $8\frac{1}{2}$ ounce glass of water has a capacity of about $250 \text{ ml} \left(\dfrac{1}{4} \text{ L}\right)$; d.

49. $6 \cdot 4 + 5 \div 1 = 24 + 5 = 29$

53. $3 + 5(19 - 17) - 8 = 3 + 5(2) - 8$
$= 3 + 10 - 8$
$= 13 - 8$
$= 5$

57. $\text{BSA} = \sqrt{\dfrac{90 \times 182}{3600}} \approx 2.13$
The BSA is approximately 2.13 sq m.

61. $60 \text{ in.} = \dfrac{60 \text{ in.}}{1} \cdot \dfrac{2.54 \text{ cm}}{1 \text{ in.}} = 152.4 \text{ cm}$
$150 \text{ lb} \approx \dfrac{150 \text{ lb}}{1} \cdot \dfrac{0.45 \text{ kg}}{1 \text{ lb}} = 67.5 \text{ kg}$
$\text{BSA} \approx \sqrt{\dfrac{67.5 \times 152.4}{3600}} \approx 1.690$
The BSA is approximately 1.69 sq m.

65. $20 \text{ m} \times 40 \text{ m} = 800 \text{ sq m}$
$20 \text{ m} \approx \dfrac{20 \text{ m}}{1} \cdot \dfrac{3.28 \text{ ft}}{1 \text{ m}} \approx 65.6 \text{ ft}$
$40 \text{ m} \approx \dfrac{40 \text{ m}}{1} \cdot \dfrac{3.28 \text{ ft}}{1 \text{ m}} = 131.2 \text{ ft}$
$20 \text{ m} \times 40 \text{ m} \approx 65.6 \text{ ft} \times 131.2 \text{ ft} \approx 8606.72 \text{ sq ft}$
The area is 800 sq m or approximately 8606.72 sq ft.

Chapter 5 Test

1. $\dfrac{\$75}{\$10} = \dfrac{75}{10} = \dfrac{5 \cdot 15}{5 \cdot 2} = \dfrac{15}{2}$

5. $\dfrac{414 \text{ ft}}{231 \text{ ft}} = \dfrac{414}{231} = \dfrac{3 \cdot 138}{3 \cdot 77}$
$= \dfrac{138}{77}$

9.
$$\begin{array}{r} 0.148 \approx 0.15 \\ 8{\overline{\smash{\big)}\,1.190}} \\ \underline{-\ 8} \\ 39 \\ \underline{-\ 32} \\ 70 \\ \underline{-\ 64} \\ 6 \end{array}$$
The 8-oz size costs approximately \$0.15/ounce.

$$\begin{array}{r} 0.157 \\ 12\overline{)\,1.890} \end{array} \approx 0.16$$
$$\begin{array}{r} -12 \\ \hline 69 \\ -60 \\ \hline 90 \\ -84 \\ \hline 6 \end{array}$$

The 12-ounce size costs approximately \$0.16/ounce. The 8-oz size is the better buy.

13. $\dfrac{-1.5}{5} = \dfrac{2.4}{n}$

$-1.5n = 12$

$n = \dfrac{12}{-1.5} = -\dfrac{120}{15}$

$n = -8$

17. Let $n =$ the standard dose

dose $\rightarrow$ $\dfrac{n}{80} = \dfrac{10}{15}$ $\leftarrow$ dose
pounds $\rightarrow$ $\leftarrow$ pounds

$15n = 800$

$n = \dfrac{800}{15}$

$n = \dfrac{5 \cdot 160}{5 \cdot 3}$

$n = \dfrac{160}{3} = 53\dfrac{1}{3}\,\text{g}$

21. $40\,\text{mg} = \dfrac{40\,\text{mg}}{1} \cdot \dfrac{1\,\text{g}}{1000\,\text{mg}} = \dfrac{40}{1000}\,\text{g}$

$\phantom{40\,\text{mg}} = \dfrac{4}{100}\,\text{g} = 0.04\,\text{g}$

25. $5\text{ gal }2\text{ qt} \div 2$
$= 22\text{ qt} \div 2$
$= 11\text{ qt}$
$= 2\text{ gal }3\text{ qt}$

29. $88\,\text{m} + 340\,\text{cm} = 88\,\text{m} + 3.40\,\text{m} = 91.4\,\text{m}$
The span is 91.4 meters

33. $5\,\text{km} \approx \dfrac{5\,\text{km}}{1} \cdot \dfrac{0.62\,\text{mi}}{1\,\text{km}} \approx 3.1\,\text{mi}$
5 km is about 3.1 mi.

CHAPTER 6

Exercise Set 6.1

1. $\dfrac{81}{100} = 81\%$

5. Most people preferred chocolate chip cookies. The percent is
$\dfrac{52}{100} = 52\%$

9. $6\% = 6(0.01) = 0.06$

13. $61.3\% = 61.3(0.01) = 0.613$

17. $0.6\% = 0.6(0.01) = 0.006$

21. $32.58\% = 32.58(0.01) = 0.3258$

25. $4\% = 4 \cdot \dfrac{1}{100} = \dfrac{4}{100} = \dfrac{1}{25}$

29. $175\% = 175 \cdot \dfrac{1}{100} = \dfrac{175}{100} = \dfrac{7 \cdot 25}{4 \cdot 25} = \dfrac{7}{4}$ or $1\dfrac{3}{4}$

33. $10\dfrac{1}{3}\% = \dfrac{31}{3}\% = \dfrac{31}{3} \cdot \dfrac{1}{100} = \dfrac{31}{300}$

37. $0.003 = 0.003(100\%) = 0.3\%$

41. $5.3 = 5.3(100\%) = 530\%$

45. $0.3328 = 0.3328(100\%) = 33.28\%$

49. $0.7 = 0.7(100\%) = 70\%$

53. $\dfrac{2}{5} = \dfrac{2}{5}(100\%) = \dfrac{200}{5}\% = 40\%$

57. $\dfrac{3}{8} = \dfrac{3}{8}(100\%) = \dfrac{300}{8}\% = \dfrac{75}{2}\% = 37\dfrac{1}{2}\%$

61. $2\dfrac{1}{2} = \dfrac{5}{2} = \dfrac{5}{2}(100\%) = \dfrac{500}{2}\% = 250\%$

65. $\dfrac{7}{11} = \dfrac{7}{11}(100\%) = \dfrac{700}{11}\% \approx 63.64\%$

$$\begin{array}{r} 63.636\ldots \approx 63.64 \\ 11\overline{)\,700.000} \end{array}$$
$$\begin{array}{r} -66 \\ \hline 40 \\ -33 \\ \hline 7\,0 \\ -6\,6 \\ \hline 40 \\ -33 \\ \hline 70 \\ -66 \\ \hline 4 \end{array}$$

69.

Percent	Decimal	Fraction
35%	35% = 0.35	35% = $\dfrac{35}{100} = \dfrac{7}{20}$
$\dfrac{1}{5} = \dfrac{20}{100} = 20\%$	$\dfrac{1}{5} = \dfrac{2}{10} = 0.2$	$\dfrac{1}{5}$
$0.5 = 0.50 = 50\%$	0.5	$0.5 = \dfrac{5}{10} = \dfrac{1}{2}$
70%	70% = 0.7	70% = $\dfrac{70}{100} = \dfrac{7}{10}$
$\dfrac{3}{8} = \dfrac{375}{1000} = \dfrac{37.5}{100}$ $= 37.5\%$	$\dfrac{3}{8} = \dfrac{375}{1000} = 0.375$	$\dfrac{3}{8}$

73.

Percent	Decimal	Fraction
200%	200% = 2.00 = 2	200% = $\dfrac{200}{100} = 2$
$2.8 = \dfrac{28}{10} = \dfrac{280}{100}$ $= 280\%$	2.8	$2.8 = 2\dfrac{8}{10} = 2\dfrac{4}{5}$
705%	705% = 7.05	705% = $\dfrac{705}{100}$ $= 7\dfrac{5}{100} = 7\dfrac{1}{20}$
$4\dfrac{27}{50} = 4\dfrac{54}{100}$ $= \dfrac{454}{100} = 454\%$	$4\dfrac{27}{50} = 4\dfrac{54}{100} = 4.54$	$4\dfrac{27}{50}$

77. $23\% = 0.23$
$23\% = \dfrac{23}{100}$

81. $12\% = 0.12$
$12\% = \dfrac{12}{100} = \dfrac{3 \cdot 4}{25 \cdot 4} = \dfrac{3}{25}$

85. $6 \cdot n = 72$

$$\frac{6 \cdot n}{6} = \frac{72}{6}$$

$$n = 12$$

89. a. $6.5\% = 0.065$, not 0.65.

b. $7.8\% = 0.078$ True.

c. $120\% = 1.2$, not 0.12.

d. $0.35\% = 0.0035$ True.

Parts b and d are correct.

93. $\frac{3}{4}$ is shaded.

$$\frac{3}{4} = \frac{3}{4}(100\%) = \frac{300}{4}\% = 75\%$$

75% is shaded.

97.
$$
\begin{array}{r}
0.2658 \approx 0.266 \\
79 \overline{)\ 21.0000} \\
-15\,8 \\ \hline
5\,20 \\
-4\,74 \\ \hline
460 \\
-395 \\ \hline
650 \\
-632 \\ \hline
18
\end{array}
$$

$\frac{21}{79} \approx 0.266$ or 26.6%

101. $49\% = 0.49$

Exercise Set 6.2

1. 15% of 72 is what number?

$$\downarrow \quad \downarrow \ \downarrow \ \downarrow \qquad \downarrow$$

$$15\% \quad \cdot \quad 72 = \qquad n$$

5. 1.9 is 40% of what number?

$$\downarrow \ \downarrow \ \downarrow \ \downarrow \qquad \downarrow$$

$$1.9 = 40\% \cdot \qquad n$$

9. What number is 9% of 43?

$$\downarrow \qquad \downarrow \ \downarrow \ \downarrow \ \downarrow$$

$$n \qquad = 9\% \ \cdot \ 43$$

13. $n = 14\% \cdot 52$

$n = 0.14 \cdot 52$

$n = 7.28$

7.28 is 14% of 52.

17. $1.2 = 12\% \cdot n$

$1.2 = 0.12n$

$$\frac{1.2}{0.12} = n$$

$10 = n$

1.2 is 12% of 10.

21. $16 = n \cdot 50$

$$\frac{16}{50} = n$$

$0.32 = n$

$32\% = n$

16 is 32% of 50.

25. $125\% \cdot 36 = n$

$1.25 \cdot 36 = n$

$45 = n$

125% of 36 is 45.

29. $126 = n \cdot 31.5$

$$\frac{126}{31.5} = n$$

$4 = n$

$400\% = n$

126 is 400% of 31.5.

33. $n \cdot 150 = 67.5$

$$n = \frac{67.5}{150}$$

$n = 0.45$

$n = 45\%$

45% of 150 is 67.5.

37. $2.4\% \cdot 26 = n$

$0.024 \cdot 26 = n$

$0.624 = n$

2.4% of 26 is 0.624.

41. $6.67 = 4.6\% \cdot n$

$6.67 = 0.046 \cdot n$

$$\frac{6.67}{0.046} = n$$

$145 = n$

6.67 is 4.6% of 145.

45. $\dfrac{27}{n} = \dfrac{9}{10}$

$27 \cdot 10 = 9 \cdot n$

$270 = 9n$

$$\frac{270}{9} = n$$

$30 = n$

49. $\dfrac{17}{12} = \dfrac{n}{20}$

53. In the equation $5 \cdot n = 32$, the step that should be taken to find the value of n is to divide by 5, obtaining $n = \dfrac{32}{5}$, which is choice c.

57. $n = 33\dfrac{1}{3}\% \cdot 24$ in words is "some number equals thirty-three and one third percent of twenty-four."

61. Since 55% is less than 100%, which is 1, 55% of 45 is less than 45; c.

65. Since 100% is 1, and 100% of n is 45, then n is 45; a.

69. $1.5\% \cdot 45{,}775 = n$

$0.015 \cdot 45{,}775 = n$

$686.625 = n$

1.5% of 45,775 is 686.625.

Exercise Set 6.3

1. 32% of 65 is what number?

$$\downarrow \qquad \downarrow \qquad \downarrow$$

$$\text{percent base} \qquad \text{amount} = a$$

$$\frac{a}{65} = \frac{32}{100}$$

5. 2.3 is 58% of what number?

$$\downarrow \qquad \downarrow \qquad \downarrow$$

$$\text{amount percent} \qquad \text{base} = b$$

$$\frac{2.3}{b} = \frac{58}{100}$$

9. What percent of 200 is 70?

$$\downarrow \qquad \downarrow \qquad \downarrow$$

$$\text{percent} = p \ \ \text{base amount}$$

$$\frac{70}{200} = \frac{p}{100}$$

13. $\dfrac{a}{105} = \dfrac{18}{100}$

$\dfrac{a}{105} = \dfrac{9}{50}$

$a \cdot 50 = 9 \cdot 105$

$50a = 945$

$a = \dfrac{945}{50}$

$a = 18.9$

Therefore, 18.9 is 18% of 105.

17. $\dfrac{7.8}{b} = \dfrac{78}{100}$

$7.8 \cdot 100 = 78 \cdot b$

$780 = 78b$

$\dfrac{780}{78} = b$

$10 = b$

Therefore, 7.8 is 78% of 10.

21. $\dfrac{14}{50} = \dfrac{p}{100}$

$\dfrac{7}{25} = \dfrac{p}{100}$

$7 \cdot 100 = p \cdot 25$

$700 = 25p$

$\dfrac{700}{25} = p$

$28 = p$

Therefore, 14 is 28% of 50.

25. $\dfrac{a}{80} = \dfrac{2.4}{100}$

$a \cdot 100 = 2.4 \cdot 80$

$100a = 192$

$a = \dfrac{192}{100}$

$a = 1.92$

Therefore, 2.4% of 80 is 1.92.

29. $\dfrac{348.6}{166} = \dfrac{p}{100}$

$348.6 \cdot 100 = p \cdot 166$

$34{,}860 = 166p$

$\dfrac{34{,}860}{166} = p$

$210 = p$

Therefore, 348.6 is 210% of 166.

33. $\dfrac{3.6}{8} = \dfrac{p}{100}$

$3.6 \cdot 100 = p \cdot 8$

$360 = 8p$

$\dfrac{360}{8} = p$

$45 = p$

Therefore, 45% of 8 is 3.6.

37. $\dfrac{a}{48} = \dfrac{1.8}{100}$

$a \cdot 100 = 1.8 \cdot 48$

$100a = 86.4$

$a = \dfrac{86.4}{100}$

$a = 0.864$

Therefore, 1.8% of 48 is 0.864.

41. $\dfrac{3.5}{b} = \dfrac{2.5}{100}$

$3.5 \cdot 100 = 2.5 \cdot b$

$350 = 2.5b$

$\dfrac{350}{2.5} = b$

$140 = b$

Therefore, 3.5 is 2.5% of 140.

45. $-\dfrac{11}{16} + \left(-\dfrac{3}{16}\right) = \dfrac{-11 + (-3)}{16} = \dfrac{-14}{16} = -\dfrac{7 \cdot 2}{8 \cdot 2} = -\dfrac{7}{8}$

49. $\begin{array}{r} \overset{1}{0.41} \\ +0.29 \\ \hline 0.70 \end{array}$

53. answers may vary

57. answers may vary

61. $\dfrac{8652}{b} = \dfrac{119}{100}$

$8652 \cdot 100 = 119 \cdot b$

$865{,}200 = 119b$

$\dfrac{865{,}200}{119} = b$

$7270.6 \approx b$

Exercise Set 6.4

1. 24 is 1.5% of what number?
Method 1

$24 = 1.5\% \cdot n$

$24 = 0.015n$

$\dfrac{24}{0.015} = n$

$1600 = n$

1600 bolts were inspected.
Method 2

$\dfrac{24}{b} = \dfrac{1.5}{100}$

$24 \cdot 100 = 1.5 \cdot b$

$2400 = 1.5b$

$\dfrac{2400}{1.5} = b$

$1600 = b$

1600 bolts were inspected.

5. 300 is what percent of 2000?
Method 1

$300 = n \cdot 2000$

$300 = 2000n$

$\dfrac{300}{2000} = n$

$\dfrac{15}{100} = n$

$15\% = n$

Vera spends 15% of her monthly income on food.
Method 2

$\dfrac{300}{2000} = \dfrac{p}{100}$

$\dfrac{3}{20} = \dfrac{p}{100}$

$3 \cdot 100 = p \cdot 20$

$300 = 20p$

$\dfrac{300}{20} = p$

$15 = p$

Vera spends 15% of her monthly income on food.

9. 73 is what percent of 535?
Method 1

$73 = n \cdot 535$

$73 = 535n$

$\dfrac{73}{535} = n$

$0.136 \approx n$

13.6% of the members of the 108th U.S. Congress have attended a community college.

Method 2

$$\frac{73}{535} = \frac{p}{100}$$

$$73 \cdot 100 = 535p$$

$$7300 = 535p$$

$$\frac{7300}{535} = p$$

$$13.6 \approx p$$

13.6% of the members of the 108th U.S. Congress have attended a community college.

13. 20 is what percent of 40?

Method 1

$$20 = n \cdot 40$$

$$20 = 40n$$

$$\frac{20}{40} = n$$

$$0.5 = n$$

$$50\% = n$$

50% of the total calories come from fat.

Method 2

$$\frac{20}{40} = \frac{p}{100}$$

$$20 \cdot 100 = p \cdot 40$$

$$2000 = 40p$$

$$\frac{2000}{40} = p$$

$$50 = p$$

50% of the total calories come from fat.

17. What number is 8% of 6200?

Method 1

$$n = 8\% \cdot 6200$$

$$n = 0.08 \cdot 6200$$

$$n = 496$$

The decrease was 496 chairs. The new number of chairs produced each month is $6200 - 496 = 5704$ chairs.

Method 2

$$\frac{a}{6200} = \frac{8}{100}$$

$$a \cdot 100 = 8 \cdot 6200$$

$$100a = 49,600$$

$$a = \frac{49,600}{100}$$

$$a = 496$$

The decrease was 496 chairs. The new number of chairs produced each month is $6200 - 496 = 5704$ chairs.

21. What number is 4.5% of 19,286?

Method 1

$$n = 4.5\% \cdot 19,286$$

$$n = 0.045 \cdot 19,286$$

$$n = 867.87$$

The price of the car will increase by $867.87. The new price of that model will be $19,286 + $867.87 = $20,153.87.

Method 2

$$\frac{a}{19,286} = \frac{4.5}{100}$$

$$a \cdot 100 = 4.5 \cdot 19,286$$

$$100a = 86,787$$

$$a = \frac{86,787}{100}$$

$$a = 867.87$$

The price of the car will increase by $867.87. The new price of that model will be $19,286 + $867.87 = $20,153.87.

25. What number is 80% of 35?

Method 1

$$n = 80\% \cdot 35$$

$$n = 0.80 \cdot 35$$

$$n = 28$$

The increase is projected to be 28 million. The population is projected to be $(35 + 28)$ million = 63 million.

Method 2

$$\frac{a}{35} = \frac{80}{100}$$

$$a \cdot 100 = 80 \cdot 35$$

$$100a = 2800$$

$$a = \frac{2800}{100}$$

$$a = 28$$

The increase is projected to be 28 million. The population is projected to be $(35 + 28)$ million = 63 million.

29.

Original Amount	New Amount	Amount of Increase	Percent Increase
85	187	$187 - 85 = 102$	$\frac{102}{85} = 1.2 = 120\%$

33.

Original Amount	New Amount	Amount of Decrease	Percent Decrease
160	40	$160 - 40 = 120$	$\frac{120}{160} = 0.75 = 75\%$

37. percent increase $= \dfrac{\text{amount of increase}}{\text{original amount}} = \dfrac{23.7 - 19.5}{19.5}$

$$= \frac{4.2}{19.5} \approx 0.215$$

The miles per gallon increased by 21.5%.

41. percent increase $= \dfrac{\text{amount of increase}}{\text{original amount}} = \dfrac{441 - 174}{174}$

$$= \frac{267}{174} \approx 1.534$$

The farm size increased by 153.4%.

45. percent increase $= \dfrac{\text{amount of increase}}{\text{original amount}} = \dfrac{29,000 - 16,000}{16,000}$

$$= \frac{13,000}{16,000} = 0.8125 \approx 0.813$$

The number is expected to increase by 81.3%.

49. percent decrease $= \dfrac{\text{amount of decrease}}{\text{original amount}} = \dfrac{127,333 - 99,887}{127,333}$

$$= \frac{27,446}{127,333} \approx 0.216$$

The population is expected to decrease by 21.6%.

53.
$$\begin{array}{r} {}^{1\ 1}9.20 \\ + 1.98 \\ \hline 11.18 \end{array}$$

57. The increased number is double the original number, since $n + (100\%)n = n + 1 \cdot n = n + n = 2n$.

Exercise Set 6.5

1. sales tax $= 5\% \cdot \$150 = 0.05 \cdot \$150 = \$7.50$
The sales tax is $7.50.

5. $\$57 = r \cdot \$600$

$$\frac{\$57}{\$600} = r$$

$$0.095 = r$$

The sales tax rate is 9.5%.

9. sales tax $= 6.5\% \cdot \$1800 = 0.065 \cdot \$1800 = \$117$
total price $= \$1800 + \$117 = \$1917$
The total price of the bracelet is $1917.

13. $\$98.70 = r \cdot \$1645$

$\dfrac{\$98.70}{\$1645} = r$

$0.06 = r$

The sales tax rate is 6%.

17. commission $= 4\% \cdot \$1,236,856 = 0.04 \cdot \$1,236,856 = \$49,474.24$
Her commission was \$49,474.24.

21. commission $= 1.5\% \cdot \$125,900 = 0.015 \cdot \$125,900 = \$1888.50$
His commission will be \$1888.50.

	Original Price	Discount Rate	Amount of Discount	Sale Price
25.	\$68	10%	$10\% \cdot \$68$ $= \$6.80$	$\$68 - \$6.80$ $= \$61.20$
29.	\$215	35%	$35\% \cdot \$215$ $= \$75.25$	$\$215 - \$75.25$ $= \$139.75$

33. discount $= 15\% \cdot \$300 = 0.15 \cdot \$300 = \$45$
sale price $= \$300 - \$45 = \$255$
The discount is \$45 and the sale price is \$255.

	Purchase Price	Tax Rate	Sales Tax	Total Price
37.	\$82	5.5%	$5.5\% \cdot \$82 = \$4.51$	$\$82 + \$4.51$ $= \$86.51$

	Sale	Commission Rate	Commission
41.	\$17,900	$\dfrac{\$1432}{\$17,900} = 0.08 = 8\%$	\$1432

45. $400 \cdot 0.03 \cdot 11 = 12 \cdot 11 = 132$

49. Round \$68 to \$70 and 9.5% to 10%.
$10\% \cdot \$70 = 0.10 \cdot \$70 = \$7$
$\$70 + \$7 = \$77$
The best estimate of the total price is \$77; d.

	Bill Amount	10%	15%	20%
53.	$\$72.17 \approx \$72.00$	\$7.20	$\$7.20 + \dfrac{1}{2}(\$7.20)$ $= \$7.20 + \$3.60$ $= \$10.80$	$2(\$7.20)$ $= \$14.40$

57. $7.5\% \cdot \$24,966 = 0.075 \cdot \$24,966 = \$1872.45$
$\$24,966 + \$1872.45 = \$26,838.45$
The total price of the necklace is \$26,838.45.

Exercise Set 6.6

1. simple interest $=$ principal $\cdot$ rate $\cdot$ time $= (\$200)(8\%)(2)$
$\qquad = (\$200)(0.08)(2) = \$32$

5. simple interest $=$ principal $\cdot$ rate $\cdot$ time $= (\$5000)(10\%)\left(1\dfrac{1}{2}\right)$
$\qquad = (\$5000)(0.10)(1.5) = \$750$

9. simple interest $=$ principal $\cdot$ rate $\cdot$ time $= (\$2500)(16\%)\left(\dfrac{21}{12}\right)$
$\qquad = (\$2500)(0.16)(1.75) = \$700$

13. simple interest $=$ principal $\cdot$ rate $\cdot$ time $= \$5000(9\%)\left(\dfrac{15}{12}\right)$
$\qquad = \$5000(0.09)(1.25) = \$562.50$
Total $= \$5000 + \$562.50 = \$5562.50$

17. Total amount $=$ original principal $\cdot$ compound interest factor
$\qquad = \$6150(7.61226) = \$46,815.399$
The total amount is \$46,815.40.

21. Total amount $=$ original principal $\cdot$ compound interest factor
$\qquad = \$10,000(5.81636) = \$58,163.60$
The total amount is \$58,163.60.

25. Total amount $=$ original principal $\cdot$ compound interest factor
$\qquad = \$2000(1.46933) = \$2938.66$
Compound interest $=$ total amount $-$ original principal
$\qquad = \$2938.66 - \$2000 = \$938.66$

29. perimeter $= 10 + 6 + 10 + 6 = 32$
The perimeter is 32 yards.

33. answers may vary

Chapter 6 Test

1. $85\% = 85(0.01) = 0.85$

5. $6.1 = 6.1(100\%) = 610\%$

9. $0.2\% = \dfrac{0.2}{100} = \dfrac{2}{1000} = \dfrac{1}{500}$

13. $n = 42\% \cdot 80$
$n = 0.42 \cdot 80$
$n = 33.6$
Therefore, 42% of 80 is 33.6.

17. 20% of what number is \$11,350?
$0.20n = \$11,350$
$n = \dfrac{\$11,350}{0.20}$
$n = \$56,750$
The value is \$56,750.

21. commission $= 4\% \cdot \$9875 = 0.04 \cdot \$9875 = \$395$
His commission is \$395.

25. simple interest $=$ principal $\cdot$ rate $\cdot$ time
$\qquad = (\$400)(13.5\%)\left(\dfrac{6}{12}\right)$
$\qquad = (\$400)(0.135)(0.5)$
$\qquad = \$27.00$
Total amount due the bank $= \$400 + \$27 = \$427$

CHAPTER 7

Exercise Set 7.1

1. The year with the most car symbols is 2004, so the greatest number of cars was manufactured in 2004.

5. There are 10 car symbols for 2005 and 11 car symbols for 2004, for a total of 21 car symbols. Each symbol represents 500 cars.
$500 \cdot 21 = 10,500$
Approximately 10,500 cars were manufactured in 2004 and 2005.

9. Since $\dfrac{4000}{500} = 8$, 4000 cars would be represented by 8 car symbols. Both 1999 and 2002 have 8 car symbols, so 4000 cars were manufactured in 1999 and 2002.

13. Since $\dfrac{21}{3} = 7$, 21 ounces of chicken would be represented by 7 chicken symbols. 1998, 2001, and 2004 have more than 7 chicken symbols, so more than 21 ounces of chicken were consumed per person per week in 1998, 2001, and 2004.

17. To represent 17 ounces, divide 17 by 3, the number of ounces represented by a chicken symbol. $\dfrac{17}{3} = 5\dfrac{2}{3}$, so $5\dfrac{2}{3}$ symbols represent 17 ounces.

21. The bar for May is between 15 and 20, and closer to 20, so the average number of tornado-related deaths for May is about 19.

25. The bar for Delhi, India, ends about halfway between the lines for 18 million and 19 million, so the population is about 18.5 million or 18,500,000.

29. The U.S. cities in the graph are Los Angeles and New York. The New York bar is longer and ends closer to 22 than 21, so New York City has the largest population at about 21.7 million or 21,700,000.

33. The height of the bar for 100–149 miles per week is 15, so 15 of the adults drive 100–149 miles per week.

37. 15 of the adults drive 100–149 miles per week and 9 of the adults drive 150–199 miles per week, so 15 + 9 = 24 of the adults drive 100–199 miles per week.

41. 9 of the 100 adults surveyed drive 150–199 miles per week, so the ratio is $\frac{9}{100}$.

45. According to the bar graph, approximately 21 million householders will be 55–64 years old.

49. answers may vary

53.

Class Interval (Scores)	Tally	Class Frequency (Number of Games)
90–99	~~||||~~ |||	8

57.

Class Interval (Account Balances)	Tally	Class Frequency (Number of People)
$200–$299	~~||||~~		6

61.

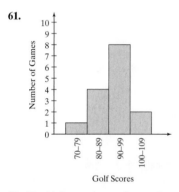

65. The highest point on the graph corresponds to 1982, so the average number of goals per game was the greatest in 1982.

69. The dot for 1990 is below the 2.5-level, so the average number of goals per game was less than 2.5 in 1990.

73. 10% of 62 is $0.10 \cdot 62 = 6.2$

77. $\frac{17}{50} = \frac{17 \cdot 2}{50 \cdot 2} = \frac{34}{100} = 34\%$

81. The lowest point on the graph of low temperatures corresponds to Sunday. The low temperature on Sunday was 68°F.

85. answers may vary

Exercise Set 7.2

1. The largest sector corresponds to the category "parent or guardian's home," thus most of the students live in a parent or guardian's home.

5. 180 of the students live in campus housing while 320 live in a parent or guardian's home.

$$\frac{180}{320} = \frac{9}{16}$$

The ratio is $\frac{9}{16}$.

9. 30% + 7% = 37%

37% of the land on Earth is accounted for by Europe and Asia.

13. Australia accounts for 5% of the land on Earth.

5% of 57,000,000 = $0.05 \cdot 57,000,000$

$= 2,850,000$

Australia is 2,850,000 square miles.

17. The second-largest sector corresponds to nonfiction, so the second-largest category of books is nonfiction.

21. Children's fiction accounts for 22% of the books.

22% of 125,600 = $0.22 \cdot 125,600$

$= 27,632$

The library has 27,632 children's fiction books.

25.

Sector	Degrees in Each Sector
United States	$58\% \times 360° = 0.58 \times 360° = 208.8° \approx 209°$
Asia	$36\% \times 360° = 0.36 \times 360° = 129.6° \approx 130°$
Europe	$6\% \times 360° = 0.06 \times 360° = 21.6° \approx 22°$

29.
$$\begin{array}{r} 5 \\ 2\overline{)10} \\ 2\overline{)20} \\ 2\overline{)40} \end{array}$$

$40 = 2 \cdot 2 \cdot 2 \cdot 5 = 2^3 \times 5$

33. answers may vary

37. The Indian Ocean accounts for 21% of Earth's oceans. 21% of 264,489,800 = $0.21 \cdot 264,489,800 = 55,542,858$. The Indian Ocean covers 55,542,858 square kilometers.

Exercise Set 7.3

1. Mean: $\frac{21 + 28 + 16 + 42 + 38}{5} = \frac{145}{5} = 29$

Median:
Write the numbers in order. 16, 21, 28, 38, 42
The middle number is 28.
Mode: There is no mode, since each number occurs once.

5. Mean: $\frac{0.2 + 0.3 + 0.5 + 0.6 + 0.6 + 0.9 + 0.2 + 0.7 + 1.1}{9} = \frac{5.1}{9}$
$$\approx 0.6$$

Median:
Write the numbers in order. 0.2, 0.2, 0.3, 0.5, 0.6, 0.6, 0.7, 0.9, 1.1
The middle number is 0.6.
Mode: Since 0.2 and 0.6 occur twice, there are two modes, 0.2 and 0.6.

9. Mean: $\frac{1483 + 1483 + 1450 + 1381 + 1283}{5} = \frac{7080}{5}$
$$= 1416 \text{ feet}$$

13. answers may vary

17. gpa $= \frac{4 \cdot 3 + 4 \cdot 3 + 3 \cdot 4 + 3 \cdot 1 + 3 \cdot 2}{3 + 3 + 4 + 1 + 2}$
$= \frac{45}{13} \approx 3.46$

21. Mode: 6.9 since this number appears twice.

25. Mean: $\frac{\text{sum of 15 pulse rates}}{15} = \frac{1095}{15} = 73$

29. There are 9 rates lower than the mean. They are 66, 68, 71, 64, 71, 70, 65, 70, and 72.

33. $\frac{18}{30} = \frac{2 \cdot 3 \cdot 3}{5 \cdot 2 \cdot 3} = \frac{3}{5}$

37. Since the mode is 35, we use 35 twice. Since there are an odd number of items in the list and the median is 37, then 37 must be in the list. Let the last missing number be n. Then

$$\frac{35 + 35 + 37 + 40 + n}{5} = 38, \text{ the mean, or}$$

$35 + 35 + 37 + 40 + n = 38 \cdot 5$ or

$147 + n = 190$ or $n = 43$.

The missing numbers are 35, 35, 37, and 43.

Exercise Set 7.4

1.

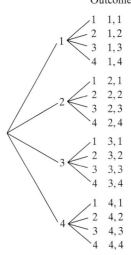

Outcomes

15 outcomes

5.

Outcomes

16 outcomes

9.

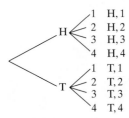

Outcomes

8 outcomes

13. A 1 or a 4 are two of the six possible outcomes. The probability is $\frac{2}{6} = \frac{1}{3}$.

17. Five of the six possible outcomes are numbers greater than 1. The probability is $\frac{5}{6}$.

21. A 1, a 2, or a 3 are three of three possible outcomes. The probability is $\frac{3}{3} = 1$.

25. One of the seven marbles is red. The probability is $\frac{1}{7}$.

29. Two of the seven marbles are either blue or red. The probability is $\frac{2}{7}$.

33. The blood pressure did not change for 10 of the 200 people. The probability is $\frac{10}{200} = \frac{1}{20}$.

37. $\frac{1}{2} \cdot \frac{1}{3} = \frac{1 \cdot 1}{2 \cdot 3} = \frac{1}{6}$

41. One of the 52 cards is the king of hearts. The probability is $\frac{1}{52}$.

45. Thirteen of the 52 cards are hearts. The probability is $\frac{13}{52} = \frac{1}{4}$.

49.

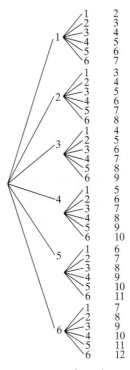

Sum

probability $= \frac{3}{36} = \frac{1}{12}$

53. answers may vary

Chapter 7 Test

1. There are $4\frac{1}{2}$ dollar symbols for the second week. Each dollar symbol corresponds to \$50. $4\frac{1}{2} \cdot \$50 = \frac{9}{2} \cdot \$50 = \frac{\$450}{2} = \$225$

\$225 was collected during the second week.

5. The shortest bar corresponds to February. The normal monthly precipitation in February in Chicago is 3 centimeters.

9. The line graph is above the 3 level for 1990, 1991, and 2000. Thus the inflation rate was greater than 3% in 1990, 1991, and 2000.

13. Services employed 31% of the labor force.

31% of 132,000,000 = 0.31 × 132,000,000

                   = 40,920,000

40,920,000 people were employed in the service industry.

17.

Class Interval (Scores)	Tally	Class Frequency (Number of Students)
40–49	I	1
50–59	III	3
60–69	IIII	4
70–79	IIII	5
80–89	IIII III	8
90–99	IIII	4

21.

Grade	Point Value	Credit Hours	$\left(\text{Point Value}\right) \cdot \left(\text{Credit Hours}\right)$
A	4	3	12
B	3	3	9
C	2	3	6
B	3	4	12
A	4	1	4
	Totals	14	43

$\dfrac{43}{14} \approx 3.07$

The grade point average is about 3.07.

25. A 3 or a 4 are two of the ten possible outcomes. The probability is $\dfrac{2}{10} = \dfrac{1}{5}$.

CHAPTER 8

Exercise Set 8.1

1. $3 + 2z = 3 + 2(-3)$
$= 3 + (-6)$
$= -3$

5. $z - x + y = -3 - (-2) + 5$
$= -3 + 2 + 5$
$= -1 + 5$
$= 4$

9. $8 - (5y - 7) = 8 - (5 \cdot 5 - 7)$
$= 8 - (25 - 7)$
$= 8 - 18$
$= -10$

13. $\dfrac{6xy}{4} = \dfrac{6(-2)(5)}{4}$
$= \dfrac{-12(5)}{4}$
$= \dfrac{-60}{4}$
$= -15$

17. $\dfrac{x + 2y}{2z} = \dfrac{-2 + 2 \cdot 5}{2(-3)}$
$= \dfrac{-2 + 10}{-6}$
$= \dfrac{8}{-6}$
$= -\dfrac{4}{3} \text{ or } -1\dfrac{1}{3}$

21. $\dfrac{xz}{y} + \dfrac{3}{10} = \dfrac{-2(-3)}{5} + \dfrac{3}{10}$
$= \dfrac{6}{5} + \dfrac{3}{10}$
$= \dfrac{12}{10} + \dfrac{3}{10}$
$= \dfrac{15}{10}$
$= \dfrac{3}{2} \text{ or } 1\dfrac{1}{2}$

25. $3x + 5x = (3 + 5)x = 8x$

29. $4c + c - 7c = (4 + 1 - 7)c$
$= (5 - 7)c$
$= -2c$

33. $4a + 3a + 6a - 8 = (4 + 3 + 6)a - 8$
$= (7 + 6)a - 8$
$= 13a - 8$

37. $3x + 7 - x - 14 = 3x - x + 7 - 14$
$= (3 - 1)x + (7 - 14)$
$= 2x + (-7)$
$= 2x - 7$

41. $\dfrac{5}{6} - \dfrac{7}{12}x - \dfrac{1}{3} - \dfrac{3}{10}x = \dfrac{5}{6} - \dfrac{1}{3} - \dfrac{7}{12}x - \dfrac{3}{10}x$
$= \left(\dfrac{5}{6} - \dfrac{1}{3}\right) + \left(-\dfrac{7}{12} - \dfrac{3}{10}\right)x$
$= \left(\dfrac{5}{6} - \dfrac{2}{6}\right) + \left(-\dfrac{35}{60} - \dfrac{18}{60}\right)x$
$= \dfrac{3}{6} + \left(-\dfrac{53}{60}\right)x$
$= \dfrac{1}{2} - \dfrac{53}{60}x$

45. $6(5x) = (6 \cdot 5)x = 30x$

49. $-0.6(7a) = (-0.6 \cdot 7)a = -4.2a$

53. $2(y + 2) = 2 \cdot y + 2 \cdot 2 = 2y + 4$

57. $-4(3x + 7) = -4 \cdot 3x + (-4) \cdot 7$
$= (-4 \cdot 3)x + (-28)$
$= -12x - 28$

61. $\dfrac{1}{2}(-8x - 3) = \dfrac{1}{2}(-8x) - \dfrac{1}{2}(3)$
$= \left(\dfrac{1}{2} \cdot -8\right)x - \dfrac{3}{2}$
$= -4x - \dfrac{3}{2}$

65. $4(6n - 5) + 3n = 4 \cdot 6n - 4 \cdot 5 + 3n$
$= 24n - 20 + 3n$
$= 24n + 3n - 20$
$= (24 + 3)n - 20$
$= 27n - 20$

69. $-2(3x + 1) - 5(x - 2)$
$= -2 \cdot 3x + (-2) \cdot 1 - 5 \cdot x - (-5) \cdot 2$
$= (-2 \cdot 3)x + (-2) - 5x - (-10)$
$= -6x - 2 - 5x + 10$
$= -6x - 5x - 2 + 10$
$= (-6 - 5)x + (-2 + 10)$
$= -11x + 8$

73. Let $l = 18$ and $w = 14$.
$P = 2l + 2w$
$= 2 \cdot 18 + 2 \cdot 14$
$= 36 + 28$
$= 64$
The perimeter is 64 feet.

77. $A = s^2 = (4y)^2 = 4y \cdot 4y = 4 \cdot 4 \cdot y \cdot y = 16y^2$
The area is $16y^2$ square centimeters.

81. $P = a + b + c = 5 + x + (2x + 1)$
$\quad = 5 + x + 2x + 1 = 3x + 6.$
The perimeter is $(3x + 6)$ feet.

85. Let $l = 12$, $w = 6$, and $h = 4$.
$V = lwh = 12 \cdot 6 \cdot 4 = 72 \cdot 4 = 288$
The volume is 288 cubic inches.

89. $-13 + 10 = -3$

93. $-4 + 4 = 0$

97. The given result is correct.
$\begin{aligned}
7x - (x + 2) &= 7x - 1(x + 2) \\
&= 7x - 1 \cdot x + (-1)(2) \\
&= 7x - x - 2
\end{aligned}$

101. The order of the terms is not changed, only the grouping within parentheses. Thus,
$-7 + (4 + y) = (-7 + 4) + y$
demonstrates the associative property of addition.

105. Add the area of the left-hand rectangle and the right-hand rectangle.
$\begin{aligned}
7(2x + 1) + 3(2x + 3) &= 7 \cdot 2x + 7 \cdot 1 + 3 \cdot 2x + 3 \cdot 3 \\
&= (7 \cdot 2)x + 7 + (3 \cdot 2)x + 9 \\
&= 14x + 7 + 6x + 9 \\
&= 14x + 6x + 7 + 9 \\
&= (14 + 6)x + 7 + 9 \\
&= 20x + 16
\end{aligned}$
The area is $(20x + 16)$ square miles.

109. $9684q - 686 - 4860q + 12,960$
$= 9684q - 4860q - 686 + 12,960$
$= (9684 - 4860)q + (-686 + 12,960)$
$= 4824q + 12,274$

Exercise Set 8.2

1. $x - 8 = 2$
$10 - 8 \overset{?}{=} 2$
$\quad\quad 2 \overset{?}{=} 2$ True
Yes, 10 is a solution of the equation.

5. $-9f = 64 - f$
$-9(-8) \overset{?}{=} 64 - (-8)$
$\quad 72 \overset{?}{=} 64 + 8$
$\quad 72 \overset{?}{=} 72$ True
Yes, -8 is a solution of the equation.

9. $a + 5 = 23$
$a + 5 - 5 = 23 - 5$
$\quad\quad a = 18$

Check:
$a + 5 = 23$
$18 + 5 \overset{?}{=} 23$
$\quad 23 \overset{?}{=} 23$ True
The solution of the equation is 18.

13. $7 = y - 2$
$7 + 2 = y - 2 + 2$
$\quad 9 = y$

Check:
$7 = y - 2$
$7 \overset{?}{=} 9 - 2$
$7 \overset{?}{=} 7$ True
The solution of the equation is 9.

17. $x + \dfrac{1}{2} = \dfrac{7}{2}$
$x + \dfrac{1}{2} - \dfrac{1}{2} = \dfrac{7}{2} - \dfrac{1}{2}$
$\quad\quad x = \dfrac{6}{2}$
$\quad\quad x = 3$

Check:
$x + \dfrac{1}{2} = \dfrac{7}{2}$
$3 + \dfrac{1}{2} \overset{?}{=} \dfrac{7}{2}$
$\dfrac{6}{2} + \dfrac{1}{2} \overset{?}{=} \dfrac{7}{2}$
$\quad \dfrac{7}{2} \overset{?}{=} \dfrac{7}{2}$ True
The solution of the equation is 3.

21. $x - 3 = -1 + 4$
$\quad x - 3 = 3$
$x - 3 + 3 = 3 + 3$
$\quad\quad x = 6$

Check:
$x - 3 = -1 + 4$
$6 - 3 \overset{?}{=} -1 + 4$
$\quad 3 \overset{?}{=} 3$ True
The solution of the equation is 6.

25. $x - 0.6 = 4.7$
$x - 0.6 + 0.6 = 4.7 + 0.6$
$\quad\quad x = 5.3$

Check:
$x - 0.6 = 4.7$
$5.3 - 0.6 \overset{?}{=} 4.7$
$\quad 4.7 \overset{?}{=} 4.7$ True
The solution of the equation is 5.3.

29. $y + 2.3 = -9.2 - 8.6$
$\quad y + 2.3 = -17.8$
$y + 2.3 - 2.3 = -17.8 - 2.3$
$\quad\quad y = -20.1$

Check:
$y + 2.3 = -9.2 - 8.6$
$-20.1 + 2.3 \overset{?}{=} -9.2 - 8.6$
$\quad -17.8 \overset{?}{=} -17.8$ True
The solution of the equation is -20.1.

33. $5 + (-12) = 5x - 7 - 4x$
$5 + (-12) = 5x - 4x - 7$
$\quad\quad -7 = x - 7$
$-7 + 7 = x - 7 + 7$
$\quad\quad 0 = x$

Check:
$5 + (-12) = 5x - 7 - 4x$
$5 + (-12) \overset{?}{=} 5(0) - 7 - 4(0)$
$5 + (-12) \overset{?}{=} 0 - 7 - 0$
$\quad\quad -7 \overset{?}{=} -7$ True
The solution of the equation is 0.

37. $\dfrac{-7}{-7} = 1$ because $-7 \cdot 1 = -7$.

41. $-\dfrac{2}{3} \cdot -\dfrac{3}{2} = \dfrac{2 \cdot 3}{3 \cdot 2} = \dfrac{6}{6} = 1$

45. To solve $-\dfrac{1}{7} = -\dfrac{4}{5} + x$, $\dfrac{4}{5}$ should be added to both sides of the equation.

49. $x - 76,862 = 86,102$
$x - 76,862 + 76,862 = 86,102 + 76,862$
$\quad\quad x = 162,964$

53. Use $I = R - E$ where $I = 705{,}000{,}000$ and $R = 24{,}547{,}000{,}000$.

$$I = R - E$$
$$705{,}000{,}000 = 24{,}547{,}000{,}000 - E$$
$$705{,}000{,}000 - 24{,}547{,}000{,}000 = 24{,}547{,}000{,}000 - 24{,}547{,}000{,}000 - E$$
$$-23{,}842{,}000{,}000 = -E$$
$$23{,}842{,}000{,}000 = E$$

Best Buy's total expenses for the year were $23,842,000,000.

Exercise Set 8.3

1. $5x = 20$

$$\frac{5x}{5} = \frac{20}{5}$$
$$x = 4$$

5. $0.4y = -12$

$$\frac{0.4y}{0.4} = \frac{-12}{0.4}$$
$$y = -30$$

9. $-0.3x = -15$

$$\frac{-0.3x}{-0.3} = \frac{-15}{-0.3}$$
$$x = 50$$

13. $\dfrac{1}{6}y = -5$

$$\frac{6}{1} \cdot \frac{1}{6}y = \frac{6}{1} \cdot -5$$
$$y = -30$$

17. $-\dfrac{2}{9}z = \dfrac{4}{27}$

$$-\frac{9}{2} \cdot -\frac{2}{9}z = -\frac{9}{2} \cdot \frac{4}{27}$$
$$z = -\frac{2}{3}$$

21. $16 = 10t - 8t$

$$16 = 2t$$
$$\frac{16}{2} = \frac{2t}{2}$$
$$8 = t$$

25. $4 - 10 = -3z$

$$-6 = -3z$$
$$\frac{-6}{-3} = \frac{-3z}{-3}$$
$$2 = z$$

29. $0.4 = -8z$

$$\frac{0.4}{-8} = \frac{-8z}{-8}$$
$$-0.05 = z$$

33. $-\dfrac{3}{5}x = -\dfrac{6}{15}$

$$-\frac{5}{3} \cdot -\frac{3}{5}x = -\frac{5}{3} \cdot -\frac{6}{15}$$
$$x = \frac{2}{3}$$

37. $5 - 5 = 2x + 7x$

$$0 = 9x$$
$$\frac{0}{9} = \frac{9x}{9}$$
$$0 = x$$

41. $-3x - 3x = 50 - 2$

$$-6x = 48$$
$$\frac{-6x}{-6} = \frac{48}{-6}$$
$$x = -8$$

45. $\dfrac{1}{4}x - \dfrac{5}{8}x = 20 - 47$

$$\frac{2}{8}x - \frac{5}{8}x = -27$$
$$-\frac{3}{8}x = -27$$
$$-\frac{8}{3} \cdot -\frac{3}{8}x = -\frac{8}{3} \cdot -27$$
$$x = 72$$

49. $\dfrac{x-3}{2} = \dfrac{5-3}{2} = \dfrac{2}{2} = 1$

53. Addition should be used to solve the equation $12 = x - 5$. Specifically, 5 should be added to both sides of the equation.

57. answers may vary

61. Use $d = r \cdot t$, where $d = 390$ and $r = 60$.

$$d = r \cdot t$$
$$390 = 60 \cdot t$$
$$\frac{390}{60} = \frac{60t}{60}$$
$$\frac{13}{2} = t$$

It will take $\dfrac{13}{2} = 6.5$ hours to make the drive.

Exercise Set 8.4

1. $2x - 6 = 0$

$$2x - 6 + 6 = 0 + 6$$
$$2x = 6$$
$$\frac{2x}{2} = \frac{6}{2}$$
$$x = 3$$

5. $6 - n = 10$

$$6 - 6 - n = 10 - 6$$
$$-n = 4$$
$$\frac{-n}{-1} = \frac{4}{-1}$$
$$n = -4$$

9. $1.7 = 2y + 9.5$

$$1.7 - 9.5 = 2y + 9.5 - 9.5$$
$$-7.8 = 2y$$
$$\frac{-7.8}{2} = \frac{2y}{2}$$
$$-3.9 = y$$

13. $3x - 7 = 4x + 5$

$$3x - 7 - 5 = 4x + 5 - 5$$
$$3x - 12 = 4x$$
$$3x - 3x - 12 = 4x - 3x$$
$$-12 = x$$

17. $9 - 3x = 14 + 2x$

$$9 - 14 - 3x = 14 - 14 + 2x$$
$$-5 - 3x = 2x$$
$$-5 - 3x + 3x = 2x + 3x$$
$$-5 = 5x$$
$$\frac{-5}{5} = \frac{5x}{5}$$
$$-1 = x$$

21. $3(x - 1) = 12$

$$3x - 3 = 12$$
$$3x - 3 + 3 = 12 + 3$$
$$3x = 15$$
$$\frac{3x}{3} = \frac{15}{3}$$
$$x = 5$$

25. $35 - 17 = 3(x - 2)$
$18 = 3x - 6$
$18 + 6 = 3x - 6 + 6$
$24 = 3x$
$\dfrac{24}{3} = \dfrac{3x}{3}$
$8 = x$

29. $2t - 1 = 3(t + 7)$
$2t - 1 = 3t + 21$
$2t - 1 - 21 = 3t + 21 - 21$
$2t - 22 = 3t$
$2t - 2t - 22 = 3t - 2t$
$-22 = t$

33. $3r + 4 = 19$
$3r + 4 - 4 = 19 - 4$
$3r = 15$
$\dfrac{3r}{3} = \dfrac{15}{3}$
$r = 5$

37. $8 - t = 3$
$8 - 8 - t = 3 - 8$
$-t = -5$
$\dfrac{-t}{-1} = \dfrac{-5}{-1}$
$t = 5$

41. $9a + 29 = -7$
$9a + 29 - 29 = -7 - 29$
$9a = -36$
$\dfrac{9a}{9} = \dfrac{-36}{9}$
$a = -4$

45. $11(x - 2) = 22$
$11x - 22 = 22$
$11x - 22 + 22 = 22 + 22$
$11x = 44$
$\dfrac{11x}{11} = \dfrac{44}{11}$
$x = 4$

49. $-3c + 1 - 4c = -20$
$-3c - 4c + 1 = -20$
$-7c + 1 = -20$
$-7c + 1 - 1 = -20 - 1$
$-7c = -21$
$\dfrac{-7c}{-7} = \dfrac{-21}{-7}$
$c = 3$

53. $-5 + 7k = -13 + 8k$
$-5 + 13 + 7k = -13 + 13 + 8k$
$8 + 7k = 8k$
$8 + 7k - 7k = 8k - 7k$
$8 = k$

57. $-8(n + 2) + 17 = -6n - 5$
$-8n - 16 + 17 = -6n - 5$
$-8n + 1 = -6n - 5$
$-8n + 1 + 5 = -6n - 5 + 5$
$-8n + 6 = -6n$
$-8n + 8n + 6 = -6n + 8n$
$6 = 2n$
$\dfrac{6}{2} = \dfrac{2n}{2}$
$3 = n$

61. $10 + 5(z - 2) = -4z + 1$
$10 + 5z - 10 = -4z + 1$
$5z = -4z + 1$
$5z + 4z = -4z + 4z + 1$
$9z = 1$
$\dfrac{9z}{9} = \dfrac{1}{9}$
$z = \dfrac{1}{9}$

65. $7(6 + w) = 6(w - 2)$
$42 + 7w = 6w - 12$
$42 - 42 + 7w = 6w - 12 - 42$
$7w = 6w - 54$
$7w - 6w = 6w - 6w - 54$
$w = -54$

69. $2(3z - 2) - 2(5 - 2z) = 4$
$6z - 4 - 10 + 4z = 4$
$10z - 14 = 4$
$10z - 14 + 14 = 4 + 14$
$10z = 18$
$\dfrac{10z}{10} = \dfrac{18}{10}$
$z = \dfrac{9}{5}$

73. "The product of" indicates multiplication.
$-5(-29) = 145$

77. "The quotient of" indicates division.
$\dfrac{100}{2(50)} = 1$

81. The number of electronically filed returns is expected to be 70 million in 2006 and 90 million in 2009. The increase is expected to be 90 million $-$ 70 million = 20 million returns.

85. The next step in solving $-3x = -1.2$ is to divide both sides of the equation by -3; a.

89. Use $C = \dfrac{5}{9}(F - 32)$ with $C = 57.8$.

$$C = \dfrac{5}{9}(F - 32)$$
$$57.8 = \dfrac{5}{9}(F - 32)$$
$$\dfrac{9}{5}(57.8) = \dfrac{9}{5} \cdot \dfrac{5}{9}(F - 32)$$
$$104.04 = F - 32$$
$$104.04 + 32 = F - 32 + 32$$
$$136.04 = F$$

The temperature was 136.04°F.

Exercise Set 8.5

1. "A number added to -5 is -7" is
$-5 + x = -7$.

5. "A number subtracted from -20 amounts to 104" is
$-20 - x = 104$.

9. "The product of 5 and the sum of -3 and a number is -20" is
$5(-3 + x) = -20$

13. "The sum of 3, 4, and a number amounts to 16" is
$3 + 4 + x = 16$
$7 + x = 16$
$x + 7 - 7 = 16 - 7$
$x = 9$

17. "Thirty less a number is equal to the product of 3 and the sum of the number and 6" is

$$30 - x = 3(x + 6)$$
$$30 - x = 3x + 18$$
$$30 - 30 - x = 3x + 18 - 30$$
$$-x = 3x - 12$$
$$-x - 3x = 3x - 3x - 12$$
$$-4x = -12$$
$$\frac{-4x}{-4} = \frac{-12}{-4}$$
$$x = 3$$

21. "Three times the difference of some number and 5 amounts to the quotient of 108 and 12" is

$$3(x - 5) = \frac{108}{12}$$
$$3x - 15 = 9$$
$$3x - 15 + 15 = 9 + 15$$
$$3x = 24$$
$$\frac{3x}{3} = \frac{24}{3}$$
$$x = 8$$

25. Let x be the number of votes that John Kerry received. Since George W. Bush received 34 more votes than John Kerry, George W. Bush received $x + 34$ votes. Since a total of 538 votes were cast for the two candidates, the sum of x and $x + 34$ is 538.

$$x + x + 34 = 538$$
$$2x + 34 = 538$$
$$2x + 34 - 34 = 538 - 34$$
$$2x = 504$$
$$\frac{2x}{2} = \frac{504}{2}$$
$$x = 252$$

Thus, John Kerry received 252 votes and George W. Bush received $252 + 34 = 286$ votes.

29. Let x be the number of universities in the United States. Since India has 2649 more universities than the United States, India has $x + 2649$ universities. Since their combined total is 14,165, the sum of x and $x + 2649$ is 14,165.

$$x + x + 2649 = 14165$$
$$2x + 2649 = 14165$$
$$2x + 2649 - 2649 = 14165 - 2649$$
$$2x = 11516$$
$$\frac{2x}{2} = \frac{11516}{2}$$
$$x = 5758$$

Thus, the United States has 5758 universities and India has $5758 + 2649 = 8407$ universities.

33. Let x be the capacity of Neyland Stadium. Since Michigan Stadium has a capacity of 4647 more than Neyland, Michigan Stadium has a capacity of $x + 4647$. Since their combined capacity is 210,355, the sum of x and $x + 4647$ is 210,355.

$$x + x + 4647 = 210{,}355$$
$$2x + 4647 = 210{,}355$$
$$2x + 4647 - 4647 = 210{,}355 - 4647$$
$$2x = 205{,}708$$
$$\frac{2x}{2} = \frac{205{,}708}{2}$$
$$x = 102{,}854$$

Thus, Neyland Stadium has a capacity of 102,854 and Michigan Stadium has a capacity of $102{,}854 + 4647 = 107{,}501$.

37. Let x be the number of ounces of food the finch consumes. Since a crow will eat five more ounces than a finch, a crow will consume $x + 5$ ounces of food. Since they eat 13 ounces of food together, the sum of x and $x + 5$ is 13.

$$x + x + 5 = 13$$
$$2x + 5 = 13$$
$$2x + 5 - 5 = 13 - 5$$
$$2x = 8$$
$$\frac{2x}{2} = \frac{8}{2}$$
$$x = 4$$

Thus, the finch consumes 4 ounces of food and the crow consumes $4 + 5 = 9$ ounces of food.

41. Let x be the amount Anthony received for the accessories. Since he received five times as much for the bike, he received $5x$ for the bike. Since he received a total of $270 for the bike and accessories, the sum of x and $5x$ is 270.

$$x + 5x = 270$$
$$6x = 270$$
$$\frac{6x}{6} = \frac{270}{6}$$
$$x = 45$$

Thus, Anthony received $5 \cdot \$45 = \$225$ for the bike.

45. 586 rounded to the nearest ten is 590.

49. 2986 rounded to the nearest thousand is 3000.

53. Use $P = A + C$, where $P = 165{,}000$ and $A = 156{,}750$.

$$P = A + C$$
$$165{,}000 = 156{,}750 + C$$
$$165{,}000 - 156{,}750 = 156{,}750 - 156{,}750 + C$$
$$8250 = C$$

The agent will receive $8250.

Chapter 8 Test

1.
$$\frac{3x - 5}{2y} = \frac{3 \cdot 7 - 5}{2(-8)}$$
$$= \frac{21 - 5}{-16}$$
$$= \frac{16}{-16}$$
$$= -1$$

5. Area $=$ length $\cdot$ width
$$A = 4 \cdot (3x - 1)$$
$$= 4 \cdot 3x - 4 \cdot 1$$
$$= 12x - 4$$
The area is $(12x - 4)$ square meters.

9.
$$-\frac{5}{8}x = -25$$
$$-\frac{8}{5} \cdot -\frac{5}{8}x = -\frac{8}{5} \cdot -25$$
$$x = 40$$

13.
$$-4x + 7 = 15$$
$$-4x + 7 - 7 = 15 - 7$$
$$-4x = 8$$
$$\frac{-4x}{-4} = \frac{8}{-4}$$
$$x = -2$$

17.
$$10y - 1 = 7y + 21$$
$$10y - 1 + 1 = 7y + 21 + 1$$
$$10y = 7y + 22$$
$$10y - 7y = 7y - 7y + 22$$
$$3y = 22$$
$$\frac{3y}{3} = \frac{22}{3}$$
$$y = \frac{22}{3}$$

21. Use $A = \frac{1}{2} \cdot b \cdot h$, where $b = 5$ and $h = 12$.

$$A = \frac{1}{2} \cdot b \cdot h = \frac{1}{2} \cdot 5 \cdot 12 = 30$$

The area is 30 square feet.

CHAPTER 9

Exercise Set 9.1

1. The figure extends indefinitely in two directions. It is line YZ, or $\overleftrightarrow{YZ}$.

5. The figure has two endpoints. It is line segment PQ or $\overline{PQ}$.

9. A right angle has a measure of $90°$.

13. $\angle S$ measures $180°$. It is a straight angle.

17. $\angle Q$ measures between $90°$ and $180°$. It is an obtuse angle.

21. The complement of an angle that measures $17°$ is an angle that measures $90° - 17° = 73°$.

25. The complement of an angle that measures $58°$ is an angle that measures $90° - 58° = 32°$.

29. $52° + 38° = 90°$, so $\angle PNQ$ and $\angle QNR$ are complementary. $60° + 30° = 90°$, so $\angle MNP$ and $\angle RNO$ are complementary.

33. $m\angle x = 120° - 88° = 32°$

37. $\angle x$ and the angle marked $35°$ are vertical angles, so $m\angle x = 35°$.
$\angle x$ and $\angle y$ are supplementary, so
$m\angle y = 180° - m\angle x = 180° - 35° = 145°$.
$\angle y$ and $\angle z$ are vertical angles so
$m\angle z = m\angle y = 145°$.

41. $\angle x$ and the angle marked $80°$ are supplementary, so
$m\angle x = 180° - 80° = 100°$.
$\angle y$ and the angle marked $80°$ are alternate interior angles, so
$m\angle y = 80°$.
$\angle x$ and $\angle z$ are corresponding angles, so $m\angle z = m\angle x = 100°$.

45. $\angle x$ can also be named $\angle ABC$ or $\angle CBA$.

49. $m\angle ABC = 15°$

53. $m\angle DBA = m\angle DBC + m\angle CBA$
$= 50° + 15°$
$= 65°$

57. $\frac{7}{8} + \frac{1}{4} = \frac{7}{8} + \frac{2}{8} = \frac{9}{8}$ or $1\frac{1}{8}$

61. $3\frac{1}{3} - 2\frac{1}{2} = \frac{10}{3} - \frac{5}{2} = \frac{20}{6} - \frac{15}{6} = \frac{5}{6}$

65. The supplement of an angle that measures $125.2°$ is an angle with measure $180° - 125.2° = 54.8°$.

69. True; since $120°$ is less than $180°$, it is possible to find the supplement of a $120°$ angle.

73. Two angles are complementary if their sum is $90°$. If two complementary angles have the same measure, then the measure of each must be $\frac{1}{2}(90°) = 45°$.

Exercise Set 9.2

1. The figure has five sides, so it is a pentagon.

5. The figure has four sides, so it is a quadrilateral.

9. All three sides of the triangle have the same length, therefore the triangle is equilateral.

13. Two sides of the triangle have the same length, therefore the triangle is isosceles.

17. $m\angle x = 180° - 95° - 72° = 13°$

21. Twice the radius of a circle is its diameter.

25. A quadrilateral with opposite sides parallel is a parallelogram.

29. $d = 2 \cdot r = 2 \cdot 7 = 14$ m

33. $d = 2 \cdot r = 2 \cdot 20.3 = 40.6$ cm

37. The solid is a cylinder.

41. The solid is a cone.

45. The object has the shape of a rectangular solid.

49. The object has the shape of a pyramid.

53. $r = \frac{1}{2}d = \frac{1}{2} \cdot 26 = 13$ miles

57. $2(18) + 2(36) = 36 + 72 = 108$

61. True; since all four sides of a square are equal in length, a square is also a rhombus.

65. False; a pentagon has five sides, so it cannot be a quadrilateral, which has four sides.

69. answers may vary

Exercise Set 9.3

1. $P = 2 \cdot l + 2 \cdot w$
$= 2 \cdot 17$ ft $+ 2 \cdot 15$ ft
$= 34$ ft $+ 30$ ft
$= 64$ ft
The perimeter is 64 feet.

5. $P = a + b + c$
$= 5$ in. $+ 7$ in. $+ 9$ in.
$= 21$ in.
The perimeter is 21 inches.

9. All sides of a regular triangle have the same length.
$P = a + b + c = 4$ in. $+ 4$ in. $+ 4$ in. $= 12$ in.
The perimeter is 12 inches.

13. Sum the lengths of the sides.
$P = 5$ ft $+ 3$ ft $+ 2$ ft $+ 7$ ft $+ 4$ ft
$= 21$ ft
The perimeter is 21 feet.

17. $P = 2 \cdot l + 2 \cdot w$
$= 2 \cdot 120$ yd $+ 2 \cdot 53$ yd
$= 240$ yd $+ 106$ yd
$= 346$ yd
The perimeter of the football field is 346 yards.

21. The amount of stripping needed is 22 feet.
22 feet $\cdot$ \$3 per foot $=$ \$66
The total cost of the stripping is \$66.

25. $P = 4 \cdot s = 4 \cdot 7$ in. $= 28$ in.
The perimeter is 28 inches.

29. The unmarked vertical side must have length 28 m $- 20$ m $= 8$ m.
The unmarked horizontal side must have length
20 m $- 17$ m $= 3$ m.
Sum the lengths of the sides.
$P = 17$ m $+ 8$ m $+ 3$ m $+ 20$ m $+ 20$ m $+ 28$ m
$= 96$ m
The perimeter is 96 meters.

33. The unmarked vertical side must have length
10 mi $+ 12$ mi $= 22$ mi.
The unmarked horizontal side must have length
8 mi $+ 34$ mi $= 42$ mi.
Sum the lengths of the sides.
$P = 42$ mi $+ 12$ mi $+ 34$ mi $+ 10$ mi $+ 8$ mi $+ 22$ mi
$= 128$ mi
The perimeter is 128 miles.

37. $C = 2 \cdot \pi \cdot r$
$= 2 \cdot \pi \cdot 8$ mi
$= 16\pi$ mi
≈ 50.24 mi

41. $C = 2 \cdot \pi \cdot r$
$= 2 \cdot \pi \cdot 5$ ft
$= 10\pi$ ft
$\approx 10 \cdot \frac{22}{7}$ ft
The distance around is about $\frac{220}{7} = 31\frac{3}{7}$ feet or about 31.43 feet.

45. Sum the lengths of the sides.
$P = 9$ mi $+ 6$ mi $+ 11$ mi $+ 4.7$ mi
$= 30.7$ mi
The perimeter is 30.7 miles.

49. The sides of a regular pentagon all have the same length. Sum the lengths of the sides.

$P = 8$ mm $+ 8$ mm $+ 8$ mm $+ 8$ mm $+ 8$ mm

$= 40$ mm

The perimeter is 40 millimeters.

53. $5 + 6 \cdot 3 = 5 + 18 = 23$

57. $(18 + 8) - (12 + 4) = 26 - 16 = 10$

61. A fence goes around the edge of a yard, thus the situation involves perimeter.

65. Paint covers the surface of a wall, thus the situation involves area.

69. a. The first age category that 8-year-old children fit into is "Under 9," thus the minimum width is 30 yards and the minimum length is 40 yards.

 b. $P = 2 \cdot l + 2 \cdot w$

$= 2 \cdot 40$ yd $+ 2 \cdot 30$ yd

$= 80$ yd $+ 60$ yd

$= 140$ yd

The perimeter of the field is 140 yards.

73. a. Smaller circle:

$C = 2 \cdot \pi \cdot r$

$= 2 \cdot \pi \cdot 10$ m

$= 20\pi$ m

≈ 62.8 m

Larger circle:

$C = 2 \cdot \pi \cdot r$

$= 2 \cdot \pi \cdot 20$ m

$= 40\pi$ m

≈ 125.6 m

 b. Yes, when the radius of a circle is doubled, the circumference is also doubled.

77. $P = 2 \cdot l + 2 \cdot w$

30 ft $= 2 \cdot 9$ ft $+ 2 \cdot w$

30 ft $= 18$ ft $+ 2 \cdot w$

12 ft $= 2 \cdot w$

6 ft $= w$

The width is 6 feet.

Exercise Set 9.4

1. $A = l \cdot w = 2$ m $\cdot 3.5$ m $= 7$ sq m

5. $A = \dfrac{1}{2} \cdot b \cdot h = \dfrac{1}{2} \cdot 6$ yd $\cdot 5$ yd $= 15$ sq yd

9. $A = s^2 = (4.2 \text{ ft})^2 = 17.64$ sq ft

13. $A = \dfrac{1}{2}(b + B) \cdot h$

$= \dfrac{1}{2}(7 \text{ yd} + 4 \text{ yd}) \cdot 4$ yd

$= \dfrac{1}{2}(11 \text{ yd}) \cdot 4$ yd

$= 22$ sq yd

17. $A = b \cdot h$

$= 5$ in. $\cdot 4\dfrac{1}{2}$ in.

$= 5$ in. $\cdot \dfrac{9}{2}$ in.

$= \dfrac{45}{2}$ sq in.

$= 22\dfrac{1}{2}$ sq in.

21.

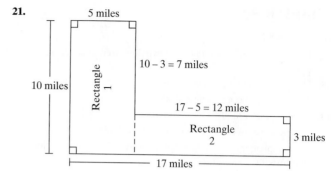

Rectangle 1: $A = l \cdot w = 10$ mi $\cdot 5$ mi $= 50$ sq mi

Rectangle 2: $A = l \cdot w = 12$ mi $\cdot 3$ mi $= 36$ sq mi

The area of the figure is 50 sq mi $+ 36$ sq mi $= 86$ sq mi.

25. $A = \pi r^2 = \pi(6 \text{ in.})^2 = 36\pi$ sq in. $\approx 113\dfrac{1}{7}$ sq in.

29. $A = l \cdot w = 505$ ft $\cdot 225$ ft $= 113{,}625$ sq ft

The area of the flag is 113,625 square feet.

33. $A = l \cdot w = 16$ in. $\cdot 8$ in. $= 128$ sq in.

128 sq in. $\cdot \dfrac{1 \text{ sq ft}}{144 \text{ sq in.}} = \dfrac{128}{144}$ sq ft $= \dfrac{8}{9}$ sq ft

The side has area 128 square inches, which is $\dfrac{8}{9}$ square foot.

37. $A = l \cdot w = 7$ ft $\cdot 6$ ft $= 42$ sq ft

$4 \cdot 42$ sq ft $= 168$ sq ft

Four panels have an area of 168 square feet.

41. $A = \dfrac{1}{2}(b + B)h$

$= \dfrac{1}{2}(25 \text{ ft} + 36 \text{ ft}) \cdot 12\dfrac{1}{2}$ ft

$= \dfrac{1}{2} \cdot 61$ ft $\cdot 12\dfrac{1}{2}$ ft

$= 381\dfrac{1}{4}$ sq ft

To the nearest square foot, the area is 381 square feet.

45. Sum the lengths of the sides.

3 ft $+ 3\dfrac{1}{2}$ ft $+ 6$ ft $+ 8\dfrac{1}{2}$ ft $+ 4$ ft $= 25$ ft

49. Note that the dimensions given are the diameters of the pizzas.

12-inch pizza:

$r = \dfrac{1}{2} \cdot d = \dfrac{1}{2} \cdot 12$ in. $= 6$ in.

$A = \pi \cdot r^2 = \pi(6 \text{ in.})^2 = 36\pi$ sq in.

Price per square inch $= \dfrac{\$10}{36\pi \text{ sq in.}} \approx \$0.0884$

8-inch pizzas:

$r = \dfrac{1}{2} \cdot d = \dfrac{1}{2} \cdot 8$ in. $= 4$ in.

$A = \pi \cdot r^2 = \pi(4 \text{ in.})^2 = 16\pi$ sq in.

$2 \cdot A = 2 \cdot 16\pi$ sq in. $= 32\pi$ sq in.

Price per square inch: $\dfrac{\$9}{32\pi \text{ sq in.}} \approx \$0.0895$

Since the price per square inch for the 12-inch pizza is less, the 12-inch pizza is the better deal.

53. The area of the shaded region is the area of the square minus the area of the circle.

Square: $A = s^2 = (6 \text{ in.})^2 = 36$ sq in.

Circle: $r = \dfrac{1}{2} \cdot d = \dfrac{1}{2}(6 \text{ in.}) = 3$ in.

$A = \pi \cdot r^2 = \pi(3 \text{ in.})^2 = 9\pi$ sq in. ≈ 28.26 sq in.

36 sq in. $- 28.26$ sq in. $= 7.74$ sq in.

The shaded region has area of approximately 7.74 square inches.

57. The skating area is a rectangle with a half circle on each end.

Rectangle: $A = l \cdot w = 22 \text{ m} \cdot 10 \text{ m} = 220 \text{ sq m}$

Half circles: $A = 2 \cdot \dfrac{1}{2} \cdot \pi \cdot r^2$

$\qquad\qquad = \pi(5 \text{ m})^2$

$\qquad\qquad = 25\pi \text{ sq m} \approx 78.5 \text{ sq m}$

$220 \text{ sq m} + 78.5 \text{ sq m} = 298.5 \text{ sq m}$

The skating surface has area of 298.5 square meters.

Exercise Set 9.5

1. $V = l \cdot w \cdot h = 6 \text{ in.} \cdot 4 \text{ in.} \cdot 3 \text{ in.} = 72 \text{ cu in.};$

$SA = 2lh + 2wh + 2lw$

$\quad = 2(6 \text{ in.})(3 \text{ in.}) + 2(4 \text{ in.})(3 \text{ in.}) + 2(6 \text{ in.})(4 \text{ in.})$

$\quad = 36 \text{ sq in.} + 24 \text{ sq in.} + 48 \text{ sq in.}$

$\quad = 108 \text{ sq in.}$

5. $V = \dfrac{1}{3} \cdot \pi \cdot r^2 \cdot h = \dfrac{1}{3} \cdot \pi \cdot (2 \text{ yd})^2 \cdot 3 \text{ yd} = 4\pi \text{ cu yd} \approx 12\dfrac{4}{7} \text{ cu yd};$

$SA = \pi r \sqrt{r^2 + h^2} + \pi r^2$

$\quad = \pi(2 \text{ yd})\sqrt{(2 \text{ yd})^2 + (3 \text{ yd})^2} + \pi(2 \text{ yd})^2$

$\quad = 2\pi \text{ yd}\sqrt{4 \text{ sq yd} + 9 \text{ sq yd}} + \pi(4 \text{ sq yd})$

$\quad = 2\pi \text{ yd}\sqrt{13 \text{ sq yd}} + 4\pi \text{ sq yd}$

$\quad = 2\pi \text{ yd} \sqrt{13} \text{ yd} + 4\pi \text{ sq yd}$

$\quad = 2\sqrt{13}\,\pi \text{ sq yd} + 4\pi \text{ sq yd}$

$\quad = (2\sqrt{13}\pi + 4\pi) \text{ sq yd} \approx 35.20 \text{ sq yd}$

9. $V = \pi \cdot r^2 \cdot h$

$\quad = \pi(1 \text{ in.})^2 \cdot 9 \text{ in.}$

$\quad = 9\pi \text{ cu in.} \approx 28\dfrac{2}{7} \text{ cu in.}$

13. $V = s^3 = \left(1\dfrac{1}{3} \text{ in.}\right)^3$

$\quad = \left(\dfrac{4}{3} \text{ in.}\right)^3$

$\quad = \dfrac{64}{27} \text{ cu in.}$

$\quad = 2\dfrac{10}{27} \text{ cu in.}$

17. Note: $1\dfrac{3}{10} \text{ in.} = \dfrac{13}{10} \text{ in.}$

$V = \dfrac{1}{3}s^2h$

$\quad = \dfrac{1}{3}(5 \text{ in.})^2 \cdot \dfrac{13}{10} \text{ in.}$

$\quad = \dfrac{1}{3} \cdot 25 \cdot \dfrac{13}{10} \text{ cu in.}$

$\quad = 10\dfrac{5}{6} \text{ cu in.}$

21. $V = \dfrac{4}{3}\pi r^3$

$\quad = \dfrac{4}{3}\pi(7 \text{ in.})^3$

$\quad = \dfrac{1372}{3}\pi \text{ cu in. or } 457\dfrac{1}{3}\pi \text{ cu in.}$

$SA = 4\pi r^2$

$\quad = 4\pi(7 \text{ in.})^2$

$\quad = 4\pi(49 \text{ sq in.})$

$\quad = 196\pi \text{ sq in.}$

25. $r = \dfrac{1}{2} \cdot d = \dfrac{1}{2} \cdot 4 \text{ cm} = 2 \text{ cm}$

$V = \dfrac{1}{3}\pi \cdot r^2 \cdot h$

$\quad = \dfrac{1}{3}\pi \cdot (2 \text{ cm})^2 \cdot 3 \text{ cm}$

$\quad = 4\pi \text{ cu cm}$

$\quad \approx 12\dfrac{4}{7} \text{ cu cm}$

There are approximately $12\dfrac{4}{7}$ cubic centimeters of ice cream in the cone.

29. $5^2 = 5 \cdot 5 = 25$

33. $1^2 + 2^2 = 1 \cdot 1 + 2 \cdot 2 = 1 + 4 = 5$

37. a. The first age category that 9-year-old children fit into is "Under 10," thus the minimum width is 40 yards and the minimum length is 60 yards.

b. $A = l \cdot w = 40 \text{ yd} \cdot 60 \text{ yd} = 2400 \text{ sq yd}$

The area of the field is 2400 square yards.

41. $V = \dfrac{1}{3} \cdot s^2 \cdot h$

$\quad = \dfrac{1}{3} \cdot (344 \text{ m})^2 \cdot 65.5 \text{ m}$

$\quad \approx 2{,}583{,}669 \text{ cu m}$

The original volume of the pyramid was about 2,583,669 cubic meters.

45. answers may vary

Exercise Set 9.6

1. The triangles are congruent by Side-Side-Side.

5. The triangles are congruent by Angle-Side-Angle.

9. $\dfrac{22}{11} = \dfrac{14}{7} = \dfrac{12}{6} = \dfrac{2}{1}$

The ratio of corresponding sides is $\dfrac{2}{1}$.

13. $\dfrac{n}{3} = \dfrac{9}{6}$

$6 \cdot n = 3 \cdot 9$

$6n = 27$

$n = \dfrac{27}{6}$

$n = 4.5$

17. $\dfrac{n}{3.75} = \dfrac{12}{9}$

$9 \cdot n = 12 \cdot 3.75$

$9n = 45$

$n = \dfrac{45}{9}$

$n = 5$

21. $\dfrac{n}{3.25} = \dfrac{17.5}{3.25}$

$3.25 \cdot n = 17.5 \cdot 3.25$

$3.25n = 56.875$

$n = \dfrac{56.875}{3.25}$

$n = 17.5$

25. $\dfrac{n}{34} = \dfrac{10}{16}$

$16 \cdot n = 10 \cdot 34$

$16n = 340$

$n = \dfrac{340}{16}$

$n = 21.25$

29. $\dfrac{x}{25} = \dfrac{40}{2}$

$2 \cdot x = 40 \cdot 25$

$2x = 1000$

$x = \dfrac{1000}{2}$

$x = 500$

The building is 500 feet tall.

33. $\dfrac{n}{18} = \dfrac{24}{30}$

$\dfrac{n}{18} = \dfrac{4}{5}$

$5 \cdot n = 4 \cdot 18$

$5 \cdot n = 72$

$n = \dfrac{72}{5}$

$n = 14.4$

The shadow of the tree is 14.4 feet long.

37. Average $= \dfrac{14 + 17 + 21 + 18}{4} = \dfrac{70}{4} = 17.5$

41. $\dfrac{n}{7} = \dfrac{5}{9}$

$9 \cdot n = 5 \cdot 7$

$9n = 35$

$n = \dfrac{35}{9} = 3\dfrac{8}{9}$

The print is $3\dfrac{8}{9}$ inches wide, so it is too wide to fit on a 3-by-5-inch index card.

Chapter 9 Test

1. The complement of an angle that measures 78° is an angle that measures $90° - 78° = 12°$.

5. $\angle x$ and the angle marked 73° are vertical angles, so $m\angle x = 73°$.
$\angle x$ and $\angle y$ are alternate interior angles, so $m\angle y = m\angle x = 73°$.
$\angle x$ and $\angle z$ are corresponding angles, so $m\angle z = m\angle x = 73°$.

9. Circumference:

$C = 2 \cdot \pi \cdot r$

$\quad = 2 \cdot \pi \cdot 9$ in.

$\quad = 18\pi$ in.

$\quad \approx 56.52$ in.

Area:

$A = \pi r^2$

$\quad = \pi (9 \text{ in.})^2$

$\quad = 81\pi$ sq in.

$\quad \approx 254.34$ sq in.

13. $V = l \cdot w \cdot h = 5 \text{ ft} \cdot 3 \text{ ft} \cdot 2 \text{ ft} = 30$ cu ft;

$SA = 2lh + 2wh + 2lw$

$\quad = 2(5 \text{ ft})(2 \text{ ft}) + 2(3 \text{ ft})(2 \text{ ft}) + 2(5 \text{ ft})(3 \text{ ft})$

$\quad = 20 \text{ sq ft} + 12 \text{ sq ft} + 30 \text{ sq ft} = 62 \text{ sq ft}$

17. First find the area of the lawn.

$A = l \cdot w = 123.8 \text{ ft} \cdot 80 \text{ ft} = 9904$ sq ft

0.02 ounce per square foot is $\dfrac{0.02 \text{ oz}}{1 \text{ sq ft}}$.

$\dfrac{0.02 \text{ oz}}{1 \text{ sq ft}} \cdot 9904 \text{ sq ft} = 198.08$ oz

Vivian needs to purchase 198.08 ounces of insecticide.

APPENDIX A

Exercise Set A.1

1. $\begin{array}{r} 1 \\ +4 \\ \hline 5 \end{array}$

5. $\begin{array}{r} 3 \\ +9 \\ \hline 12 \end{array}$

9. $\begin{array}{r} 9 \\ +5 \\ \hline 14 \end{array}$

13. $\begin{array}{r} 5 \\ +5 \\ \hline 10 \end{array}$

17. $\begin{array}{r} 2 \\ +9 \\ \hline 11 \end{array}$

21. $\begin{array}{r} 6 \\ +4 \\ \hline 10 \end{array}$

25. $\begin{array}{r} 9 \\ +8 \\ \hline 17 \end{array}$

29. $\begin{array}{r} 7 \\ +5 \\ \hline 12 \end{array}$

33. $\begin{array}{r} 4 \\ +3 \\ \hline 7 \end{array}$

37. $\begin{array}{r} 7 \\ +1 \\ \hline 8 \end{array}$

41. $\begin{array}{r} 2 \\ +4 \\ \hline 6 \end{array}$

45. $\begin{array}{r} 3 \\ +6 \\ \hline 9 \end{array}$

49. $\begin{array}{r} 2 \\ +5 \\ \hline 7 \end{array}$

53. $\begin{array}{r} 8 \\ +3 \\ \hline 11 \end{array}$

57. $\begin{array}{r} 0 \\ +5 \\ \hline 5 \end{array}$

61. $\begin{array}{r} 6 \\ +7 \\ \hline 13 \end{array}$

65. $\begin{array}{r} 0 \\ +7 \\ \hline 7 \end{array}$

69. $\begin{array}{r} 4 \\ +1 \\ \hline 5 \end{array}$

73. $\begin{array}{r} 7 \\ +9 \\ \hline 16 \end{array}$

77. $\begin{array}{r} 1 \\ +0 \\ \hline 1 \end{array}$

81.
$$\begin{array}{r} 2 \\ +8 \\ \hline 10 \end{array}$$

85.
$$\begin{array}{r} 5 \\ +0 \\ \hline 5 \end{array}$$

89.
$$\begin{array}{r} 9 \\ +2 \\ \hline 11 \end{array}$$

93.
$$\begin{array}{r} 2 \\ +7 \\ \hline 9 \end{array}$$

97.
$$\begin{array}{r} 6 \\ +8 \\ \hline 14 \end{array}$$

Exercise Set A.2

1.
$$\begin{array}{r} 1 \\ \times 1 \\ \hline 1 \end{array}$$

5.
$$\begin{array}{r} 8 \\ \times 4 \\ \hline 32 \end{array}$$

9.
$$\begin{array}{r} 2 \\ \times 2 \\ \hline 4 \end{array}$$

13.
$$\begin{array}{r} 3 \\ \times 2 \\ \hline 6 \end{array}$$

17.
$$\begin{array}{r} 4 \\ \times 6 \\ \hline 24 \end{array}$$

21.
$$\begin{array}{r} 5 \\ \times 8 \\ \hline 40 \end{array}$$

25.
$$\begin{array}{r} 9 \\ \times 6 \\ \hline 54 \end{array}$$

29.
$$\begin{array}{r} 6 \\ \times 9 \\ \hline 54 \end{array}$$

33.
$$\begin{array}{r} 4 \\ \times 9 \\ \hline 36 \end{array}$$

37.
$$\begin{array}{r} 9 \\ \times 4 \\ \hline 36 \end{array}$$

41.
$$\begin{array}{r} 8 \\ \times 6 \\ \hline 48 \end{array}$$

45.
$$\begin{array}{r} 9 \\ \times 0 \\ \hline 0 \end{array}$$

49.
$$\begin{array}{r} 3 \\ \times 5 \\ \hline 15 \end{array}$$

53.
$$\begin{array}{r} 1 \\ \times 0 \\ \hline 0 \end{array}$$

57.
$$\begin{array}{r} 0 \\ \times 6 \\ \hline 0 \end{array}$$

61.
$$\begin{array}{r} 9 \\ \times 2 \\ \hline 18 \end{array}$$

65.
$$\begin{array}{r} 6 \\ \times 6 \\ \hline 36 \end{array}$$

69.
$$\begin{array}{r} 7 \\ \times 5 \\ \hline 35 \end{array}$$

73.
$$\begin{array}{r} 8 \\ \times 5 \\ \hline 40 \end{array}$$

77.
$$\begin{array}{r} 9 \\ \times 1 \\ \hline 9 \end{array}$$

81.
$$\begin{array}{r} 1 \\ \times 5 \\ \hline 5 \end{array}$$

85.
$$\begin{array}{r} 3 \\ \times 7 \\ \hline 21 \end{array}$$

89.
$$\begin{array}{r} 8 \\ \times 2 \\ \hline 16 \end{array}$$

93.
$$\begin{array}{r} 4 \\ \times 1 \\ \hline 4 \end{array}$$

97.
$$\begin{array}{r} 3 \\ \times 6 \\ \hline 18 \end{array}$$

APPENDIX C

Exercise Set C.1

1. $(2x + 3) + (-7x - 27) = (2x - 7x) + (3 - 27)$
$$= -5x + (-24)$$
$$= -5x - 24$$

5. $(12y - 20) + (9y^2 + 13y - 20)$
$$= 9y^2 + (12y + 13y) + (-20 - 20)$$
$$= 9y^2 + 25y - 40$$

9. $(5a - 6) - (a + 2) = (5a - 6) + (-a - 2)$
$$= (5a - a) + (-6 - 2)$$
$$= 4a - 8$$

13. $(10y^2 - 7) - (20y^3 - 2y^2 - 3)$
$$= (10y^2 - 7) + (-20y^3 + 2y^2 + 3)$$
$$= (-20y^3) + (10y^2 + 2y^2) + (-7 + 3)$$
$$= -20y^3 + 12y^2 - 4$$

17.
$$\begin{array}{r} 13y^2 - 6y - 14 \\ -(5y^2 + 4y - 6) \end{array} \qquad \begin{array}{r} 13y^2 - 6y - 14 \\ + -5y^2 - 4y + 6 \\ \hline 8y^2 - 10y - 8 \end{array}$$

21. $(4y + 4) - (3y + 8) = (4y + 4) + (-3y - 8)$
$$= (4y - 3y) + (4 - 8)$$
$$= y - 4$$

25. $(10x + 4.5) + (-x - 8.6) = (10x - x) + (4.5 - 8.6)$
$$= 9x - 4.1$$

29. $(21y - 4.6) - (36y - 8.2)$
$$= (21y - 4.6) + (-36y + 8.2)$$
$$= (21y - 36y) + (-4.6 + 8.2)$$
$$= -15y + 3.6$$

33. $(b^3 - 2b^2 + 10b + 11) + (b^2 - 3b - 12)$
$$= b^3 + (-2b^2 + b^2) + (10b - 3b) + (11 - 12)$$
$$= b^3 - b^2 + 7b - 1$$

37. $\left(3z + \dfrac{6}{7}\right) - \left(3z - \dfrac{3}{7}\right)$
$$= \left(3z + \dfrac{6}{7}\right) + \left(-3z + \dfrac{3}{7}\right)$$
$$= (3z - 3z) + \left(\dfrac{6}{7} + \dfrac{3}{7}\right)$$
$$= \dfrac{9}{7}$$

41. $x^2 - 6x + 3$

Let $x = 2$.
$$(2)^2 - 6(2) + 3 = 4 - 12 + 3 = -5$$

45. $2x + 10$

Let $x = 5$.
$$2(5) + 10 = 10 + 10 = 20$$

49. $2x^2 + 4x - 20$

Let $x = 5$.
$$2(5)^2 + 4(5) - 20 = 2(25) + 20 - 20 = 50$$

53. $3000 + 20x$

Let $x = 10$.
$$3000 + 20(10) = 3000 + 200 = 3200$$

It costs \$3200 to manufacture 10 file cabinets.

57. $(2x + 1) + (x + 11) + (5x - 10)$
$$= (2x + x + 5x) + (1 + 11 - 10)$$
$$= 8x + 2$$

The perimeter is $(8x + 2)$ inches.

61.
$$\begin{array}{r} 3x^2 + \_\,x - \_ \\ +\,\_\,x^2 - 6x + 2 \\ \hline 5x^2 + 14x - 4 \end{array}$$
$$\left[\begin{array}{l}(3 + \_\,)x^2 = 5x \\ (3 + 2)x^2 = 5x^2\end{array}\right]$$
$$\left[\begin{array}{l}(\_ - 6)x = 14x \\ (20 - 6)x = 14x\end{array}\right]$$
$$\left[\begin{array}{l}(\_ + 2) = -4 \\ (-6 + 2) = -4\end{array}\right]$$
$$\begin{array}{r} 3x^2 + 20x - 6 \\ +\,2x^2 - 6x + 2 \\ \hline 5x^2 + 14x - 4 \end{array}$$

65. When $t = 8$ seconds:
$$1053 - 16t^2 = 1053 - 16(8)^2$$
$$= 1053 - 16 \cdot 64$$
$$= 1053 - 1024$$
$$= 29$$

The height of the object above the river after 8 seconds is 29 feet.
When $t = 9$ seconds:
$$1053 - 16t^2 = 1053 - 16(9)^2$$
$$= 1053 - 16 \cdot 81$$
$$= 1053 - 1296$$
$$= -243$$

The height of the object above the river after 9 seconds is -243 feet. The object hits the water between 8 and 9 seconds.

Exercise Set C.2

1. $x^5 \cdot x^9 = x^{5+9} = x^{14}$

5. $3z^3 \cdot 5z^2 = (3 \cdot 5)(z^3 \cdot z^2) = 15z^5$

9. $(-5x^2y^3)(-5x^4y) = (-5)(-5)(x^2 \cdot x^4)(y^3 \cdot y)$
$$= 25x^6y^4$$

13. $2x \cdot 3x \cdot 7x = (2 \cdot 3 \cdot 7)(x \cdot x \cdot x) = 42x^3$

17. $(x^5)^3 = x^{5 \cdot 3} = x^{15}$

21. $(b^7)^6 \cdot (b^2)^{10} = b^{7 \cdot 6} \cdot b^{2 \cdot 10}$
$$= b^{42} \cdot b^{20}$$
$$= b^{42+20}$$
$$= b^{62}$$

25. $(a^{11}b^8)^3 = a^{11 \cdot 3}b^{8 \cdot 3} = a^{33}b^{24}$

29. $(-3y)(2y^7)^3 = (-3y) \cdot 2^3(y^7)^3$
$$= (-3y) \cdot 8y^{21}$$
$$= (-3)(8)(y^1 \cdot y^{21})$$
$$= -24y^{22}$$

33. $A = S^2$
$$= (4x^6 \text{ in.})^2$$
$$= (4)^2(x^6)^2(\text{in.})^2$$
$$= 16x^{12} \text{ in.}^2$$
$$= 16x^{12} \text{ sq in.}$$

The area is $16x^{12}$ sq in.

37. $(14a^7b^6)^3(9a^6b^3)^4$
$$= (14)^3(a^7)^3(b^6)^3(9)^4(a^6)^4(b^3)^4$$
$$= 2744a^{21}b^{18} \cdot 6561a^{24}b^{12}$$
$$= (2744 \cdot 6561)(a^{21} \cdot a^{24})(b^{18} \cdot b^{12})$$
$$= 18{,}003{,}384a^{45}b^{30}$$

41. answers may vary

Exercise Set C.3

1. $3x(9x^2 - 3) = 3x \cdot 9x^2 + 3x \cdot (-3)$
$$= (3 \cdot 9)(x \cdot x^2) + (3)(-3)(x)$$
$$= 27x^3 + (-9x)$$
$$= 27x^3 - 9x$$

5. $7x^2(6x^2 - 5x + 7)$
$$= (7x^2)(6x^2) + (7x^2)(-5x) + (7x^2)(7)$$
$$= (7 \cdot 6)(x^2 \cdot x^2) + (7)(-5)(x^2 \cdot x) + (7 \cdot 7)x^2$$
$$= 42x^4 - 35x^3 + 49x^2$$

9. $(2x - 6)(x + 4) = 2x(x + 4) - 6(x + 4)$
$$= 2x \cdot x + 2x \cdot 4 - 6 \cdot x - 6 \cdot 4$$
$$= 2x^2 + 8x - 6x - 24$$
$$= 2x^2 + 2x - 24$$

13. $(a + 6)(a^2 - 6a + 3)$
$$= a(a^2 - 6a + 3) + 6(a^2 - 6a + 3)$$
$$= a \cdot a^2 + a(-6a) + a \cdot 3 + 6 \cdot a^2 + 6(-6a) + 6 \cdot 3$$
$$= a^3 - 6a^2 + 3a + 6a^2 - 36a + 18$$
$$= a^3 - 33a + 18$$

17. $(x^3 + 2x + x^2)(3x + 1 + x^2)$
$$= x^3(3x + 1 + x^2) + 2x(3x + 1 + x^2)$$
$$ + x^2(3x + 1 + x^2)$$
$$= x^3 \cdot 3x + x^3 \cdot 1 + x^3 \cdot x^2 + 2x \cdot 3x + 2x \cdot 1$$
$$ + 2x \cdot x^2 + x^2 \cdot 3x + x^2 \cdot 1 + x^2 \cdot x^2$$
$$= 3x^4 + x^3 + x^5 + 6x^2 + 2x + 2x^3$$
$$ + 3x^3 + x^2 + x^4$$
$$= x^5 + 4x^4 + 6x^3 + 7x^2 + 2x$$

21. $-2y^2(3y + y^2 - 6)$
$$= -2y^2 \cdot 3y + (-2y^2) \cdot y^2 + (-2y^2)(-6)$$
$$= -6y^3 - 2y^4 + 12y^2$$

25. $(2a + 3)(2a - 3)$
$$= 2a(2a - 3) + 3(2a - 3)$$
$$= 2a \cdot 2a + 2a(-3) + 3 \cdot 2a + 3(-3)$$
$$= 4a^2 - 6a + 6a - 9$$
$$= 4a^2 - 9$$

29. $\left(b + \dfrac{3}{5}\right)\left(b + \dfrac{4}{5}\right) = b\left(b + \dfrac{4}{5}\right) + \dfrac{3}{5}\left(b + \dfrac{4}{5}\right)$
$$= b^2 + \dfrac{4}{5}b + \dfrac{3}{5}b + \dfrac{3}{5} \cdot \dfrac{4}{5}$$
$$= b^2 + \dfrac{7}{5}b + \dfrac{12}{25}$$

33. $(7x + 5)^2 = (7x + 5)(7x + 5)$
$$= 7x(7x + 5) + 5(7x + 5)$$
$$= 49x^2 + 35x + 35x + 25$$
$$= 49x^2 + 70x + 25$$

37. $(2x^2 - 3)(4x^3 + 2x - 3)$
$$= 2x^2(4x^3 + 2x - 3) - 3(4x^3 + 2x - 3)$$
$$= 8x^5 + 4x^3 - 6x^2 - 12x^3 - 6x + 9$$
$$= 8x^5 - 8x^3 - 6x^2 - 6x + 9$$

41.
$$
\begin{array}{r}
2z^2 - z + 1 \\
\times\ \ 5z^2 + z - 2 \\
\hline
-4z^2 + 2z - 2 \\
2z^3 - z^2 + z \\
10z^4 - 5z^3 + 5z^2 \\
\hline
10z^4 - 3z^3 \qquad + 3z - 2
\end{array}
$$

45. larger area − smaller area
$$= (x^2 - 1)(x^2 - 1) - (x)(x)$$
$$= x^2(x^2 - 1) - 1(x^2 - 1) - (x)(x)$$
$$= x^4 - x^2 - x^2 + 1 - x^2$$
$$= x^4 - 3x^2 + 1$$
The area of the shaded figure is $(x^4 - 3x^2 + 1)$ sq m.

APPENDIX D

Exercise Set

1. inductive

5. deductive

9. A, Z, B, Y, C

These are letters of the alphabet in forward order in positions 1 and 3; the second and fourth letters are the letters of the alphabet in reverse order. So, the fifth letter must be the letter that comes directly after B, namely C.

13. O, T, T, F, F, S, S, E

17. 2, 7, 4, 8, 6, 9

The numbers in the odd positions (first, third, and fifth) are even numbers and the numbers in the even positions (second and fourth) are counting numbers beginning at 7. So, the sixth number should be the next counting number after 8, namely 9.

21. 1, 11, 38, 84, 151, 241
$$
\begin{array}{ccccc}
& \vee & \vee & \vee & \vee & \vee \\
& 10 & 27 & 46 & 67 & 90 \\
& & \vee & \vee & \vee & \vee \\
& & 17 & 19 & 21 & 23 \\
& & & \vee & \vee & \vee \\
& & & 2 & 2 & 2
\end{array}
$$

45. 1st: Sal
2nd: Mark
3rd: Joey
4th : Bob

49. Based on statement a, either Marty or Maria is the electrical engineer. From statement b we can conclude that either Aaron or Donna is the civil engineer. Since statement c says that Aaron works on the same floor as the civil engineer, then this tells us Aaron is not the civil engineer. So Donna must be the civil engineer.

53. 10 people said they drink Coke and Pepsi. A total of 65 people said they drink Coke. This means that $65 - 10 = 55$ is the number of people that drink only Coke. Since a total of 40 people said they drink Pepsi, $40 - 10 = 30$ people only drink Pepsi. This means that $55 + 10 + 30 = 95$ people drink Coke or Pepsi. Since 100 people were polled, $100 - 95 = 5$ people drink neither Coke nor Pepsi.

INDEX

Photo Credits

LICENSING AGREEMENT
CHAPTER TEST PREP VIDEO CD, BASIC COLLEGE MATHEMATICS WITH EARLY INTEGERS
ELAYN MARTIN-GAY

0-13-222751-7
© 2007 Pearson Education, Inc.
Pearson Prentice Hall
Pearson Education, Inc.
Upper Saddle River, NJ 07458
Pearson Prentice Hall™ is a trademark of Pearson Education, Inc.

YOU SHOULD CAREFULLY READ THE TERMS AND CONDITIONS BEFORE USING THE CD-ROM PACKAGE. USING THIS CD-ROM PACKAGE INDICATES YOUR ACCEPTANCE OF THESE TERMS AND CONDITIONS.

Pearson Education, Inc. provides this program and licenses its use. You assume responsibility for the selection of the program to achieve your intended results, and for the installation, use, and results obtained from the program. This license extends only to use of the program in the United States or countries in which the program is marketed by authorized distributors.

LICENSE GRANT
You hereby accept a nonexclusive, nontransferable, permanent license to install and use the program ON A SINGLE COMPUTER at any given time. You may copy the program solely for backup or archival purposes in support of your use of the program on the single computer. You may not modify, translate, disassemble, decompile, or reverse engineer the program, in whole or in part.

TERM
The License is effective until terminated. Pearson Education, Inc. reserves the right to terminate this License automatically if any provision of the License is violated. You may terminate the License at any time. To terminate this License, you must return the program, including documentation, along with a written warranty stating that all copies in your possession have been returned or destroyed.

LIMITED WARRANTY
THE PROGRAM IS PROVIDED "AS IS" WITHOUT WARRANTY OF ANY KIND, EITHER EXPRESSED OR IMPLIED, INCLUDING, BUT NOT LIMITED TO, THE IMPLIED WARRANTIES OF MERCHANTABILITY AND FITNESS FOR A PARTICULAR PURPOSE. THE ENTIRE RISK AS TO THE QUALITY AND PERFORMANCE OF THE PROGRAM IS WITH YOU. SHOULD THE PROGRAM PROVE DEFECTIVE, YOU (AND NOT PEARSON EDUCATION, INC. OR ANY AUTHORIZED DEALER) ASSUME THE ENTIRE COST OF ALL NECESSARY SERVICING, REPAIR, OR CORRECTION. NO ORAL OR WRITTEN INFORMATION OR ADVICE GIVEN BY PEARSON EDUCATION, INC., ITS DEALERS, DISTRIBUTORS, OR AGENTS SHALL CREATE A WARRANTY OR INCREASE THE SCOPE OF THIS WARRANTY.

SOME STATES DO NOT ALLOW THE EXCLUSION OF IMPLIED WARRANTIES, SO THE ABOVE EXCLUSION MAY NOT APPLY TO YOU. THIS WARRANTY GIVES YOU SPECIFIC LEGAL RIGHTS AND YOU MAY ALSO HAVE OTHER LEGAL RIGHTS THAT VARY FROM STATE TO STATE.

Pearson Education, Inc. does not warrant that the functions contained in the program will meet your requirements or that the operation of the program will be uninterrupted or error-free. However, Pearson Education, Inc. warrants the CD-ROM(s) on which the program is furnished to be free from defects in material and workmanship under normal use for a period of ninety (90) days from the date of delivery to you as evidenced by a copy of your receipt. The program should not be relied on as the sole basis to solve a problem whose incorrect solution could result in injury to person or property. If the program is employed in such a manner, it is at the user's own risk and Pearson Education, Inc. explicitly disclaims all liability for such misuse.

LIMITATION OF REMEDIES
Pearson Education, Inc.'s entire liability and your exclusive remedy shall be:
1. the replacement of any CD-ROM not meeting Pearson Education, Inc.'s "LIMITED WARRANTY" and that is returned to Pearson Education, or
2. if Pearson Education is unable to deliver a replacement CD-ROM that is free of defects in materials or workmanship, you may terminate this agreement by returning the program.

IN NO EVENT WILL PEARSON EDUCATION, INC. BE LIABLE TO YOU FOR ANY DAMAGES, INCLUDING ANY LOST PROFITS, LOST SAVINGS, OR OTHER INCIDENTAL OR CONSEQUENTIAL DAMAGES ARISING OUT OF THE USE OR INABILITY TO USE SUCH PROGRAM EVEN IF PEARSON EDUCATION, INC. OR AN AUTHORIZED DISTRIBUTOR HAS BEEN ADVISED OF THE POSSIBILITY OF SUCH DAMAGES, OR FOR ANY CLAIM BY ANY OTHER PARTY.

SOME STATES DO NOT ALLOW FOR THE LIMITATION OR EXCLUSION OF LIABILITY FOR INCIDENTAL OR CONSEQUENTIAL DAMAGES, SO THE ABOVE LIMITATION OR EXCLUSION MAY NOT APPLY TO YOU.

GENERAL
You may not sublicense, assign, or transfer the license of the program. Any attempt to sublicense, assign or transfer any of the rights, duties, or obligations hereunder is void.

This Agreement will be governed by the laws of the State of New York.

Should you have any questions concerning this Agreement, you may contact Pearson Education, Inc. by writing to:
ESM Media Development
Higher Education Division
Pearson Education, Inc.
1 Lake Street
Upper Saddle River, NJ 07458

Should you have any questions concerning technical support, you may write to:
New Media Production
Higher Education Division
Pearson Education, Inc.
1 Lake Street
Upper Saddle River, NJ 07458

YOU ACKNOWLEDGE THAT YOU HAVE READ THIS AGREEMENT, UNDERSTAND IT, AND AGREE TO BE BOUND BY ITS TERMS AND CONDITIONS. YOU FURTHER AGREE THAT IT IS THE COMPLETE AND EXCLUSIVE STATEMENT OF THE AGREEMENT BETWEEN US THAT SUPERSEDES ANY PROPOSAL OR PRIOR AGREEMENT, ORAL OR WRITTEN, AND ANY OTHER COMMUNICATIONS BETWEEN US RELATING TO THE SUBJECT MATTER OF THIS AGREEMENT.

System Requirements
Windows
Pentium II 300 MHz processor
Windows NT, 2000, ME, or XP
64 MB RAM (128 MB RAM required for Windows XP)
4.3 MB available hard drive space (optional-for minimum QuickTime installation)
800 x 600 resolution
8x or faster CD-ROM drive
QuickTime 6.x
Sound card

Macintosh
PowerPC G3 233 MHz or better
Mac OS 9.x or 10.x
64 MB RAM
10 MB available hard drive space for Mac OS 9, 19 MB on OS X (optional—if QuickTime installation is needed)
800 x 600 resolution
8x or faster CD-ROM drive
QuickTime 6.x

Support Information
If you are having problems with this software, call (800) 677-6337 between 8:00 a.m. and 8:00 p.m. EST, Monday through Friday, and 5:00 p.m. through 12:00 a.m. EST on Sundays. You can also get support by filling out the web form located at: http://247.prenhall.com/mediaform

Our technical staff will need to know certain things about your system in order to help us solve your problems more quickly and efficiently. If possible, please be at your computer when you call for support. You should have the following information ready:
• Textbook ISBN
• CD-ROM ISBN
• corresponding product and title
• computer make and model
• Operating System (Windows or Macintosh) and Version
• RAM available
• hard disk space available
• Sound card? Yes or No
• printer make and model
• network connection
• detailed description of the problem, including the exact wording of any error messages.

NOTE: Pearson does not support and/or assist with the following:
• third-party software (i.e. Microsoft including Microsoft Office suite, Apple, Borland, etc.)
• homework assistance
• Textbooks and CD-ROMs purchased used are not supported and are non-replaceable. To purchase a new CD-ROM, contact Pearson Individual Order Copies at 1-800-282-0693.